FACILITY FIRE BRIGADES

SECOND EDITION

Technical Writer and Lead Senior Editor
Jeff Fortney

Lead Instructional Developers
Lindsey Dugan
Tara Roberson-Moore

Graphic Designer
Errick Braggs

INTERNATIONAL FIRE SERVICE TRAINING ASSOCIATION
Validated by the International Fire
Service Training Association

Published by
Fire Protection Publications
Oklahoma State University

RECYCLABLE

The International Fire Service Training Association (IFSTA) was established in 1934 as a *nonprofit educational association of fire fighting personnel dedicated to the advancement of fire fighting techniques and firefighter safety through training.* To carry out the IFSTA mission, Fire Protection Publications (FPP) was established at Oklahoma State University in the College of Engineering, Architecture and Technology. The primary purpose of FPP is to publish and distribute training materials as proposed, developed, and validated by IFSTA. FPP also develops state of the art teaching and learning materials to support the adoption and use of the manuals. The print products are supported by a full array of eBooks, online learning and apps.

IFSTA holds two meetings each year, one in January and one in July. During these meetings, selected committees of subject matter experts, who are acknowledged leaders in their fields, review draft materials and ensure that the content is accurate and meets the National Fire Protection Association professional qualification standards. These assemblies bring together individuals from several related and allied occupations:

- Fire department executives, training officers, and line personnel
- Educators from colleges and universities
- Representatives from governmental agencies
- Delegates of firefighter associations and industrial organizations

Validation committee members receive no fees for their work and their travel expenses are only partially funded by FPP. Members participate because of a personal commitment to the fire service and its future through training. Serving on a committee is prestigious in the fire and emergency response community. This unique process to validate the content of training textbooks creates a close relationship between IFSTA, the publications and the fire service community.

The manuals and associated instructional materials are the primary source of training and education for most fire departments and training agencies in North America, the U.S. Department of Defense, fire service related higher education programs, and other emergency response organizations worldwide. Some of the manuals are available in other languages including French, Arabic, Japanese and Chinese.

ISBN 978-0-87939-636-7   *Library of Congress Control Number: 2019933111*

Second Edition, First Printing, March 2019   *Printed in the United States of America*

10   9   8   7   6   5   4   3   2   1

If you need additional information concerning the International Fire Service Training Association (IFSTA) or Fire Protection Publications, contact:

Customer Service, Fire Protection Publications, Oklahoma State University
930 North Willis, Stillwater, OK 74078-8045
800-654-4055   Fax: 405-744-8204   customer.service@osufpp.org

For assistance with training materials, to recommend material for inclusion in an IFSTA manual, or to ask questions or comment on manual content, contact:

Editorial Department, Fire Protection Publications, Oklahoma State University
930 North Willis, Stillwater, OK 74078-8045
405-744-4111   Fax: 405-744-4112   E-mail: editors@osufpp.org

Table of Contents

Section A: Incipient Facility Fire Brigade Member

Section B: Common Advanced Exterior and Interior Structural Facility Fire Brigade Member Training Requirements

Section D: Interior Structural Facility Fire Brigade Member Only

Section E: Facility Fire Brigade Leader

Section G: Support Member

List of Tables

List of Key Terms

Acknowledgments

This Second Edition of **Facility Fire Brigades** will assist corporate and fire and emergency services personnel in establishing and training facility fire brigades within their jurisdictions. Chapters 4, 5, 6, 7, 8, and 9 of NFPA Standard 1081, *Standard for Facility Fire Brigade Member Professional Qualifications*, 2018 edition, and Chapters 4, 5, and 6 of NFPA Standard 600, Standard on Facility Fire Brigades, 2015 Edition, identify the qualification and certification requirements for facility fire brigade members.

Acknowledgment and special thanks are extended to the members of the IFSTA validating committee who contributed their time, wisdom, and knowledge to make this manual a reality.

IFSTA Facility Fire Brigades, 2nd Edition Validation Committee

Chair
Ed Hawthorne
Global Emergency Response Manager
Shell Oil Company
Haslet, TX

Vice Chair
Bob Taylor
Secretary and Past Chairman
PRB Coal User's Group
Newburgh, IN

Secretary
Patricia Thomas, CSP, CHMM, CET
President/Owner
Thomas Loss Control Enterprises
Coffeyville, TX

Committee Members

Doug Bledsoe
Fire Captain
Port Neches Fire Department
Groves, TX

Jonathan Lund, PE
Fire Marshal
Des Moines Fire Department
Des Moines, IA

Mark Butterfield
Principal/Chief Instructor
Butterfield Associates
Hutchinson, KS

Robert Mathis
Assistant Fire Chief
Port of Portland Airport Fire and Rescue
Portland, OR

Richard Hermo
Assistant Chief/Training Officer
Georgia Pacific Fire Department
Clatskanie, OR

Jim Pendergast
Fire Chief
Town of Penhold Fire Department
Penhold, Alberta, Canada

Emory Johnson
Assistant Fire Chief
Waste Isolation Pilot Plant Fire Department
Nuclear Waste Partnership, LLC
Carlsbad, NM

Dan Ripley
Fire Captain
Lincoln Fire and Rescue
Lincoln, NE

Committee Members (continued)

Scott L. Shear
Fire Protection Instructor
Duke Energy
Kings Mountain, NC

Craig Shelley
CEO
World Safe International
Pine Plains, NY

Steven Stokely, Sr.
PSM/Quality Team Leader
INEOS Nitriles
Green Lake, TX

Paul Valentine
Senior Fire Consultant
Fire Protection Engineering
Global Risk Consultants
Chicago, IL

The following individuals and organizations contributed design drawings, information, photographs, or other assistance that made the completion of this manual possible:

Moe Abdulrahman

Diane Anderson

Pedro Arellano

Bonnie Barlow

Shane Barnhill

John Barzyk

Mike Bauschka

Hunter Beckcom

James Belluomini

Boeing Company

Josiah Bouthillier

Travis Boyd

Zachary Brackin

James Bradshaw

Greg Bridges

Tim Bridgewater

Seth Brignac

Larry Brown

Edward Lee Brown III

Shad Bryant

Jerry Burtner

Brain Canady

John Cedeno

Landon Clause

Carson Combest

Jonny Conover

Daniel Crewes

Shawn Crowell

Dallas-Fort Worth Airport Fire Rescue

Dallas-Fort Worth Airport Fire Training Research Center

Seth Davis

Dylan Delso

Dustin Dicharry

Nicholas Duggan

Ben Duvall

Jeff Edgecombe

Michael Ellis

Brian Epperson

Darin Fields

Kathy Fraser

Frontier Fire Protection, Stillwater (OK)

Jordan Glass

Global Product Solutions (GPS), Shawnee (OK)

Ryan Gonzalez

Mark W. Gray

Steven Hager

Ed Hawthorne

John Hendricks

Hillcrest Medical Center, Tulsa (OK)

Darren Himes

Jacob Ingham

Mark Jackson

Kyle Jenkins

Christopher D. Jones

Johnathon Jones

Stanley M. Jones

Randy Kelley

Dane Kepka

Ethan Khuelman

Thomas David Kimbrough

Kohl Kramp

Thomas D. Kuglin, Jr.

Justin Lalicker

Mike Lampson

Delmar Langan

Colton Leaning

Jameson Lewis

Kerry Louque

Byron J. Mack

Michael Magdaleno

Mike Mallory

Dakota Markes

Marathon Petroleum Company LP, Louisiana Refining Division, Garyville (LA)

Rob Mathis

Gage McCartney

John McEnany

Kristina Mendez

Bryan Moody

Jeff Morrissette

Elio Mosqueda

Tracy Neathery

Victor Ojeda

Oklahoma State University, Stillwater (OK)

- Energy Services
- Environmental Health & Safety
- Water Treatment Plan

Joshua Peak

Travis Peetoom

Terry Perilloux

Jason Petrillo

Phillips 66, Ponca City (OK) Refinery

Bill Piganelli

David Pittman, Jr.

Freddy Pitts

Ponca City Fire Department, Ponca City (OK)

Bradyn Pressnall

Jay Prigmore

Ryan Ray

Chuck Rice

Casey Richardson

Brandon Robicheaux

Brandon Samrow

James R. Sapp

Bernie Schulte

Edward Scioneaux

Shell Oil Deer Park Training Center, Houston (TX)

Michael Shrader

Taylor Siemsen

Chris Simmel

Felton D. Simpson

Paul Smith

Bart Snyder

Gregg Southard

Tina Stackhouse

Scott Steichen

Stillwater Fire Department (OK)

Corey Sudduth

Robert D. Taylor

Texas A&M Emergency Services Training Institute (ESTI), College Station (TX)

Thomas Tharp

Tulsa Fire Department, Tulsa (OK)

Ray L. Werner

Jeffrey M. Williams

Gary Wilson

Chris Yancey

Patrick Younes

Mark Young

Special thanks are also extended to the personnel of Oklahoma Fire Service Training for their timely and efficient assistance. In particular, we would like to thank Bryan West, Rhett Strain, Terry Blackburn, Connor Bunch, Steve George, Robert Goode, Greg Hewin, Matt Phippen, and Jacob Smith for their help with acquiring photographs for this manual.

Last, but certainly not least, gratitude is also extended to the members of the Fire Protection Publications Facility Fire Brigade Project Team whose contributions made the final publication of this manual possible.

NOTE: Any omissions are purely accidental and the lead senior editor apologizes profusely.

Facility Fire Brigade Project Team

Project Manager/Writer/Editor/Photographer
Jeff Fortney, Senior Editor

Director of Fire Protection Publications
Craig Hannan

Associate Director of Fire Protection Publications
Mike Wieder

Managing Editor
Colby Cagle

Editorial Manager
Clint Clausing

Curriculum Managers
Colby Cagle
Leslie Miller

Production Coordinators
Ann Moffatt
Missy Hannan

eProducts Manager
Justin Smola

Senior Editors
Alex Abrams, Senior Editor
Cindy Brakhage, Senior Editor
Kimberly Edwards, Senior Editor
Mike Fox, Senior Editor
Libby Snyder, Senior Editor

Instructional Development
Lindsey Dugan
Tara Roberson-Moore

Illustrators and Layout Designers
Errick Braggs, Senior Graphic Designer

IFSTA/FPP Photographers
Lindsey Dugan
Kimberly Edwards
Jeff Fortney
Brett Noakes
Veronica Smith
Mike Wieder

eProducts Staff
Kelly Naas
Ryan Souders

Editorial Assistant
Tara Gladden

Indexer
Nancy Kopper

The IFSTA Executive Board at the time of validation of **Facility Fire Brigades, 2nd edition** was as follows:

IFSTA Executive Board

Executive Board Chair
Bradd Clark
Fire Chief
Owasso Fire Department, Retired
Program Manager/Instructor
Florida State Fire College
Ocala, Forida

Vice Chair
Mary Cameli
Fire Chief
City of Mesa Fire Department
Mesa, Arizona

IFSTA Executive Director
Mike Wieder
Associate Director
Fire Protection Publications
Oklahoma State University
Stillwater, Oklahoma

Board Members

Steve Ashbrock
Fire Chief
Madeira & Indian Hill Fire Department
Cincinnati, Ohio

Steve Austin
Project Manager
Cumberland Valley Volunteer Firemen's Association
Newark, Delaware

Dr. Larry Collins
Associate Dean
Eastern Kentucky University
Safety, Security, & Emergency Department
Richmond, Kentucky

Dennis Compton
Fire Chief
Mesa & Phoenix Fire Departments, Retired
Chairman, Board of Directors
National Fallen Firefighters
Mesa, Arizona

Elizabeth Hendel
Deputy Chief
Phoenix Fire Department
Phoenix, Arizona

John Hoglund
Director Emeritus
Maryland Fire & Rescue Institute
New Carrollton, Maryland

Tonya Hoover
Superintendent
National Fire Academy
Emmitsburg, Maryland

Tom Jenkins
Fire Chief
Rogers Fire Department
Rogers, Arkansas

Dr. Scott Kerwood
Fire Chief
Hutto Fire Rescue
Hutto, Texas

Wes Kitchel
Assistant Chief, Retired
Sonoma County Fire & Emergency Services
Department
Santa Rosa, California

Dedication

This manual is dedicated to the men and women who hold devotion to duty above personal risk, who count on sincerity of service above personal comfort and convenience, who strive unceasingly to find better and safer ways of protecting people, homes, and property from the ravages of fire, medical emergencies, and other disasters

...The Firefighters of All Nations.

Introduction

Employers who choose to have a facility fire brigade are mandated by Occupational Safety & Health Administration (OSHA) Regulation 29 *CFR* 1910.156 to prepare and maintain a statement or written policy that establishes the existence of the facility fire brigade. The organizational statement must outline employee responsibilities and actions in the event of a fire or other emergency in the workplace.

National Fire Protection Association (NFPA) 600, *Standard on Facility Fire Brigades*, and NFPA 1081, *Standard for Facility Fire Brigade Member Professional Qualifications*, outline the general requirements for an organized facility fire brigade and define the minimum standards and the professional requirements for the facility fire brigade members. However, the functions that the industrial fire brigade will be expected to perform in the workplace are site-specific and will vary from facility to facility and from company to company. While the organizational plan must specify which functions the fire brigade will perform, it must also specify which ones the fire brigade members are not to perform. Thus, the plan serves to both define and limit the duties and responsibilities of the fire brigade.

The name *industrial fire brigades*, was used prior to 2015, at which point NFPA 600 implemented the name change to *facility fire brigades*, when NFPA 1081 adopted the change as well. This necessitated a name change for IFSTA's **Industrial Exterior and Structural Fire Brigades** manual which has become **Facility Fire Brigades, 2nd edition**.

NFPA 1081 establishes the following levels of facility fire brigade personnel and the job performance requirements (JPR) for each:

- Incipient Facility Fire Brigade Member
- Advanced Exterior Facility Fire Brigade Member
- Interior Structural Facility Fire Brigade Member
- Facility Fire Brigade Leader
- Fire Brigade Training Coordinator
- Support Member

This manual addresses the training requirements for each level of facility fire brigade personnel. The focus of this book is for facility fire brigade members and management personnel who are responsible for developing procedures and training for the fire brigade.

The information contained in **Facility Fire Brigades, 2nd edition**, will help fire brigade members meet the requirements of NFPA 1081 (2018 edition). This edition of NFPA 1081 contains significant updates to the 2001 version which was referenced in the previous edition of this manual. The NFPA 1081 (2018 edition) updates include: qualifications, knowledge, and skills for job performance at each level; introduced new JPRs for the Fire Brigade Leader on leadership, management, and supervising training evolutions; and introduced the position of Fire Brigade Training Coordinator. This manual incorporates the JPRs for the position of Support Member that was first introduced in NFPA 1081 (2012).

At the beginning of each chapter, the applicable JPRs are listed along with the chapter learning objectives. The associated JPR is also listed under each section heading. More specific directions on where JPRs are covered within each chapter are contained in **Appendix A**. NFPA 1081 does not require that the objectives be mastered in the order in which they appear in the standard. Local agencies may choose the order in which they wish the material to be presented. This edition of the manual also incorporates skill sheets as a tool for learning basic skills required by the standard.

Separating the written text from the step-by-step procedures makes the manual easier to read and the skills easier to locate and use. Therefore, skill sheets describing the step-by-step procedures for many of the tasks described in the Skill Sheet section between Chapter 24 and the Appendix A. Note that the skill sheets contain written information on the key steps in that skill; they may not have a photo or illustration for each step.

Purpose and Scope

This 2nd edition of **Facility Fire Brigades** is written for personnel assigned to facility fire brigades. The **Purpose** of this manual is to train facility personnel to the following job performance levels for facility fire brigade members:

- Incipient Facility Fire Brigade Member
- Advanced Exterior Facility Fire Brigade Member
- Interior Structural Facility Fire Brigade Member
- Facility Fire Brigade Leader
- Facility Fire Brigade Training Coordinator
- Support Member

The manual also assists management personnel with compliance to applicable laws and regulations regarding training and management of facility fire brigades. The manual can be used to train facility fire brigade members to higher performance levels, to expand their knowledge of facility fire fighting, or as a foundation for a training program.

The **Scope** of this manual is to meet the requirements of NFPA 1081, *Standard for Facility Fire Brigade Member Professional Qualifications (2018)*. The manual covers the entire standard and can be used to train to any of the job performance levels found in chapters 5-9 of 1081. **Appendix A** includes correlation information showing where each portion of the standard is addressed in the manual text.

To support the scope of the manual, references to the following standards and regulations are contained throughout:

- NFPA 600, *Standard on Facility Fire Brigades*, (2015)
- NFPA 1500™, *Standard on Fire Department Occupational Safety, Health, and Wellness Program*, (NFPA 1500™ is trademarked by the National Fire Protection Association, Quincy, MA.)
- OSHA regulations in Title 29 of the *Code of Federal Regulations*, Part 1910

Book Organization

Facility Fire Brigades, 2nd edition, is organized with the materials for each level into separate sections subdivided into chapters with one section that shares common requirements for Advanced Exterior and Interior Structural positions. This altered format will allow the student to locate and study material required to meet the appropriate level. It will also assist the instructor in presenting material for each level or for a course that combines all levels of instruction. The major sections within this manual are:

Section A: Incipient Facility Fire Brigade Member

Section B: Common Advanced Exterior and Interior Structural Facility Fire Brigade Member Training Requirements

Section C: Advanced Exterior Facility Fire Brigade Member Only

Section D: Interior Structural Facility Fire Brigade Member Only

Section E: Facility Fire Brigade Leader

Section F: Facility Fire Brigade Training Coordinator

Section G: Support Member

Review Sections

NFPA 1081, *Standard for Facility Fire Brigade Member Professional Qualifications*, contains numerous JPRs where training requirements introduced at one level (Incipient) is repeated at other levels (Advanced Exterior and/or Interior Structural). To address this without repeating large volumes of material, we have inserted Review Sections into some chapters beyond the Incipient Level. The information in these Review Sections covers the essential information from the previous locations but in a condensed format. These Review Sections are identified in the A- or B-heads. (For example: Review Section: Facility Fire Brigade Organizational Structure.) If identified in the A-head, then all information in that A-head and its subordinate B- and C-heads is review information. If identified in the B-head, then all information in that B-head and its subordinate C-heads is review information.

Skill Sheets

For the safety of the students and optimal educational structure, we are trying something new with the skill sheets for this manual. Instead of being at the end of each chapter, they will be located between Chapter 24 and Appendix A. At the end of each chapter will be a reference list of each skill sheet that applies to that chapter.

Terminology

This manual is written with a global, international audience in mind. For this reason, it often uses general descriptive language in place of regional- or agency-specific terminology (often referred to as *jargon*). Additionally, in order to keep sentences uncluttered and easy to read, the word *state* is used to represent both state and provincial level governments (or their equivalent). This usage is applied to this manual for the purposes of brevity and is not intended to address or show preference for only one nation's method of identifying regional governments within its borders.

The glossaries of key terms at the end of each chapter will assist the reader in understanding words that may not have their roots in the fire and emergency services. The sources for the definitions of fire-and-emergency-services-related terms will be the IFSTA **Fire Service Orientation and Terminology** manual.

Key Information

Various types of information in this book are given in shaded boxes marked by symbols or icons (information, key information, and case histories). See the following examples:

Information

Information boxes give facts that are complete in themselves but belong with the text discussion. It is information that needs more emphasis or separation. In the text, the title of information boxes will change to reflect the content.

Review Box

Review boxes summarize information from lower certification levels that should be revisited when studying for higher certification levels. Review boxes are primarily used when information in NFPA standards is repeated from one certification level to the next.

A **key term** is designed to emphasize key concepts, technical terms, or ideas that fire brigade members need to know. They are highlighted in red in the text. Definitions are listed in alphabetical order at the end of the chapter. An example of a key term is:

Three key signal words are found in the book: **WARNING**, **CAUTION**, and **NOTE**. Definitions and examples of each are as follows:

WARNING: Indicates information that could result in death or serious injury to industrial fire brigade members.

CAUTION: Indicates important information or data that industrial fire brigade members need to be aware of in order to perform their duties safely.

NOTE: Indicates important operational information that helps explain why a particular recommendation is given or describes optional methods for certain procedures.

U.S. to Canadian Measurement Conversion

Measurements	Customary (U.S.)	Metric (Canada)	Conversion Factor
Length/Distance	Inch (in)	Millimeter (mm)	1 in = 25 mm
	Foot (ft) [3 or less feet]	Millimeter (mm)	1 ft = 300 mm
	Foot (ft) [3 or more feet]	Meter (m)	1 ft = 0.3 m
	Mile (mi)	Kilometer (km)	1 mi = 1.6 km
Area	Square Foot (ft^2)	Square Meter (m^2)	1 ft^2 = 0.09 m^2
	Square Mile (mi^2)	Square Kilometer (km^2)	1 mi^2 = 2.6 km^2
Mass/Weight	Dry Ounce (oz)	gram	1 oz = 28 g
	Pound (lb)	Kilogram (kg)	1 lb = 0.5 kg
	Ton (T)	Ton (T)	1 T = 0.9 T
Volume	Cubic Foot (ft^3)	Cubic Meter (m^3)	1 ft^3 = 0.03 m^3
	Fluid Ounce (fl oz)	Milliliter (mL)	1 fl oz = 30 mL
	Quart (qt)	Liter (L)	1 qt = 1 L
	Gallon (gal)	Liter (L)	1 gal = 4 L
Flow	Gallons per Minute (gpm)	Liters per Minute (L/min)	1 gpm = 4 L/min
	Cubic Foot per Minute (ft^3/min)	Cubic Meter per Minute (m^3/min)	1 ft^3/min = 0.03 m^3/min
Flow per Area	Gallons per Minute per Square Foot (gpm/ft^2)	Liters per Square Meters Minute (L/(m^2.min))	1 gpm/ft^2 = 40 L/(m^2.min)
Pressure	Pounds per Square Inch (psi)	Kilopascal (kPa)	1 psi = 7 kPa
	Pounds per Square Foot (psf)	Kilopascal (kPa)	1 psf = .05 kPa
	Inches of Mercury (in Hg)	Kilopascal (kPa)	1 in Hg = 3.4 kPa
Speed/Velocity	Miles per Hour (mph)	Kilometers per Hour (km/h)	1 mph = 1.6 km/h
	Feet per Second (ft/sec)	Meter per Second (m/s)	1 ft/sec = 0.3 m/s
Heat	British Thermal Unit (Btu)	Kilojoule (kJ)	1 Btu = 1 kJ
Heat Flow	British Thermal Unit per Minute (BTU/min)	watt (W)	1 Btu/min = 18 W
Density	Pound per Cubic Foot (lb/ft^3)	Kilogram per Cubic Meter (kg/m^3)	1 lb/ft^3 = 16 kg/m^3
Force	Pound-Force (lbf)	Newton (N)	1 lbf = 0.5 N
Torque	Pound-Force Foot (lbf ft)	Newton Meter (N.m)	1 lbf ft = 1.4 N.m
Dynamic Viscosity	Pound per Foot-Second (lb/ft.s)	Pascal Second (Pa.s)	1 lb/ft.s = 1.5 Pa.s
Surface Tension	Pound per Foot (lb/ft)	Newton per Meter (N/m)	1 lb/ft = 15 N/m

Conversion and Approximation Examples

Measurement	U.S. Unit	Conversion Factor	Exact S.I. Unit	Rounded S.I. Unit
Length/Distance	10 in	1 in = 25 mm	250 mm	250 mm
	25 in	1 in = 25 mm	625 mm	625 mm
	2 ft	1 in = 25 mm	600 mm	600 mm
	17 ft	1 ft = 0.3 m	5.1 m	5 m
	3 mi	1 mi = 1.6 km	4.8 km	5 km
	10 mi	1 mi = 1.6 km	16 km	16 km
Area	36 ft²	1 ft² = 0.09 m²	3.24 m²	3 m²
	300 ft²	1 ft² = 0.09 m²	27 m²	30 m²
	5 mi²	1 mi² = 2.6 km²	13 km²	13 km²
	14 mi²	1 mi² = 2.6 km²	36.4 km²	35 km²
Mass/Weight	16 oz	1 oz = 28 g	448 g	450 g
	20 oz	1 oz = 28 g	560 g	560 g
	3.75 lb	1 lb = 0.5 kg	1.875 kg	2 kg
	2,000 lb	1 lb = 0.5 kg	1 000 kg	1 000 kg
	1 T	1 T = 0.9 T	900 kg	900 kg
	2.5 T	1 T = 0.9 T	2.25 T	2 T
Volume	55 ft³	1 ft³ = 0.03 m³	1.65 m³	1.5 m³
	2,000 ft³	1 ft³ = 0.03 m³	60 m³	60 m³
	8 fl oz	1 fl oz = 30 mL	240 mL	240 mL
	20 fl oz	1 fl oz = 30 mL	600 mL	600 mL
	10 qt	1 qt = 1 L	10 L	10 L
	22 gal	1 gal = 4 L	88 L	90 L
	500 gal	1 gal = 4 L	2 000 L	2 000 L
Flow	100 gpm	1 gpm = 4 L/min	400 L/min	400 L/min
	500 gpm	1 gpm = 4 L/min	2 000 L/min	2 000 L/min
	16 ft³/min	1 ft³/min = 0.03 m³/min	0.48 m³/min	0.5 m³/min
	200 ft³/min	1 ft³/min = 0.03 m³/min	6 m³/min	6 m³/min
Flow per Area	50 gpm/ft²	1 gpm/ft² = 40 L/(m².min)	2 000 L/(m².min)	2 000 L/(m².min)
	326 gpm/ft²	1 gpm/ft² = 40 L/(m².min)	13 040 L/(m².min)	13 000 L/(m².min)
Pressure	100 psi	1 psi = 7 kPa	700 kPa	700 kPa
	175 psi	1 psi = 7 kPa	1225 kPa	1200 kPa
	526 psf	1 psf = 0.05 kPa	26.3 kPa	25 kPa
	12,000 psf	1 psf = 0.05 kPa	600 kPa	600 kPa
	5 psi in Hg	1 psi = 3.4 kPa	17 kPa	17 kPa
	20 psi in Hg	1 psi = 3.4 kPa	68 kPa	70 kPa
Speed/Velocity	20 mph	1 mph = 1.6 km/h	32 km/h	30 km/h
	35 mph	1 mph = 1.6 km/h	56 km/h	55 km/h
	10 ft/sec	1 ft/sec = 0.3 m/s	3 m/s	3 m/s
	50 ft/sec	1 ft/sec = 0.3 m/s	15 m/s	15 m/s
Heat	1200 Btu	1 Btu = 1 kJ	1 200 kJ	1 200 kJ
Heat Flow	5 BTU/min	1 Btu/min = 18 W	90 W	90 W
	400 BTU/min	1 Btu/min = 18 W	7 200 W	7 200 W
Density	5 lb/ft³	1 lb/ft³ = 16 kg/m³	80 kg/m³	80 kg/m³
	48 lb/ft³	1 lb/ft³ = 16 kg/m³	768 kg/m³	770 kg/m³
Force	10 lbf	1 lbf = 0.5 N	5 N	5 N
	1,500 lbf	1 lbf = 0.5 N	750 N	750 N
Torque	100	1 lbf ft = 1.4 N.m	140 N.m	140 N.m
	500	1 lbf ft = 1.4 N.m	700 N.m	700 N.m
Dynamic Viscosity	20 lb/ft.s	1 lb/ft.s = 1.5 Pa.s	30 Pa.s	30 Pa.s
	35 lb/ft.s	1 lb/ft.s = 1.5 Pa.s	52.5 Pa.s	50 Pa.s
Surface Tension	6.5 lb/ft	1 lb/ft = 15 N/m	97.5 N/m	100 N/m
	10 lb/ft	1 lb/ft = 15 N/m	150 N/m	150 N/m

Incipient Facility Fire Brigade Member

Chapter Contents

JPRs addressed in this chapter

This chapter provides information that addresses the following job performance requirements of NFPA 1081, *Standard for Facility Fire Brigade Member Professional Qualifications (2018)*.

4.1.2.1	4.1.2.3	4.1.3
4.1.2.2	4.1.2.5	4.2.3

1. Identify the duties of the different levels of the fire brigade organization.

2. Recognize the responsibilities of facility management.

3. Identify the elements that must be included in a written fire brigade organizational statement or policy.

4. Recognize the elements that must be included in a written emergency response operations site plan. [4.1.3, 4.1.2.1, 4.1.2.3]

5. Identify the information necessary to complete an incident report. [4.1.2.5]

6. Describe the topics SOPs should cover. [4.1.3, 4.2.3]

7. Describe the communications necessary at an emergency incident. [4.1.2.2, 4.1.3]

8. Explain the components and functions of the National Incident Management System-Incident Command System (NIMS-ICS).

Chapter 1
Facility Fire Brigade Organization and Responsibilities

A facility fire brigade is composed of employees of an industry or facility occupancy who are knowledgeable, trained, and skilled enough to perform basic fire fighting operations. These personnel may be workers who are trained to serve as fire brigade members during emergencies or full-time fire fighting personnel hired to protect that facility. This chapter defines the responsibilities of a facility's management regarding a facility fire brigade, which includes preparing an organizational statement as well as an employee emergency action plan. This chapter also describes the general duties of a facility fire brigade member.

Fire Brigade Organization

The duties of **facility fire brigade** members are specified in the applicable **Occupational Safety and Health Administration (OSHA)** regulation (29 *CFR* 1910.156); **National Fire Protection Association (NFPA)** 600, *Standard on Facility Fire Brigades* (2015); and NFPA 1081, *Standard for Facility Fire Brigade Member Professional Qualifications* (2018). Management is required to meet, as a minimum, the requirements of OSHA 29 *CFR* 1910.156. NFPA 600 was developed as a recommended standard for professional qualifications of the facility fire brigade and designed to be consistent with OSHA regulations. NFPA 1081 defines the minimum job requirements necessary for the members of an organized facility fire brigade providing services at a specific facility or facility site.

A facility fire brigade leader requires additional training and must be able to size up the situation and determine whether conditions exceed the fire brigade's response abilities. These conditions are based upon the response duties and limitations placed on each type of facility fire brigade:

- Incipient
- Advanced exterior only
- Interior structural only
- Advanced exterior and interior structural

 Fires Beyond the Incipient Stage

If a fire develops beyond the incipient (beginning) stage, an incipient fire brigade should not attempt to combat the fire. The local fire department should be called if a fire is beyond the abilities and limitations of the incipient, advanced exterior only, interior structure only, or advanced exterior and interior structural brigades. Some fire brigade organizations automatically contact the local fire department. Each agency must follow its local emergency response plan.

Incipient Fire Brigades

Members of incipient fire brigades are trained to fight incipient stage fires. They must be able to safely combat the fire without having to enter an environment that is **Immediately Dangerous to Life and Health (IDLH)**. Incipient fire brigade members are not required to wear **self-contained breathing apparatus (SCBA)** or **thermal protective clothing (Figure 1.1)**. They must be able to fight the fire effectively using only portable fire extinguishers or small handlines, which flow up to 125 gallons per minute (gpm) (473 L/min).

Figure 1.1 Incipient fire brigade members do not wear thermal protective clothing or use SCBA while extinguishing fires.

Depending on the facility or authority having jurisdiction (AHJ), incipient fire brigade members may combat exterior fires defensively from outside the hot or warm zones of the incident. In order to follow this strategy, the organizational statement of the fire brigade must identify the strategy as a response duty of the brigade and cover it in the brigade's **standard operating procedures (SOPs)**. The incipient fire brigade members must also have received training for each particular authorized activity. The incipient fire brigade members may use portable fire extinguishers, handlines that flow up to 125 gpm (473 L/min), master streams appliances, or similar devices to manually apply specialized agents.

NOTE: During a facility fire incident, the facility fire brigade leader must decide which fire fighting strategy to use to mitigate the incident. There are two basic strategies from which the fire brigade leader may choose: defensive and offensive. In the defensive fire fighting mode, the only fire suppression activities taken are those necessary to prevent a fire from spreading from one place to another. In the offensive fire fighting mode, the fire suppression activities focus on reducing the fire's size to achieve extinguishment. Should conditions change, the fire brigade leader may call for a strategic transition from offensive to defensive or defensive to offensive. IFSTA's **Structural Fire Fighting: Initial Response Strategy and Tactics** manual provides more information on this topic.

Advanced Exterior Only Fire Brigades

Members of an advanced exterior only fire brigade may take offensive fire fighting action within the incident hot zone only from the exterior of a structure. The fire brigade's organizational statement must identify this action as a response duty of the brigade and must cover it in the brigade's SOPs. Advanced exterior only fire brigade members must also have received training for the particular activity. The employer must provide the appropriate types of SCBA and thermal protective clothing to fire brigade members, and the fire brigade members must be trained in the proper use of these items. Some advanced exterior only fire brigades use proximity protective clothing to allow them to get close to the fire during fire fighting operations. The advanced exterior only fire brigade members must be able to use handlines that flow up to 300 gpm (1 140 L/min), master streams, or similar devices to manually apply specialized agents **(Figure 1.2)**.

Figure 1.2 Advanced exterior fire brigade members must wear the thermal protective clothing and SCBA during fire fighting operations.

Interior Structural Only Fire Brigades

Members of an interior structural only fire brigade may take offensive fire fighting action from only within the incident hot zone of the interior of a structure. The fire brigade's organizational statement must identify this as a response duty of the brigade and must cover it in the brigade's SOPs. Interior structural only fire brigade members must have received training for each particular activity. The employer must provide the appropriate types of SCBA and thermal protective clothing to fire brigade members, and the fire brigade members must be trained in the proper use of these items **(Figure 1.3)**. The interior structural only fire brigade members must be able to use handlines that flow up to 300 gpm (1 140 L/min), master streams, or similar devices to manually apply specialized agents.

Figure 1.3 Interior structural fire brigade members wear thermal protective clothing and SCBA when conducting interior fire attacks.

Advanced Exterior/Interior Structural Fire Brigades

As the name implies, members of this type of fire brigades may take offensive fire fighting action within the incident hot zone from the exterior of a structure or from within the structure itself. The fire brigade's organizational statement must identify this action as a response duty of the brigade and must cover it in the brigade's SOPs. Advanced exterior/interior fire brigade members must also have received training for each particular activity. The employer must provide the appropriate types of SCBA and thermal protective clothing to fire brigade members, and the fire brigade members must be trained in the proper use of these items. Proximity protective clothing must not be used for interior structural fire fighting operations. The advanced exterior/interior structural fire brigade members must be able to use handlines that flow up to 300 gpm (1 140 L/min), master streams, or similar devices to manually apply specialized agents.

Responsibilities of Facility Management

Facility management must establish a written policy outlining employee responsibilities and actions in the event of a fire or other emergency in the workplace. Management personnel should conduct a **risk assessment** study to determine the level of emergency response, prepare an organizational statement and an employee emergency action plan, and ensure that employees complete a performance-based training program with periodic refresher training. Training must correspond to the duties and functions assigned. The quality and frequency of training must ensure that employees can perform their assigned duties and functions in a manner that does not present a hazard to themselves or to others. To accomplish these objectives, management must first decide upon one or more of the following options:

- **Option 1.** All employees evacuate the workplace without taking any action to deal with a fire, other than to report it. Training on evacuation and fire-reporting procedures are required for this option.

- **Option 2.** Designated employees are trained in the use of portable extinguishers and/or small handlines. Therefore, they are authorized to attempt extinguishment of an incipient fire in their immediate work areas if it appears safe and prudent to do so. Initial training and annual refreshers are required.

- **Option 3.** Employees are trained in the use of portable extinguishers and/or small handlines to extinguish an incipient fire in their immediate work areas. Initial training and annual refreshers are required.

- **Option 4.** Designated employees are provided required training based upon the level of response selected and are assigned to an emergency response team or brigade for an organized response to fires, including interior structure or advanced exterior fires, or to other emergencies in all areas of the facility. Initial training and quarterly refreshers are required.

Another possible option for management is to form a full-time, dedicated emergency response organization or facility fire brigade. Its primary responsibility is to provide the necessary training for response to fires and other emergencies in all areas of the facility. Full-time facility fire brigades are functionally equivalent to operating a fire and emergency services organization **(Figure 1.4)**. Additional training information for such fire brigades may be found in IFSTA's **Essentials of Fire Fighting** manual.

NOTE: See **Appendix B**, Facility Emergency Response and Safety Needs Assessment, to assist those in facility management who must select training levels in response to OSHA and other related government regulations.

Facility Fire Brigade Organizational Statement

OSHA 29 *CFR* 1910.156 mandates that employers who choose to have a facility fire brigade must prepare and maintain a statement or written policy that establishes the existence of the facility fire brigade. The organizational statement must outline employee responsibilities and actions in the event of a fire or other emergency in the workplace. This policy must include, as a minimum, the following elements:

Figure 1.4 A full-time fire brigade member cleaning one of the brigade's fire apparatus.

Figure 1.5 A fire brigade leader (in the red helmet) receiving a report from three of his personnel during an incident.

- Basic organizational structure
- Description of training and education (type, amount, and frequency)
- Size of the facility fire brigade or emergency organization
- Facility fire brigade entrance requirements
- Facility fire brigade equipment and apparatus

   Other information that may be in the organizational statement may include:

- Descriptions of functions that the facility fire brigade is to perform at the
- Shifts during which the brigade members are available to respond

Basic Organizational Structure

The organizational statement for the emergency response organization (facility fire brigade) must be site-specific and assign responsibilities to positions, establish operational limitations, and show how the facility fire brigade fits into the company emergency plan. The organizational statement should also describe the relationship of the facility fire brigade to other response agencies, including both municipal and contractual organizations.

   In order for the facility fire brigade to function properly, qualified individuals have to be assigned positions of leadership. The necessary position titles and their assigned duties are described as follows:

- **Senior facility manager** – Is ultimately responsible for the actions of the facility fire brigade and for defining its level or type of response. This person also bears the responsibility for ensuring that the facility fire brigade is both adequately trained and properly equipped to fulfill established duties.
- **Fire brigade management official** – Is responsible for the organization, management, and operation of the facility fire brigade.
- **Fire brigade leader** – Is responsible for directing the actions of the brigade, coordinating the training of members assigned to his or her shift, and ensuring that the predetermined response capability is maintained at all times **(Figure 1.5)**. The fire brigade leader should have a good working knowledge of the facility's construction and the associated fire risk(s). This knowledge allows the fire brigade leader to correctly assess the potential hazards associated with an emergency at the facility.

- **Fire brigade member** – Is responsible for carrying out actions as directed by the facility fire brigade chief or facility fire brigade leader, SOPs, and for maintaining the knowledge and competency level required of the position.
- **Fire brigade training coordinator** – Is a designated company representative responsible for coordinating effective, consistent, and quality training within the facility fire brigade training and education program **(Figure 1.6)**.

Figure 1.6 The fire brigade training coordinator (in the lower left) is evaluating one of his instructors.

- **Fire brigade support member** - Provide support functions to the emergency response brigade. Support members are personnel from the electrical; plumbing; heating, ventilation, and air conditioning; process control; and site security departments of the facility. Specific assignments, along with the necessary training programs and record keeping, should be developed for each position that supports the brigade.
- **Other personnel** – Provide technical expertise in hazardous materials response, technical rescue, emergency medicine, industrial safety, and other topics.

Training and Education

OSHA and the NFPA have established the minimum standards for facility fire brigades. As specified in 29 *CFR* 1910.156 (2), emergency response personnel must be provided with both the education and the training necessary to enable them to safely and effectively perform any particular task or evolution that may be required under the emergency action plan. NFPA 1081 outlines the basic job performance requirements for fire brigade members at all levels.

The fire brigade training coordinator or other qualified instructors should deliver the training. The training, based on written performance objectives, usually includes both lecture and hands-on practice. All emergency response personnel must be able to perform their functions to the established performance level in a safe and timely manner. Training should include both the positive and the negative lessons learned from previous emergency responses (postincident critiques) and from drills. After a postincident critique, training should be conducted in any areas found to be in need of improvement.

Training and drills are separate and distinct functions. **Training** involves teaching/learning new or additional information and/or skills. **Drills** are exercises conducted to practice and/or evaluate training already received. Both training and drills provide a safe environment in which the trainee may make and correct mistakes that would be unacceptable in an actual emergency **(Figure 1.7)**.

Figure 1.7 Training (left and center photos) can occur in classrooms or on the training ground. Drills (right) provide a safe yet realist environment to practice and/or evaluate the training already received.

For the facility fire brigade to maintain proficiency and effectiveness, regular periodic drills should be held for each shift or team. Any deficiencies discovered during a drill should then be resolved. The fire brigade training coordinator should ensure that all training and drills are documented and each member's individual training file is kept current. Copies of all course materials should also be maintained (see Record Keeping section).

NOTE: The company should provide the local fire jurisdiction with site-specific information and training opportunities with its fire brigade if the fire department will be responding to the company's facilities.

Size of Emergency Organization

The number of members in a facility fire brigade depends on the following:

- Type of fire brigade
- Number of employees working in the facility
- Size of the facility
- Number and type of potential hazards in the facility
- Availability of emergency equipment on site
- Potential availability of mutual aid from another agency

A facility fire brigade may be composed of employees who volunteer or are assigned to it. The members from each work shift and each department in the facility so that there will be an adequate number of personnel available during any given period of the day or night.

If a brigade is expected to conduct interior fire brigade operations, it is expected to follow OSHA's *two-in/two-out* regulation. This regulation requires that when two fire brigade members enter a structure fire that has developed beyond the incipient stage, there must be two fully equipped and qualified fire brigade members outside to rescue the attack team in an emergency. If there are not enough personnel to conform to this rule, then no one enters until additional resources arrive. However, if there is a known life safety hazard to a victim that can be saved without undue risk to fire brigade members, this rule can be amended to allow the two-person attack team to enter the structure leaving one person outside. The fire brigade leader or fire brigade member giving the order must be able to justify his or her actions based upon local SOPs or NFPA standards.

Facility Fire Brigade Entrance Requirements

Both NFPA 600 and 1081 outline the general requirements for an organized facility fire brigade and define the minimum standards and the professional requirements for the facility fire brigade members. However, the functions that the facility fire brigade will be expected to perform in the workplace are site-specific and will vary between facilities and companies. While the organizational plan must specify which functions the brigade will perform, it must also identify which ones the brigade members are *not* to perform. Therefore, the plan serves to both define and limit the duties and responsibilities of the fire brigade.

Before performing any brigade duties or functions, each member should undergo a complete medical examination. This examination is conducted to ensure that the member is physically capable of performing all assigned duties and responsibilities. The examination also establishes a baseline against which the results of subsequent examinations can be compared.

Facility fire brigade members shall be evaluated annually to ensure that they meet their job-related physical performance requirements. Facility fire brigade members who are under the influence of alcohol or drugs shall not participate in any facility fire brigade operation, training, or drill.

Facility Fire Brigade Equipment and Apparatus

Facility fire brigades use a wide variety of tools, equipment, and apparatus. Each fire brigade should select and purchase the equipment that meets the needs and hazards of the specific facility. Because this equipment must be readily accessible, adequate storage space must be made available. Fire brigade members must have access to the operations and maintenance manuals and equipment maintenance reports for all assigned equipment. An equipment inventory list should be developed, maintained, reviewed annually, and updated as needed to ensure the equipment is properly accounted for. Each piece of facility equipment should be inspected and undergo maintenance per manufacturer's requirements, NFPA requirements, or in accordance with the AHJ.

Some facility fire brigades have **fire apparatus** at their sites **(Figure 1.8)**. Safety should always be the primary consideration in the selection, operation, inspection, maintenance, and repair of any facility apparatus. Fire brigade apparatus must be maintained as the manufacturer's procedures recommend. Apparatus should be inspected at least weekly and within 24 hours of any use or repair. Unsafe apparatus must be removed from service until properly repaired. Fire pumps must be tested in accordance with NFPA 1911, *Standard for Service Tests of Fire Pump Systems on Fire Apparatus*. Aerial devices must be inspected and service tested in accordance with NFPA 1914, *Standard for Testing Fire Department Aerial Devices*.

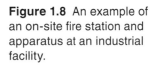

Figure 1.8 An example of an on-site fire station and apparatus at an industrial facility.

Facility fire brigade apparatus may only be driven and operated by personnel who have been selected by the fire brigade manager, who are properly trained in their use, and who meet the requirements of NFPA 1002, *Standard for Fire Apparatus Driver/Operator Professional Qualifications*. **Fire apparatus driver/operators** must hold valid driver's licenses for the type of apparatus being used and must obey all traffic regulations and safety procedures when driving or operating an apparatus. Personnel riding within a fire brigade apparatus must be seated and wearing their seat belts while the vehicle is moving.

Emergency Response Operations Site Plan

NFPA 1081 (2018): 4.1.2.1

OSHA regulations written and enforced by the United States Department of Labor (under 29 *CFR* 1910.38, *Employee Emergency Plans and Fire Prevention Plans*) require a written emergency response operations site plan covering those actions of both employers and employees during a fire or other emergency. The employee emergency action plan is independent of the facility fire brigade organizational statement. The action plan must address all potential emergencies that can be anticipated in the workplace. The plan should be reviewed annually with each employee, and it should include, as a minimum, the following elements:

- Emergency escape route assignments from individual work areas and assembly areas
- Procedures to be followed by employees who must remain in the work area to continue or shut down critical plant operations
- Procedures to account for all employees after an emergency evacuation has been completed
- Specified rescue and medical duties for those employees responsible for performing them
- Preferred means for reporting fires and other emergencies
- List of names or regular job titles of persons or departments to be contacted for further information or explanation of duties under the plan
- Fire prevention plan that includes housekeeping standards, guidelines for storage of fuels, and guidelines for maintenance of fire equipment

Reporting Emergencies

NFPA 1081 (2018): 4.1.2.1

Every employee in the plant or facility must know how to report an emergency via the facility's intercom, telephone, fire alarm, or radio communication systems. This requirement allows other employees to be made aware of the emergency and alerts fire brigade members of the emergency. Reporting an emergency can be accomplished in several different ways, depending on the policies that management adopts. Reporting an emergency can be as simple as shouting for help or sounding an alarm, or it can involve using other means as specified in the emergency action plan. Appropriate signs with phone numbers and instructions should be posted throughout the facility. Employees should practice the procedure periodically as part of the facility emergency action plan and training program.

Fire brigade members must be able to receive a report of an emergency, gather the appropriate infor-

> **CAUTION:** Each facility may have a different way of reporting an emergency, and all employees must know the procedure for their facility.

mation regarding the emergency, and relay the information to the other members of the fire brigade. To accomplish this task, fire brigade members must be proficient in using the facility's telephone, radio, intercom, or installed alarm systems.

If the report is from an installed alarm system, the fire brigade member may only be able to identify the location of the emergency and possibly the type. If the report comes from someone at the facility, the fire brigade member should gather the following information:

- Location of the emergency
- Type of emergency
- Number of personnel involved, including those injured or missing
- Determine if evacuation has been initiated

Emergency Response Procedures

NFPA 1081 (2018): 4.1.2.3

Facility fire brigade members must be thoroughly trained in the facility's layout, special hazards, and the emergency response procedures to be followed at that location. Personnel must be:

- Provided the equipment appropriate to the fire brigade level at the facility.
- Trained to use each piece of equipment safely and effectively.
- Trained to recognize response hazards.
- Able to respond to an emergency so that all team members arrive safely.

Facility Personnel Accountability

NFPA 1081 (2018): 4.1.3

The facility or plant's emergency response operations site plan should include an accountability system that tracks all personnel on the incident scene. An accountability system is essential to personnel safety because it maintains records of work durations, exposures, and other critical incident factors. The **Incident Commander (IC)** may appoint a representative to ensure that all personnel are accounted for during an incident. A method of accounting for all personnel must be part of any evacuation plan. Designated employees report to the IC regarding the status of the evacuation and identify any unaccounted for individuals. Personnel include emergency responders (both internal and external), employees and contractors, and visitors at the facility or plant during the time of the incident. This information is essential so that a search can be initiated quickly for any missing individuals (see Accounting for Evacuated Employees section). Any individuals who are not accounted for are reported to the IC so that the local fire and emergency services organization can conduct a search for the missing individuals.

Evacuation Planning

NFPA 1081 (2018): 4.1.3

Just as each facility may have different means of reporting emergencies, each facility may have its own unique **evacuation** requirements. As a minimum, every employee emergency action plan must outline the procedures for a complete evacuation of the facility. Depending on variables that include the facility's layout and the number of employees normally on site, the plan may also specify both the type (level) and the method of evacuation for each work area. Every evacuation plan should include detailed floor plans or workplace maps to show both the emergency exit routes and any alternative escape routes. Management should clearly mark escape routes on the evacuation plan and post copies of the plan prominently in each work area. The evacuation plan should also show designated safe areas where evacuees may assemble for an accounting of personnel. Fire brigade members should be trained to assist with the evacuation of personnel, as required by the facility emergency response operations site plan. The facility fire brigade should conduct evacuation drills at least annually to eliminate confusion during actual emergencies.

Levels of Evacuation

Facility management must consider and specify the levels of evacuation and then incorporate them into the employee emergency action plan. The level (type) of evacuation in an emergency situation can range from evacuating a specific work area or a single floor to conducting a total evacuation of the premises. Facility management can then establish policies defining the level of evacuation needed according to the scope and complexity of each anticipated type and level of emergency.

Exit Identification

In facilities, all exits must be clearly identified and must remain unobstructed and accessible. For specific exit marking requirements, see NFPA 101, *Life Safety Code®*, 29 *CFR* 1910.37 (q), Exit Marking, or applicable building code as adopted by the AHJ.

Assembly Areas

An **area of assembly**, designated by the facility's emergency response operations site plan, is a predetermined point of assembly that is free from any hazards. A primary and secondary area of assembly should be identified and communicated to the evacuating employees, contractors, and visitors. The selection of assembly areas should take into account varying conditions, such as weather and expected emergency conditions. The following types of areas are typically designated:

- Open areas adjacent to the building
- Other buildings
- Parking lots
- Designated locations, such as safe rooms, **safe havens**, or other areas of refuge as approved by the AHJ

Accounting for Evacuated Employees
NFPA 1081 (2018): 4.1.3

During an emergency, management is responsible to ensure complete evacuation of all employees, visitors, and contractors and account for them. The accounting system can be easily completed by designated employees checking off the names of employees, visitors, and contractors from established lists as individuals arrive in the designated assembly area **(Figure 1.9)**. Established lists must be kept current.

Figure 1.9 An evacuation warden conducting a roll-call to verify personnel accountability.

Employees Who Remain Behind
NFPA 1081 (2018): 4.1.3

Critical facility operators or essential employees may have to stay behind and stabilize machinery or the facility's processes during some types of emergencies, such as fires and chemical or gas leaks. When some machines and/or processes are shut down abruptly or incorrectly, they may create conditions more dangerous than the emergency necessitating the evacuation. Management may decide to protect these employees by having them **shelter in place** and not immediately evacuate the area. Such situations must be clearly and specifically identified in the emergency action plan. These employees should remain in their work areas only if the emergency does not put them in imminent danger.

Other personnel may need to remain in the emergency area to ensure that other employees have evacuated and are proceeding to the designated assembly area. Designated employees may be trained to deal with specific emergencies, and they may be required to respond to the emergency area to maintain certain critical processes or assist with emergency shutdown procedures. Other personnel may be trained in the skills needed for special rescue and medical duties, which can also necessitate a response to the emergency scene.

Explanation of Duties under the Plan

To maintain each employee's personal safety, each person must know his or her duties and responsibilities during an emergency. Management must make information readily available to employees. Employees also have the responsibility to know their emergency duties. This information must be communicated to all employees through required orientation and training sessions and reinforced periodically thereafter. If, prior to an emergency occurring, any employee is not certain about what the appropriate action should be, that employee should seek clarification either from an immediate supervisor or from the person in charge of fire protection and safety in the facility.

Incident Reports

NFPA 1081 (2018): 4.1.2.5

Following a fire brigade response to an emergency incident, an accurate report describing the details of the event should be completed. From legal, statistical, and record-keeping standpoints, incident reports are vital to both facility and fire brigade operations. Incident reports must be complete and written in terminology that can be understood. Because incident reports are legal documents, there are possible legal consequences if the reports are inaccurate or incomplete.

Incident reports can be handwritten or electronically produced. The information gathered on reports could be used for:

- Assessing facility and fire brigade needs
- Budgeting
- Determining trends in fire cause, types of responses, and brigade member injuries
- Providing information for fire safety databases and to insurance rating agencies
- Determining requirements for fire and life safety education programs

When completing an incident report, fire brigade members should follow facility guidelines. These guidelines should address the content requirements for incident reports. The following is a general list of information that may be required **(Figure 1.10)**:

- Facility name, incident number, district name/number, shift number, and number of alarms
- Names and addresses of the occupant(s) and/or owner(s)
- Type of structure, primary use, construction type, and number of stories
- How the emergency was reported (telephone, walk-in, radio)
- Type of call (fire, rescue, medical)
- Action that was taken (investigation, extinguishment, rescue)
- Property use information (single-family dwelling, commercial occupancy)
- Number of injuries and/or fatalities

Sample Facility Incident Report Form

Facility Incident Report

Incident Number: [ ] Incident Date: [ ]

Report Completed By: [ ] Corporate ID: [ ]

Number of Personnel That Responded: [ ] Apparatus That Responded: [ ]

Time Out: [ ]

On Location: [ ]

In Service: [ ]

Facility Name: [ ] Facility Function: [ ]

Building Number: [ ]

Address: [ ]

City: [ ] State: [ ] Zip Code: [ ]

Type of Incident: ☐ Fire ☐ Rescue ☐ Medical ☐ Other: [ ]

Location Description: [ ]

Floor/Level: [ ] Door/Room: [ ]

Actions Taken: [ ]

Figure 1.10 Incident reports require a wide range of information that relate to a fire or other emergency at a facility.

- Number of personnel who responded and type of apparatus that responded
- How and where the fire started
- Method used to extinguish the fire
- Estimated cost of damage
- Remarks/comments (the officer in charge usually writes a narrative of the incident)

If a computer-based incident report system is used, fire brigade members should be trained in its operation. They should also know how to gather the information necessary to complete a report and proofread the report to ensure its accuracy.

Standard Operating Procedures (SOPs)

NFPA 1081 (2018): 4.2.3

Each facility fire brigade must develop site specific standard operating procedures (SOP) or standard operating guidelines (SOG) for administrative, emergency operations, and safety purposes. Regardless of whether they are called SOPs or SOGs, they provide a written reference for how the fire brigade operates in both routine and emergency situations **(Figure 1.11)**. For the purposes of this manual, we will use the terms standard operating procedure and.

Figure 1.11 An example of a facility SOP that relates to fire brigade personnel accountability.

Sample Standard Operational Procedure

Whitman Refining Inc. - Facility #3
Section 8 Accountability

Section 8.0 Fire Brigade Personnel Accountability System

8.1 Purpose
To insure accountability of all fire brigade members who respond to and function within fire suppression activities or provide fireground support.

8.2 Application
All fire brigade members shall be assigned accountability tags for accountability on the scene.

8.3 Fire Brigade Members Responsibility
Prior to entry into a hazardous environment, each fire brigade member shall give his/her tag to the incident accountability officer (IAO). Fire brigade members must work in teams of two (2) or more. Upon leaving the hazardous environment, the fire brigade members retrieve their tags from the IAO.

8.4 Fire Officers Responsibility
All fire officers will be aware of the location of their assigned crews at all times. The IAO is to note the following:
a.   Time of entry into the hazardous environment.
b.   The location where entry was made.
c.   Number of personnel making entry.
d.   Tactical considerations for personnel placement.

8.5 Evacuation Call
When all personnel on the fireground must be accounted for or there is a need to evacuate an unsafe structure or area, the Incident Commander (IC) or other fire officer will issue an evacuation order over the radio and will sound an air horn for no less than a thirty (30) second interval upon receiving such order. This order should be issued judiciously in extreme emergencies, which will include:
a.   Imminent danger of structural collapse.
b.   Rapidly deteriorating fire conditions.
c.   Any condition that warrants the accountability of fire brigade members.

8.6 References
A. NFPA 1500, Standard on Firefighter Occupational Safety, Health, and Wellness Program.

Each fire brigade member must read and thoroughly understand the SOPs that the brigade develops. Fire brigade members should also be encouraged to actively contribute to the development of these documents. SOPs do not replace the need for **size-up** during an incident.

NOTE: The IC conducts a size-up of the situation to determine and evaluate all existing factors that are used to develop objectives, strategy, and tactics for fire suppression before committing personnel and equipment to a course of action.

SOPs do, however, provide a basic set of operating guidelines and procedures to assist the fire brigade leader in dealing with a particular incident. While each incident is different, there are enough similarities in each type of incident to develop SOPs that can establish basic procedures to be followed during an incident.

Administrative SOPs should include the following:

- Fire brigade organizational structure

- Information management and record keeping

- Work schedule and policies

- Fire equipment inspection procedures
- Routine radio and telephone communications

  SOPs for emergency operations should follow the most commonly accepted order of incident priorities:

  1) Life safety
  2) Incident stabilization
  3) Property conservation
  4) Incident mitigation and restoration to normal conditions

The SOPs should address fire and hazardous materials incidents, medical emergencies, natural disasters, and any other site-specific incidents that a facility risk assessment identifies. They should also cover:

- Incident management systems
- Personnel accountability systems
- Communication procedures
- Emergency evacuation procedures
- Safe havens
- Interfacing with outside or mutual aid agencies

  SOPs should address both routine and emergency safety needs, such as:

- Normal work clothing
- Risk management for emergency response
- Personal protective equipment to be worn during an emergency
- Thermal protective clothing to be worn in the warm zone
- Thermal protective clothing and respiratory protection to be worn in the hot zone
- Hazardous processes conducted at the site
- Methods for reporting a hazard
- Welding or cutting (hot work) standby requirements
- Fuel storage and transfer
- Flammable and combustible liquids storage
- Site-specific conditions and hazards
- Notification for fire brigade leaders regarding any major fire protection system or equipment outages
- First-aid procedures and equipment

Information Management and Record Keeping

Information management and record keeping are important tasks that should be covered in the fire brigade's SOPs. Fire brigade information and records may be required for the following uses:

- Federal and state verification of compliance with safety regulations
- Routine verification of compliance with fire brigade training requirements
- Budget development
- Documentation or evidence in a court case involving an incident at a site

Documents such as fire safety surveys, training sessions and drills, and equipment records must be documented and maintained. Provisions must be made in the organizational statement and in the brigade's SOPs that identify what documentation is necessary, who must prepare it, and how this information is to be maintained.

Record keeping assists with:

- Verifying compliance with any regulation or requirement regardless of whether OSHA, an insurance carrier, or company policy mandates it.

- Revealing training needs by showing the amount of time that has passed since a given member or team has had training on any given topic.

- Keeping all members current with mandated renewals of certifications, licenses, and inoculations.

For each individual and emergency response team, records should be kept on at least the following items in addition to any others that may be required by the particular organization:

- Training

- Drills

- Actual responses (incident reports)

- Critiques of incident responses

- Lessons learned

- Near misses

- Inspections of personal protective equipment

- Inspection dates and inventory of brigade equipment, including who performed it

- Maintenance records for all equipment

- Specifications for all equipment purchased

- Fit testing for any respirator equipment or self-contained breathing apparatus

- Employee medical histories

- Exposures (or suspected exposures) to hazardous materials

Training records, whether for an individual or a team, should list the date, time, location, equipment used, and topic or training objective of the session as well as the names of all participants and instructors. In addition, the records should show each participant's level of achievement in the session. Data recorded should include test scores achieved, skills demonstrated, exercises completed, and any other measures of proficiency. This documentation may be the only proof that the facility fire brigade member has been trained and is qualified to perform as indicated in the plan. Copies of training materials, such as lesson plans, textbooks, and manuals, should also be maintained.

ANSI Z490.1

ANSI Z490.1-2016, *Criteria for Accepted Practices in Safety, Health, and Environmental Training*, provides a comprehensive list of guidelines for training documentation.

Maintaining Records

In addition to maintaining records on people and teams, records should be maintained on a facility for the life of that facility. In other words, if a facility is still standing, there should be records of the facility kept at the company level, if not at the local level. By maintaining a file on a facility throughout its lifetime, it will be possible to note the changes that have been made to the facility and how proposed changes may be affected by the previous uses of the facility. If a structure is demolished, the company should maintain the files for a reasonable period of time before the records and files are destroyed. Local policy, legal recommendations, and corporate policy will dictate how long this period will be.

All facility fire brigade files and records are corporate documents. Obviously, some information contained in the reports may be considered proprietary or confidential in nature. Officials who are responsible for overseeing the storage of inspection records should understand company policies regarding such documentation. This practice will provide guidance for them on what documents may be released to the public and those documents that must be withheld.

NOTE: Remember that employee medical records are confidential documents.

Written Records

Even in facility fire brigades that have been diligent and kept up with technological advances, there tend to be a large number of written inspection records and documentation that need to be filed and maintained. These records include older records that were generated before computerization and hard copy documents that are used in computer filing systems. Some facility fire brigades that have a computerized documentation process have also chosen to print hard copies of the information and maintain them in a written file. This practice ensures that new records are stored with older records to keep the file complete and consistent. These copies also provide an additional backup in the event that a computer system failure ever makes the files inaccessible for any period of time.

Each inspected facility should have a file that contains copies of all building and inspection records for that facility, particularly for the fire detection and suppression systems installed within that facility. Each time further action is taken in a facility, records of those actions should be added to the file. The file should be kept as up to date as possible.

The methods for cataloging and storing the files vary. Much of how this procedure is done depends on the size of the facility fire brigade and the number of facilities it is responsible for protecting.

Electronic Records

Many facility fire brigades are taking advantage of advances in computer technology to maintain and store records electronically. Computerized record systems can also assist in planning and scheduling future fire detection and suppression system needs. The level of sophistication of the computer system depends on the facility fire brigade's needs **(Figure 1.12)**. Few facility fire brigades have the resources or the need to develop their own data management system, so most use a program procured from an outside firm.

Figure 1.12 Fire brigade personnel must be familiar with the computer systems and programs used by their facility fire brigade.

Two primary methods by which data may be logged into the computer system are as follows:

- Use a laptop computer or handheld electronic data recording equipment and then download the information into the system.
- Record the information on written forms and then enter the information manually into the computer system.

The ability to electronically record information in the field and then download it into the computer system is the most efficient of the two methods. The use of small, portable computer equipment such as tablets and cell phones has become a more common practice.

Many aspects of computer system management must be given careful consideration when using the system to store inspection records and data. Several questions that must be answered are as follows:

- How will the information be filed?
- How can the information be retrieved?
- What portion of the information will be stored in a read-only format so that records cannot be accidentally or purposely changed without authorization?
- Which personnel will be given access to retrieve information from the system?

Safety of the Facility Fire Brigade Member

Fires at a facility may have a tremendous impact on the local responders, the local fire and emergency services organization, and the community. Facility incidents can result in serious injuries to or deaths of facility fire brigade members as well as major property losses.

Other losses may include damaged equipment or facilities (which are expensive to repair or replace) and legal expenses. In order to prevent these losses, it is necessary to prevent the incidents that cause them. Reducing incidents prevents injuries and saves lives and money. The safety of all facility fire brigade members is paramount during all phases of their assigned duties.

An effective safety program becomes a matter of developing, promoting, and practicing an ongoing attitude of involvement throughout the organization. Safety requires effort on everyone's part. The assignment of a safety officer for each response should be standard protocol **(Figure 1.13)**.

Figure 1.13 A safety officer (in the white helmet) talking with fire brigade members during a training evolution.

Team Integrity in Hazardous Areas
NFPA 1081 (2018): 4.2.3

Teamwork is the basis of all fire control and emergency operations. Emergency scenes are inherently dangerous, and as a result, facility fire brigade members to should work in teams of two or more personnel. To maintain team integrity, facility fire brigade members should follow these guidelines:

- Have a charged hoseline and a backup safety device (fixed monitor or hoseline) ready prior to approaching a fire.

- Always enter and exit areas with teammates.

- When necessary, establish a Rapid Intervention Crew (RIC) or Rapid Intervention Team (RIT) at an incident and be prepared for deployment in the event of a member rescue.

- Personnel positioned in fire zones should be able to relocate to alternate positions in the event of changes in fire conditions.

- More experienced personnel should oversee the activities of less experienced personnel.

- Have one or more means of communication between the team and personnel outside the hazardous area.

- Hoselines and/or safety ropes may be used to prevent becoming lost in a structure.

- At no point should a team member separate from the rest of the team. Separating from the team can be dangerous in vision-obscured conditions such as a large, smoke filled area, room, or structure. To prevent becoming separated in this type of condition, fire brigade members should maintain physical contact with walls, hoselines, search rope, and/or other members while crawling through an area to be searched.

- Exit the hazardous area immediately if the fire grows beyond the incipient stage or other hazards occur.

- All facility fire brigade members should know the locations of any safe havens or shelter in place locations at their site. No safe haven can provide protection from all of the potential hazards at a facility.

To provide protection for personnel who must monitor continuing operations or conduct shutdown operations, control rooms are usually designed to protect equipment and personnel against heat, smoke, corrosive vapors, and electrical hazards. Fire brigade members should be familiar with the locations of and access points into safe havens provided at their site. Fire brigade members may use these safe havens during an emergency.

Two-In/Two-Out Rule

The fire brigade should have an SOP that outlines how it will implement OSHA's *two-in/two-out* regulation during certain emergency situations. These situations may include but are not limited to interior fire attacks, hazardous materials incidents, or confined space search and rescue operations.

Personnel Accountability Systems for Fire Brigade Members
NFPA 1081 (2018): 4.1.3

Personnel accountability systems are designed to track personnel, both in and out of the IDLH environment. All departments use some type of accountability system at every incident. All personnel should be trained in its use, and it should be part of all training exercises.

An accountability system can help save a team member's life if that person's SCBA malfunctions, the member becomes lost or trapped, or there is an unexpected change in a fire's behavior. If the IC does not know the location of personnel at a fire scene, determining whether someone is trapped inside is daunting. Firefighters and fire brigade members have died because they were not known to be missing until it was too late.

A variety of accountability systems exist including the Passport Accountability System®, SCBA tag systems, and computer-based electronic systems **(Figure 1.14)**. These systems are only effective if the IC implements them and personnel use them at the incident.

Figure 1.14 The fire brigade member on the left just handed his accountability tag to the accountability officer on the right.

Tag (Passport) System

In a tag or passport system, the fire brigade leaders or Accountability Officer (AO) have a passport listing for every crew member. Fire brigade members give their passports/tags to their supervisor or a designated AO per fire brigade policy. Passports are then attached to a control board or personnel identification chart. Fire brigade members collect their passports after leaving the IDLH. This system allows Command to know which personnel are operating on the incident scene and their location.

SCBA Tag System

A tag attached to each SCBA can be used to provide accountability data. Fire brigade members give their tags to an AO who records time of entry and the expected time of exit. Exit time is based on the air pressure in the lowest-reading SCBA in the team. Brigade members leaving the IDLH environment take back their tags so that the AO knows who is still inside the IDLH environment. On extended operations, relief crews are sent in before interior crews run low on air.

Computer-based Electronic Accountability Systems

Computer-based electronic accountability systems use radio-based tracking or radar-based transmitters attached to PPE. Most systems sound an alarm if a fire brigade member becomes immobile or calls for assistance. They can also sound a MAYDAY or evacuation alarm and verify that the IC or other brigade members have received it.

Some SCBA manufacturers have developed units with digital accountability features. At the beginning of the work shift, personnel "log-in" to their assigned SCBA. When they arrive at an incident, their position and air supply automatically register on the IC's tracking software within the command unit.

Electronic systems should never fully replace manual accountability systems, such as passport and SCBA tag systems. They should only be used as a supplemental safety measure.

Environmental Awareness

Fire brigade SOPs should address environmental awareness. Many incidents, as well as some training exercises, may have a harmful impact on the local environment. As a result, training exercises that involve the use of certain types of extinguishing media(s) (such as dry chemical or powder) may be restricted. Check with the local jurisdiction to ensure compliance of the approved extinguishing media before the start of any training exercise. Training to provide brigade members with the appropriate level of environmental awareness is beyond the scope of this document. However, management must ensure that all personnel are made aware of the capabilities and limitations of available resources as well as of the requirements of applicable laws and regulations. The local fire and emergency services organization and hazardous materials team may be of assistance in meeting this need.

Communications

NFPA 1081 (2018): 4.1.2.2, 4.1.3

Routine and emergency communications play a vital role in the success of a facility fire brigade's operations. Fire brigade members should be taught how to:

- Operate the facility's and brigade's communications systems and equipment
- Transmit and receive routine and emergency messages
- Use proper communications procedure and etiquette
- Recognize areas where radio communications are ineffective or prohibited

The strategic and tactical orders given at an incident should be clear and easily understood by personnel involved in the incident. During an emergency, a combination of verbal and nonverbal communications may be used to transmit and receive these orders.

Figure 1.15 Portable radios provide an effective means of communications between fire brigade members.

The fire brigade's SOPs should identify appropriate language to be used, unit identifiers, common terminology, and nonverbal signals. An important signal that usually is nonverbal is the "evacuate immediately" signal, such as a continuous air/steam horn blast, which is used to clear members from areas that are rapidly becoming too dangerous to occupy, such as imminent structural collapse or storage vessel failure. Fire brigade members should practice these signals until their use becomes second nature.

Fire brigade members must be provided adequate communications equipment and training in order to support their operational needs **(Figure 1.15)**. During incidents involving chemical/vapor/gas/dust releases, fire brigade members must use intrinsically safe communications equipment that is designed and approved for use in flammable atmospheres and is incapable of releasing sufficient electrical energy to cause the ignition of a flammable atmospheric mixture. Portable radios, cellular telephones, and cellular walkie-talkie phones are examples of communication devices that fire brigade members may use during an incident. Call signs for each unit can be relatively simple to develop. For example, the Incident Commander could be called Command or IC. Attack crews could be called Attack 1, Attack 2, and so on. Ventilation crews could be called Vent 1 or Ventilation.

Communications between units should identify who is being called and who is the caller. For example: "Command, this is Rescue." Or "Attack 1 from Command." Plain language or clear text should be used in all communications. Radio communication codes have largely been discontinued because of differences in the codes between agencies that can and often do work together. Plain language transmissions reduce or prevent confusion and misunderstanding from interfering with a response to an incident. An example of such plain language could be: "Attack 2 from Command. I want two handlines on the fire on the second floor."

Nonverbal hand signals are often used at emergency scenes to communicate between fire brigade members. The following are common examples of these signals **(Figure 1.16)**:

- *To charge a hoseline:* A handline team leader rotates one hand in the air above his or her head to signal the hydrant/valve operator.

- *To adjust the fog pattern:* A team leader signals the nozzle operator by holding his or her hands together at the wrist and moving the finger tips apart to show a widening angle.

- *To move forward:* A team leader signals his or her handline operator by applying gentle pressure forward to the operator's shoulders.

- *To move backwards:* A team leader signals his or her handline operator by pulling gently backwards on the operator's shoulders.

Because facility fire brigades can work together with municipal fire departments during emergencies, personnel with both agencies should be trained in proper communication protocols with each other. This training will greatly reduce confusion and chaos during mutual responses and ensure coordination between units from each agency.

Proper communications protocols and procedures aid the IC in assigning tasks to subordinates. The IC and fire brigade members must be able to convey assignments, orders, or messages under stressful conditions including inherently dangerous incident scenes with loud noises and distractions. Use the following guidelines when giving commands and assignments:

- Use plain language or clear text.

- Be accurate, brief, and clear.

Figure 1.16 Hand signals are often used during training evolutions and at emergency scenes when noise can interfere with communications.

- Identify the unit(s) designated to carry out the task.

- Identify the task(s) to be carried out.

- Ask for acknowledgement from the crew receiving the assignment. The crew leader can paraphrase the assignment back to Command to confirm the team's task.

For example, Command radios the Operations Chief the following message: "Ops from Command. Assign two attack crews and one rescue team to the fire at the southeast corner of the facility. We have a report of one victim in that area." The Operations Chief responds: "Command from Ops, understood. Two attack crews and one rescue crew to the southeast corner. One victim in that area." The Ops Chief then radios: "Attack 1, Attack 2, and Rescue 1. Attack the fire at the southeast corner of the facility and begin rescue operations. One victim reported in the area."

The fire brigade's SOPs should include a procedure for members to transmit an emergency call for assistance, if necessary. The exact procedure may vary between facilities, but usually includes the following:

1. Declaring a Mayday over the fire brigade's emergency radio channel

2. Providing information about your emergency

3. Activating Personal Alert Safety System (PASS) device

4. Taking other actions to call attention to your location

National Incident Management System – Incident Command System (NIMS-ICS)

The United States government mandated that all emergency services organizations use common terminology and command structures to improve their interoperability. The **National Incident Management System - Incident Command System (NIMS-ICS)** was created as a result. NIMS-ICS is designed to be applicable to both small, single-unit incidents that may last a few minutes to complex, large-scale incidents involving several agencies and many mutual aid units that possibly last for days or weeks. NIMS-ICS combines command strategy with organizational procedures. It provides a functional, systematic organizational structure. The ICS organizational structure clearly shows the lines of communication and chain of command.

NIMS-ICS involves five major organizational functions **(Figure 1.17)**:

- Command
- Planning
- Finance/Administration
- Operations
- Logistics

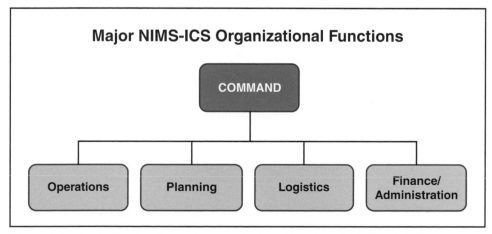

Figure 1.17 Illustrating the five major organizational function within NIMS-ICS.

Components of NIMS-ICS

Fire brigade personnel need to understand the roles and responsibilities of each component and position within NIMS-ICS and how they are utilized within the brigade. It is advantageous for all emergency personnel to receive NIMS-ICS training as part of their entry level training, recurring proficiency training, and professional development. NIMS-ICS courses are offered through the online resources of the National Fire Academy, the Federal Emergency Management Agency (FEMA), and many state/tribal and local agencies.

Command

The Incident Commander is the person in overall command of an incident. The IC is ultimately responsible for all incident activities, including the development and implementation of a strategic plan that sets long-term goals and objectives for an incident. This process may include making a number of critical decisions and being responsible for the results of those decisions. The IC has the authority to call resources to the incident and release them from it.

If the size and complexity of the incident require it, the IC may delegate authority for various duties to others, who together with the IC form the Command staff. Positions within the Command staff include the following (**Figure 1.18**):

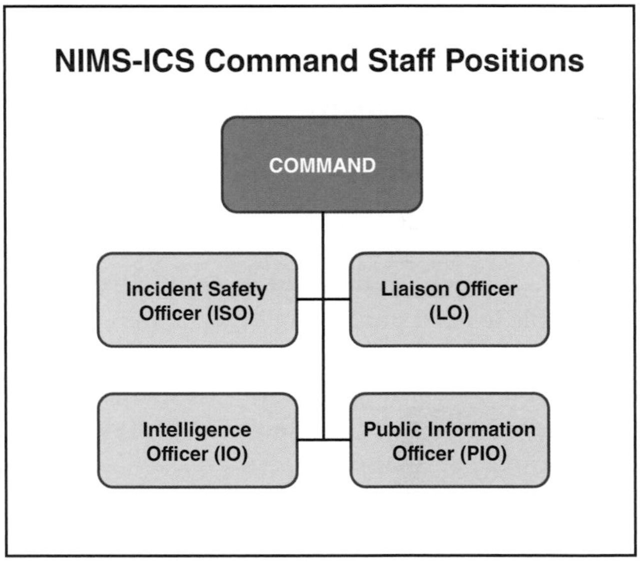

NIMS-ICS Command Staff Positions

COMMAND

Incident Safety Officer (ISO)

Liaison Officer (LO)

Intelligence Officer (IO)

Public Information Officer (PIO)

Figure 1.18 Examples of positions within the Command Staff.

- **Incident Safety Officer (ISO)** — The ISO is the most commonly implemented position at a scene. An ISO should be appointed to monitor activities at incidents that are involved with life safety/hazardous situations. The ISO plays a vital role in the IMS. The ISO should have the authority to immediately suspend, terminate, or alter any operation that jeopardizes the safety of personnel. Fire brigade members need to be familiar with NFPA 1500™, *Standard on Fire Department Occupational Safety and Health Program* (2017), and NFPA 1521, *Standard for Fire Department Safety Officer Professional Qualifications* (2015).

- **Intelligence Officer (IO)** — The Intelligence Officer may be part of the Command Staff, a unit in the Planning Section, a branch within Operations, or a separate general staff section. The IO's role is to support incident management activities by managing internal information, intelligence, and operational security requirements. This responsibility includes providing information and operational security activities and safeguarding sensitive information while ensuring it reaches those individuals who need access to it in the performance of their duties.

- **Liaison Officer (LO)** — The LO coordinates with representatives of other agencies who are assisting with the incident/emergency. These agencies may include but are not limited to the local fire, law enforcement, and emergency medical departments.
- **Public Information Officer (PIO)** — The PIO interfaces with the public, the media, and other agencies. The PIO provides information related to the incident to keep these other group aware of the status of the incident.

Operations

The Operations Section Chief reports to the IC and is responsible for the management of all operations that affect the primary mission of eliminating the problem. The function of the Operations Section Chief is to direct the tactical operations to meet the strategic goals the IC develops. The Operations Section may be subdivided into as many Branches as needed **(Figure 1.19)**.

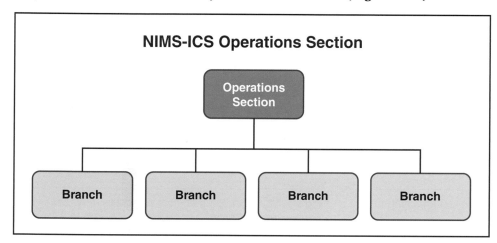

Figure 1.19 Common positions with the Operations Section of NIMS-ICS.

Planning

The Planning Section is responsible for the collection, evaluation, dissemination, and use of information concerning the development of the incident. Planning is also responsible for maintaining the status of all resources assigned to the incident. Command will use the information that the Planning Section compiles to develop strategic goals and contingency plans. Specific units under Planning include the following **(Figure 1.20)**:

- Resource Unit
- Situation Status Unit
- Demobilization Unit
- Technical specialists whose services are required

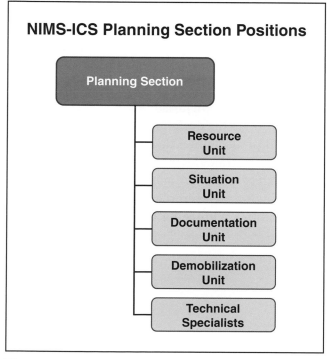

Figure 1.20 Examples of positions with the Planning Section of NIMS-ICS.

Logistics

The Logistics Section is responsible for providing the facilities, services, and materials necessary to support the incident. There are two branches within Logistics: the support branch and the service branch. The support branch includes supplies, facilities, and ground support (vehicle services). The service branch includes medical, communications, and food services **(Figure 1.21)**.

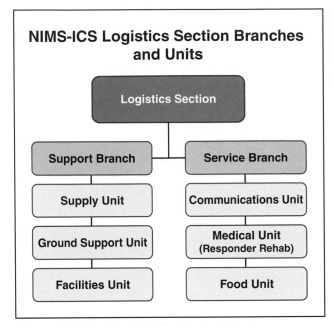

Figure 1.21 The Logistics Section includes two branches: support and services.

Figure 1.22 Examples of units within the Finance/Administration Section of NIMS-ICS.

Finance/Administration

The Finance/Administration Section is responsible for tracking and documenting all costs and financial aspects of the incident **(Figure 1.22)**. Generally, the Finance/Administration Section is activated only on large-scale, long-term incidents.

Unified Command

Unified command is established when more than one agency has incident jurisdiction or when incidents cross political jurisdictions. These agencies work together through the designated members of the Unified Command, often the senior person from the agencies and/or disciplines that are participating in the Unified Command, to establish a common set of objectives and strategies and a single incident action plan. The object is to include those "players" necessary to successfully mitigate a large-scale incident that has complex legal and financial ramifications. The following are examples of persons who may be included in Unified Command during incidents in fixed facilities **(Figure 1.23)**:

- Facility IC
- Local fire department IC
- State environmental control
- Local or state emergency management agency
- Police agencies and federal agencies

 Unity of Command and Span of Control

All facility fire brigades adhere to the same basic organizational principles. To function effectively as a member of a fire brigade, each member must understand **unity of command** and **span of control**.

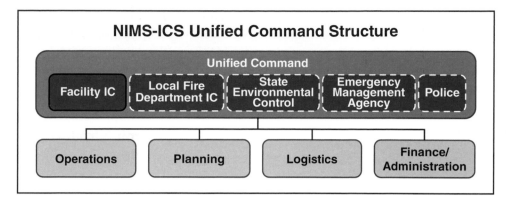

NIMS-ICS Unified Command Structure

Unified Command

Facility IC | Local Fire Department IC | State Environmental Control | Emergency Management Agency | Police

Operations | Planning | Logistics | Finance/ Administration

Figure 1.23 An example of agencies working under a Unified Command within NIMS-ICS.

Communications

Communications during an emergency incident takes a variety of forms. Face-to-face, verbal communication is clearly the most efficient form of communication, but the size and complexity of an operation may necessitate using telephone and radio communication as well. In most cases, mobile and portable radios are the primary communications media.

The radio communications system should reflect the size and complexity of the incident. Routine incidents can usually be handled on a single channel, but larger incidents may require using several channels to allow for clear and timely exchanges of information. Separate channels may be needed for command, tactical, and support functions.

Under NIMS-ICS, all radio communications should be transmitted in plain English ("clear text"). Codes, abbreviations, and acronyms should not be used because they may not be universally understood.

In addition, personnel should exercise proper radio discipline and follow all protocols. They should also confine transmissions to essential information and keep them as brief as possible. Long messages should be interrupted at frequent intervals to allow other individuals to break in with high-priority traffic. Obviously, emergency transmissions always have priority over other traffic, and personnel should avoid transmitting whenever anyone declares he or she has emergency traffic.

Local protocols dictate how messages are phrased, but in NIMS-ICS everyone should be called by the NIMS-ICS position he or she occupies. For example, regardless of who is the Incident Commander, that individual is always called "IC." The incident name may be included ("Warehouse IC") if more than one incident is in progress.

Radio communications should be established between the **emergency operations center (EOC)** and any mutual aid or automatic aid agencies that would respond to an incident at a facility site. This allows the IC to communicate with those agencies.

Implementing the System

The first person arriving on the scene of an emergency should initiate NIMS-ICS. If it has not already been done, this person should sound an alarm to notify the other employees in the facility of the emergency. Once the alarm has been sounded, this individual should begin to evaluate the situation in order to determine the answers to the following questions:

- What has occurred?
- What is the current status of the emergency?
- Is anyone injured or trapped?
- What is likely to happen in the foreseeable future?
- Can the emergency be handled with the resources on scene or en route?
- Is there a pre-plan for this emergency?
- Does the emergency fall within the scope of the training received?

The individual making the evaluation is at least temporarily in command of the incident. If the evaluation reveals that the actions required to eliminate the emergency are beyond the scope of this individual's training, Command should be transferred to someone more qualified at the earliest opportunity. In the meantime, the individual should do whatever he or she is qualified to do, such as notifying plant safety personnel of the situation, assisting with evacuations, and initiating the IMS by naming the incident and announcing the location of the incident Command Post (CP).

If there is no life-threatening situation that demands immediate action, the IC should begin to formulate an incident action plan taking into account any existing pre-plan. The plan should reflect the following priorities:

- Ensuring personnel safety and survival
- Rescuing or evacuating endangered occupants
- Eliminating the hazard
- Confining the emergency to its initial area when responders arrived
- Protecting exposures
- Extinguishing the fire/eliminating the hazard
- Performing loss control (overhaul and salvage)
- Cleaning up and protecting the environment
- Conducting termination (returning situation to as near normal as possible)
- Documenting the incident response

Whenever the NIMS-ICS is implemented, there should be only ONE Incident Commander. Even when Unified Command is used, the chain of command must be clearly defined. To avoid the confusion that conflicting orders cause, the IC should issue all orders through the chain of command.

For example, company policy may dictate that an employee, such as the facility manager, must be in charge of anything on company property. When the expertise and resources of the municipal fire and emergency services organization are needed, the manager can act on behalf of the company in the decision-making process but defer to the IC for the strategic and tactical decisions needed to mitigate the emergency.

With advice from the Operations Section Chief (if activated), the IC will gather and organize enough resources to handle the incident in a way that ensures that orders are carried out promptly, safely, and efficiently. Having sufficient resources on scene helps to ensure the safety of all personnel involved. The organization must be structured so that all available resources can be used to achieve the goals of the incident action plan. If necessary, the Incident Commander can appoint a Command staff to help gather, process, and disseminate information.

All incident personnel must function according to the incident action plan. Fire brigade leaders should follow SOPs, and every action should be directed toward achieving the goals and objectives specified in the plan.

Transfer of Command

A smooth and efficient transfer of command can contribute greatly to bringing the incident to a timely and successful conclusion. If both the nature and the scope of an incident are beyond the incipient level, the facility fire brigade member must be prepared to transfer command to the next arriving person with a higher level of expertise or authority. Transfer should be done face to face; however, if this interaction is not feasible, it can be done over the radio **(Figure 1.24)**.

Regardless how it's done, command can only be transferred to someone who is on the scene. As an incident grows, command may be transferred several times before the incident is brought under control,

Figure 1.24 Transfer of command is best accomplished face-to-face.

but it is recommended that command be passed as infrequently as possible for the continuity of the action plan. The person relinquishing command must provide the person assuming command with a situation status report, which is an updated version of the incident evaluation generated on arrival. The situation status report should include the following information:

- What happened
- Whether anyone was injured or trapped
- What has been done so far
- What is currently underway
- Whether the problem has stabilized or is getting worse
- What resources are on scene or en route and their assignments
- Whether it appears that current resources are adequate for the situation or that more resources need to be called in

An example of a complete situation status report might be the following:

"A fire is burning in a large trash container inside the warehouse at the northeast corner. No one is hurt and the fire appears to be confined to the trash container, but it is close to the wall and the smoke is heavy. When I sounded the alarm, I ordered everyone out of the building and called the fire brigade. The brigade is currently stretching a 1¾-inch handline to the fire to extinguish the fire. The fire does not seem to be getting any larger. Plant environmental is responding to contain any runoff water. I believe this will be adequate to control the fire, but I suggest we call the container supplier to have it removed from the site after extinguishment."

The person assuming on-scene command should acknowledge receipt of the status report by repeating it back to the other person. If the reiteration is accurate, the person assuming on-scene command is ready to accept control of and responsibility for the management of the incident. The former on-scene IC can then be reassigned to an operating unit or retained at the CP as an aide or as a member of the Command staff. The IC can call for any additional resources that might be needed.

Command and control of the incident does not transfer automatically when the information has been exchanged. If the problem does not exceed the level of training of the first on-scene IC and the senior member is satisfied with the manner in which the first on-scene IC is handling the situation, he or she may choose to leave the first on-scene IC in command. If the senior member is unsatisfied with how the situation is being handled, he or she assumes on-scene command and control of the incident.

If command is transferred, the former on-scene IC should announce the change to avoid any possible confusion caused by other personnel hearing a different voice issuing orders and acknowledging messages. However, if personnel involved follow the chain of command and use correct radio protocols, the member should not be calling anyone by his or her name, rank, or job title. Therefore, it should not matter who answers the radio messages. Anything that can reduce the confusion during the early stages of an emergency should be done, and announcing a transfer of on-scene command is one way of accomplishing that objective.

Tracking Resources

NIMS-ICS provides a means of tracking all personnel and equipment assigned to the incident. Most units responding to a facility incident will arrive fully staffed and ready to be assigned an operational objective; other personnel may have to be formed into units at the scene. To handle these and other differences in the resources available, the incident action plan must contain a tracking and accountability system with the following elements:

- A procedure for checking in at the scene
- A way of identifying the location of each unit and all personnel on scene
- A procedure for releasing units no longer needed

Incident Documentation

An important duty at an incident is the proper written documentation of everything that was done at an emergency. Someone should be specifically assigned to keep track of exactly what was done, who was on the scene, resources requested, and a time line of events as they occurred. All documentation should be secured with the incident report for reference and proof of actions, if needed.

Terminating the Incident

Once the incident has been brought under control the resources that are no longer needed should be released from the incident. This release is especially important when mutual aid units have been called in. Having NIMS-ICS in place will assist in demobilizing in a methodical and efficient manner. Adhering to a formal demobilization plan helps to recover loaned equipment, such as portable radios, and in identifying and documenting any damaged or lost equipment.

Chapter Review

1. Describe the levels of facility fire brigades.
2. What are the options that facility management must choose from when outlining employee responsibilities?
3. What elements must be included in a written fire brigade organizational statement or policy?
4. What elements must be addressed in a written emergency response operations site plan?
5. What information is included in incident reports?
6. What are three types of personnel accountability systems?
7. What are some nonverbal hand signals that may be communicated at an incident?
8. What are the components of NIMS-ICS?
9. How is command transferred in the NIMS-ICS system?

Key Terms

Area of assembly — A predetermined point of assembly that is free from any hazards.

Drill — Exercise conducted to practice and/or evaluate training already received; the process of skill maintenance.

Emergency Operations Center (EOC) — Facility that houses communications equipment, plans, contact/notification list, and staff that are used to coordinate the response to an emergency.

Evacuation — Controlled process of leaving or being removed from a potentially hazardous location, typically involving relocating people from an area of danger or potential risk to a safer place.

Facility Fire Brigade — Team of employees organized within a private company, industrial facility, or plant who are assigned to respond to fires and emergencies on that property. *Formerly* Industrial Fire Brigade.

Fire Apparatus — Any fire department or fire brigade emergency vehicle used in fire suppression or other emergency situations.

Fire Apparatus Driver/Operator — Fire brigade member who is charged with the responsibility of operating fire apparatus to, during, and from the scene of a fire operation, or at any other time the apparatus is in use. The driver/operator is also responsible for routine maintenance of the apparatus and any equipment carried on the apparatus. This is typically the first step in the fire department promotional chain. Also known as Chauffeur, Driver/Operator, or Engineer.

Immediately Dangerous to Life and Health (IDLH) — Description of any atmosphere that poses an immediate hazard to life or produces immediate irreversible, debilitating effects on health; represents concentrations above which respiratory protection should be required. Expressed in parts per million (ppm) or milligrams per cubic meter (mg/m³); companion measurement to the permissible exposure limit (PEL).

Incident Commander (IC) — Person in charge of the incident command system and responsible for the management of all incident operations during an emergency.

National Fire Protection Association (NFPA) — U.S. nonprofit educational and technical association devoted to protecting life and property from fire by developing fire protection standards and educating the public. Located in Quincy, Massachusetts.

National Incident Management System - Incident Command System (NIMS-ICS) — The U.S. mandated incident management system that defines the roles, responsibilities, and standard operating procedures used to manage emergency operations; creates a unified incident response structure for federal, state, and local governments.

Occupational Safety and Health Administration (OSHA) — U.S. federal agency that develops and enforces standards and regulations for occupational safety in the workplace.

Risk Assessment — (1) Determining the risk level or seriousness of a risk. (2) Process for evaluating risk associated with a specific hazard defined in terms of probability and frequency of occurrence, magnitude and severity, exposure, and consequences. *Also known as* Risk Evaluation.

Safe Haven — A designated location within a facility that has been designed to provide protection from one or more hazards associated with the facility.

Self-Contained Breathing Apparatus (SCBA) — Respirator worn by the user that supplies a breathable atmosphere that is either carried in or generated by the apparatus and is independent of the ambient atmosphere. Respiratory protection is worn in all atmospheres that are considered to be Immediately Dangerous to Life and Health (IDLH). *Also known as* Air Mask *or* Air Pack.

Shelter in Place — Having occupants remain in a structure or vehicle in order to provide protection from a rapidly approaching hazard, such as a fire or hazardous gas cloud. *Also known as* Protection-in-Place, Sheltering, *and* Taking Refuge.

Size-Up — Ongoing evaluation of influential factors at the scene of an incident.

Span of Control — Maximum number of subordinates that that one individual can effectively supervise; ranges from three to seven individuals or functions, with five generally established as optimum.

Standard Operating Procedure (SOP) — Formal methods or rules to guide the performance of routine functions or emergency operations. Procedures are typically written in a handbook, so that all firefighters can consult and become familiar with them. Also known as Operating Instruction (OI), Predetermined Procedures, or Standard Operating Guideline (SOG).

Thermal Protective Clothing — Garments emergency responders must wear to protect themselves while fighting fires, mitigating hazardous materials incidents, performing rescues, and delivering emergency medical services.

Training — (1) Supervised activity or process for achieving and maintaining proficiency through instruction and hands-on practice in the operation of equipment and systems that are expected to be used in the performance of assigned duties. (2) The transfer of knowledge regarding vocational or technical skills.

Unity of Command — Organizational principle in which workers report to only one supervisor in order to eliminate conflicting orders.

Skill Sheet List

The following skill sheets should be used to evaluate the skills described in this chapter:

NOTE: Students should wear the PPE appropriate to the NFPA 1081 level (Incipient, Advanced Exterior, Interior Structural, etc...) being evaluated.

Incipient Facility Fire Brigade Member

Chapter Contents

JPRs addressed in this chapter

This chapter provides information that addresses the following job performance requirements of NFPA 1081, *Standard for Facility Fire Brigade Member Professional Qualifications (2018).*

4.3.5

Learning Objectives

1. Explain the purpose of fire safety surveys. [4.3.5]

2. Describe the general procedures for conducting a fire safety survey. [4.3.5]

Chapter 2
Fire Safety Surveys

The hazards found at a site vary depending upon the type of facility or facilities found at that site and the manner in which each facility is constructed. The design layout, materials, and type of construction may also be different for each occupancy/industry for which the structure is intended. For example, an automobile manufacturing building is not constructed using the same design or with the exact same materials as an institutional facility such as a hospital or prison.

Fire brigade members need to be familiar with the different uses for the structures at their site. The basic uses for buildings in the industrial setting include the following:

- Offices
- Process units
- Warehouses
- Laboratories
- Control rooms
- Assembly lines

Fire safety surveys are a part of the fire prevention activities at a site and may serve a vital function in facility fire brigade operations. Fire safety surveys familiarize a facility fire brigade member to areas within the facility and help identify the hazards found at a site.

Introduction to Fire Safety Surveys
NFPA 1081 (2018): 4.3.5

Figure 2.1 A fire brigade member looks for fire hazards during a facility fire safety survey.

Fire safety surveys involve those activities that have been planned or legislated to ensure that personnel have a safe physical work environment. The survey process requires that fire brigade members become familiar with the structures and operations at their facility and to quickly recognize fire and safety hazards. The findings make fire brigade members aware of potential hazards and permit them to communicate unsafe conditions to building/facility managers and occupants **(Figure 2.1)**. Observed problems should be resolved diplomatically before an incident occurs. Additional guidance regarding inspection practices can be found in IFSTA's **Fire Inspection and Code Enforcement** manual and the OSHA *General Industry Standards*, 29 *CFR* 1910.

Fire safety survey and fire incident records contain the documented fire history of a facility and can improve fire prevention efforts. Studying previous incidents, reviewing data obtained from various fire reports, and comparing statistical data can accomplish many informational benefits. Such a review helps identify conditions or problems that were noted during previous surveys, such as:

- Hazardous conditions and acts
- Damage from previous incidents
- Recurring trends (poor maintenance and housekeeping)
- Out of date fire system service and test records

If fire brigade personnel conduct a fire safety survey at their facility, they should focus on identifying fire and safety hazards. Their purpose is to ensure that facility personnel have done everything in their means to prevent fires from occurring and to provide a means of egress for occupants if a fire does occur.

NOTE: Fire brigade members have a vested interest in the prevention of fires. Fire prevention is always safer and more effective when compared to actual fire suppression.

Fire Safety Survey Procedures
NFPA 1081 (2018): 4.3.5

Fire brigade personnel should follow their organization's procedures for conducting fire safety surveys. As explained in this section, a fire brigade member should be familiar with the following at a minimum:

- Personal requirements for the fire safety survey
- Survey equipment
- Conducting the fire safety survey
- Exit interview
- Reports and records

Personal Requirements for the Fire Safety Survey

When performing a fire safety survey, the fire brigade member should project a professional appearance. A professional appearance gains the respect of the personnel being dealt with and bolsters the fire brigade's image. In addition to appearance, a fire brigade member's knowledge and experience will contribute to his or her overall professional bearing.

Fire brigade members should possess a basic understanding of fire prevention principles and should approach their assignments with confidence. They can aggressively tackle assigned situations they are trained to handle and may offer corrective advice. They should also be aware of their limitations in the field of fire prevention.

A fire brigade member's ability to judge conditions will improve with formal training, experience, and on-the-job training. The fire brigade manager, leaders, training coordinator, fire prevention personnel, and other individuals from a wide range of technical backgrounds can provide needed insight on those occasions when answers to hazardous situations are required. Fire brigade members should feel comfortable to ask for help when needed.

Survey Equipment

While performing a fire safety survey, fire brigade members may use one set of equipment at the survey site and then a different set at the fire brigade office/station.

Equipment at the Survey Site (Figure 2.2):

- Coveralls or other specialized clothing
- Appropriate protective equipment such as safety glasses, hearing protection, head protection, and gloves
- At least one portable radio if the members are to remain available for fire fighting duty during the survey

Figure 2.2 Flashlights, safety glasses, a tape measure, and other equipment can be useful to a fire brigade member conducting a facility fire safety survey.

- Clipboard, grid or engineering paper, copy of the prefire plan, copy of NFPA or locally used standard plan symbols, and any fire brigade facility survey forms, if used
- Pen or pencil
- Measuring device such as measuring tapes, wheels, or lasers
- Flashlight
- Camera, if allowed

Equipment at the Fire Brigade Office or Station:

- Reference books/manuals/procedures
- Survey reports and forms
- Survey file, preferably on a computer database
- Code and inspection manuals
- Accurate facility records
- Drawing board
- Drawing scales, rulers, and materials

Fire brigades can select the time and place to perform fire prevention activities. Fire brigade management should set a schedule for survey activities and ensure the fire brigade leaders and members perform these activities in an efficient and professional manner.

The fire brigade leader should contact the facility manager ahead of time to schedule the survey. The fire brigade leader will inform the facility manager of the purpose of the fire safety survey and find out what day and time would be most suitable. Coordinating with the facility manager will ensure that the survey coincides with the availability of the building personnel. This procedure enables fire safety surveys to be scheduled at a time that will not inflict a hardship on either the occupants or the fire brigade.

Conducting the Fire Safety Survey

Fire safety surveys can reduce the number of fire incidents, injuries, and deaths occurring at an industrial site. When fire brigade members conduct a fire safety survey, their main objectives should include the following:

- Preventing accidental fires
- Improving life safety conditions
- Helping the facility manager and occupants to understand and improve existing conditions
- Complying with appropriate codes and regulations

While conducting a fire safety survey in larger facilities in which workers may not know one another or work in all areas of the facility, the following guidelines may apply **(Figure 2.3)**:

Figure 2.3 During a facility fire safety survey, the fire brigade member surveys the interior and exterior of the facility. When terminating the survey, the fire brigade member should thank those who helped.

- Report to the department supervisor and state the purpose of your visit.
- Have a fire brigade member working in the area help with the survey/inspection because of his or her familiarity with the area, the processes, and personnel.
- Maintain a courteous attitude at all times.
- Compliment employees when favorable conditions are found.
- Make constructive comments regarding the elimination of hazardous conditions.

NOTE: Understand that it is acceptable to say "I don't know" or "I will have to check and get back with you" when appropriate.

- Survey the entire building or facility both inside and outside.
- Thank the supervisor(s) and employees for their time and assistance in the survey.

Fire Hazards

A **fire hazard** is a condition that encourages a fire to start or increases the extent or severity of a fire. Basic fire chemistry suggests fire cannot survive without a fuel supply, sufficient heat source, oxygen supply, and a self-sustained chemical reaction (fire tetrahedron). Therefore, eliminating one or all of these elements can prevent hazardous fire conditions.

Control of the oxygen supply is difficult if the fire cannot be separated from airflow, whether via containment or smothering using suppression solutions. Because 21 percent of the earth's atmosphere is composed of oxygen, any amount of airflow is likely to support the reaction. Controlling the hazards associated with fuel supply and heat sources may be the simplest option. If heat sources are kept separated from fuel supplies, the condition remains safe. Not all fuel supplies can be ignited easily, but misuse of any fuel under extreme heat conditions can lead to a fire. Some common fuel hazards include the following:

- Ordinary combustibles such as wood, cloth, or paper
- Flammable and combustible gases such as natural gas, liquefied petroleum gas (LPG), and compressed natural gas (CNG)
- Flammable and combustible liquids such as gasoline, oils, lacquers, or alcohol
- Chemicals such as nitrates, oxides, or chlorates
- Dusts such as particles from grain, wood, metal, or coal
- Metals such as magnesium, sodium, or potassium
- Plastics, resins, and cellulose

Heat source hazards relate to a source of heat energy that may start a fire. These hazards include the following:

- **Chemical heat energy** — The result of an oxidizer and reducing agent reacting with one another to generate heat
- **Electrical heat energy** — Produced by poorly maintained or misused electrical appliances/equipment, exposed wiring, and lighting
- **Mechanical heat energy** — Generated by moving parts on machines, such as belts and bearings
- **Nuclear heat energy** — Heat generated by nuclear fission
- **Heat of decomposition** — Heat created by decomposing organic materials.

> **CAUTION:** Any heat source may be dangerous.

Common Fire Hazards

A **common fire hazard** is a condition that is prevalent in almost all areas and brings a fuel source and an ignition source together. Fire brigade members need to be alert to the dangers posed by the following common hazards **(Figure 2.4)**:

Figure 2.4 Common fire hazards include poor housekeeping, oily rags, combustible dust buildups, and improper wiring. *Combustible dust and improper wiring photos courtesy of Rich Mahaney.*

- Poor housekeeping and improper storage of materials can:
  — Complicate movement through an area
  — Increase the fire load of an area
  — Increase the chance that a flammable or combustible material may come in contact with an ignition source
  — Hide fire hazards
- Defective or improperly used heating, lighting, or power equipment
- Improper use, storage, and disposal of floor cleaning compounds
- Misuse of fumigation substances and flammable or combustible liquids
- Improper disposal or storage of oil/chemical soaked rags
- Buildups of combustible dusts
- Improper storage of small quantities of flammable or combustible liquids
- Improper storage of flammable or combustible materials in electrical or mechanical rooms
- Improper storage of materials in exit ways or stair wells
- Improper smoking and disposal of smoking materials
- Improper electrical wiring or temporary electrical wiring used in place of permanent power sources
  Factors that can contribute to the spread or severity of a fire include the following:
- Blocking fire doors open, which can contribute to the spread of a fire
- Existence of party walls, common attics, cocklofts, and other open voids in multiple occupancies
- The quantity and types of fuel(s) to which a fire may spread (fuel loading)

A comprehensive program geared toward public awareness, fire and life safety education, and good safety practices can reduce the hazards caused by unsafe personal acts. Many industries have permitting programs to evaluate the amount of combustibles that are permitted in a given area. Transient combustibles that are not properly managed can create a situation where the fire load increases in excess of the design of the fire suppression system.

Target Hazard Properties

A **target hazard** is a facility in which there is a great potential for life or property loss from a fire. These occupancies should receive special attention during surveys. The following are examples of target hazard facilities **(Figure 2.5)**:

- Lumber mills and yards
- Paper manufacturing plants
- Consumer goods manufacturing facilities
- Electrical power generation plants
- Chemical manufacturing facilities
- Oil refineries and bulk storage facilities
- Fabrication and machining facilities
- Paint facilities

Figure 2.5 Target hazard facilities include lumber mills, power plants, chemical plants, and oil refineries. *Lumber mill photo courtesy of Paul Pestel and chemical plant photo courtesy of Rich Mahaney.*

Special Fire Hazards

A **special fire hazard** arises as a result of the processes or operations that are characteristic of the individual occupancy. Commercial, manufacturing, and large meeting occupancies have particular hazards. The fire brigade management will need to brief the personnel conducting a fire safety survey on the special fire hazards of that occupancy. The NFPA Handbook is a good source of information on special fire hazards.

Each facility can present special hazards to workers and fire brigade members. These hazards may be related to the facility's specific industry, construction, or occupancy type. Fire brigade members must be trained on the site-specific hazards found at their location.

Many special fire hazards are related to the types of mechanical or chemical processes used within the facility. Fire brigade members should be aware of the processes used in their facilities and where they are located. Some of these processes will be contained at specific facilities designed for their operations while others may be present during inspections of other types of occupancies. There are locations where these hazardous processes may exist only during the use of the process and will require a permit to perform.

Survey Concerns

There are a number of items or concerns that fire brigade members should check during a fire safety survey. Some of these items are commonly found in the interior of the facility while others may be encountered on the exterior.

Interior Survey Concerns

During the interior survey of the building or facility, brigade members should look for the following concerns **(Figure 2.6, p. 50)**:

- **Combustible materials** — Are unused components, cardboard boxes, papers, and other materials stored properly? Are combustibles stored in close proximity to high-temperature devices or processes? Are they stored in racks?
- **Mechanical devices** — Inquire about proper operations, maintenance, and conditions, including power cords.

| Mechanical Devices | Flammable Storage | Emergency Equipment |

Figure 2.6 During the interior portion of a facility fire safety survey, the fire brigade member should check mechanical devices, flammable storage lockers and rooms, and emergency equipment.

- **Electrical wiring and equipment** — Check for old, frayed, or exposed wiring and improperly installed electrical conductors. Check for unprotected light bulbs or improperly maintained equipment, such as exhaust fans encrusted with dust and dirt. Check that the electrical fixtures are properly rated and labeled for a hazardous location. Is temporary power being used in place of permanent power sources? Are electrical conduit fittings in a hazardous area rated for that environment and intact?

- **Portable heating units** — Note whether equipment is listed with Underwriters Laboratories (UL), Factory Mutual (FM), or some other laboratory and determine if it is adequately separated from combustible furniture or other materials.

- **General housekeeping practices** — Are trash cans kept empty? Are exhaust vents and dryer vents clean? Are spray booths clean? Are filters coated with overspray? Are there accumulations of combustible materials/particles on horizontal or vertical surfaces?

- **Fire detection and suppression systems** — Check the status of fire detection and suppression systems and conduct operational testing on a regular basis. Ensure that systems that are out of service are properly tagged or labeled. Are sprinkler heads free from paint, intact, clean, and with control valves properly marked? Are stand pipes clear and in good condition?

- **Electrical distribution panels** — Are panels, switches, and breakers labeled? Are any breakers missing or tripped?

- **Gas appliances** — Check for the following: improper clearance to combustible materials, the existence of automatic gas control safety devices, manual supply line shutoff, corroded piping, the condition of vents, and possible gas leaks.

- **Oil-burning installations** — Check for the existence of annual service records and the condition of oil burners, chimney pipes, supply tanks, and piping.

- **Furnaces, hot water heaters, and vent pipes** — Is the unit properly installed and clear of combustibles? Is the vent pipe in good condition? Inquire about hot water temperature settings to protect against scalds and burns.

- **Accumulated waste and dust** — Note stacks of paper, cardboard, discarded components, old rags, and improperly stored items. Are rafters, floors, and conveyors free from accumulated dust? Are spray booths clean and filters not coated with overspray? Do vents have any grease or chemical build-up around them or on the decking's surface?

- **Flammable and combustible liquid and other hazardous materials** — Are flammable sprays, chemicals, and other dangerous solutions being properly labeled, used, and stored? Are dispensing drums grounded, and are bonding cords in good condition? Check that non-rated electrical equipment is not in the area. Are storage cabinets properly rated and contain only the flammable liquids with no combustibles, such as cardboard boxes inside? Check that the maximum capacity of the cabinet has not been exceeded.

- **Emergency markings, postings, and equipment inspections** — Are the locations of fire extinguishers and exits properly marked? Are exits unobstructed? Are emergency telephone numbers and procedures properly posted? Have fire extinguishers and other emergency equipment been inspected, as required? Are emergency lights working and regularly tested?

Exterior Survey Concerns

During the exterior survey of the building or facility, brigade members should look for the following concerns (**Figure 2.7**):

Figure 2.7 When surveying the exterior of a facility, the fire brigade member should check for unkempt vegetation and inspect outbuildings and security devices.

- **Facility access** — Check clearances for emergency apparatus (such as pumpers and aerials) to reach or escape from the facility.
- **Roof** — Check the condition of the roof as well as the access and egress to/from the roof to check condition of caged ladders and fire escapes.
- **Chimneys and spark arrestors** — Check condition of chimneys and spark arrestors.
- **Wildland or landscaped areas, open storage areas, utility substation, and remote storage facilities** — Are the grounds clear of unkempt vegetation? Are these areas accessible? Are there distinct separations of combustible materials?
- **Fuel storage areas** — Is fuel stored properly? Is the area properly marked to prevent smoking or the introduction of flame into the area? Are containment areas provided for spills? Are appropriate fire extinguishers available? Is there an accessible emergency shutoff valve?
- **Outside waste burners** — Discourage use of outside waste burners. Check for conformity to local restrictions.
- **Garages, sheds, barns, and outbuildings** — Are these structures in good repair? Note storage of dangerous chemicals or other substances. Are there combustible materials stored against buildings? Are trash and/or dumpsters located at proper standoff distances? Are appropriate fire extinguishers available?
- **Flammable liquids and gases** — Recommend that flammable liquids be kept in a can rated for flammable liquids and stored only in a flammable storage locker indicated for that use.
- **Lightning protection** — Recommend that the components of fixed lightning protection systems on structures be tested periodically. Visually check that the building's grounding system is intact.

- **Security devices** — Note security devices (window bars, security fences, and electronic security devices) and guard dogs that may hamper ingress or egress.
- **Permanently installed fire protection systems and equipment** — Visually check the accessibility, condition, and operational readiness of such systems and equipment. Ensure systems and equipment are not being used for non-emergency purposes.

Exit Interview

Reporting findings to the person responsible for the building or facility being surveyed can do much to maintain a cooperative attitude of the department supervisor and employees. To leave the premises without consulting that person might give the impression that the survey was unimportant or incomplete. During this interview, a fire brigade member or the fire brigade leader should comment on the conditions that were found. An exit interview also gives fire brigade members an opportunity to express thanks for the courtesies extended to the fire brigade and opens the way to explain how fire brigade members will study these reports from the standpoint of fire fighting procedures (pre-incident planning). In the final portion of the exit interview, fire brigade members should answer any questions they can and refer the facility manager/occupant to the fire brigade office for further assistance.

Reports and Records

The findings of the fire safety survey should be reported to facility management in accordance with company policy. This report should identify any hazards found, recommended corrections, and the time limits for making such corrections. A reinspection is conducted to ensure that corrections have been made. Fire safety survey records should be maintained in accordance with company policy.

Chapter Review

1. How can studying previous incidents improve fire prevention efforts?

2. What are some exterior fire survey concerns?

Discussion Question

1. What common fire hazards have you seen in your facilities?

Key Terms

Common Fire Hazards — Those that are prevalent in almost all occupancies and encourage a fire to start.

Fire Hazard — Any material, condition, or act that contributes to the start of a fire or that increases the extent or severity of fire.

Fire Safety Surveys — Those activities that have been planned or legislated to ensure that personnel have a safe physical work environment.

Special Fire Hazards — Hazards that arise from or are related to the particular processes or operation in an occupancy.

Target Hazard — Any facility in which a fire, accident, or natural disaster could cause substantial casualties or significant economic harm, through either property or infrastructure damage.

Skill Sheet List

The following skill sheets should be used to evaluate the skills described in this chapter:

NOTE: Students should wear the PPE appropriate to the NFPA 1081 level (Incipient, Advanced Exterior, Interior Structural, etc...) being evaluated.

Incipient Facility Fire Brigade Member

Chapter Contents

JPRs addressed in this chapter

This chapter provides information that addresses the following job performance requirements of NFPA 1081, *Standard for Facility Fire Brigade Member Professional Qualifications (2018)*.

4.1.2   4.3.1

1. Explain the basic principles of fire science. [4.1.2, 4.3.1]

2. Describe how thermal energy impacts fire behavior. [4.1.2]

3. Explain the function of fuel within the combustion process. [4.1.2]

4. Explain the function of oxygen within the combustion process. [4.1.2]

5. Explain the self-sustained chemical reaction involved in flaming combustion. [4.1.2]

6. Differentiate among the stages of fire development. [4.1.2, 4.3.1]

7. Explain how fire brigade operations can influence fire behavior in a structure. [4.1.2, 4.3.1]

8. Describe how building construction and layout affects fire development. [4.1.2, 4.3.1]

9. Describe how fire can affect common building materials. [4.1.2, 4.3.1]

10. Identify special industry hazards fire brigades may encounter. [4.1.2]

Chapter 3
Fire Dynamics

Fire dynamics describes the meeting point between fire science, materials science, fluid dynamics of gases, and heat transfer. Understanding the basic physics of these sciences can give fire brigade members the knowledge needed to forecast fire growth at a scene and predict the likely consequences of various tactical options available for controlling a fire. All of the following provide fire brigade members with pieces of the total picture about a fire's likely behavior during fireground operations:

- Fire science
- The combustion process
- Fire behavior and its relationship to various materials and environments
- Classifications of fires and their corresponding extinguishing agents
- Recognition of fire behavior indicators, fire development patterns, and the potential for rapid fire development
- Various ventilation and fire suppression tactics used as tools for controlling fires

Science of Fire

NFPA 1081 (2018): 4.1.2, 4.3.1

Fire brigade members should have a scientific understanding of **combustion**, **fire**, **heat**, and **temperature**. Fire can take various forms, but all fires involve a heat-producing chemical reaction between some type of fuel and an oxidizer, most commonly oxygen in the air. Oxidizers are not combustible but will support or enhance combustion. **Table 3.1** lists some common oxidizers.

Table 3.1 Common Oxidizers	
Substance	**Common Use**
Calcium Hypochlorite (granular solid)	Chlorination of water in swimming pools
Chlorine (gas)	Water purification
Ammonium Nitrate (granular solid)	Fertilizer
Hydrogen Peroxide (liquid)	Industrial bleaching (pulp and paper and chemical manufacturing)
Methyl Ethyl Ketone Peroxide	Catalyst in plastics manufacturing

Coutesy of Ed Hartin.

Physical Science Terminology

Physical science is the study of **matter** and **energy** and includes chemistry and physics. This theoretical foundation must be translated into a practical knowledge of fire dynamics. To remain safe, you need to be able to identify the fire dynamics present in a given situation and anticipate what the next stages of the fire will be along with how fire fighting operations may impact the fire's behavior **(Figure 3.1)**.

Figure 3.1 The conditions found at a fire scene offer indications of a fire's current behavior and potential future behavior.

The world around you is made up of matter in the form of physical materials that occupy space and have mass. While matter can undergo many types of physical and chemical changes, this chapter will concentrate on those changes related to fire.

A physical change occurs when a substance remains chemically the same but changes in size, shape, or appearance. Examples of physical change are water freezing (liquid to solid) and boiling (liquid to gas).

A chemical reaction occurs when a substance changes from one type of matter into another, such as two or more substances combining to form compounds. **Oxidation** is a chemical reaction involving the combination of an oxidizer, such as oxygen in the air, with other materials. Oxidation can be slow, such as the combination of oxygen with iron to form rust, or rapid, as in combustion of methane (natural gas) **(Figure 3.2)**.

Figure 3.2 The timeline of oxidation illustrates the speed differences among each type of oxidation.

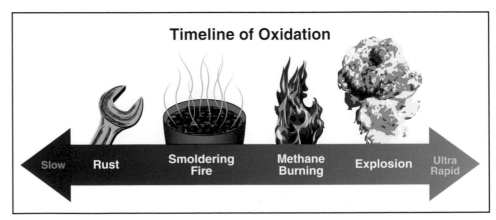

Energy is the capacity to perform work. Work occurs when a force is applied to an object over a distance or when a substance undergoes a chemical, biological, or physical change. In the case of heat, work means increasing a substance's temperature.

Forms of energy are classified as either potential or kinetic **(Figure 3.3)**. Potential energy represents the amount of energy that an object can release at some point in the future. Fuels have a certain amount of potential energy before they are ignited, based on their chemical composition. This potential energy available for release in the combustion process is known as the heat of combustion. The rate at which a fuel releases energy over time depends on many variables including:

- Chemical composition
- Arrangement
- Density of the fuel
- Availability of oxygen for combustion

Figure 3.3 Potential energy is stored energy, while kinetic energy is actively being released. *Courtesy of Dan Madrzykowski, NIST.*

Kinetic energy is the energy that a moving object possesses. While a fuel such as wood is not "moving" as you might define it, when heat is introduced, the molecules within the fuel begin to vibrate. As the heat (thermal energy) increases, these molecules vibrate more and more rapidly. The fuel's kinetic energy is the result of these vibrations in the molecules.

There are many types of energy including:

- Chemical
- Thermal
- Mechanical
- Electrical
- Light
- Nuclear
- Sound

All energy can change from one type to another. For example, mechanical energy from a machine can convert to thermal energy when friction between moving parts generates heat. In terms of fire behavior, the potential chemical energy of a fuel converts into heat and light during combustion.

Energy is measured in **joules (J)** in the International System of Units (SI). The quantity of heat required to change the temperature of 1 gram of water by 1 degree Celsius is 4.2 joules. In the customary system, the unit of measurement for heat is the British thermal unit (Btu). A British thermal unit is the amount of heat required to raise the temperature of 1 pound of water by 1 degree Fahrenheit. While not used in scientific and engineering texts, the Btu is still frequently used in the fire service. When comparing joules and Btu, 1 055 J = 1 Btu.

Chemical and physical changes almost always involve an exchange of energy. A fuel's potential energy releases during combustion and converts to kinetic energy. Reactions that emit energy as they occur are **exothermic reactions**. Fire is an exothermic chemical reaction that releases energy in the form of heat and sometimes light.

Reactions that absorb energy as they occur are **endothermic reactions (Figure 3.4)**. For example, converting water from a liquid to a gas (steam) requires the input of energy resulting in an endothermic reaction. Converting water to steam is a tactic for controlling and extinguishing some types of fires.

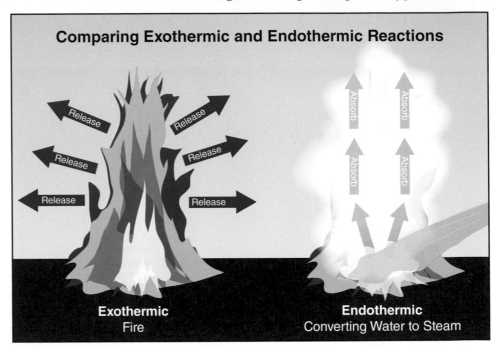

Figure 3.4 Exothermic reactions release energy while endothermic reactions absorb energy.

Fire Triangle and Tetrahedron

The **fire triangle** and **fire tetrahedron** models are used to explain the elements of fire and how fires can be extinguished **(Figure 3.5)**. The oldest and simplest model, the fire triangle, shows three elements necessary for combustion to occur: fuel, oxygen, and heat. Remove any one of these elements and the fire will be extinguished. The fire triangle was used prior to the general adaptation of the fire tetrahedron, which includes a **chemical chain reaction**.

An uninhibited chemical chain reaction must also be present for a fire to occur. The fire tetrahedron model includes the chemical chain reaction to explain flaming or gas-phase combustion (fire is an example of gas-phase combustion).

Ignition

Fuels must be in a gaseous state to burn; therefore, solids and liquids must become gaseous in order for ignition to occur. When heat is transferred to a liquid or solid, the substance's temperature increases and the substance starts to convert to a gaseous state (off-gassing). In solids, off-gassing is a chemical change known as **pyrolysis**; in liquids, a physical change called **vaporization (Figure 3.6)**.

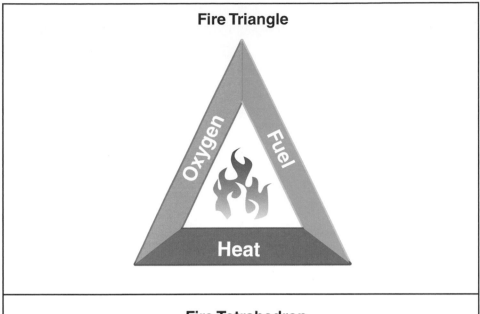

Fire Triangle

Oxygen

Fuel

Heat

Fire Tetrahedron

Reducing Agent (Fuel)

Oxidizing Agent

Chemical Chain Reaction

Heat

Chemical Chain Reaction

Reducing Agent

Oxidizing Agent

Heat

Figure 3.5 The fire triangle illustrates the three components needed for a fire, while the fire tetrahedron demonstrates the four components needed for a self-sustaining fire.

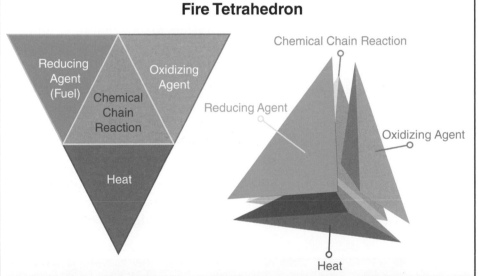

Pyrolysis

Vaporization

Figure 3.6 Pyrolysis occurs when a solid fuel is converted into a gaseous fuel. Vaporization is the conversion of a liquid to a vapor by the heat energy of combustion. *Courtesy of Dan Madrzykowski, NIST.*

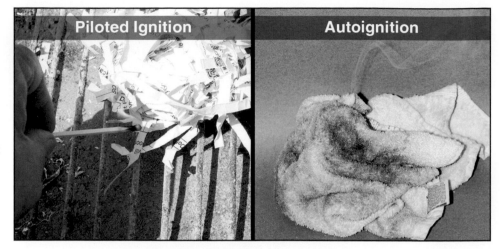

Figure 3.7 Piloted ignition involves the introduction of an external ignition source, while autoignition occurs under special conditions without the heat of a spark or other source.

Piloted ignition is the most common form of ignition and occurs when a mixture of fuel and oxygen encounter an external heat source with sufficient heat or thermal energy to start the combustion reaction. **Autoignition** occurs without any external flame or spark to ignite the fuel gases or vapors. The fuel's surface is heated to the point at which the combustion reaction occurs **(Figure 3.7)**.

Once the fuel is ignited, the energy released from combustion transfers to the remaining solid fuel resulting in the production and ignition of additional fuel vapors or gases. This exchange of energy from the burning gases to the fuel results in a sustained combustion reaction.

Autoignition temperature (AIT) is the minimum temperature at which a fuel in the air must be heated in order to start self-sustained combustion. The autoignition temperature of a substance is always higher than its piloted ignition temperature.

Combustion

Fire and combustion are similar conditions. Both words are commonly used to mean the same thing. Combustion, however, is a chemical reaction while flaming combustion is only one possible form of combustion. Combustion can occur without visible flames. There are two modes of combustion: nonflaming and flaming **(Figure 3.8)**.

Figure 3.8 Nonflaming combustion (left) features lower temperatures and smoldering conditions. Flaming combustion (right) displays visible flames above the burning fuel.

Nonflaming Combustion

Nonflaming combustion occurs more slowly and at a lower temperature, producing a smoldering glow in the material's surface. The burning may be localized on or near the fuel's surface where it is in contact with oxygen. Examples of nonflaming or smoldering combustion include burning charcoal or smoldering wood or fabric. The fire triangle illustrates the elements/conditions required for this mode of combustion.

Flaming Combustion

Flaming combustion is commonly referred to as fire. It produces a visible flame above the material's surface. Flaming combustion occurs when a gaseous fuel mixes with oxygen in the correct ratio and heats to ignition temperature. Flaming combustion requires liquid or solid fuels to be converted to the gas-phase through the addition of heat (vaporization or pyrolysis, respectively). When heated, both liquid and solid fuels will emit vapors that mix with oxygen, producing flames above the material's surface if the gases ignite. The fire tetrahedron accurately reflects the conditions required for flaming combustion.

Each element of the tetrahedron must be in the proper proportion and in close physical proximity for flaming combustion to occur. Removing any element of the tetrahedron interrupts the chemical chain reaction and stops flaming combustion. However, the fire may continue to smolder depending on the characteristics of the fuel.

Ignition is where the combustion process begins. A heat source pyrolizes a fuel, creating fuel gases. Those gases mix with oxygen and ignite, creating a fire. The fire can be compared to a pump. Fresh oxygen is "pumped in" and mixes with fuel gases. Then as it burns, the fire "pumps out" combustion products that have larger amounts of mass and a higher level of energy than the inlet air. In the case of open burning, the "pump" does not have a well-defined inlet or outlet, as the air is being **entrained** (drawn in) from all around the burning fuel. **Figure 3.9** illustrates the intake flow to the fire and the exhaust flow from the fire.

The fire also generates heat. As the **heat transfers** to the gaseous combustion products, they expand and begin to rise and move away from the fire due to buoyancy. In other words, the density of the hot combustion products is less than the surrounding air, and the combustion products "float" on the dense cool air surrounding the fuel, creating the layers of smoke and fuel gases that fill a compartment during a fire.

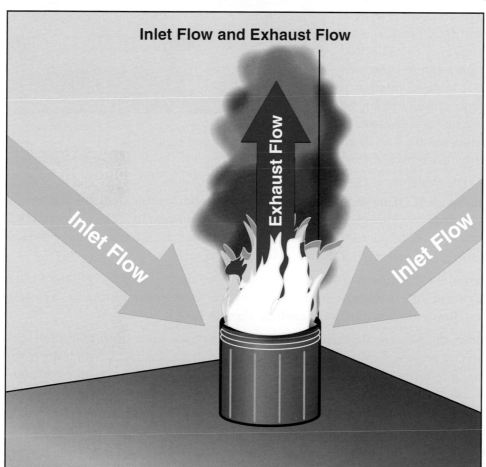

Figure 3.9 This illustration demonstrates the concepts of inlet flow and exhaust flow.

Products of Combustion

As a fuel burns, its chemical composition changes, which produces new substances. These **products of combustion** are often simply described as heat and smoke. While the heat from a fire is a danger to anyone directly exposed to it, exposure to toxic gases found in smoke and/or lack of oxygen cause most fire deaths. Smoke is an aerosol comprised of gases, vapor, and solid particulates.

Smoke is the product of **incomplete combustion**. Simply stated, combustion is incomplete when any of the fuel is left after combustion has occurred. Smoke and ash are examples of left over fuel from incomplete combustion.

By comparison, under ideal conditions, the entire fuel would undergo a chemical conversion from its current form into an equal amount of new materials. For example, complete combustion of methane in air results in the production of heat, light, water vapor, and carbon dioxide.

However, combustion is incomplete in a structure fire, meaning that some of the fuel does not burn, but instead gets entrained with hot gases and rises aloft. This unburned fuel is smoke, and it has the potential to burn **(Figure 3.10)**.

Most structure fires involve multiple types of fuels (**carbon-based fuels** [wood, cotton], **hydrocarbon fuels** [plastics, synthetic fabrics], and other types), and the fires tend to have a limited air supply. When the air supply is limited, the level of incomplete combustion is higher, which produces more smoke. These factors result in complex chemical reactions that generate a wide range of products of combustion including toxic and flammable gases, vapors, and particulates that comprise smoke.

Figure 3.10 Smoke is composed of a wide range of toxic and flammable gases and particulates.

Gases such as **carbon monoxide (CO)** are generally colorless, while vapor and particulates give smoke its varied colors. Most components of smoke are toxic and dangerous to human life. The materials that make up smoke vary from fuel to fuel, but generally all smoke is toxic. The toxic effects of smoke inhalation are the result of the interrelated effect of all the toxic products present.

Keep in mind that the combustion process consumes oxygen from the air, effectively removing it from the environment. As part of the chemical reaction, the consumed oxygen combines with carbon in the smoke to form combustion products like CO or **carbon dioxide (CO_2)**.

Low oxygen concentrations alone can result in hypoxia or death. The toxic gases in combination with a low oxygen concentration can reduce the time that a victim could survive. **Table 3.2** lists some of the more common products of combustion and their toxic effects. Concentrations of the products of combustion and/or low oxygen concentrations can cause **asphyxiation** (fatal level of oxygen deficiency in the blood).

Carbon monoxide (CO) is a toxic and flammable product of the incomplete combustion of organic (carbon-containing) materials. Carbon monoxide is a colorless, odorless gas present at almost every fire. It is released when an organic material burns in an atmosphere with a limited supply of oxygen. CO exposure is frequently identified as the cause of death in civilian fatalities.

Table 3.2
Common Products of Combustion and Their Toxic Effects

Carbon Monoxide	Colorless, odorless gas. Inhalation of carbon monoxide causes headache, dizziness, weakness, confusion, nausea, unconsciousness, and death. Exposure to as little as 0.2 percent carbon monoxide can result in unconsciousness within 30 minutes. Inhalation of high concentration can result in immediate collapse and unconsciousness.
Formaldehyde	Colorless gas with a pungent, irritating odor that is highly irritating to the nose. 50-100 ppm can cause severe irritation to the respiratory tract and serious injury. Exposure to high concentrations can cause injury to the skin. Formaldehyde is a suspected carcinogen.
Hydrogen Cyanide	Colorless, toxic, and flammable liquid below 79°F (26°C) produced by the combustion of nitrogen-bearing substances. It is a chemical asphyxiant that acts to prevent the body from using oxygen. It is commonly encountered in smoke in concentrations lower than carbon monoxide.
Nitrogen Dioxide	Reddish-brown gas or yellowish-brown liquid, which is highly toxic and corrosive.
Particulates	Small particles that can be inhaled and deposited in the mouth, trachea, or the lungs. Exposure to particulates can cause eye irritation, respiratory distress (in addition to health hazards specifically related to the particular substances involved).
Sulfur Dioxide	Colorless gas with a choking or suffocating odor. Sulfur dioxide is toxic and corrosive, and can irritate the eyes and mucous membranes.

Source: *Computer Aided Management of Emergency Operations (CAMEO)* and *Toxicological Profile for Polycyclic Aromatic Hydrocarbons.*

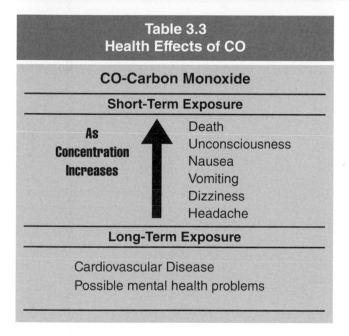

Table 3.3
Health Effects of CO

CO-Carbon Monoxide

Short-Term Exposure

As Concentration Increases

Death
Unconsciousness
Nausea
Vomiting
Dizziness
Headache

Long-Term Exposure

Cardiovascular Disease
Possible mental health problems

CO acts as a chemical **asphyxiant**. CO poisoning is a sometimes lethal condition in which carbon monoxide molecules attach to hemoglobin, decreasing the blood's ability to carry oxygen. CO combines with hemoglobin about 200 times more effectively than oxygen does. CO does not act on the body, but excludes oxygen from the blood, leading to hypoxia of the brain and tissues. Death will follow if the process is not reversed. **Table 3.3** illustrates the effects of CO on humans.

Hydrogen cyanide (HCN), a toxic and flammable substance produced in the combustion of materials containing nitrogen, is also commonly found in smoke, although at lower concentrations than CO. Incomplete combustion of substances that contain nitrogen and carbon produce HCN.

The following materials produce HCN:

- Natural fibers such as wool, cotton and silk
- Resins such as carbon fiber or fiberglass
- Synthetic polymers such as nylon or polyester
- Synthetic rubber such as neoprene, silicone and latex

These materials are found in:

- Upholstered furniture
- Bedding
- Insulation
- Carpets
- Clothing
- Other common building materials and household items

HCN is a significant byproduct of the combustion of polyurethane foam used in many household furnishings. HCN is also released during off-gassing as an object is heated. It may also be found in vehicle fires, where new insulation materials give off high amounts of gases and cause fires to last longer.

HCN is 35 times more toxic than CO. HCN acts as a chemical asphyxiant but with a different mechanism of action than CO. HCN prevents the body from using oxygen at the cellular level. HCN can be inhaled, ingested, or absorbed into the body, where it then targets the heart and brain. Inhaled HCN enters the bloodstream and prevents the blood cells from using oxygen properly, killing the cells. The effects of HCN depend on the concentration, length, and type of exposure. Large amounts, high concentrations, and lengthy exposures are more likely to cause severe effects, including permanent heart and brain damage or death. **Table 3.4** illustrates the effects of HCN on the human body.

Table 3.4 Health Effects of HCN Exposure
HCN Cyanide
Low Concentration
Eye Irritation Headache Confusion Nausea Vomiting Coma (in some cases) Fatality (in some cases)
High Concentration
Immediate central nervous system, cardiovascular, and respiratory distress leading to death within minutes.

CAUTION: Wear full personal protective equipment (PPE) and self-contained breathing apparatus (SCBA) anytime there is a possibility of exposure to smoke, heat, or toxic gases.

Carbon dioxide (CO_2) is a product of complete combustion of organic materials. It is not toxic in the same manner as CO or HCN, but it displaces existing oxygen which creates an oxygen deficient atmosphere. CO_2 also acts as a respiratory stimulant, increasing respiratory rate.

NOTE: Fire gases also contain many other gases than the three highlighted in this section. These additional gases have their own effects and exposure times. The exposure time is based on the combination of gases or the lethal effective dose.

Irritants in smoke are substances that cause breathing discomfort and inflammation of the eyes, respiratory tract, and skin. Smoke can contain a wide range of irritating substances depending on the fuels involved. More than 20 irritants in smoke have been identified including hydrogen chloride, formaldehyde, and acrolein.

Smoke also contains significant amounts of unburned fuels in the form of solid and liquid particulates and gases. Smoke must be treated with the same respect as any other flammable gas because it may burn or explode. Particulates can interfere with vision and breathing.

> **WARNING:** Smoke is fuel and is potentially flammable. Smoke can be oxygen deficient and contain chemicals, which may be acutely toxic, and/or carcinogens which may cause cancer.

Pressure Differences

Pressure is the force per unit of area applied perpendicular to a surface. For example, atmospheric pressure (1 atmosphere [app. 101 kPa]) at standard temperature (68° F [20° C]) indicates the amount of pressure the atmosphere applies to the surface of the earth. At standard temperature and atmospheric pressure, gases remain calm and move very little. Differences in pressure above or below standard pressure create movement in gases. Gases always move from areas of higher pressure to areas of lower pressure. Even small differences in pressure, such as the 0.1 kPa or less differences created in most compartment fires, create this movement.

Heat from a fire increases the pressure of the surrounding gases. This increased pressure will seek to expand and equalize with areas of lower pressure. Heated gases will rise, remain aloft (**buoyant**) and generally travel up and out. At the same time, cooler, fresh air will generally travel inward toward the fire. This exchange of air creates a convective flow. As the pressure difference between high and low pressure areas increases, the speed with which gases will move from high to low also increases. It is critical for fire brigade members to understand how small changes to the gas pressure within a structure can dramatically affect fire behavior **(Figure 3.11)**.

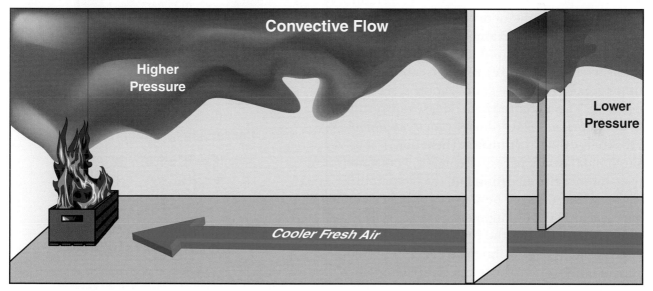

Figure 3.11 Heated gases will travel upward and outward from a fire while cooler, fresher air is drawn in toward the fire creating a convective flow.

Thermal Energy (Heat)

NFPA 1081 (2018): 4.1.2

A working knowledge of fire dynamics requires an understanding of temperature, energy, and power or **heat release rate**. Fire brigade members often use these terms interchangeably because the differences between the terms are not always understood.

Difference Between Heat Release Rate and Temperature

Heat is the thermal kinetic energy needed to release the potential chemical energy in a fuel. As heat begins to vibrate the molecules in a fuel, the fuel begins a physical change from a solid or liquid to a gas. The fuel emits flammable vapors which can ignite and release thermal energy. This new source of thermal energy begins to heat other, uninvolved fuels converting their energy and spreading the fire.

Temperature is the measurement of heat. More specifically, temperature is the measurement of the average kinetic energy in the particles of a sample of matter. A block of wood at room temperature has stable molecules and is in no danger of ignition. When thermal energy transfers to the wood, the wood is heated, and the temperature of the wood rises because the molecules have begun to vibrate and move more freely and rapidly.

Temperature can be measured using several different scales. The most common are the **Celsius** scale, used in the **International System of Units (SI)** (metric system), and the **Fahrenheit scale**, used in the customary system. The freezing and boiling points of water provide a simple way to compare these two scales **(Figure 3.12)**.

A dangerous misconception is that temperature is an accurate predictor or measurement of heat transfer. It is not. For example, one candle burns at the same temperature as ten candles. However, the heat release rate (kW) of the ten candles is ten times greater than one candle at the same temperature. The increased heat release rate results in an increased heat transfer rate to an object. This energy flow to a unit area (**heat flux**) is measured in kilowatts per square meter. Translated to an interior fire environment, the temperature in the structure may be within tolerances for personal protective equipment however, the heat flux to the PPE from the fire indicates the real measurement of how long the PPE will protect you. In other words, the temperature tells you it is safe to go in, but the heat transfer rate – not the temperature – tells you how long you can stay in.

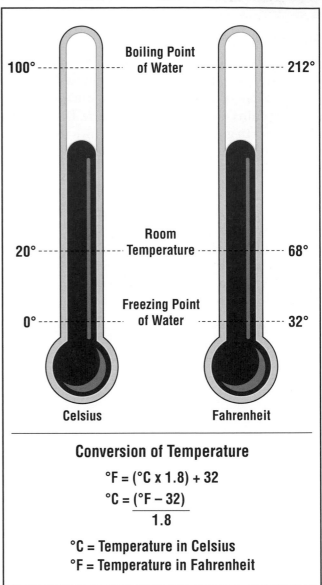

Conversion of Temperature

$$°F = (°C \times 1.8) + 32$$
$$°C = \frac{(°F - 32)}{1.8}$$

°C = Temperature in Celsius
°F = Temperature in Fahrenheit

Figure 3.12 The two common scales used to measure temperature are the Celsius scale (International System of Units [SI or metric system]) and the Fahrenheit scale used in the Customary System.

Sources of Thermal Energy

Chemical, electrical, and mechanical energy are common sources of heat that result in the ignition of a fuel. They can all transfer heat, cause the temperature of a substance to increase, and are most frequently the ignition sources of structure fires.

Chemical Energy

Chemical energy is the most common source of heat in combustion reactions. The potential for oxidation exists when any combustible fuel is in contact with oxygen. The oxidation process almost always results in the production of thermal energy **(Figure 3.13)**.

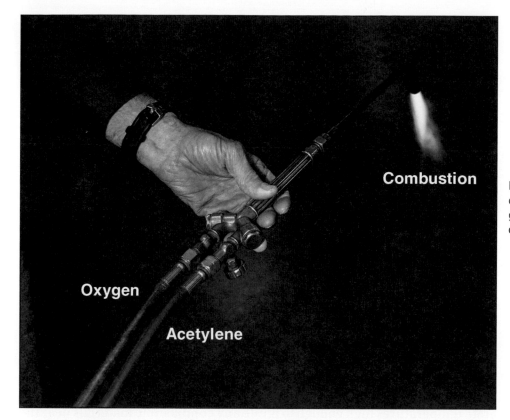

Combustion

Oxygen

Acetylene

Figure 3.13 The flame of a cutting torch illustrates the generation of heat from a chemical reaction.

Self-heating, a form of oxidation, is a chemical reaction that increases the temperature of a material without the addition of external heat. Self-heating can lead to spontaneous ignition, which is ignition without the addition of external heat.

Oxidation normally produces thermal energy slowly. The energy dissipates almost as fast as it is generated. An external heat source such as sunshine can initiate or accelerate the process. For self-heating to progress to spontaneous ignition, the following factors are required:

- The insulation properties of the material immediately surrounding the fuel must be such that the heat cannot dissipate as fast as it is generated.

- The rate of heat production must be great enough to raise the temperature of the material to its autoignition temperature.

- The available air supply in and around the heated material must be adequate to support combustion.

Rags soaked in linseed oil, rolled into a ball, and thrown into a corner have the potential for spontaneous ignition. The natural oxidation of this vegetable oil and the cloth will generate heat if some method of heat transfer such as air movement around the rags does not dissipate the heat. The cloth could eventually increase in temperature enough to cause ignition.

The rate of most chemical reactions increases as the temperature of the reacting materials increases. The oxidation reaction that causes heat generation accelerates as the fuel generates and absorbs more heat. When the heat generated exceeds the heat being lost, the material may reach its autoignition temperature and ignite spontaneously. **Table 3.5, p. 68** lists some common materials that are subject to self-heating.

Table 3.5	
Spontaneous Heating Materials and Locations	
Type of Material	**Possible Locations**
Charcoal	Convenience stores Hardware stores Industrial plants Restaurants Residences
Linseed oil-soaked rags	Woodworking shops Lumber yards Furniture repair shops Picture frame shops Residential/Commercial Construction/Remodeling sites
Hay and manure	Farms Feed stores Arenas Feedlots

Electrical Energy

Electrical energy can generate temperatures high enough to ignite any combustible materials near the heated area. Electrical heating can occur in several ways, including the following (**Figure 3.14**):

Figure 3.14 Examples of resistance heating, overcurrent or overload heating, arcing, and sparking.

Resistance

Overload

Arcing

Sparking

- **Resistance heating** — Electric current flowing through a conductor produces heat. Some electrical appliances, such as incandescent lamps, ranges, ovens, or portable heaters, are designed to make use of resistance heating. Other electrical equipment is designed to limit resistance heating under normal operating conditions.

- **Overcurrent or overload** — When the current flowing through a conductor exceeds its design limits, the conductor may overheat and present an ignition hazard. Overcurrent or overload is unintended resistance heating.

- **Arcing** — In general, an arc is a high-temperature luminous electric discharge across a gap or through a medium such as charred insulation. Arcs may be generated when there is a gap in a conductor such as a cut or frayed wire or when there is high voltage, static electricity, or lightning.

- **Sparking** — When an electric arc occurs, luminous (glowing) particles can form and splatter away from the point of arcing.

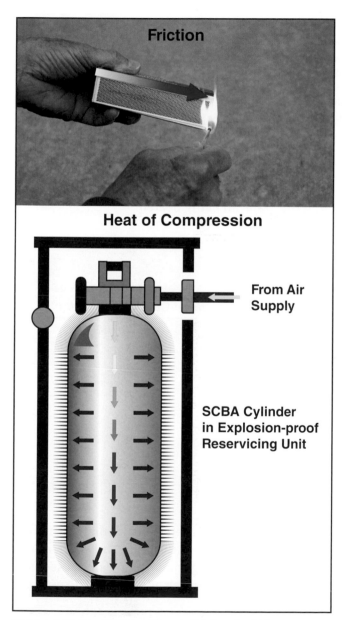

Figure 3.15 The friction of the match head rubbing across the box's striker generates the heat needed to ignite the match. As air is forced into the cylinder, it becomes compressed generating heat of compression.

Mechanical Energy

Friction or **compression** generates mechanical energy **(Figure 3.15)**. The movement of two surfaces against each other creates heat of friction that generates heat and/or sparks. Heat is generated when a gas is compressed. Diesel engines use this principle to ignite fuel vapors without spark plugs. This principle is also the reason that SCBA cylinders feel warm to the touch after they are filled. When a compressed gas expands, the gas absorbs heat. This absorption accounts for the way the cylinder cools when a CO_2 extinguisher is discharged.

Heat Transfer

The transfer of heat from one point or object to another is part of the study of thermodynamics. Heat transfer from the initial fuel package (burning object) to other fuels in and beyond the area of fire origin affects the growth of any fire and is part of the study of fire dynamics. Heat transfers from warmer objects to cooler objects because heated materials will naturally return to a state of thermal equilibrium in which all areas of an object are a uniform temperature. Objects at the same temperature do not transfer heat.

The rate at which heat transfers is related to the temperature differential of the bodies and the thermal conductivity of the materials involved. The greater the temperature differences between the bodies, the greater the transfer rate. A material with higher thermal conductivity will transfer heat more quickly than other materials. Heat transfers from one body to another by three mechanisms: conduction, convection, and radiation.

Conduction

Conduction is the transfer of heat through and between solids. Conduction occurs when a material is heated as a result of direct contact with a heat source (**Figure 3.16**). Conduction results from increased molecular motion and collisions between a substance's molecules, resulting in the transfer of energy through the substance. The more closely packed the molecules of a substance

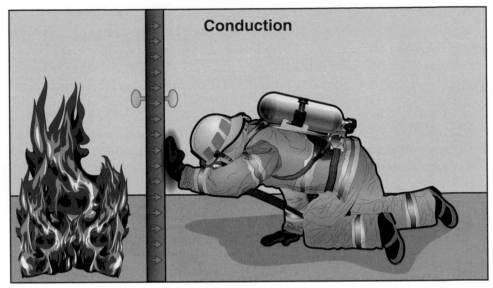

Figure 3.16 Conduction occurs when heat is transferred between solid objects, in this case, between the door and the firefighter's hand.

are, the more readily it will conduct heat. For example, if a fire heats a metal pipe on one side of a wall, heat conducted through the pipe can ignite wooden framing components in the wall or nearby combustibles on the other side of the wall.

Heat transfer due to conduction is dependent upon three factors:

- Area being heated
- Temperature difference between the heat source and the material being heated
- Thermal conductivity of the heated material

Table 3.6 shows the thermal conductivity of various common materials at the same ambient temperature (68°F [20°C]). For example, copper will conduct heat more than seven times faster than steel. Likewise, steel is nearly forty times as thermally conductive as concrete. Air is the least able to conduct heat of most substances, so it is a very good insulator.

Table 3.6 Thermal Conductivity of Common Substances		
Substance	**Temperature**	**Thermal Conductivity (W/mK)**
Copper	68°F (20°C)	386.00
Steel	68°F (20°C)	36.00 – 54.00
Concrete	68°F (20°C)	0.8 – 1.28
Gypsum Wall Board	68°F (20°C)	0.50
Wood (pine)	68°F (20°C)	0.13
Air	68°F (20°C)	0.03

Insulating materials slow the conduction of heat from one solid to another. Good insulators are materials that do not conduct heat well because their physical makeup disrupts the point-to-point transfer of heat or thermal energy. The best commercial insulators used in building construction are those made of fine particles or fibers with void spaces between them filled with a gas such as air. Gases do not conduct heat very well because their molecules are relatively far apart.

Figure 3.17 Convection is the transfer of heat by the circulation of liquids or gases.

Convection

Convection is the transfer of thermal energy by the circulation or movement of a fluid (liquid or gas) **(Figure 3.17)**. In the fire environment, convection usually involves transfer of heat through the movement of hot smoke and fire gases. As with all heat transfer, the heat flows from the hot fire gases to the cooler structural surfaces, building contents, and air. Convection may occur in any direction. Vertical movement is due to the buoyancy of smoke and fire gases. Lateral movement is usually the result of pressure differences (movement from high to low pressure).

Heat transfer due to convection is dependent upon three factors:

- Area being heated
- Temperature difference between the hot fluid or gas and the material being heated
- Turbulence and velocity of moving gases

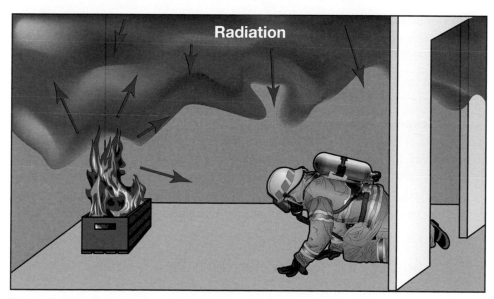

Figure 3.18 Radiation is the transfer of heat by electromagnetic waves without another medium to transfer the heat energy.

Radiation

Radiation is the transmission of energy as electromagnetic waves, such as light waves, radio waves, or X-rays, without an intervening medium **(Figure 3.18)**. Radiant heat can become the dominant mode of heat transfer as the fire grows in size and can have a significant effect on the ignition of objects located some distance from the fire. Radiant heat transfer is also a significant factor in fire development and spread in compartments.

Numerous factors influence radiant heat transfer, including:

- **Nature of the exposed surfaces** — Dark-colored materials emit and absorb heat more effectively than light-colored materials; smooth or highly-polished surfaces reflect more radiant heat than rough surfaces.

- **Distance between the heat source and the exposed surfaces** — Increasing distance reduces the effect of radiant heat **(Figure 3.19)**.

- **Temperature of the heat source** — Unlike other methods of heat transfer that depend on the temperature of both the heat source and exposed surface, radiant heat transfer only depends on the temperature of the heat source. As the temperature of the heat source increases, the radiant energy also increases **(Figure 3.20)**.

As an electromagnetic wave, radiated heat energy travels in a straight line at the speed of

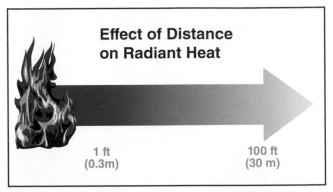

Figure 3.19 The effects of radiant heat diminish as the distance between the origin point and an exposure increases.

Figure 3.20 As the heat release rate or temperature of the source increases, the thermal radiation given off will also increase. The fire on the right is giving off more thermal radiation than the fire on the left. *Courtesy of NIST.*

light. The heat of the sun is the best example of radiated heat transfer. The energy travels at the speed of light from the sun through space (a vacuum) until it strikes and warms the surface of the earth.

Radiation is a common cause of **exposure fires**. As a fire grows, it radiates more energy which other objects absorb as heat. In large fires, it is possible for the radiated heat to ignite buildings or other fuel packages a considerable distance away. Radiated heat travels through vacuums and air spaces that would normally disrupt conduction or convection. However, materials that reflect, absorb, or scatter radiated energy will disrupt the heat transmission. While flames have high temperature resulting in significant radiant energy emission, hot smoke or flames in the upper layer can also radiate significant heat.

The Importance of Understanding Temperature and Heat Transfer Rate

Heat flux (kW/m²) from radiated heat emitted from flames or hot surfaces such as the walls and ceiling may cause PPE failure even when the temperature of the gases within a compartment are within acceptable limits. Traditionally, fire brigade members have focused on the gas temperature, stated in degrees on the Fahrenheit or Celsius scale, within a compartment that is on fire as being the best indicator of the thermal hazard. However, National Institute of Standards and Technology (NIST) laboratory tests show that these temperature measurements may not accurately account for radiated heat. SCBA facepieces, especially, are susceptible to radiated heat flux.

PPE is designed to insulate the wearer from a specified amount of heat long enough to extinguish the fire or exit the compartment under a limited set of conditions. PPE will not protect you indefinitely. While temperature measurements are a useful tool, relying upon personal, situational awareness "in the moment" is still essential for monitoring PPE's performance during operations.

Interaction Among the Methods of Heat Transfer

The methods of heat transfer rarely occur individually during a fire. The fire radiates heat, causes convection of heat through hot fuel gases, and conducts heat through burning materials or metals that are involved in the fire.

Convected heat and radiated heat that reaches walls and ceilings heats those surfaces which, in turn, begin to conduct heat to whatever extent possible based upon the material's thermal conductivity. One side of the object is warm and slowly warms through the object until the opposite side is of equal temperature with the heated side.

A heated surface will then, in turn, begin to radiate heat which could lead to ignition, combustion, convection, and so on. This cycle continues until interrupted.

A good example of this interaction is how your PPE absorbs heat during interior operations. Convected and radiated heat will begin to heat the exterior of your PPE. The longer you are in the heated environment, the more heat that surface will absorb. The PPE has low thermal conductivity, so it will conduct heat slowly. However, eventually the interior surface of the PPE will heat to the same level as the exterior. Wherever the gear is compressed against skin or underclothing, heat will be conducted faster. **Table 3.7** shows various responses of human skin and PPE as they are heated.

Where the PPE is not in contact, it will radiate heat to the insulating air layer between your body and the interior surface of the gear. This transferred heat can cause heat stress and will eventually cause PPE to fail. The heat absorption and build-up in PPE is a direct result of all of the heat transfer methods acting at the same time.

Table 3.7 Response to Temperature of an Object Being Heated	
Temperature °F (°C)	**Response**
98.6 °F (37 °C)	Normal human oral/body temperature
111 °F (44 °C)	Human skin begins to feel pain
118 °F (48 °C)	Human skins receives a first degree burn injury
131°F (55 °C)	Human skin receives a second degree burn injury
140 °F (62 °C)	A phase where burned human tissue becomes numb
162 °F (72 °C)	Human skin is instantly destroyed
212 °F (100 °C)	Water boils and produces steam
284 °F (140 °C)	Glass transition temperature of polycarbonate
446 °F (230 °C)	Melting temperature of polycarbonate
482 °F (250 °C)	Charring of natural cotton begins
>572 °F (>300 °C)	Charring of modern protective clothing fabrics begins
>1,112 °F (>600 °C)	Temperatures inside a post-flashover room fire

Source: Underwriter's Laboratories, Inc.

Fuel

NFPA 1081 (2018): 4.1.2

Fuel is the oxidized or burned material or substance in the combustion process. A fuel may be found in any of three physical states of matter: gas, liquid, or solid.

The fuel in a combustion reaction is known as the reducing agent. Fuels may be inorganic or organic. Inorganic fuels, such as hydrogen or magnesium, do not contain carbon. Most common fuels are organic, containing carbon and other elements. Organic fuels can be divided into hydrocarbon-based fuels, such as:

- Gasoline
- Plastics
- Fuel oil
- Cellulose-based materials (wood and paper)

A fuel's chemical content influences both its heat of combustion and heat release rate. The fuel's heat of combustion is the total amount of thermal energy released when a specific amount of that fuel burns. In other words, different materials release more or less heat than others based on their chemical makeup. Many plastics, flammable liquids, and flammable gases contain more potential thermal energy than wood **(Table 3.8)**.

Synthetic materials are common in modern construction and furnishings. These materials are synthesized from petroleum products, and as a result, they have higher heats of combustion and may generate higher heat release rates than wood on a per-mass basis.

Table 3.8 Representative Peak Heat Release Rates (HRR) During Unconfined Burning		
Fuel Material	**Peak HRR in kilowatts**	**Common Locations for Material**
Small wastebasket	4-50	Homes, businesses, shops
Cotton mattress	40-970	Homes, furniture stores, motels
Cotton easy chair	290-370	Homes, furniture stores, office buildings
Small pool of gasoline	400	Traffic crash, fuel stations
Dry Christmas tree	3000-5000	Homes, trash facilities, dumpsters, recycling sites
Polyurethane mattress	810-2630	Homes, furniture stores, motels, dormitories, jails
Polyurethane easy chair	1350-1990	Homes, furniture stores, motels
Polyurethane sofa	3120	Homes, furniture stores, motels, dormitories, office buildings

Adapted from NFPA® 921, 2014 edition

Power is the rate at which energy transfers. Another way to describe power is the rate at which energy converts from one form to another. The standard international (SI) unit for power is the watt (W). One watt is 1 joule per second (J/s).

In terms of fire behavior, power is the heat release rate during combustion. When a fuel is heated, work is being performed (energy is being transferred). The speed with which this work occurs, heat release rate, is the amount of generated power. Heat release rate is the energy released per unit of time as a fuel burns and is usually expressed in kilowatts (kW) or megawatts (MW). Heat release rate depends on the type, quantity, and orientation of the fuel. Heat release rate directly relates to oxygen consumption because the combustion process requires a continuous supply of oxygen to continue. Typically, the more oxygen is available, the higher the heat release rate. Similarly, the heat release rate decreases if all available oxygen is consumed and not replenished. **Figure 3.21** shows an example of the heat release rate produced by various sizes of fires.

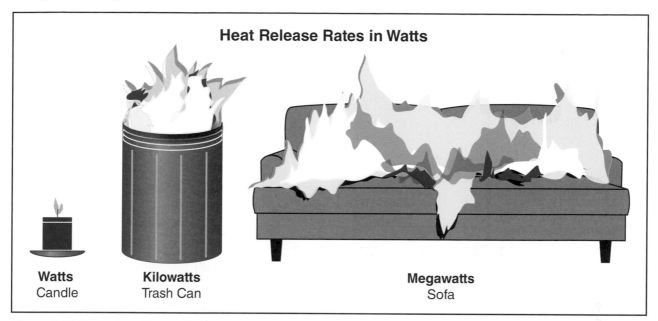

Heat Release Rates in Watts

Watts	Kilowatts	Megawatts
Candle	Trash Can	Sofa

Figure 3.21 Examples of heat release rate conditions that may be measured in watts, kilowatts, or megawatts.

 Prefixes for Units of Measure: Kilo and Mega

The standard international system of units (SI) specifies a set of prefixes that precede units of measure to indicate a multiple or fraction of that unit. Two common prefixes encountered when discussing energy (joules) and heat release rate (watts) are *kilo* and *mega*. The prefix *kilo* indicates a multiple of 1 thousand and *mega* indicates a multiple of 1 million. For example, a kilowatt is 1 thousand watts and a megawatt is 1 million watts.

Gases

For flaming combustion to occur, fuels must be in the gaseous state. As previously described, thermal energy is required to change solids and liquids into the gaseous state. *Vapor* is the common term used to describe the gaseous state of a fuel that would normally exist as a liquid or a solid at standard temperature and pressure.

Gaseous fuels such as methane (natural gas), hydrogen, and acetylene, can be the most dangerous of all fuel types because they are already in the physical state required for ignition. When wood burns inefficiently, the combustion products may contain methane, acetylene and other fuel gases. **Table 3.9** contains characteristics of common flammable gases.

Table 3.9 Characteristics of Common Flammable Gases		
Material	**Vapor Density**	**Ignition Temperature**
Methane (Natural Gas)	0.55	(1004°F) 540°C
Propane (Liquefied Petroleum Gas)	1.52	(842°F) 450°C
Carbon Monoxide	0.96	(1,128°F) 620°C

Source: *Computer Aided Management of Emergency Operations* (CAMEO)

Vapor density describes the density of gases in relation to air. Air has a vapor density of 1. Gases with a vapor density of less than 1, such as methane, will rise while those having a vapor density of greater than 1, such as propane, will sink (**Figure 3.22**). Vapor densities are based upon the assumption that the density is measured at standard temperature and pressure. Heated gases expand and become less dense; when cooled they contract and become more dense.

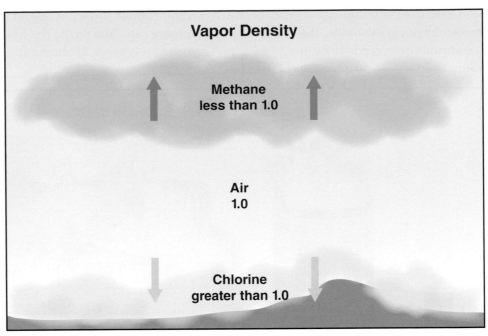

Figure 3.22 The vapor density of a gas provides an indication of where a gas will collect at an incident.

Liquids

Liquids have mass and volume but no definite shape except for a flat surface or the shape of their container. Unlike gases, liquids will not expand to fill all of a container. When released on the ground, liquids will flow downhill and pool in low areas. Just as gas density is compared to air, liquid density is compared to water. Specific gravity is the ratio of the mass of a given volume of a liquid compared to the mass of an equal volume of water at the same temperature. Water is assigned a specific gravity of 1. Liquids with a specific gravity less than 1, such as gasoline and most other flammable liquids, are lighter than water and will float on its surface. Liquids with a specific gravity greater than 1, such as corn syrup, are heavier than water and will sink (**Figure 3.23**).

To burn, liquids must vaporize. Vaporization is the transformation of a liquid to vapor or a gaseous state. Unlike solids, liquids retain their

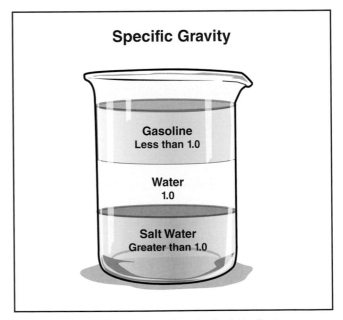

Figure 3.23 The specific gravity of a liquid indicates whether the liquid will float on the surface of water or sink.

state of matter partly due to standard atmospheric pressure. For vaporization to occur, the escaping vapors must be at a greater pressure than atmospheric pressure. The pressure that vapors escaping from a liquid exert is known as vapor pressure. *Vapor pressure* indicates how easily a substance will evaporate into air. Flammable liquids with a high vapor pressure present a special hazard to fire brigade members.

The vapor pressure of the substance and the amount of thermal energy applied to it determines the rate of vaporization. For example, a puddle of water eventually evaporates because of slow heat transfer from the sun. When the same amount of water is heated on a stove, however, it vaporizes much more rapidly because there is more thermal energy applied. The volatility or ease with which a liquid gives off vapor influences how easily it can ignite. The size of a liquid's surface area also influences the extent to which the liquid will give off vapor. In many open containers, the surface area of liquid exposed to the atmosphere is limited.

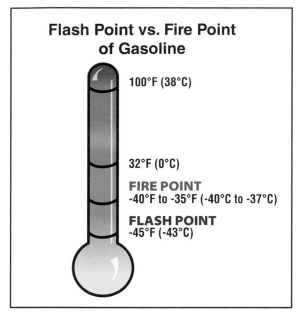

Figure 3.24 The flashpoint of a liquid indicates the temperature at which the liquid will ignite temporarily, while the fire point indicates the temperature at which the liquid, once ignited, will continue to burn.

Flash point is the minimum temperature at which a liquid gives off sufficient vapors to ignite, but not sustain combustion, in the presence of a piloted ignition source. **Fire point** is the temperature at which a piloted ignition of sufficient vapors will begin a sustained combustion reaction **(Figure 3.24)**. Flash point is commonly used to indicate the flammability hazard of liquid fuels. Liquid fuels that vaporize sufficiently to burn at temperatures under 100°F (38°C) present a significant flammability hazard.

Fire brigade members must know how liquid fuels react with water. **Solubility** describes the extent to which a substance (in this case a liquid) will mix with water. Solubility may be expressed in qualitative terms (*slightly* or *completely*) or as a percentage (20 percent soluble). Materials that are **miscible** in water will mix in any proportion. Liquids such as hydrocarbon fuels (gasoline, diesel, and fuel oil) are lighter than water and do not mix with it. Flammable liquids called **polar solvents** such as alcohols (methanol, ethanol) will mix readily with water.

Table 3.10 — Characteristics of Common Flammable and Combustible Liquids				
Material	**Water Soluble**	**Specific Gravity**	**Flash Point**	**Autoignition Temperature**
Gasoline	No	0.72	(-36°F) -38°C	(853°F) 486°C
Diesel	No	<1.00	(125°F) 52°C	(410°F) 210°C
Ethanol	Yes	0.78	(55°F) 13°C	(689°F) 365°C
Methanol	Yes	0.79	(52°F) 11°C	(867°F) 464°C

Source: *Computer Aided Management of Emergency Operations* (CAMEO)

Liquids that are less dense (lighter) than water are more difficult to extinguish using water as the sole extinguishing agent. Because the liquid fuel is less dense and will not mix with water, adding water to the liquid fuel may disperse the burning liquid instead of extinguishing it, which could potentially spread the fire to other areas. Fire brigade members should use the appropriate foam or chemical agent to extinguish liquid fuels that are not water-soluble.

Water-soluble liquids will mix with some water-based extinguishing agents, such as many types of fire fighting foam. The extinguishing agent will mix with the burning liquid and become much less effective at extinguishing the fire. To avoid this mixture, fire brigade members should use alcohol-resistant fire fighting foams specifically designed for polar solvents. **Table 3.10** lists the characteristics of common flammable and combustible liquids.

Solids

Solids have definite size and shape. Different solids react differently when exposed to heat. Some solids such as wax and metals will change their state and melt, while others such as wood and plastics will not. When solid fuels are heated, they begin to pyrolize (off-gas) and release fuel gases and vapors. If there is enough fuel and heat, the process of pyrolysis generates sufficient flammable vapors to ignite in the presence of sufficient oxygen or another oxidizer.

When wood first heats, it begins to pyrolize and decompose into its volatile components and carbon. These vapors are usually white in color. Pyrolysis of wood begins at temperatures below 400°F (204°C), which is lower than the temperature required for ignition of the released vapors. **Table 3.11** outlines the pyrolysis effects within different temperature zones. The pyrolysis process is similar with synthetic fuels such as plastics and some fabrics.

Table 3.11 Pyrolysis of Wood and Polyurethane Foam	
Wood	**Polyurethane Foam (PUF)**
Stage 1	**Stage 1**
Temperature: Less than 392°F (200°C)	**Temperature:** Less than 392°F (200°C)
Physical and Chemical Changes: Moisture is released as the wood begins to dry; combustible and noncombustible materials are released to the atmosphere although there is insufficient heat to ignite them.	**Physical and Chemical Changes:** As flexible polyurethane foam (PUF) thermally degrades (pyrolyzes), it transforms into combustible gases and liquid.
Stage 2	**Stage 2**
Temperature: 392°F – 536°F (200°C) – (280°C)	**Temperature:** 392°F – 536°F (200°C) – (280°C)
Physical and Chemical Changes: The majority of the moisture has been released; charring has begun; the primary compound being released is carbon monoxide (CO); ignition has yet to occur.	**Physical and Chemical Changes:** As the liquid polyols continue to be heated, they will vaporize into combustible gases, as well. Ignition of these gases may occur in this stage.
Stage 3	**Stage 3**
Temperature: 536°F – 932°F (280°C) – (500°C)	**Temperature:** 536°F – 932°F (280°C) – (500°C)
Physical and Chemical Changes: Rapid pyrolysis takes place; combustible compounds are released and ignition can occur; charcoal is formed by the burning process.	**Physical and Chemical Changes:** Pyrolysis continues at an increased rate. Ignition of PUF occurs 698°F (370°C). Auto-ignition of PUF can occur at temperatures in the range of 797°F to 833°F (425° to 445°C). No char layer is formed.
Stage 4	
Temperature: Greater than 932°F (500°C)	
Physical and Chemical Changes: Free burning exists as the wood material is converted to flammable gases.	

Sources: Wood data adapted from NFPA *Fire Protection Handbook*®, 19th edition, Volume II, pages 8-35 and 36. Polyurethane foam data from UL-FSRI, ASTM 1929 test (NIST NCSTAR 2); SFPE *Handbook of Fire Protection Engineering*, 4th edition; and *The Ignition Handbook* (V. Babrauskas).

Solid fuels have a definite shape and size which significantly affects how easily they ignite. The primary consideration is the surface area of the fuel in proportion to its mass, called the **surface-to-mass ratio**. One of the best examples is that of a large tree:

1. To produce lumber, the tree must be felled and cut into a log. The surface area of this log is low compared to its mass; therefore, the surface-to-mass ratio is low.

2. The log is then cut into planks. This reduces the mass of the individual planks compared to the log. The resulting surface area increases, thus increasing the surface-to-mass ratio.

3. The chips and sawdust produced as the planks are cut into boards have an even higher surface-to-mass ratio.

Surface-to-Mass Ratio

Lower

Log

Boards

Coarse Sawdust

Fine Sawdust

Higher

Energy Required for Ignition

Higher

Lower

4. If the boards are milled or sanded, the shavings or sawdust have the highest surface-to-mass ratio of any of the examples.

As this ratio increases, the fuel particles become more finely divided like shavings or sawdust. Therefore, the particles' ability to ignite increases tremendously. As the surface area increases, more of the material is exposed to the heat and generates combustible pyrolysis products more quickly **(Figure 3.25)**.

The proximity and orientation of a solid fuel relative to the source of heat also affects the way the fuel burns **(Figure 3.26)**. For example, if you ignite one corner of a sheet of ⅛-inch (3 mm) plywood paneling that is lying horizontally (flat), the fire will consume the fuel at a relatively slow rate. The same type of paneling in a vertical position (standing on edge) burns much more rapidly because the heated vapors rise over more surface area and transfer more heat to the paneling.

Oxygen

NFPA 1081 (2018): 4.1.2

Oxygen in the air is the primary oxidizing agent in most fires. Normally, air consists of about 21 percent oxygen. The energy release in fire is directly proportional to the amount of oxygen available for combustion. When a fire ignites in an open area where air is plentiful, the fire

Figure 3.25 (left) As the surface-to-mass ratio of a fuel becomes higher (increases), the energy required for ignition is lower (reduced).

Figure 3.26 (below) This illustration demonstrates how the position (orientation) of a fuel impacts fire spread.

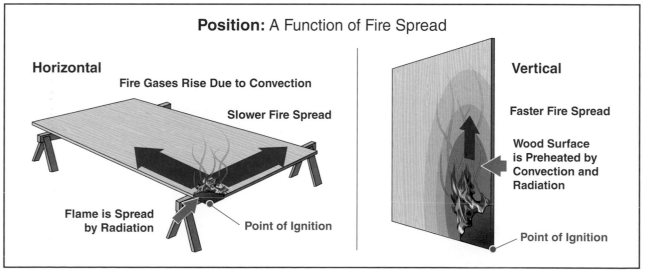

Position: A Function of Fire Spread

Horizontal

Fire Gases Rise Due to Convection

Slower Fire Spread

Flame is Spread by Radiation

Point of Ignition

Vertical

Faster Fire Spread

Wood Surface is Preheated by Convection and Radiation

Point of Ignition

will release energy based on the given surface area. In contrast, when a fire ignites within a compartment with limited air supply the fire can only react with oxygen from the compartment's air and any additional oxygen supplied through openings. Thus, in most compartment fires, the energy released is proportional to the limited amount of oxygen available, not the amount of fuel available to burn.

At normal ambient temperatures (68°F [20°C]), materials can ignite and burn at oxygen concentrations as low as 15 percent. When oxygen concentration is limited, the flaming combustion will diminish, causing combustion to continue in the nonflaming mode. Nonflaming or smoldering combustion can continue at extremely low oxygen concentrations even when the surrounding environment's temperature is relatively low. However, at high ambient temperatures, flaming combustion may continue at considerably lower oxygen concentrations.

 Effects of Oxygen Concentration

Oxygen concentration in the atmosphere has a significant effect on both fire behavior and our ability to survive. Typically, an atmosphere having less than 19.5 percent oxygen is considered oxygen deficient and presents a hazard to persons not wearing respiratory protection, such as SCBA, to provide fresh air. When the oxygen concentration in the atmosphere exceeds 23.5 percent, the atmosphere is considered oxygen enriched and presents an increased fire risk.

When the oxygen concentration is higher than normal, materials exhibit different burning characteristics. Materials that burn at normal oxygen levels will burn more intensely and may ignite more readily in oxygen-enriched atmospheres. Some petroleum-based materials will autoignite in oxygen-enriched atmospheres.

Many materials that do not burn at normal oxygen levels will burn in oxygen-enriched atmospheres. One such material is Nomex® **fire-resistant** fabric, which is used in many types of protective clothing. At normal oxygen levels, Nomex® does not burn. When placed in an oxygen-enriched atmosphere of approximately 31 percent oxygen, Nomex® ignites and burns vigorously.

Fires in oxygen-enriched atmospheres are more difficult to extinguish and present a potential safety hazard. Fire brigade members may find these conditions in hospitals and other healthcare facilities, some industrial occupancies, and even private homes where occupants use breathing equipment containing pure oxygen.

For combustion to occur after a fuel converts into a gaseous state, the fuel must be mixed with air (an oxidizer) in the proper ratio. The range of concentrations of the fuel vapor and air is called the **flammable (explosive) range**. The fuel's flammable range is reported using the percent by volume of gas or vapor in air for the **lower explosive (flammable) limit (LEL)** and for the **upper explosive (flammable) limit (UEL)**. The LEL is the minimum concentration of fuel vapor and air that supports combustion. Concentrations below the LEL are said to be *too lean* to burn. The UEL is the concentration above which combustion cannot take place. Concentrations above the UEL are said to be *too rich* to burn. Within the flammable range, there is an ideal concentration at which there is exactly the correct amount of fuel and oxygen required for combustion **(Figure 3.27)**.

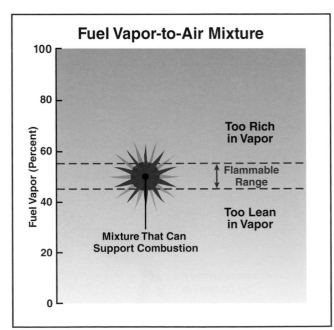

Figure 3.27 The flammable range is a relatively narrow band of conditions at which a mixture of fuel vapors and air will burn.

Table 3.12
Flammable Ranges of Common Flammable Gases and Liquids (Vapor)

Substance	Flammable Range
Methane	5%–15%
Propane	2.1%–9.5%
Carbon Monoxide	12%–75%
Gasoline	1.4%–7.4%
Diesel	1.3%–6%
Ethanol	3.3%–19%
Methanol	6%–35.5%

Source: *Computer Aided Management of Emergency Operations* (CAMEO)

The flammable ranges for some common materials are listed in **Table 3.12**. Chemical handbooks and documents such as the National Fire Protection Association (NFPA) *Fire Protection Guide to Hazardous Materials* present the flammable limits for combustible gases. *The Guide* and other sources normally report the limits at standard temperature and atmospheric pressures. Variations in temperature and pressure can cause the flammable range to vary considerably.

Self-Sustained Chemical Reaction
NFPA 1081 (2018): 4.1.2

The self-sustained chemical reaction involved in flaming combustion is complex. As flaming combustion occurs, the molecules of a fuel gas and oxygen (O_2) break apart to form **free radicals** (electrically charged, highly reactive parts of molecules). Free radicals combine with oxygen or with the elements released from the fuel gas to form new substances (molecules) and even more free radicals. The process also increases the speed of the oxidation reaction.

The combustion of a simple fuel such as methane and oxygen provides a good example. Complete oxidation of methane releases the elements needed to create carbon dioxide and water as well as release energy in the form of heat and light. The elements released when methane molecules breakdown (carbon and hydrogen) recombine with oxygen in the air to form CO_2 and H_2O (carbon dioxide and water) **(Figure 3.28, p. 82)**.

At various points in the combustion of methane, this process results in production of carbon monoxide and formaldehyde, which are both flammable and toxic. When more chemically complex fuels burn, their combustion creates different types of free radicals and intermediate combustion products, many of which are also flammable and toxic.

Flaming combustion is one example of a chemical chain reaction. Sufficient heat will cause fuel and oxygen to form free radicals and initiate the self-sustained chemical reaction. The fire will continue to burn until it consumes the fuel or oxygen or an extinguishing agent, applied in sufficient quantity, interferes with the ongoing reaction. **Chemical flame inhibition** occurs when an extinguishing agent, such as dry chemical or Halon-replacement agent, interferes with this chemical reaction, forms a stable product, and terminates the combustion reaction.

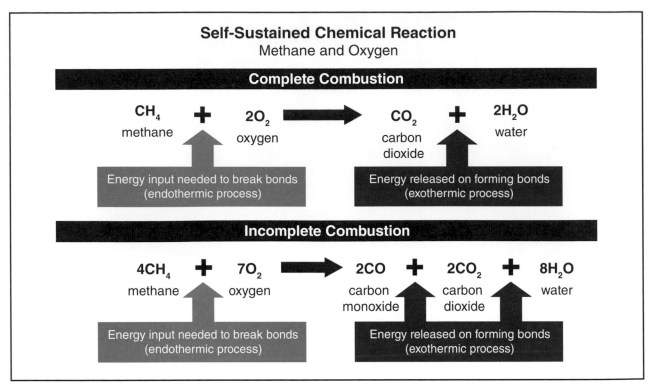

Figure 3.28 Illustrating the concepts of complete and incomplete combustion of methane.

Compartment Fire Development

NFPA 1081 (2018): 4.1.2, 4.3.1

Typically, when we think about a fire, we tend to limit our perspective to the burning fuel itself. However, in the sections that follow, we will see that the compartment surrounding that burning fuel has a significant impact on the available **ventilation**, access to additional fuel, and heat losses or gains.

Compartment fire development depends upon whether the fire is **fuel-limited** or **ventilation-limited**. When sufficient oxygen is available for flaming combustion, the fire is said to be fuel-limited. Under fuel-limited conditions, the fuel's characteristics such as heat release rate and configuration control fire development. As long as the fire can reach more ignitable fuel, it will continue to burn.

Conversely, ventilation-limited fires have access to all of the fuel needed to maintain combustion. However, the fire does not have access to enough oxygen to continue to burn or to spread to all available fuels.

All compartment fires begin in the incipient stage as fuel-limited fires. Once the fire reaches the growth stage, the fire will either remain fuel-limited if there is enough oxygen to support continued growth, or the fire will consume all available oxygen and become ventilation-limited. A fuel-limited fire will usually progress through the stages of fire development in order. Ventilation-limited fires tend to enter an early state of decay at the end of the growth stage because there is no longer enough available oxygen for the fire to become fully developed.

This section will define the stages of fire development and then describe the progression of a fire in a compartment. The examples in the information boxes describe fire behavior in a room with one exterior window, an exterior doorway, and typical modern furnishings found in a residential living room.

Stages of Fire Development

Fires develop through four stages: incipient, growth, fully developed, and decay. These stages can occur with any fire; however, there are three key factors that control how the fire develops: the fuel properties, the ventilation available, and heat conservation. Depending on these factors, the fire development stages exhibit different characteristics or may occur in a different sequence.

The four stages of fire development can be generally defined as follows:

- **Incipient Stage** — The incipient stage starts with ignition when the three elements of the fire triangle come together and the combustion process begins. At this point, the fire is small and confined to a small portion of the fuel first ignited.

- **Growth Stage** — As the fire transitions from incipient to growth stage, more of the initial fuel package becomes involved and the production of heat and smoke increases. If there are other fuels close to the initial fuel package, radiant heat from the fire may begin to pyrolyze nearby fuels which could spread the fire to new fuel packages. The fire may continue to grow to become fully developed or may enter an early state of decay depending upon available oxygen.

- **Fully Developed Stage** — The fully developed stage occurs when all combustible materials in the compartment are burning at their peak heat release rate based on the available oxygen. The fire is consuming the maximum amount of oxygen that it can. If the fire is limited to one fuel package, the fully developed stage occurs when the entire fuel package is on fire and the fire has reached its peak heat release rate.

- **Decay Stage** — As the fire consumes the available fuel or oxygen and the heat release rate begins to decline, the fire enters the decay stage. Fuel-limited fires may self-extinguish in this stage or reduce to smoldering fires. Ventilation-limited fires may also self-extinguish. However, if oxygen becomes available during the decay stage before complete extinguishment, these fires are likely to reenter the growth stage and rapidly become fully developed.

Open burning or a *free burn* condition provides the most basic fire growth curve, as shown in Figure **3.29a and b**. Open burning is representative of a fuel-limited fire, such as a campfire, a pile of wood pallets, or a sofa in a large, open, empty warehouse. This fire is considered fuel controlled because a single item burning either outside or in a large, well-ventilated space means there is sufficient oxygen available to burn the fuel until it can no longer sustain combustion. As heat and fire gases are produced, they move away from the fuel and disperse throughout the environment remote from the burning fuel. The only limit or control on the heat release rate of a fire burning out in the open is the fuel itself.

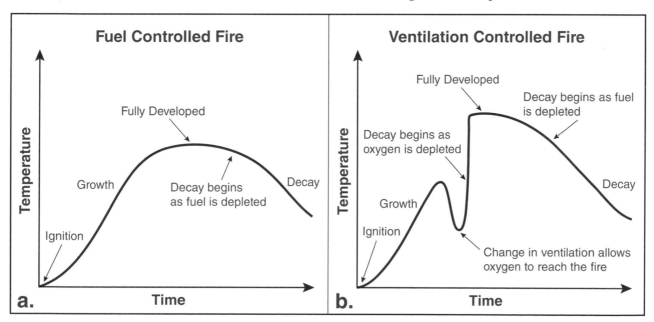

Figure 3.29a A line graph showing the progression of a fuel-controlled fire. *Courtesy of Dan Madrzykowski, NIST.*
Figure 3.29b A line graph showing the progression of a ventilation-controlled fire. *Courtesy of Dan Madrzykowski, NIST.*

Incipient Stage

The incipient stage is where a fire begins **(Figure 3.30)**. Once ignition occurs and the combustion process begins, development in the incipient stage depends largely upon the characteristics and configuration of the fuel involved (fuel-limited fire). Air in the compartment provides adequate oxygen to continue fire development. The following describe what occurs when a compartment fire enters the incipient stage:

Figure 3.30 An example of an incipient fire on a couch. *Courtesy of Dan Madrzykowski, NIST.*

- Radiant heat warms the adjacent fuel and continues the process of pyrolysis. A thin plume of hot gases and flame rises from the fire and mixes with the cooler air in the compartment.

- The hot gases in the plume rise until they encounter the ceiling and then begin to spread horizontally. This flow of fire gases is called the **ceiling jet**.

- Hot gases in contact with the surfaces of the compartment and its contents transfer heat to other materials.

In this early stage of fire development, the fire has not yet influenced the environment within the compartment to a significant extent. The temperature, while increasing, is only slightly above ambient in areas that the fire, plume, and ceiling jet directly affect. During the incipient stage, occupants can safely escape from the compartment, and a portable extinguisher or small hoseline can safely extinguish the fire.

The transition from incipient to growth stage can occur quickly (in some cases in seconds), depending on the type and configuration of fuel involved. A visual indicator that a fire is leaving the incipient stage is flame height. When flames reach 2.5 feet (750 mm) high, radiated heat begins to transfer more heat than convection. The fire will then enter the growth stage.

CAUTION: Transition from the incipient to growth stages can occur in a matter of seconds depending upon the type and configuration of fuel.

Example Compartment: Incipient Stage

To begin our example of a compartment fire's development, let's assume that a fire started in the cushions of a chair in the corner of a room. The window and the door are closed. Within the room, there is enough oxygen for the incipient fire to entrain ("pump in") air and create ("pump out") fuel gases and smoke. The fire begins to spread from the cushions to the rest of the chair. The polyurethane foam of the cushions burns quickly, creating black, fuel-rich smoke which begins to form a plume above the chair **(Figure 3.31)**.

Figure 3.31 The graph in the lower left of the photo shows the progression of the fire in its incipient stage. *Courtesy of Dan Madrzykowski, NIST.*

Growth Stage

Within the growth stage, a variety of fire behaviors can occur, depending upon the number of ventilation sources. The fire may consume all of its available oxygen and enter a ventilation-limited state of decay or ventilation may provide enough oxygen for rapid fire development and/or growth to full development. Rapid fire development usually occurs during the growth stage. Understanding fire dynamics is largely an understanding of everything that can happen during the growth stage.

NOTE: Keep in mind that if the fire enters ventilation-limited decay that does not indicate that the fire is in its final stage of development.

As the fire transitions from incipient to growth stage, it begins to influence more of the compartment's environment and has grown large enough for the compartment configuration and amount of ventilation to influence it. The first effect is the amount of air that is entrained into the fire.

Unconfined fires draw air from all sides and the **entrainment** (drawing in) of air cools the plume of hot gases, reducing flame length and vertical extension **(Figure 3.32)**. In a compartment fire, the location of the fuel package in relation to the compartment walls affects the amount of air that is entrained and thus the amount of cooling that takes place. The following tenets describe entrainment based on the positioning of fuel packages:

- Fires in fuel packages in the middle of the room can entrain air from all sides.
- Fires in fuel packages near walls can only entrain air from three sides.
- Fires in fuel packages in corners can only entrain air from two sides.

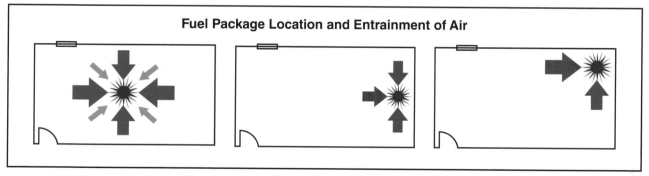

Figure 3.32 The location of a fire in a compartment influences the entrainment of air into the fire.

Therefore, when the fuel package is not in the middle of the room, the **combustion zone** (the area where sufficient air is available to feed the fire) expands vertically and a higher plume results. A higher plume increases the temperatures in the developing hot gas layer at ceiling level and increases the speed of fire development. In addition, heated surfaces around the fire radiate heat back toward the burning fuel which further increases the speed of fire development.

A fire is said to be in the growth stage until the fire's heat release rate has reached its peak, either because of a lack of fuel or a lack of oxygen. In other words, when a fire cannot grow without the introduction of a new fuel source or a new oxygen source, it has left the growth stage and become fully developed. Two common routes to full development are as follows:

- Fires that consume all available oxygen and transition to a state of ventilation-limited decay.
- Fires that have enough oxygen and move to the growth stage and possibly through rapid fire development.

As the fire spreads to the chair, the entire chair becomes involved. Air entrains from only two sides, so the fire releases more energy than it would in the middle of the room and thus accelerates the fire's growth. The side table next to the chair begins to heat and pyrolize. The ceiling above the chair begins to blacken as the plume grows taller and transfers heat to the ceiling and surrounding walls. A ceiling jet begins to form **(Figure 3.33)**.

Figure 3.33 The graph in this image shows the transition of a fire from the incipient stage into the growth stage. *Courtesy of Dan Madrzykowski, NIST.*

Thermal Layering

Once the ceiling jet reaches the walls of the fire compartment, the hot gas layer begins to develop. **Thermal layering** is the tendency of gases to form into layers according to temperature, gas density, and pressure. Provided that there is no mechanical mixing from a fan or a hose stream, the hottest gases will form the highest layer, while the cooler gases will form the lower layers **(Figure 3.34)**. In addition to the effects of heat transfer through radiation and convection described earlier, radiation from the hot gas layer also acts to heat the interior surfaces of the compartment and its

Figure 3.34 The image on the left shows the visible conditions within a compartment that is on fire. The infrared image on the right shows the thermal layering of gases from the top (hottest) of the compartment to the bottom (coolest). *Courtesy of NIST.*

contents. Changes in ventilation and **flow path** can significantly alter thermal layering. The flow path is defined as the space between the air intake and the exhaust outlet. Multiple openings (intakes and exhausts) create multiple flow paths.

The products of combustion from the fire begin to affect the environment within the compartment. As the fire continues to grow, the hot gas layer within the fire compartment gains mass and energy. As the mass and energy of the hot gas layer increases, so does the pressure. Higher pressure causes the hot gas layer to spread downward within the compartment and laterally through any openings such as doors or windows. If there are no openings for lateral movement, the higher pressure gases have no lateral path to follow to an area of lower pressure. As a result, the hot gases will begin to fill the compartment starting at the ceiling and filling down.

Isolated flames (intermittent flames) may move through the hot gas layer. Combustion of these hot gases indicates that portions of the hot gas layer are within their flammable range, and that there is sufficient heat to cause ignition. As these hot gases circulate to the outer edges of the plume or the lower edges of the hot gas layer, they find sufficient oxygen to ignite. This phenomenon frequently occurs before more substantial involvement of flammable products of combustion in the hot gas layer. The appearance of isolated flames is sometimes an immediate indicator of **flashover**.

The interface between the hot gas layers and cooler layer of air is commonly referred to as the **neutral plane** because the net pressure is zero, or neutral, where the layers meet. The neutral plane exists at openings where hot gases exit and cooler air enters the compartment. At these openings, hot gases at

Figure 3.35 Illustrating the location of the neutral plane in a compartment fire. Hot gases are exiting through the upper part of the doorway while cooler air enters through the lower part. *Courtesy of Dan Madrzykowski, NIST.*

higher than ambient pressure exit through the top of the opening above the neutral plane. Lower pressure air from outside the compartment entrains into the opening below the neutral plane **(Figure 3.35)**.

Transition to Ventilation-Limited Decay

Most compartment fires that develop beyond the incipient stage become ventilation-limited. Even when doors and windows are open, insufficient air entrainment may prohibit the fire from developing based on the available fuel. When windows are intact and doors are closed, the fire may move into a ventilation-limited state of decay even more quickly. While a closed compartment reduces the heat release rate, fuel may continue to pyrolize, creating fuel-rich smoke.

As the interface height of the hot gas layer descends toward the floor, the greater volume of smoke begins to interrupt the entrainment of fresh air and oxygen to the seat of the fire and into the plume. This interruption causes the fire within the compartment to burn less efficiently. As the efficiency of combustion decreases (incomplete combustion), the heat release rate decreases and the amount of unburned fuel within the hot gas layer increases.

Example Compartment: Growth Stage – Thermal Layering

Figure 3.36 This image shows the growth stage of a compartment fire as thermal layering begins to occur within the compartment. *Courtesy of Dan Madrzykowski, NIST.*

The plume coming from the chair has now reached the ceiling and become a ceiling jet. Hot fire gases and fuel-rich smoke begin to spread horizontally across the ceiling. Both the door and the window are closed, so the smoke has no way to leave the compartment. The compartment begins to fill with hot gases and smoke. The dividing line between the dwindling air in the compartment and the increasing amount of smoke in the compartment steadily lowers toward the floor. The end table is completely involved with flames now. The walls and ceiling have also heated and are radiating heat back into the room. The coffee table has begun to pyrolize and the flat-screen television has begun to melt. The hydrocarbon materials in the compartment burn quickly and inefficiently, creating fuel-rich, black smoke. The heat release rate is high, though the environment near the floor where there is still air might be tenable for fire brigade members **(Figure 3.36)**.

The fire is now in a state of ventilation-limited decay because:

- There is not enough oxygen to maintain combustion.

- The heat release rate has decreased to the point that fuel gases will not ignite.

Although the heat release rate decreases when a fire is ventilation-limited, the temperature in the room may remain high. Because there is not enough oxygen to maintain combustion, the fire has a lower heat release rate, but that does not mean that the environment is tenable. The compartment fills with fuel-rich gases that only need more oxygen to ignite because of the higher temperatures in the compartment.

Even if temperatures decrease, pyrolysis can continue. Under these conditions, a large volume of flammable products of combustion can accumulate within the compartment. These gases are fuel that can ignite, given a new source of oxygen.

If no other source of oxygen exists, the compartment will fill with black smoke and slowly cooling fuel gases. The compartment will show no visible flames. The characteristics of the fuel and **fuel load** in today's typical fires will cause fires to quickly become ventilation-limited.

In order for a ventilation-limited fire to grow, it needs a new supply of oxygen. Ventilation introduces outside air to the fire as this new source of oxygen. If windows or doors fail, the sudden introduction of fresh air creates a rapid increase in the heat release rate and growth of the fire. This rapid increase can also occur when fire brigade members open a door or window to enter the compartment for extinguishment, which creates a new flow path **(Figure 3.37)**.

Figure 3.37 By breaking the window, the firefighter introduces new oxygen into the compartment increasing the fire's heat release rate and growth. *Courtesy of Dan Madrzykowski, NIST.*

WARNING: Even coordinated tactical ventilation increases the combustion rate in ventilation-limited fires.

The pressure outside the compartment is lower than the pressure inside the compartment **(Figure 3.38)**. Because of these pressure differences, any ventilation to the outside – opening an interior or exterior door, or breaking or opening a window – provides a flow path along which the hot gases can now move from the high pressure area inside to the low pressure area outside.

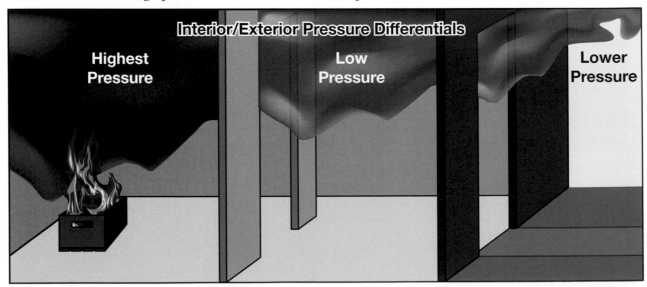

Figure 3.38 The pressure differences between the interior of a compartment (higher) and the exterior (lower) provide a flow path that hot gases may move along.

Example Compartment: Growth Stage – Transition to Ventilation-Limited Decay

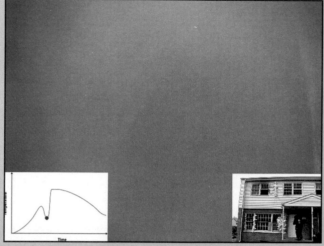

Figure 3.39 This image shows a fire's transition to ventilation-limited decay. *Courtesy of Dan Madrzykowski, NIST.*

The window in the compartment has not failed and the door is still closed. The hot gas layer in the room has lowered to about 2 feet (0.6 m) off the floor. The small amount of oxygen left below the gas layer is no longer sufficient to sustain flaming combustion **(Figure 3.39)**. No flames are visible, but the remainder of the furnishings in the room slowly continue to pyrolize and add fuel gases to the compartment. The walls and ceiling still radiate heat. Though the heat release rate is low, use of a thermal imager from outside the compartment shows temperatures hot enough to ignite flammable gases. From outside the window, only smoke is visible, and there are pulses of smoke in the cracks around the door.

Rapid Fire Development

Rapid fire development refers to the rapid transition from the growth stage or early decay stage to a ventilation-limited, fully developed stage **(Figure 3.40)**. Among these events are flashover and backdraft.

NOTE: Smoke explosions are also incidents of rapid fire development, but they involve more than just one compartment of a structure. Smoke explosions will be described later in this chapter.

Rapid Fire Development

| Growth | Decay | 5 seconds after door is opened | Post-flashover 60 seconds after door is opened |

Figure 3.40 This series of images show the evolution of a fire from the growth stage through decay and then shows rapid fire development that occurs once a door is opened. *Courtesy of Dan Madrzykowski, NIST.*

Rapid fire development has been responsible for numerous fire brigade member deaths and injuries. To protect yourself and your crew, you must be able to:

- Recognize the indicators of rapid fire development
- Know the conditions created by each of these situations
- Determine the best action to take before they occur

In this section, rapid fire development conditions are described along with their indicators.

Flashover. Rapid transition from the growth stage to the fully developed stage is known as flashover. When flashover occurs, the combustible materials and fuel gases in the compartment ignite almost simultaneously; the result is full-room fire involvement. Flashover typically occurs during the fire's growth stage, but may occur during the fully developed stage as the result of a change in ventilation.

Flashover conditions are defined in various ways; however, during flashover, the environment of the room changes from a two-layer condition (hot on top, cooler on the bottom) to a single, well mixed hot gas condition from floor to ceiling. The environment is untenable, even for fully protected fire brigade members. As flashover occurs, the gas temperatures in the room reach 1,100 °F (593°C) or higher.

A significant indicator of flashover is **rollover**. Rollover describes a condition where the unburned fire gases that have accumulated at the top of a compartment ignite and flames propagate through the hot gas layer or across the ceiling.

Rollover may occur during the growth stage as the hot gas layer forms at the ceiling of the compartment. Flames may appear in the layer when the combustible gases reach their ignition temperature. While the flames add to the total heat generated in the compartment, this condition is not flashover. Rollover will generally precede flashover, but it may not always result in flashover. Rollover contributes to flashover conditions because the burning gases at the upper levels of the room generate tremendous amounts of radiant heat which transfers to other fuels in the room. The new fuels begin pyrolysis and release the additional gases necessary for flashover.

The transition period between preflashover fire conditions (growth stage/ventilation-limited decay) to postflashover (fully developed stage) can occur rapidly. Radiation from the compartment's upper layer heats the compartment's contents until they reach their ignition temperature simultaneously. When the upper layer ignites, the amount of radiation increases to levels that rapidly ignite contents in the room, even if they are remote from the fire. During flashover, the volume of burning gases can increase from approximately ¼ to ½ of the room's upper volume to fill the room's entire volume and extend out of any openings from the room. When flashover occurs, burning gases push out of compartment openings (such as a door to another room) at a substantial velocity.

There are four common elements of flashover:

- **Transition in fire development** — Flashover represents a transition from the growth stage to the fully developed stage.

- **Rapidity** — Although it is not an instantaneous event, flashover happens rapidly, often in a matter of seconds, to spread fire completely throughout the compartment.

- **Compartment** — There must be an enclosed space such as a single room or enclosure.

- **Pyrolysis of all exposed fuel surfaces** — Fire gases from all of the combustible surfaces in the enclosed space ignite, provided that there is sufficient oxygen to support flaming combustion.

Two interrelated factors determine whether a fire within a compartment will progress to flashover. First, there must be sufficient fuel and the heat release rate must be sufficient for flashover conditions to develop. For example, ignition of discarded paper in a small metal wastebasket may not have sufficient heat to develop flashover conditions in a large room lined with gypsum drywall. On the other hand, ignition of a sofa with polyurethane foam cushions placed in the same room will likely result in flashover provided the fire has sufficient oxygen.

The second factor is ventilation. Regardless of the type, quantity, or configuration of fuel, heat release depends on oxygen. A developing fire must have sufficient oxygen to reach flashover, an amount that a sealed room may not provide. The available air supply limits the heat release. If there is insufficient natural ventilation, the fire may enter the growth stage but not reach the heat release rate or gaseous fuel production to transition through flashover to a fully involved fire.

NOTE: The autoignition temperature of CO, the most abundant fuel gas created in most fires, is approximately 1,100° F (595°C).

Survival rates for fire brigade members are extremely low in a flashover. At the floor level, a heat flux of approximately 20 kW/m² is also typical of rollover conditions at the start of the flashover. Once flames begin to affect a surface, the heat flux could range from 60 to 200 kW/m². For frame of reference on heat flux, consider that NIST testing conducted in 2013 (Purtoti, 2013) has shown that SCBA face pieces begin to fail after 5 minutes of exposure to a heat flux of 15 kW/m². You must be aware of the following flashover indicators to protect yourself:

- **Building indicators** — Interior configuration, fuel load, thermal properties, and ventilation
- **Smoke indicators** — Rapidly increasing volume, turbulence, darkening color, optical density, and lowering of the hot gas layer and/or neutral plane
- **Heat indicators** — Rapidly increasing temperature in the compartment, pyrolysis of contents or fuel packages located some distance away from the fire, or hot surfaces
- **Flame indicators** — Isolated flames or rollover in the hot gas layers or near the ceiling

Levels of the neutral plane observed from the exterior of the structure are also good indicators of fire behavior within the structure as follows **(Figure 3.41)**:

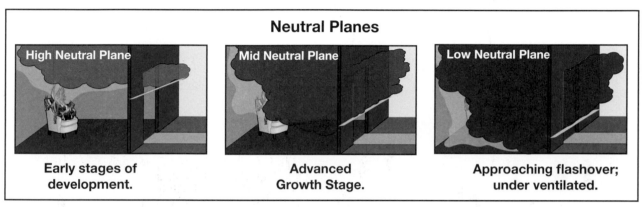

Neutral Planes

| High Neutral Plane | Mid Neutral Plane | Low Neutral Plane |

Early stages of development. | Advanced Growth Stage. | Approaching flashover; under ventilated.

Figure 3.41 Observing the neutral plane from outside a structure can provide indications of the behavior of the fire within.

- **High neutral plane** — May indicate that the fire is in the early stages of development.

  Remember that high ceilings can hide a fire that has reached a later development stage. A high neutral plane can also indicate a fire above your level.

- **Mid-level neutral plane** — Could indicate that the compartment has not yet ventilated or that flashover is approaching.

- **Very low-level neutral plane** — May indicate that the fire is reaching backdraft conditions. This occurrence could also mean that a fire is below you (basement fire or lower story).

When a fire is in ventilation-limited decay, the introduction of new oxygen can trigger flashover quickly. Flashover may occur whenever sufficient oxygen and ventilation are available for fire growth. However, in an uncontrolled situation, it may be difficult to identify what stage a fire is in, so fire brigade members should assume that flashover may occur at any time that the conditions are right.

Flashover may not occur in every compartment fire, such as in large-area compartments or compartments with high ceilings. Fire development may take an alternative path in a compartment that quickly becomes ventilation-limited, before the thermal energy can build within the compartment. The fire may not progress to flashover but instead become ventilation-limited, limiting heat release rate and causing the fire to enter the decay stage while continuing the process of pyrolysis and increasing the fuel content of the smoke.

Example Compartment: Growth Stage – Flashover

Let's back up a moment and change the conditions of our example. When the hot gas layer reaches about halfway down the compartment, a fire brigade member opens the door to ventilate the room. When the door was closed, the fire was on its way to ventilation-limited decay. With the introduction of fresh air from outside, the fire grows rapidly **(Figure 3.42)**. Fire brigade members can observe the neutral plane in the doorway with smoke exiting the top half of the door. The amount of smoke increases, and the neutral plane lowers in the doorway as more of the surfaces in the room pyrolize. Fire brigade members observe flames moving through the top of the hot gas layer. These flames radiate a large amount of energy to the compartment contents, causing the contents to pyrolize and release more fuel while rapidly heating to their ignition temperature. Suddenly, the hot gases and incoming oxygen reach the correct mix, and the isolated flames become a room full of flames. All of the hot gases ignite at once. The heat release rate rises dramatically, igniting all of the flammable fuels within the compartment. Flames extend up and around the door frame of the open door.

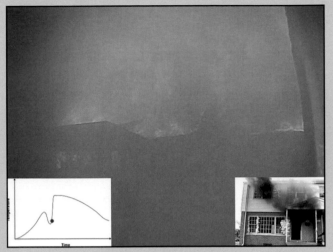

Figure 3.42 In this image, the fire grows rapidly as fresh oxygen is introduced into the compartment. *Courtesy of Dan Madrzykowski, NIST.*

Backdraft. A ventilation-limited compartment fire can produce a large volume of flammable smoke and other gases due to incomplete combustion. While the heat release rate from a ventilation-limited fire decreases, elevated temperatures may still be present within the compartment. An increase in ventilation such as opening a door or window can result in an explosively rapid combustion of the flammable gases, called a **backdraft**. Backdraft occurs in a space containing a high concentration of heated flammable gases that lack sufficient oxygen for flaming combustion.

When potential backdraft conditions exist in a compartment, the introduction of a new source of oxygen will return the fire to a fully involved state rapidly (often explosively). A backdraft can occur with the creation of a horizontal or vertical opening. All that is required is the mixing of hot, fuel-rich smoke with air. Backdraft conditions can develop within a room, a void space, or an entire building. Anytime a compartment or space contains hot combustion products, fire brigade members must consider potential for backdraft before creating any openings into the compartment. Backdraft indicators include:

- **Building indicators** — Interior configuration, fuel load, thermal properties, amount of trapped fuel gases, and ventilation

- **Smoke indicators** — Pulsing smoke movement around small openings in the building; smoke-stained windows

- **Air flow indicators** — High velocity air intake

- **Heat indicators** — High heat, crackling or breaking sounds

- **Flame indicators** — Little or no visible flame

   The effects of a backdraft can vary considerably depending on a number of factors, including:

- Volume of smoke

- Degree of confinement

- Temperature of the environment

- Pressure

- Speed with which fuel and air mix

Do not assume that a backdraft will always occur immediately after an opening is made into the building or involved compartment. You must watch the smoke for indicators of potential rapid fire development including the air currents changing direction, or smoke rushing in or out. To some degree, the violence of a backdraft depends upon the extent to which the fuel/air mixture is confined in the compartment. The more confined, the more violent the backdraft will be.

Example Compartment: Growth Stage – Backdraft

Let's again change the conditions in our compartment. The compartment is ventilation-limited, and all of the petroleum products in the room (chair cushions, plastic in the flat-screen TV) have produced large amounts of fuel-rich, black smoke. The bottom of the hot gas layer is barely off the floor. There is nothing visible but dense, black smoke through the window. At this moment, the window fails. The high volume of confined smoke rushes to the new area of low pressure and billows out the window. Air from the outside rushes in at the same speed. The hot gases and air mix so quickly that they reach their explosive limit almost immediately. Flames propagate through the hot gases seemingly all at once, and an explosion of fire erupts out of the open window.

Fully Developed Stage

The fully developed stage occurs when the heat release rate of the fire has reached its peak, because of lack of either fuel or oxygen. There are two main types of fully developed fires: ventilation-limited and fuel-limited fires. The factor limiting the peak heat release rate is used to identify which type of fully developed fire exists.

Fire brigade members often misinterpret the term "fully developed" to mean that the fire can no longer grow. A more accurate description would be that the fire has grown *as much as it can*. New sources of fuel introduced after full development will allow fuel-limited fires to grow. Likewise, new sources of oxygen introduced after full development will allow ventilation-limited fires to grow.

Fuel-Limited Conditions

The available fuel limits the peak heat release in a fuel-limited, fully developed fire. The most effective method of increasing the heat release rate is to provide more fuel. A campfire located in a fire ring is a good example of fuel-limited conditions. The fire reaches its peak when all the fuel becomes involved. The fire ring separates the burning fuel from other potential fuel resulting in a fuel-limited, fully developed fire. Adding additional fuel or firewood would increase the energy release of the fire to a new peak heat release rate.

Technically speaking, most compartment fires, even those that are ventilated and have untenable interior environments, are ventilation-limited. Adding ventilation points to a compartment fire that is already ventilated will add oxygen that will allow the fire to grow. Fuel-limited full development usually occurs when fires are not contained within compartments such as wildland fires, vehicular fires, or fires burning in collapsed structures.

Example Compartment: Fully Developed – Fuel-Limited Conditions

Let's assume that the compartment flashed over shortly after a fire brigade member opened the door for ventilation. As a result of flashover, all of the available fuels in the compartment burned. Let's further assume that the compartment burned until one of the walls and the adjoining part of the ceiling collapsed. The fire then had access directly to the outside air without the ventilation limitations of the doorway. The fire now has access to an unlimited, unimpeded supply of oxygen and is consuming oxygen at the highest capacity that it can. Any available fuel burns, and flames, smoke, heated fire gases, and embers exit the compartment through the opening. At this point, fire brigade members have no choice but to protect surrounding exposures (neighboring buildings or vegetation) and contain the fire from the exterior.

Ventilation-Limited Conditions

In contrast, a fully developed, ventilation-limited fire lacks the oxygen available to grow because the number and size of openings in the compartment limit the entrainment of air. The fire reaches a peak when it consumes all the available oxygen from the air intake, typically with incomplete combustion. Additional fuel is available and gaseous fuel is leaving the compartment in the smoke; however, the fire cannot release any more energy. Allowing additional air into the compartment via an additional opening or enlarging the existing opening will provide more oxygen, resulting in a higher peak heat release rate.

WARNING: Additional ventilation will cause an already ventilated fire to grow.

Ventilation-limited, fully developed fires present a hazardous situation to fire brigade members. The potential for a window failure to provide fresh oxygen and increase the peak heat release rate can endanger both fire brigade members and potential victims. To reduce the risk of the unpredictable window failure, fire brigade members must transition the fire from ventilation-limited to fuel-limited. With the high heat of combustion found in modern furnishings, the only mechanism to transition the fire is to extinguish some of the burning fuel. It is not possible to make enough openings in a compartment to transition a fire from ventilation-limited to fuel-limited conditions.

WARNING: Additional ventilation alone will not transition a ventilation-limited fire to a fuel-limited fire.

Example Compartment: Fully Developed – Ventilation-Limited Conditions

Again, let's take a step back in the development of our fire. Let's assume this time that the window is already ventilated, and fire brigade members are planning to enter the compartment through the doorway for an interior attack. The amount of smoke exiting the window is significant and larger than earlier in the fire's development, but the amount of smoke is no longer increasing, an indicator that the fire is consuming as much oxygen as it can through the window opening **(Figure 3.43)**.

The fire brigade members have two choices for controlling this type of fire. First, they could enter through the door low and under the smoke to attack the seat of the fire directly. They know, however, that opening the door will introduce a new flow

Figure 3.43 In this image, the fire reaches the fully developed stage. *Courtesy of Dan Madrzykowski, NIST.*

path for air that could allow the fire to grow. So they choose their second option. One team cools the hot gas layer using a straight stream from outside the window, which lowers the temperature in the compartment. Once this tactic reduces the heat release rate, another team takes a charged handline through the door. The exterior team disrupts the fully developed conditions of the fire, minimizing the impact of a new ventilation source at the doorway. The interior attack crew encounters an environment with a lower heat release rate and more tenable conditions than they would have in option one. They are able to accomplish full extinguishment of the fire with greater ease.

Decay Stage

A fire is said to be in the decay stage when it runs out of either fuel or oxygen. Either fuel or oxygen is an integral part of the fire triangle introduced earlier in the chapter. Without all three components of the triangle, the fire will decay and extinguish.

In fuel-limited fires, the decay stage is usually the fire's final stage, leading to the fire's self-extinguishment when it runs out of available fuel. Ventilation-limited fires can also self-extinguish due to lack of oxygen. Both of these situations can result in the termination of the combustion reaction. However, just like throwing another log on top of a smoldering campfire, introducing new oxygen to a ventilation-limited fire can cause it to reenter the growth stage.

Fuel-Limited Decay

After a fuel-limited fire reaches the fully developed stage the fire will decay as the fuel is consumed. As the fire consumes the available fuel and the heat release rate begins to decline, the fire enters the decay stage. The heat release rate will decrease, but the temperature of surrounding objects may remain high for some time due to absorbed heat.

Compartment fires rarely enter a state of fuel-limited decay unless the compartment burns all the way to the ground. If the compartment fails and the fire opens to the atmosphere, then the amount of fuel available would limit the fire's ability to grow.

Example Compartment: Fuel-Limited Decay

After the wall and ceiling fail and the fire continues to burn, the compartment now collapses into a pile of slowly cooling fuel and embers. Some flames still show, but there is no longer enough fuel to sustain flaming combustion. There are embers and small amounts of smoke, but the fire is basically over.

Assuming there were fire brigade members at the scene, the fire could have reached the decay stage when the fire brigade members applied enough water to the fuels that the fire's heat would no longer pyrolize the contents or structural members. The water would have also greatly reduced the heat release rate to tenable or even negligible levels **(Figure 3.44)**.

Figure 3.44 After water application, the fire's heat has been reduced so that pyrolysis of the contents and structural members no longer occurs. *Courtesy of Ron Moore, McKinney (TX) Fire Department.*

Ventilation-Limited Decay

When a fire enters a ventilation-limited state of decay, this stage is not necessarily the last stage of the fire's development. As stated earlier, the fire awaits a new supply of oxygen to return to the growth stage. This statement is true even if compartment ventilation has already occurred.

To ensure that the decay stage of a ventilation-limited fire is the fire's final stage, a controlled transition from ventilation-limited to fuel-limited must take place. To provide this control, fire brigade members must cool the hot fire gases before any further ventilation occurs or immediately following any forcible entry. This tactic will lessen the likelihood of the gases igniting when supplied fresh oxygen.

If the compartment has no ventilation openings, the heat release rate will eventually decrease to the point that the heat in the compartment naturally transfers through the compartment itself to the outside. This process takes time and is rarely a viable fire fighting strategy because fire brigade members must ensure that no ventilation occurs until the compartment transfers all of the heat.

Example Compartment: Ventilation-Limited Decay

Let's back up to the point where the compartment was in ventilation-limited decay. Remember, the temperatures in the compartment indicate high enough levels of heat to ignite fuel gases, but there is not enough oxygen to support combustion.

Fire brigade members on the scene wait until they have charged and ready hoselines in place before opening the door to access the fire. The Incident Commander assigns one fire brigade member to door control, two more to fire attack, and two more as a rapid intervention crew. The door control fire brigade member opens the door. The heat release rate increases for a moment, but the attack fire brigade members open their nozzle utilizing a straight stream to cool the gases. The smoke changes in color (it whitens) and after a few moments a high neutral plane appears in the doorway. Thermal imagers show a reduction in temperature in the compartment. The hoseline team slowly advances through the doorway and applies water to the seat of the fire **(Figure 3.45)**.

The fire brigade's coordination has controlled the transition from a ventilation-limited environment to a fuel-limited environment. As a result, the compartment is still standing and in a state of fuel-limited decay. It is ventilated and free of smoke, releases very little heat, and presents a tenable temperature.

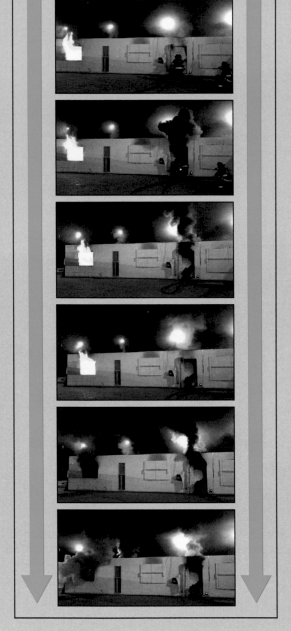

Figure 3.45 This sequence of images shows the effects of water as it cools the heated fire gases within the structure. *Photos courtesy of Dan Madrzykowski, UL-FSRI.*

Structure Fire Development

NFPA 1081 (2018): 4.1.2, 4.3.1

Structures are essentially composed of individual compartments connected by hallways, stairways, or openings such as doorways. If a fire starts within one of the compartments, how it grows or decays is based on the model growth curves presented in previous sections. However, in a structure, the fire has the potential to involve more than one compartment or could spread beyond the contents of a compartment and involve the structural members of the building itself. Fighting a fire in a structure, as opposed to a stand-alone single compartment, is challenging because fire brigade members will need to size up the building, find the fire, and then find a way to attack the fire.

Flow Path

In a structure fire, the method by which the fire receives the needed oxygen to sustain the combustion reaction occurs through one or many flow paths. The flow path is composed of two regions: the ambient air flow in and the hot exhaust flow out **(Figure 3.46)**. The flow is always unidirectional due to pressure differences where the ambient air flows toward the seat of the fire and reacts with the fuel. The products of combustion flow away from the fire toward the low pressure outlet.

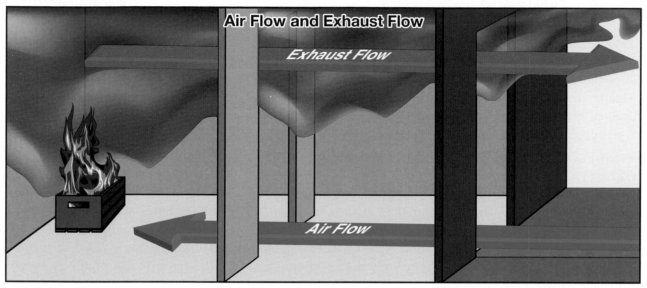

Figure 3.46 Illustrating the concepts of air flow and exhaust flow.

In a structure fire, the floor plan and openings within the structure determine the available flow path. For example, hot gases from a fire in a bedroom will travel out of the doorway and into the hallway if the door is open. If other doors in the structure are also open, the adjoining rooms also become possible parts of the flow path. The pressure in these other rooms is lower than the pressure in the fire room; therefore, hot fire gases and smoke will travel toward those areas unless the direction of flow is altered, for example, through tactical ventilation or door control **(Figure 3.47)**. Air in those rooms will entrain toward the fire as the structure fills with fuel gases and the fire grows and spreads.

A flow path's effectiveness to transport ambient air to the seat of the fire is based on the following:

- Size of the ventilation opening
- Length of the path traveled
- Number of obstructions
- Elevation differences between the base of the fire and the opening

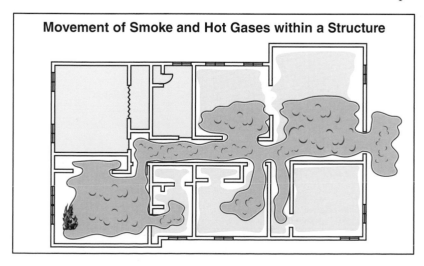

Figure 3.47 This image illustrates how the floor plan and openings within a structure determine the available flow path of hot gases.

When fire brigade members advance a hoseline or ventilate windows to make entry into a building, they establish new flow paths between the fire compartment and exterior vents of the building. These new flow paths may allow air and thus oxygen to reach the fire, increasing the heat release rate. In addition, hot, fuel-rich fire gases may flow toward a vent opened to the building's exterior because the hot gases are at a higher pressure than the lower pressure air outside the vent. When the hot gases mix with the outside oxygen, they may be hot enough to autoignite. Since any ventilation creates new flow paths for oxygen and hot gases, fire brigade members must use tactics that control the oxygen available to the fire and the fire's generated heat to prevent unwanted fire spread.

When hot gases follow the flow path from areas of high to low pressure, they convect heat to a larger portion of the structure. They also carry the products of combustion into new areas of the structure. Since these gases are also fuel, fire can propagate through them, out of the fire room. As a result, fire brigade members should know the location of the flow path for these gases in the structure and coordinate their ventilation and interior activities accordingly.

Fire brigade members working in the exhaust portion of the flow path will feel the increase in temperature as the velocity and/or turbulence increases, causing increased convective heat transfer. Convective heat transfer is a similar phenomenon to wind chill, except energy is transferred from a hot fluid (gas) to a solid surface (your PPE) rather than from a hot surface (your skin) to a cooler fluid (air). If ventilation is not well coordinated, this heat transfer – such as that associated with flashover or backdraft – can be unsurvivable even when wearing PPE. If you must perform operations in the flow path, recognize that these operations are risky and potentially life threatening. The time that fire brigade members are operating in the flow path should be strictly limited. They should not be in the area any longer than necessary.

A structure fire that extends beyond the room of origin may have two compartments involved, each in different stages of development. The room of origin may be in a fully developed, ventilation-limited stage while the adjacent compartment may be in the growth stage and nearing flashover. Understanding the model growth curves and what conditions to expect based on fire dynamics will aid fire brigade members in finding or establishing a tenable environment for their interior operations. Tactics employed for **fire suppression**, ventilation, and search and rescue will directly relate to the fire dynamics occurring on a given incident.

Ventilation and Wind Considerations

Beginning an attack on a ventilation-limited structure fire with ventilation alone will progressively increase the fire's heat release rate and spread as additional vents are made. Once the fire has filled the structure's compartments with hot, unburned, gaseous fuel, using ventilation as the only tactic will not enable you to get ahead of the fire and limit fire growth and spread **(Figure 3.48)**.

Figure 3.48 A model showing the evolution of a compartment fire. *Courtesy of UL, Inc.*

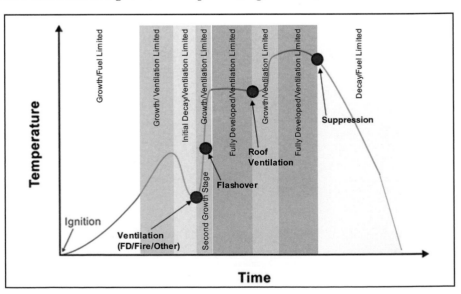

Unplanned Ventilation

Unplanned ventilation occurs when a structural member fails – usually because of exposure to heat – and introduces a new source of oxygen to the fire. This new oxygen source could result from the failure of a:

- Window **(Figure 3.49)**
- Doorway
- Roof
- Wall

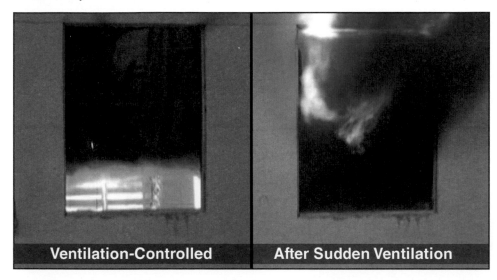

Ventilation-Controlled **After Sudden Ventilation**

Figure 3.49 The sudden ventilation of a compartment fire can lead to rapid fire development. *Courtesy of Dan Madrzykowski, NIST.*

The source of new oxygen does not have to originate from outside the building. When floors fail above basement fires, the interior air in the structure becomes a new oxygen source.

Unplanned ventilation is often the result of:

- Occupant action
- Fire effects on the building (such as window glazing)
- Actions other than planned, systematic, and coordinated tactical ventilation

Unplanned ventilation, by definition, is unexpected. When it occurs, situational awareness is essential to ensure your safety and that of other crew members.

Wind Conditions

The wind can increase the pressure inside the structure, drive smoke and flames into unburned portions of the structure and onto advancing fire brigade members, and/or upset tactical ventilation efforts. You must be aware of the wind direction and velocity and use it to your advantage to assist in tactical ventilation.

> **WARNING:** Wind-driven conditions can occur in any type of structure. Wind speeds as low as 10 mph (16 km/h) can create wind-driven fire conditions.

Wind conditions can also create differences in pressure that can cause windows to fail. The exterior pressure on the upwind side of a structure will be higher than the pressure on the downwind side of the structure. As a result, the ambient air on the outside of the structure is constantly trying to move through the structure along the path from high to low pressure. If heat exposure weakens windows in this path, wind pressure could cause them to fail which introduces a new flow path for oxygen and hot fire gases.

> **CAUTION:** A strong wind can overpower the natural convective effect of a fire and drive the smoke and hot gases back into the building.

Smoke Explosions

A smoke explosion occurs when a mixture of unburned fuel gases and oxygen comes in contact with an ignition source. When smoke travels away from the fire it can accumulate in other areas and mix with air. When the fuel and oxygen are within the flammable range and contact an ignition source, the result will be explosive, rapid combustion. Smoke explosions are violent because they involve premixed fuel and oxygen.

Smoke Effects on Fire Fighting Operations

Limiting or interrupting one or more of the essential elements in the combustion process depicted in the fire tetrahedron controls and extinguishes fire. Fire brigade members can influence fire dynamics in a number of ways:

- **Temperature reduction** — Using water or a foam agent to cool fire gases and hot surfaces for the purposes of extinguishment.

- **Fuel removal** — Eliminating sources of fuel in the path of the fire's spread that could provide a new source of fuel; typically a tactic in wildland fires or liquid and gas fires.

- **Oxygen exclusion/flow path control** — Using door control and tactical ventilation techniques to control the amount of air available to the fire.

- **Chemical flame inhibition** — Using extinguishing agents other than water and foam, such as some dry chemicals, halogenated agents (Halons), and Halon-replacement "clean" agents, to inhibit or interrupt the combustion reaction and stop flame production.

Reaction of Building Construction to Fire

NFPA 1081 (2018): 4.1.2, 4.3.1

As buildings burn, the fire creates a variety of dangerous conditions. You must be aware of these conditions to remain safe during an emergency incident. An already serious situation can worsen if fire brigade members fail to recognize the potential of the situation and take the wrong actions.

Two primary types of dangerous building conditions are:

- Conditions that contribute to the spread and intensity of the fire
- Conditions that make the building susceptible to collapse

These two conditions are related; conditions that contribute to the spread and intensity of the fire will increase the likelihood of structural collapse. The following sections describe some of these conditions.

Construction Type and Elapsed Time of Structural Integrity

Most building codes rate the various construction types according to how long each construction type maintains its structural integrity over a certain period of time. **Table 3.13** shows some examples of the expected fire resistance of the five types of construction. How long a building will maintain structural integrity is not an exact science. Observations made at a fire scene must be used to reevaluate estimations based upon building construction type. When you respond to a fire, there are many unknown factors that are not reflected in fire resistance estimates, such as the following:

- The duration of the fire up to the time of arrival
- The building's contents
- Way(s) the building contents affect the heat release rate
- The heat release rate and intensity of the fire
- Renovations to the interior that may have compromised fire resistance

	Type I		Type II			Type III		Type IV	Type V	
	442	332	222	111	000	211	200	2HH	111	000
Exterior Bearing Walls										
Supporting more than one floor, columns, or other bearing walls	4	3	2	1	0	2	2	2	1	0
Supporting one floor only	4	3	2	1	0	2	2	2	1	0
Supporting a roof only	4	3	1	1	0	2	2	2	1	0
Interior Bearing Walls										
Supporting more than one floor, columns, or other bearing walls	4	3	2	1	0	1	0	2	1	0
Supporting one floor only	3	2	2	1	0	1	0	1	1	0
Supporting roofs only	3	2	1	1	0	1	0	1	1	
Columns										
Supporting more than one floor, columns, or other bearing walls	4	3	2	1	0	1	0	H	1	0
Supporting one floor only	3	2	2	1	0	1	0	H	1	0
Supporting roofs only	3	2	1	1	0	1	0	H	1	0
Beams, Girders, Trusses, and Arches										
Supporting more than one floor, columns, or other bearing walls	4	3	2	1	0	1	0	H	1	0
Supporting one floor only	2	2	2	1	0	1	0	H	1	0
Supporting roofs only	2	2	1	1	0	1	0	H	1	0
Floor-Ceiling Assemblies	2	2	2	1	0	1	0	H	1	0
Roof-Ceiling Assemblies	2	1½	1	1	0	1	0	H	1	0
Interior Nonbearing Walls	0	0	0	0	0	0	0	0	0	0
Exterior Nonbearing Walls	0	0	0	0	0	0	0	0	0	0

Adapted from Table 4.1.1 of NFPA 220.

H: Heavy timber members

Reprinted with permission from NFPA 220-2015, *Standard on Types of Building Construction*, Copyright © 2014, National Fire Protection Association, Quincy, MA. This reprinted material is not the complete and official position of the NFPA on the referenced subject, which is represented only by the standard in its entirety.

Information gathered at the scene provides the best indicators of structural integrity. You can then compare this immediate knowledge with any known information about the structure, such as its construction type, to form opinions about safety on the fireground.

Fuel Load of Structural Members and Contents

The total quantity of combustible contents of a building, space, or fire area is referred to as the fuel load (some documents may use the term *fire load*). All combustible materials in the building's construction comprise the fuel load, such as:

- Wood framing
- Floors
- Ceilings
- Furnishings
- Combustible materials within the building

The more materials that are combustible, the more fuel is available to pyrolize and burn. Your knowledge of building construction and occupancy types will be essential to determining fuel loads. At a scene, you will only be able to estimate the fuel load based upon your knowledge and experience. For example, a concrete block structure with a steel roof assembly containing stored steel pipe will have a much smaller fuel load than a wood-frame structure used for storing flammable

Figure 3.50 The wood frame of this building served as fuel to the fire. *Courtesy of Mike Wieder.*

liquids. In buildings where the construction materials are flammable, the materials themselves add to the structure's fuel load. For example, in wood-frame buildings, the structure itself is a source of fuel **(Figure 3.50)**.

The orientation of the fuels as well as their surface-to-mass ratio will also influence the rate and intensity of fire spread. The contents of a structure are often the most readily available fuel source, significantly influencing fire development in a compartment fire. When contents release a large amount of heat rapidly, both the intensity of the fire and speed of development will increase. For example, synthetic furnishings, such as polyurethane foam, begin to pyrolize rapidly under fire conditions even when the contents are located some distance from the fire's origin. The chemical makeup of the foam and its high surface-to-mass ratio speed the process of fire development **(Figure 3.51)**.

Figure 3.51 These images demonstrate how the polyurethane foam in the chair pyrolizes rapidly under fire conditions. *Courtesy of Dan Madrzykowski, NIST.*

The proximity and continuity of contents and structural fuels also influence fire development. Fuels located in the upper level of adjacent compartments will pyrolize more quickly because of heat radiating from the hot gas layer. Continuous fuels such as combustible interior finishes will rapidly spread the fire through compartments.

Similarly, the fire's location within the building will influence fire development. Fires originating on upper levels generally extend downward much more slowly following the fuel path or as a result of structural collapse. When the fire originates in a low level of the building, such as in the basement or on the first floor, convected heat currents will cause vertical extension through:

- Atriums
- Vertical shafts
- Stairways
- Concealed spaces

Additionally, if the structural elements of the building become involved in the fire, not only does the structure itself provide a new source of fuel, but the fire may be burning in hidden cavities throughout the building. These hidden spaces make finding and extinguishing the fire more difficult and increase the potential risk of building collapse.

In commercial, industrial, and storage facilities with large fuel loads, the fire can overwhelm the capabilities of a fire suppression system and make it difficult for fire brigade members to gain access during fire suppression operations **(Figure 3.52)**. Performing and updating preincident surveys is the most effective means of establishing awareness of these hazards.

Figure 3.52 These rolls of printing paper are an example of a heavy fuel load.

Assuming that there is available oxygen, the higher the fuel load, the more likely the fire will behave in the following ways:

- If structural members are part of the fuel load, structural integrity of the building will deteriorate faster.
- The longer the fire burns, the more fire spread accelerates.
- The fire may have a higher heat release rate.
- The structure may self-ventilate, introducing even more oxygen to the fuel-limited fire and accelerating fire development and involvement of combustible structural members.

If fires are ventilation-limited, higher fuel loads indicate a greater amount of unburned fuel that could reignite with the introduction of a new oxygen source. There may also be a greater amount of unburned fuel gases in the air because fuel packages pyrolized but did not begin combustion before the building became oxygen-limited. Such buildings are subject to backdrafts and flashovers if fire brigade members do not coordinate ventilation.

Furnishings and Finishes

In addition to structural members, combustible interior **finishes** and furnishings, can be a significant factor that influences fire spread and are a major factor in the loss of lives in fires. The interior finishes include the window, wall, and floor coverings such as drapes, wallpaper, and carpet. Furnishings may include:

- Tables
- Bookcases/shelves
- Desks
- Other items found in occupancies

Combustible Exterior Wall Coverings

Flammable material that contributes to the structure's fuel load often covers exterior walls. Exterior wall coverings may add carbon fuels (wooden siding) or petroleum fuels (vinyl siding) to the fuel load. The wall coverings may be installed atop exterior insulation which, in turn, is another fuel source. When exterior coverings become exposed to heat and catch fire, they can spread the fire to other areas of the structure or to adjacent exposures such as vegetation or neighboring buildings **(Figure 3.53)**.

Combustible Roof Materials

The combustibility of a roof's surface is a basic concern to the fire safety of an entire community. Some of the earliest fire regulations imposed in North America related to combustible roof coverings because they were blamed for several conflagrations caused by flaming embers flying from roof to roof.

Wood shakes, even when treated with fire retardant, can significantly contribute to fire spread. This is a problem in **wildland/urban interface** fires where wood shake roofs have contributed

Figure 3.53 The vinyl siding on the exterior of this building provided fuel for exterior fire spread up two sides of the building. *Courtesy of Ron Jeffers, Union City, NJ.*

to large fires. Fire brigade members must use exposure protection tactics to protect combustible roofs on structures adjacent to a fire building or wildland fire.

Fire-resistant metal roof decking may be covered with combustible layers of foam insulation and felt paper covered with asphalt waterproofing. A fire below the metal deck can melt and ignite combustible materials, causing a second fire above the roof.

Building Compartmentation

The arrangement of compartments in a building directly affects fire development, severity, possible duration, and intensity. Building **compartmentation** is the layout of the various open spaces in a structure and includes:

- Number of stories above or below ground
- Openings between floors
- Barriers to fire spread
- Floor plan
- Continuous voids or concealed spaces

Each of these elements may contribute to either fire spread or containment. For instance, an open floor plan space may contain furnishings that provide fuel sources on all sides of a point of ignition. Conversely, a compartmentalized configuration may have fire rated barriers, such as walls, ceilings, and doors, separating fuel sources and limiting fire development to an individual compartment **(Figure 3.54)**.

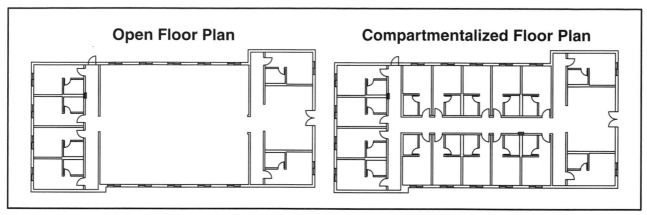

Figure 3.54 Illustrating the differences between open and compartmentalized floor plans.

Any open space with no complete fire barrier dividing it is considered a compartment. Two rooms that a doorway connects are considered two compartments only if the door between them is closed. When the door is open, a fire in either room can access the oxygen from the adjoining room. The rooms will affect one another more slowly than if the intervening wall weren't there at all, but a closed door will slow the effect of a fire in one room on the adjoining room even further. Fire brigade members should use doors to their advantage during interior operations, closing doors whenever appropriate to control available oxygen sources.

Given enough available fuel, fire will follow oxygen through a building along any available flow path. Fire brigade members can take advantage of compartmentation to control the flow path to create more predictable fire behavior during operations.

Effects of Building Construction Features

Building features such as lightweight materials or open floor plans have direct effects on how fire will spread in the structure. If you do not take building construction features into account, then fire fighting activities may worsen an emergency – possibly catastrophically – rather than help to extinguish the fire. Remember, a structure fire is the place where fire dynamics and building construction interact. The sections that follow highlight some of the construction features that fire brigade members should consider when fighting structure fires.

Compartment Volume and Ceiling Height

A fire in a large compartment will normally develop more slowly than one in a small compartment. Slower fire development is due to the greater volume of air and the increased distance radiated heat must travel from the fire to the contents that must be heated. However, a large volume of air will support the development of a larger fire before the lack of ventilation becomes the limiting factor.

A high ceiling can also make determining the extent of fire development more difficult. In structures with high ceilings, a large volume of hot smoke and fire gases can accumulate at the ceiling level, while conditions at floor level remain relatively unchanged. Fire brigade members may mistake floor-level conditions for the actual state of fire development. If the large hot gas layer ignites, the situation becomes immediately hazardous.

Large, open spaces in buildings contribute to the spread of fire throughout. Such spaces may be found in **(Figure 3.55)**:

- Warehouses
- Theaters
- Churches
- Large atriums
- Large-area mercantile buildings

Large spaces may also exist between roofs and ceilings and under rain roofs. In these concealed spaces, fire can travel undetected, feeding on combustible, exposed wood rafters. When smoke appears through openings in the roof or around the eaves, the exact point of origin may be deceiving.

Figure 3.55 Example of commercial structures with an open floor plans and potentially high fuel loads.

Thermal Properties of the Building

The thermal properties of the building can contribute to rapid fire development. The thermal properties can also make extinguishment more difficult and reignition possible. Thermal properties of a building include:

- **Insulation** — Contains heat within the building that causes a localized increase in the temperature and fire growth and may introduce an additional fuel source

- **Heat reflectivity** — Increases fire spread through the transfer of radiant heat from wall surfaces to adjacent fuel sources

- **Retention** — Maintains temperature by slowly absorbing and releasing large amounts of heat

Effects of Fire on Common Building Materials

NFPA 1081 (2018): 4.1.2, 4.3.1

Facilities are constructed of a wide variety of materials. Some materials, such as wood and plastic, will contribute fuel to a fire in the structure while other materials, such as concrete and masonry, will prevent or limit the spread of fire. All materials react differently when exposed to the heat of a fire. Your knowledge of how these materials react to fire will help you understand what to expect from a fire in a particular type of construction. More information about how building materials react under fire conditions can be found in the IFSTA manual, **Building Construction Related to the Fire Service**.

Common building materials include:

- Wood
- Reinforced concrete
- Glass/fiberglass
- Masonry
- Gypsum
- Plastic
- Metals
- Lath and plaster
- Composite materials

Wood

Wood is the most common building material used in North America. Size and moisture content affect how wood reacts to fire conditions. The smaller the dimensions of the wood, the easier it is to ignite and the faster it will lose structural integrity. Large wooden beams, such as those used in heavy-timber construction, are difficult to ignite and retain their structural integrity even after prolonged exposure to direct flame impingement. Lumber of smaller dimensions needs to be protected by gypsum drywall or other insulation to increase its resistance to heat or fire.

Figure 3.56 Illustrating the similarities and differences between three common engineered wood products.

The wood's moisture content affects the rate at which it burns. Wood with a high moisture content (sometimes referred to as **green wood**) does not ignite as readily nor burn as fast as wood that has been kiln-dried or dehydrated by exposure to air over a long period of time. In some cases, wood is pressure-treated with fire-retardant chemicals to reduce the speed at which it ignites or burns. However, fire retardants are not always effective in reducing fire spread. Pressure-treating wood also weakens the wood's load-carrying ability by as much as 25 percent.

Newer construction often contains composite building components and materials that are made of wood fibers, plastics, and other substances joined by glue or resin binders. Such materials include plywood, particleboard, fiberboard, **oriented strand board (OSB)**, and paneling **(Figure 3.56)**. Some of these products may be highly combustible, can produce significant toxic gases, or can rapidly deteriorate under fire conditions.

Masonry

Masonry includes bricks, stones, and concrete blocks **(Figure 3.57)**. Brick and stone are generally used to create **veneer walls**, which are decorative covers for wood, metal, and concrete-block load-bearing walls. Fire and exposure to high temperature has a minimal effect of masonry. Bricks rarely show signs of loss of integrity or serious deterioration. Stones and concrete may lose small portions of their surface when heated, a condition called **spalling (Figure 3.58)**. Concrete blocks may crack, but they usually retain most of their strength and basic structural stability. Heat may degrade the mortar between the bricks, blocks, and stone, which could show signs of weakening.

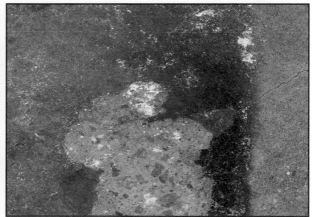

Figure 3.57 Bricks (left) and blocks (right) are common masonry materials.

Figure 3.58 An example of heat-spalled concrete.

Metals

Metal building materials commonly include iron, steel, aluminum, and other metals. They are used to provide structural support, decorative covering on exterior walls, stairs, door and window frames, ductwork, pipes, and fasteners, including nails, screws, and plates. The effect of heat and fire on metal materials will depend on the type of metal and whether the metal is exposed or covered. Metals expand when heated and may lose structural strength depending on the duration and intensity of the heat exposure.

Iron

Two types of iron can be found in buildings in North America: cast iron and wrought iron. Cast iron was commonly used in the 19th century for structural support beams and columns, stairs, balconies, railings, and elevators, and building facades. Facades consisted of large exterior wall sections fastened to the masonry on the front of the building. Cast iron has high resistance to fire and intense heat, but it may crack or shatter when rapidly cooled with water. During a fire, bolts or other connections that hold cast iron components to the building can fail, causing the entire façade to fall. Failure can also result from bolts rusting through or mortar becoming loose around the bolt.

Wrought iron was used in buildings of the early 1800s for nails, straps, tie rods, railings, and balconies. After 1850, it was used for rail and I-beams, channels, and support columns. Today, wrought iron is used for decorations in the construction of gates, fences, and balcony railings. Wrought iron is usually riveted or welded together while cast iron is bolted or screwed.

Steel

Steel is the primary material used for structural support in the construction of large modern buildings and processing units. Steel is also used for stairs, wall studs, window and door frames, and balconies and railings **(Figure 3.59)**. It is also used to reinforce concrete floors, roofs, and walls.

Figure 3.59 Examples of steel usage in building construction.

Although steel is highly useful and durable, steel structural members lengthen (elongate) when heated. A 50-foot (15 m) beam may elongate by as much as 4 inches (100 mm) when heated from room temperature to about 1,000°F (538°C). If the steel is restrained from movement at the ends, it buckles and fails somewhere in the middle. The failure of steel structural members can be anticipated at temperatures near or above 1,000°F (538°C). The temperature at which a specific steel member fails depends on many variables, including the size of the member, the load it is under, the composition of the steel, and the geometry of the member. For example, a **lightweight steel truss** will fail much quicker than a large, heavy I-beam. To reduce the effect of heat on steel structural members, fireproofing materials should be applied in a manner that meets the relevant fire code or AHJ.

> **CAUTION:** Straight or solid streams striking insulated steel members may degrade the integrity of the fireproofing materials.

During preincident planning, the presence and type of steel members should be noted. This will allow fire brigade members responding to a fire to calculate the duration of heat exposure to the steel structural members, and provide an indication of when the structural members might fail. The critical temperature for steel, 1,000°F (538°C), can easily be reached at ceiling level from the rising heat and smoke. Always consider what effect the heat is having on these structural elements even if you cannot see them.

In addition to buckling, elongating steel may push out load-bearing walls and cause a collapse. If the walls can withstand the lateral force, the steel will fail and sag somewhere in the middle, potentially causing collapse of upper floors, the roof, and/or support structures. Water can cool steel structural members and stop elongation, which reduces the risk of a structural collapse.

Aluminum

The use of aluminum increased throughout the 20th century. Initial uses included decorative features, such as the tower portion of the Empire State Building in New York City. Other decorative and functional uses include roofing, flashing, gutters, downspouts, window and door frames, and exterior **curtain wall** panels. Aluminum studs have replaced wood in many commercial and residential buildings. Acoustical tile ceilings are supported by aluminum framing and support wires that can create entanglement hazards for fire brigade members. Heat will affect aluminum more rapidly than steel when comparing equal masses.

Other Metals

Other metals may be found in building construction. Tin has been used to produce metal ceiling tiles for over a century and is used as a roof covering. Copper is found in wiring, pipes, gutters, and other decorative elements. Lead is still found in pipes, flashing, and as a component of stained glass or leaded glass windows. These metals will fail when exposed to sufficient levels of heat.

Figure 3.60 Concrete being poured around rebar to form a reinforced concrete building component.

Reinforced Concrete

Concrete can be poured in place at the construction site or formed into precast sections and transported to the site. Reinforced concrete is internally fortified with steel reinforcement bars (**rebar**) or wire mesh **(Figure 3.60)**. This support gives the material the compressive strength (the ability to withstand pressure on the surface) of concrete along with the tensile strength (the ability to withstand being pulled apart or stretched) of steel. While reinforced concrete performs well under fire conditions, it can lose strength through spalling. Prolonged heating can cause a failure of the bond between the concrete and the steel reinforcement. Cracks and spalling in reinforced concrete surfaces are an indication that damage has occurred and that strength may be reduced. In addition, prolonged exposure to chemicals can cause the steel reinforcing bars to corrode and the concrete bond to weaken before any exposure to fire, significantly reducing the time to failure. The occupancy history of the structure may yield clues as to any potential weakening of structural components.

Gypsum Board

Gypsum board, also known as drywall or Sheetrock®, is an inorganic product from which plaster and wallboards are constructed. It is unique because it has high water content that absorbs a great deal of heat as the moisture evaporates. The water content gives gypsum excellent heat-resistant and fire-retardant properties. Because it breaks down gradually under fire conditions, gypsum is commonly used to insulate steel and structural members. In areas where the gypsum has failed, the structural members behind it will be subjected to higher temperatures and could fail as a result.

Glass/Fiberglass

Glass is not typically used for structural support and is instead used in sheet form for doors and windows and in block form for nonload-bearing walls **(Figure 3.61)**. Wire-reinforced glass may provide some thermal protection as a separation, but conventional glass is an ineffective barrier to fire extension. Heated glass may crack and shatter when a cold fire stream strikes it.

Fiberglass is typically used for insulation purposes and is located between interior/exterior walls and between ceilings and roofs. The glass component of fiberglass is not a significant fuel, but the materials used to bind the fiberglass may be combustible and difficult to extinguish.

Glass Sheets | Wire-reinforced Glass

Figure 3.61 Glass sheets in an exterior wall (left) and wire reinforced glass in a door (right).

 Types of Insulation

There are several types of insulation that have been used in construction. Modern types of insulation include:

- **Fiberglass** — A soft wool-like material used as insulation and for textiles such as drapes. To reduce the loss of heated air, fiberglass was installed inside heating ducts between the 1960s and 1980s. Fiberglass insulation may release small particles that can irritate the eyes, nose, and lungs. OSHA requires fiberglass insulation to carry a cancer label.

- **Foam** — Foam insulation is applied in rigid boards called *extruded and expanded polystyrene (EPS)* or blown into wall cavities or voids in spray form. Spray foam can irritate the respiratory system. There are several types of foam insulation, including:

  — Polyisocyanurate

  — Polyurethane

  — Polystyrene

NOTE: Several of the foams are human **sensitizers** and known carcinogens.

- **Cellulose** — Most cellulose insulation is approximately 80 percent post-consumer recycled newspaper by weight; the rest is comprised of fire-retardant chemicals and, in some products, acrylic binders. Over time, cellulose loses its fire retardant properties. It is also a respiratory irritant when inhaled.

- **Mineral wool** — The term refers to two different materials: slag wool and rock wool. Accounting for approximately 80 percent of mineral wool produced, slag wool is produced primarily from iron ore blast furnace slag, an industrial waste product. Rock wool is produced from natural rocks. Prior to the 1960s, mineral wool was the most common type of insulation. It is becoming more popular as an insulation material.

- **Cotton** — A type of insulation made of cotton and polyester mill scraps, plastic fiber, and borates for fire resistance. It is as effective as fiberglass or cellulose, has fewer documented health risks than fiberglass, and is easy to install. It costs more than fiberglass, however, and is not widely available.

Types of insulation that are no longer manufactured but may be found in older structures include:

- **Asbestos** — A mineral fiber that was used historically for insulation and as a fire retardant. It was most commonly used for pipe and furnace insulation, around door gaskets on furnaces, and for insulation on steam and hot water pipes and electric wires. Asbestos is a known carcinogen. Although its use has been banned in the U.S. since 1989, it may still be encountered in older buildings. Since 2000, studies have determined that vermiculite insulation, used in attics and walls, may contain asbestos. Known as Zonolite®, this insulation can produce dangerous levels of airborne asbestos when heated.

- **Urea Formaldehyde Foam Insulation (UFFI)** — Originally used in the 1970s for insulating walls, this material caused high levels of formaldehyde emissions when improperly installed. Although it is no longer in use, it may still be found in some older structures. Formaldehyde is a known carcinogen. Vapors can be given off when it is heated.

There are potential risks from all types of insulation. Some insulation presents health risks while others may contribute to fire spread if the fire retardant has deteriorated. Some insulation may emit a toxic or harmful gas when heated. From a personal safety standpoint, personnel must wear the appropriate type of respiratory protection when performing overhaul operations.

Plastics

Plastics are used in many forms as a building material. On building exteriors, vinyl siding may be applied over older siding, foam insulation panels, or other materials. Vinyl siding does not require painting or continued maintenance like wood, and it adds additional insulation when applied properly. Water and sewer pipes made from varying sizes of plastic pipe and fittings, and are used to replace lead pipes **(Figure 3.62)**. Other decorative plastic materials include moldings, wall coverings, and mantel pieces. Most plastic will melt and can contribute to the fuel load within a structure.

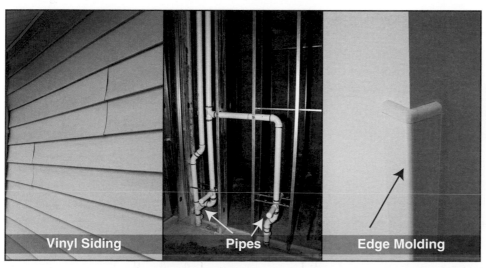

Figure 3.62 Examples of plastics being used for various construction purposes.

NOTE: Several the plastics are human sensitizers and known carcinogens. The products of combustion have the same properties as the materials in their active-use state, which is why personnel must wear respiratory protection at all times during the fire and subsequent overhaul or cleanup.

Composite Materials

The construction industry is using **composite materials** more frequently than in the past. One reason for this shift is a shortage of high-quality and large-diameter timber. Another reason is a on-going trend to use recycled materials in place of hardwoods and other materials.

Generally, composite materials are manufactured by combining two or more distinctly different materials. Structural composites are engineered to create lightweight materials with high structural strength, resistance to chemical wear, corrosion resistant, and heat resistance. The materials are cost effective and fairly easy to manufacture.

Examples of composite building materials include:

- **Finger-jointed timber** — Small pieces of wood that are joined into longer boards using epoxy resins and glues.

- **Laminated timber** — Also known as plywood or glulam (glue-laminated) wood, these materials are sheets of wood used for roof and floor decking, walls, and stair treads among other uses.

- **Medium density fiberboard (MDF)** — Another type of laminated wood product, MDF is closer in appearance and strength to hardwood. It is used for doors and door-surrounds, decorative moldings, rails, skirtings, and cornices.

- **Particle board** — Made from small particles and flakes generated in the manufacture of lumber, particle board is used for exterior and interior wall panels and furniture. Urea formaldehyde is one of the types of glues used to manufacture particle board and can pose a health hazard due to outgassing when heated.

- **Synthetic wood** — This material, produced in sheets and boards, is manufactured from recycled plastic from liquid containers, primarily milk bottles. Synthetic wood is primarily used for exterior rails, stairs, and decks.

Special Industrial Considerations

NFPA 1081 (2018): 4.1.2

An industrial fire brigade may face unique fire behavior situations due to the materials, situations, operations, or equipment found at its particular facility. The organizational statement, procedures, training program, and exercise program must include the necessary special practices and precautions that special industry hazards require. Some of the special industry hazards that fire brigade management must be aware of, if present in their workplace are **(Figure 3.63)**:

- Liquid petroleum storage fires, particularly involving crude oil

- **Liquid petroleum gas (LPG)** hazards with particular attention to **Boiling Liquid Expanding Vapor Explosions (BLEVE)**

- Biological hazards

- Fire in facilities with radioactive materials

    NOTE: Specialized training for these types of hazards is available at a number of training facilities across the world.

Figure 3.63 Examples of special industrial hazards such as a large-volume petroleum fire, a tank-car fire, biological waste, and radiological materials. *Petroleum storage fire photo courtesy of Williams Fire & Hazard Control Inc / Brent Gaspard. Kingman BLEVE photo courtesy of Mohave Museum of History and Arts, Kingman, AZ.*

Chapter Review

1. What is the difference between a physical change and a chemical reaction?

2. What is the difference between the fire triangle and the fire tetrahedron?

3. What is the difference between piloted ignition and autoignition?

4. List the various products of combustion that may be found in a fire.

5. How does fire influence the pressure of the surrounding gases?

6. What is the difference between heat and temperature?

7. Contrast the three methods of heat transfer.

8. How are gaseous, liquid, and solid fuels different?

9. How does oxygen concentration relate to flammability?

10. How are free radicals produced in the chemical reaction that takes place during flaming combustion?

11. How do the four stages of fire development differ?

12. What are the differences between different types of rapid fire development?

13. What does the fully developed stage look like during fuel-limited conditions and ventilation-limited conditions?

14. How can fire brigade members impact fire behavior during fire brigade operations?

15. How does the construction or configuration of a building impact fire development within it?

16. How are different types of metal building materials affected by fire?

17. What are some special industry hazards that fire brigade management must be aware of?

Discussion Questions

1. Why is it important for fire brigade members to understand the principles of fire science?

2. Provide an example of each of the methods of heat transfer: conduction, convection, and radiation.

3. Why is important for fire brigade members to understand the properties of fuels?

4. How does understanding the stages of fire development help incipient-level fire brigade members?

5. Think of buildings at your individual facilities. How will building construction features of those structures impact fire development within them?

6. What are some special industry hazards present in your local facilities?

Chapter 3 End Notes

Putorti, Anthony Jr., Amy Mensch, Nelson Bryner, and George Braga, "*Thermal Performance of Self-Contained Breathing Apparatus Facepiece Lenses Exposed to Radiant Heat Flux*," NIST Technical Note 1785 (NIST.TN 1785), February 2013.

SFPE Handbook of Fire Protection Engineering. Hurley, M.J. et al. editors, Springer, 2016.

Key Terms

Asphyxiant — Any substance that prevents oxygen from combining in sufficient quantities with the blood or from being used by body tissues.

Asphyxiation — Fatal condition caused by severe oxygen deficiency and an excess of carbon monoxide and/or other gases in the blood.

Autoignition — Initiation of combustion by heat but without a spark or flame. (NFPA 921)

Autoignition Temperature — The lowest temperature at which a combustible material ignites in air without a spark or flame. (NFPA 921)

Backdraft — Instantaneous explosion or rapid burning of superheated gases that occurs when oxygen is introduced into an oxygen-depleted confined space. The stalled combustion resumes with explosive force; may occur because of inadequate or improper ventilation procedures.

Boiling Liquid Expanding Vapor Explosion (BLEVE) — Rapid vaporization of a liquid stored under pressure upon release to the atmosphere following major failure of its containing vessel. Failure is the result of over-pressurization caused by an external heat source, which causes the vessel to explode into two or more pieces when the temperature of the liquid is well above its boiling point at normal atmospheric pressure.

Buoyant — The tendency or capacity of a liquid or gas to remain afloat or rise.

Carbon-Based Fuels — Fuels in which the energy of combustion derives principally from carbon; includes materials such as wood, cotton, coal, or petroleum.

Carbon Dioxide (CO_2) — Colorless, odorless, heavier than air gas that neither supports combustion nor burns; used in portable fire extinguishers as an extinguishing agent to extinguish Class B or C fires by smothering or displacing the oxygen. CO_2 is a waste product of aerobic metabolism.

Carbon Monoxide (CO) — Colorless, odorless, dangerous gas (both toxic and flammable) formed by the incomplete combustion of carbon. It combines with hemoglobin more than 200 times faster than oxygen does, decreasing the blood's ability to carry oxygen.

Ceiling Jet — Horizontal movement of a layer of hot gases and combustion by-products from the center point of the plume, when a horizontal surface such as a ceiling redirects the vertical development of the rising plume.

Celsius — International temperature scale on which the freezing point is 0°C (32°F) and the boiling point is 100°C (212°F) at normal atmospheric pressure at sea level.

Chemical Chain Reaction — One of the four sides of the fire tetrahedron representing a process occurring during a fire. Vapor or gases are distilled from flammable materials during initial burning; atoms and molecules are then released from these vapors and combine with other radicals to form new compounds; these compounds are again disturbed by the heat, releasing more atoms and radicals that again form new compounds and so on. Interrupting the chain reaction will stop the overall reaction; this is the extinguishing mechanism utilized by several extinguishing agents.

Chemical Flame Inhibition — Extinguishment of a fire by interruption of the chemical chain reaction.

Combustion — A chemical process of oxidation that occurs at a rate fast enough to produce heat and usually light in the form of either a glow or flame. (Reproduced with permission from NFPA 921-2011, Guide for Fire and Explosion Investigations, Copyright©2011, National Fire Protection Association®)

Combustion Zone — Area surrounding a heat source in which there is sufficient air available to feed a fire.

Compartmentation — The way that the arrangement of compartments creates or does not create a series of barriers designed to keep flames, smoke, and heat from spreading from one room or floor to another.

Composite Materials — Plastics, metals, ceramics, or carbon-fiber materials with built-in strengthening agents.

Compression — Vertical and/or horizontal forces that tend to push the mass of a material together; for example, the force exerted on the top chord of a truss.

Curtain Wall — Nonload-bearing exterior wall attached to the outside of a building with a rigid steel frame. Usually the front exterior wall of a building intended to provide a certain appearance.

Endothermic Reaction — Chemical reaction in which a substance absorbs heat.

Energy — Capacity to perform work; occurs when a force is applied to an object over a distance, or when a chemical, biological, or physical transformation is made in a substance.

Entrain — To draw in and transport solid particles or gases by the flow of a fluid.

Entrainment — The drawing in and transporting of solid particles or gases by the flow of a fluid.

Exothermic Reaction — Chemical reaction between two or more materials that changes the materials and produces heat.

Exposure Fire — A fire ignited in fuel packages or buildings that are remote from the initial fuel package or building of origin.

Fahrenheit Scale — Temperature scale on which the freezing point is 32°F (0°C) and the boiling point at sea level is 212°F (100°C) at normal atmospheric pressure.

Finish — Fine or decorative work required for a building or one of its parts.

Fire — A rapid oxidation process, which is a gas-phase chemical reaction resulting in the evolution of light and heat in varying intensities.

Fire Point — Temperature at which a liquid fuel produces sufficient vapors to support combustion once the fuel ignites. The fire point is usually a few degrees above the flash point.

Fire Resistant — Capacity of structural components to resist higher heat temperatures for certain periods of time. Lesser degree of resistance to fire than *fireproof.*

Fire Suppression — All work and activities connected with fire-extinguishing operations, beginning with discovery and continuing until a fire is completely extinguished.

Fire Tetrahedron — Model of the four elements/conditions required to have a fire. The four sides of the tetrahedron represent fuel, heat, oxygen, and self-sustaining chemical chain reaction.

Fire Triangle — Plane geometric model of an equilateral triangle that is used to explain the conditions/elements necessary for combustion. The sides of the triangle represent heat, oxygen, and fuel. The fire triangle was used prior to the general adaptation of the fire tetrahedron, which includes a chemical chain reaction.

Flammable (Explosive) Range — Range between the upper flammable limit and lower flammable limit in which a substance can ignite.

Flashover — (1) Stage of a fire at which all surfaces and objects within a space have been heated to their ignition temperature, and flame breaks out almost at once over the surface of all objects in the space. (2) Rapid transition from the growth stage to the fully developed stage.

Flash Point — Minimum temperature at which a liquid gives off enough vapors to form an ignitable mixture with air near the surface of the liquid.

Flow Path — Composed of at least one intake opening, one exhaust opening, and the connecting volume between the openings. The difference in pressure determines the direction of the flow. Heat and smoke in a high pressure area will flow toward areas of lower pressure.

Free Radical — Electrically charged, highly reactive parts of molecules released during combustion reactions.

Friction — Resistance between two surfaces moving while in contact with each other. May generate heat and contribute to combustion.

Fuel-Limited — Fire with adequate oxygen in which the heat release rate and growth rate are determined by the characteristics of the fuel, such as quantity and geometry. *Also known as* Fuel-controlled (Reproduced with permission from NFPA 921-2011, *Guide for Fire and Explosion Investigations*, Copyright 2011, National Fire Protection Association).

Fuel Load — The total quantity of combustible contents of a building, space, or fire area, including interior finish and trim, expressed in heat units of the equivalent weight in wood.

Green Wood — Wood with high moisture content.

Heat — Form of energy associated with the motion of atoms or molecules in solids or liquids that is transferred from one body to another as a result of a temperature difference between the bodies, such as from the sun to the earth. To signify its intensity, it is measured in degrees of temperature.

Heat Flux — The measure of the rate of heat transfer to or from a surface, typically expressed in kilowatts/m2.

Heat Release Rate — Total amount of heat released per unit time. The heat release rate is typically measured in kilowatts (kW) or Megawatts (MW) of output.

Heat Transfer — Flow of heat from a hot substance to a cold substance; may be accomplished by convection, conduction, or radiation.

Hydrocarbon Fuel — Petroleum-based organic compound that contains only hydrogen and carbon; may also be used to describe those materials in a fuel load which were created using hydrocarbons such as plastics or synthetic fabrics.

Hydrogen Cyanide (HCN) — Colorless, toxic, and flammable liquid until it reaches 79°F (26°C). Above that temperature, it becomes a gas with a faint odor similar to bitter almonds; produced by the combustion of nitrogen-bearing substances.

Incomplete Combustion — Result of inefficient combustion of a fuel; the less efficient the combustion, the more products of combustion are produced rather than burned during the combustion process.

International System of Units — Modern metric system, based on units of ten.

Irritant — Liquid or solid that, upon contact with fire or exposure to air, gives off dangerous or intensely irritating fumes.

Isolated Flames — Flames in the hot gas layer that indicate the gas layer is within its flammable range and has begun to ignite; often observed immediately before a flashover.

Joule (J) — Unit of work or energy in the International System of Units (SI); the energy (or work) when a unit force (1 newton) moves a body through a unit distance (1 meter). Joules are defined in terms of mechanical energy. In terms of thermal energy, joules refer to the amount of additional heat needed to raise the temperature of a substance, such as the 4.2 Joules needed to raise the temperature of 1 gram of water 1 degree Celsius. Takes the place of calorie for heat measurement (1 calorie = 4.19 J).

Lightweight Steel Truss — Structural support made from a long steel bar that is bent at a 90-degree angle with flat or angular pieces welded to the top and bottom.

Liquefied Petroleum Gas (LPG) — Any of several petroleum products, such as propane or butane, stored under pressure as a liquid.

Lower Explosive (Flammable) Limit (LEL) — Lower limit at which a flammable gas or vapor will ignite and support combustion; below this limit the gas or vapor is too *lean* or *thin* to burn (lacks the proper quantity of fuel). *Also known as* Lower Flammable Limit (LFL).

Masonry — Bricks, blocks, stones, and unreinforced and reinforced concrete products.

Matter — Anything that occupies space and has mass.

Miscible — Materials that are capable of being mixed in all proportions.

Neutral Plane — Level at a compartment opening where the difference in pressure exerted by expansion and buoyancy of hot smoke flowing out of the opening and the inward pressure of cooler, ambient temperature air flowing in through the opening is equal.

Oriented Strand Board (OSB) — Wooden structural panel formed by gluing and compressing wood strands together under pressure. This material has replaced plywood and planking in the majority of construction applications. Roof decks, walls, and subfloors are all commonly made of OSB.

Oxidation — Chemical process that occurs when a substance combines with an oxidizer such as oxygen in the air; a common example is the formation of rust on metal. *See* Decomposition and Pyrolysis.

Piloted Ignition — Moment when a mixture of fuel and oxygen encounters an external heat (ignition) source with sufficient heat or thermal energy to start the combustion reaction.

Polar Solvents — Flammable liquids that have an attraction to water, much like a positive magnetic pole attracts a negative pole; examples include alcohols, esters, ketones, amines, and lacquers.

Pressure — Force per unit area exerted by a liquid or gas measured in pounds per square inch (psi) or kilopascals (kPa).

Products of Combustion — Materials produced and released during burning.

Pyrolysis — The chemical decomposition of a solid material by heating. Pyrolysis precedes combustion of a solid fuel.

Rebar — Short for reinforcing bar. These steel bars are placed in concrete forms before the cement is poured. When the concrete sets (hardens), the rebar within it adds considerable strength and reinforcement.

Rollover — Condition in which the unburned fire gases that have accumulated at the top of a compartment ignite and flames propagate through the hot-gas layer or across the ceiling. These superheated gases are pushed, under pressure, away from the fire area and into uninvolved areas where they mix with oxygen. When their flammable range is reached and additional oxygen is supplied by opening doors and/or applying fog streams, they ignite and a fire front develops, expanding very rapidly in a rolling action across the ceiling.

Sensitizer — Material that can cause an allergic reaction of the skin or respiratory system. *Also known as* Allergen.

Smoke Explosion — Form of fire gas ignition; the ignition of accumulated flammable products of combustion and air that are within their flammable range.

Solubility — Degree to which a solid, liquid, or gas dissolves in a solvent (usually water).

Spalling — Expansion of excess moisture within masonry materials due to exposure to the heat of a fire, resulting in tensile forces within the material, and causing it to break apart. The expansion causes sections of the material's surface to violently disintegrate, resulting in explosive pitting or chipping of the material's surface.

Surface-To-Mass Ratio — Ratio of the surface area of the fuel to the mass of the fuel.

Temperature — (1) Measure of a material's ability to transfer heat energy to other objects; the greater the energy, the higher the temperature. (2) Measure of the average kinetic energy of the particles in a sample of matter, expressed in terms of units or degrees designated on a standard scale.

Thermal Layering (of Gases) — Outcome of combustion in a confined space in which gases tend to form into layers, according to temperature, with the hottest gases found at the ceiling and the coolest gases at floor level.

Upper Explosive (Flammable) Limit (UEL) — Upper limit at which a flammable gas or vapor will ignite; above this limit the gas or vapor is too *rich* to burn (lacks the proper quantity of oxygen). *Also known as* Upper Flammable Limit (UFL).

Vapor Density — Weight of pure vapor or gas compared to the weight of an equal volume of dry air at the same temperature and pressure. A vapor density less than 1 indicates a vapor lighter than air; a vapor density greater than 1 indicates a vapor heavier than air.

Vaporization — Physical process that changes a liquid into a gaseous state; the rate of vaporization depends on the substance involved, heat, pressure, and exposed surface area.

Veneer Walls — Walls with a surface layer of attractive material laid over a base of a common material.

Ventilation — Systematic removal of heated air, smoke, gases or other airborne contaminants from a structure and replacing them with cooler and/or fresher air to reduce damage and facilitate fire fighting operations.

Ventilation-Limited — Fire with limited ventilation in which the heat release rate or growth is limited by the amount of oxygen available to the fire. *Also known as* Ventilation-controlled (Reproduced with permission from NFPA 921-2011, *Guide for Fire and Explosion Investigations*, Copyright 2011, National Fire Protection Association).

Wildland/Urban Interface — Line, area, or zone where an undeveloped wildland area meets a human development area.

Incipient Facility Fire Brigade Member

Chapter Contents

JPRs addressed in this chapter

This chapter provides information that addresses the following job performance requirements of NFPA 1081, *Standard for Facility Fire Brigade Member Professional Qualifications (2018)*.

4.2.1

4.3.2

Learning Objectives

1. Explain the classifications of portable fire extinguishers. [4.2.1, 4.3.2]

2. Describe the types of portable fire extinguishers. [4.3.2]

3. Explain the processes for selecting and using portable fire extinguishers. [4.2.1]

Chapter 4
Portable Fire Extinguishers

Portable fire extinguishers can be found in fixed facilities, such as residences, retail stores, and businesses, onboard ships and aircraft, and on vehicles, including fire apparatus. NFPA 10, *Standard for Portable Fire Extinguishers*, addresses portable fire extinguishers, which are intended for use on small, incipient fires or those in the early growth stage. Primarily intended for occupant use, fire brigade members may also use portable fire extinguishers in a variety of circumstances **(Figure 4.1)**.

Figure 4.1 A fire brigade member using a dry chemical extinguisher during a training exercise.

According to NFPA 1081, fire brigade members must know the following about portable fire extinguishers:

- Classifications of fires
- Risks associated with each class of fire
- Operating methods and limitations of portable fire extinguishers

A fire brigade member must be able to:

- Select appropriate extinguisher for size and type of fire.
- Safely carry portable fire extinguishers.
- Approach fire with portable fire extinguishers.
- Operate portable fire extinguishers.

This chapter describes the various types of portable fire extinguishers, how they are rated, and the proper way to inspect them. This chapter also covers the steps involved in the selection and use of portable fire extinguishers.

Classifications of Portable Fire Extinguishers

NFPA 1081 (2018): 4.2.1, 4.3.2

Portable **fire extinguishers** are classified according to the type of fire that each one is designed to extinguish, though they are suitable to extinguish more than one class of fire. In the U.S. and Canada, there are five classes of portable fire extinguishers to match the five classes of fire: Class A, B, C, D, and K. Other nations add other fire and extinguisher classifications for their territories **(Table 4.1)**. Portable fire extinguishers are identified by combinations of the letters A, B, and/or C or the symbols for each class of fire. The three most common combinations are Class A-B-C, Class A-B, and Class B-C. All new portable fire extinguishers must be labeled with their appropriate markings. Firefighters should use an extinguisher only for the fire type for which it is intended. To choose the appropriate portable fire extinguisher for a given fire, first determine what is burning. Certain **extinguishing agents** are only effective on certain classes of fire or fuels.

Table 4.1 Comparing U.S./Canadian Fire Classifications to United Kingdom/European Union Fire Classifications		
U.S. Classes of Fires	**Types of Fires**	**UK and EU Classes of Fires**
A	Ordinary Combustibles: wood, paper, plastics, and textiles	A
B	Flammable and Combustible Liquids	B
B	Flammable Gases	C
C	Live Electrical Fires	(no letter)
D	Combustible Metals	D
K	Kitchen/Cooking Oils/Fats	F

Class A and B extinguishers are classified with both letter and numerical rating systems. Underwriters Laboratories (UL) and Underwriters Laboratories of Canada (ULC) conduct tests that determine the classification and numerical rating system. These tests are designed to determine the extinguishing capability for each size and type of extinguisher. **Table 4.2** compares the ratings of each class of portable extinguisher.

The ratings for each separate class of extinguisher are independent and do not affect each other. For example, a common-sized extinguisher, such as the multipurpose extinguisher rated 4-A 20-B:C, should extinguish a Class A fire that is 4 times larger than a 1-A fire, extinguish approximately 20 times as much Class B fire as a 1-B extinguisher, and extinguish a deep-layer flammable liquid fire of 20 square feet (1.8 m²) in area. It must also be nonconductive so it is safe to use on fires involving energized electrical equipment. Refer to the section later in this chapter about Class B extinguishers for more information.

Portable fire extinguishers are identified in two ways. One system uses geometric shapes of specific colors with the class letter shown within the shape. The second system uses pictographs to make the selection of the most appropriate fire extinguishers easier. It also shows the types of fires on which extinguishers should *not* be used. **Table 4.3** compares the two identification systems.

Table 4.2
Portable Fire Extinguisher Ratings

Class	Ratings	Explanations
A	1-A through 40-A (A = 1¼ gallons of water)	1-A (1¼ gallons [5 L] of water) 2-A (2½ gallons [10 L] of water) 3-A (3¾ gallons [15 L] of water) etc.
B	1-B through 640-B	Based on the approximate square foot (square meter) area of a flammable liquid fire a non-expert can extinguish
C	No extinguishing capability tests	Tests are to determine non-conductivity
D	No numerical ratings	Tested for reactions, toxicity, and metal burn out time
K	No numerical rating	Tested to ensure effectiveness against 2.25 square feet (0.2 m²) of light cooking oil in a deep fat fryer

Table 4.3
Fire Extinguisher Letter/Image/Picture Symbols

U.S./Canadian System
Letter Symbol   Image Symbol

A — Ordinary Combustibles

B — Flammable Liquids

C — Electrical Equipment

D — Combustible Metals

K — Cooking Oils

U.K./E.U. System
Picture Symbol

A — Wood, Paper, Textiles, etc.

B — Flammable Liquids

C — Flammable Gases

D — Metals

Electrical

F — Cooking Oil and Fat Fires

Reproduced with permission from Wayne State University, Detroit, MI.

Class A

Class A fires involve ordinary combustibles such as **(Figure 4.2)**:

- Textiles
- Paper
- Plastics
- Rubber
- Wood

Water and water-based agents such as Class A foam can extinguish all of these fuels. Multi-purpose **dry chemicals** will also extinguish fires fueled by Class A materials.

The Class A rating of water extinguishers is primarily based on the amount of extinguishing agent and the duration

Figure 4.2 A variety of Class A materials found inside a warehousing facility.

and range of the discharge used in extinguishing test fires. Class A portable fire extinguishers are rated from 1-A through 40-A. For a 1-A rating, 1¼ gallons (5 L) of water are required. A 2-A rating requires 2½ gallons (10 L) or twice the 1-A capacity.

Class B

Class B fires involve flammable and combustible liquids and gases, including **(Figure 4.3)**:

- Alcohol
- Gasoline
- Lubricating oils
- Liquefied petroleum gas (LPG)

All of these fuels require the same extinguishing agents. Agents used to extinguish special hazard Class B fires include carbon dioxide (CO_2), dry chemicals, and Class B foam.

Figure 4.3 Flammable and combustible liquids and gases are examples of Class B materials.

Class B portable fire extinguishers are classified with numerical ratings ranging from 1-B through 640-B. The rating is based on the approximate square foot (square meter) area of a flammable liquid fire that a nonexpert operator can extinguish using one full extinguisher. The nonexpert operator is expected to extinguish 1 square foot (0.09 m^2) for each numerical rating or value of the extinguisher rating.

Class C

Class C fires involve energized electrical equipment **(Figure 4.4)**. Once the power supply has been turned off or disconnected, the fire can be treated as a Class A or B fire.

Water and water-based agents conduct electrical current and cannot be used on Class C fires until the electricity has been shut off. Class C extinguishing agents will not conduct electricity, making them suitable for electrical fires.

NOTE: Some companies have designed and manufactured water-mist extinguishers designed for use on Class C fires.

Fire extinguishing capability tests are not specifically conducted for Class C ratings. Class C extinguishers receive that letter rating because Class C fires are essentially Class A or Class B fires involving energized electrical equipment. The extinguishing agent is tested for electrical nonconductivity. The Class C rating, which confirms that the extinguishing agent will not conduct electricity, is assigned in addition to the rating for Class A and/or Class B fires.

Figure 4.4 When energized, a fire in this electric motor would be considered a Class C fire.

Figure 4.5 The combustible metal filings in this bin would create a Class D fire if ignited.

Class D

Class D fires are those involving combustible metals and alloys such as **(Figure 4.5)**:

- Titanium
- Lithium
- Magnesium
- Potassium
- Sodium

Magnesium fires can be identified by the bright white emissions during the combustion process. Some common uses of magnesium are in:

- Cameras
- Laptops
- Metal box springs for beds
- Wheels and transmission components for automobiles or aircraft

> **CAUTION:** The use of water or water-based agents on Class D fires will cause the fire to react violently, emit bits of molten metal, and possibly injure nearby firefighters.

Class D **dry powder** extinguishers work best on these types of fires. Do *not* confuse dry powder extinguishers with dry chemical units used on Class A, B, and C fires. Only liquid or powder extinguishers rated for Class D fires should be used to extinguish metal fires.

> **CAUTION:** Use only Class D-rated fire extinguishers to extinguish metal fires.

Test fires for establishing Class D ratings vary with the type of combustible metal being tested. The following factors are considered during each test:

- Reactions between the metal and the agent
- Toxicity of the agent
- Toxicity of the fumes produced and the products of combustion
- Time to allow metal to burn completely without fire suppression compared to the time to extinguish the fire using the extinguisher

When an extinguishing agent is determined to be safe and effective for use on a combustible metal, the application instructions are included on the faceplate of the extinguisher, although no numerical rating is given. Class D agents cannot be given a rating for use on other classes of fire.

Class K

Class K fires involve combustible cooking oils, such as vegetable or animal fats and oils that burn at extremely high temperatures **(Figure 4.6)**. These fuels can be found in commercial and institutional kitchens and industrial cooking facilities. **Wet chemical systems** and portable fire extinguishers are used to control and extinguish Class K fires.

Class K-rated extinguishers must be capable of **saponification**,

Figure 4.6 A large scale fryer that uses combustible cooking oils, such as this one in a food production facility, could cause a Class K fire.

which is the conversion of the fatty acids or fats in the following oils to a soap:

- Vegetable oil
- Peanut oil
- Canola oil
- Other oils with little or no fatty acids

Wet chemical agents containing an alkaline mixture, such as potassium acetate, potassium carbonate, or potassium citrate, work by suppressing the vapors and smothering the fire. Agents capable of extinguishing a fire from a deep fryer using these light oils with a surface area of 2.25 square feet (0.2 m²) meet the minimum criteria for Class K rating.

Types of Portable Fire Extinguishers

NFPA 1081 (2018): 4.3.2

Along with classifying portable fire extinguishers by the type of fire they will extinguish, extinguishers are also organized by the type of extinguishing agent and the method used to expel the contents. Extinguishing agents use at least one of the following methods to extinguish fire:

- **Smothering** — Excluding oxygen from the burning process
- **Cooling** — Reducing the burning material below its ignition temperature
- **Chain breaking** — Interrupting the chemical chain reaction in the burning process
- **Saponification** — Forming an oxygen-excluding soapy foam surface

Table 4.4 lists the primary and secondary extinguishing methods of various extinguishing agents. Extinguishing agents that work by smothering are ineffective on materials that contain their own oxidizing agent. For example, a fire in magnesium or other combustible metals will flare and intensify if water is applied. **Table 4.5, p. 128** shows the operational characteristics of different types of portable fire extinguishers.

NOTE: Water-type extinguishers must be protected against freezing if exposed to temperatures lower than 40°F (4°C). Adding a manufacturer's approved, biodegradable antifreeze to the water or storing them in warm areas may provide freeze protection.

Table 4.4 Extinguishing Agent Characteristics		
Agent	**Primary Method**	**Secondary Method**
Water	Cooling	Oxygen depletion
Carbon Dioxide	Oxygen depletion	Cooling
Foam	Oxygen depletion	Vapor suppression
Clean Agent	Chain inhibition	Cooling
Dry Chemical	Chain inhibition	Oxygen depletion
Wet Chemical	Oxygen depletion	Vapor suppression
Dry Powder	Oxygen depletion	Heat transfer cooling

All portable fire extinguishers expel their contents using one of the following mechanisms:

- **Manual pump** — The operator physically applies pressure to a pump that increases pressure within the container, forcing the agent out a nozzle at the end of a hose.
- **Stored pressure** — Compressed air or inert gas within the container forces the agent out a nozzle at the end of a hose when the operator presses the handle.

Table 4.5
Operational Characteristics of Portable Fire Extinguishers

Extinguisher	Type	Agent	Fire Class	Size	Stream Reach	Discharge Time
Pump-Tank Water	Hand-carried; backpack	Water	A only	1½-5 gal (6 L to 20 L)	30-40 ft (9.1 m to 12.2 m)	45 sec to 3 min
Stored-Pressure Water	Hand-carried	Water	A only	1¼-2½ gal (5 L to 10 L)	30-40 ft (9.1 m to 12.2 m)	30-60 sec
Aqueous Film Forming Foam (AFFF)	Hand-carried	Water and AFFF	A & B	2½ gal (10 L)	20-25 ft (6.1 m to 7.6 m)	Approx. 50 sec
Halon 1211*	Hand-carried; wheeled	Halon	B & C	Hand-carried: 2½-20 lb (1 kg to 9 kg) Wheeled: to 150 lb (68 kg)	8-18 ft (2.4 m to 5.5 m) 20-35 ft (6.1 m to 10.7 m)	8-18 sec 30-44 sec
Halon 1301	Hand-carried	Halon	B & C	2½ lb (1 kg)	4-6 ft (1.2 m to 1.8 m)	8-10 sec
Carbon Dioxide	Hand-carried	Carbon Dioxide	B & C	2½-20 lb (1 kg to 9 kg)	3-8 ft (1 m to 2.4 m)	8-30 sec
Carbon Dioxide	Wheeled	Carbon Dioxide	B & C	50-100 lb (23 kg to 45 kg)	8-10 ft (2.4 m to 3 m)	26-65 sec
Dry Chemical	Hand-carried stored-pressure; cartridge-operated	Sodium bicarbonate, potassium bicarbonate, ammonium phosphate, potassium chloride	B & C	2½-30 lb (1 kg to 14 kg)	5-20 ft (1.5 m to 6.1 m)	8-25 sec
Multipurpose Dry Chemical	Hand-carried stored-pressure; cartridge-operated	Monoammonium phosphate	A, B, & C	2½-30 lb (1 kg to 14 kg)	5-20 ft (1.5 m to 6.1 m)	8-25 sec
Dry Chemical	Wheeled; ordinary or multipurpose		A, B, & C	75-350 lb (34 kg to 159 kg)	Up to 45 ft (13.7 m)	20 sec to 2 min
Dry Powder	Hand-carried; wheeled	Various, depending on metal fuel (this description for sodium chloride plus flow enhancers)	D only	Hand Carried: to 30 lb (14 kg) Wheeled: 150 lb & 350 lb (68 kg & 159 kg)	4-6 ft (1.2 m to 1.8 m)	28-30 sec
Wet Chemical	Hand-carried	Potassium Acetate	K only	2.5 gal (9.43 L)	8-12 ft (2.4 m to 3.6 m)	75-85 sec

*Rating: Those larger than 9 lb (4 kg) capacity have small Class A Ratings (1-A to 4-A)

- **Pressure cartridge** — Compressed inert gas is contained in a separate cartridge on the side of the container. When the operator punctures the cartridge seal, the expellant enters the container, forcing the agent out a nozzle on the end of a hose.

Common portable fire extinguishers include:

- Pump-type water extinguishers
- **Water mist extinguishers** (stored-pressure)
- Clean agent extinguishers
- Dry chemical extinguishers
- Dry powder extinguishers

- Stored-pressure water extinguishers
- Aqueous film forming foam (AFFF) extinguishers
- Carbon dioxide (CO_2) extinguishers
- Cart-mounted extinguishers
- Wet chemical extinguishers

Pump-Type Water Extinguishers

Pump-type water extinguishers are intended primarily for use on ground cover fires although they may also be used for small Class A fires. They may be hand-carried tanks or designed to be worn on the back with a manually operated slide pump **(Figure 4.7)**. The nozzle produces a straight stream, fog, or water-mist pattern.

Stored-Pressure Water Extinguishers

Stored-pressure water extinguishers, also called air-pressurized water (APW) extinguishers or pressurized water extinguishers, are useful for all types of small Class A fires **(Figure 4.8)**. Fire brigade personnel may use these types of extinguishers for confined hot spots during overhaul operations.

Water is stored in a tank along with compressed air or nitrogen. A gauge located on the valve assembly shows the extinguisher's pressurize level. When the operating valve is activated, the stored pressure forces water up the siphon tube and out through the hose.

Class A foam concentrate is sometimes added to pump-type or stored-pressure water extinguishers to increase their effectiveness. The Class A foam concentrate serves as a wetting agent and can aid in extinguishing deep-seated fires in upholstered furniture or vehicle seats and wildland fires in densely matted vegetation. Class A foam concentrate reduces the surface tension of water, allowing the water to quickly penetrate the surface.

Water-Mist Stored-Pressure Extinguishers

Similar in appearance to stored-pressure water extinguishers, water-mist extinguishers use **deionized water** as the agent and nozzles that produce a fine spray instead of a solid stream **(Figure 4.9, p. 130)**. Because impurities in water make it conduct electricity, the deionized water also makes these Class A extinguishers safe to use on energized electrical equipment (Class C). The fine spray also enhances the water's cooling and soaking characteristics and reduces scattering of the burning materials.

Figure 4.7 A fire brigade member practicing the operation of a backpack pump-type water extinguisher.

Figure 4.8 An example of a common air-pressurized water fire extinguisher.

Figure 4.9 An example of a water-mist fire extinguisher.

Figure 4.10 An example of an AFFF fire extinguisher.

Aqueous Film Forming Foam (AFFF) Extinguishers

Aqueous film forming foam (AFFF) extinguishers are intended for Class B fires, particularly in combating fires in or suppressing vapors from small liquid fuel spills **(Figure 4.10)**. AFFF extinguishers are different from stored-pressure water extinguishers in two ways:

- The AFFF extinguisher tank contains a specified amount of AFFF concentrate mixed with the water to produce a foam solution.

- It has an **air-aspirating foam nozzle** that aerates the foam solution, producing a better-quality foam than a standard extinguisher nozzle provides.

NOTE: Some manufacturers market AFFF foam concentrates that can be used on Class A fires.

The water/AFFF solution is expelled using compressed air or nitrogen stored in the tank with the solution. The finished foam floats on the surface of fuels that are lighter than water. The vapor seal created by the film of finished foam extinguishes the flame and prevents reignition. To avoid disturbing the foam blanket when applying the foam, personnel should not apply it directly onto the fuel; instead, they should let it rain down gently onto the fuel's surface or deflect off a nearby object or surface.

AFFF extinguishers are most effective on static pools of flammable liquids. They are not suitable for fires in Class C, Class D, or Class K fuels or for such situations as fuel flowing down from an elevated point and fuel under pressure spraying from a leak.

Figure 4.11 This clean agent extinguisher hangs in an electrical utility room.

Figure 4.12 An example of a carbon dioxide fire extinguisher.

Clean Agent Extinguishers

Clean agents are replacing halogenated extinguishing agents commonly called Halons. Halons were effective for extinguishing fires in computer rooms, aircraft engines, and areas that contained materials that water or dry chemical agents could damage easily. However, halogenated extinguishing agents also have a damaging effect on the atmosphere's ozone layer. The U.S. Environmental Protection Agency (EPA) has approved Halotron extinguishers, which offer an alternative to Halons.

Clean agents are discharged as rapidly evaporating liquids that leaves no residue. These agents effectively cool and smother fires in Class A and Class B fuels, and the agents are nonconductive so they can be used on energized electrical equipment (Class C) fires **(Figure 4.11)**.

Carbon Dioxide (CO_2) Extinguishers

Carbon dioxide (CO_2) fire extinguishers, found as both handheld and wheeled units, are most effective in extinguishing Class B and Class C fires. The discharge is in the form of a gas, has a limited reach, and can be dispersed by wind. They do not require freeze protection **(Figure 4.12)**.

Carbon dioxide is stored under its own pressure as a liquefied gas. The agent is discharged through a plastic or rubber horn on the end of either a short hose or tube. The gaseous discharge usually forms dry ice crystals or carbon dioxide "snow." Shortly after discharge, this snow changes from a solid to a gas without becoming a liquid. When released, the carbon dioxide gas displaces available oxygen and smothers the fire. Even though CO_2 discharges at subzero temperatures, it has little if any cooling effect on fires. Carbon dioxide produces no vapor-suppressing film on the surface of the fuel; therefore, reignition is always a danger.

Carbon dioxide wheeled units are considerably larger than handheld units. CO_2 wheeled units usually have 50-to-100 pound (23 Kg to 45 Kg) capacities. Wheeled units are most commonly used in airports and industrial facilities. After being moved to the fire, the hose (usually less than 15 feet [5 m] long) must be deployed or unwound from the unit before use. The principle of operation is the same as in the smaller handheld units.

Dry Chemical Extinguishers

The terms *dry chemical* and *dry powder* are often incorrectly used interchangeably. Dry chemical agents are for use on Class A-B-C fires and/or Class B-C fires; dry powder agents are used only on Class D fires. Dry chemical extinguishers are among the most common portable fire extinguishers in use. There are two basic types of dry chemical extinguishers:

• Regular B:C-rated

• Multipurpose and A:B:C-rated (see Extinguisher Rating System section)

Unless specifically noted in this section, the characteristics and operation of both types of dry chemical extinguishers are exactly the same. The following are commonly used dry chemicals:

• Sodium bicarbonate

• Urea-potassium bicarbonate

• Monoammonium phosphate

• Potassium bicarbonate

• Potassium chloride

During manufacture, dry chemical agents are mixed with additives that make the agents moisture-resistant and prevent them from caking (drying or hardening into a mass). This process keeps the agents ready for use and free-flowing even after being stored for long periods.

The dry chemical agents themselves are nontoxic and generally considered safe to use. However, the cloud of chemicals discharged from the extinguisher may reduce visibility and create respiratory problems just like any other airborne particulate. Some dry chemicals are compatible with foam, but others are not. Monoammonium phosphate and some sodium bicarbonate agents will cause the foam blanket to deteriorate when applied in conjunction with or after foam to a Class B fire or spill.

On Class A fires, firefighters should direct the discharge at whatever is burning in order to cover it with chemical. When the flames have been knocked down, personnel should apply intermittently as needed on any smoldering areas. Many dry chemical agents can be mildly corrosive to all surfaces.

Handheld Units

There are two basic designs for handheld dry chemical extinguishers: stored-pressure and cartridge-operated. The stored-pressure type is similar in design to the air-pressurized water extinguisher. A constant pressure of about 200 psi (1 400 kPa) is maintained in the agent storage tank. Cartridge-operated extinguishers employ a pressure cartridge connected to the agent tank. The agent tank is not pressurized until a plunger is pushed to release the gas from the cartridge. Both types of extinguishers use either nitrogen or carbon dioxide as the pressurizing gas **(Figure 4.13)**.

Wheeled Units

Dry chemical wheeled units are similar to the handheld units but larger **(Figure 4.14)**. They are rated for Class A, B, and C fires based on the dry chemical in the unit.

Operating the wheeled dry chemical extinguisher is similar to operating the handheld, cartridge-operated dry chemical extinguisher. Some units are internally pressurized. In other units, the extinguishing agent is kept in one tank and the pressurizing gas is stored in a separate cylinder. When the

Figure 4.13 A pressurized dry chemical fire extinguisher (left) and a cartridge-operated dry chemical fire extinguisher (right).

CAUTION: When pressurizing a cartridge-operated extinguisher, do not place your head or any other part of your body above the top of the extinguisher. If the fill cap was not properly screwed back on, the cap and/or a cloud of agent can be forcibly discharged.

extinguisher is in position at a fire, the hose should first be stretched out completely. Once the agent storage tank and hose are charged, it can make removing the hose more difficult and the powder can sometimes clog in any sharp bends in the hose. Fire brigade members should introduce the pressurizing gas into the agent tank and allow a few seconds for the gas to fully pressurize the tank before they open the nozzle. The operator should prepare for a significant nozzle reaction when the nozzle is opened. Firefighters should apply the agent in the same manner as described for the handheld, cartridge-operated dry chemical extinguishers.

Figure 4.14 Comparing the sizes of a pressurized dry chemical fire extinguisher (left) and a wheeled dry chemical fire extinguisher (right).

Cart-Mounted Extinguishers

Some larger fire extinguishing units are mounted on carts or trailers so that they can be moved more easily. The extinguishing agents used in these units can include dry chemical, foam, or a combination of dry chemical and foam. Propellant gases for these units may be stored inside the agent tank (stored pressure) or in a separate propellant storage tank (pressure cartridge) **(Figure 4.15)**. Some cart-mounted extinguisher units are equipped with automatic fire detection and suppression equipment to activate the unit if a fire occurs.

Figure 4.15 An example of a cart-mounted fire extinguisher.

Dry Powder Extinguishers

Special dry powder extinguishing agents and application techniques control and extinguish fires involving Class D combustible metals **(Figure 4.16)**. No single extinguishing agent will control or extinguish fires in all combustible metals. Some agents are effective against fires in several metals; others are effective on fires in only one type of metal. Personnel can apply some powdered agents with portable extinguishers, but some agents require fire brigade members to apply them with a shovel or a scoop. The manufacturer's technical sales literature describes the appropriate application technique for any given dry powder. You should be thoroughly familiar with the information that applies to all agents carried on your apparatus.

Figure 4.16 An example of a dry powder fire extinguisher.

Class D portable fire extinguishers come in both handheld and wheeled models. Whether a particular dry powder is applied with an extinguisher or with a scoop, it must be applied in sufficient depth to completely cover the burning area in order to create a smothering blanket. Fire brigade personnel should gently apply the agent to avoid breaking any crust that may form over the burning metal. If the crust is broken, the fire may flare and expose more uninvolved material to combustion. Avoid scattering the burning metal. Additional applications may be necessary to cover any hot spots that develop.

If a small amount of burning metal is on a combustible surface, the fire should first be covered with powder. Then, a layer of powder 1 to 2 inches (25 mm to 50 mm) deep should be spread nearby and the burning metal shoveled onto this layer with more powder added as needed. After extinguishment, the material should be left undisturbed until the mass has cooled completely before disposal is attempted.

Figure 4.17 A Class K fire extinguisher in kitchen.

Wet Chemical Extinguishers

Similar in appearance to standard stored-pressure water extinguishers, wet chemical fire extinguishers are intended for use on Class K fires involving cooking fats, greases, and vegetable and animal oils in commercial kitchens **(Figure 4.17)**. These fire extinguishers contain a special potassium-based, low-pH agent formulated to operate on the principle of saponification in which the agent combines with the oils to create a soapy foam surface over the cooking appliance. Some fire departments carry Class K extinguishers on their apparatus.

 Refilling Fire Extinguishers

Depending upon your jurisdiction's requirements, you may be responsible for refilling various types of fire extinguishers. You should refer to your local training, standard operating procedures, and manufacturer's instructions before refilling any extinguisher. Most portable fire extinguisher manufacturers offer specialized training courses for servicing each type of extinguisher.

Selecting and Using Portable Fire Extinguishers

NFPA 1081 (2018): 4.2.1

In most cases, your supervisor will make the decision on the need to use a portable fire extinguisher and will tell you the correct type to use. If you are the only one present and must make your own selection, there are a number of factors to consider when deciding which portable fire extinguisher to select for the situation. In addition, there are a number of factors to remember when using the extinguisher you selected. This section explains these considerations. This information is also important when you are instructing others in the selection and use of extinguishers.

REACT and RACE

Prior to selecting and using an extinguisher, the fire brigade member should ensure that other personnel evacuate the area, the location is isolated, an alarm is sounded to notify others of the emergency, and the fire extinguisher is rated for use on the class of fire encountered. Two methods used to accomplish task this are REACT and RACE.

REACT:

R – Remove those in immediate danger.

E – Ensure that the room door is closed.

A – Activate the fire alarm or notify law enforcement agency, depending on the nature of the emergency if it has not already been done.

C – Call the fire department or local law enforcement agency.

T – Try to extinguish or control the fire or remove those at risk without endangering additional lives.

RACE:

R – Remove (patients)

A – Alert (call 9-1-1)

C – Confine (close off the area of origin)

E – Extinguish (if able to do so)

Selecting the Proper Fire Extinguisher

Select extinguishers that minimize the risk to life and property and are effective in extinguishing the fire. To make this selection, consider the following factors:

- Classification of the burning fuel
- Hazards to be protected
- Atmospheric conditions
- Ease of handling extinguisher
- Rating of the extinguisher
- Size and intensity of the fire
- Availability of trained personnel
- Any life hazard or operational concerns

Do not select dry chemical extinguishers for use in areas where highly sensitive computer equipment is located. The residue left afterward could potentially do more damage to the sensitive electronic equipment than the fire. In these particular areas, clean agent or carbon dioxide extinguishers are better choices.

Using Portable Fire Extinguishers

Portable fire extinguishers come in many types and sizes. While the operating procedures of each type of extinguisher are similar, you should become familiar with the detailed instructions found on the extinguisher's label.

NOTE: Wear appropriate protective clothing when using fire extinguishers during fire fighting operations and all live-fire training evolutions.

After selecting the appropriate size and type of extinguisher for the situation, make a quick visual inspection. This inspection is necessary to ensure that the extinguisher is charged and operable. This check may protect you from injury caused by a defective or depleted extinguisher. When inspecting an extinguisher immediately before use, check the following **(Figure 4.18)**:

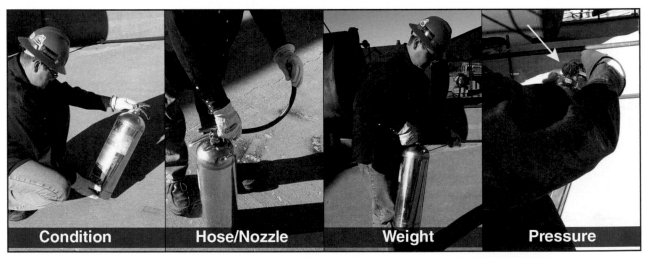

Figure 4.18 When inspecting a portable fire extinguisher, you should check the extinguisher's condition, hose and nozzle, weight, and pressure.

- **External condition** — No apparent damage
- **Hose/nozzle** — In place
- **Weight** — Feels as though it contains agent
- **Pressure gauge (if available)** — In operable range. A pressure gauge, if present, should register a reading within the operable range.

NOTE: If the extinguisher appears to be in working order, you can then use it to extinguish the fire.

After performing the visual inspection, pick up the extinguisher by its handles and carry it to the point of application. Approach the fire from the windward side with the wind at your back. Once in position to attack the fire, use the PASS application method **(Figure 4.19)**:

Figure 4.19 Illustrating the PASS method of using a portable fire extinguisher.

CAUTION: If the fire is too large and other fire brigade members are not yet on location, withdraw to a safe location and attempt to isolate by closing doors if you can do so safely.

P – Pull the pin, breaking the thin wire or plastic seal.

A – Aim the nozzle at the base of the fire.

S – Squeeze the handles together to release a short burst to test the extinguisher, then squeeze continuously to release the agent.

S – Sweep the nozzle back and forth to cover the burning material.

Considerations relating to suppressing incipient fires of all classes include:

- An advantage of fire extinguishers are they are quick to deploy over a hoseline.
- Remember that a portable extinguisher is a first-aid fire fighting appliance and does not take the place of an appropriate-sized hoseline.
- Be sure the extinguishing agent reaches the fire — if it cannot, the agent will be wasted.
- Ensure that there is a clear exit for immediate escape should you need it.
- Smaller extinguishers require a closer approach to the fire than larger units, though radiant heat or smoke may prevent you from getting close enough for the agent to reach the fire.
- Adverse winds can limit the reach of an agent.
- Operating an extinguisher close to the fire can sometimes scatter lightweight solid fuels or penetrate the surface of liquid fuels.
- Apply the agent from a point where it reaches but does not disturb the fuel surface. Releasing the handles will stop the flow of agent.
- After the fire is reduced in size, you may move closer to achieve final fire extinguishment.
- If extinguishment is not achieved after an entire extinguisher has been discharged onto the fire, withdraw and reassess the situation.
- If the fire is in a solid fuel that has been reduced to the smoldering phase, it may be overhauled using an appropriate tool to pull it apart. A charged hoseline can then be used to soak it to achieve complete extinguishment.
- If the fire is in a liquid fuel, it may be necessary to either apply the appropriate type of foam through a hoseline or simultaneously attack the fire with more than one portable fire extinguisher.
- For Class B fires involving the gaseous state, always attempt to shut off the fuel source prior to extinguishment.
- For fires involving an energized electrical component (Class C), attempt to shut off the electricity to the component before attempting to extinguish the fire.

- If more than one extinguisher is used simultaneously, work in unison with the other firefighters and maintain a constant awareness of each other's actions and positions **(Figure 4.20)**.

- Lay empty fire extinguishers on their sides after use. This cue signals to other fire brigade personnel that they are empty and reduces the chance of someone taking one and approaching a fire with an empty extinguisher.

Figure 4.20 Fire brigade members need to work in unison while using portable fire extinguishers on a fire.

Chapter Review

1. Name each class of fire and types of combustible materials that they may involve.

2. What are the methods that extinguishing agents use to extinguish fire?

3. What are dry powder extinguishers designed to extinguish?

4. What factors should be considered when selecting a fire extinguisher?

5. What are some considerations when using a fire extinguisher to extinguish an incipient fire?

Key Terms

Air-Aspirating Foam Nozzle — Foam nozzle designed to provide the aeration required to make the highest quality foam possible; most effective appliance for the generation of low-expansion foam.

Aqueous Film Forming Foam (AFFF) — Synthetic foam concentrate that, when combined with water, can form a complete vapor barrier over fuel spills and fires and is a highly effective extinguishing and blanketing agent on hydrocarbon fuels.

Class A Fire — Fires involving ordinary combustibles such as wood, paper, cloth, and similar materials.

Class B Fire — Fires of flammable and combustible liquids and gases.

Class C Fire — Fires involving energized electrical equipment.

Class D Fire — Fires of combustible metals such as magnesium, sodium, and titanium.

Class K Fire — Fires in cooking appliances that involve combustible cooking media, such as vegetable or animal oils and fats; commonly occurring in commercial cooking facilities, such as restaurants and institutional kitchens.

Deionized Water — Water from which ionic salts, minerals, and impurities have been removed by ion exchange.

Dry Chemical — Any one of a number of powdery extinguishing agents used to extinguish fires.

Dry Powder — Extinguishing agent suitable for use on combustible metal fires.

Extinguishing Agent — Any substance used for the purpose of controlling or extinguishing a fire.

Fire Extinguisher — Portable fire fighting device designed to combat incipient fires.

Saponification — Phenomenon that occurs when mixtures of alkaline based chemicals and certain cooking oils come into contact, resulting in the formation of a soapy film.

Smothering — Act of excluding oxygen from a fuel.

Water Mist Extinguisher — Fire extinguisher capable of discharging atomized water through a special applicator; pressurized water mist extinguishers use distilled water, whereas back-pump water mist extinguishers use ordinary water.

Wet Chemical System — Extinguishing system that uses a wet chemical solution as the primary extinguishing agent; usually installed in range hoods and associated ducting where grease may accumulate.

Skill Sheet List

The following skill sheets should be used to evaluate the skills described in this chapter:

NOTE: Students should wear the PPE appropriate to the NFPA 1081 level (Incipient, Advanced Exterior, Interior Structural, etc...) being evaluated.

Incipient Facility Fire Brigade Member

Chapter Contents

JPRs addressed in this chapter

This chapter provides information that addresses the following job performance requirements of NFPA 1081, *Standard for Facility Fire Brigade Member Professional Qualifications (2018)*.

4.3.1   4.3.4

4.3.3

1. Describe the principles of water supply systems. [4.3.4]

2. Explain fire hose components and tools. [4.3.1, 4.3.4]

3. Describe the methods for making hose rolls and hose loads. [4.3.1, 4.3.4]

4. Describe the methods for deploying, advancing, and operating hoselines. [4.3.1, 4.3.4]

5. Describe the extinguishing properties of water.

6. Explain the factors the affect pressure gain and loss in fire streams. [4.3.4]

7. Identify the types of fire stream patterns and nozzles. [4.3.3]

8. Describe the operating procedures of nozzles and master streams. [4.3.3]

Chapter 5
Water Supply, Hose, and Fire Streams

Water is the primary extinguishing agent used on most fires because it is readily available and inexpensive to use. A municipal, rural, private facility, or mobile water supply system usually supplies water. Water-based fire suppression operations are ineffective without an adequate water supply.

Fire hose carries water from the **fire hydrant** or water source to the pumper/quint and then to the fire. Supply hoses transfer the water from the supply source to an apparatus' fire pump. The pump controls the pressure and forwards the water through **attack lines** to where it is needed. Nozzles create fire streams to apply the water to the fire to accomplish extinguishment.

This chapter describes the background and skill knowledge you will need to learn about:

- Principles of water supply systems
- Fire streams
- Fire hose
- Service testing fire hose

Principles of Water Supply Systems
NFPA 1081 (2018): 4.3.4

There are two basic types of **water supply** systems in North America: public and private. Public water supply distribution systems are generally a function of local government. For example, a municipal water department is usually a separate city utility whose main function is to provide sanitary water that is safe for human use. In contrast, a state-authorized water district is governed via an elected board.

A private water supply system may provide water under contract to a municipality, region, or single property. Private water supply distribution systems may take a variety of forms, including systems that are specific to an industrial facility or complex such as a refinery or that provide water to a residential subdivision **(Figure 5.1)**. In the former case, the facility owner/occupant has the responsibility for the inspection, testing, and maintenance of the system. The water source may be a public supply distribution system that is separated from the private system by a water meter and check valve or an on-site water supply such as a well or lake. In the case where a private water supply also serves a particular area, such as a residential subdivision, the owners' association for the area may maintain the system. The water sources may be the same as those used for industrial facilities.

Figure 5.1 Private water supplies may include water towers (left), reservoirs (center), and pump stations (right).

The design of public and private water supply systems may vary depending upon the region. However, systems may be composed of the following basic components, which are explained in the following sections:

- Sources of water supply
- Means of moving water
- Water treatment or processing facilities
- Distribution systems

Sources of Water Supply

Water is supplied from natural freshwater sources, such as wells, springs, rivers, lakes, and ponds. Groundwater or snow-melt at higher elevations may feed streams and springs. Rainfall replenishes lakes, ponds, and groundwater. The ocean can also be a water source though seawater is 220 times saltier than fresh water. Along with the salt, ocean water contains other impurities that must be removed to make the water potable for humans and useful for agricultural use. Salt water from rivers or the ocean supplies some private fire water systems (nonpotable).

The volume of water that a community or facility needs for both domestic use and fire protection can be calculated based on the history of consumption and estimates of anticipated needs. Cities and other water providers track their average and maximum daily water consumption. Some providers also track their peak hourly consumption. Engineers add to these calculations based upon anticipated fire flow requirements needed for fire protection within the jurisdiction's boundaries. To be considered adequate, a system must be capable of supplying the water needed for fire protection in addition to the domestic requirement. In most cities, the domestic/industrial requirements exceed that required for fire protection. However, in small towns the requirements for fire protection may exceed other requirements. The amount of water in a private fire water system is determined by the daily utility water use added to the credible or largest credible fire scenario, with the expectation that fire water use must be maintained for 4-12 hours.

To ensure constant pressure, water distribution systems may incorporate elevated storage tanks throughout the system to create pressure through gravity. Elevated gravity storage tanks are usually constructed of steel or concrete. These tanks may be located on high towers or on hilltops **(Figure 5.2)**. The higher the tank in comparison to its supply destination, the more elevation head pressure is generated. Gravity tank capacities range from 5,000 gallons (20 000 L) to over 1 million gallons (greater than 4 000 000 L).

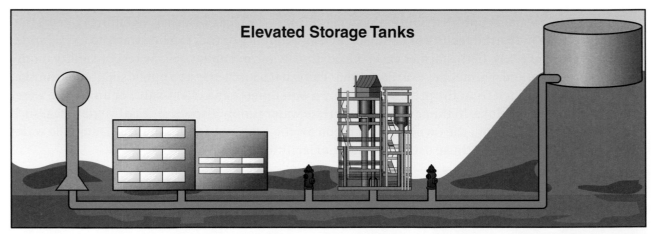

Elevated Storage Tanks

Figure 5.2 Elevated storage tanks help provide adequate water pressure to facilities.

Means of Moving Water

Water must be moved from its original source to the point it is distributed and used. Most systems include an intermediary step between the source and distribution points for water quality evaluation and treatment. Three methods for moving water through the system are gravity, direct pumping, and a combination system using both gravity and direct pumping **(Figure 5.3)**.

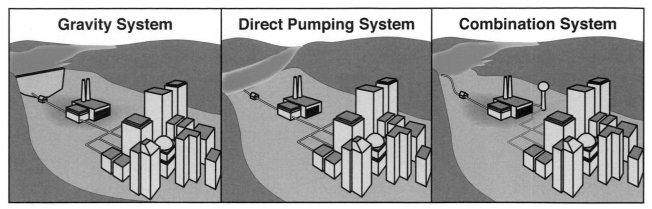

| Gravity System | Direct Pumping System | Combination System |

Figure 5.3 Water may be moved via gravity, direct pumping, or combination water systems.

Gravity Systems

A **gravity system** delivers water from the source or the treatment plant to the distribution system without pumping equipment. The difference between the height of the water source and the point of use creates elevation pressure (also known as *elevation head pressure*). The elevation pressure forces the water throughout the water distribution system. Gravity pressure is adequate for fire flow and most industrial functions only when the primary water source is located more than 100 feet (30 m) higher than the highest point in the water distribution system. The most common examples of gravity systems are those supplied from an alpine lake or a mountain reservoir.

Direct Pumping Systems

When elevation pressure cannot provide sufficient pressure to meet the facility's needs, a pump is placed near the water source or treatment plant to create the required pressure within the distribution system. This system for moving water is called a **direct pumping system**.

A few cities have direct pumping water systems that are dedicated for fire protection. In contrast, most direct pumping systems are found in agricultural and industrial settings. Rural fire departments are often equipped to tap into agricultural irrigation systems when water is needed for fire fighting. In direct pumping systems, one or more pumps draw water from the primary source and transport it to the point of use. The main disadvantages of direct pumping systems are their total dependence on pumps (subject to mechanical failure) and on electricity (subject to power outages) to run the pumps. System reliability enhancements include the addition of emergency generators, duplicate pumps and piping.

Industrial private fire water systems are often direct pumping systems. These high-volume systems frequently incorporate a combination of power sources (electricity, diesel, natural gas, or steam) to provide protection from power failures. These private systems are often designed with the largest electric pump being considered out of service for the purposes of determining the proper design flow rate.

Combination Systems

Most communities use **combination systems** that consist of both gravity tanks and the direct pumping process to provide adequate pressure. Water is pumped into the distribution system and elevated storage tanks (that provide gravitational pressure). When the consumption demand is greater than the rate at which the water is pumped, water flows from the storage tanks into the distribution system. Conversely, when consumption demand is reduced, water is pumped into the storage tanks.

Industrial facilities often have their own combination water supply systems with elevated storage tanks **(Figure 5.4, p. 146)**. These water supplies may be available to the local fire department in an emergency when a prior agreement exists. Water for fire protection may be available to some communities from storage systems, such as underground cisterns (tanks used to store rainwater), that are considered a part of the distribution system. Fire department pumpers draft (draw water from a static source) from these sources and provide the pressure needed to transport the water to a fire.

Figure 5.4 This elevated water tower provides water to a facility.

Water Treatment or Processing Facilities

Potable water is commonly used in water distribution systems. Before water can be used as potable water, it must be processed to remove impurities and minerals that can be harmful to humans, animals, and plants. Most communities operate water treatment plants and/or water desalination plants. Before water can enter the distribution system, it must pass through these facilities. A disruption in the facility's pumping capacity, such as mechanical breakdown, natural disaster, loss of power supply, or fire could reduce or halt the volume and pressure of water available for fire fighting operations.

Distribution Systems

The water distribution system consists of a network of piping and isolation and control valves throughout the community or service area that carry the water under pressure to the points of use. The following sections describe each of these system components.

Piping

In addition to the water storage tanks, the condition and carrying capacity of the system's network of underground pipes, is a significant factor in the ability of a water system to deliver adequate pressure. Underground water pipes, often called **water mains** are generally made of cast iron, ductile iron, asbestos cement, steel, polyvinyl chloride (PVC) plastic, or concrete. When water flows through any pipe, the internal surface of the pipe and the movement of the water itself causes friction that reduces the water pressure at the distribution end.

The term **grid system** describes the interlocking network of water mains that compose a water distribution system. A water distribution system consists of three types of water mains **(Figure 5.5)**:

- **Primary feeders** — Large pipes, also known as arterial mains, with relatively widespread spacing. These mains convey large quantities of water to various points in the distribution system and supply smaller secondary feeder mains. Arterial mains can be large, ranging from 16 inches (400 mm) to 72 inches (1 825 mm) in diameter or greater. Fire hydrants are rarely attached directly to these mains.

- **Secondary feeders** — Intermediate pipes that interconnect with the primary feeder lines to create a grid. They are 12 to 14 inches (300 mm to 350 mm) in diameter. Control valves can be used to isolate each secondary feeder.

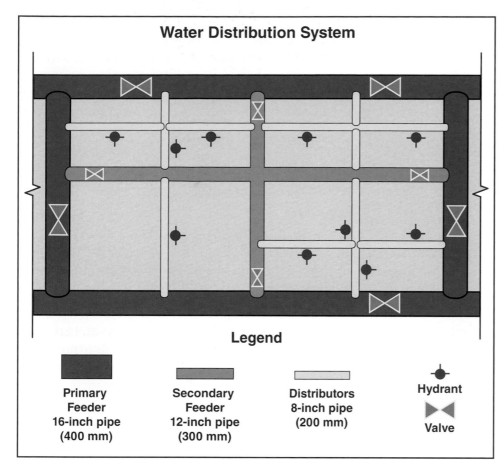

Figure 5.5 This illustration shows the types of water mains within a common water distribution system.

- **Distributors** — Small water mains, 6 to 8 inches (150 to 200 mm) in diameter, that serve individual fire hydrants and commercial and residential consumers. Distributors may form an intermediate grid between secondary feeders or may be dead-end lines with the hydrant or supplied property at the end of the line.

To ensure a sufficient water supply, two or more primary feeders should run from the supply source to the high-risk and industrial districts of the community along separate routes. Similarly, secondary feeders should provide water from the primary feeders along two directions to any end point. This arrangement increases the capacity of the supply at any given point and ensures that a break in a feeder main will not completely cut off the supply.

Water distribution systems are generally designed using computer programs and hydraulic calculations that ensure constant pressure and quantity throughout the system. The grid or **loop system** is designed to provide constant pressure or flow when pipes or the grid must be repaired. Another advantage of the grid system is that high demand in one area does not reduce water flow in other areas. Dead-end lines may exist but have disadvantages such as allowing water to stagnate in the pipes, requiring constant flushing and causing services to be turned off when pipes are repaired.

The ability to deliver adequate quantities of water under pressure depends on the capacity of the system's network of pipes. Eight-inch (200 mm) pipe is often the minimum size used, although some communities are allowing 6-inch (150 mm) pipes in residential subdivisions.

Access to the water supply system is made through connections to the piping system. These connections may be through waterflow control valves and flow meters at the point that customers gain water from the system or through fire hydrants that are used for fire protection.

Isolation and Control Valves

Sometimes parts of a water supply system may need to be shut down or the water flow to them interrupted to stop leaks or make repairs. When interrupting water flow, it is standard procedure to start with the smallest area or part of the system affected, the individual hydrants or properties. If that is insufficient to interrupt the water flow to the affected area, then it would be necessary to shut off distribution lines. The process is repeated until the necessary level of isolation is achieved. Water supply systems contain valves to interrupt water flow to:

- Individual hydrants or properties
- Distribution lines
- Secondary feeders
- Primary feeders
- Entire water systems

Most valves are constructed of brass, steel, or cast iron. There are two types of valves generally used in public water supply systems: isolation valves and control valves.

Isolation valves. These valves may also be known as *stop* or *shutoff valves* and are either **gate valves** or **butterfly valves**. Isolation valves are used to isolate sections for maintenance and repair, to replace hydrants, or to make new connections to the system. Isolation valves are located strategically to minimize the disruption to customers while the system is down. Isolation valves should be tested (opened and closed) at least once a year to ensure that they are in good working condition. The municipal water department responsibilities generally stop at the property line or water meter. In many industrial facilities, the facility is responsible for the testing of the isolation valves within their facilities.

Isolation valves are generally located on municipal easement (on or adjacent to streets, sidewalks, and alleys) and below ground. They are usually marked with the word WATER or the name of the municipality or jurisdiction. This cover should be removed to access the nonindicating type valve. Either a residential or commercial water shutoff key can then be inserted into the opening to turn the valve stem 90 degrees to the direction of flow to shut off the water. All valves and hydrants are opened by rotating the stem or operating nut to the left or counterclockwise. Rotating the stem or nut to the right or clockwise closes the valve or hydrant.

NOTE: Some hydrants operate in the other direction. For best practice, look at the bonnet on the fire hydrant for the arrow to indicate the opening direction.

Isolation valves for private water supply systems are usually indicating-type valves. An indicating valve shows whether the gate valve seat is open, closed, or partially closed. Two common indicating valves are the **post indicator valve (PIV)** and the **outside stem and yoke (OS&Y) valve**. The post indicator valve is a hollow metal post that houses the valve stem. A plate attached to the valve stem inside this post has the words *OPEN* and *SHUT* printed on it so that the position of the valve is shown **(Figure 5.6)**. The OS&Y valve has a yoke on the outside with a threaded stem that opens or closes the gate inside the valve. The threaded portion of the stem is visible when the valve is open and not visible when the valve is closed **(Figure 5.7)**.

Control valves. Control valves are also located between public water supply distribution systems and private water supply distribution systems. The configuration of these valves may be unique to each location and would be considered site specific training. Typical types of control valves include:

- Pressure-reducing valves
- Pressure-relief valves
- Throttling valves
- Check valves

- Pressure-sustaining valves
- Flow-control valves
- Float valves

Figure 5.6 The PIV on the left is open while the one on the right is shut.

Figure 5.7 An OS&Y valve is open when the stem is visible (left) and closed/shut when the stem is wound into the valve housing (right).

In addition to these waterflow control valves, a water flowmeter and a backflow preventer will be installed on the water supply pipeline. The water flowmeter determines the quantity of water that the facility is using for billing purposes. The backflow preventer prohibits any water from flowing back into the public water system **(Figure 5.8)**.

Types of Pressure

Pressure is defined as *force per unit area*. In fire service hydraulics, pressure is the force that moves water through a conduit, whether a pipe or a hose. In water supply systems, pressure is measured in different ways for different purposes. In this context, pressure is measured in pounds per square inch (psi) or kilopascals (kPa). Firefighters need to understand the following terms that identify the pressure measurements that are relevant to water supply:

- Static pressure
- Residual pressure
- Flow (velocity) pressure

Figure 5.8 Examples of a system of backflow preventers in a power generation facility.

Static Pressure

Pumps or gravity create the pressure in a public or private water system. Systems with little or no water flow are considered to have **static pressure**. *Static pressure* is stored potential energy that is available to force water through mains, valves, hydrants, and fire hose. True static pressure is rarely found in a public water supply system due to leaks and domestic consumption. Therefore, static pressure is defined in this context as the normal pressure existing on a system before water is released from a hydrant.

Residual Pressure

The term **residual pressure** represents the pressure left in the distribution system at a specific location when water is flowing. *Residual pressure* is that part of the total available pressure that is not used to overcome friction or gravity while forcing water through pipes, valves, hydrants, or fire hose. Residual pressure also provides an indication of the availability of additional water.

Flow (Velocity) Pressure

When water is released from a fire hydrant or nozzle, the forward movement of the water stream exerts a pressure that a pitot tube and gauge can measure. **Flow pressure** is the forward velocity pressure at a discharge opening while water is flowing.

Some private industrial fire water systems are designed to supply fixed fire protection equipment at pressures normally supplied by the fire department engine boosting the pressure. As a result, the private fire water system may have a static pressure of 150-175 psi and a residual pressure of 125-150 psi. This pressure allows for the use of fixed monitors without the use of fire department engines to pump the fire water.

Fire Hydrants

Fire hydrants are often the most dependable water sources near the incident site. When they are fully operational, fire hydrants can provide a consistent volume of water under constant pressure. On the other hand, fire hydrants and water supply systems can fail, with failures or reduction in water supply (volume) or pressure resulting from:

- Damaged hydrant valves and connections
- Broken water mains
- Greater demand than the system can provide
- Hydrants located on dead-end water mains
- Closed isolation valves
- Restricted mains caused by sediment and mineral deposits
- Frozen pipes or hydrants

When hydrants fail to provide sufficient volume or pressure, fire brigade members must select an alternate water supply. Alternate water supplies are discussed later in this chapter.

Because fire hydrants are a basic resource used in fire fighting, you must know fire hydrant types, markings, use, inspections, and maintenance. Fire brigade members, inspectors, water department personnel, or private contractors may perform fire hydrant testing.

In general, all fire hydrant bonnets, barrels, and foot pieces are made of cast iron. The internal working parts are usually made of bronze, but valve facings may be made of rubber, leather, or composite materials. A commonly found hydrant discharge outlet configuration includes **(Figure 5.9)**:

Figure 5.9 This industrial facility hydrant is equipped with two steamer connections and two 2½-inch outlets.

- At least one large (4 or 4½ inches [100 mm or 115 mm]) outlet often referred to as the pumper outlet nozzle or steamer connection
- Two hose outlet **nozzles** for 2½-inch (65 mm) **couplings**

Hydrant specifications require a 5-inch (125 mm) valve opening for standard three-way hydrants and a 6-inch (150 mm) connection to the water main. Fire brigades and local fire departments must ensure that their fire hose couplings match the male threads of the fire hydrants within their jurisdiction. NFPA 1963, *Standard for Fire Hose Connections*, sets regulations for the number of threads per inch and the outside diameter of the male thread.

Fire hydrants are located along all portions of a water distribution system and are generally connected at specified intervals by 6-inch (150 mm) connecting pipes. Water department personnel usually determine the location, spacing, and distribution of fire hydrants. In general, fire hydrants should not be spaced more than 300 feet (100 m) apart in high-value districts. Hydrants should be located at every other intersection so that every building on a given street is within one block of a hydrant. Additional intermediate hydrants may be required where distances between intersections exceed 350 to 400 feet (105 m to 120 m). In some locations, **hydrant manifolds**, or simply called manifolds, are used in place of hydrants and serve the same function **(Figure 5.10)**.

Other factors that affect hydrant location and spacing include:

- Types of building construction
- Types of occupancies
- Building densities (number of structures within the facility/site)
- Sizes of water mains
- Required fire flows for occupancies within a given area

Friction loss and location of hydrants can reduce pressure in the distribution system. Encrustations of minerals and sediment that accumulate inside the mains over a period of years can cause friction loss in water mains that serve fire hydrants. Friction loss reduces the water pressure available from fire hydrants. The location of hydrants can also affect the water volume and pressure. For instance, a fire hydrant that receives water from only one direction, known as a **dead-end hydrant**, has a limited water supply **(Figure 5.11)**.

To overcome this issue and ensure greater pressure, fire hydrants can be located so they receive water from two or more directions. **Circulating hydrants** that receive water from more than one direction are said to have **circulating feed** or a looped system. A distribution system that provides circulating feed from all directions is called a grid system **(Figure 5.12)**.

Figure 5.10 This hydrant manifold has a master stream monitor built into it.

Figure 5.11 The hydrant in this illustration receives water from only one direction.

Figure 5.12 This hydrant is able to receive water from two directions.

The locally adopted building or fire code determines the type and location of fire hydrants on the system. The two primary types of fire hydrants used in North America are dry-barrel and wet-barrel. While they serve the same purpose, their designs and operating principles are quite different. The following sections discuss fire hydrants in greater detail.

Dry-Barrel Hydrants

Designed for use in climates that have freezing temperatures, the main control valve of the dry-barrel hydrant is located at the base or foot of the hydrant below the frost line with an isolation valve located on the distribution line **(Figure 5.13)**. The stem nut used to open and close the control valve is located on top of the hydrant. Water is only allowed into the hydrant when the stem nut is operated. Any water remaining in a closed dry-barrel hydrant drains through small drains called *weep holes* at the bottom of the hydrant when the main valve approaches a closed position. A hydrant wrench is used to open the valve by turning the stem in a counterclockwise direction or to close it by turning the stem in a clockwise direction.

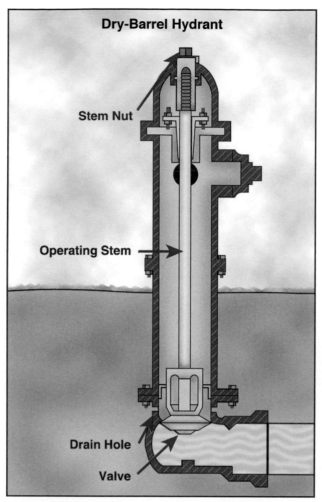

Figure 5.13 Dry-barrel hydrants are needed in areas that experience freezing temperatures.

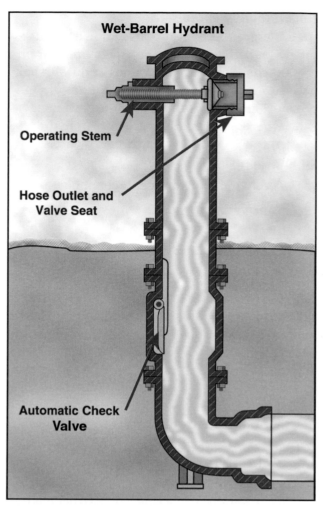

Figure 5.14 Wet-barrel hydrants are common in regions with warm climates.

Wet-Barrel Hydrants

Wet-barrel hydrants are designed to have water in the hydrant at all times **(Figure 5.14)**. These hydrants are usually installed in warmer climates where prolonged periods of subfreezing weather are uncommon. Horizontal compression valves are usually at each outlet, but another control valve may be in the top of the hydrant to control the water flow to all outlets.

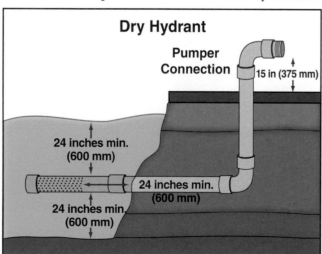

Figure 5.15 Dry hydrants are common at facilities that have static water sources and provide a means for fire apparatus to easily draft from the water source.

Dry Hydrants

In areas without a water distribution system, **dry hydrants** may be utilized to supply water from a static water supply (pond, lake, or reservoir) **(Figure 5.15)**. Dry hydrants are non-pressurized and require a pump (typically a fire apparatus) to **draft** water from the static source. They typically consist of a short section of piping (steel, iron, or PVC) with one end that extends up from the ground terminating with a threaded outlet for connection to the fire apparatus while the other end extends through the ground and into the water supply terminating in a strainer.

Underground Hydrants

An underground hydrant (also known as flush, pit, recessed, or chuck hydrants) is a fire hydrant that sits completely underground in a durable box enclosure and is accessible by lifting the in-ground box steel door that is flush with the pavement or floor where it is installed. Most flush hydrants consist of an operating nut and two 2½ inch (65 mm) outlets **(Figure 5.16)**.

Underground fire hydrants are commonly found in facilities such as:

- Airports
- Aircraft manufacturing facilities
- Manufacturing and other industrial installations

These hydrants are used where a fire hydrant projecting above grade would hinder the facility's operation or be subject to damage from or cause damage to:

- Taxiing aircraft
- Forklifts
- Other vehicular traffic

Due to the discreet appearance of underground hydrant boxes, they must be conspicuously and obviously identified with painted warning markings to prevent parking or placement of obstructions on or near the hydrant **(Figure 5.17)**. Adequate area to facilitate hose connection, operation, and maintenance of the hydrant must be identified and maintained at all times. Underground hydrants require consistent and frequent inspection and maintenance due to their nature of being underground where dirt, sand, and other debris can wash into the box. As always, fire brigade members should be knowledgeable of all hydrant and fire control devices within the confines of their facility, including their location and operation of each.

Out-of-Service Hydrants

When a hydrant is taken out-of-service, the water or fire department, or facility AHJ should take the following actions:

- Place "Out-of-Service" tags or devices on the hydrant **(Figure 5.18)**.
- Notify fire station personnel within the response district the hydrant serves that it is out-of-service and approximately when it will return to service.
- Notify hydrant repair personnel.

Figure 5.16 An example of an underground hydrant at an airport facility.

Figure 5.17 The cover of this underground hydrant is painted bright red to identify its location.

Figure 5.18 Hydrants that no longer work or are undergoing maintenance should be marked "out-of-service".

If water is seen bubbling up out of the ground at the base of a dry-barrel hydrant when the hydrant is fully open, a broken component in the hydrant barrel is allowing water to get past the drain opening. This hydrant should be reported to the water authority, which will mark it out-of-service until it is repaired.

> **CAUTION:** If water is coming up from the ground around a fire hydrant, the ground may rapidly become unstable, creating deep mud.

Other reasons for a hydrant to be out-of-service may include:

- Damage to the hydrant, water system piping, or pump that support that location.
- Repairs or upgrades being performed on the water system.
- Obstructions placed within the hydrant.
- A frozen hydrant during cold temperatures.

Fire Hydrant Connection Tools and Appliances

Firefighters use a variety of tools when making fire hydrant connections, including **(Figure 5.19)**:

- Hose clamps
- Hydrant wrenches
- Gate valves
- Spanner wrenches
- Rubber mallets
- Hydrant valves

A hose clamp can be used to stop the flow of water in a hoseline for the following reasons:

- To prevent charging the **hose bed** during a **forward hose lay** from a hydrant
- To allow replacement of a burst section of hose without stopping the water supply
- To allow extension of a charged hoseline without stopping the water supply

Some of the most common tools used to tighten or loosen hose couplings are the **spanner wrench**, **hydrant wrench**, and the rubber mallet. The most common valves used in hoseline and hydrant work are gate valves and hydrant valves.

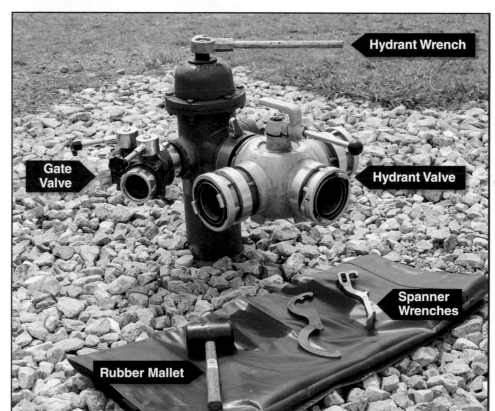

Figure 5.19 Examples of the many tools and appliances fire brigade members use to make hydrant connections. *Courtesy of Oklahoma City (OK) Fire Department/Lt. Ray Lujan.*

Although the primary purpose of the spanner wrench is to tighten or loosen couplings, a number of other features have been built into some spanner wrenches:

- Wedge for prying
- Opening that fits gas utility valves
- Slot for pulling nails
- Flat surface for hammering

Hydrant wrenches are primarily used to remove discharge caps from fire hydrant outlets and to open fire hydrant valves. The hydrant wrench is usually equipped with a pentagonal opening in its head that fits most standard fire hydrant operating nuts. The lever handle may be threaded into the operating head to make it adjustable, or the head and handle may be of the ratchet type. The head may also be equipped with a spanner to help make or break coupling connections.

A rubber mallet is sometimes used to strike the lugs to tighten or loosen intake hose couplings. Intake hose couplings have long operating lugs for hand tightening the intake connection. A rubber mallet can be used to further tighten the intake connection and achieve an airtight connection when setting up a drafting operation.

Gate valves are used to control the flow from a hydrant outlet. They have a baffle that is lowered into the path of the water by turning a screw-type handle.

A variety of hydrant valves are available for use in **supply line** operations. Known by a variety of regional names, these valves are used when a forward lay is made from a low-pressure hydrant to the fire scene. A hydrant valve has four main functions:

- Allow additional hoselines to be laid to the hydrant
- Connect a supply pumper to the hydrant
- Boost the pressure in the original supply line without interrupting the flow of water in the line
- Allow the original supply line to be connected to the hydrant and charged before the arrival of another pumper at the hydrant

NOTE: Some facilities with a private high pressure system that can directly supply fire attack lines.

Fire Hydrant Connections

To ensure that wet- and dry-barrel hydrants are ready for use, they must be inspected and operated at least once a year. You must know how to operate fire hydrants in order to:

- Provide water through hoses for fire suppression operations
- Flow water from hydrant discharge openings to flush sediment **(Figure 5.20)**
- Perform periodic inspections
- Ensure proper operation of valves and caps
- Assist in flow tests

Figure 5.20 Fire brigade members should flush a hydrant to remove any sediment before connecting a hoseline.

Considerations for wet- and dry-barrel hydrants. All hydrants must be opened and closed slowly to prevent damage to fire hose, hydrants, and other equipment, or possible injury to firefighters. Opening a hydrant too fast may cause the fire hose connected to it to flail violently as the water pressure straightens the hose. Closing a hydrant too fast may cause a sudden increase in pressure (**water hammer**) within the water supply system, which can result in damage to the system piping or appliances attached to the system, such as water heaters in adjacent structures.

Considerations specific to dry-barrel hydrants. To prevent freezing, the dry-barrel hydrant main valve is located underground below the frost line. Normally, the hydrant barrel from the top of the stem down to the main valve is empty. This approach prevents water in the barrel from freezing during extended periods of subfreezing temperatures.

When the stem nut is turned counterclockwise, the main valve moves downward allowing water to flow into the hydrant. As the main valve moves downward, a drain valve plate attached to the stem closes a drain hole located near the bottom of the hydrant, allowing water to flow past it into the hydrant barrel.

Most hydrants are shut down by slowly turning the stem nut clockwise, causing the main valve to rise and shutting off the flow of water into the hydrant barrel. At the same time, the drain valve plate rises, opening the drain hole. The water that remains in the hydrant barrel empties through the drain hole into the surrounding soil.

NOTE: There are some hydrants that require turning the stem nut counterclockwise to close the main valve. Fire brigade members should be familiar with the operation of all hydrants within their facility.

Additional precautions should be taken when operating dry-barrel hydrants that are installed in areas where prolonged periods of subfreezing weather are common. If a dry-barrel hydrant is not opened fully, the drain may be left partially open. The resulting flow through the drain hole can cause erosion of the soil around the base of the hydrant, sometimes called "undermining" the hydrant. Over time, this erosion can destroy the hydrant's support and cause it to leak badly. This damage can put the hydrant out of service and necessitate it being reinstalled. Therefore, dry-barrel hydrants must be either completely open or completely closed.

When a dry-barrel hydrant is shut down, fire brigade members must verify that the water left in the hydrant barrel is draining out. The following steps can test whether the draining is occurring:

1. Close the main valve by turning the stem nut clockwise until resistance is felt, then turn it a quarter-turn counterclockwise.

2. Cap all discharges except one.

3. Place the palm of one hand over the open discharge.

If the hydrant is draining, a slight vacuum should be felt pulling the palm toward the discharge. If this vacuum is not felt, repeat the process and try again. If the hydrant still is not draining, the drain hole is probably plugged. Notify the water authority to have it inspect the hydrant. If this issue occurs in winter, the hydrant must be pumped until empty to prevent the water from freezing in the barrel before the hydrant is repaired or replaced.

In some areas, the **Environmental Protection Agency (EPA)** has required drain holes to be closed to prevent contamination of the water supply. In these areas, dry-barrel hydrants must be pumped until empty after each use.

Alternative Water Supplies

Many rural areas lack public water distribution systems or have systems with inadequate volume and pressure for fire fighting operations. In these areas, rural water supply operations must frequently be performed. Two common operations are **water shuttle operations** and **relay pumping operations**. For these operations to succeed, preincident planning and frequent practice are required. The following sections briefly explain each of these operations. For additional information on rural water supply operations, see the IFSTA **Pumping Apparatus Driver/Operator Handbook** and NFPA 1142, *Standard on Water Supplies for Suburban and Rural Fire Fighting*.

Static water sources that may be accessed through drafting include:

- Lakes
- Ponds/reservoirs
- Rivers
- Oceans or other salt water sources in private fire water systems.
- Swimming pools
- Large above-ground watering tanks for agricultural use
- **Portable tanks**
- Cooling tower basins

NOTE: Some static water sources are equipped with a dry-hydrant connection that allows the pumping apparatus to draw water from the lowest point of the water source. These sources and connections should be checked annually.

Vehicle access and drafting capability are critical in using static water sources. If the water source is inaccessible or the ground around the water source will not safely support the pumping apparatus, then it will not work as a static water source.

Water Shuttle Operations

Water shuttle operations involve hauling water from a supply source (fill site) to the incident scene. The water is then transferred to an attack pumper's tank or to portable tanks (dump sites) from which water may be drawn to fight a fire **(Figure 5.21)**. If large diameter hoselines are not available, water shuttle operations can be used for distances greater than ½ mile (0.8 km) from the nearest fire hydrant or water source or greater than the fire department's capability of laying supply hoselines. A sufficient number of **mobile water supply apparatus** are needed to maintain the needed fire flow (water flow).

Fast-fill and fast-dump capabilities are critical to efficient water shuttle operations. Radio equipped water supply officers are assigned at both the fill and dump sites to coordinate these operations. Also important are traffic control, hydrant operations, hookups, and tank venting. Mobile water supply apparatus driver/operators should remain in their vehicles during filling/dumping operations.

There are three key components to water shuttle operations **(Figure 5.22)**:

- **Fill site** at the water source
- **Dump site** at the fire scene
- Mobile water supply apparatus to haul water from the fill site to the dump site

Figure 5.21 Water tenders can be used to carry and dump water into portable tanks.

The dump site is generally located near the fire or incident. The dump site usually consists of one or more portable water tanks into which mobile water supply apparatus deposit water before returning to the fill site. Apparatus attacking the fire may draft directly from the portable tanks, or other apparatus may draft from the tanks and supply the attack apparatus. Low-level intake devices enable drafting operations to permit use of most of the water in the portable tank.

Portable tanks have capacities beginning at 1,000 gallons (4 000 L). In general, there are two types of portable water tanks. One type is the collapsible or folding style that uses a square metal frame and a synthetic or canvas duck liner. The other type is a round, self-supporting synthetic tank with a floating collar that rises as the tank is filled. These frameless portable tanks are widely used in wildland fire fighting operations.

Before opening a portable tank, a salvage cover or heavy tarp should be spread on the ground to protect the tank's liner once water is dumped into it. When the situation permits, portable tanks should be as level as possible to ensure maximum capacity. The tank should be positioned in a location that allows easy access from multiple directions but does not inhibit access of other apparatus to the fire scene. Portable tanks should be set up so that more than one mobile water supply apparatus can off-load at the same time. Ensure that the drain is located on the downhill side of the tank and away from the drafting tank.

Multiple portable tanks are set up when large quantities of water must be maintained. A portable tank is used for the attack pumper, while the mobile water supply apparatus dump into the other tanks. When two portable tanks are used, they can be interconnected through their drain fittings. If multiple portable tanks are needed, **jet siphon** devices can be used to transfer water from one tank to another. A jet siphon uses a 1½-inch (38 mm) discharge line connected to the siphon. The siphon is then attached to a hard sleeve placed between two tanks.

There are four basic methods by which mobile water supply apparatus unload:

- Gravity dumping through large (10- or 12-inch [250 mm or 300 mm]) dump valves
- Jet-assist dumps that increase the flow rate
- Apparatus-mounted pumps that off-load the water
- Combination of these methods

To quickly fill mobile water supply apparatus, use the best fill site or hydrant available, large hoselines, multiple hoselines, and, if necessary, a pumper for adequate flow. In some situations, multiple portable pumps may be necessary. Both fill sites and dump sites should be arranged so that a minimum of backing or maneuvering of apparatus is required.

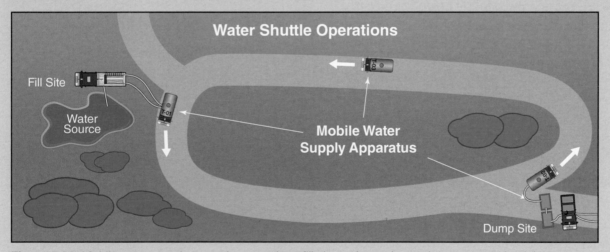

Figure 5.22 Mobile water supply operations require a fill site, a dump site, and apparatus to haul the water from one to the other.

Fire Hose

NFPA 1081 (2018): 4.3.1, 4.3.4

Fire hose is a flexible, portable extension of the water distribution system that carries water from the fire hydrant, manifold, or **standpipe system** through attack hoselines to the point where water is needed **(Figure 5.23)**. Fire brigade members must know:

- Fire hose characteristics, including construction and sizes
- Types of fire hose couplings
- Types of hose appliances
- Tools used in hose operations

In addition, you need to be able to perform the following skills:

- Rolling and folding hose
- Loading supply hose on apparatus
- Loading preconnected attack lines
- Maintaining and cleaning hose

The primary characteristics used to describe fire hose include the type of construction and the materials used, the internal diameter, and the type of couplings used to make connections. Fire hose is used as either supply hose or attack hose. Supply hose transports water from a fire hydrant or other water supply source to an apparatus equipped with a pump **(Figure 5.24)**. Attack hose transports water or other agents, at increased pressure, from the following sources:

- From the pump-equipped apparatus to a nozzle or nozzles
- From a pump-equipped apparatus to a **fire department connection (FDC)** mounted on a structure
- From a **hose cabinet**, **hose box** (also called a hose house), or standpipe to the point the water is applied to the fire

Fire hose is manufactured in various diameters and lengths based upon specifications in NFPA 1961, *Standard on Fire Hose* **(Figure 5.25)**. The diameter of a fire hose refers to its inside diameter. For example, hose labeled 3 inches (77 mm) in diameter must have an internal diameter of 3 inches (77 mm) **(Figure 5.26, p. 162)**. Some types of fire hose can expand beyond their actual manufactured internal diameter because of the elastic qualities of modern materials used in hose construction.

Figure 5.23 A fire brigade member extending a hoseline from an industrial facility hydrant.

Figure 5.24 The hoseline in this photo is an example of a supply line.

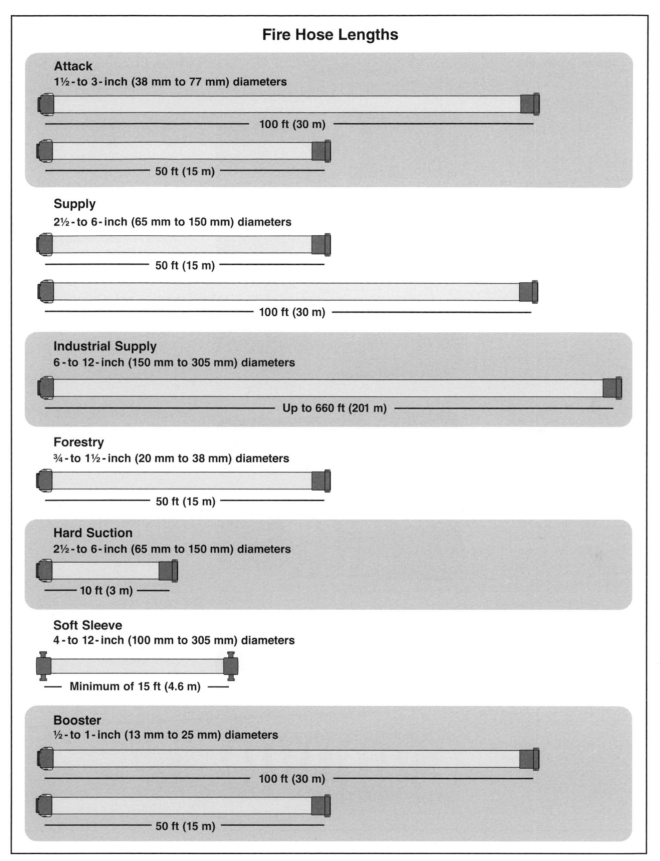

Figure 5.25 Examples of the various sizes and lengths of fire hose.

Fire Hose Construction Features

Hose Types and Diameters	Cutaway Views	Linings, Coverings, and Reinforcements
Booster Hose ¾ or 1 inch (20 mm or 25 mm)	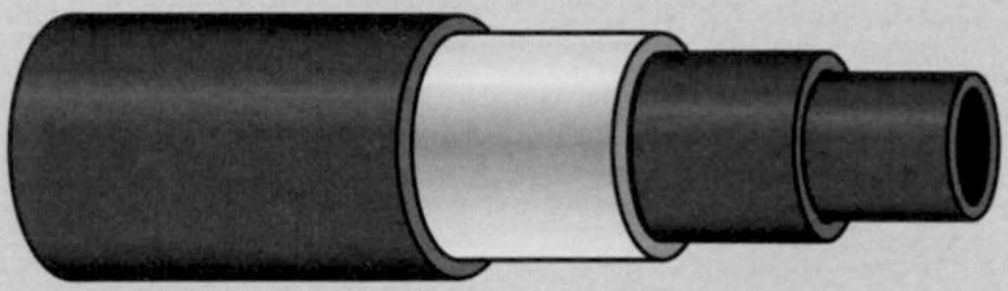	• Rubber Covered • Rubber Lined • Fabric Reinforcement
Woven-Jacket Hose 1 to 6 inches (25 mm to 150 mm)	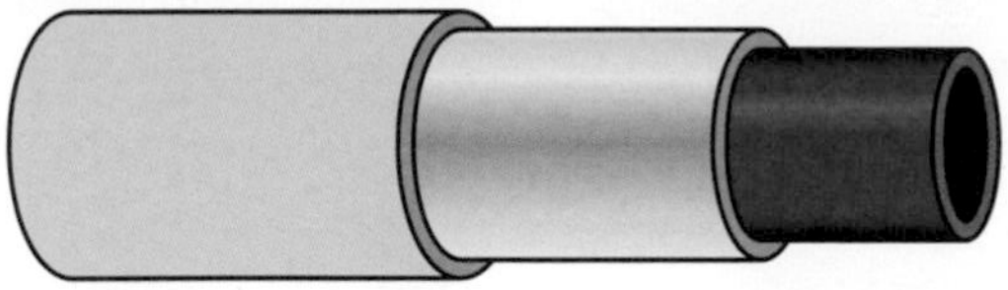	• One or More (Two Showing) Woven-Fabric Jackets • Rubber Lined
Rubber-Covered Hose 1 to 6 inches (25 mm to 150 mm)	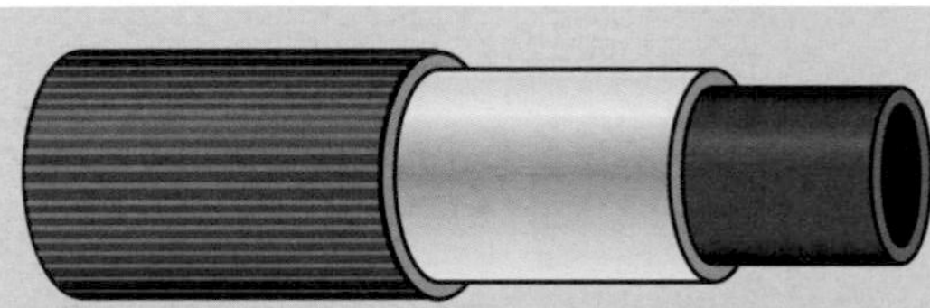	• Woven Polyester Tube • Nitrile Rubber • Synthetic Rubber Outer Cover
Impregnated Single-Jacket Hose 1½ to 5 inches (38 mm to 125 mm)		• Woven Polyester Nylon or Combination of Synthetic Fibers Form Tube • Polymer Covered • Polymer Lined
Noncollapsible Intake Hose 2½ to 6 inches (65 mm to 150 mm)	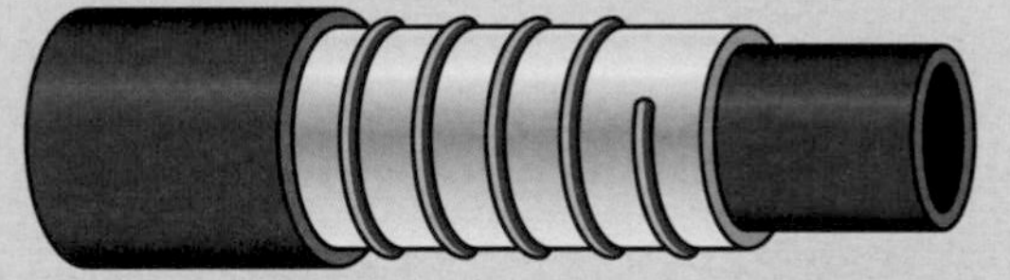	• Rubber Covered • Fabric and Wire (Helix) Reinforcement • Rubber Lined
Flexible Noncollapsible Intake Hose 2½ to 6 inches (65 mm to 150 mm)	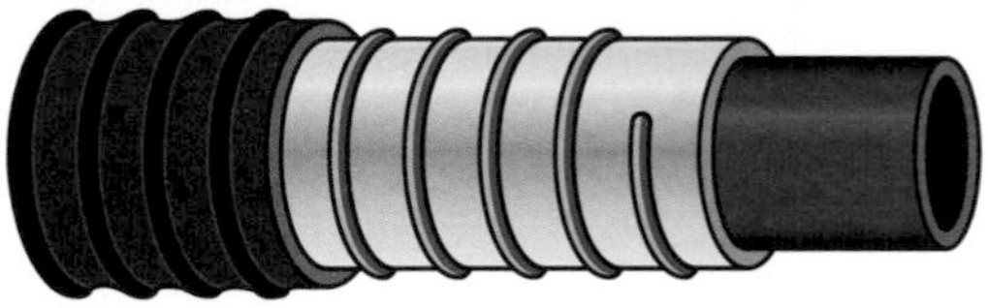	• Rubber Covered • Fabric and Plastic (Helix) Reinforcement • Rubber Lined
Flexible Noncollapsible Clear Intake Hose 2½ to 6 inches (65 mm to 150 mm)	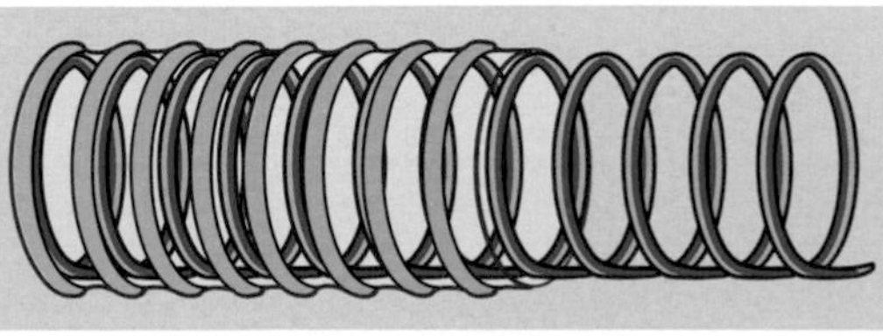	• Polyvinyl Tube • Polyvinyl Reinforcement (Helix)

Figure 5.26 Illustrating the construction features and diameters of various types of fire hose.

Figure 5.27 This supply hose is made from synthetic nitrile rubber.

Figure 5.28 The lightweight hose in this hose cabinet is designed for lower working pressures and for use by building occupants.

Expansion results in a larger interior diameter when the hoseline is pressurized with water and lower friction loss. Not all fire hose exhibit these characteristics. The performance of a particular hoseline depends on the materials and methods used in its construction.

Both attack and supply hose are commonly manufactured in 50 or 100 foot (15 or 30 m) lengths, referred to as a section. The traditional length of fire hose in North America is 50 feet (15 m) per section. Modern hose may be carried in longer sections because it is often constructed of high-strength, lightweight synthetic materials that have the same relative weight of traditional sections of hose. Synthetic nitrile rubber hoses are more chemical resistant than traditional fire hose, dry faster, and can be decontaminated and cleaned more easily **(Figure 5.27)**.

Given the potential need for carrying the hose up several flights of stairs or deep within a horizontal facility, lightweight hose has become increasingly more common. Most types of lightweight hose are **single-jacket hose**. Lightweight hose may not have the same durability (heat and abrasion resistance) as conventional fire attack hose, and for this reason, lightweight hose for standpipe/high-rise firefighting should be only used in applications without exposure to significant heat and abrasion. Lightweight hose that is designed for fire fighting operations specifically in a high-rise or standpipe application is frequently referred to as high-rise hose. These hoses are subject to the same testing procedures as other fire attack hose and are able to withstand working pressures needed for operations. This hose is specifically designed to be lightweight and easy to maneuver.

Lightweight hose is ideal for some applications, such as Class II standpipe systems or fire hose reels strategically located in a facility **(Figure 5.28)**. Hose used in this application typically has a lower working pressure than fire attack hose and is typically designed for occupant use without PPE.

Booster hose is another type of lightweight hose that can be used in fire fighting applications. It has a stiff outer membrane to maintain the shape of the hose and is coiled around a reel for storage **(Figure 5.29, p. 164)**. This type of hose, frequently referred to as booster hose, is typically used for small fires (such as trash, wildland, or car fires). It is most often found as preconnected hoseline on a fire fighting apparatus.

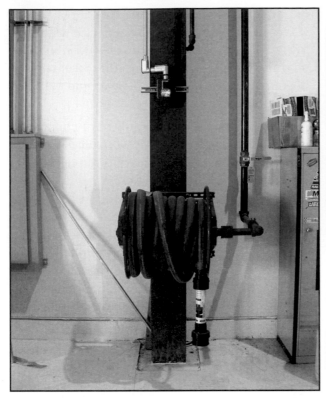

Figure 5.29 Booster hose is commonly coiled around reels in buildings or on apparatus.

Figure 5.30 Suction hose is used for drafting water from static water sources because it will not collapse during drafting operations.

Suction hose (also called *intake hose*), is used to connect the pumper to a hydrant or other water source because it will not collapse under the vacuum conditions needed during drafting and intake. This hose is manufactured in minimum lengths specified in NFPA 1901, *Standard for Automotive Fire Apparatus*, usually in 10-foot (3 m) long sections, for drafting water from static water supplies or connecting to a fire hydrant **(Figure 5.30)**. Some hard-suction hose is constructed of a rubberized, reinforced material; other hoses are made of heavy-duty corrugated plastic. Hard-suction hose is also available in sizes ranging from 2½ to 6 inches (65 mm to 150 mm) in diameter.

Large **soft sleeve hose** is used to connect the pumper intake to a pressurized water source **(Figure 5.31)**. Traditionally referred to as soft suction hose, soft sleeve hose is not rigid and cannot be used for drafting because it will collapse under vacuum. Soft sleeve hose is available in diameters ranging from 2½ to 6 inches (65 mm to 150 mm).

Fire Hose Couplings

Fire hose couplings are designed to connect hose sections to form a continuous hoseline and to connect fire hoses to nozzles, hydrants, pumper connections, and fire department connections (FDCs). To ensure compatibility between all brands of fire hose, NFPA 1963, *Standard for Fire Hose Connections*, specifies fire hose coupling design and construction. Threaded couplings must meet the dimensions required of American National Fire Hose Connection Screw Threads, commonly called *National Hose (NH)*. Using fire hose with national standard threads means that two or more fire departments that respond together can connect their fire hose sections with those from the other departments.

NOTE: Some facilities and jurisdictions do not use national standard threads. When connecting to hydrants or apparatus in those jurisdictions as part of mutual aid, hose adapters may be needed to complete the connection. Preplanning is required to identify the presence of non-standard threads and acquire the appropriate adapters.

Figure 5.31 Large supply lines are usually constructed as soft sleeve hose.

Both attack hose and supply hose may be equipped with either threaded or nonthreaded couplings. All types of couplings may be connected or disconnected quickly and simply with practice. The skills needed for attack and supply hoses must be present before they are tested under emergency conditions. Nozzles are connected or removed from the fire hose using the same methods as those used for coupling and uncoupling sections of hose. The sections that follow describe the characteristics of threaded and nonthreaded couplings.

Figure 5.32 Examples of male (left) and female (right) couplings.

Threaded Couplings

One of the oldest coupling designs involves the casting or machining of a spiral thread into the face of two distinctly different couplings dubbed male and female. A male coupling thread is cut on the exterior surface, while a female coupling thread is on the interior surface of a free-turning ring called a swivel. The swivel permits connecting two sections of hose without twisting the entire hose **(Figure 5.32)**. Each section of fire hose with threaded couplings has a male coupling at one end and a female coupling at the other.

> **CAUTION:** Connect couplings hand-tight to avoid damage to the coupling and gasket.

A threaded coupling has several other parts. The portion of the coupling that serves as a point of attachment to the hose is called the shank. A flattened angle at the end of the threads on the male and female couplings called the Higbee cut prevents cross-threading when couplings are connected. The Higbee indicator (indentation) on the exterior of the coupling marks where the Higbee cut begins. This indicator aids in matching the start of the male coupling thread to the start of the female coupling thread during low light situations or when the threaded end of the coupling is not readily visible **(Figure 5.33)**.

Unlike common pipe threads that are relatively fine, fire hose coupling threads are coarse (with wide tolerances), which allow the couplings to be connected quickly. Some manufacturers design the larger coupling sizes (3½ inches [90 mm] and above) with either ball bearings or roller bearings under the swivel to ensure their smooth operation. Removable rubber **gaskets** are located inside the base of the female coupling to ensure a tight fit, and reduce water leaks.

Threaded couplings are manufactured with lugs or handles to aid in tightening and loosening the connection. Lugs are located on the shank of a male coupling and on the swivel of a female coupling. Lugs are grasping points where firefighters can easily hold the coupling when making and breaking coupling connections. Connections may be made manually or with the assistance of spanner wrenches (special wrenches that fit against the lugs, also called spanners). The three types of lugs are rocker, recessed, and pin **(Figure 5.34)**.

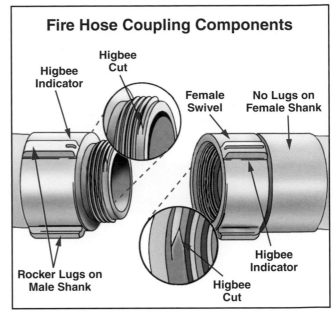

Figure 5.33 Examples of common fire hose coupling components.

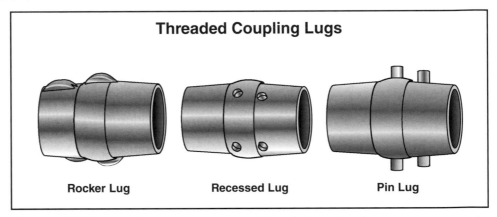

Figure 5.34 There are three common types of threaded coupling lugs: rocker, recessed, and pin lugs.

Handles, or extended lugs, are located on the swivels of large intake supply or suction hoses. Firefighters can grasp these handles when manually tightening the large coupling that connects the hose to a pump valve intake. If necessary, striking the handles with a rubber mallet can help loosen the coupling or tighten leaking couplings on a charged line. You may need to use the mallet for tightening during the setup for a drafting operation.

Pin lugs, usually found on old fire hose couplings, resemble small pegs. Pin-lug couplings are still available but are not commonly ordered with new fire hose, because they tend to catch when hose is dragged over objects or deployed from the hose bed of a pumping apparatus.

Recessed lugs, simply shallow holes drilled into the coupling, are normally found on booster hose. This lug design prevents abrasion that would occur if the hose had protruding lugs and was wound onto reels. Firefighters need to use a pin-lug spanner wrench inserted into the recessed lug holes to tighten or loosen the couplings.

Rounded rocker lugs are used on modern threaded couplings. The rounded shape of rocker lugs (unlike pin lugs) helps prevent the hose from catching on objects. On the couplings, one of the rocker lugs on the swivel is scalloped with a shallow indentation (the Higbee indicator) to mark where the Higbee cut begins.

Nonthreaded Couplings

Nonthreaded couplings are connected with locks or cams rather than screw threads. Although there are some nonthreaded couplings that have male and female ends, *two-way couplings* are more prevalent in North America. A two-way coupling set has no distinct male and female components and both couplings are identical. There are two kinds of two-way couplings: quarter-turn and Storz **(Figure 5.35)**.

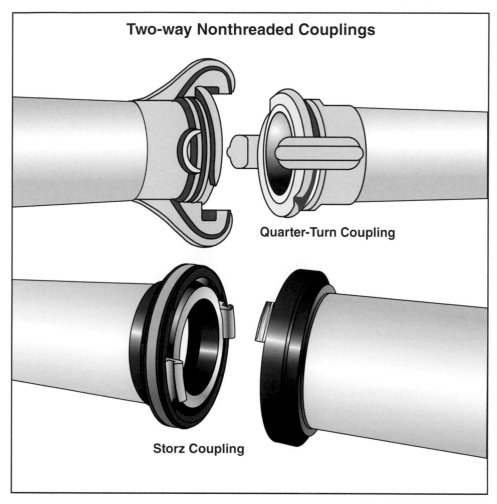

Two-way Nonthreaded Couplings

Quarter-Turn Coupling

Storz Coupling

Figure 5.35 There are two common types of non-threaded couplings: quarter-turn and Storz couplings.

The quarter-turn coupling has two hook-like lugs on each coupling. The lugs, which are grooved on the underside, extend past a raised lip or ring on the open end of the coupling. When the couplings are mated, the lug of one coupling slips over the ring of the opposite coupling and then rotates 90 degrees clockwise to lock. A gasket on the face of each coupling seals the connection to prevent leakage.

Storz couplings are most commonly found on large diameter hose (LDH). Like quarter-turn couplings, they are joined and then rotated until locked in place to form a connection. Unlike quarter-turn couplings, the locking components consist of grooved lugs and inset rings built into the face of each coupling swivel. When mated, the lugs of each coupling fit into recesses in the opposing coupling ring and then slide into locking position behind the ring with a one-third-turn rotation. External lugs at the rear of the swivel provide leverage for connecting and disconnecting couplings. On most manufacturers' couplings, the lugs align to give a visual indicator of a connected coupling (couplings properly aligned and locked in place).

Nonthreaded couplings have the following advantages:

- Fire hose can be connected quickly. However, the use of spanner wrenches to ensure a complete connection slightly slows the connecting operation.

- There is no risk of damaging a coupling from cross-threading the connection because there are no threads.

- Double-male or double-female adapters (adapters connecting two threaded couplings of the same thread type, size, and sex) are not needed, so hose can be deployed from the hose bed regardless of hose load type.

Nonthreaded couplings also have the following disadvantages:

- Hose can become uncoupled, often suddenly and violently, if a complete connection has not been made.

- Hydrants require an adapter to make connections with nonthreaded couplings. The time needed to attach the adapter increases the time required to connect to the hydrant and begin deploying hose.

- Dirt and other large debris can become lodged inside the coupling's grooves, giving the impression that a tight seal has been made when the hose is not connected.

NOTE: Some fire and emergency service organizations that have adopted two-way couplings for their supply hose operations use permanent adapters installed on hydrants for fire hydrant connections.

Hose Appliances and Hose Tools

Hose appliances and hose tools are used in conjunction with hose and nozzles to complete hose layouts. Hose appliances are devices that route water in a variety of ways and make different types of hose connections. Hose tools are devices that assist with the movement, handling, protection, and connecting of hose. A simple way to remember the difference between hose appliances and hose tools is that water flows through appliances but not through tools.

Hose appliances include valves and valve-controlled devices such as wyes, Siameses, water thieves, large-diameter hose appliances, and hydrant valves, as well as fittings such as adapters and intake strainers. Hose tools include hose rollers, spanner wrenches, hose strap and hose rope tools, hose chain tools, hose ramps, hose jackets, blocks, and hose clamps.

Hose Appliances

A hose appliance is any piece of hardware used with fire hose to control the flow of water and create a variety of pathways for water through hose layouts. Common hose appliances include valves and valve devices, fittings, and intake strainers.

Valves. The following valves are used in hoselines and at hydrants and pumpers to control the flow of water (**Figure 5.36**):

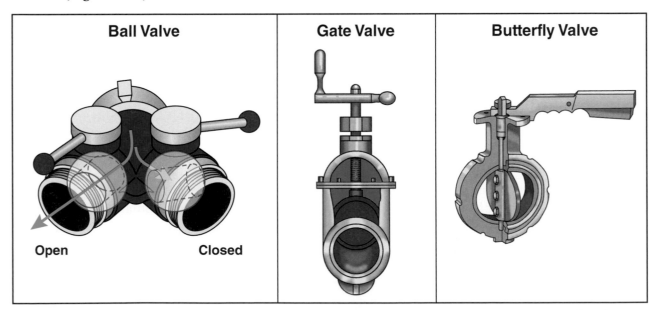

Figure 5.36 There are three common types of valves used by fire brigade members: ball, gate, and butterfly valves.

- **Ball valves** — Used in pumper discharges and gated wyes. Ball valves are open when the handle is in line with the hose and closed when it is at a right angle to the hose. Ball valves are also used in fire pump piping systems.

- **Butterfly valves** — Used on large pump intakes and incorporates a flat baffle that turns 90 degrees. Most are operated manually using a quarter-turn handle, but some are operated using an electric motor and can be controlled remotely. The baffle pivots in the center of the waterway and aligned with the flow when the valve is open.

- **Clapper valves** — Used in Siamese appliances and fire department connections (FDC) to allow water to flow in only one direction. Clapper valves prevent water from flowing out of unused ports when one intake hose is connected and charged before adding more hose. The clapper is a flat disk hinged at the top or one side, which swings open and closed like a door.

Valve Devices. Valve devices allow the number of hoselines operating on the fireground to be increased or decreased. These devices include wye appliances, Siamese appliances, water thief appliances, large-diameter hose appliances, and hydrant valves **(Figure 5.37)**.

Figure 5.37 Examples of various valve devices used by fire brigade members.

- **Wye appliances** — Wye appliances are used to divide a single hoseline into two or more lines. All wyes have a single female inlet and multiple male outlet connections. Wyes that have valve-controlled outlets are called gated wyes. Ball valves are generally used in *gated wyes*. One of the most common wyes has a 2½-inch (65 mm) inlet that divides into two 1½-inch (38 mm) outlets, although many other combinations are available. For high water volume operations, wyes with a large-diameter hose (LDH) inlet and two 2½-inch (65 mm) outlets are used.

- **Siamese appliances** — Siamese and Wye appliances are similar in appearance. While wyes divide a single hoseline into multiple lines, a Siamese combines multiple lines into one line. These appliances permit multiple supply hoselines to be laid parallel to supply a pumper or high-output device. Siamese appliances usually consist of two female inlets, with either a center clapper valve or two clapper valves (one on each side) and a single male outlet. Some Siamese appliances are equipped with three clappered inlets, commonly called triamese appliances or manifolds. The clapper valves are used to control the flow of the inlet streams into the single outlet stream. Siamese and triamese appliances are commonly used when LDH is not available to overcome friction loss in exceptionally long hose lays or those that carry a large flow. These appliances are also used when supplying ladder pipes that are not equipped with a permanent waterway.

- **Water thief appliances** — In operation, the water thief is similar to the wye appliance; however, there is an inlet and outlet of matching size combined with smaller outlets that "steal" water from the main line. Larger volume water thief appliances consist of an LDH inlet and outlet and two or more 2½-inch (65 mm) valve-controlled male outlets.

- **Large-diameter hose appliances** — Some fire fighting operations require water to be distributed at various points along the main supply line. In these cases, an LDH water thief can be used. In other cases, when a large volume of water is needed near the end of the main supply line, an LDH manifold appliance can be used. A typical LDH manifold consists of one LDH inlet and three 2½-inch (65 mm) valve-controlled male outlets. Depending on the locale and the configuration of the appliance, these devices are sometimes called *portable hydrants*, *phantom pumpers*, or *large-diameter distributors*.

Fittings. Fittings are used to connect hose of different diameters and thread types or to protect the couplings on standpipes and on apparatus intakes and outlets. There are two main types of fittings: adapters and reducers **(Figure 5.38)**.

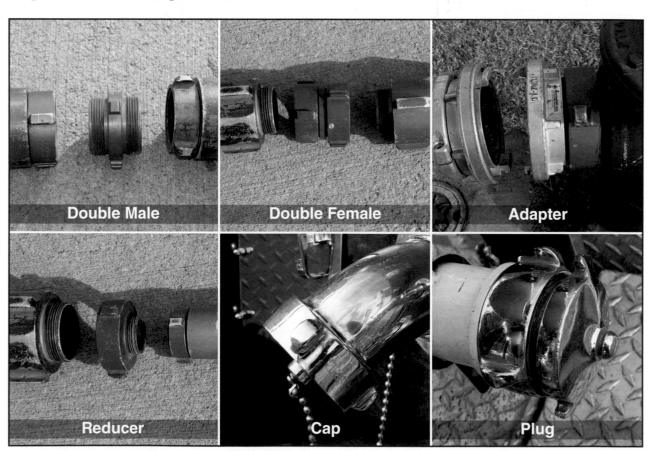

Figure 5.38 Examples of common fire hose fittings.

An adapter is a fitting for connecting hose couplings with similar threads and the same inside diameter. The double-male and double-female adapters are among the most often-used hose fittings. These adapters allow two male couplings or two female couplings of the same diameter and thread type to be connected. An increasingly common fitting is used to connect a sexless coupling to a threaded outlet on a hydrant.

Reducers connect a smaller-diameter hoseline to the end of a larger one. However, using a reducer limits the larger hose to supplying only one smaller line. Using a wye appliance allows the larger hose to supply two smaller ones.

Other common fittings include elbows that provide support for intake or discharge hose at the pumping apparatus. These elbows are also used on the standpipe outlets in stairway risers to prevent kinks in the attack line. The threads on pump male discharge outlets are protected with hose caps. Female inlets on some FDCs are capped with hose plugs.

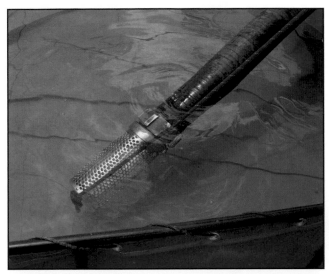

Figure 5.39 Strainers such as this one prevent debris from being drawn into the pump during drafting operations.

Intake Strainers. Intake strainers are devices attached to the drafting end of a hard-suction hose when pumping from a static water source. They are designed to keep debris from entering the apparatus or portable pump. Such debris can damage the pump or pass through it to clog the nozzle.

Intake strainers must not rest on the bottom of a static water source except when the bottom is clean and hard, such as the bottom of a swimming pool. To prevent a strainer from resting on the bottom of a lake or pond, tie one end of a length of rope to the eyelet on the strainer and the other to an apparatus or another anchor point. Floating intake strainers are also available to keep the intake strainer off the bottom of a static water source **(Figure 5.39)**.

Hose Tools

Hose tools are used to protect, move, handle, store, and connect hose. Common hose tools include **(Figure 5.40, p. 172)**:

- Hose roller
- Hose jacket
- Hose clamp
- Hose strap, hose rope, and hose chain
- Hose bridge or ramp
- Chafing block

Hose Roller. Hose rollers protect hose from the mechanical damage of dragging hose over sharp corners, such as roof edges and windowsills. This device consists of a metal frame with two or more rollers. The notch of the frame is placed over the potentially damaging edge or windowsill, and the frame is secured with a rope or clamp. The hose is then pulled across the rollers. The hose roller can also protect rope when hoisting tools over similar edges.

Hose Jacket. When a hoseline ruptures but must remain charged to continue a fire attack, a hose jacket can sometimes be installed at the point of rupture. A hose jacket consists of a hinged two-piece metal cylinder. The rubber lining of each half of the cylinder seals the rupture to prevent leakage. A locking device clamps the cylinder closed when in use. Hose jackets are made in two sizes: 2½ inches and 3 inches (65 mm and 77 mm). The hose jacket encloses the hose so effectively that it can continue to operate at full pressure. A hose jacket can also connect hose with mismatched or damaged screw-thread couplings.

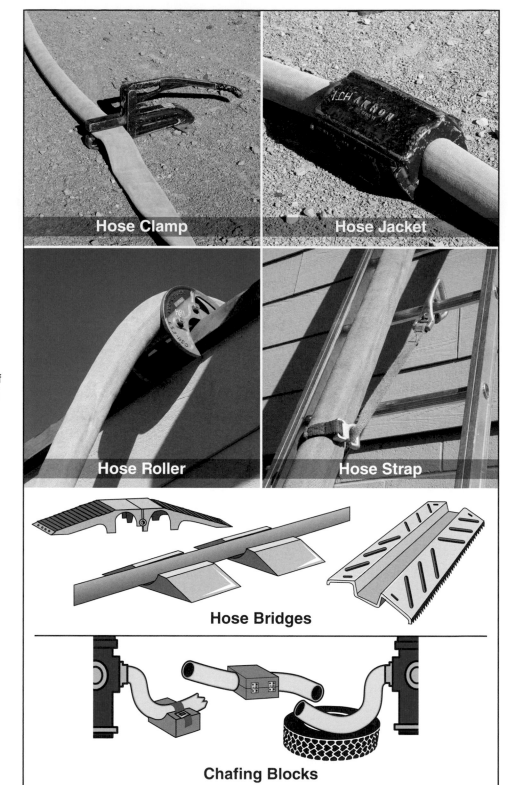

Figure 5.40 Examples of common hose tools used by fire brigades.

Hose Clamp. There are three types of hose clamps: screw-down, press-down, and hydraulic press. If applied incorrectly, a hose clamp can injure fire brigade members or damage the hose. Some general rules that apply to hose clamps are as follows:

- Apply the hose clamp at least 20 feet (6 m) behind the rear of the apparatus.

- Apply the hose clamp approximately 5 feet (1.5 m) from the coupling on the supply side.

- Center the hose evenly in the jaws to avoid pinching the hose.

- Close and open the hose clamp slowly to avoid water hammer.
- Stand to one side when applying or releasing any type of hose clamp (the operating handle or frame can snap open suddenly).
- Use proper lifting techniques when moving LDH clamps and placing them around hose as the clamps and hose are heavy.

> **CAUTION:** Never stand over the handle of a hose clamp when applying or releasing it. The handle or frame may pop open and swing violently upward.

> **CAUTION:** When LDH hose is charged, the hose may cause the LDH hose clamp to shift its position rapidly or cause the clamp to open, possibly violently, and allow water.

Hose Strap, Hose Rope, and Hose Chain. Hose straps, ropes, and chains are used to carry, pull, or handle charged hoselines. They provide a more secure means to handle pressurized hose when applying water. They may also be used to secure hose to ladders and other fixed objects.

Hose Bridge or Ramp. Hose bridges or ramps help prevent damage to fire hose when vehicles must drive over it. They should be used wherever a hoseline is laid across a street or another area where it may be driven over. Hose ramps can be used as chafing blocks or positioned over small spills to keep hoselines from becoming contaminated.

Chafing Block. Charged hoselines vibrate and rub against other surfaces, which can cause abrasions. Chafing blocks are devices used to protect fire hose from these abrasions. They are particularly useful near pumpers where intake hose comes in contact with pavement or curbs because vibrations from the pumper may keep the intake hose in constant motion. Chafing blocks may be made of wood, leather, or sections of old truck tires.

Hose Rolls

There are a number of different methods for rolling fire hose, depending on whether it is intended to be used or stored. In all methods, care must be taken to protect the couplings. Some of the more common hose rolls include:

- Straight Roll
- Donut Roll
- Twin Donut Roll

Straight Roll

The single section straight roll is the simplest of all hose rolls. To make this roll, start at the male coupling end and roll toward the female coupling end of the hose. When the roll is completed, the female end is exposed and the male end is protected in the center of the roll **(Figure 5.41)**. The straight roll is commonly used for hose in the following situations:

- Transporting damaged or dirty hose to the station for repair, replacement, or cleaning
- Storing sections of hose in a storage rack or other location
- Carrying spare sections of hose in apparatus compartments
- Making hose loading easier

To indicate that a section of hose must be repaired and/or tested before being placed back in service, some departments use a variation of the straight roll. This roll is started at the female

Figure 5.41 An example of hose rolled into a straight hose roll.

coupling so that when the roll is completed, the male coupling is exposed. Another method is to tie a knot in the exposed end or attach a tag indicating the type and location of damage.

Donut and Twin Donut Rolls

The *donut roll* is commonly used in situations where hose is likely to be deployed for use directly from a roll **(Figure 5.42)**. The donut roll has certain advantages over the straight roll:

- The firefighter has control of both couplings, which protects them from damage.

- The hose rolls out easier with fewer twists or kinks.

- Holding both couplings enables a quicker connection to other couplings.

The twin donut roll usually works best on 1½-inch (38 mm) and 1¾-inch (45 mm) hose, although 2-, 2½-, or 3-inch (50 mm, 65 mm, or 77 mm) hose can also be rolled in this manner. The purpose of this hose roll is to create a compact roll that can be easily transported and carried for special applications, such as high-rise or standpipe operations.

Figure 5.42 An example of a donut roll.

Figure 5.43 An example of a twin donut roll being carried by a strap.

If the couplings are offset by about 1 foot (0.3 m) at the beginning, they can be coupled together after the roll is tied or strapped. A hose strap, inserted into the center of the roll, is used to carry the hose roll **(Figure 5.43)**.

Basic Hose Loads

NFPA 1901, *Standard for Automotive Fire Apparatus*, lists the minimum quantity of hose in various sizes to be carried on a standard pumping apparatus. There must be a minimum 800 feet (240 m) of 2½-inch (65 mm) or larger fire supply hose and 400 feet (120 m) of 1½-inch (38 mm), 1¾-inch (45 mm), or 2-inch (52 mm) attack fire hose. Supply and attack hose is generally carried in open compartments called hose beds. Hose beds vary in location, size, and shape, and are sometimes built for specific needs. The front of the hose bed is closest to the front of the apparatus, and the rear of the hose bed is closest to the rear of the apparatus. Most hose beds have open aluminum slats in the bottom that allow air to circulate throughout the hose load to prevent mildew damage to woven-jacketed hose.

Apparatus hose beds may be a single compartment, or a vertical panel that runs from the front to the rear of the hose compartment may divide or separate them. This division creates a split hose bed, allowing the apparatus to have hose loaded that can be deployed as a single or double supply line or for both forward and reverse hose lays at the same time. Fire brigade members should store hose in a split bed so that both beds may be connected when a long hose lay is required.

The three most common loads for supply hoselines are the *flat*, *accordion*, and *horseshoe* loads. Hose loads may also have a finish, an additional section connected to the hose load and arranged on the top of the load, which can be rapidly deployed for forward or reverse supply hose lays or as an attack line.

Additional supply and attack hose may be carried in compartments on the apparatus. A common type of hose bundle is the high-rise pack, described later in this section.

 Hose Load Finishes

Hose load finishes are added to the basic hose load to increase the versatility of the load. Finishes are normally loaded to provide enough hose to connect the hoseline to a hydrant and to provide an attack hoseline at the fire scene.

Finishes fall into two categories: finishes used for forward hose lays (straight finish) and finishes used for reverse hose lays (reverse horseshoe and skid load finishes). Finishes for forward lays facilitate making a hydrant connection and are not as elaborate as finishes for reverse lays. Finishes for reverse lays provide an adequate amount of hose at the scene for initial fire attack.

Straight Finish. A straight finish consists of the last section of hose arranged loosely back and forth across the top of the hose load. A hydrant wrench, gate valve, and any necessary adapters are usually strapped to the hose at or near the female coupling **(Figure 5.44)**.

Figure 5.44 An example of a straight finish.

Reverse Horseshoe Finish. This finish is similar to the horseshoe load except that the bottom of the "U" portion of the horseshoe is at the rear of the hose bed. It is made of one or two 100-foot (30 m) sections of hose, each connected to one side of a gated wye. Any size attack hose can be used: 1½, 1¾, or 2½ inches (38 mm, 45 mm, or 65 mm). The smaller sizes require a 2½-x 1½-inch (65 mm by 38 mm) gated wye. The 2½-inch (65 mm) hose requires a 2½-x 2½-inch (65 mm by 65 mm) gated wye. A nozzle of the appropriate size is also needed for each attack line **(Figure 5.45)**.

Figure 5.45 An example of a reverse horseshoe finish.

The reverse horseshoe finish can also be used for a preconnected line and can be loaded in two or three layers. With the nozzle extending to the rear, firefighters can place the finish over one shoulder and extend the opposite arm through the loops of the layers to pull the hose from the bed for an arm carry. A second preconnected line can be located in the hose bed below when there is sufficient depth.

Skid Load Finish. A skid load finish consists of folding the last three sections (150 feet [45 m] of 2½-inch [65 mm] hose) into a compact bundle on top of the rest of the hose load. To begin the load, form three or more pull loops that extend beyond the end of the hose load. The rest of the hose, with nozzle attached, is accordion-folded across the hose used to form the pull loops in the hose bed **(Figure 5.46)**.

Figure 5.46 An example of a skid load finish.

Hose Loading Guidelines

Loading hose on fire apparatus must be done correctly to allow it to deploy correctly during an emergency operation. During an emergency, properly loaded hose can be efficiently and effectively deployed for supply or attack operations. The following guidelines should be followed, regardless of the type of hose load used:

- Check gaskets and swivel before connecting any coupling.
- Keep the flat sides of the hose in the same plane when two sections of hose are connected. Lugs on the couplings do not need to be aligned.
- Tighten the couplings hand-tight.
- Remove kinks and twists from fire hose when it is bent to form a loop in the hose bed.
- Make a short fold or reverse bend, called a *Dutchman*, in the hose during the loading process so that couplings are not too close to the front or rear of the hose bed and will not flip over when pulled out of the bed. The Dutchman serves two purposes: It changes the direction and location of a coupling. The reverse bends should not be overused in the same layer because it can result in couplings becoming wedged in the bed.

- Load large diameter hose (3½-inch [90 mm] or larger) with all couplings near the front of the bed. This load saves space and allows the hose to lay flat.

- Do not pack hose too tightly. This action puts excess pressure on the folds of the hose and may cause couplings to snag when the hose pays out of the bed. A general rule is that the hose should be loose enough to allow a gloved hand to be easily inserted between the folds.

Loading large diameter hose can be laborious and time-consuming work. To make the work more efficient, apparatus equipped with LDH often carry LDH rollers. The roller is a wider version of the hose roller previously mentioned. It mounts temporarily on the tailboard of the pumper. With the hoseline laid between the wheels along the length of the apparatus, the apparatus is slowly driven along the hoseline. As the apparatus moves, the hose is pulled up over the roller and into the hose bed. Because the hose may need to be guided over the roller, this task is one of the few times that firefighters are permitted to stand on the tailboard or ride in the hose bed while the apparatus is in motion. Firefighters riding on the apparatus while loading hose should be safety harnessed to the apparatus to prevent falling from it.

Another version of a combination load has large diameter supply hose loaded on one side of the bed and smaller-diameter hose that can be used for either supply or attack loaded on the other side. A pumper loaded in this manner can lay LDH when the fire requires the pumper to lay its own supply line and work alone (laying it forward so the pumper stays at the incident scene). Fire brigade members can use small diameter hose as a supply line at fires with less demanding water flow requirements as well as for attack lines on large fires. Therefore, a split hose bed gives fire brigade leaders the greatest number of choices when determining the best way to use limited resources. Three supply hose loads are: flat load, accordion load, and combination load.

Figure 5.47 The flat hose load is one of the most commonly used loads in the fire service.

Flat Load

The flat load is the simplest way to load supply hose. It is suitable for any size of supply hose and is the best way to load large diameter hose. As the name implies, the hose is laid so that its folds lie flat rather than on edge **(Figure 5.47)**. Hose loaded in this manner is less subject to wear from apparatus vibration during travel. A disadvantage of this load is that the hose folds contain sharp bends at both ends of the bed, which requires that the hose be reloaded periodically to change the location of the bends within each length to prevent damage to the lining.

In a single hose bed, the flat load may be started on either side. In a split hose bed, lay the first length against the partition with the coupling hanging far enough below the hose bed so that the coupling can be connected to the last coupling of the load on the opposite side and laid on top of the load. This placement allows the couplings to be easily disconnected when the load must be divided to lay dual lines. How far the coupling needs to hang is based on your estimate of the anticipated height of the hose bed.

The hose load for large diameter hose should be started 12 to 18 inches (300 mm to 450 mm) from the front of the hose bed. This extra space should be reserved for couplings, and all couplings should be laid in a manner that allows them to deploy without flipping over. It may be necessary to make a short fold or reverse bend in the hose to do this.

Accordion Load

The accordion load is named for the manner in which the hose appears after loading. The hose is laid on edge in folds that lie adjacent to each other. The first coupling is placed in the rear of the bed. In a single hose bed, it can be placed in either corner. An accordion load is easy to load, only requiring two or three people, although four people are optimal for the task **(Figure 5.48)**. Another advantage is that firefighters can easily pick up a number of folds and place them on one shoulder to carry the hose from the bed.

Combination Load

Combination loads are used with split hose beds that are loaded with threaded coupling hose. This load permits the apparatus to make a forward lay from the water source to the fire, then a reverse lay back to the water source follows. One half of the bed is loaded with the female coupling exposed and the other half has the male coupling exposed. A double-female adapter fitting is used where the two beds are connected. This load can be a flat, accordion, or horseshoe load **(Figure 5.49)**.

Figure 5.48 Another common hose load is the accordion load.

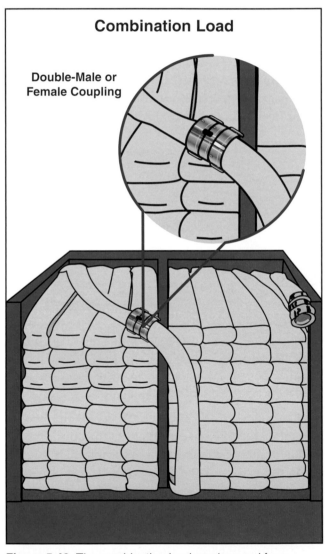

Figure 5.49 The combination load can be used for a forward or reverse hose lay.

Horseshoe Load

The horseshoe load is another hose arrangement named for the way it appears after loading. Like the accordion load, the hose is loaded on its edge, but in this case the hose is laid in a U-shaped configuration around the perimeter of the hose bed working toward the center **(Figure 5.50)**. Each length is progressively laid from the outside of the bed toward the inside so that the last length is at the center of the horseshoe. The primary advantage of the horseshoe load is that it has fewer sharp bends in the hose than the accordion or flat loads.

Figure 5.50 Illustrating the layout of a horseshoe load.

Horseshoe loads in single hose beds have certain disadvantages. Excess hose may be deployed because the hose is pulled alternately from one side of a bed and then the other creating a wavy or snakelike lay. Another disadvantage is that folds for a shoulder carry cannot be pulled as easily as they can with an accordion load. With the horseshoe load, two fire brigade members are required to make the shoulder folds for the carry. Like the accordion load, the hose is loaded on its edge, which can result in wear on hose edges. The horseshoe load does not work for large diameter hose because the hose remaining in the bed tends to fall flat as the hose is deployed, which can cause the hose to become entangled.

In a single hose bed, the horseshoe load may be started on either side. In a split hose bed, lay the first length against the partition with the coupling hanging far enough below the hose bed so that the coupling can be connected to the last coupling of the load on the opposite side and laid on top of the load. This placement allows the couplings to be easily disconnected when the load must be divided to lay dual lines. How far the coupling needs to hang is based on your estimate of the anticipated height of the hose bed.

Preconnected Hose Loads for Attack Lines

Preconnected hoselines, simply called *preconnects*, are the primary lines most fire departments use for fire attack. These hoselines are connected to a discharge valve and placed in an area other than the main hose bed. Preconnected hoselines generally range from 50 to 250 feet (15 m to 75 m) in length. Preconnected attack lines can be carried in the following places:

- Longitudinal beds
- Raised trays
- Transverse beds (sometimes called *cross lays* or *Mattydale hose beds*)
- Tailboard compartments
- Side compartments or bins
- Front bumper wells (sometimes called *jump lines*)
- Reels

Figure 5.51 An example of a preconnected flat load on a facility hose trailer.

The following sections describe some common loads for preconnects. Special loads to meet local requirements may be developed based on individual experiences and apparatus configurations. Regardless of the type of load used, the preconnected attack hose must be fully deployed from the hose bed before the line is charged. In some departments, this practice is referred to as "clearing the bed" and is the responsibility of the driver/operator or firefighter pulling the hose.

Preconnected Flat Load

The preconnected flat load is adaptable for varying sizes of hose beds and is often used in transverse beds **(Figure 5.51)**. This load is similar to a flat load for larger supply hose except that exposed loops are provided for pulling the load from the bed. Place the loops at regular intervals within the load so that equal portions of the load are pulled from the bed. The number of loops and the intervals at which they are placed depend on the size and total length of the hose.

Triple Layer Load

The triple layer load gets its name because the load begins with hose folded in three layers. The three folds are then laid into the bed in an S-shaped fashion **(Figure 5.52)**. One fire brigade member can pull this load.

The layers in a triple layer load may be as long as 50 feet (15 m) each. All of this hose must be completely removed from the bed before deploying the nozzle end of the hose, which can be difficult or impossible if the space directly behind the hose bed is restricted. While this hose load can be used for all sizes of attack lines, it is often preferred for larger (2- and 2½-inch [50 mm and 65 mm]) attack lines that may be too cumbersome for shoulder carries.

Minuteman Load

One person can pull and advance the minuteman load. This load can be carried on the shoulder, completely clear of the ground, which makes it less likely that the hose will catch on obstacles. The load deploys from the shoulder as the firefighter advances toward the fire. The load is also particularly well-suited for a narrow hose bed **(Figure 5.53)**. However, this load can be awkward to carry when wearing an SCBA. If the load is in a single stack, it may also collapse on the shoulder if not held tightly in place.

Booster Hose Reels

Booster hoselines are rubber-covered hose of varying lengths and diameters that are usually carried preconnected and coiled on reels, making it ideal for quick first-attack on small exterior fires. These hoses retain their internal capacity while on the reel and do not have to be fully unreeled before use. Direct connection provides instant water flow no matter what length of hose is needed. These booster hose reels may be mounted in any of several places on the apparatus according to specified needs and the design of the apparatus. Some booster hose reels are mounted above the pump panel and behind the apparatus cab **(Figure 5.54)**. This arrangement provides booster hose that can be unrolled from either side of the apparatus. Other booster hose reels are mounted on the front bumper of the apparatus or in rear compartments. Manual- and power-operated reels are available. In order to load the maximum amount of hose with the easiest removal from the reel, booster hose should be wound onto the reel one layer at a time in an even manner.

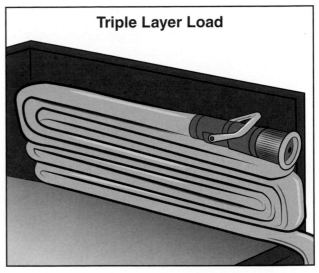

Figure 5.52 Illustrating the layout of the triple layer load.

Figure 5.53 Illustrating the layout of the minuteman load.

> **WARNING:** Booster lines are not appropriate for interior fire fighting or fires that have the potential for sudden, large escalation because they do not deliver a sufficient volume of water to protect firefighters if conditions suddenly deteriorate.

Figure 5.54 Booster hose reels may be mounted within a facility or on apparatus.

Figure 5.55 Standpipe/high-rise packs are useful in transporting multiple lengths of hose and tools and equipment to where they are needed.

Standpipe/High-Rise Packs

Standpipe/high-rise packs are preassembled hose rolls, bundles, or packs. These packs are carried on an apparatus or stored in a hose house or hose box. Being preassembled, these packs are ready to carry aloft (or into a building) and connect to the building's standpipe system. How these standpipe/high-rise hose packs are constructed is a matter of local preference, but the most common are hose bundles that are easily carried on the shoulder or in specially designed hose packs complete with nozzles, fittings, and tools **(Figure 5.55)**.

Hose selection for use with standpipe systems should take into consideration multiple factors: diameter, weight, durability, and system design. When standpipes are used to fight a fire, fire brigade members made need to transport the hose up several flights of stairs or extend hoselines within structures that encompass large areas. The diameter of the hose must also be considered. Hose with larger diameter has lower friction loss. Friction loss in hose must be considered when determining the needed nozzle pressure and comparing that to the available pressure and flow from the standpipe.

Deploying Hoselines

Attack hoselines carry water from a fire pump that provides pressure to where the water is needed. As a fire brigade member, you will be trained to deploy hoselines from their stored or preconnected locations in a hose cabinet or from an apparatus.

Preconnected Hoselines

The steps of deploying preconnected hoselines vary with the type of hose load. Speed and efficiency increase with practice. Your local SOPs may vary from the steps listed in this section and the referenced skill sheets.

Preconnected flat loads can be easily deployed from a hose cabinet or an apparatus. To advance the preconnected flat load, grasp the hose loop in one hand and the nozzle in the other hand, pull the hose from the compartment, and advance towards the fire **(Figure 5.56, p. 182)**. Spread the hose and straighten it to remove any kinks before charging the line. The minuteman load is deployed without dragging the hose on the ground. The hose deploys by unfolding from the top of the stack carried on the shoulder as the firefighter advances toward the fire **(Figure 5.57, p. 182)**. The hoseline should also deploy with fewer kinks and bends in it than deployments of other types of loads. Advancing the triple layer load involves placing the nozzle and the fold of the first tier on the firefighter's shoulder and walking away from the apparatus toward the fire **(Figure 5.58, p. 182)**.

Figure 5.56 A fire brigade member deploying a preconnected flat hose load from a hose trailer.

Figure 5.57 A minuteman load being deployed.

Figure 5.58 A fire brigade member preparing to deploy a triple layer load from a facility hose trailer.

Other Hoselines

While some 2½-inch (65 mm) or larger attack hoselines may be preconnected, others may be deployed using supply hose as attack line. The hose may be deployed from either side of the hose bed and may require an adapter to mate the coupling with a nozzle or connect the hose to an FDC.

Hoselines equipped with wye appliances are normally used in connection with a reverse layout because the wye connection is fastened to the 2½- or 3-inch (65 mm or 77 mm) supply hose. A fire brigade member performing two consecutive operations can unload these hoselines. Remove the attack lines in hose bundles or disconnect the preconnected hoselines and place them on the ground behind the apparatus with any necessary nozzles and adapters. Then remove the wye and enough hose to supply the smaller attack lines connected or to be connected to the wye.

To deploy individual sections from flat, accordion, or horseshoe loads, load one section of hose on another firefighter's shoulder one at a time. Multiple firefighters carry the hose to the desired location once it is disconnected from the remainder of the hose in the bed. Because all of the folds in an accordion load and a flat load are nearly the same length, they can be loaded on the shoulder by taking several folds at a time directly from the hose bed.

Hose Team Duties

Fire brigade members may operate larger hoselines in teams of two or three responders. Each team member has specific duties under direction of the fire brigade leader. The nozzle operator is responsible for controlling the nozzle, selecting the appropriate discharge pattern, appropriately applying the agent, and directing the agent to where it will be most effective. The nozzle operator should slowly open and close the nozzle's **bale** to reduce nozzle reaction and prevent water hammer **(Figure 5.59)**.

The second member on the line helps maintain control of the hoseline, maneuver the hoseline, and guide it around obstacles **(Figure 5.60)**. If it becomes necessary to retreat, the second member can help by pulling or moving the hose along the exit path. Larger attack hoselines may require a third fire brigade member be assigned to help maintain control of the line and with maneuvering it at the scene.

Figure 5.59 The bale of the nozzle is used to open and close the nozzle's built-in valve.

Figure 5.60 The backup member helps the nozzleman maintain control of the hoseline.

Advancing Hoselines to Final Positions

Once hoselines have been laid out from the attack pumper or stand pipe, they must be advanced into position for applying water onto the fire. Deploying hose over flat surfaces with no obstacles is very simple using most deployment methods. Advancing hoselines is considerably more difficult when hoses must be deployed up or down stairways, from standpipes, up ladders, and/or deep into buildings. Hoselines can be deployed more easily before they are charged because water adds weight, rigidity, and pressure that makes the hose difficult to maneuver. Because of the size of many industrial and commercial facilities, fire brigade members may need to enter the involved structure with uncharged or charged hoselines and connect to the water supply once near the fire's location. You must also know how to add more hose to extend a hoseline as well as how to secure and replace a ruptured section of hose if necessary.

Working Line Drag

The working line drag is one of the quickest and easiest ways to advance a charged hoseline at ground level. The fire brigade members place the hose over their shoulders with the coupling or nozzle resting on their chests.

Extending a Section of Hose

Occasionally, fire brigade members may need to extend the length of a hoseline with hose of the same size or perhaps even smaller hose. The fire brigade members interrupt the water flow, add the new sections, then restore the water flow.

Retrieving a Loose Hoseline

A *loose hoseline* is one in which water is flowing through a nozzle, an open butt, or a broken line and is not under control by fire brigade members. This situation is dangerous because the loose hoseline may whip back and forth and up and down. Fire brigade members and bystanders may be seriously injured or killed if the uncontrolled whipping end hits them.

Closing a valve at the pump or hydrant to turn off the flow of water is the safest way to control a loose line. Another method is to position a hose clamp at a stationary point in the hoseline. It may also be possible to put a kink in a smaller diameter hose at a point away from the break until the appropriate valve is closed. To put a kink in the hose, obtain sufficient slack in the line, bend the hose over on itself, creating a "Z" in the hose (this does not apply to LDH due to its size and weight when charged), and apply body weight to the bends in the hose. During this operation, it is helpful to place one knee directly upon the bend and apply pressure at this point **(Figure 5.61)**.

Figure 5.61 A fire brigade member demonstrating the "Z" method of stopping the flow of water through a hoseline.

Replacing Burst Sections

A hose clamp or a kink in the hose can also be used to stop the flow of water when replacing a burst section of hose. Two additional sections of hose should be used to replace a broken section. This practice is necessary because hoselines stretch to longer lengths when under pressure; the couplings in the line are invariably farther apart than the length of a single replacement section.

Operating Handlines

Fire brigade members operate hoselines and nozzles to apply fire streams to control and extinguish fires. The method used will vary depending on the size of the hoseline and the strength and personal preference of the fire brigade member(s). Optional methods are described in the following sections.

Operating Small Attack Lines

One or two fire brigade members can operate small hoselines, such as booster lines and 1½-, 1¾-, and 2-inch (38 mm, 45 mm, and 50 mm) hoselines. Small hoselines can require additional fire brigade members when the hose is charged and obstructions must be negotiated.

One-Fire Brigade Member Method. Assigning one fire brigade member to operate an attack hoseline may occur when performing exterior fire suppression activities to fight a small ground cover fire, rubbish or trash fire, vehicle fire, small structure fire, or during overhaul operations.

Figure 5.62 A nozzle operator opening the bale of a fog nozzle.

Figure 5.63 The backup person should be within 3 feet (1 m) or an arm's length of the nozzleman.

The **nozzle operator** holds the nozzle with one hand and holds the hose just behind the nozzle with the other hand. The hoseline is then rested against the waist and across the hip. Holding nozzles equipped with a pistol grip is slightly different: hold the pistol grip in one hand while holding the operating bale in the other **(Figure 5.62)**.

Two-Fire Brigade Members Method. Two fire brigade members are the minimum number required for handling any attack line during interior structural operations. The nozzle operator holds the nozzle with one hand and holds the hose just behind the nozzle with the other hand. The hoseline is then rested against the waist and across the hip.

Holding nozzles equipped with a pistol grip is slightly different: hold the pistol grip in one hand while holding the operating bale in the other. The backup fire brigade member takes a position on the same side of the hose about 3 feet (1 m) or approximately an arm's length behind the nozzle operator **(Figure 5.63)**. The second fire brigade member holds the hose with both hands and rests it against the waist and across the hip or braces it with the leg. The backup fire brigade member is responsible for keeping the hose straight behind the nozzle operator and at a level comfortable for the nozzle operator. The backup person takes the majority of the reaction forces for the nozzle operator. During extended operations, either one or both fire brigade members may apply a hose strap or rope hose tool to reduce the effects of nozzle reaction.

Three-Fire Brigade Members Method. Three fire brigade members can easily maneuver a small handline. There are several methods for three brigade members to control small hoselines. In all cases, the positioning of the nozzleperson is the same as previously described for the two-fire brigade member method. The only differences will be in the position of the second and third brigade members on the hoseline. Some fire brigades prefer the first backup fire brigade member to stand directly behind the brigade member at the nozzle, with the third fire brigade member kneeling on the hose behind the second brigade member. Another method is for both backup fire brigade members to serve as anchors by kneeling on opposite sides of the hoseline. Another technique is for all brigade members to use hose straps and remain in a standing position, which is the most mobile method.

Operating Large Attack Lines

Once a large attack hoseline has been deployed and advanced to the fire, fire brigade members must place it in operation. The methods that the following sections describe can be used with large attack hoselines of 2½-and 3-inch (65 mm and 77 mm) or larger hose.

One-Fire Brigade Member Method. During exposure protection or overhaul operations, one fire brigade member may be assigned to operate a large hoseline if a **master stream device** is unavailable. A large loop is formed that crosses over the hoseline about 2 feet (0.6 m) behind the nozzle. The fire brigade member sits on the intersection where the hose crosses over itself and directs the fire stream to the point of application **(Figure 5.64)**. To reduce fatigue during extended operations, the nozzle operator can either use a hose strap or rope hose tool looped over the shoulder or reduce the nozzle flow if conditions allow. Except for limited lateral (side-to-side) motion, this method does not permit much maneuvering of the nozzle.

Figure 5.64 A fire brigade member operating a large hoseline for exposure control.

Two-Fire Brigade Members Method. When two fire brigade members are assigned to handle a large hoseline, they may need a means of anchoring the hoseline to offset nozzle reaction. This may include the use of hose straps or rope hose tools to assist in anchoring the hose. The nozzle operator loops a hose strap or rope hose tool around the hose a short distance from the nozzle, placing the large loop across the back and over the outside shoulder. The operator then holds the nozzle with one hand and the hose just behind the nozzle with the other hand. The hoseline rests against the body. Leaning slightly forward helps control the nozzle reaction. The backup fire brigade member again serves as an anchor about 3 feet (1 m) back. The backup fire brigade member also has a hose strap or rope hose tool around the hose and leans his or her shoulder forward to absorb some of the nozzle reaction **(Figure 5.65)**.

Figure 5.65 Two fire brigade members operating a large hoseline during a training exercise.

Three-Fire Brigade Members Method. When using a large-size hoseline, the minimum recommended approach is the three-fire brigade member method if mobility of the hoseline is needed. There are several methods for three brigade members to control large hoselines. In all cases, the positioning of the nozzle operator is the same as previously described for the two-fire brigade member method. The only differences will be in the position of the second and third brigade members on the hoseline. Some fire brigades prefer the first backup fire brigade member to stand directly behind the brigade member at the nozzle, with the third fire brigade member kneeling on the hose behind the second brigade member. Another method is for both fire brigade members to serve as anchors by kneeling on opposite sides of the hoseline. Another technique is for all brigade members to use hose straps and remain in a standing position, which is the most mobile method.

Fire Streams

NFPA 1081 (2018): 4.3.3

A *fire stream* is a stream of water or other extinguishing agent after it leaves a fire hose nozzle until it reaches the desired target. The following factors have an effect on a fire stream:

- Velocity of the water/extinguishing agent
- Wind direction and velocity
- Operating pressure
- Condition of the nozzle opening
- Gravity
- Air friction
- Nozzle design and adjustment

Fire streams are used for the following:

- Apply water or foam directly onto burning material to reduce its temperature and access to oxygen
- Apply water or foam into open flames to reduce the temperature so that firefighters can advance handlines
- Reduce the temperature of the upper gas layers
- Disperse hot smoke and fire gases from a heated area
- Create a water curtain to protect firefighters and property from heat
- Create a barrier between a fuel and a fire by covering the fuel with a foam blanket

Fire streams can be best described in terms of the following information:

- The patterns they form
- The nozzles that create those patterns
- The types of control valves that permit the flow of water through the nozzle
- The factors that limit a fire stream

The size of the nozzle opening or orifice and nozzle pressure determines the quantity of water flowing from the nozzle. The size of the opening also influences the reach or distance of the fire stream. Finally, the type of nozzle determines the shape of the fire stream. A smooth bore nozzle produces a tightly-packed solid stream of water. A fog nozzle produces a fog or straight stream. The sections that follow provide more detailed information about fire streams.

Extinguishing Properties of Water

Several characteristics of water are valuable for fire extinguishment of Class A fires, including:

- Water is readily available.
- Water is relatively inexpensive.
- Water has a greater heat-absorbing capacity (high specific heat) than most other common extinguishing agents.
- Water changing into steam requires a relatively large amount of heat (high latent heat of vaporization).
- Water can be applied in a variety of ways.

To understand how water is used to extinguish fire, you must know how it is converted to vapor when heat is applied and the properties of steam. These topics are covered in the following sections.

The primary way that water extinguishes fire is by absorbing heat, which creates a cooling effect. When heated to its boiling point, water converts into water vapor or steam in a process called *vaporization*. Vaporization of water creates steam.

At 212° F (100°C) water expands approximately 1,700 times its original volume as it turns to steam **(Figure 5.66)**. As the temperature increases, steam (like any gas) continues to expand. The volume of steam produced depends on the amount of water that is applied. The effects of this steam on conditions inside a compartment depend on where the steam is produced.

In order for complete vaporization to occur, boiling temperatures must be maintained long enough for the entire volume of water to be vaporized. A solid stream of water has a smaller surface area and absorbs heat less efficiently. When the water is broken into small particles or droplets, such as a fog pattern, it absorbs heat and converts into steam more rapidly because more of the water's surface is exposed to the heat. For example, 1 cubic inch (1 638.7 mm^3) of ice dropped into a glass of water takes some time to absorb its capacity of heat. This reaction is because a surface area of only 6 square inches (387 mm^2) of the ice is exposed to the water. If that cube of ice is divided into 1/8-cubic inch (204.8 mm^3) cubes and dropped into the water, a surface area of 48 square inches (3 096 mm^2) of ice is exposed to the water. The finely divided particles of ice absorb heat more rapidly. This same principle applies to water in the liquid state.

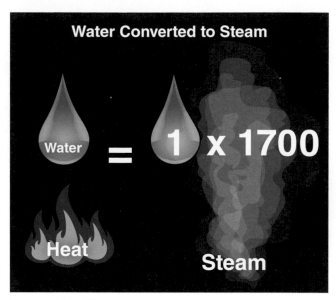

Figure 5.66 When converted to steam, water expands approximately 1,700 times its original volume.

While steam production is necessary for effective and efficient use of water as an extinguishing agent, care must be taken to apply the appropriate amount of water in the right place to achieve the desired effect. When steam is produced on contact with hot surfaces, such as burning fuel or walls and ceiling materials that are hotter than 212°F (100°C), water is vaporized into steam, adding to the total volume of the upper layer of hot smoke and fire gases. This creates a heat inversion as the volume increases and the room fills with the mixture of hot smoke, fire gases, and steam. That heated layer expands downward, making conditions uncomfortable or even dangerous for firefighters inside the room.

When water is introduced into the upper layer of hot smoke and fire gases, the water vaporizes, the hot gases are cooled, and the upper layer contracts toward the ceiling. Because the energy required to heat and vaporize water is much greater than that required to cool the hot gases, the temperature of the hot gases drops faster and farther than the temperature of the steam rises. In other words, products of combustion will cool down faster than steam can heat up when water is applied directly to the gases.

NOTE: Good nozzle control and coordination with tactical ventilation are necessary for effective, efficient, and safer fire stream operation and fire control.

 Effects of Stream Patterns on Vaporization at Ceiling Level

Both examples involve a fire in a 10 x 20 foot (3 m by 6 m) compartment with a 10-foot (3 m) ceiling, providing a total volume of 2,000 ft^3 (57 m^3). The hot layer of smoke and fire gases is 5 feet (1.5 m) deep and has an average temperature of 932°F (500°C).

Example 1: The nozzle operator uses a straight stream or narrow fog pattern to discharge sufficient water upward towards the ceiling to lower the temperature in the compartment to 392°F (200°C). The nozzle pattern causes most of the water to reach the ceiling. Only 10 percent of the water is vaporized in the hot upper layer. The remaining 90 percent is vaporized on contact with the hot ceiling surface. The volume of the upper layer will almost double, filling the room with hot smoke, fire gases, and steam.

Example 2: The nozzle operator uses a fog nozzle set on a wider pattern and applies the same volume of water as in Example 1 using short pulses of water fog, lowering the temperature in the compartment to 392°F (200°C). In this case, 40 percent of the water is vaporized in the upper layer of hot gases and 60 percent is vaporized on contact with the hot ceiling surface. This reaction results in a slight decrease in the volume of the upper layer comprised of hot smoke, fire gases, and steam.

Pressure Loss/Gain

To produce effective fire streams, fire brigade members should know the factors affecting pressure loss and gain. Friction loss and evaluation are two factors that affect pressure loss and gain in a fire stream. Pressure changes are possible due to friction loss in hose and appliances. A loss or gain in pressure may result due to elevation and the direction of water flow uphill or downhill.

Friction Loss

Friction loss is a fraction of total water pressure that is lost while forcing water through pipes, fittings, fire hose, and adapters. When water flows through these constricting spaces, the water molecules rub against the insides and slow down, reducing the pressure at the nozzle. The difference in pressure in a hoseline between a pumper and the nozzle (excluding pressure changes due to elevation differences) is the most common example of friction loss **(Figure 5.67)**.

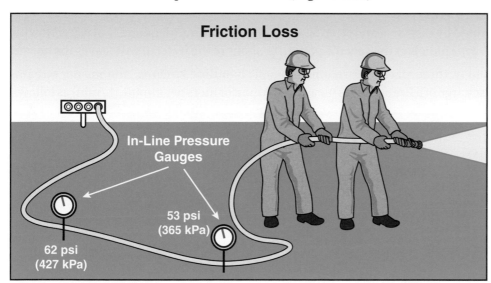

Figure 5.67 Illustrating the friction loss that occurs as water flows through a hoseline.

Certain characteristics of hose layouts, such as hose size and length of the hose lay, also affect friction loss. In general, the smaller the hose diameter and the longer the hose lay, the higher the friction loss at a given pressure and flow rate. For example, with a 1½-inch (38 mm) hose laid out over 200 feet (60 m) with 150 psi pump pressure, friction loss can significantly reduce the **gallons per minute (gpm)** flow at the nozzle from the expected rate.

The following conditions increase friction loss in fire hose:

- Rough linings in fire hose
- Sharp bends in hose
- Length of hose lay
- Damaged hose couplings
- Number of adapters
- Small hose diameter

Friction loss can be addressed and potentially overcome by addressing any of the factors above, whether separately or in combination. Two other ways to overcome friction loss include adding parallel hoselines and increasing pump pressure.

Elevation Loss/Gain

Elevation refers to the position of an object above or below ground level. In a fire fighting operation, elevation refers to the position of the nozzle in relation to the pumping apparatus, which is at ground level. Elevation pressure refers to a gain or loss in a hoseline caused by a change in elevation. When a nozzle is *above* the fire pump, there is a *pressure loss*. When the nozzle is *below* the pump, there is a *pressure gain* (**Figure 5.68**). These losses and gains occur because of gravity acting on the water.

Figure 5.68 Illustrating the concepts of pressure loss and pressure gain due to changes in elevation.

Fire Stream Patterns and Nozzles

Fire stream patterns are defined by their size and type. Size refers to the volume or quantity of water flowing from the nozzle per minute. *Type* indicates the specific pattern or shape of the water after it leaves the nozzle.

Fire streams are classified in three sizes: low-volume streams, handline streams, and master streams (**Figure 5.69**). The rate of discharge of a fire stream is measured in gpm or liters per minute (L/min) as follows:

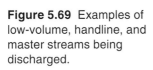

Figure 5.69 Examples of low-volume, handline, and master streams being discharged.

- **Low-volume stream** — Discharges less than 40 gpm (160 L/min). Typically supplied by ¾-inch (20 mm), 1-inch (25 mm), or 1½-inch (38 mm) hoselines.

- **Handline stream** — Supplied by 1½-to 3-inch (38 mm to 77 mm) hose, with flows from 40 to 350 gpm (160 L/min to 1 400 L/min). Nozzles with flows in excess of 350 gpm (1 400 L/min) are not recommended for handlines.

- **Master stream** — Discharges more than 350 gpm (1 400 L/min) and is fed by one or more 2½- or 3-inch (65 mm or 77 mm) hoselines or large-diameter hoselines connected to a master stream nozzle. Nozzle pressures of 80 to 100 psi (560 to 700 kPa) are common with master stream devices. Master streams are large-volume fire streams created by master stream appliances such as:

  - Apparatus-mounted **turrets** or **ladder pipes**.   - Fixed monitors

  - Quick attacks on pick-up trucks   - Trailer-mounted master stream devices

The nozzle's design and the water pressure at the nozzle determines the volume of water discharged. To be effective, a fire stream must deliver a volume of water sufficient to absorb heat faster than the fire generates it. If the heat-absorbing capability of a fire stream does not exceed the heat output from the fire, extinguishing the fire by cooling is impossible.

Fire Stream Patterns

The *type* of fire stream indicates a specific pattern or shape of the stream as it leaves the nozzle. In general, the pattern must be compact enough for the majority of the water to reach the burning material. Effective fire streams must meet or exceed the critical flow rate. They must also have sufficient reach to put water where it is needed.

To produce an effective fire stream, several factors are needed. All fire streams must have an agent (water), a pressuring device (pump), a means for the agent to reach the discharge device (hoseline), and a discharge device (nozzle).

The major types of fire stream patterns are solid, fog, straight, and broken **(Figure 5.70)**. The fire stream pattern may be any one of these in any size classification. The following sections more closely examine the characteristics of different types of fire streams.

Figure 5.70 Examples of the four major types of hose stream patterns.

Solid Streams. A solid stream pattern is produced from a fixed orifice, smooth bore nozzle. Smooth bore nozzles are designed to produce a stream as compact as possible with little shower or spray. A solid stream has the ability to reach areas that other streams might not reach. It can also penetrate and saturate burning materials or debris. Gravity, friction with air, and wind can affect the reach of a solid stream.

Characteristics of solid streams include:

- Has good reach and stream penetration
- Produces a stream at low nozzle pressure
- Produces less steam conversion
- Provides less heat absorption per gallon (liter)
- Has the potential to conduct electricity

> **CAUTION:** Do not use solid streams on energized electrical equipment.

The effective range of streams can be determined via observations and tests. Some qualities of an effective stream are:

- A stream that maintains continuity until it reaches the point where it loses its forward velocity (breakover) and falls into showers of spray that are easily blown away **(Figure 5.71)**.

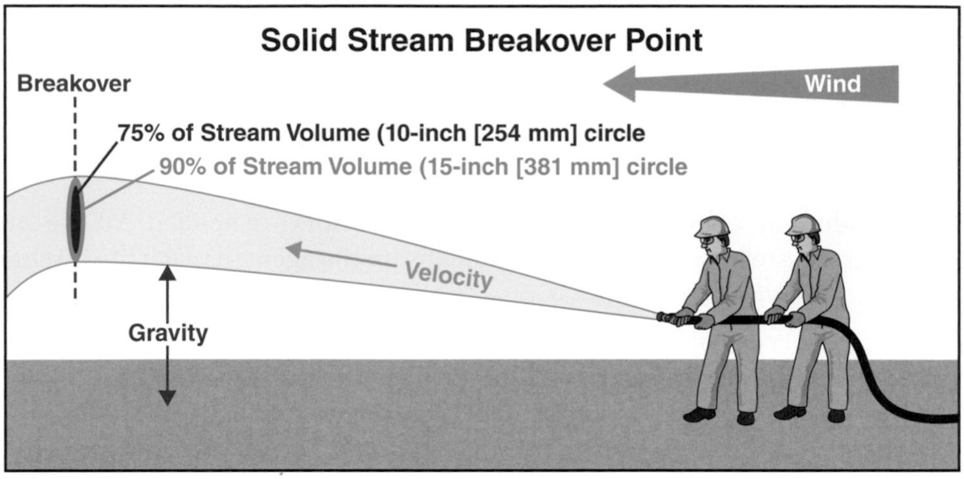

Figure 5.71 Illustrating the concept of the solid stream breakover point.

Solid Stream Breakover Point

Breakover

Wind

75% of Stream Volume (10-inch [254 mm] circle
90% of Stream Volume (15-inch [381 mm] circle

Velocity

Gravity

- A stream that is cohesive enough to maintain its original shape and attain the required height even in a light, gentle wind (breeze).

The performance of a solid stream depends on the velocity of the stream resulting from the pump pressure and the size of the nozzle orifice. A nozzle pressure (NP) of 50 psi (350 kPa) will produce fire streams from smooth bore nozzles with good reach and volume. If greater reach and volume are needed, the nozzle pressure may be increased to 65 psi (450 kPa). Above this pressure, the nozzle and hoseline will require additional fire brigade members to handle safely.

Straight Streams. A straight stream pattern is a semi-solid stream produced by a fog nozzle. The nozzle operator rotates the stream shaper on a fog nozzle until a straight stream is produced. Characteristics of straight stream patterns are similar to those of the solid stream although the straight stream is slightly less cohesive than a solid stream.

Fog Streams. A fog stream is a fine spray composed of tiny water droplets. Fog nozzles are used to produce fog streams and designed to permit adjustment of the tip to produce different fog-stream patterns. Water droplets, in either a shower or spray, are formed to expose the maximum water surface for heat absorption. The desired performance of a fog stream is characterized by the amount of heat that it absorbs and the rate by which the water is converted into steam or vapor.

Fog streams have the following characteristics:

- Patterns can be adjusted to suit the situation.
- Can be used for hydraulic ventilation, vapor dispersion, and crew protection.
- Reduce heat by exposing the maximum water surface for heat absorption.
- Cool the hot fire gas layer as well as hot surfaces.
- Have shorter reach or penetration than solid or straight fire streams.
- Are more affected by wind than are solid or straight fire streams.
- May disturb thermal layering in a room or compartment if applied incorrectly.
- May intensify the fire by pushing fresh air into the fire area if used incorrectly.

Fog streams range from narrow to wide angles (cones). A narrow-angle fog pattern (sometimes called a power cone) has the highest forward velocity and its reach varies in proportion to the pressure applied. A wide-angle fog pattern (sometimes called full fog) has less forward velocity and a shorter reach than

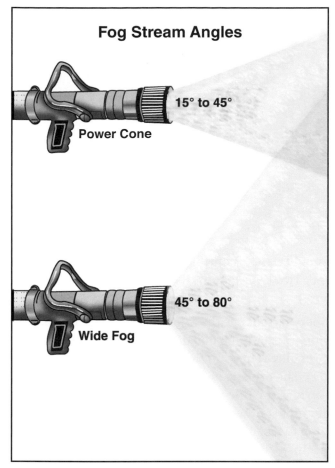

Fog Stream Angles

Power Cone

15° to 45°

Wide Fog

45° to 80°

Figure 5.72 Examples of a power cone pattern and a wide fog pattern.

other fog settings **(Figure 5.72)**. Like all fire streams, any fog pattern will have a maximum reach. The standard nozzle pressure for fog nozzles is 100 psi (700 kPa). Once the nozzle pressure has produced a fire stream with maximum reach, further increases in nozzle pressure have little effect on the stream, except to increase the volume.

Broken Streams. A broken stream pattern is a fire stream that has been broken into coarsely divided water droplets by specialized nozzles, such as cellar nozzles, piercing (penetrating) nozzles, and chimney nozzles. While a solid stream may become a broken stream past the breakover point, a true broken stream takes on that form as it leaves the discharge device. The effects of a broken stream can also be produced by deflecting solid or straight streams off a wall or ceiling so they break up over the fire. Broken streams are used to extinguish fires in attics, cocklofts, basements, and other confined spaces.

Broken streams have the following characteristics:

- Coarse droplets absorb more heat per gallon (liter) than a solid stream.

- Greater reach and penetration than a fog stream.

- May be effective on fires in confined spaces.

- May have sufficient continuity to conduct electricity.

- Stream may not reach some fires.

Fire Stream Limiting Factors. There are five limiting factors that affect the reach of a fire stream:

- **Gravity** — Gravity not only limits the vertical and horizontal distance the fire stream will travel, it also causes solid streams to separate and lose their compact shape.

- **Water velocity** — Effective forward velocity of the fire stream ranges from 60 to 120 feet per second (18.3 to 36.6 meters per second). Nozzle pressures of 25 to 100 psi (175 kPa to 700 kPa) generate this velocity.

- **Fire stream pattern** — Solid stream patterns have greater reach than straight, fog, or broken patterns.

- **Water droplet friction with air** — Air friction has greater effect on the multiple finely-formed water droplets in a fog stream than it does on the outer surfaces of a compact solid stream.

- **Wind** — Wind direction and speed can shorten the reach and deteriorate the shape of the fire stream. The negative effect is increased on fog streams.

Under ideal circumstances shown in mathematical models, the greatest horizontal reach for a fire stream is attained at 45 degrees from the horizontal plane. In actual operation, fire stream angles between 30 degrees and 34 degrees provide the maximum effective horizontal reach **(Figure 5.73, p. 194)**.

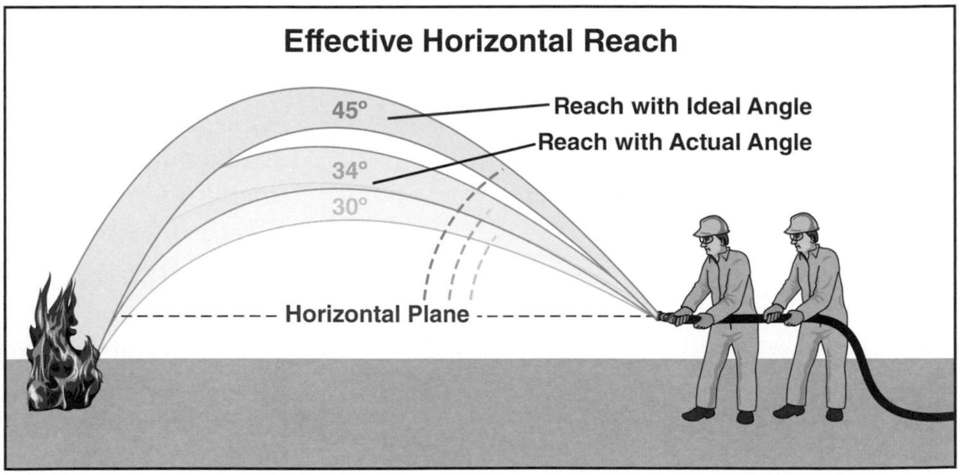

Effective Horizontal Reach

45°

34°

30°

─── Reach with Ideal Angle
─── Reach with Actual Angle

Horizontal Plane ─────────

Figure 5.73 During fire stream operations, the actual angle of greatest effectiveness is between 30 and 34 degrees.

Water-Flow Adjustment — Fire brigade members might want to control the rate of water flow through a fog nozzle, such as when the water supply is limited. Two types of nozzles provide this capability — manually adjustable and automatic (constant pressure):

- **Manually adjustable nozzles** — Fire brigade members can change the rate of discharge from a manually adjustable fog nozzle by rotating the selector ring — usually located directly behind the nozzle tip — to a specific gpm (L/min) setting. Each setting provides a constant flow rate as long as the operator maintains the proper nozzle pressure **(Figure 5.74)**. The brigade member has the choice of making flow-rate adjustments either before opening the nozzle or while water is flowing. Depending upon the size of the nozzle, the fire brigade member may adjust flow rates from 10 gpm to 250 gpm (40 L/min to 1 000 L/min) for handlines and from 300 gpm to 2,500 gpm (1 200 L/min to 10 000 L/min) for master streams. Most of these nozzles also have a "flush" setting to rinse debris from the nozzle.

NOTE: Be aware that some nozzles have a preset gpm ratings.

> **CAUTION:** Make adjustments to the flow rate in increments. Large, quick adjustments can cause an abrupt change in the reaction force of the hoseline that may throw a fire brigade member off balance.

Figure 5.74 A fire brigade member turning the discharge rate selector ring of a manually adjustable nozzle.

Figure 5.75 A fire brigade member adjusting the pattern selector of an automatic (constant-pressure) nozzle.

- **Automatic (constant-pressure) nozzles** — Constant-pressure nozzles automatically vary the rate of flow to maintain an effective nozzle pressure. Obviously, a certain minimum nozzle pressure is needed to maintain a good spray pattern **(Figure 5.75)**. With this type of nozzle, the nozzle operator can change the rate of flow by opening or closing the shutoff valve. Automatic nozzles allow the nozzle operator to deliver large quantities of water at constant operating pressures or to reduce the flow to allow for mobility while maintaining an effective discharge pattern.

Handling Fog Stream Nozzles. Although nozzle designs differ, the water pattern that the nozzle setting produces may affect the ease with which a particular nozzle is operated. Fire stream nozzles, in general, are not easy to control. If water travels at angles to the direct line of discharge, the reaction forces may be made to counterbalance each other and reduce the nozzle reaction. This balancing of forces is the reason a wide-angle fog pattern can be handled more easily than a straight-stream pattern.

Advantages:

- The discharge pattern of fog streams may be adjusted to suit the situation.

- Some fog-stream nozzles have adjustable settings to control the amount of water being used.

- Fog streams aid ventilation by entraining air into or out of the fire area.

- Fog streams dissipate heat by exposing the maximum water surface for heat absorption.

Disadvantages:

- Fog streams do not have the reach or penetrating power of solid streams.

- Fog streams are more susceptible to wind currents than are solid streams.

- Fog streams may create heat inversion and cause steam burns to fire brigade members when improperly used during interior attacks.

Using Water on Combustible Dust Fires. Some facilities generate large quantities of combustible dust **(Figure 5.76)**. If this dust ignites, water may be used as an extinguishing agent only if the materials in the dust are not water reactive. Water should be applied gently using a medium to wide-pattern with a low pressure nozzle. The stream should be lofted onto the burning materials from the greatest distance the stream will reach. This approach will reduce the risk of dispersing more of the dust into the air or introducing more air into the mixture.

Figure 5.76 Facilities like this saw mill generate large quantities of combustible dust. *Courtesy of Paul Pestel.*

Solid streams should only be used when greater reach is needed. If the area is still subject to the potential of explosion, fire brigade members can set up a master stream device while other streams protect the fire brigade members. The solid stream can then be left without an operator.

> **CAUTION:** Fire brigade members should avoid applying water to water-reactive materials. Applying water to such materials may cause a violent reaction.

Nozzles and Nozzle Control Valves

NFPA 1963, *Standard for Fire Hose Connections*, establishes two general categories of fire stream nozzles: straight tip nozzles and spray nozzles. For this manual, straight tip nozzles will be referred to as *smooth bore nozzles* and spray nozzles will be referred to as *fog nozzles*. Smooth bore and fog nozzles are used on handlines and on master stream appliances, such as fixed apparatus-mounted monitors, portable monitors, and elevated monitors mounted on aerial devices. Delivery devices for broken fire streams, not covered by the standard, can be used to apply water in confined spaces that attack hoselines cannot reach. Both categories of nozzles as well as the broken-stream delivery devices perform three main functions: controlling water flow, creating reach, and shaping the fire stream. The following sections describe the most commonly used types of nozzle and nozzle control valves.

Smooth Bore Nozzles. Smooth bore nozzles are designed so that the shape of the water in the nozzle is gradually reduced until it reaches a point a short distance from the orifice **(Figure 5.77)**. At this point, the nozzle becomes a smooth cylinder with a length between 1 to 1½ times its inside diameter. The purpose of this short, cylindrical section is to give the water its round shape before discharge.

NOTE: The smooth bore nozzle tip size should not be larger than one-half the diameter of the hose.

Characteristics of smooth bore nozzles:

- Operate at low nozzle pressures
- Are less prone to clogging with debris
- Can be used to apply compressed-air foam
- May allow hoselines to kink due to less pressure
- Do not allow for selection of different stream patterns

The velocity of the stream is a result of the nozzle pressure. This pressure and the size of the discharge opening determine the flow from a smooth bore nozzle. When smooth bore nozzles are used on handlines, they are usually operated at 50 psi (350 kPa) nozzle pressure. Most smooth bore master stream appliances are operated at 80 psi (560 kPa).

The flow rate from smooth bore nozzles depends on the velocity of the stream resulting from the pump pressure and the size of the nozzle orifice. Some smooth bore nozzles are equipped with a single-size tip for a single flow rate and others have stacked tips to provide varied flows. When

Figure 5.77 Three types of smooth bore nozzles. *Courtesy of Elkhart Brass Manufacturing Company, Inc., Task Force Tips, and Akron Brass Company.*

using nozzles equipped with a stacked tip, remove low-flow tips before placing the nozzle in operation if higher flows are required. Changing the flow rate requires that the nozzle be shut off and the tip changed. **Table 5.1** shows the flow rates available through various size tips at a constant pressure.

Fog Nozzles. Fog nozzles may be manually or automatically adjusted, resulting in straight stream, narrow-angle fog, and wide-angle fog patterns. Fog nozzles should be operated at their designed operating pressures. Characteristics of fog nozzles include:

Table 5.1 (Customary)
Flow in GPM from Various-Sized Solid Stream Nozzles

Nozzle Diameter in Inches

Nozzle Pressure in psi	1	1⅛	1¼	1⅜	1½	1⅝	1¾	1⅞	2	2¼
50	209	265	326	396	472	554	643	740	841	1065
55	219	277	342	415	495	581	674	765	881	1118
60	229	290	357	434	517	607	704	810	920	1168
65	239	301	372	451	537	631	732	843	958	1215
70	246	313	386	469	558	655	761	875	994	1260
75	256	324	399	485	578	678	787	905	1030	1305
80	264	335	413	500	596	700	813	935	1063	1347

Table 5.1 (Metric)
Flow in L/min from Various-Sized Solid Stream Nozzles

Nozzle Diameter in Millimeters

Nozzle Pressure in kPa	25	29	32	35	38	42	45	48	50	57
350	791	1 003	1 234	1 499	1 786	2 097	2 434	2 801	3 183	4 031
385	829	1 048	1 294	1 571	1 873	2 200	2 551	2 896	3 334	4 232
420	867	1 098	1 351	1 643	1 957	2 297	2 665	3 066	3 483	4 421
455	905	1 139	1 408	1 707	2 033	2 389	2 771	3 191	3 626	4 600
490	931	1 185	1 461	1 775	2 112	2 480	2 880	3 312	3 763	4 770
525	969	1 226	1 510	1 835	2 188	2 567	2 980	3 425	3 899	4 940
560	1 000	1 000	1 563	1 893	2 256	2 650	3 077	3 539	4 024	5 099

- Can have their discharge pattern adjusted.
- Can provide protection to firefighters with a wide fog pattern.
- Can provide exposure protection.
- Offer a variety of nozzle choices.
- Can apply certain types of foam.

There are four types of fog nozzles commonly used by the fire service (**Figure 5.78**):

Basic Fog Nozzle | **Constant Gallonage Fog Nozzle** | **Constant Pressure (Automatic) Fog Nozzle** | **Constant/Select Gallonage Fog Nozzle**

Figure 5.78 Examples of various types of fog nozzles. *Basic and constant gallonage fog nozzle pictures courtesy of Shad Cooper, Wyoming State Fire Marshal's Office.*

- **Basic fog nozzle** — An adjustable-pattern fog nozzle in which the rated discharge is delivered at a designated nozzle pressure and nozzle setting
- **Constant gallonage fog nozzle** — An adjustable-pattern fog nozzle that discharges a constant discharge rate throughout the range of patterns from a straight stream to a wide fog at a designed nozzle pressure
- **Constant pressure (automatic) fog nozzle** — An adjustable-pattern fog nozzle in which the pressure remains relatively constant through a range of discharge rates
- **Constant/select gallonage fog nozzle** — A constant discharge rate fog nozzle with a feature that allows manual adjustment of the orifice to affect a predetermined discharge rate while the nozzle is flowing

The rate of discharge from a manually adjustable fog nozzle can be changed by rotating the selector ring — usually located directly behind the nozzle tip — to a specific gpm (L/min) setting. Each setting provides a constant rate of flow as long as there is adequate nozzle pressure. The nozzle operator has the choice of making flow rate adjustments either before opening the nozzle or while water is flowing. Depending upon the size of the nozzle, the operator may adjust flow rates from 10 gpm to 250 gpm (40 L/min to 1 000 L/min) for handlines and from 350 gpm to 2,500 gpm (1 200 L/min to 10 000 L/min) for master streams. A specified minimum nozzle pressure is needed to maintain a good fog pattern. Most of these nozzles also have a "flush" setting to rinse debris from the nozzle.

Adjust the flow rate in small increments. Large, quick adjustments can cause an abrupt change in the reaction force of the hoseline and may throw firefighters off balance.

Constant-pressure fog nozzles automatically vary the rate of flow to maintain a reasonably constant nozzle pressure through a specified flow range. With this type of nozzle, the nozzle operator can change the rate of flow by opening or closing the shutoff valve. Automatic fog nozzles allow the nozzle operator to vary the flow rate while maintaining a consistent nozzle pressure.

Automatic fog nozzles for handlines are designed for the following flow rates:

- Low flows such as 10 gpm (40 L/min) to 125 gpm (500 L/min)
- Midrange flows such as 70 gpm (280 L/min) to 200 gpm (800 L/min)
- High flows such as 70 gpm (280 L/min) to 350 gpm (1 400 L/min)

Automatic master stream fog nozzles are typically designed to flow between 350 gpm (1 400 L/min) and 1,250 gpm (5 000 L/min). Large-diameter or multiple hoselines supply these nozzles, which could be directly connected to a fire pump by piping.

NOTE: Water flow adjustments in manual and automatic fog nozzles require close coordination between the nozzle operator, the company officer, and the pump operator.

Fog nozzles are designed to operate at a variety of nozzle pressures. The designed operating pressure for most fog nozzles is 100 psi (700 kPa). Nozzles with a designed operating pressure of 45, 50, or 75 psi (315, 350, or 525 kPa) are also available. Although these nozzles have less nozzle reaction compared to nozzles designed to operate at 100 psi (700 kPa), droplet size is much greater, fog pattern density is lower, and the fire stream has less velocity.

Broken-Stream Delivery Devices. A broken stream pattern can be used to extinguish fires in concealed spaces in basements, chimneys, attics, or other types of concealed spaces. The special nozzles that can be used to produce a broken stream pattern include **(Figure 5.79)**:

- **Piercing nozzles** — Used to access fires in concealed spaces. This nozzle can pierce material such as stucco, block, wood, and lightweight steel. The nozzle consists of a piercing tip, shaft, hose connection, and striking plate at the end. A nozzle control valve can be attached between the nozzle's hose connection and the supply hose. The nozzle is usually driven into place with a mallet, sledgehammer, or flathead axe.

Figure 5.79 Examples of a piercing nozzle, a Bresnan distributor nozzle, and a cellar nozzle. *Bresnan distributor photo courtesy of Shad Cooper, Wyoming State Fire Marshal's Office.*

- **Cellar nozzles** — Consist of a rotating head with multiple outlets that distribute water in a circular pattern. The nozzle may be supplied by a 1½-inch (38 mm) or 2½-inch (65 mm) supply hose with a control valve located one section of hose from the nozzle. The nozzle and hose are lowered into the cellar, attic, cockloft, or confined space through a hole cut in the overhead surface. The Bresnan distributor and the Rockwood cellar pipe are two commonly used cellar nozzles.

Electrically Safe Nozzles. A type of nozzle specifically designed to be used on fires involving Class C, electrically energized components. Electrically safe nozzles produce a fog pattern that is safe to use at 10 feet (3 m) or more from the energized equipment. Fire brigade members must be thoroughly familiar with the specific electrically safe nozzle(s) their organization has and trained on how to use the nozzle(s) safely and effectively. A 10-degree fog pattern is the tightest pattern most electrically safe nozzles will make. It is recommended that fire brigade members approach no closer than 10 feet (3 m) when using 1½ inch (38 mm) hose and no closer than 20 feet (6 m) when using 2½ inch (65 mm) or larger hose. Fire brigade members should remember that the water runoff is never electricity safe. When using electrically safe nozzles, fire brigade members should follow the manufacturer's recommendations.

Nozzle Control Valves. Nozzle control or shutoff valves enable the nozzle operator to start, stop, increase, or decrease the flow of water while maintaining effective control of the nozzle. These valves allow the operator to open the nozzle slowly, to control the nozzle as the reaction increases, and to close it slowly to prevent water hammer. There are three main types of nozzle control valves found on smooth bore, fog nozzles, and broken-stream delivery devices **(Figure 5.80)**:

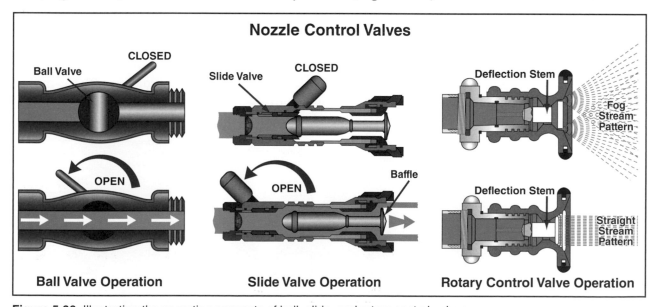

Figure 5.80 Illustrating the operating concepts of ball, slide, and rotary control valves.

- **Ball Valve** — Ball valves, the most common nozzle control valves, provide effective nozzle control with a minimum of effort. The ball, perforated by a smooth waterway, is suspended from both sides of the nozzle body and sealed against a seat. The ball can be rotated up to 90 degrees by moving the valve handle or bale backward to open it and forward to close it. With the valve in the closed position, the waterway is perpendicular to the nozzle body, blocking the flow of water through the nozzle. With the valve in the open position, the waterway is in line with the axis of the nozzle, allowing water to flow through it. Although the nozzle will operate in any position between fully closed and fully open, operating it with the valve in the fully open position gives maximum flow and performance. When a ball valve is used with a smooth bore nozzle, a partially open valve will cause turbulence that may affect the quality of the solid stream.

- **Slide Valve** — The cylindrical slide valve control seats a movable cylinder against a shaped cone to turn off the flow of water. When the shutoff handle is in the forward position, the cylinder is closed, preventing water flow past the shaped cone. As the handle is pulled back, the cylinder slides open, permitting water to flow through the nozzle without creating turbulence.

- **Rotary Control Valve** — Rotary control valves are found only on rotary control fog nozzles. They consist of an exterior barrel guided by a screw that moves the exterior barrel forward or backward, rotating around an interior barrel. Rotary control valves also control the discharge pattern of the stream. This type of nozzle is commonly found in standpipe cabinets attached to occupant-use hoselines.

Nozzle Terminology

Many terms are used to describe nozzle used by facility fire brigades. Some fire brigades may also use terms, such as:

NFPA Terms

- Straight tip nozzle
- Spray nozzle

Alternate Terms

- Smooth bore nozzle
- Solid bore nozzle
- Solid stream nozzle
- Combination nozzle
- Fog nozzle
- Adjustable fog nozzle

Maintenance of Nozzles

Nozzles should be inspected after each use and at least annually to ensure they are in proper working condition. Basic maintenance, care, and cleaning should be performed in accordance with the manufacturer's recommendations. Qualified maintenance technicians should perform technical nozzle maintenance. Inspections include the following actions **(Figure 5.81)**:

Figure 5.81 A fire brigade member inspecting a fog nozzle.

External Damage   **Ease of Operation**   **Missing Teeth**

- Inspect the swivel gasket for damage or wear. Replace worn or missing gaskets.
- Look for external damage to the nozzle body, coupling, and tip.
- Look for internal damage and debris.
- Check for ease of operation of the nozzle parts.
- Ensure that the pistol grip (if applicable) is secured to the nozzle.
- Ensure that all parts are in place and in good condition.
- Check for missing teeth on fog nozzle rings.
- Ensure spinning rings on fog nozzles move freely, if so equipped.

  General nozzle care includes:

- Thoroughly cleaning nozzles after each use with soap and water using a soft bristle brush.
- Following the manufacturer's recommendations for cleaning and lubricating any moving parts that are sticking.
- Storing nozzle with the control valve bale in the closed position.
- Never dropping or dragging nozzles.
- Using the flush setting on fog nozzles to remove any internal debris. If debris remains, shut off the water supply, remove the nozzle, and physically remove the debris.

Operating Nozzles

Because of the differing designs of handline nozzles, each one handles somewhat differently when operated at the recommended pressure. Variable pattern nozzles may also handle differently at different settings. Handline nozzles are not always easy to control at or above standard operating pressures. The following sections discuss considerations while handling common types of nozzles.

Smooth Bore Nozzle Operation

When water flows from a smooth bore nozzle, it creates force in the direction of the stream and equal force in the opposite direction. The force in the opposite direction pushes back on the nozzle operator. The velocity, flow rate, and discharge pattern of the stream causes this nozzle reaction. The reaction acts against both the nozzle and the curves in the hoseline, sometimes making the nozzle difficult to handle. Increasing the nozzle discharge pressure and flow rate increases nozzle reaction.

The operator should control the nozzle as follows:

- Cradle the hoseline under one arm while holding the nozzle or nozzle pistol grip in one hand.
- Pull back slowly on the bale with the other hand to open the nozzle.
- As the action increases, lean forward with legs apart, one foot forward, weight evenly distributed on both feet.

During interior operation, the nozzle can be operated in a similar fashion while kneeling on one knee. One fire brigade member can usually operate a smooth bore nozzle on a 1½-inch (38 mm) or smaller hoseline. Hoselines that are 1¾ (45 mm) and larger require additional fire brigade members to overcome the reaction and maneuver the hoseline.

Fog Nozzle Operation

The reaction that a fog nozzle causes will vary depending on the setting of the fog nozzle. When the fog nozzle is set on straight stream or narrow stream pattern, the reaction is similar to that of a smooth bore nozzle. As the fog pattern widens, the reaction decreases, making the nozzle easier to handle.

Handling the fog nozzle is the same as that of the smooth bore nozzle. Information on operating hoselines during fire attack is included in Chapter 8, Initial Fire Fighting Operations and in later chapters.

Operating Master Stream Devices

Master streams are usually deployed in situations where the fire is beyond the effectiveness of handlines or there is a need for fire streams in areas that are unsafe for fire brigade members. The four main uses for a master stream are as follows:

- Direct fire attack
- Indirect fire attack
- Supplementation of handlines that are already attacking the fire from the exterior
- Exposure protection

Master streams can have an effect on search and rescue, ventilation, and property conservation. Master streams should not be operated in occupied structures. There should also be consideration for the volume of water being applied. The high volume of water that master streams deliver could cause structural collapse if the structure is incapable of supporting the additional weight.

> **WARNING:** Do not pull the master stream device's twist-lock or elevation safety stop pins or activate overrides while water is flowing. This action can cause the monitor to separate from its base or operate in an unstable manner. Fire service personnel have been injured and killed by making this mistake.

Figure 5.82 The fire brigade member can adjust the stream from this master stream device up, down, and to the right or left.

Master stream devices must be properly positioned to apply an effective stream on a fire, particularly when using a fog nozzle because fog streams do not have the stream reach and penetration of solid streams. While a master stream nozzle can be adjusted up and down and right and left, it must be shut down before it can be relocated **(Figure 5.82)**. Moving a master stream device can be a time-consuming and labor-intensive process, causing the device to be out of operation for a period of time.

A consideration for master stream placement is the angle at which the stream enters the structure. Fire brigade members should aim the stream so that it enters the structure at an upward angle, causing it to deflect off the ceiling or other overhead objects. This angle makes the stream diffuse into smaller droplets that rain down on the fire, providing maximum extinguishing effectiveness. Streams that enter the opening at an angle that is horizontal or at a lower angle are not as effective.

Finally, place the master stream device in a location that allows the stream to cover the most surface area of the building, especially where there is a large volume of fire and a limited number of master stream devices. Doing so allows fire brigade members to change the direction of the stream and to direct it into more than one opening if necessary.

A master stream device can provide effective exposure protection to other structures. There are two approaches for providing exposure protection. The first and most effective approach is to direct the stream at the structure's surface that faces the fire. The stream should strike the surface and run down it. If the surface is wide, multiple devices can be used or one unit can sweep the face and keep it wet. The second approach is to create a water curtain between the fire and the exposure. This approach can be effective if the exposure is not a single surface, such as densely placed trees. The water curtain will stop the radiated heat as long as the water drops are compact.

Master stream devices flow a minimum of 350 gpm (1 400 L/min), which can mean high friction loss in supply hose. Therefore, except for small quick-attack devices that are designed to operate from a single 2½-inch (65 mm) line, it is not practical to supply master stream appliances with anything less than two 2½-inch (65 mm) hoselines because of the high friction loss in the supply hose. Conventional master stream devices may be temporarily supplied by one 2½-inch (65 mm) line while adding additional hoselines. When greater quantities of water are required, a third 2½-inch (65 mm) or large-diameter supply line will be required. Some master stream devices are equipped to handle a large-diameter (4-inch [100 mm] or larger) supply line.

The operation of master stream devices consumes large volumes of water that accumulate inside structures when master streams are directed into buildings. This water accumulates on floors, and the building contents may absorb some of this water as well. Both accumulation and absorption of water add weight that affects structural integrity and increases the potential for structural collapse during overhaul and fire investigation activities.

CAUTION: Added water weight from master stream operations increases the potential for structural collapse.

Because master streams are used primarily in defensive operations, fire brigade members may need to shut down other handlines in order to maintain effective fire streams from the master stream devices. The IC will make the decision on joint handline and master stream operations based on your local SOPs.

Aside from apparatus-mounted deck guns, deploying a master stream device and the necessary water supply hoselines will usually require a minimum of two fire brigade members, although more firefighters can accomplish it faster. Once a device is in place, one firefighter can operate it. When water is flowing, at least one fire brigade member should be stationed at the master stream device at all times unless the device is being used in a hazardous position such as close to a fire-weakened wall or near a liquid propane gas (LPG) tank. The fire brigade member tending the device can change the direction of the stream when required and prevent pressure in hoselines from moving the device.

If the situation is too dangerous to have fire brigade members stationed at the device, it can be securely anchored in position. Once the device is deployed, hoselines are attached and charged, and the desired stream is developed, fire brigade members can be withdrawn to a safe distance. If the device starts to move, the pump operator can decrease the pressure at the apparatus to stop any movement.

Elevated master stream devices are used to apply water to the upper stories of multistory buildings, either as a direct fire attack or as a water supply for handlines. They can also provide exposure protection to endangered structures. A number of different types of aerial apparatus can deliver elevated master streams, most commonly **quintuple combination pumpers (quints)**, aerial ladders, aerial platforms, and water towers. Under a variety of circumstances, you may be assigned to operate an elevated master stream device or to support such an operation.

Chapter Review

1. What is the difference between gravity and direct pumping systems?

2. Name and describe the different types of fire hydrants.

3. What are three hose tools that are used to protect, move, handle, store, or connect hose?

4. What are the three types of hose rolls?

5. Name and describe the different techniques for advancing hoseline.

6. What is vaporization and how does it affect extinguishment?

7. What conditions can increase friction loss in fire hose?

8. What are the advantages of different types of fire streams?

9. In what types of situations would master streams be deployed?

Discussion Question

1. What type of nozzles are often used in your facilities?

Key Terms

Attack Line — Hoseline connected to a pump discharge of a fire apparatus ready for use in attacking a fire; may or may not be preconnected. In contrast, supply lines are connected to a water supply with a pump. *Also called* Attack Hose *or* Attack Hose Line.

Bale — The handle for a nozzle's control valve. It is moved towards the nozzle operator to open the nozzle's control valve and away from the nozzle operator to close the valve.

Booster Hose — Non-collapsible rubber-covered, rubber-lined hose usually wound on a reel and mounted somewhere on an engine or water tender; used for the initial attack and extinguishment of incipient and smoldering fires. This hose is most commonly found in ½-, ¾-, and 1-inch (13 mm, 19 mm, and 25 mm) diameters and is used for extinguishing low-intensity fires and mop-up. *Also known as* Booster Line, Hard Line, *and* Red Line.

Butterfly Valve — Control valve that uses a flat circular plate in a pipe that rotates 90 degrees across the cross section of the pipe to control the flow of water.

Circulating Feed — Fire hydrant that receives water from two or more directions.

Circulating Hydrant — Fire hydrant that is located on a secondary feeder or distributor main that receives water from two directions.

Combination System — Water supply system that is a combination of both gravity and direct pumping systems. It is the most common type of municipal water supply system.

Coupling — Fitting permanently attached to the end of a hose; used to connect two hoselines together, or to connect a hoseline to a device such as a nozzle, appliance, discharge valve, or hydrant.

Dead-End Hydrant — Fire hydrant located on a dead-end main that receives water from only one direction.

Direct Pumping System — Water supply system supplied directly by a system of pumps rather than elevated storage tanks.

Draft — Process of acquiring water from a static source and transferring it into a pump that is above the source's level; atmospheric pressure on the water surface forces the water into the pump where a partial vacuum was created.

Dry Hydrant — Permanently installed pipe that has pumper suction connections installed at static water sources to speed drafting operations.

Dump Site — Location at which tankers/tenders offload their contents during a water shuttle operation.

Environmental Protection Agency (EPA) — U.S. federal regulatory agency designed to protect the air, water, and soil from contamination; responsible for researching and setting national standards for a variety of environmental programs.

Fill Site — Location at which tankers/tenders will be loaded during a water shuttle operation.

Fire Department Connection (FDC) — Point at which the fire department can connect into a sprinkler or standpipe system to boost the water pressure and flow in the system. This connection consists of a clappered siamese with two or more 2½-inch (65 mm) intakes or one large-diameter (4-inch [100 mm] or larger) intake. *Also known as* Fire Department Sprinkler Connection.

Fire Hydrant — Upright metal casing that is connected to a water supply system and is equipped with one or more valved outlets to which a hoseline or pumper may be connected to supply water for fire fighting operations. *Also known as* Hydrant.

Flow Pressure — Pressure created by the rate of flow or velocity of water coming from a discharge opening. *Also known as* Plug Pressure.

Forward Hose Lay — Process where hose is deployed from the water source to the incident.

Friction Loss — That part of the total pressure lost as water moves through a hose or piping system; caused by water turbulence and the roughness of interior surfaces of hose or pipe.

Gallons per Minute (GPM) — Unit of volume measurement used for water movement.

Gaskets — Rubber seals or packings used in joints and couplings to prevent the escape or inflow of fluids (liquids and gases).

Gate Valve — Control valve with a solid plate operated by a handle and screw mechanism. Rotating the handle moves the plate into or out of the waterway. *See* Butterfly Valve.

Gravity System — Water supply system that relies entirely on the force of gravity to create pressure and cause water to flow through the system. The water supply, which is often an elevated tank, is at a higher level than the system.

Grid System — Water supply system that utilizes lateral feeders for improved distribution.

Hose Bed — Main hose-carrying area of a pumper or other piece of apparatus designed for carrying hose. *Also known as* Hose Body.

Hose Box — Free standing protective enclosure that often contains a hydrant, fire hose, nozzles, and hose tools used for incipient fire fighting. *Also known as* Hose House.

Hose Cabinet — Recessed wall cabinet that contains a wall hydrant and preconnected fire hose for incipient fire fighting. *Also known as* Hose Rack.

Hydrant Manifold — A type of hydrant equipped with multiple discharges that is commonly found in or at industrial facilities.

Hydrant Wrench — Specially designed tool used to open or close a hydrant and to remove hydrant caps.

Jet Siphon — Section of pipe or hard suction hose with a 1-inch (25 mm) discharge line inside that bolsters the flow of water through the tube. The jet siphon is used between portable tanks to maintain a maximum amount of water in the tank from which the pumper is drafting.

Ladder Pipe — Master stream nozzle mounted on an aerial ladder.

Loop System — Water main arranged in a complete circuit so that water will be supplied to a given point from more than one direction. *Also known as* Belt System, Circle System, *or* Circulating System.

Master Stream Device — Manifold device and nozzle capable of delivering a water stream of 350 gpm (1 325 L/min) or more and is usually supplied by combining two or more hoselines into the device.

Mobile Water Supply Apparatus — Fire apparatus with a water tank of 1,000 gallons (3 785 L) or larger whose primary purpose is transporting water; may also carry a pump, some hose, and other equipment. *Also known as* Tanker *or* Tender.

Nozzle — Appliance on the discharge end of a hoseline that forms a fire stream of definite shape, volume, and direction.

Nozzle Operator — Individual assigned to operate a fire department nozzle. *Also known as* Nozzleperson *or* Nozzleman.

Outside Stem and Yoke (OS&Y) Valve — Outside stem and yoke valve; a type of control valve for a sprinkler system in which the position of the center screw indicates whether the valve is open or closed. *Also known as* Outside Screw *and* Yoke Valve.

Portable Tank — Collapsible storage tank used during a relay or shuttle operation to hold water from water tanks or hydrants; this water can then be used to supply attack apparatus. *Also known as* Catch Basin, Fold-a-Tank, Porta-Tank, *or* Portable Basin.

Post Indicator Valve (PIV) — Type of valve used to control underground water mains that provides a visual means for indicating "open" or "shut" positions; found on the supply main of installed fire protection systems. The operating stem of the valve extends above ground through a "post," and a visual means is provided at the top of the post for indicating "open" or "shut."

Potable Water — Filtered, purified, or treated water that can be used for drink or food preparation without risk of health problems.

Quintuple Combination Pumper (Quint) — Apparatus that serves as an engine and as a ladder truck; equipped with a fire pump, water tank, ground ladders, hose bed, and aerial device.

Relay Pumping Operation — Using two or more pumpers to move water over a long distance by operating them in series; water discharged from one pumper flows through hoses to the inlet of the next pumper, and is then pumped to the next pumper in line. *Also known as* Relay Pumping.

Residual Pressure — Pressure measured at the hydrant to which a pressure gauge is attached while water is flowing from one or more other hydrants during a hydrant flow test. It represents the pressure remaining in the water supply system while the test water is flowing and is that part of the total pressure that is not used to overcome friction or gravity while forcing water through fire hose, pipe, fittings, and adapters.

Single-Jacket Hose — Type of hose construction consisting of one woven jacket; usually lined with an inner rubber tube.

Soft Sleeve Hose — Large diameter, collapsible piece of hose used to connect a fire pump to a pressurized water supply source; sometimes incorrectly referred to as *soft suction hose.*

Spanner Wrench — Small tool primarily used to tighten or loosen hose couplings; can also be used as a prying tool or a gas key. *Also called* Spanners.

Standpipe/High-Rise Pack — Special, preassembled kit containing hose, adapters, nozzle, and spanner wrenches for use during standpipe or high-rise operations.

Standpipe System — Wet or dry system of pipes in a large single-story or multistory building, with fire hose outlets installed in different areas or on different levels of a building to be used by firefighters and/or building occupants. This system is used to provide for the quick deployment of hoselines during fire fighting operations.

Static Pressure — Pressure at a given point in a water system when no testing or fire protection water is flowing.

Static Water Source — Body of water that is not under pressure (other than atmospheric) or in a supply piping system, and must be drafted from in order to be used. Static sources include ponds, lakes, rivers, and wells.

Suction Hose — Intake hose that connects pumping apparatus or portable pump to a water source.

Supply Line — Hoseline connecting a water supply with a pump. In contrast, an attack line is connected to a pump discharge of a fire apparatus ready for use in attacking a fire and may or may not be preconnected. Also called *Supply Line* or *Supply Hose Line.*

Turret — Large, preplumbed master stream appliance connected directly to a pump that is mounted on a pumper, a trailer, and some airport rescue and fire fighting apparatus, and is capable of sweeping from side to side and designed to deliver large volumes of foam or water. *Also known as* Deck Gun, Deck Pipe, *or* Turret Pipe.

Water Hammer — Force created by the rapid deceleration of water, causing a violent increase in pressure that can be powerful enough to rupture piping or damage fixtures. Generally results from closing a valve or nozzle too quickly.

Water Main — Principal pipe in a system of pipes for conveying water, especially one installed underground.

Water Shuttle Operation — Method of water supply by which mobile water supply apparatus continuously transport water between a fill site and the dump site located near the emergency scene.

Water Supply — Any source of water available for use in fire fighting operations.

Skill Sheet List

The following skill sheets should be used to evaluate the skills described in this chapter:

NOTE: Students should wear the PPE appropriate to the NFPA 1081 level (Incipient, Advanced Exterior, Interior Structural, etc...) being evaluated.

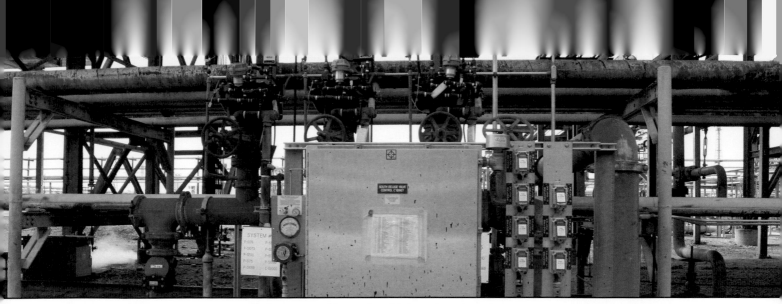

Incipient Facility Fire Brigade Member

Chapter Contents

JPRs addressed in this chapter

This chapter provides information that addresses the following job performance requirements of NFPA 1081, *Standard for Facility Fire Brigade Member Professional Qualifications (2018)*.

4.2.2	4.3.4
4.3.2	4.3.5

Learning Objectives

1. Identify the basic components of fire detection systems.

2. Describe the types of fire alarm systems.

3. List the types of fixed fire extinguishing systems. [4.2.2, 4.3.2]

4. Describe the components of sprinkler systems. [4.2.2, 4.3.2]

5. Identify the types of sprinkler systems. [4.2.2, 4.3.2]

6. Describe the methods of activation and safety precautions for sprinkler systems. [4.2.2, 4.3.2]

7. Explain fire brigade support responsibilities when using sprinkler systems. [4.2.2, 4.3.2]

8. Describe the types of special extinguishing systems. [4.2.2, 4.3.2]

9. Describe the types, components, and uses of standpipe systems. [4.2.2, 4.3.4]

10. Identify the importance and documents of system inspection reports. [4.3.5]

Chapter 6

Fire Protection, Detection, and Suppression Systems

Key components of any industrial facility's fire protection program are the fire detection and suppression systems found at the site. The early detection of a fire and the signaling of an appropriate alarm remain the most significant factors in preventing large losses. Suppression systems, such as automatic sprinkler, carbon dioxide (CO_2), dry chemical, and clean agent (halons and halocarbons) systems, can extinguish most fires in the early stages.

Fire brigade members must be trained in the function and operation of fire protection, detection, and suppression systems at their facilities. This chapter covers:

- Fire detection systems
- Special extinguishing systems
- Fixed fire extinguishing systems
- Standpipe systems
- Sprinkler systems
- System inspection records

Fire Detection Systems

Fire brigade members must be able to recognize and interpret fire alarm system conditions during an emergency. To accomplish this, a fire brigade member should understand these systems and how they function to:

- Detect the presence of fire or products of combustion.
- Notify building occupants to escape in the event of a fire.
- Summon organized assistance to initiate or assist in fire control activities.
- Initiate fire control and suppression systems and sounding an alarm.
- Supervise fire control and suppression systems to maintain operational .
- Operate ventilation systems to allow smoke and other products of combustion to escape.
- Initiate auxiliary functions involving environmental, utility, and process controls, including control of elevators.

Basic System Components

Several components that make up a typical alarm system include the:

Figure 6.1 This fire alarm control unit controls and monitors the fire alarm system in an industrial facility.

- **Fire alarm control unit (FACU)** — The FACU contains the electronics that control and monitor the fire alarm system. It receives signals from alarm initiating devices, processes the signals, and produces output signals **(Figure 6.1)**.

- **Power supplies** — Primary and secondary power supply alarm systems. The building's electrical supply usually supplies primary power. If the primary power supply gets interrupted due to a loss of power, a trouble signal should be indicated on the FACU. A secondary power supply must also be provided for the system to ensure that the system will operate if the primary system fails. Secondary power sources can include batteries with chargers and auxiliary generators **(Figure 6.2)**.

Figure 6.2 FACUs require primary and secondary power supplies. Some FACUs rely on generators instead of batteries for their secondary power supply.

- **Initiating devices** — Initiating devices may be manually operated (pull stations) or automatic (smoke and/or heat detectors). Automatic devices sense the presence of products of combustion or other hazardous conditions and send a signal to the FACU **(Figure 6.3)**.

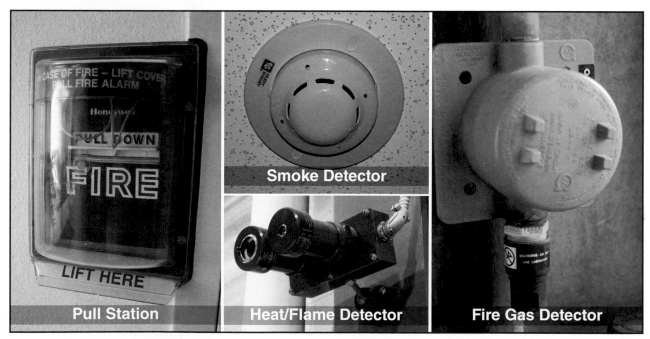

Figure 6.3 Examples of four types of fire alarm system initiating devices.

- **Manually operated pull stations** — Devices placed at strategic locations within facilities to allow facility workers to manually initiate the fire signaling system by pulling a lever.

- **Smoke detectors** — Devices designed to detect the products of combustion found in smoke.

— **Heat detectors** — Devices designed to recognize a change of temperature that a fire causes within the protected area.

— **Flame detectors** — Devices that detect light in the ultraviolet wave spectrum (UV detectors), in the infrared wave spectrum (IR detectors), or in both.

— **Fire gas detectors** — Devices that monitor the levels of carbon dioxide and carbon monoxide within the protected area.

— **Combination detectors** — Devices that combine the various detection systems into single devices, such as heat/smoke detectors and smoke/fire gas detectors.

— **Very Early Smoke Detection Appliance (VESDA)** - Devices that draw air through a network of pipes to detect smoke. VESDA systems monitor the atmosphere within production, labs, computer/server room, or any area where a potential exists for considerable financial loss from fire or activation of a suppression system. If a VESDA detects an atmosphere with smoke or particulate contamination, it transmits an alarm signal. These signals are sent to an alarm monitoring center where they are continually monitored.

Figure 6.4 Two of the most common fire alarms are the audible alarm bell (top) and the visual flashing strobe (bottom).

- **Notification appliances** — Once an initiating device sends a signal to the FACP, the control unit processes the signal and activates local and remote notification appliances. Notification appliances are categorized as follows **(Figure 6.4)**:

  — **Audible** — Approved sounding devices, such as horns, bells, or speakers, that indicate a fire or emergency

  — **Visual** — Approved lighting devices, such as strobes or flashing lights, that indicate a fire or emergency condition

  — **Textual** — Visual text or symbols indicating a fire or emergency condition

  — **Tactile** — Indication of a fire or emergency condition through sense of touch or vibration

- **Auxiliary services** — Devices designed to perform the following special functions

  — Shut down or exhaust the heating, ventilation, and air-conditioning (HVAC) system for smoke control.

  — Close smoke and/or fire doors and dampers.

  — Pressurize stairwells for evacuation purposes.

  — Override control of elevators and prevent them from opening on the fire floor.

  — Automatically return the elevator to the main floor.

— Operate heat and smoke vents.

— Activate special fire extinguishing systems, such as preaction and deluge sprinkler systems, or a variety of fixed extinguishing agents.

— Monitor certain aspects of the fire pump, pump driver, and generator.

— Shut down processes or equipment.

Types of Fire Alarm Systems

There are three broad categories of fire alarm systems: protected premises (local), auxiliary fire alarm, and supervisory station alarm systems. The following sections describe these categories and the types of systems within them.

Protected Premises (Local) Systems

Protected premise fire alarm systems, also called *local alarm systems*, provide notification only to building occupants **(Figure 6.5)**. There are no provisions for automatic off-site reporting. Manual or automatic initiating devices may be used to activate the system. A local system may be capable of annunciating a supervisory or trouble condition. The three basic types of local alarm systems include:

- **Noncoded** — When an alarm-initiating device sends a signal to the FACU, all of the alarm-signaling devices operate simultaneously.

- **Zoned/annunciated** — This system enables emergency responders to identify the general location (zone) of alarm device activation on an annunciator panel screen, FACU, or a computer printout.

- **Addressable** — Fire brigade members or building personnel responding to the alarm can use the system to pinpoint the specific device that has been activated.

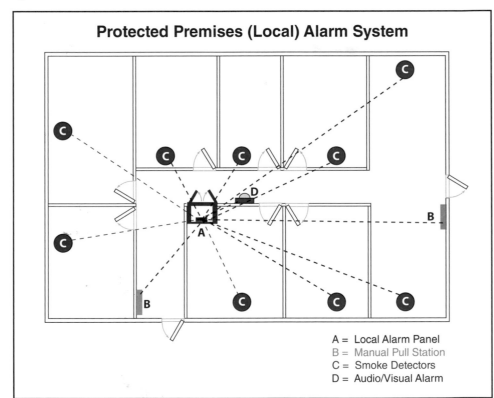

Figure 6.5 Illustrating the layout of a protected premises (local) alarm system.

Protected Premises (Local) Alarm System

A = Local Alarm Panel
B = Manual Pull Station
C = Smoke Detectors
D = Audio/Visual Alarm

Auxiliary Fire Alarm Systems

Auxiliary alarm systems are usually connected to a municipal fire alarm system. Alarms are transmitted over this system to a public fire telecommunications center where the appropriate response agencies are selected and dispatched to the alarm. There are two types of auxiliary alarm systems: local energy systems and shunt systems.

- **Local energy system** — This type of system has its own power. In these systems, initiating devices can be activated even when the power supply to the municipal system is interrupted. Interruption may result in the alarm only sounding locally and not being transmitted to a fire department telecommunications center.

- **Shunt system** — This is a type of system in which the municipal alarm circuit extends into the protected property. When a manual or automatic alarm is initiated on the premises, the alarm is instantly transmitted to the alarm center over the municipal system.

Supervising Station Alarm Systems

These systems continuously monitor remote locations to report supervisory, trouble, or alarm signals to the appropriate authorities. Types of supervising station systems include:

- **Proprietary alarm systems** — These systems protect large commercial and industrial buildings, high-rise structures, and groups of commonly owned facilities. Each building or area is wired into a common receiving point the facility owner operates **(Figure 6.6)**.

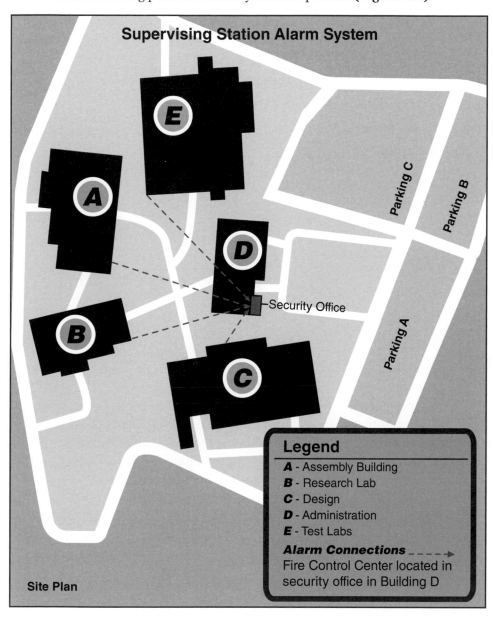

Figure 6.6 Illustrating the layout of a proprietary alarm system.

- **Central station systems** — These systems are monitored by contracted services at a central station. Employees at a central station relay information to local emergency services and occupancy representatives.

- **Remote receiving systems** — These systems connect to the emergency services telecommunications center usually using a telephone or a dedicated radio frequency.

- **Emergency voice/alarm communications systems** — These supplementary systems may be placed in a facility in addition to one of the other types of systems previously discussed. These systems communicate detailed information to facility personnel and facility fire brigade members in the facility. They may be stand-alone systems or integrated into the overall fire detection and signaling system. Occupant notification must be part of the system.

Fixed Fire Extinguishing Systems

NFPA 1081 (2018): 4.2.2, 4.3.2

Fire brigade members should be familiar with fixed fire extinguishing systems in their facility. They should be able to describe each system, how it is activated, the safety precautions that apply when the system actuates, how to support the system, and how to reset it after an incident. The following text describes fixed fire extinguishing systems and where and why they are used. The objectives of this text are to:

- Provide a basic overview of systems and describe how they operate.
- Identify how fire brigade members can support these systems.
- Identify safety issues related to these systems.

    Fixed fire extinguishing systems include:

- Sprinklers
- Water-mist
- Carbon dioxide (CO_2)
- Dry chemical
- Foam
- Wet chemical
- Clean agent

Sprinkler Systems

NFPA 1081 (2018): 4.2.2, 4.3.2

An automatic sprinkler system is an integrated system of pipes, sprinklers (sometimes called sprinkler heads), and control valves designed to automatically discharge sufficient water or extinguishing agent to extinguish a fire or prevent its spread until fire brigade members arrive. Sprinklers are arranged so that they will distribute enough water or extinguishing agent in the protected area. Sprinklers can either extend from exposed pipes or protrude through the ceiling or walls from hidden pipes.

According to National Fire Protection Association (NFPA) 13, there are two general types of sprinkler coverage: full and partial sprinkler coverage. A full coverage sprinkler system protects the entire building. A partial sprinkler system protects only certain areas, such as high-hazard areas, exit routes, or designated locations.

Automatic sprinkler systems rarely fail to operate. When they do fail, it is generally because of:

- Partially or completely closed main water control valve
- Interruption to the municipal water supply
- Damaged, painted-over, or dirty sprinklers
- Excess debris or sediment in the pipes
- Tampering and vandalism
- Frozen or broken pipes
- Failure of a secondary water supply
- Sprinklers obstructed by objects stacked too close

Sprinkler System Fundamentals

Figure 6.7 illustrates the main parts of an automatic wet-pipe sprinkler system. The system includes many more components, starting with a water main and continuing into the control valve. The riser is the vertical piping to which the sprinkler valve, one-way check valve, fire department connection (FDC), alarm valve, main drain, and other components get attached. The feed main is the pipe connecting the riser to the cross mains. Cross mains service branch lines on which the sprinklers are installed. Cross mains extend past the last branch lines and are capped to facilitate flushing. System piping decreases in size from the riser outward. Hangers and clamps support the system.

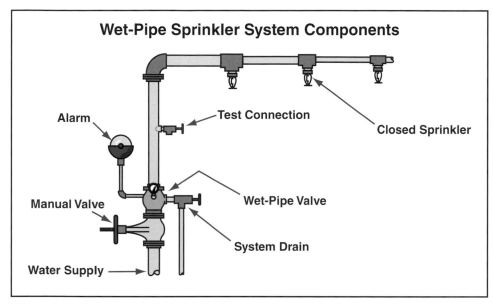

Wet-Pipe Sprinkler System Components

Figure 6.7 This illustration shows the main parts of an automatic wet-pipe sprinkler system.

Sprinkler Heads

Sprinklers are fixed-spray nozzles that are opened individually. When a heat-responsive element such as a fusible link activates, the cap or plug in the sprinkler opens, allowing water to discharge. Personnel could also encounter open-type sprinklers with no heat-responsive element, especially in deluge systems. A later section will describe deluge systems. Engineers have designed devices known as early-suppression fast-response (ESFR) sprinklers, which react five to ten times faster than traditional sprinklers. ESFR sprinklers can usually be quickly identified because they are larger than traditional sprinklers. Sprinklers are commonly rated according to the temperature at which they are designed to operate. This temperature is usually identified by color-coding the sprinkler frame arms and the liquid in frangible bulb-type sprinklers as well as stamping the temperature into the sprinkler itself.

Three of the most commonly used release mechanisms respond to heat to activate sprinklers include **(Figure 6.8)**:

- **Fusible link** — A fusible link holds two levers together, which hold a cap in place that stops water flow. When heat from a fire melts the link, then water or air pressure in the pipe pushes the levers and cap out of the way, allowing water to flow.

Figure 6.8 Fusible links, frangible bulbs, and chemical pellets are three of the most commonly used sprinkler release mechanisms.

- **Frangible bulb** — During a fire, heat expands a heat-sensitive liquid inside the frangible bulb. The internal pressure increases until the bulb shatters at the proper temperature. When the bulb shatters, the valve cap is released and water is allowed to flow.

- **Chemical pellet** — A plunger and a small pellet made of solder holds the sprinkler valve cap in place. The solder melts when heated to a certain temperature, releasing the plunger and opening the valve.

Sprinkler Types

Sprinklers are described by their orientation within the system or purpose. Common sprinkler orientation types include the following **(Figure 6.9)**:

- **Pendant** — Used where it is impractical or unsightly to use sprinklers in an upright position. The deflector on this type of sprinkler breaks the pattern of water into a circular pattern of small droplets directed downward.

- **Upright** — Used typically in dry systems and designed to deflect the spray of water downward in a hemispherical pattern. Upright sprinklers cannot be inverted for use in the hanging or pendant position because the spray would be deflected toward the ceiling.

- **Sidewall** — Used where it is desirable or required to install sprinklers on a wall at the side of a room or space. This decision may be for cost-savings or appearance. By modifying the deflector, a sprinkler can be made to discharge most of its water to one side. Sidewall sprinklers are useful in corridors, offices, breakrooms, and kitchens.

- **Concealed** — Hidden by a removable decorative cover that releases when exposed to a specific temperature.

- **Flush** — Mounted in a ceiling with the body of the sprinkler, including the threaded shank, above the plane of the ceiling.

- **Recessed** — Installed in recessed housing within the ceiling of a compartment or space; all or part of the sprinkler other than the threaded shank is mounted in the housing.

- **In-Rack** — Typically used in storage facilities. In-rack sprinklers incorporate a protective disk that shields the heat-sensing element from water discharged from the sprinklers above.

- **Special Purpose** — Designed and listed to protect special hazards, such as locations with corrosive atmospheres.

- **Deluge** — Open sprinklers without fusible links that a fire detection system activates, opening the water or foam control valve.

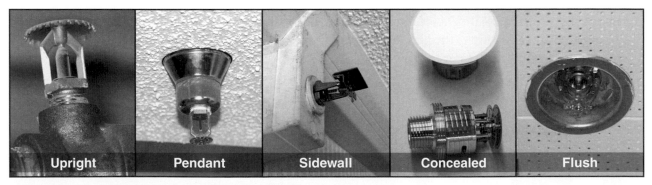

Figure 6.9 Examples of common sprinkler orientations.

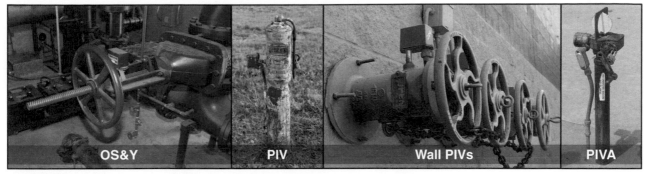

Figure 6.10 Indicating control valves include the OS&Y, PIV, WPIV, and PIVA.

Control Valves

Every sprinkler system is equipped with a fire protection system's main water control valve. Control valves are used to interrupt the water supply to the system in order to replace sprinklers, perform maintenance, or interrupt operations. Most main water control valves are of the indicating type and manually operated. An indicating valve shows at a glance if it is open.

Types of indicating control valves include the following **(Figure 6.10)**:

- **Outside stem and yoke (OS&Y) valve** — Has a yoke on the outside with a threaded stem that opens and closes the gate inside the valve housing. The threaded portion of the stem is visible beyond the yoke when the valve is open and not visible when the valve is closed.

- **Post indicator valve (PIV)** — Hollow metal post that houses the valve stem. Attached to the valve stem is a movable plate with the words OPEN or SHUT visible through a small glass window on the side of the housing. When not in use, the operating handle is locked to the valve housing.

- **Wall post indicator valve (WPIV)** — Similar to a PIV, except that it extends horizontally through the wall with the target and valve operating nut on the outside of the building.

- **Post indicator valve assembly (PIVA)** — Does not use a plate with words OPEN and SHUT as does a PIV. Instead, a PIVA uses a circular disk inside a flat plate on top of the valve housing. When the valve is open, the disk is perpendicular to the surrounding plate. When the valve is closed, the disk is in line with the plate that surrounds it. The PIVA is operated with a built-in crank.

NOTE: Underground, water key operated valves similar to a water system's primary valve may have replaced some PIVs.

NOTE: Any damage or impairment to a control valve must be reported so that repair or replacement of the valve can be accomplished. During an emergency, water for extinguishment must come from another source, such as a pumper supplying water through a fire department connection.

Water Flow Alarms

Some sprinkler systems are equipped with an audible local alarm. There are two versions of this alarm **(Figure 6.11)**:

Figure 6.11 Audible sprinkler system alarms include water motor gongs and water flow detectors.

- **Water motor gong** — As the sprinkler system activates, water flows through the piping and out through the sprinklers. This water flow turns a small water wheel inside the unit sounding the alarm by causing a small hammer to strike a gong.

- **Electronic water flow detectors** — An electro-mechanical device that activates when water flows through sprinkler system piping. Upon activation, it sends a signal to a fire alarm panel.

Water Supply

The system's water supply should be capable of delivering the required volume of water to the highest sprinkler at a residual pressure of at least 15 psi (105 kPa). The minimum flow depends on the hazard, what is being protected, the occupancy, and building contents. A connection to a public system with adequate volume, pressure, and reliability is a good source of water for automatic sprinklers. It is often the only water supply available. Automatic sprinkler systems are typically equipped with a waterflow device that initiates an alarm when water begins to flow in the system.

Figure 6.12 A fire pump can be incorporated into a sprinkler system to provide adequate water volume and pressure.

To ensure that adequate water volume and pressure for fire suppression operations are maintained during periods of peak demand, a fire pump is typically incorporated into the sprinkler system **(Figure 6.12)**. An electric, diesel, or steam pump driver powers the fire pump. The pump controller activates the driver and pump when the system pressure falls below a predetermined level. To ensure system reliability, personnel must regularly run and test the site's fire pump.

NOTE: Most facility fire systems have a jockey pump installed to maintain a basic pressure of 50 psi (350 kPa) for site use, and the big pump kicks on when it senses a larger flow or pressure drop.

Fire Department Connections (FDC)

In many cases, the water supply for sprinkler systems is designed to supply only a portion of the sprinklers installed on the system. If a large fire occurs or a pipe breaks, the sprinkler system will need an outside source of water and pressure to do its job effectively. A pumper connected to the sprinkler fire department connection (FDC) can provide additional water and pressure. FDCs for sprinklers usually consist of a Siamese inlet with at least two 2½-inch (65 mm) female connections with a clapper valve in each connection or one large-diameter connection that is attached to a clappered inlet **(Figure 6.13)**.

Figure 6.13 Fire department connections provide a means for connecting fire hose to a sprinkler or standpipe system.

Sprinkler FDCs should be supplied with water from pumpers that have a capacity of at least 1,000 gpm (4 000 L/min) or greater. A minimum of two 2½-inch (65 mm) or larger hoses should be attached to the FDC. Whenever possible, fire pumpers supplying attack lines should operate from hydrants connected to mains other than the one supplying the sprinkler system.

After water flows through the fire department connection into the sprinkler system, it passes through a check valve that prevents the water from flowing back into the FDC. The proper direction of water flow through a check valve is usually indicated by an arrow on the valve or by observing the appearance of the valve casing. A ball drip valve may also be installed at the check valve and FDC. This valve is designed to keep the valve and connection dry and operating properly during freezing conditions.

Departmental preincident plans may identify the pressure at which a sprinkler system should be supported, as well as any special circumstances. In some jurisdictions, the use of large diameter hose (LDH) is not recommended for connection to FDCs because the pressures these hoses are tested to are lower than other supply/attack lines.

Types of Sprinkler Systems

There are basically five types of sprinkler systems used in facilities:

Figure 6.14 Water discharging from a sprinkler.

- **Wet-Pipe Sprinkler Systems** — Wet-pipe sprinkler systems, sometimes referred to as straight stick systems, are used in locations where temperatures remain above 40°F (4°C). A wet-pipe sprinkler system is the simplest type of automatic fire sprinkler system and requires little maintenance. This system contains water under pressure at all times. It is connected to a water supply so an open sprinkler will immediately discharge a water spray in the area and activate an alarm **(Figure 6.14)**.

- **Dry-Pipe Sprinkler Systems** — Dry-pipe sprinkler systems are used in locations where the piping may be subjected to temperatures below 40°F (4°C). Pipes in dry-pipe systems are pitched (sloped) to help drain the water in the system toward the main drain. In these systems, air or nitrogen under pressure replaces water in the sprinkler piping above the dry-pipe valve (device that keeps water out of the sprinkler piping until a fire actuates a sprinkler). When a sprinkler activates, pressurized air escapes. Then the dry-pipe valve automatically opens to permit water into the piping system. In a large dry-pipe system, several minutes could be lost while the air gets expelled from the system. Standards require that a quick-opening device is installed in systems that have a water capacity of over 500 gallons (2 000 L). An accelerator is one type of quick-opening device. Its basic purpose is to redirect system air to accelerate the opening of the dry-pipe valve, which allows water into the sprinkler system more quickly. Exhausters, another quick-opening device, expel air from the system to allow water to flow in its place.

- **Preaction Sprinkler Systems** — Preaction sprinkler systems are dry systems that employ a deluge-type valve, fire detection devices, and closed sprinklers **(Figure 6.15, p. 222)**. This type of system is used when it is important to prevent water damage. The system will not discharge water into the sprinkler piping, except in response to either smoke- or heat-detection system actuation, which operates a release switch located in the system actuation unit. This release switch opens the deluge valve and permits water to enter the distribution system so that water is ready when the sprinklers activate. Once water is in the system it will only discharge through sprinklers that have been activated.

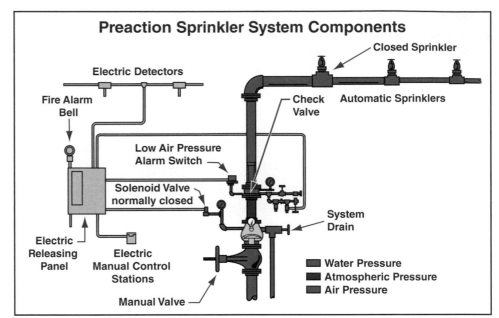

Figure 6.15 Illustrating the major components of a preaction sprinkler system.

- **Deluge Sprinkler Systems** — Deluge sprinkler systems are similar to dry-pipe systems in that there is no water in the distribution piping before system activation. However, in a deluge system, all sprinklers are open at all times (these are known as open-head sprinklers) **(Figure 6.16)**. This feature means that when the system is activated and water enters the piping, the water will discharge simultaneously from all of the sprinklers. A deluge valve controls the flow of water into the system. Fire detection devices (heat, smoke, or flame detectors) installed in the area protected by the system control the operation of the deluge valve.

Normally installed in high-hazard occupancies such as aircraft hangars, deluge systems are designed to quickly supply a large volume of water or extinguishing agent to the protected area. A variation of this system is the partial deluge system in which some sprinklers are open and some are not. A water curtain system is another form of deluge system designed to provide exposure protection.

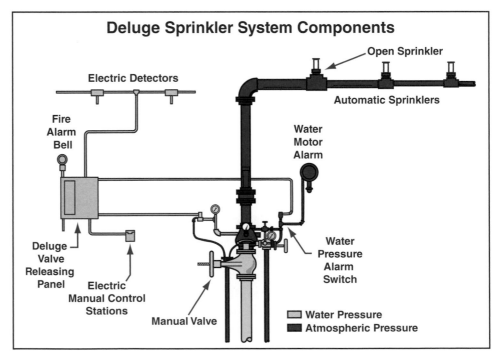

Figure 6.16 Illustrating the major components of a deluge sprinkler system.

System Activation

Sprinkler systems are activated in the following ways:

- **Automatically** — Triggered by either a detector or a combination of detectors that may be responsive to heat, smoke, or gases.
- **Manually** — Triggered by someone operating a manual station and putting the system through its complete cycle of operation, including the predischarge alarm.

Safety Precautions

Where required, sprinkler systems should be equipped with warning devices to alert employees to immediately evacuate the area. Run-off water from sprinkler system operations in industrial plants or other facilities may be contaminated with oils or other hazardous materials and should be retained for cleanup.

Figure 6.17 A fire brigade member shutting off a sprinkler system PIV.

Fire Brigade Support

The fire brigade should inspect sprinkler systems regularly. Fire brigade members should be trained to activate the system, if necessary. They are also responsible for assisting in the evacuation of affected personnel, accounting for everyone displaced by the evacuation, and preventing unauthorized entry into the affected area.

Personnel should be prepared to help supplement the water supply to a sprinkler system. Supplemental water may come from operating auxiliary fire pumps or connecting hoselines from pumpers to the system's fire department connections (FDCs).

Fire brigade members should be prepared to shut down sprinkler systems or close off individual sprinklers to reduce water damage **(Figure 6.17)**. Exercise caution in shutting down sprinkler systems prior to reaching extinguishment as this response may result in additional fire damage to the facility. When it is necessary to shut down a sprinkler system, the shutdown needs to be coordinated with the fire brigade leader. A fire brigade member should be stationed at the control valve with a two-way radio in case the system needs to be turned back on.

Special Extinguishing Systems

NFPA 1081 (2018): 4.2.2, 4.3.2

Special extinguishing systems typically use an extinguishing agent other than water or in addition to water. These extinguishing agents are unique to their application in specific occupancies. Some facilities, such as industrial manufacturing plants, may incorporate several special extinguishing systems depending on the materials and processes used.

Types of special extinguishing systems include the following:

- Water-mist
- Dry chemical
- Wet chemical

- Carbon dioxide
- Foam
- Clean-agent

Water-Mist Extinguishing Systems

A water-mist system resembles a water-spray fixed system, except that the water-mist system discharges a fine mist of water. The mist absorbs larger quantities of heat than water-spray or automatic sprinkler systems. Theoretically, the water-mist system raises the humidity of the room high enough to halt combustion. The fine spray also controls or extinguishes fire by displacing oxygen and blocking radiant heat production. Because more fire can be controlled with less water damage, the water-mist system can work as a replacement for fixed fire suppression systems that used halogenated hydrocarbon agents.

Water-mist systems are used to protect the following hazards:

- Gas jet fires
- Flammable and combustible liquids
- Marine vessels
- Computer equipment and rooms
- Aircraft passenger cabins
- Ordinary Class A combustibles

These systems are designed to protect lives and property by extinguishing Class A and Class B fires, controlling fire temperatures in compartments, and preventing flashover with extension to other compartments in a structure. Research also indicates that water-mist systems may be suitable for use in residential occupancies and flammable and combustible storage facilities.

Water-mist systems are designed to be operated at considerably higher pressures than standard sprinkler systems. The basic pressure ranges in which these systems operate include the following **(Figure 6.18)**:

- Low-pressure system — 175 psi (1 225 kPa) or less
- Intermediate-pressure system — 175 to 500 psi (1 225 kPa to 3 500 kPa)
- High-pressure systems — 500 psi (3 500 kPa) or greater

Compressed-air, nitrogen, or high-pressure water pumps create these higher pressures. Storage cylinders or air pumps may supply compressed air to the system. Air pressure may be applied to the water through the water tube itself (single-fluid system) or through a second air tube to each spray nozzle (twin-fluid system).

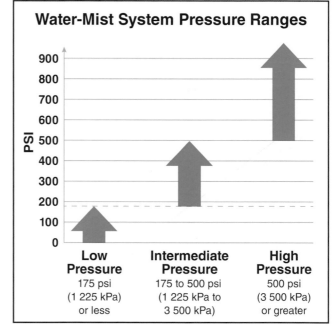

Figure 6.18 Illustrating the various pressure ranges for low, intermediate, and high pressure water-mist systems.

In general, a water-mist system is composed of small-diameter, pressure-rated copper, or stainless-steel tubing. Small-diameter spray nozzles are spaced evenly on the tubing. Depending on the system's design, the nozzles may be of the open or closed sprinkler variety. A product-of-combustion detection system activates the system, and may have a set amount of time to discharge. These systems should also have a means of manual operation if individuals discover the fire before the activation of the system.

The most common type of water-mist system works similarly to a deluge sprinkler system. All of the spray nozzles in a particular room or zone are open, and when the detection devices activate, the water discharges from the nozzles.

System Activation

There are two ways in which water-mist systems are activated:

- **Automatically** — Triggered by either a detector or a combination of detectors that may be responsive to heat, smoke, or gases.

- **Manually** — Triggered by someone operating a manual station and putting the system through its complete cycle of operation, including the predischarge alarm.

Safety Precautions

Systems that have automatic actuation should be equipped with appropriate warning signals to alert employees of the need to immediately evacuate the area. This evacuation reduces the employees' exposure to the fire's products of combustion and the pressurized mist that the system produces.

Fire Brigade Support

The fire brigade should inspect water-mist systems on a regular basis, and its members should be trained to activate the system, if necessary. Members should monitor the operation of water-mist systems to ensure they are working properly. Other fire fighting equipment, such as water-mist extinguishers, hoselines, or monitors, may be needed to supplement water-mist system operations.

Figure 6.19 The extinguishing agent supply cylinders for a facility's CO_2 fire suppression system.

Carbon Dioxide Extinguishing Systems

Three types of carbon dioxide (CO_2) systems — total flooding systems, local application systems, and hoselines — are used to protect different types of hazards in industrial settings. All systems must conform to the requirements of NFPA 12, *Standard on Carbon Dioxide Extinguishing Systems.*

The components of carbon dioxide systems include actuation devices, agent storage containers, piping, and discharge devices. Discharge devices for total flooding systems may be either the high- or low-velocity type, although high-velocity discharge devices promote better disbursement of the agent throughout the area. The discharge devices used for local application are typically designed to produce a low-velocity discharge that limits the possibility of splashing the burning product.

Both total flooding and local application systems can be designed using either high-pressure or low-pressure CO_2 containers **(Figure 6.19)**. In high-pressure systems, carbon dioxide is stored in standard federal Department of Transportation (DOT) cylinders at a pressure of about 850 psi (5 950 kPa) at 70° F (21° C). In low-pressure systems, the carbon dioxide is stored in large refrigerated tanks at 300 psi (2 100 kPa) at a temperature of 0° F (-18° C).

Total Flooding Systems

As the name implies, total flooding systems fill the enclosed space with CO_2, which displaces the oxygen and smothers the fire. For CO_2 to be effective as an extinguishing agent, a concentration of at least 34 percent must be achieved and maintained throughout the flooded space. This percentage may have to be increased for some types of hazards, such as fires involving hydrogen. The concentration must be maintained for a sufficient period of time to extinguish the embers and allow the residue to cool, so the space must be relatively airtight to limit the loss of CO_2. Carbon dioxide flooding systems are required to have a preactuation alarm to notify occupants of the impending actuation of the system and self-locking exit doors prevent inappropriate reentry into the flooded space.

NOTE: When these systems fail to operate properly or do not extinguish the fire, it is usually due to premature entrance by personnel or failure to maintain the integrity of the enclosure.

Local Application Systems

Local application systems are designed to discharge CO_2 onto a specific hazard that is on fire **(Figure 6.20)**. Actuation of the system usually shuts down the fuel source as well. The agent is delivered at the rate and the quantity specified by NFPA 12, and this type of system does not require a preactuation alarm because the agent is only applied in a specific area (see Safety Precautions section).

Hand Hoselines

In this type of system, hoselines (generally rolled onto hose reels) are attached to the CO_2 system piping at critical locations around the industrial site. When needed, a fire brigade member unrolls the hoseline from the hose reel, charges the hoseline, and approaches the fire with the nozzle. If a fire brigade member operates a CO_2 handline within an enclosed space, the CO_2 can displace the oxygen within the area, so the member must wear a self-contained or supplied air breathing apparatus.

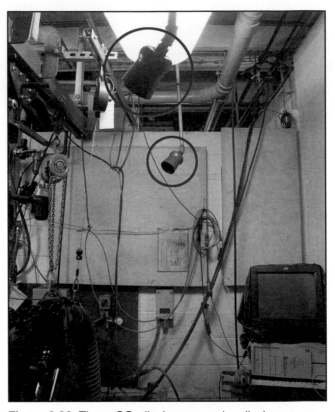

Figure 6.20 These CO_2 discharge nozzles discharge extinguishing agent onto an engine in a test cell in the event of a fire.

System Activation

Three means of actuating carbon dioxide systems are as follows:

- **Automatic** — Triggered by either a detector or a combination of detectors that may be responsive to heat, smoke, or gases.

- **Normal manual** — Triggered by someone operating a manual station and putting the system through its complete cycle of operation, including the predischarge alarm. In some facilities, this manual activation can be done remotely from the Control Room.

- **Emergency manual** — Used only when the other actuation modes fail. This actuation is a manual dump that causes the system to immediately discharge without advance warning.

Safety Precautions

The reduction of oxygen in a confined space is the most serious problem involving carbon dioxide systems. Any level of oxygen that will not support combustion will also not support human life. Predischarge alarms may use horns, bells, flashing lights, or sirens.

In addition to the predischarge alarms required in total flooding systems, an appropriate time delay between the actuation of the predischarge alarm and the actual discharge of the agent must also be provided. All employees working in areas that these systems protect must be educated about the dangers of carbon dioxide and trained in emergency evacuation procedures.

In local application systems, carbon dioxide is delivered directly onto the hazard rather than released to fill the space with the gas. However, if the hazard is enclosed in either a shroud or a hood that could trap the gas, the enclosed area may be as dangerous as the space would be with a total flooding system. Signage should be placed on the entrance or openings of any enclosed space or shroud to warn emergency responders of the hazardous conditions.

> **WARNING:** If a total flooding system has discharged, anyone entering the affected area(s) must don an SCBA or perform atmospheric testing of the environment to ensure oxygen is present within the safe limits — 19.5 to 21 percent.

If local fire and emergency services organization responds to the incident, fire brigade members should inform responders that the space has been flooded with CO_2 so they can take appropriate precautions. However, ventilating the space may rekindle the fire. These systems provide little rekindle protection. Fire brigade members should be prepared to extinguish any remaining fire as well as overhaul operations.

After a fire is extinguished, the room in which the fire occurred and any adjacent spaces (particularly those below the fire level) should be treated as hazardous confined spaces. Mechanical ventilation should be set up to eliminate residual CO_2 and other fire gases. Before employees are allowed to reenter the space without SCBA, personnel should sample the atmosphere within the space to determine it is safe to do so.

Fire Brigade Support

As with other extinguishing systems, the fire brigade should inspect CO_2 systems on a regular basis. There is little that fire brigade members can do to directly support an operating carbon dioxide system. Their responsibilities are limited to assisting in the evacuation of affected personnel, accounting for everyone displaced by the evacuation, and preventing unauthorized entry into the affected area.

Industrial fire brigade members should ensure that doors leading into and out of the affected area are closed, HVAC systems for that area are shut down, and the vents for the area remain closed to contain the agent. Entry should be denied to anyone not wearing SCBA until personnel have sampled and determined that the atmosphere in any space where the agent has been discharged is within safe limits.

Dry Chemical Extinguishing Systems

Dry chemical extinguishing systems are used in a variety of locations, including places where:

- A rapid fire knockdown is required.
- Water damage must be minimized.
- Contamination with and cleanup of extinguishing agent is acceptable.
- Reignition is unlikely.
- Freezing would be a problem.

Some example locations include storage areas for flammable and combustible liquids, flammable solids, chemicals, or ammunition. These systems are most commonly used to protect the following:

- Quenching processes
- Paint spray booths
- Exhaust duct systems
- Dip tanks
- Commercial cooking areas

There are two main types of dry chemical systems: total flooding systems and local application systems. All dry chemical systems must meet the requirements of NFPA 17, *Standard for Dry Chemical Extinguishing Systems.*

System Description

All dry chemical systems have similar components: a storage tank(s) for extinguishing agent and expellant gas, piping through which the gas moves the agent, nozzles to disperse the agent, and an actuating mechanism. Actuation of most systems automatically stops the fuel and/or power to the protected hazard.

There are no standard tank sizes for dry chemical agents **(Figure 6.21)**. Both the agent and expellant gas may be contained in the storage tank or they may be stored separately. The expellant gas is either nitrogen or carbon dioxide. The tanks resemble those used for portable fire extinguishers, but are much larger. Although uncommon, some agent tanks may hold as much as 4,000 pounds (1 800 kg) of agent. However, most tanks are in the 30- to 500-pound (14 kg to 227 kg) range. The tanks must be located as close to the discharge point as possible and in an area subject to temperatures within a range of -40° F to 120° F (-40° C to 49° C).

Figure 6.21 Dry chemical extinguishing agent is stored in these tanks which are part of a fire suppression system for a vehicle painting facility.

Dry chemical agent is discharged onto the fire from nozzles attached to a system of fixed piping. The piping is specially designed to accommodate the unique flow characteristics of dry chemical agents. The pipe size, the number of fittings, the number and radius of bends, and total friction loss are calculated into each system design. The agent is discharged through nozzles designed for the specific hazard to be protected. The two types of dry chemical systems are the:

- **Total Flooding Systems** — Dry chemical flooding systems are designed to introduce a dense concentration of agent into an enclosed area, such as a paint booth or a flammable-liquid storage room. For this type of system to be effective, the discharge area must be totally enclosed or have openings equipped with automatic closers that operate whenever the system is actuated.

- **Local Application Systems** — Local application systems are the most common dry chemical extinguishing systems in use. They discharge agent onto a specific surface, such as the liquid surface area of a dip tank or a commercial cooking area.

System Activation

There are two ways in which dry chemical systems can be activated:

- **Automatically** — Triggered by a detector or a combination of detectors that may be responsive to heat (such as fusible links), smoke, or gases.

- **Manually** — Triggered by someone operating a manual station and putting the system through its complete cycle of operation, including the predischarge alarm. Manual actuation devices should be located near the protected operation or area but positioned so that personnel will not be endangered if manual activation of the system is required.

Safety Precautions

Systems that have automatic actuation should be equipped with warning signals to alert employees of the need to immediately evacuate the area. This evacuation reduces the employees' exposure to airborne particles of the agent. The chemicals used as extinguishing agents are not toxic but can irritate the eyes and respiratory tract. If a dry chemical system has discharged into a confined space, no one should enter the space without SCBA until the space is thoroughly ventilated.

Fire Brigade Support

The fire brigade should inspect dry chemical extinguisher systems regularly. Members should be trained to activate the system, if necessary. There is little that fire brigade members can do to directly support an operating dry chemical system. Their responsibilities are limited to assisting in the evacuation of affected personnel, accounting for everyone displaced by the evacuation, and preventing unauthorized entry into the affected area. These systems provide little to no rekindle protection. Fire brigade members should be ready to search for any remaining fire as well as overhaul operations.

Foam Extinguishing Systems

Foam extinguishing systems are best suited for use on fires involving flammable or combustible liquids, and most of these systems are found in manufacturing and industrial areas where these hazards are present. These systems may be either the total flooding type or the local application type. Depending on the type of system, the requirements of one of the following NFPA standards must be met in the design of the system:

- NFPA 11, *Standard for Low-, Medium, and High-Expansion Foam Systems*
- NFPA 16, *Standard for the Installation of Foam-Water Sprinkler and Foam-Water Spray Systems*
- NFPA 18A, *Standard on Water Additives for Fire Control and Vapor Mitigation*
- NFPA 409, *Standard on Aircraft Hangars*

System Description

A foam extinguishing system must have an adequate water supply, a supply of the correct foam concentrate, a piping system, a proportioning system, and discharge devices. Automatic foam systems also include detection devices. A complete foam extinguishing system includes the central station from which the foam solution is pumped, the piping through which it flows, and the devices from which the finished foam is discharged **(Figure 6.22)**.

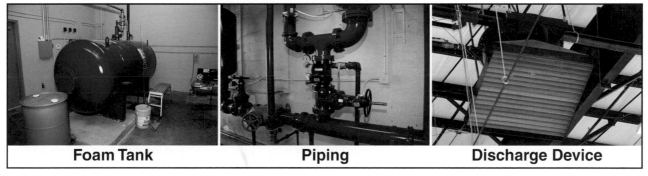

| Foam Tank | Piping | Discharge Device |

Figure 6.22 Three major components of a foam extinguishing system.

The foam that these systems deliver is light enough to float on the surface of flammable and combustible liquids, with a sufficient water content to resist breakdown. Foams create a cohesive blanket over the flammable liquid, separating the liquid from the oxygen in the air and reducing evaporation of the liquid. At the same time, the water within the foam has a cooling effect on the fire and upon hot objects such as steel tanks.

There are two basic types of foam extinguishing systems:

- **Total Flooding** — A total flooding system is designed to introduce a heavy application of foam over a large surface area, such as a truck loading area, unloading area, fuel, storage tanks, an aircraft hangar, or a warehouse.
- **Local Application** — A local application system is designed to discharge foam on a specific surface or area, such as a dip tank or a storage tank.

Specific Foam Concentrates

Numerous types of foam concentrates are available for specific applications according to their properties and performance. Some foam concentrates are thick and viscous and form tough, heat-resistant finished foam blankets over burning liquid surfaces; other foam concentrates are thinner and spread more rapidly as finished forms. Some foam concentrates produce a vapor-sealing film of surface-active water solution on a liquid surface. Other foam concentrates, such as medium- and high-expansion foam concentrates, are used in large volumes for vapor suppression or to flood confined spaces. The sections that follow highlight each of the common foam concentrate types.

Regular Protein Foam. The use of regular protein foam concentrates started before World War II. These foams are virtually nonexistent in today's municipal, industrial, or military fire and emergency services. Although rare, regular protein foam concentrate may still be found in a fixed fire-suppression system, especially in shipboard systems. Regular protein foam generally has good heat stability, but it is not as mobile or fluid on the fuel surface as synthetic-based foam concentrates or modern fluoroprotein derivatives. Regular protein foam concentrate is susceptible to fuel pickup; consequently, care should be taken to minimize submergence through plunging of the foam stream into the fuel.

Fluoroprotein Foam. Fluoroprotein foam concentrate, a combination protein-based and synthetic-based foam concentrate, is derived from protein foam concentrates to which **fluorosurfactants** are added. The fluorosurfactants are similar to those developed for aqueous film forming foam (AFFF) concentrates (described later) but are used in much lower concentrations. The addition of these chemicals produces finished foam that flows across fuel surfaces more rapidly than regular protein foam. Because of these surfactants, fluoroprotein foam concentrates are **oleophobic** (oil shedding) and well-suited for subsurface injection: a process by which foam is pumped into the bottom of a burning tank containing certain hydrocarbons and then floats to the top to form a fire-extinguishing finished foam.

Fluoroprotein foam concentrates can be formulated to be alcohol-resistant by adding ammonia salts that are suspended in organic solvents. Alcohol-resistant fluoroprotein foam concentrate maintains its alcohol-resistive properties for extended periods of time depending on a number of factors. Alcohol-resistant fluoroprotein foam concentrates have a very high degree of heat resistance and water retention.

Film Forming Fluoroprotein Foam. Film forming fluoroprotein (FFFP) foam concentrate is based on fluoroprotein foam technology with AFFF concentrate capabilities (see the following section). FFFP foam concentrate incorporates the benefits of AFFF concentrate for fast fire knockdown and the benefits of fluoroprotein foam concentrate for long-lasting heat resistance.

Alcohol-resistant FFFP concentrate has all the fire-fighting capabilities of regular FFFP concentrate, including some of the following advantages:

- **Multipurpose** — Can be used on polar solvent fuels at 6 percent concentrations and on hydrocarbon fuels at 3 percent concentrations. New concentrates that can be used at 3 percent concentrations on either type of fuel are also available.

- **Storage** — Can be stored at temperatures ranging from 35°F to 120°F (2°C to 49°C).

- **Premixable** — Can be mixed into a solution and stored ready for use.

- **Subsurface injection** — Can be used for subsurface injection applications.

Aqueous Film Forming Foam (AFFF). Aqueous Film Forming Foam (known as AFFF and commonly pronounced as "A-triple-F") is the most commonly used foam concentrate. This synthetic concentrate consists of fluorosurfactants and **hydrocarbon surfactants** combined with high-boiling-point solvents and water. Fluorochemical surfactants reduce the surface tension of water to a degree less than the surface tension of the hydrocarbon so that a thin aqueous film can spread across the fuel.

When AFFF (as well as the previously mentioned FFFP finished foam) is applied to a hydrocarbon fire, the following three results occur:

- An air/vapor-excluding film is released ahead of the foam blanket.
- The fast-moving foam blanket then moves across the surface and around objects, adding further insulation.
- As the aerated foam blanket continues to drain its water, more film is released. This result gives AFFF finished foam the ability to "self-heal" areas where the foam blanket is disturbed.

Alcohol-Resistant AFFF (AR-AFFF). Alcohol-resistant concentrates (AR-AFFF) composes another class of AFFF concentrates. They are available from most foam manufacturers. On hydrocarbons, AR-AFFF's performance is similar to AFFF and proportioned (usually 1 or 3 percent) in accordance with the manufacturer's recommendation. On most polar solvents, alcohol-resistant AFFF concentrates are proportioned at 3 or 6 percent (3:97 or 6:94 concentrate/water ratios), depending on the particular brand selected. When alcohol-resistant AFFF concentrates are applied to polar solvent fuels, they create a membrane rather than a film over the fuel. This membrane separates the water in the foam blanket from the attack of the solvent. Apply alcohol-resistant AFFF to the fuel so that the membrane can form first. Do not plunge alcohol-resistant AFFF into the polar solvent fuel.

Alcohol-resistant AFFF may be used in subsurface injection applications on certain light hydrocarbons, such as gasoline, kerosene, and jet propulsion fuels. AR-AFFF concentrate is generally not used in premix applications.

Vapor-Mitigating Foam. Technological advances in the area of hazardous-material foam concentrates have recently produced AR-AFFF concentrates that can help stop some acidic or alkaline reactions. Some vapor-mitigating foams are designed solely for use on unignited spills of hazardous liquids. Some vapor-mitigating foams are not effective in fire fighting situations. Because of the presence of water, this type of foam is unsuited for many water-reactive mixtures.

High-Expansion Foam. High-expansion foam concentrates are special-purpose foam concentrates that are chemically similar to Class A foams. They can minimize water damage because they have relatively low water content, which is also useful when runoff is undesirable. The use of high-expansion finished foam outside is generally not recommended because the slightest breeze may remove the foam blanket in sheets and re-expose the hazard to stray ignition sources.

Emulsifiers. Emulsifiers are liquid chemicals that are designed to mix with a fuel, breaking it into small droplets and encapsulating them. The resulting emulsion is rendered nonflammable.

Emulsifiers should only be used with fuels that are 1 inch (25 mm) or less in depth. If the fuel is deeper, it is almost impossible to mix the emulsifier thoroughly with the fuel. Once an emulsifier is thoroughly mixed with the fuel, it renders the fuel unsalvageable. Fire brigade members should be aware that emulsifiers do not work effectively with water-soluble or water-miscible fuels because an emulsion cannot be formed between the concentrate and the fuel.

NOTE: Emulsifiers can have a negative environmental impact on bodies of water, including the fish and other aquatic life.

System Activation

There are two ways in which foam systems are activated:

- **Automatically** — Triggered by either a detector or a combination of detectors that may be responsive to heat, smoke, or gases.
- **Manually** — Triggered by someone operating a manual station and putting the system through its complete cycle of operation, including the predischarge alarm.

Safety Precautions

Foam systems are installed for fuels that produce tremendous heat and flame. With certain types of fuels (crudes and some other heavy oils), there may be potential for **boilovers**, **slop-overs** and **froth-overs (Figure 6.23)**. Brigade members should stay away from large fires involving flammable liquids, and they should avoid walking through or otherwise disturbing a foam blanket. Disturbing the foam blanket can allow flammable vapors to escape and reignite.

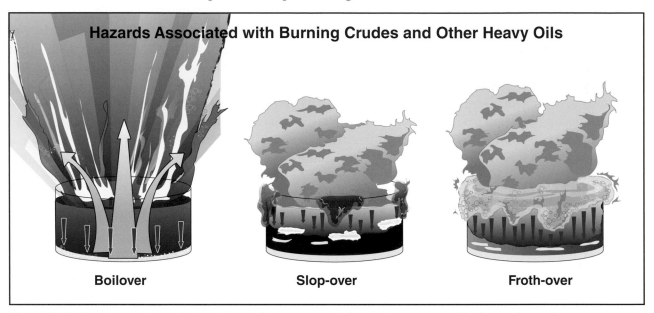

Hazards Associated with Burning Crudes and Other Heavy Oils

| Boilover | Slop-over | Froth-over |

Figure 6.23 Burning crudes and other heavy oils can create boilover, slop-over, and froth-over hazards.

Fire Brigade Support

The fire brigade should regularly inspect foam extinguishing systems and be trained to activate the system, if necessary. They are also responsible for assisting in the evacuation of affected personnel, accounting for everyone displaced by the evacuation, and preventing unauthorized entry into the affected area.

Fire brigade members may have to help supplement the water and foam supplies to a foam system. Supplemental water may come from operating auxiliary fire pumps or connecting hoselines from pumpers to the system's fire department connections (FDCs). Foam may come from storage tanks or smaller containers.

Fire brigade members should exercise caution in shutting down foam systems prior to extinguishment. This action may result in additional fire damage to the facility. Personnel should be prepared to shut down foam systems or close off individual sprinklers to reduce damage from water and foam.

Fixed Monitors

Fixed monitors are commonly used in industrial facilities. The purpose of these master stream devices is to deliver large quantities of water or foam over a known distance in either a straight stream or a fog pattern. Preplumbed fixed monitors reduce the need to deploy extensive hose layouts to supply portable master stream devices and/or handline nozzles **(Figure 6.24)**. Either type may be used defensively to protect structures and process

Figure 6.24 An example of a fixed monitor at an oil refinery facility.

components endangered by flame or radiant heat as well as to provide large quantities of water for fire suppression. Fixed fire-water monitor systems should meet the requirements of NFPA 24, *Standard for the Installation of Private Fire Service Mains and Their Appurtenances.*

System Description

Fixed monitors are similar to portable master stream devices in design and function. However, they are usually elevated from 3 to 40 feet (1 m to 12 m) above the ground and attached to a water pipe or fire hydrant that is part of the facility's water system. The term "fixed" refers to their permanent installation, but not necessarily to a prepositioned spray direction. Many fixed monitors can be trained laterally and either elevated or depressed to direct the stream. Some monitors require that this manipulation be done manually; other monitors allow it to be done automatically or by remote control.

All fixed monitor systems consist of a large-volume water supply, foam tanks (for foam monitors), a control valve, and a monitor nozzle. Some fixed monitors have self-educting nozzles attached to them to facilitate foam-making when needed. Some facilities may have their fixed monitors attached to a separate water system that is used exclusively for fire protection. In the absence of elevated water tanks, these systems may use fire water pumps to achieve the needed flows and pressures.

Figure 6.25 A fire brigade member manually operating a fixed monitor.

System Activation

Personnel can operate fixed monitors manually from the base of the assembly or hydraulically from a remote location **(Figure 6.25)**. Manual actuation simply requires turning on the control valve, but depending on the installation, operating the monitor may involve adjusting the pattern and/ or directing the stream.

An operator can perform remote actuation of a hydraulically controlled monitor by manipulating a joystick or operating a series of switches. Personnel can accomplish this task from a remotely located control room so they are not exposed to fire or hazardous vapors.

Safety Precautions

Fire brigade members should use caution when manually operating fixed monitors. Once a monitor is in operation, members should withdraw to a safe area in case a situation suddenly deteriorates. If a remotely controlled monitor does not work properly, personnel should not endanger themselves trying to repair it during an emergency. Members should also be aware of the impact force of master streams as well as the fact that so much water can make the area slippery. An operating monitor creates a signification reaction force, so any movements to redirect monitors should be done slowly to avoid overstressing the mounting assembly. Fire brigade members must not enter the fire stream that a monitor creates, as doing so can cause serious personal injury.

Fire Brigade Support

The fire brigade should inspect fixed monitor systems on a regular basis. As long as a fixed monitor system has an adequate water supply at operating pressure, there is little that fire brigade members need to do to support the system. Their most important function should be to ensure that all necessary valves are in the correct positions for the system to function as designed. If fire water pumps are used as part of the system, fire brigade members should also make sure the pumps are functioning properly. If water supplies are limited, personnel will have to monitor them during the operation and refill them afterward.

Wet Chemical Extinguishing Systems

Because wet chemical agents react with animal fats or vegetable oils to form a nonflammable soap (saponification), these systems are best suited for Class K applications in commercial fryers, grills, range hoods, plenums, and ducts **(Figure 6.26)**. Wet chemical agents can extinguish grease or oil fires in four ways: fuel removal, cooling, smothering, and flame inhibition. Wet chemical agents can cause floors to become slippery.

Figure 6.26 If a fire occurs in the deep fat fryers in this cooking area, these nozzles will discharge a Class K wet chemical agent to extinguish the fire.

System Description

Wet chemical systems are similar to dry chemical local application systems, except that the agent is a liquid instead of a powder. A wet chemical agent is typically a solution of water and/or potassium carbonate or potassium acetate sprayed onto the fire. These agents are not recommended for electrical fires because they are conductive.

 Wet Chemical Systems

Wet chemical systems can be messy, particularly when food greases are involved. The spray from a wet chemical system can also migrate to surrounding surfaces, causing corrosion of electrical wires or damage to hot cooking equipment. Personnel must ensure a prompt cleanup after activation of a wet chemical system. In some jurisdictions, a Class K extinguisher is also required wherever a wet chemical system is installed.

System Activation

Fire brigade members should realize that the activation of these systems might shut down or disconnect fuel supplies and trip the circuit breakers for the electrical control devices. There are two ways in which wet chemical systems are activated:

- **Automatically** — Triggered by either a detector or a combination of detectors that may be responsive to heat, smoke, or gases.

- **Manually** — Triggered by someone operating a manual station and putting the system through its complete cycle of operation, including the predischarge alarm.

Fire Brigade Support

Fire brigade members can support a wet chemical extinguishing system by assisting in the evacuation personnel from the affected area. They also need to ensure the fire is extinguished and that it has not spread to adjacent combustibles. After the system has discharged, a certified technician should service and recharge it.

Clean Agent Extinguishing Systems

Clean agents are gaseous or volatile fire extinguishing chemicals that do not conduct electricity and do not leave a residue when they evaporate. Examples of clean agents include Halon 1301, Halon 1211, Halotron™, and Inergen™ agents.

Halon 1301 and Halon 1211 are the agents most commonly used in halogenated agent extinguishing systems. Applicable standards for clean agent systems include:

- NFPA 12A, *Standard on Halon 1301 Fire Extinguishing Systems*
- NFPA 408, *Standard for Aircraft Hand Portable Fire Extinguishers*
- NFPA 2001, *Standard on Clean Agent Fire Extinguishing Systems*

Because of its toxicity, use of Halon 1211 is not permitted in habitable areas such as computer rooms. Halon 1301 may be used in habitable areas, because it is effective at such low concentrations that it poses little threat to occupants. However, because both of these agents may produce toxic decomposition products in fires and displace oxygen, the systems should include a predischarge alarm. The Montreal Protocols address the elimination of halon and halon extinguishing systems. In most cases, these materials and systems have been removed from service with the exception of the military and other special government installations. Common approved replacement agents include Halotron™, Inergen™, FE-200™, and FE-13™.

As a result of the signing of the Montreal Protocols, the Significant New Alternatives Policy (SNAP) program under Section 612 of the Clean Air Act of 1990 mandated the U.S. Environmental Protection Agency (EPA) to evaluate alternative chemicals and processes intended to replace ozone-depleting substances. In February of 1994, EPA published two lists of acceptable alternatives as part of a SNAP final rule.

The SNAP final rule said that halon alternatives must meet five basic criteria. They must (1) be effective fire fighting agents, (2) have acceptable environmental impact, (3) have low toxicity, (4) be relatively clean (volatile), and (5) be commercially available soon. The rule also divided halon alternatives into two categories: streaming agents and total flooding agents. For copies of the EPA-approved halon alternatives lists, contact the U.S. EPA. See NFPA 2001 for additional information. The facility fire protection specialist should complete a fire risk analysis to ensure that a suitable substitute is found.

Alternatives to the use of halons include Halotron™, Inergen™, FM-200™, and FE-13™. These systems are just a few of the alternatives on the ever-growing list of clean agents that meet the requirements of the Montreal Protocols. Facility fire brigade members should become familiar with the manufacturer's specifications for alternative systems found at their sites.

System Description

Clean agent extinguishing systems are available in local application and total flooding types. Local application systems apply the extinguishing agent onto the fire. Total flooding systems permeate the entire space with enough agent to extinguish or prevent a fire.

Most system designs, in either category, allow automatic and manual actuation. Components common to all clean agent systems include:

- Agent tanks
- Nozzles
- Manual releases
- Selector valves
- Actuators
- Detectors
- Control panels

The agent is stored in tanks as a liquefied compressed gas that is super-pressurized with nitrogen gas to promote discharge over wide temperature ranges **(Figure 6.27)**. There are no standard tank sizes, shapes, or colors. Halon tank capacities range from 5 to 600 pounds (2 kg to 272 kg). The size and number of tanks vary with the system design. Gauges are used to indicate the pressure in the tanks; however, because of super pressurization with nitrogen, pressure gauge readings may not give a true indication of the amount of agent in the tanks. They are connected to a system of fixed piping that terminates at the nozzles.

Figure 6.27 These tanks contain FM 200™, a clean extinguishing agent.

System Activation

There are two ways in which clean agent systems are activated:

- **Automatically** — Triggered by either a detector or a combination of detectors that may be responsive to heat, smoke, or gases.

- **Manually** — Triggered by someone operating a manual station and putting the system through its cycle of operation, including the predischarge alarm.

All extinguishing agent storage tanks have one or more valves to permit the release of agent into the hazard area. While the valves are operated either mechanically or pneumatically, the systems are actuated manually or electrically in response to signals from smoke detectors.

Safety Precautions

In terms of physiological effects on humans, Halon 1301 is considered to be safer than carbon dioxide. However, the effects of the decomposition products of both halons make it necessary to treat them in much the same way as CO_2. Brigade members and other personnel working near these systems should be trained in how to react when the predischarge alarm sounds. Industrial fire brigade members should ensure that doors leading into and out of the affected area are closed, HVAC systems for that area are shut down, and the vents for the area are closed to contain the agent. Entry should be denied to anyone not wearing SCBA or SAR until personnel have sampled and determined that the atmosphere in any space where the agent has been discharged is within safe limits.

Fire Brigade Support

The fire brigade should inspect clean agent extinguisher systems on a regular basis. They should be trained to activate the system, if necessary. There is little that fire brigade members can do to directly support an operating clean agent system. Their responsibilities are limited to assisting in the evacuation of affected personnel, accounting for everyone displaced by the evacuation, and preventing unauthorized entry into the affected area.

NOTE: Many industrial fire brigades have SOPs to allow for a seat time prior to opening these areas post system discharge to ensure time for the clean agent to be effective. While waiting, additional fire equipment can be staged in case the fire needs to be overhauled.

Standpipe and Hose Systems

NFPA 1081 (2018): 4.2.2, 4.3.4

Standpipe and hose systems are designed to provide a means for rapidly deploying fire hoses and operating fire streams at locations that are remote from the fire apparatus. Standpipe systems can be found in buildings and structures where the AHJ requires it.

The value of standpipes in large-area, one-story structures is primarily based on expediency. Horizontal standpipes reduce the time and effort needed to manually advance a hoseline several hundred feet (meters) to reach the seat of the fire. During overhaul, horizontal standpipes can also reduce the amount of hose needed to reach areas that sprinklers already control. In many high-rise buildings, a standpipe is the primary means for manual extinguishment and overhaul of a fire and an essential element in a building's design.

Depending on the type of system installed, either fire brigade members or properly trained occupants may use standpipe systems. A reliable water supply may be in place to service the standpipe system. Fire brigades may provide the water supply or augment the existing supply using a FDC. The standpipe system may also be part of or separate from an automatic sprinkler, water spray, water mist, or foam-water system.

Although standpipe systems are required in many buildings, they do not take the place of automatic sprinkler systems, nor do they lessen the need for sprinklers. Automatic sprinklers continue to be the most effective method of fire control.

Components found in standpipe systems commonly include the following:

- Hose stations
- Waterflow control valves
- Pressure-regulating devices

- Water supply
- Risers
- Fire department connection (FDC)

There are three classes of standpipe systems based on the intended use of the hose stations or discharge outlets. These classes are **(Figure 6.28)**:

Figure 6.28 Examples of the three classes of standpipes.

- **Class I** — Class I standpipe systems are primarily for use by fire suppression personnel trained in handling large hoselines. A Class I system provides 2½-inch (65 mm) hose connections or hose stations attached to the standpipe riser. The 2½-inch (65 mm) hose connections may be equipped with a reducer on the cap that allows for the connection of a 1½-inch (38 mm) hose coupling.

- **Class II** — A Class II system, sometimes referred to a house lines, is designed for trained building occupants or fire brigade personnel to use. These systems are equipped with 1½-inch (38 mm) hose and nozzle and stored on a hose reel or rack system. These systems typically use a single-jacket type hose and are equipped with a lightweight, twist-type shut-off nozzle.

- **Class III** — A Class III system combines the features of Class I and Class II systems. Class III systems provide 1½-inch (38 mm) hose stations to supply water for trained building occupants and 2½-inch (65 mm) hose connections to supply a larger volume of water for use by fire brigades and other personnel trained in handling heavy fire streams. The system must allow both Class I and Class II services to be used simultaneously.

There are different types of standpipe systems that include the following:

- **Automatic wet** — This system contains water at all times. Wet standpipe systems cannot be used in cold environments.

- **Automatic dry** — This system contains air under pressure to maintain the integrity of the piping. Water is admitted to the system through a dry-pipe valve upon the opening of a hose valve.

- **Semiautomatic dry** — Standpipe system attached to a water supply that is capable of supplying the system demand at all times; it requires activation of a control device to provide water at hose connections. The system is designed to admit water into the system when a dry-pipe valve is activated at the hose station.

- **Manual dry** — This system does not have a permanent water supply. It is instead designed to have water only when the system is being supplied through the FDC.

- **Manual wet** — Standpipe system that is maintained full of water but has no water supply; the water in the system is maintained to identify leaks. The fire brigade must provide water to the system.

Pressure Regulating Valves

Where the discharge pressure at a hose outlet exceeds 175 psi (1 225 kPa), NFPA 14 requires a pressure-regulating device to limit the pressure to 100 psi (700 kPa), unless the AHJ approves it. The use of a pressure-regulating device prevents pressures that make a fire hose difficult or dangerous to handle. This device enhances system reliability because it extends individual zones to greater heights. In some instances, it may improve system economy because its use may eliminate some pumps.

Pressure-regulating devices (PRDs) make the system design more complex. The three basic categories of pressure-regulating devices are as follows:

- **Pressure-restricting devices** — Consist of a simple restricting orifice inserted into the waterway. The amount of pressure drop through the orifice plate depends on the orifice diameter and available flow and pressure within the system. Each standpipe discharge connection is fitted with a restricting orifice with different sizes being required for each floor and application. They are limited to systems with 1½-inch (38 mm) hose discharges and 175 psi (1 225 kPa) maximum pressure. This device is not a preferred type because it does not control or reduce the system water pressure.

- **Pressure-control devices** — Preferred for managing excessive pressure and considered to be the most reliable method of pressure control. They use a pitot tube and gauge to read the pressure and automatically reduce the flow through the discharge. Some of the devices are field adjustable; others are preset at the factory.

- **Pressure-reducing devices** — Preferred for managing excessive pressure; uses a spring mechanism that compensates for variations in pressure. These mechanisms balance the available pressure within the system with the pressure required for hoseline use. Inspectors need to know that the second pipe is for testing of the PRDs.

NOTE: Refer to NFPA 25 for specific testing requirements for these devices.

Standpipe systems that are equipped with pressure-regulating devices are designed to be routinely tested. Systems must have dedicated drainage pipes with connections on each floor and a means for determining water flow.

A pressure-regulating device must be specified and/or adjusted to meet the pressure and flow requirements of the individual installation. For factory-set devices, the pressure-regulating device must be installed on the proper hose outlet. A pressure-regulating device that is not properly installed or adjusted for the required inlet pressure, outlet pressure, and flow may result in reduced available flow and impaired suppression capabilities.

System Activation

Standpipe systems are activated manually. Fire brigade members should be trained to operate the standpipes systems and ensure that pressure regulating valves are used and functioning properly. Once handlines are attached, if necessary, and deployed, then the appropriate valves should be opened.

Safety Precautions

All standpipe discharges should be equipped with pressure regulating device. The fire brigade should flush the standpipe prior to connecting any hose lines.

Fire Brigade Support

In most cases, little is required of fire brigade members in supporting operating sprinkler systems. They should make sure that the control valve is open so that the system can function as designed and ensure that it remains open until water flow is no longer required. Well-meaning individuals may want to do this task in an attempt to limit water damage. Only the IC should authorize the closing of the system control valve. Fire brigade members can also communicate with incoming fire and emergency services units to direct them to the appropriate FDC.

A qualified member equipped with a two-way radio should stand by the sprinkler control valve when it is closed and until protection is restored. The member should be ready to reopen the valve should the need arise.

NOTE: During building and facility inspections, fire brigade members should look for changes in stored materials or in the structure itself that may block the spray pattern.

System Inspection Records

NFPA 1081 (2018): 4.3.5

Organizational policies should require that the readiness of fire detection and suppression systems be documented for the record and systematically stored. Records should be kept on all inspections performed on fire detection and suppression systems. Most often the fire alarm or suppression system contractor and/or the facility manager maintain these records. These records provide a historical perspective of fire protection activities within that facility. Record-keeping must be accurate since these records could be subpoenaed for legal actions.

All documents and records pertaining to a facility's fire detection and suppression systems should be kept within the company's document management system. These documents and reports include the following:

- Inspection reports, forms, and letters
- Fire reports
- Investigation reports

Chapter Review

1. Name and describe four basic system components for fire detection systems.

2. What are the most commonly used release mechanisms used to activate sprinklers?

3. What are the four types of control valves?

4. Name and describe the two types of sprinkler system activation.

5. What responsibilities should fire brigade support be prepared to carry out pertaining to sprinkler system?

6. What are some different types of special extinguishing systems?

7. Describe the three classes of standpipes.

8. What documents should be included in system inspection records?

Discussion Questions

1. What type of fixed systems are present in your facilities?

2. What type of special extinguishing systems have you come in contact with?

Key Terms

Boilover — An event in the burning of certain oils in an open-top tank when, after a long period of quiescent burning, there is a sudden increase in fire intensity associated with expulsion of burning oil from the tank. (Reprinted with permission from NFPA 1-2018, Fire Code, Copyright © 2017, National Fire Protection Association, Quincy, MA. This reprinted material is not the complete and official position of the NFPA on the referenced subject, which is represented only by the standard in its entirety which may be obtained through the NFPA website at www.nfpa.org.)

Film Forming Fluoroprotein Foam (FFFP) — Foam concentrate that combines the qualities of fluoroprotein foam with those of aqueous film forming foam. See Foam Concentrate.

Fluoroprotein Foams — Protein foam concentrate with synthetic fluorinated surfactants added. These surfactants enable the foam to shed, or separate from, hydrocarbon fuels. See Foam Concentrate.

Fluorosurfactants — Fluorine-based chemicals that lower the surface tension of a liquid, in this case fire fighting foams.

Froth-over — Froth-overs occur when water is present or enters a tank containing hot viscous oil and the sudden conversion of water to steam causes a portion of the tank contents to overflow.

Hydrocarbon Surfactants — Hydrocarbon-based chemicals that lower the surface tension of a liquid, in this case fire fighting foams.

Oleophobic — The physical property of a molecule that is repelled from oil.

Slop-over — Situation that occurs when burning oil that is stored in a tank is forced over the edge of the tank by water that is heated to the boiling point and has accumulated under the surface of the oil.

Skill Sheet List

The following skill sheets should be used to evaluate the skills described in this chapter:

NOTE: Students should wear the PPE appropriate to the NFPA 1081 level (Incipient, Advanced Exterior, Interior Structural, etc...) being evaluated.

Incipient Facility Fire Brigade Member

Chapter Contents

JPRs addressed in this chapter

This chapter provides information that addresses the following job performance requirements of NFPA 1081, *Standard for Facility Fire Brigade Member Professional Qualifications (2018)*.

4.2.2

1. Identify property conservation tools and equipment. [4.2.2]

2. Describe the actions taken in property conversation operations. [4.2.2]

3. Explain the different water management methods. [4.2.2]

4. Describe the procedures for closing and securing facilities. [4.2.2]

Chapter 7
Property Conservation Operations

Property conservation operations (also called salvage or loss control operations) are a primary task of fire brigade members. The fire service uses the term *loss control* to describe the activities that personnel perform before, during, and after a fire has been extinguished to minimize losses to property. Properly applied loss control activities include:

- Minimizing damage to the structure, exposures, and contents
- Minimizing environmental impacts such as contaminated water run-off
- Eliminating the chance that a fire will reignite in the structure
- Reducing the amount of time needed to repair and reopen the facility
- Minimizing financial loss for the company, insurance company, and facility

Property conservation is perhaps the most important aspect in loss control. During salvage, fire brigade members attempt to save property and reduce further damage from water, smoke, heat, and exposure during or immediately after a fire. Proper salvage operations involve preincident planning, knowledge of salvage procedures, and the tools and equipment necessary to perform the job. Improvisation is often necessary when personnel are presented with unique situations and limited equipment. The protection of damaged property from weather and trespassers is also critical.

Fire brigade members must do everything they can to protect property without compromising their first priority — protecting life and health. Fire and smoke are not the only factors that contribute to property damage. If not carefully performed, fire suppression activities can cause more damage than the initial fire. Protecting property requires fire brigade members to practice good loss control techniques during all phases of an incident.

Two types of damage result from a fire. Fire and smoke cause primary damage. Fire suppression activities, such as forcible entry, ventilation, and fire extinguishment operations, cause secondary damage. A structure's vulnerability to weather and vandalism following fire suppression is also considered a form of secondary damage.

This chapter will describe the operations and procedures relating to:

- Loss control tools and equipment
- Property conservation
- Closing and securing the facility

Property Conservation Tools and Equipment

NFPA 1081 (2018): 4.2.2

Property conservation operations will vary depending on the fire brigade's size and organization as well as the type and size of facility or facilities. Fire brigade members should know where to find the loss control tools and equipment that their brigade uses. Personnel should also be trained on how to properly use them.

Tools and equipment for loss control operations should be stored in a specially designated salvage toolbox or in other containers that make them easier to carry. Salvage materials and supplies may be kept in a plastic tub and brought into the structure as soon as possible **(Figure 7.1)**. The tub provides a useful water-resistant container to protect items such as computers, pictures, and other water-sensitive materials.

Figure 7.1 Plastic tubs can be used to hold and carry many salvage materials and supplies.

Typical tools and equipment used in salvage operations include:

- Electrical
- Mechanical
- Plumbing
- General carpentry
- Pumps, mops, squeegees, and buckets that are useful for removing water

Other specialized tools and equipment used in loss operations may include:

- **Automatic sprinkler kit** — The tools in a sprinkler kit stop the flow of water from an open sprinkler. Water flowing from an open sprinkler can do considerable damage to property on lower floors after a fire has been controlled in a commercial building. Sprinkler tongs or stoppers and wooden sprinkler wedges are suggested tools to include in a sprinkler kit.

- **Carryalls** — Carryalls are used to catch and carry debris, and to provide a water basin for immersing small burning objects. Carryalls should be constructed of nonflammable material.

- **Floor runners** — Fire brigade members often unintentionally damage flooring with their boots and equipment during fire suppression operations. Using floor runners may protect these floor coverings. Floor runners can be unrolled from an entrance to almost any part of a building. Commercially prepared vinyl-laminated nylon floor runners are:

  — Lightweight   — Flexible

  — Tough   — Heat-resistant

  — Water-resistant   — Easy to maintain

> **CAUTION:** Do not attempt to use sprinkler tongs or wedges if the system has a fire pump running. The pressure and volume of water that the fire pump creates can cause an injury.

> **CAUTION:** In some localities, the AHJ has established the policy that sprinklers should be shut off by closing control valves instead of using sprinkler wedges. The rationale for closing the valve is because of the potential for chemicals mixed with the water (antifreeze solutions and anti-corrosion additives) in the sprinkler piping.

Routing Water Out of a Sprinklered Building

After the sprinkler system main control valve is shut, water will continue to flow from open sprinklers for a time. **Catchalls** and chutes can be used to capture and route the water out of the building. In addition, where only one sprinkler is flowing, a 2½- or 3-inch (65 mm or 77 mm) hoseline can be fitted over the sprinkler and directed out a door or window.

NOTE: The AHJ determines responsibility for restoring automatic sprinkler systems to service. You may only restore systems if you are authorized and trained to do so.

Property Conservation Operations

NFPA 1081 (2018): 4.2.2

Property conservation operations consist of those methods and operating procedures that aid in reducing damage from fire and fire control operations. Proper salvage operations involve early planning, knowing the procedures necessary to do the job, and being familiar with the various tools and equipment to be used. Personnel may need to improvise when equipment is limited.

Planning

Efficient salvage operations require planning and training for the facility fire brigade leader and members. Standard operating procedures should be developed to address early and well-coordinated salvage operations. Special preincident plans may be needed for commercial and industrial facilities with special target hazards that can present more challenging solutions to loss control.

In commercial and industrial occupancies, personnel should be aware of the value associated with the contents vital to business survival **(Figure 7.2)**. The value of the contents may exceed the replacement cost of the structural materials. The data, documents, and information stored in or on computers, filing cabinets filled with records, and computer backup drives are critical to the operation of a business.

Figure 7.2 Commercial and industrial facilities may contain high-stack rack storage for manufacturing components and stock that hold thousands or millions of dollars in materials.

Fire brigade leaders and members can facilitate efforts before an incident by working with the loss control representative(s) of the facilities or companies. Identify critical records and components needed for business continuation (such as stock protection in warehouses and target hazards in storage areas) and provide backup copies of critical records in a remote or protected location.

Fire brigade leaders should consider the salvage requirements for completing the anticipated tasks and stock an adequate amount of the following materials:

- Rolls of plastic
- Tarps
- Duct tape
- Absorbent materials (sand and "kitty litter")
- Tools (water vacuums, sprinkler chocks or tongs, squeegees, mops, and buckets)

Another important part of planning concerns the removal of water used during and after fire, spill, leak, and release control operations. This water will be contaminated, and the fire brigade should have a plan in place for its removal, retention, and ultimate disposition.

Procedures

Salvage operations begin upon arrival and continue until the last unit leaves the scene. When the on-scene resources are sufficient and the situation permits, the Incident Commander (IC) may order salvage operations to be conducted at the same time suppression activities are underway. In some instances, the contents of the area or room(s) immediately near or below the fire's location can be protected with **salvage covers** while fire suppression operations are being conducted on the floor above. In other instances, personnel may need to delay suppression activities for a short time in order to remove vital contents. In these cases, primary damage often results in less financial loss than secondary damage caused by the fire suppression efforts. The IC should take into consideration the preincident plan, fire development, and any unsafe structural conditions before making any decisions about delaying fire suppression.

The choice of salvage procedures will depend on:

- Number of personnel available
- Extent and location of the fire
- Type, size, and quantity of the contents
- Current weather conditions

Salvage procedures include:

- Moving contents to a safe location in the structure
- Removing contents from the structure
- Protecting the contents in place with salvage covers

One useful salvage technique is to move contents from inside the structure to areas away from concentrations of smoke, where they are not in danger of fire extension and where water will not reach. This method is most effective when the fire is limited and not likely to spread, and when weather conditions would damage contents if they were moved outside. You should cover these contents with salvage covers or raise them off the floor as a precaution against secondary damage.

Removing contents from the structure will help protect them from further primary and potential secondary damage. However, this method may interfere with fire suppression and ventilation crews that are using the same doors to enter the structure. Opening and closing the doors may also interfere with the flow path of air to the fire. Contents should be stacked on surfaces that are dry, such as a parking lot or driveway, and not near areas where fire brigade members may be collecting debris for disposal. Contents that are stored outside must also be protected from theft or vandalism before and after the fire is extinguished. The owner/occupant must be told that the contents have been stored outside or the contents should be secured in some fashion.

The method most often used to protect contents is to leave them in the room in which they are found. Fire brigade members gather contents into compact piles that they can cover with a minimum of salvage covers. Grouping contents in this manner allows more items to be protected than if they were covered in their original position. If possible, group items to be protected in the center of the room when arranging for salvage. In many cases, one salvage cover can protect the contents of a small room.

When arranging grouped items in a room, a tall object should be placed in such a way that it can support a salvage cover. For example, in an office, a filing cabinet should be placed at the end of a desk. Other furniture should be grouped around the cabinet and desk, creating a high point in the furniture group that allows water to run off without pooling in depressions of the cover.

Furniture or boxes of contents that sit on wet carpet can absorb water and become damaged, even though they are well covered. To prevent this damage, the furniture or other objects should be raised off the wet floor with water-resistant materials, such as precut plastic or foam blocks. If blocks are unavailable, you can improvise with items such as pallets or pieces of lumber.

Commercial occupancies present challenges for fire brigade members who are trying to perform salvage functions. They may have difficulty covering contents in these occupancies when large stocks and display features are involved. In addition, display shelves are frequently built to the ceiling and directly against the wall. This construction feature makes contents difficult to cover because when water flows down a wall, it naturally comes into contact with shelving and wets the contents. Contents stacked too close to the ceiling also present a salvage problem. Ideally, there should be enough space between the inventory and ceiling to allow fire brigade members to easily apply salvage covers.

Stock that is susceptible to water damage should be raised off the floor to prevent saturation. Skids or pallets are commonly used for stacking in these instances, if available **(Figure 7.3)**. Even if

Figure 7.3 Pallet storage allows products or materials to be raised off the floor preventing water damage.

susceptible stock is raised off the floor, it must be covered. However, when the number of salvage covers is limited, it is good practice for personnel to use available covers for water chutes and catchalls even though the water must be routed to the floor and removed later. Some large facilities may have sumps with pumps already in place. These features should be noted on pre-fire plans along with their rated capacity.

Figure 7.4 These large rolls of print paper could collapse if they become saturated with water.

They can be activated during an emergency. In some cases, the Control Room Operators can activate them remotely. In other configurations, they are automatically or manually activated. Personnel should confirm these pumps are running and free of debris. Understand that these pumps may not be able to remove deep layers of fire fighting foams.

Fire brigade members must be cautious of high-piled stock, such as boxed materials or rolled paper that becomes wet at the bottom **(Figure 7.4)**. The wetness often causes the material to expand and push out interior or exterior walls. Wetness also reduces the material's strength and may cause the piles to collapse. Some rolls of paper can weigh a ton (900 kg) or more. If one of these rolls were to fall on fire brigade members, it could seriously injure or kill them.

Salvage Covers

Salvage covers are manufactured from waterproof canvas or vinyl in various sizes. These covers have reinforced corners and edge hems into which grommets are placed for hanging or draping. Vinyl covers are lightweight, easy to handle, economical, and practical for both indoor and outdoor use. They may melt if used to cover hot objects and may tear if used to cover sharp corners or edges.

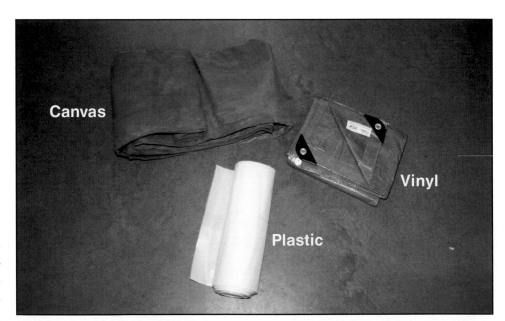

Figure 7.5 Salvage covers are made of canvas, vinyl, or rolls of plastic.

Fire brigades may also use disposable heavy-duty plastic covers. The plastic is available on rolls and can be extended as needed to cover large areas **(Figure 7.5)**. Salvage covers can also be cut from the rolls in different shapes and sizes, as needed.

Figure 7.6 One fire brigade member can easily spread a rolled salvage cover over an object or objects to be protected.

Figure 7.7 One fire brigade member can also spread a folded salvage cover easily.

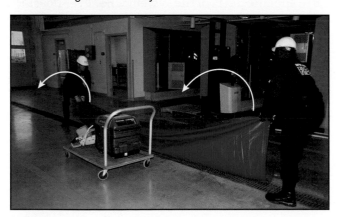

Figure 7.8 Two fire brigade members can quickly cover an object or objects with a salvage cover using the balloon throw method.

When objects or groupings are too large to be covered using a single cover or when long chutes or catchalls need to be made, personnel must splice covers with watertight joints. There are many methods for splicing salvage covers, and your fire brigade will train you on the specific procedure to use. Disposable rolled plastic sheeting can also be used as long chutes that can be cut to size as needed. The use of plastic rolls saves time and property because it eliminates the need for splicing and reduces the risk of leakage.

The proper folding and deploying of salvage covers is critical to successful salvage operations. The following sections describe the basic methods used to fold and deploy salvage covers.

One-Fire Brigade Member Spread with a Rolled Salvage Cover

The main advantage of the one-fire brigade member salvage cover roll is that one person can quickly unroll a cover across the top of an object (**Figure 7.6**). A salvage cover rolled for a one-fire brigade member spread may be carried on the shoulder or under the arm.

One-Fire Brigade Member Spread with a Folded Salvage Cover

Some brigades prefer to carry salvage covers that have been folded, as opposed to rolled (**Figure 7.7**). Two fire brigade members are needed to make this fold, performing the same functions simultaneously. Carrying a folded salvage cover on the shoulder is typically most convenient, but any safe carrying method is acceptable.

Two-Fire Brigade Member Spread with a Folded Salvage Cover

A single fire brigade member cannot easily handle a large salvage cover. These covers should be folded for two-fire brigade member deployment. The most convenient way to carry this fold is on the shoulder with the open edges next to the neck. It makes little difference which end of the folded cover is placed in front of the carrier because two open-end folds will be exposed. Position the cover so that the fire brigade member carrying it holds the lower pair of corners, and the second fire brigade member holds the uppermost pair.

A method called the *balloon throw* is commonly used for two fire brigade members to deploy a large salvage cover. The balloon throw works best when sufficient air is pocketed under the cover. This pocketed air gives the cover a parachute effect that allows it to float into place over the article(s) to be covered (**Figure 7.8**).

Water Management

NFPA 1081 (2018): 4.2.2

After fire brigade members have protected the building's contents, their next salvage consideration is normally to remove excess water. Water accumulates or is absorbed in areas that may lack adequate drainage. Accumulations of water place additional weight on structural members and can contribute to their collapse. Water weighs 8.33 pounds per gallon (1 kg per liter); therefore 1,000 gallons (4 000 liters) of water equates to 8,330 pounds (4 000 kg) of additional weight to a structure. Such accumulations can damage machinery, utilities, and stored merchandise. Elevator and heating, ventilation, and air conditioning (HVAC) equipment can be adversely affected, as well. Due to environmental concerns, fire suppression runoff water may need to be retained and treated.

Trapping Water

Water traps made of plastic sheeting can be constructed in various ways. Using plastic sheeting is appropriate for collecting small amounts of water, such as water leaking from an area above.

Diverting Water

Fire brigade members can use salvage covers, plastic sheeting, duct tape, and a stapler to construct troughs to divert water. Lightweight and flexible plastic sheeting can be shaped or wrapped around almost anything to create a trough. With plastic sheeting, personnel can divert water through a door or window or into a nearby drain. Dikes made of salvage covers or plastic can also be positioned across doorways or stairways to limit water spread.

Limiting Water Spread

Facility fire brigade members may be able to stop water from flowing or prevent it from spreading into undamaged areas. One way to limit water damage is to stop the flow of water from sprinklers after a fire is extinguished. Sprinklers can be plugged with wedges or sprinkler tongs.

Sprinkler control valves can be isolated or closed to control the flow of water to the system, but they should never be closed unless the fire is extinguished and the IC authorizes the valve closing. Floor or unit valves should be used to terminate the water flow to specific parts of the system whenever possible so that the rest of the system remains in service. Immediately after the correct valve has been closed, personnel should open the drains (main or auxiliary) to relieve system pressure. This action allows water remaining in the system to flow to the building's exterior rather than into the building through open sprinklers. The facility fire brigade member assigned to close the control valve must remain at the valve so that it may be quickly reopened if necessary. The industrial fire brigade or fire and emergency services organization must explain the limitations of the sprinkler system before returning it to service.

Routing Water

The primary objective of industrial fire brigade members when removing water is to remove it quickly and safely without damaging unaffected areas of the building **(Figure 7.9)**. Several of the following means are used to route water:

- Sewer drains or soil-pipe openings
- Water chutes
- **Scuppers**
- Stairways
- Catchalls
- Hoselines

Depending on potential damage to process areas and equipment, some drains must be protected from runoff water, and care should be used to avoid introducing contaminates to non- containment systems. Fire brigade personnel should always keep in mind environmental concerns and local procedures when diverting or routing water.

Figure 7.9 Fire fighting water runoff being directed out exterior doorways.

Sewer Drains or Soil-Pipe Openings

Sewer drains and soil pipes service sinks and toilets throughout the buildings and drain to an exterior sewer system. Soil pipes can remove the cleanout plugs, and sewer drains can be accessed by lifting toilets from floor connections. During either procedure, personnel must be careful to not damage the pipes. Damage to these pipes can result in costly repairs and even leakage of sewer gas. To remove the plug from the soil pipe, tap the edge of the pipe bell to help loosen the plug. Then use a wrench to remove the plug. Place a screen or a drain guard over the opening to prevent debris from entering the pipe.

To lift a toilet from its sewer-drain connection, shut off the water valve to the toilet. This valve is usually located on the wall adjacent to the drain connection. Flush the toilet to empty the water tank and disconnect the tubing that connects the toilet to the water valve. Remove the fasteners that attach the base of the toilet to the flooring, and gently rock the fixture to dislodge it from the wax or putty seal of the connection. Lift the toilet and set it aside so that it will not obstruct water flow to the drain. Cover the drain opening with a screen or drain guard to prevent debris from entering.

NOTE: Immediately after completing water removal procedures, close sewer drains and soil pipes to prevent contamination of the building with sewer gas. A crew member needs to form a makeshift plug from available materials, making sure that it will not hurt the pipe and that it can be removed at a later date.

Stairways

Stairways that are conveniently located may be used to route water. After occupants have been evacuated, water chutes can be constructed to provide protection for the stairwell and channel the water to an exit point.

Water Chutes

Water collected in a catchall can be routed to a drain channeled outside the building by using chutes in conjunction with the catchall. Water chutes, constructed of salvage covers and pike poles, ladders, or other available materials, can also route water from the structure.

A water chute is one of the most practical methods of removing water that comes through the ceiling from upper floors. Water chutes may be constructed on the floor below fire fighting operations to drain runoff out of the structure through windows or doors. Some fire brigades have prepared chutes, approximately 10 feet (3 m) long, as regular equipment. Other brigades find it more practical to construct chutes when and where needed using floor runners or one or more salvage covers **(Figure 7.10)**. Plastic sheeting, a heavy-duty stapler, and duct tape can be used to construct water diversion chutes.

Catchalls

A catchall is constructed from a salvage cover or plastic cover that has been placed on the floor to hold small amounts of water **(Figure 7.11)**. The catchall also may be used as a temporary means to control large amounts of water until chutes can be constructed to route the water to the outside. Properly constructed catchalls hold several hundred gallons (liters) of water and often save considerable time during salvage operations.

In order to catch as much water as possible, place the cover into position as soon as possible, even if the sides of the cover have not been uniformly rolled. Two fire brigade members are usually needed to construct a catchall.

A plan should be developed to remove water from a catchall as soon as it is constructed, especially if it appears that the volume of water will be greater than the catchall's capacity. Submersible pumps may be used if available and if there is a significant and constant flow of water into the catchall. A commonly used method of water removal is to splice a water chute to the catchall. An advantage to this system is that as soon as water accumulates in the catchall it is drained to the outside.

Figure 7.10 Two fire brigade members practicing the construction of a water chute.

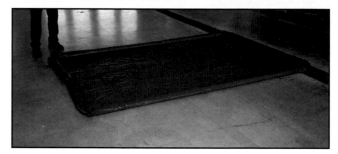

Figure 7.11 A fire brigade member examining a completed catchall.

Scuppers

Scuppers may be available in commercial occupancies. Scuppers are holes in a wall through which water may be drained from the structure. Fire brigade members can route water towards the scuppers using squeegees or water chutes.

Hoselines

Hoselines that are partially pressurized to give them weight can be used as temporary dikes. Fire brigade members can place a hoseline around the perimeter of a room and then pull the loop of the hose out the exit, removing the water. They can also use the hose to scrape the water out like a squeegee. Two lengths of hoseline that personnel position so they are parallel to each other can form a water chute to route water.

Removing Water

Although industrial fire brigade members may not remove water at some incidents – such as when contamination of hazardous materials is a factor – they must often remove a lot of water from a structure after a fire. Methods of removing large amounts of water from shafts or from areas below ground level involve either draining or pumping. Small amounts of water within a building can be removed with water vacuums, mops, brooms, and squeegees.

Portable and Submersible Pumps

When internal devices such as sump pumps and drains are insufficient for handling large quantities of water, personnel must use other means of removal. Devices that generally are used include portable pumps, submersible pumps, or dewatering devices. Portable and submersible pumps should be placed in an area that allows discharged water to flow into soil pipes, storm drains, ditches, or trenches **(Figure 7.12)**. All pumps must be equipped with strainers, and water removal should be from the lowest point available.

Dewatering Devices

Dewatering devices are pumps used to remove water from basements, elevator shafts, and sumps. Portable pumps capable of passing grey water filled with debris, jet-siphons, and submersible pumps are best suited for salvage operations. These devices can be moved to any point where a line of hose can be placed and an outlet for water can be provided.

Water Vacuum

A water vacuum is one of the easiest and fastest ways to remove water. These vacuums can be used to remove water from:

Figure 7.12 Fire brigade members can use portable, submersible pumps to remove water from a structure.

- Floors
- Carpets
- Areas where water cannot be picked up by a submersible pump or siphon ejector

The water vacuum appliance consists of a tank (worn on the back or mounted on wheels), a pump, a hose, and a nozzle. Backpack-type tanks normally have a capacity of 4 to 5 gallons (18 L to 20 L) and use a lanyard that empties the water through the nozzle or a separate drain hose. Floor models on rollers may have capacities up to 20 gallons (80 L). They may be emptied using an attached hoseline or by conventional means (upending the basin).

Closing and Securing the Facility

NFPA 1081 (2018): 4.2.2

Following an incident, personnel must ensure the building is closed and secured to prevent further damage. Doors, windows, and ventilation openings should be covered with plastic or plywood to keep out rain or snow and to prevent heat loss in cold weather. If you anticipate the need to "make a temporary door" to secure a building, plan to stock materials such as plastic, lath, nails/staples, a few sheets of plywood, hasps, locks, and hinges. With planning, cost to keep supplies is low and potential benefit is high.

Another critical aspect of salvage operations is covering openings to prevent further damage to the property from weather and trespassers. Doors or windows that have been broken or removed during suppression activities should be covered with plywood, heavy plastic, or some similar materials to keep out rain. Plywood, hinges, a hasp, and a padlock can be used to fashion a temporary door. Openings in roofs should be covered with plywood, roofing paper, heavy plastic sheeting, or tar paper. Use appropriate roofing nails if roofing paper, tar paper, or plastic is used. Place strips of lath along the edges of the material and nail them in place. Fire brigade members must ensure these openings are covered with lumber or thick plywood that will support a person's weight.

Chapter Review

1. What are some specialized tools and equipment that may be used during property conservation?

2. What operations may be included in salvage procedures?

3. What are the different ways of routing water?

4. How should facilities be secured to prevent further damage to the property from weather and trespassers?

Key Terms

Carryall — Waterproof carrier used to carry and catch debris or used as a water sump basin for immersing small burning objects.

Catchall — Retaining basin, usually made from salvage covers, to impound water dripping from above.

Property Conservation — Methods and operating procedures by which firefighters attempt to save property and reduce further damage from water, smoke, heat, and exposure during or immediately after a fire; may be accomplished by removing property from a fire area, by covering it, or by other means.

Salvage Cover — Waterproof cover made of cotton duck, plastic, or other material used by fire departments to protect unaffected furniture and building areas from heat, smoke, and water damage; a tarpaulin or tarp.

Scupper — Form of drain opening provided in outer walls at floor or roof level to remove water to the exterior of a building in order to reduce water damage.

Skill Sheet List

The following skill sheets should be used to evaluate the skills described in this chapter:

NOTE: Students should wear the PPE appropriate to the NFPA 1081 level (Incipient, Advanced Exterior, Interior Structural, etc...) being evaluated.

Incipient Facility Fire Brigade Member

Chapter Contents

JPRs addressed in this chapter

This chapter provides information that addresses the following job performance requirements of NFPA 1081, *Standard for Facility Fire Brigade Member Professional Qualifications (2018)*.

4.2.3   4.3.1

1. Describe the methods of fire extinguishment during initial fire control operations. [4.2.3, 4.3.1]

2. Explain the different fuel-specific fire suppression operations. [4.2.3, 4.3.1]

Chapter 8
Initial Fire Fighting Operations

The success or failure of initial fire control operations often depends upon the skill and knowledge of the personnel involved in initial attack. A well-trained team of fire brigade members who have an attack plan and adequate tools and equipment can handle the vast majority of emergency situations at their facilities. Personnel must be prepared to control hazards ranging from spills, leaks, and releases as well control fires should they occur on company property.

This chapter provides information on fire control procedures for incipient fires including fire brigade tactics for small structures, vehicle, and trash container fires. This chapter also focuses on hazards during response to fires involving Class A, B, C, D, and K materials.

Fire Control Operations
NFPA 1081 (2018): 4.2.3, 4.3.1

Fire control operations include the use of portable extinguishers and handlines flowing up to 125 gpm (473 L/min) to fight fires involving:

- Class A materials — stacked and piled materials, small unattached structures, and trash containers
- Class B materials — flammable/combustible liquids and gases
- Class C materials — energized electrical equipment
- Class D materials — flammable metals
- Class K materials — combustible cooking oils

United Kingdom and European Fire Classifications

The United Kingdom and Europe use a slightly different fire classification system. In that system:

- Class A materials include wood, paper, and textiles
- Class B materials are flammable liquids
- Class C materials are flammable gases
- Class D materials are metals
- Class F materials include cooking oils and fats

NOTE: Fires involving electrified equipment or facilities are not given a class identifier in this system.

The Science Behind Fire Extinguishment Methods

To understand fire control methods, you need to know how fires are extinguished. The following sections describe methods that fire brigade members use to interrupt the fire tetrahedron and extinguish a fire. These methods include:

- Temperature reduction
- Fuel removal
- Oxygen exclusion
- Chemical flame inhibition

Temperature Reduction

Temperature reduction is a strategy that disrupts the fire tetrahedron by cooling the fuel below the point at which it can sustain combustion. Water is one of the most common resources used for cooling. To be effective, fire brigade members must apply enough water to the burning fuel to absorb the combustion-generated heat and stop the gas phase chemical reaction **(Figure 8.1)**. Cooling extinguishes solid fuels by reducing the temperature of a fuel to a point where it does not produce sufficient vapors to burn. The use of water for cooling is also the most effective method available for the extinguishment of smoldering fires.

Water can also be used to control burning gases and reduce the temperature of hot products of combustion in the upper gas layer. This approach limits or stops flaming combustion in the upper layer and slows the pyrolysis process of combustible materials by reducing radiant heat flux from the upper layer, which in turn reduces the potential for flashover.

A coordinated combination of cooling hot fire gases from the exterior of a fire compartment using a straight stream paired with tactical ventilation lowers the risk that a ventilation-limited fire will reignite and reenter the growth stage when it receives more oxygen.

Water absorbs significant heat as its temperature is raised, but it has its greatest effect when it

Figure 8.1 Water application is used to reduce the temperature of the fuel below the point at which combustion is sustained.

is vaporized into steam. When water is converted to steam, it absorbs five times more energy than warming the liquid to the boiling point. A volume of water also rapidly expands approximately 1,700 times when it converts into steam. Excess steam production can reduce visibility, increase the chances for steam burns, and disrupt the thermal layer.

Fire brigade members can control steam production in the following ways:

- Use good nozzle technique.
- Apply the appropriate amount of water.
- Apply water using the most effective form (fog, straight, or solid stream based upon existing conditions).

If an appropriate amount of water is used with good nozzle technique, as described later in this chapter, the hot gases within the fire compartment will contract. The contraction of the hot gases may offset the expansion of the steam. If the cooling process is effective, steam production will be kept to a minimum.

Fuel Removal

Removing the fuel source effectively extinguishes any fire, though it is rarely an option as an extinguishment method at structure fires. Removing fuel is more common tactic at fires involving materials such as:

- Exterior stacked materials
- Flammable liquids/gases
- Vehicles

Some facilities may have remote shutoff valves in place to accomplish the safer shutdown of fuel flow **(Figure 8.2)**. Fire brigade members should be aware of where these valves are located and how they operate.

Figure 8.2 A trained facility worker closing a valve to stop the flow of a flammable fuel.

WARNING: Only personnel who are trained to operate shutoff systems should do so.

Another example of fuel removal is allowing a fire to burn until all available fuel is consumed while fire brigade members protect exposures. For instance, flammable liquid spills may create greater environmental harm if they are extinguished with water, creating substantial runoff and contaminating soil or bodies of water. When exposures or other hazards are not a consideration, the best solution may be to allow the fire to burn, maximizing thermal damage but minimizing groundwater pollution.

A fuel source may also be removed in the following ways:

- Stopping the flow of a liquid fuel
- Closing valves to stop the emission of gaseous fuels
- Moving solid fuels out of the path of the fire

Oxygen Exclusion

Reducing the oxygen available to the combustion process slows a fire's growth and may result in complete extinguishment over time. In its simplest form, this method is used to extinguish stovetop fires when a cover is placed on a pan of burning grease. Limiting the fire's air supply can be a highly effective fire control action. The simplest example of this method is when a building occupant closes the door to the fire room before leaving the building. This action limits the air supply to the fire and can sometimes prevent flashover. Control of doors and windows into and within the structure can aid in controlling the flow path of oxygen to heated, fuel-rich products of combustion.

On a larger scale, flooding a compartment with an inert gas such as carbon dioxide displaces the oxygen and disrupts the combustion process **(Figure 8.3)**. Displacing oxygen in a compartment must be coordinated carefully because it also reduces the chance for occupant survivability. Blanketing some fuels with foam can displace the oxygen. Removing or limiting a fire's access to ambient oxygen will not work on fuels that are self-oxidizing, such as ammonium nitrate found in fertilizer. A variety of industrial operations may be designed with the ability to pipe in steam for the purpose of extinguishing a fire in a vessel or container.

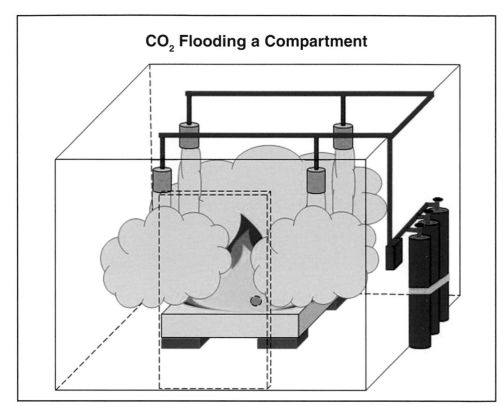

Figure 8.3 An example of how a CO_2 system can flood a compartment and displace the compartment's oxygen supply.

Chemical Flame Inhibition

Extinguishing agents, such as some dry chemicals, halogenated agents (Halons), and Halon-replacement "clean" agents, inhibit or interrupt the chemical chain reaction and stop flame production. This method of extinguishment is effective on flaming (gas phase) fires. These agents do not easily extinguish non-flaming (condensed phase) fires because there is no effective means to cool the fuel and stop the chemical chain reaction. The high agent concentrations and extended time periods necessary to extinguish smoldering fires make these agents impractical in these cases.

Hoseline Selection and Fire Stream Application Methods

Water application as a fire suppressant is only successful if a sufficient volume of water is applied to the correct location in or near the fuels that are burning. The selection of an appropriate hoseline and an appropriate attack method are important to the effectiveness of fire streams.

Hoseline Selection

Hoseline selection should be based upon fire conditions and other factors such as the following:

- Fire load and material involved
- Volume of water needed for extinguishment
- Reach needed
- Number of persons available to handle the hoseline(s)
- Mobility requirements
- Tactical requirements
- Speed of deployment
- Potential fire spread

Table 8.1 gives a simple analysis of hose stream characteristics. This table is intended to provide an overview of options, not to replace the judgment of fire brigade personnel in selecting hoselines.

| Table 8.1 | | | | | | | | | |
| Hose Stream Characteristics | | | | | | | | | |
Size in (mm)	GPM (L/min)	Reach (Max) ft (m)	FBM on Nozzle	Mobility	Damage Control	Direction Control	When Used		Effective Area
1½ inches (38 mm)	40–125 gpm (160 L/min to 500 L/min)	25–50 feet (8 m–15 m)	1 or 2	Good	Good	Excellent	• Developing fire — still small enough or sufficiently confined to be stopped with relatively limited quantity of water • For quick attack		One to Three Rooms
1¾ inches (45 mm)	40–175 gpm (160 L/min to 700 L/min)	25–50 feet (8 m–15 m)	2	Good to Fair	Good	Good	• For rapid relocation of streams • When personnel are limited • When ratio of fuel load to area is relatively light • For exposure protection		
2 inches (50 mm)	100–250 gpm (400 L/min to 1 000 L/min)	40–70 feet (12 m–21 m)	2 or 3	Fair	Fair	Good	• When size and intensity of fire are beyond reach, flow, or penetration of 1½-inch (38 mm) line • When both water and personnel are ample		One Floor or More; Fully Involved
2½ inches (65 mm)	125–350 gpm (500 L/min to 1 400 L/min)	50–100 feet (15 m–30 m)	2–4	Fair to Poor	Fair	Good	• When safety of crew dictates • When larger volumes or greater reach are required for exposure protection		
Master Stream	350–2,000 gpm (1 400 L/min to 8 000 L/min)	100–200 feet (30 m–60 m)	1	Poor to None (Aerial Master Sreams can be good)	Poor	Good	• When size and intensity of fire are beyond reach, flow, or penetration of handlines • When water is ample, but personnel are limited • When safety of personnel dictates • When larger volumes or greater reach are required for exposure protection • When sufficient pumping capability is available • When massive runoff water can be tolerated • When interior attack can no longer be maintained		Large Structures; Fully Involved

Fire Stream Application Methods

Incipient fire brigade members will use fire streams to apply agent on incipient fires. Personnel commonly apply fire streams using the following methods **(Figure 8.4)**:

Figure 8.4 A fire brigade member demonstrating the direct, indirect, and combination attack methods.

- **Direct Attack** — A direct attack applies water onto the combustible materials at the base of the fire.
- **Indirect Attack** — An indirect attack can be made by:
  - Bouncing or deflecting the stream off a wall or an object including the ceiling.
  - Spraying from outside the fire area through a door way or window.
- **Combination Attack** — The combination method uses the steam-generating technique of a ceiling-level attack combined with a direct attack on materials burning near the floor level. The nozzle may be moved in a *T*, *Z*, or *O* pattern, starting with a solid, straight, or penetrating fog stream directed into the heated gases at the ceiling level and then dropped down to attack the combustibles burning near the floor level. The *O* pattern of the combination attack is probably the most common method of attack. When performing the *O* pattern, personnel should direct the stream at the ceiling and rotate it with the stream edge reaching the ceiling, wall, floor, and opposite wall.

Master stream devices are useful in controlling larger incipient fires. Incipient fire brigade members may use master stream devices if the fire brigade is equipped and properly trained to use them.

Use of Fixed Master Stream Devices

Fixed **master stream** devices are appliances that are permanently located in an area of a facility, and are not portable, as they are attached to the ground or structure **(Figure 8.5)**. The facility's fire suppression water system usually supplies fixed master stream devices. Where available, fixed master stream devices may be one of the first lines of control for incipient fire brigade members in facility situations, particularly in locations unsafe for personnel or with limited personnel available. The three main uses for a master stream are as follows:

- For direct fire attack
- As exposure protection and/or cooling
- To supplement hoselines that are operating in the area

Fixed master stream devices should be used as specified in the facility's emergency plan or SOPs. A fire brigade member should be stationed at the master stream device while water is flowing. This position allows the fire brigade member to change the direction or pattern of the stream when required, or shut down the master stream device as the situation changes **(Figure 8.6)**.

Figure 8.5 (left) Fixed master stream devices such as this one can discharge large quantities of water and foam during fire fighting operations.

Figure 8.6 (right) Fire brigade members should be trained to operate fixed master stream devices found at their facility.

WARNING: Fire streams from master stream devices can seriously injure fire brigade members and damage property.

Exiting Hazardous Areas

In some instances, a fire may progress beyond the incipient stage despite the efforts of the incipient fire brigade efforts to control the fire. Fire brigade members should be taught to continuously evaluate the hazards at a fire and recognize when a fire has grown beyond their capabilities. They should be familiar with the fire brigade's methods of communicating an evacuation or exit from a hazardous area, and of possible evacuation routes within the site or facility. Once a fire exceeds the incipient stage, the incipient fire brigade members should exit the hazardous area as a team, and move to a safe area or safe haven by the safest route. Once outside the hazardous area, the fire brigade or team leader should account for all team members.

WARNING: Incipient level personnel should exit the hazardous area if the fire progresses to the point that PPE and SCBA are required, visibility has been impaired, or if the incipient members are NOT making visible progress in suppressing the fire.

Fuel-Specific Fire Suppression Operations

NFPA 1081 (2018): 4.3.1

The type of fuel that is involved in a fire will make a significant difference in what resources and strategies should be used to mitigate it. The following sections discuss the suppression of fires based on their primary fuel type, with a focus on hazards unique to each fuel type.

Suppressing Class A Fires

To extinguish an incipient fire involving Class A fuels such as wood or paper, fire brigade members may use fire extinguishers or hoselines depending on the size and location of the fire and the type and orientation of the materials that are on fire. Your duties and assigned tasks will depend on:

- Fire brigade standard operating procedures (SOPs)
- Assigned duties
- Amount of fire involvement
- Type of structure involved

To suppress an incipient Class A fire, fire brigade members should choose the appropriate extinguisher(s)

ℹ️ Situational Awareness: Class A Fires

Fire brigade members should observe and communicate the following conditions when responding to Class A fires:

- Changes to the configuration of the materials
- Changes to the positions of personnel in relation to the fire based upon changes to fire spread or other factors
- Indicators of imminent collapse
- Spread of fire to exposures
- Wind direction and speed
- Effectiveness of fire attack

---

or handline(s) available at their facility and operate in accordance with brigade's SOPs. They should test the extinguisher or handline prior to approaching the fire to ensure it is operational **(Figure 8.7)**. Approach the fire with caution while maintaining an escape route should the fire grow beyond the incipient stage. If possible, personnel should direct the agent at the base of the fire and sweep from side-to-side. If direct application is not possible, then an indirect attack should be attempted. As flaming combustion subsides and the fire darkens down, the fire brigade members may move closer and adjust the fire stream pattern. In stacked or piled materials, the fire brigade member should break apart the materials using a pike pole to allow agent to reach the seat of the fire. Once the fire is extinguished, overhaul the fire scene and ensure the fire is fully extinguished by exposing hidden fires.

Suppressing Class B Fires

Class B fires involve flammable and combustible liquids and gases. **Flammable liquids** are materials that are liquid at room temperature and have flash points less than 100°F (38°C); examples are gasoline and acetone. **Combustible liquids** are materials that are liquid at room temperature and have flash points higher than 100°F (38°C);

Figure 8.7 Hoselines should be tested before approaching a fire.

examples are kerosene and fuel oils. Flammable and combustible liquids can be further divided into hydrocarbons (do not mix with water) and polar solvents (mix with water). No attempt should be made to extinguish a **flammable gas** fires without first shutting off the fuel supply or safety control the gas release.

Other Definitions of Flammable and Combustible Liquids

This manual is written to meet the NFPA standards for training facility fire brigade members, and the definitions for flammable and combustible liquids used here reflect the NFPA definitions. Other standards and regulatory agencies in the U.S. and other countries may have different definitions for these types of liquids. For example, OSHA definitions for flammable and combustible liquids were similar to those of the NFPA. However, OSHA has adopted the Global Harmonized System of Classification and Labeling of Chemicals (GHS). Under GHS, all liquids with a flash point of no more than 199.4°F (93°C) are categorized as flammable liquids. Flammable liquids are then subdivided into four categories:

- Category 1 liquids have flash points below 73.4°F (23°C) and boiling points at or below 95°F (35°C).

- Category 2 liquids have flash points below 73.4°F (23°C) and boiling points above 95°F (35°C).

- Category 3 liquids have flash points at or above 73.4°F (23°C) and at or below 140°F (60°C). When Category 3 liquids with flash points at or above 100°F (37.8°C) are heated to within 30°F (16.7°C) of their flash point, they must be handled in accordance with the requirements for a Category 3 liquid with a flash point below 100°F (37.8°C).

- Category 4 liquids have flash points above 140°F (60°C) and at or below 199.4°F (93°C). When Category 4 flammable liquids are heated to within 30°F (16.7°C) of their flash points, they must be handled in accordance with the requirements for a Category 3 liquid with a flash point at or above 100°F (37.8°C).

- In addition, the new rules specify that when a liquid with a flash point greater than 199.4°F (93°C) is heated to within 30°F (16.7°C) of its flash point, it must be handled in accordance with the requirements for a Category 4 flammable liquid.

NOTE: Fire brigade personnel should learn and follow the definitions that their organization uses.

Data drawn from *Flammable and Combustible Liquids Standard, 29 CFR 1910.106.*

Fire brigade members must exercise caution when attacking fires involving flammable and combustible liquids. The first precaution is to avoid standing in pools of fuel or water runoff containing fuel. Protective clothing can absorb fuel in a **wicking** action. When protective clothing is saturated, points of contact with skin may develop chemical burns or absorb toxic materials, and materials can catch fire if an ignition source is present. Even if the wicking action does not occur, the pool of liquid itself may ignite and present extreme danger.

Unburned vapors are usually heavier than air and form pools or pockets of vapors in low spots where they may ignite. Fire brigade personnel should not enter a flammable liquid vapor cloud because their PPE will not protect them if ignition occurs. Fire brigade members must control all ignition sources in a leak area.

Vehicles, smoking materials, electrical fixtures, and sparks from steel tools can provide an ignition source sufficient to ignite leaking flammable vapors. An increase in the intensity of sound or fire issuing from a relief valve may indicate that rupture of the vessel is imminent. Fire brigade members should not assume that relief valves are sufficient to safely relieve excess pressures under severe fire conditions. Large and small flammable liquid vessels have killed fire brigade members, firefighters, and bystanders after rupturing when exposed to flames.

WARNING: Large and small flammable liquid vessels may fail violently and kill fire brigade members, firefighters, and bystanders when exposed to flames.

Class B foam is the recommended agent for controlling flammable liquid fires involving polar solvents, such as alcohols and lacquers, that mix with liquids. Alternately, water can be used to control

Class B fires involving hydrocarbon liquids, such as gasoline, kerosene, and other petroleum products, that do not mix with water. Accidents involving vehicles transporting flammable fuels and gas utilities also require Class B fire control techniques. The following sections describe applications of water on Class B fires as a:

- Cooling agent
- Substitute medium
- Vapor dispersion tool

- Mechanical tool
- Protective cover
- Ventilation tool

WARNING: Use care in choosing water or foam for response to Class B fires.

Cooling Agent

One of the most useful applications for water is as a cooling agent for protecting exposures that may weaken or collapse, such as metal tanks or support beams **(Figure 8.8)**. To be effective, water streams should be applied so that they form a protective sheet of water on the endangered exposure surfaces. When using only water to extinguish a Class B fire, the fire brigade member must use an aggressive sweeping motion of the nozzle. Working this way, the fire brigade member effectively lifts the flame away from the fuel source and allows the water droplets to cool the fuel source below its ignition temperature. Fires involving heavier oils (such as raw crude) can be extinguished with less aggressive actions, provided sufficient quantities of water in droplet form.

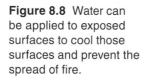

Figure 8.8 Water can be applied to exposed surfaces to cool those surfaces and prevent the spread of fire.

Mechanical Tool

For small quantities of Class B fuels only, fire brigade members can use water under pressure from hoselines to move the fuels (whether burning or not) to areas where they can safely burn or where ignition sources are more easily controlled. Because of the risk of environmental contamination, fuels must never be flushed down drains or sewers. Fire brigade members should use appropriate fog patterns, both for protection from radiant heat and to prevent "plunging" (pushing) the stream into the liquid. Plunging a stream into burning flammable liquids disrupts the surface of the liquid and increases fire intensity by causing a higher production of flammable vapors. To minimize disruption, sweep the stream slowly from side to side, and move the fuel or fire to the desired location. Care must be taken to keep the leading edge of the fog pattern in contact with the fuel surface. If that contact is broken, the fire may run underneath the stream and flash back around the attack crew. When responding to small leaks in a container, a solid stream may be applied directly to the opening to keep back the escaping liquid. The stream's pressure must exceed that of the leaking material in order for this procedure to work properly. Care must be taken not to overflow the container.

CAUTION: Do not flush fuels down drains or sewers.

Through the use of fog streams, water may also be used to dissipate and dilute flammable vapors. Fog streams can also control, to a small degree, the movement of the vapors to a desired location away from people and other operating equipment.

Substitute Medium

Water can be used to displace fuel from leaking pipes or tanks. When the fuel is lighter than water, fire brigade members can pump water back into the leaking fuel pipe or fill the tank with water to a level above the leak. This displacement floats the volatile product on top of the water as long as the water application rate equals the leak rate. Water is seldom used to dilute flammable liquids for fire control due to the large volume of water necessary in comparison to the volume of product. However, this technique may be useful for small fires when the runoff can be contained.

Protective Cover

Fire brigade personnel can use hoseline fire streams as a protective cover for teams advancing to shut off liquid or gaseous fuel valves. Coordination and slow, deliberate movements provide relative safety from flames and heat. While one hoseline may be sufficient as a protective cover, two lines with a backup line are recommended for fire control and safety.

WARNING: Prior to an emergency, fire brigade members must be well-trained and have extensive practice in the use of hoselines to provide a protective cover.

When containers or tanks of flammable liquids or gases are exposed to **flame impingement**, fire brigade members should apply streams from their maximum effective reach until relief valves close. Sufficient water application can best be achieved by lobbing a stream along the top of a tank so that water runs down both sides. This film of water cools the vapor space of the tank. Steel supports under tanks should also be cooled to prevent their collapse.

Fire brigade members can then advance under progressively widened protective fog patterns to make temporary repairs or shut off the fuel source. A backup line supplied by a separate water source and pump should be provided to protect fire brigade members in the event other lines fail or additional tank cooling is needed. Approach storage vessels exposed to fire at right angles to the tanks, never from the ends of the vessels.

WARNING: Never approach horizontal vessels exposed to fire from the ends because of the danger of ruptures; vessels frequently split and form projectiles.

Vapor Dispersion Tool

Pressurized water streams from hoselines or unattended master streams may be used for **vapor dispersion (Figure 8.9)**. These streams create turbulence, which increases the rate of the materials mixing with air and reduces the concentration of the hazardous material. After using water streams for vapor dispersion, responders must confine and analyze runoff water for possible contamination.

Figure 8.9 Vapors can be dispersed by the application of water streams.

Ventilation Tool

Ventilation is the control of air movement using natural or mechanical means. When spills occur inside structures, ventilation can remove and/or disperse harmful airborne particles, vapors, or gases. Ventilation techniques for smoke removal may also be applied to hazmat incidents (see IFSTA's **Essentials of Fire Fighting** manual). As with other types of spill control, responders should ensure the compatibility of their ventilation equipment with the hazardous atmosphere. When conducting negative-pressure ventilation, personnel should ensure the fans and other ventilators are compatible with the atmosphere. Equipment must be **intrinsically safe** in a flammable atmosphere. When choosing the type of ventilation to use, remember that positive-pressure ventilation removes atmospheric contaminants more effectively than negative-pressure ventilation.

Suppressing Class C Fires

Fires in electrical equipment (Class C fires) occur quite frequently. After the equipment is de-energized, malfunctioning equipment can be handled with relative ease. Electrical hazards can be found in:

Figure 8.10 Some facilities have transformers that create the potential for Class C (electrical) fires.

- Cable trays

- Process areas

- Transformers **(Figure 8.10)**

- Control centers

- Electrical distribution panels

 Procedures for fighting Class C fires should be established in preincident plans. The primary danger to fire brigade members while mitigating electrical fires is the failure to recognize the safety hazard. Safety is every fire brigade member's responsibility, and all members must understand the risks involved in their response area. When the brigade is ready to respond to the fire, the fire brigade leader should ensure that appropriate power breakers are opened to disconnect power flow into structures. Once the power has been turned off, fires in electrical equipment may self-extinguish or the type of fire will change from Class C to another fire class based on its fuel if it continues.

> **WARNING:** Stop the flow of electricity to the object involved before initiating fire suppression activities.

When handling fires in delicate electronic or computer equipment, clean extinguishing agents, such as carbon dioxide, Halon, or FM-200 should be used to prevent further damage to equipment. Multi-purpose dry chemical agents may require significant clean-up after use in addition to being chemically active with some electrical components. The use of water on energized equipment is discouraged because of the inherent shock hazard. If fire brigade personnel must use water, they should apply it from a distance in the form of a fog stream following the local fire brigade's SOPs.

The following sections discuss Class C fire suppression techniques needed for fires involving transmission lines and equipment, underground lines, and commercial high-voltage installations. These sections also address controlling electrical power, electrical hazards, and guidelines for electrical emergencies.

Transmission Lines and Equipment

A common electrical emergency in facility settings involves fires in bulk electrical transmission lines and equipment. When fires occur as a result of transmission lines breaking, an area equal to a span between poles should be cleared on either side of the break. To reduce the risk to life and property in these incidents, consultation and cooperation with qualified electrical personnel is essential.

Transformers are classified as either dry or wet. Wet transformers contain mineral oil that is specially blended for that purpose. While small wet transformers can contain a few gallons of this oil, larger transformers at power generation sites can contain 7,000-18,000 gallons of oil. Ensure high voltage power is turned off prior to attempting extinguishment. While dry chemical extinguishing agents will be effective on smaller transformers, transformers may reflash due to the heat they can retain. On larger transformers, large volumes of Class B foams or water additives/encapsulators are needed for safe extinguishment. Always work with your utility company for these types of events.

Fires in wet transformers may have additional hazards if the coolant liquids contain polychlorinated biphenyls (PCBs). These oil-based liquids are flammable and carcinogenic (cancer-causing). In many places around the world, including the U.S and Canada, most transformers no longer contain PCBs.

Figure 8.11 Underground utility vaults may contain power control units and cables.

Underground Lines

Underground transmission systems consist of cableways and vaults beneath the surface of a roadway or facility floor **(Figure 8.11)**. Explosions in this environment may blow utility covers a considerable distance. Explosions are triggered when a spark from fuses blowing or short-circuit arcing ignites an accumulation of gases. Explosions may be dangerous to the public as well as fire brigade members.

Fire brigade members should avoid entering a utility vault, except to attempt a rescue. Fire control can be accomplished from outside the space. Fire brigade personnel should simply discharge carbon dioxide or dry chemical into the utility vault and replace the cover, and then place a wet blanket or salvage cover over the utility cover to exclude oxygen and assist in extinguishing the fire. Water is not suggested for extinguishment in this environment because of the close proximity of electrical equipment. The runoff of water also creates puddles that conduct electricity.

Commercial High-Voltage Installations

Many facilities have electrical equipment that uses current in excess of 600 volts. Areas within a facility with this usage should include high-voltage signs on the doors of vaults or fire-resistive rooms housing equipment, such as transformers or large electric motors. Some transformers use combustible oils as coolants. Water should not be used in this environment, even in the form of fog, because the hazard of shock is great, and extensive damage may occur to electrical equipment not involved in the fire.

Controlling Electrical Power

Some fire control operations are more safely handled when the electricity is connected to the response area. For example, interior lighting, ventilation equipment, and special pumps may all rely on the structure's electrical service. Fire brigade members must control the flow of electricity into structures, or areas of a structure, where emergency operations are being performed. Especially when a fire involves only one area, it may not be necessary to shut down electricity for the entire building. When the building becomes damaged to the point that electrical service is interrupted or creates an electrical hazard, power should be turned off. When the fire brigade must take this step, only trained personnel who are aware of the hazards should be assigned the task.

A fire brigade member should control the power at the panel box by opening the main switch or removing the fuses. If further control of the electricity becomes necessary, utility personnel using approved, tested equipment should perform this task. With some industrial meters, disruption of a circuit does not stop the flow of electricity.

Historically, it had been a best practice to pull the electrical meter to turn off the electricity in structural fires. In modern applications, fire brigade members should be alert for emergency power capabilities such as emergency generators. In such cases, removing the meter or turning off the master switch does not turn off the power entirely.

WARNING: Only trained utility personnel, with correct equipment, should remove fuses or open switches at a power box.

Electrical Hazards

In order to avoid injury and protect electrical equipment, fire brigade members should be familiar with the properties and hazards of electrical transmission systems. For example, conventional electrical current (such as 110 or 120 volts) is sufficiently powerful to deliver fatal shocks. High-voltage equipment delivers a higher energy output and can do significantly more damage. When electricity flow is restricted, the hazards are reduced, especially in terms of risk of injury or fatal shock, and the danger of igniting combustibles or unauthorized powering on of electrical equipment.

The physical consequences to a person affected by an electrical shock and arc flash can include:

- Cardiac arrest
- Involuntary muscle contractions
- Damage to joints
- Ultraviolet arc burns to the eyes

- Ventricular fibrillation
- Paralysis
- Major organ damage

- Respiratory arrest
- Surface and/or internal burns
- Hearing loss

Factors most affecting the seriousness of the electrical shock delivered to a person include:

- Path of electricity through the body
- Degrees of skin resistance — wet (low) or dry (high)
- Length of exposure
- Available current — amperage flow
- Available voltage — electromotive force
- Frequency — alternating current (AC) or direct current (DC)

Guidelines for Electrical Emergencies

Electrical emergencies can be more safely managed with some foresight. The following list is intended to advise personnel on ways to maintain a safe working environment:

- Establish an exclusion zone equal to the distant between power poles (one span) in all directions when downed power line wires are encountered. Note the condition of nearby wires. A short circuit could weaken other wires, and they may fall at a later time.

Figure 8.12 (left) A facility electrician attaches a lockout/tagout device to an electrical control panel.
Figure 8.13 (right) Fire brigade members should avoid downed electrical lines.

- Guard against electrical shock and burns by avoiding contact with electrical wiring or energized equipment. Prevent eye injuries by never looking directly at arcing electrical lines.

- Treat all wires as energized and high-voltage lines.

- Do not cut any power lines without authorization, regardless of training. When possible, wait for trained utility workers to do any necessary cutting. When necessary, properly trained and authorized personnel (other than utility workers) may cut power lines do any cutting.

- Use electrical **lockout/tagout devices** when working on energized electrical equipment **(Figure 8.12)**. Lockout devices are used with padlocks to ensure that electricity will not be restored without authorization after electricity has been shut off at the control box. The control box should also be tagged (tagout) to indicate that it is out of service. In accordance with all appropriate regulations and fire brigade guidelines, lockouts and/or safety guards should be used during incidents involving elevators, compactors, industrial process equipment, or other similar large equipment. For further description and information on lockout/tagout procedures, refer to the fire brigade's SOPs and OSHA standard 1910.147, *The Control of Hazardous Energy (lockout/tagout).*

- Exercise caution when raising or lowering ladders, hoselines, or equipment near an overhead power line.

- Avoid a **ground gradient** hazard by maintaining an extra safety distance between downed electrical wires and operating positions **(Figure 8.13)**. Ground gradient is the tendency of an energized electrical conductor to pass its current along the path of least resistance (from highest to lowest potential) to ground. Downed conductors commonly discharge their electrical current through surface objects several feet (meters) from their point of contact with the ground. The higher the voltage, the greater the possible travel distance. Fire brigade members operating near a downed wire risk entering a ground gradient situation. The difference in electrical potential between a fire brigade member's feet and an object, such as a hoseline, being dragged can allow current to pass through the fire brigade member and return to the ground through the dragged object. The passage of electricity through the fire brigade member may cause interior and exterior burns, heart fibrillation, cardiac arrest, and death.

- Do not touch any vehicle or apparatus that is in contact with electrical wires. Body contact will complete the circuit to the ground, resulting in electrical shock. To safely exit an apparatus that may be charged, jump clear of the apparatus with both legs together, avoid touching the apparatus and the ground at the same time, and avoid landing in the energized zone.

- Consider all downed electrical wires and the areas around them equally dangerous.

- Do not use solid and straight streams around energized electrical equipment. Fog patterns are recommended with at least 100 psi (700 kPa) nozzle pressure. Appliances should not be used in proximity to energized equipment.

- Give special considerations for fences. While an energized electrical line contacts a fence or metal guardrail, the entire length of the fence is charged. Longer fence lines will present more exposures.
- Proceed carefully in an area where wires are down. Because of the carbon in most fire fighting and work boots, a slight charge indicating that the ground is charged may travel through the rubber and leather exterior as a tingling sensation in the feet.

Suppressing Class D Fires

Combustible metals (Class D fuels) present the dual hazards of burning at high temperatures and being reactive to water. Water is only effective at suppressing these fires when it can be applied in large enough quantities to cool the metal below its ignition temperature. The usual method of control is to protect exposures and permit the metal to burn itself out. Fire brigade members may shovel or spray special extinguishing agents from special extinguishers in quantities large enough to cover the burning metal **(Figure 8.14)**. Be ready to reapply dry powder if the fire breaks through the extinguishing agent. Directing hose streams at burning metal can result in the violent decomposition of the water and subsequent release of flammable hydrogen gas. Small metal chips or metal dust are more reactive to water than ingots or finished products.

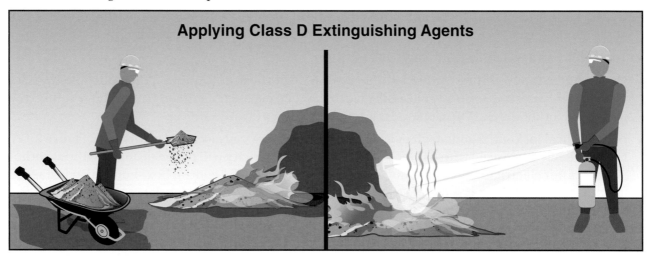

Applying Class D Extinguishing Agents

Figure 8.14 Class D fire suppressants can be applied by shovel or by a portable fire extinguisher.

> WARNING: Never use hydrogenated agents on Class D fires as phosgene gas is released as a byproduct of hydrogenated agents being burned in the fire.

Combustible metal fires emit a characteristic brilliant white light until an ash layer covers the burning material. Once this layer has formed, it may appear that the fire is out. Fire brigade members should not assume that these fires are extinguished simply because flames are not visible. It may be an extended period of time before the area or substance cools to safe levels. Combustible metal fires are hot — greater than 2,000°F (1 093°C) — even if they appear suppressed. Fire brigade members should closely monitor these types of fires using a Thermal Imager to assist in determining the amount of heat still being generated.

Suppressing Class K Fires

Some commercial cooking facilities and other industrial facilities have onsite kitchens that use high-efficiency cooking equipment (which is highly insulated and slow to cool) to heat cooking media such as vegetable or animal oil and fats (Class K fuels). Fire brigade members should be familiar with the operation of the wet chemical fire extinguishers and suppression systems intended to suppress Class K fires at their facility. If equipped, the fire suppression system should be activated before using a Class K extinguisher. Extreme care should be taken when suppressing Class K fires to avoid directing the extinguishing agent into the cooking media at too close a range or too steep of an angle. This action can cause the cooking media to be forcibly expelled from its container and spread both it and the fire.

Chapter Review

1. What factors should be considered during hose selection?

2. What are the hazards of associated with suppressing the different classifications of fire?

Key Terms

Combination Attack — Extinguishing a fire by using both a direct and an indirect attack; this method combines the steam-generating technique of a ceiling level attack with an attack on the burning materials near floor level.

Combustible Liquid — Liquid having a flash point at or above 100°F (37.8°C) and below 200°F (93.3°C).

Direct Attack (Structural) — In structural fire fighting, an attack method that involves the discharge of water or a foam stream directly onto the burning fuel.

Flame Impingement — Points at which flames contact the surface of a container or other structure.

Flammable Gas — Any material (except an aerosol) that is a gas at 68°F (20°C) or less and that (a) is ignitable and will burn at 14.7 psi (101.3 kPa) when in a mixture of 13 percent or less by volume with air, or (b) has a flammable range at 14.7 psi (101.3 kPa) by volume with air at least 12 percent regardless of the lower limit.

Flammable Liquid — Any liquid having a flash point below 100°F (37.8°C) and a vapor pressure not exceeding 40 psi absolute (276 kPa) {2.76 bar}.

Ground Gradient — Electrical field that radiates outward from where the current enters the ground; its intensity dissipates rapidly as distance increases from the point of entry.

Indirect Attack (Structural) — In structural fire fighting, a form of fire attack that involves directing fire streams toward the ceiling of a compartment in order to generate a large amount of steam in order to cool the compartment.

Intrinsically Safe — Describes equipment that is approved for use in flammable atmospheres; must be incapable of releasing enough electrical energy to ignite the flammable atmosphere. Formerly known as Explosion Proof.

Lockout/Tagout Device — Device used to secure a machine's power switches, in order to prevent accidental restart of the machine.

Master Stream — Large-caliber water stream usually supplied by combining two or more hoselines into a manifold device or by fixed piping that delivers 350 gpm (1 325 L/min) or more.

Vapor Dispersion — Action taken to direct or influence the course of airborne hazardous materials. See Dispersion and Vapor.

Wicking — Pattern that occurs when quantities of the ignitable liquid are absorbed by the material onto which the liquid is poured.

Skill Sheet List

The following skill sheets should be used to evaluate the skills described in this chapter:

NOTE: Students should wear the PPE appropriate to the NFPA 1081 level (Incipient, Advanced Exterior, Interior Structural, etc...) being evaluated.

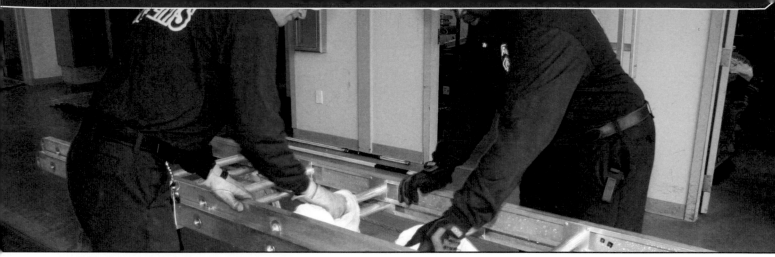

Equipment In

Incipient Facility Fire Brigade Member

Chapter Contents

JPRs addressed in this chapter

This chapter provides information that addresses the following job performance requirements of NFPA 1081, *Standard for Facility Fire Brigade Member Professional Qualifications (2018)*.

4.1.2.4

1. Describe the methods for inspecting, maintaining, and service testing ladders. [4.1.2.4]

2. Explain the methods for inspecting, maintaining, and reservicing fire extinguishers. [4.1.2.4]

3. Describe the methods for inspecting and maintaining fire hose and nozzles. [4.1.2.4]

4. Explain the methods for service testing fire hose. [4.1.2.4]

5. Explain the methods for inspecting and maintaining rope and webbing. [4.1.2.4]

6. Explain the methods for maintaining fire brigade hand tools and power equipment. [4.1.2.4]

Chapter 9
Equipment Inspection, Testing, and Maintenance

Fire brigade members may use a variety of hand tools, power equipment, and other fire fighting tools and equipment during an incident. Once these items have been used, fire brigade personnel need to inspect, clean, and conduct maintenance on them to ensure they are ready for future use. Fire brigade members should be familiar with the manufacturers' recommendations and appropriate NFPA standards for conducting inspections, testing, and maintenance. This chapter will describe the inspection, cleaning, and common maintenance procedures for the following types of tools and equipment:

- Ladders
- Maintenance, and reservicing of fire extinguishers
- General care and maintenance of fire hose and nozzles
- Inspection, maintenance, and cleaning of rope and webbing
- Other fire fighting tools and equipment

Ladders
NFPA 1081 (2018): 4.1.2.4

In response and training use, fire service ladders must withstand considerable stressors, including sudden loading, exposure to temperature fluctuations, and impacts from falling objects. To maintain functionality over time, clean and inspect ladders after each use. During inspection, you should check all parts of the ladder and note any part that shows excessive wear **(Figure 9.1)**. Inspect ladders according to departmental policy. Periodic inspections, **service tests**, cleaning, and maintenance are essential to ensure the safe operation of ground ladders.

Figure 9.1 A fire brigade member inspecting a beam on a fire service ladder.

NOTE: All ladders used in the fire service should meet the requirements of NFPA 1931, *Standard for Manufacturer's Design of Fire Department Ground Ladders* and NFPA 1932, *Standard on Use, Maintenance, and Service Testing of In-Service Fire Department Ground Ladders.*

Inspecting and Service Testing Ladders

NFPA 1932 requires fire brigade members to inspect ground ladders when placed in service, after each use, and on a monthly basis. You should refer to NFPA 1932 for a complete list of inspection items. When inspecting ground ladders, check the following **(Figure 9.2)**:

- **Heat sensor labels** on metal and fiberglass ladders for a color change indicating heat exposure

  NOTE: Replace heat sensors when their expiration date is reached.

- Heavy carbon (soot) deposits or blistered paint on tips of ladders without heat sensor labels, indicating heat exposure

Figure 9.2 When inspecting a fire service ladder, the fire brigade member should check the heat sensor to see if the ladder has been exposed to heat and inspect the rungs to ensure they are tight.

- Discoloration on fiberglass ladders that could indicate heat exposure
- **Rungs** for tightness, damage, or wear
- Bolts and rivets for tightness

  NOTE: Bolts on wooden ladders should not be so tight that they crush the wood.

- Welds for any cracks or apparent defects
- **Beams** and rungs for cracks, splintering, breaks, gouges, checks, wavy patterns, or deformation
- Worn areas caused from vibration at points of contact with apparatus or other ladders
- Ladder feet for placement and in good condition

> **WARNING:** Any ladder that has been subjected to direct flame contact, has been exposed to high heat, or has a heat sensor label that has changed color is unsafe for use until it has been service tested.

In addition to these general inspections, personnel should check other features depending on the type of ladder being inspected. If any damage is found, remove the ladder from service until it can be repaired and tested. Ladders that cannot be safely repaired must be destroyed or scrapped for parts. The following sections highlight some of these items.

Checking Ladder Markings and Labels

All fire service ground ladders are required to have factory applied markings and warning labels, although locally required markings may also be applied. These markings must be present and legible.

The following markings are commonly found on fire service ladders:

- **Designated ladder length** — Displays the ladder length on each beam within 12 inches (305 mm) of the butt plate.
- **Manufacturer's name plate** — Includes the month and year of manufacture be attached to the ladder.

- **Apparatus' designation or a locally assigned inventory number** — Stenciled on the beam as required by the AHJ.

- **White tip, or reflective tape attached to tip** — Increases the visibility of the top of the ladder. The butt of the ladder may be painted black to differentiate it from the tip. Only the top and bottom 18 inches (450 mm) of the beams should be painted.

- **Balance point stripe** — Indicates the balance point. May not be centered on the ladder's length.

> **CAUTION:** Do not paint wooden ladders as the paint may conceal damage to the wood.

NFPA 1931 requires the manufacturer to have a certification label affixed to the ladder indicating that the ladder meets the standard. A variety of warning labels are also required on all types of ladders, including:

- An electrical hazard warning label is applied to the outside of a ladder beam to warn users of the risk of electrocution if the ladder comes in contact with an electrical source.

- A ladder positioning label is placed on the outside of a ladder beam to indicate the climbing angle and the side of the ladder that must be away from the building.

- Heat sensor labels are required on metal and fiberglass ladders, placed on the inside of each beam, below the second rung from the tip of each section. The heat sensor is preset to 300°F (149°C) and must have the expiration date indicated on it. Heat sensor labels beyond the expiration date must be replaced.

Inspecting Metal Ladders

When inspecting metal ladders, look for:

- Evidence of flame impingement or heat damage
- Loose or missing rivets or fasteners
- Damaged or missing rubber on the footpads
- Dry rot or other damage to the halyard
- Corrosion or rust
- Loose or damaged rungs
- Cracks, bends, or other damage

Inspecting Fiberglass Ladders

When inspecting fiberglass ladders, look for:

- Cracks, chipping, or other damage in the fiberglass components
- Corrosion or rust on metal components
- Damaged or missing rubber on the footpads
- Loose or missing rivets or fasteners
- Evidence of flame impingement or heat damage
- Loose or damaged rungs
- Dry rot or other damage to the halyard

Wooden Ladders/Ladders with Wooden Components

When inspecting wooden ladders or ladders with wooden components, look for:

- Areas where the finish has been chafed or scraped
- Darkening (blistering or blackening) of the varnish (indicating exposure to heat)
- Dark streaks in the wood (indicating deterioration of the wood)
- Marred, worn, cracked, or splintered parts
- Shoes rounded or smooth
- Water damage

> **CAUTION:** Any indication of deterioration of the wood is reason for the ladder to be removed from service until it can be service tested.

Inspecting Roof Ladders

When inspecting **roof ladders**, make sure that the roof hook assemblies operate with relative ease **(Figure 9.3)**. In addition, the hook assemblies should not show signs of rust. The hooks should not be deformed, and the parts should be firmly attached with no sign of looseness.

Inspecting Extension Ladders

When inspecting extension ladders, look for **(Figure 9.4)**:

- **Pawl assemblies** — The hook and finger should move in and out freely.

- **Halyard** — If damage or wear is found, replace the halyard.

- **Halyard cable** — Check to see that it is taut when the ladder is in the bedded position. This check ensures proper synchronization of the upper sections during operation.

- **Pulleys** — Make sure they turn freely.

- **Ladder guides** — Check their condition and that the fly sections move freely.

Service Testing Ladders

Fire service ground ladders are designed for use in harsh conditions and to tolerate some physical stresses. To ensure continued safe functioning, they must be service tested periodically. NFPA 1932 serves as the guideline for ground ladder service testing. Test all ground ladders before they are placed in service, test annually while in service, and service test after any use that exposes them to high heat or rough treatment. The fire brigade or an approved testing agency should conduct the specified tests from the standard. NFPA 1932 recommends that personnel exercise caution when performing service tests on ground ladders to prevent injury or damage to the ladder.

Figure 9.3 Fire brigade members should open and close the hooks while inspecting a roof ladder.

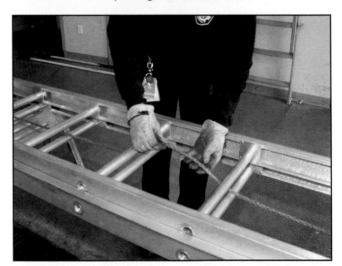

Figure 9.4 Fire brigade members should carefully examine the extension ladder lanyard for damage.

Ladder Cleaning

Regular and proper cleaning of ladders is more than a matter of appearance. More importantly, ladders that accumulate dirt or debris from a fire may harden to the point where ladder sections cannot function as designed. Therefore, fire brigade members should clean ladders after every use. Use the following guidelines when cleaning a ladder **(Figure 9.5)**:

- Use a soft bristle brush and running water to clean the ladder.

- Remove tar, oil, or greasy residues with mild soap and water or environmentally safe solvents, and occasionally apply lubrication according to departmental standard operating procedures (SOPs) and manufacturer's recommendations.

- Look for damage or wear while cleaning the ladder. Report defects according to departmental SOPs.

- Wipe the ladder dry after cleaning or use.

Figure 9.5 Ladders must be thoroughly cleaned and dried before being returned to service.

Ladder Maintenance

Ground ladder **maintenance** and **repair** refer to two separate actions for fire brigade members. Maintenance means keeping ladders in a state of usefulness or readiness. Repair means to restore or replace that which is damaged or worn out. All fire brigade members should be able to perform routine ground ladder maintenance according to departmental SOPs and the manufacturer's recommendations. Any ladders in need of repair require the service of a trained ladder repair technician.

General maintenance requirements for ground ladders include:

- Keep ground ladders free of moisture.
- Store or position ladders where they are free from vehicle exhaust or engine heat.
- Keep ladders in an area where they are not exposed to the elements of weather.
- Paint ladders only for purposes of identification or visibility.

Inspection, Maintenance, and Reservicing of Fire Extinguishers

NFPA 1081 (2018): 4.1.2.4

A fire brigade's SOPs, in coordination with NFPA 10, *Standard for Portable Fire Extinguishers*, requirements, specify the inspection, care, and maintenance of fire brigade portable fire extinguishers. Locally adopted codes and standards regulate extinguishers that private companies, organizations, and individuals own. Besides being familiar with the SOPs for taking care of extinguishers assigned to your station and apparatus, you should be aware of requirements for extinguishers in facilities at your site.

Inspection

NFPA 10 and most fire and life safety codes require that portable fire extinguishers be inspected monthly and maintained at least once each year to ensure that they are accessible and operable. Your fire brigade's SOPs will establish the monthly inspection requirements for your portable fire extinguishers. The SOPs should also cover the retention of fire extinguisher inspection records. When inspecting fire extinguishers, three factors determine the value of a fire extinguisher:

- Serviceability
- Accessibility
- Simplicity of operation

NOTE: The employees most likely to use an extinguisher should conduct the monthly inspection.

The following procedures should be part of every fire extinguisher inspection (**Figure 9.6**):

- Check that the extinguisher is in its proper location and is accessible.

- Inspect the discharge nozzle or horn for obstructions.

- Check hose for cracks and dirt or grease accumulations.

- Inspect the extinguisher container shell for any physical damage.

- Check whether the operating instructions on the extinguisher nameplate are legible.

- Check the locking pin and tamper seal to ensure that the extinguisher has not been discharged or tampered with.

- Determine whether the extinguisher is full of agent and fully pressurized. Check the pressure gauge, the weight of the extinguisher, or the agent level. An extinguisher should be less than ten percent deficient in weight.

- Check the inspection tag for the date of the previous inspection, maintenance, or recharging.

Figure 9.6 Fire extinguisher hoses should be inspected for cracks, dirt, or grease accumulations.

If any of the items listed are deficient, remove the extinguisher from service, replace it with an operational extinguisher, and report the need for service in accordance with department SOPs. Only trained personnel should repair or refill portable fire extinguishers.

Maintenance

NFPA 10 outlines the maintenance procedures for portable fire extinguishers. General guidelines for annual maintenance of fire extinguishers include checking their:

- Mechanical parts
- Extinguishing agent
- Expelling means
- Physical condition

NOTE: The fire brigade SOPs should identify the fire extinguisher maintenance processes that the facility should follow.

Reservicing

Depending on the authority having jurisdiction, qualified personnel must perform recharging of fire extinguishers in accordance with the manufacturer's instructions. Personnel should refer to NFPA 10 and the manufacturer's instructions for information relating to specific extinguishers.

General Care and Maintenance of Fire Hose and Nozzles

NFPA 1081 (2018): 4.1.2.4

Figure 9.7 A fire brigade member inspecting a section of hose for potential damage and looking at cleanliness.

Figure 9.8 Hose can be cleaned with water and a stiff scrub brush.

Thorough inspection, care, and maintenance can significantly extend the service life of fire hose. The techniques for inspecting, washing, and drying, and the provisions for storage are important functions in the care of fire hose.

Inspecting Hose

Fire hose should be inspected and service tested in accordance with NFPA 1962 or before being placed in service for the first time and at least annually thereafter. Each time a section of hose is used, whether for emergency incidents or training, it should be inspected to ensure that it is free of visible soil or damage **(Figure 9.7)**. Check couplings for ease of operation, any deformations, or other visible damage. While gathering equipment and rolling fire hose immediately following an incident, conduct a postincident inspection. This quick inspection allows firefighters to identify and mark damage on hose and couplings.

Before fire hose and couplings are stored or placed back in service after use, you should correct or report any of the following deficiencies that may be present:

- Evidence of dirt or debris on the hose jacket or couplings
- Damage to the hose jacket
- Coupling loosened from the hose
- Damage to male and female threads
- Obstructed operation of the swivel
- Absence of a well-fitting gasket in the swivel

Washing Hose

The method used to wash fire hose depends on the type of hose. Hard rubber booster hose, hard intake hose, and rubber-jacket collapsible hose only require rinsing with clean water, although a mild soap may be used if necessary.

Most **woven-jacket hose** requires a little more care. After woven-jacket fire hose is used, any dust and dirt should be thoroughly brushed or swept off of the hose. If brushing or sweeping does not remove the dirt, wash it with clean water while scrubbing with a stiff brush **(Figure 9.8)**.

When fire hose has been exposed to oil, it should be washed with a mild soap or detergent using common scrub brushes or straw brooms. Make sure that the oil is removed. The hose should then be rinsed thoroughly with clean water.

A hose washing device can make the care and maintenance of fire hose much easier. The flow of water into this device can be adjusted as desired, and the movement of the water assists in propelling the hose through the device. The hoseline that supplies the washer with water can be connected to a pumper or used directly from a hydrant (**Figure 9.9**). Higher water pressures provide better results.

Figure 9.9 A hose washing device being used to clean a section of fire hose.

A cabinet-type machine that washes, rinses, and drains fire hose is designed to be used in the station. One person can operate this machine, and it is self-propelled, and can be used with or without detergents.

Drying Hose

Fire hose should be dried before being stored. The methods used to dry hose depend on the type of hose. Hose should be dried in accordance with departmental SOPs and manufacturer's recommendations. Woven-jacket, natural fiber hose must be thoroughly dried before being reloaded on an apparatus to prevent mildew. Water should be drained from hose to prevent damage to the lining. Hard rubber booster and intake hoses may be placed back in service while wet with no ill effects.

Hose towers and drying racks must have adequate ventilation and protection so that fire hose is not exposed to excessive temperatures or direct sunlight (**Figure 9.10**). Take the following actions when drying hose in hose towers or on racks:

- Remove hose from exterior hose towers and racks as soon as it is dry to protect it from sun damage.

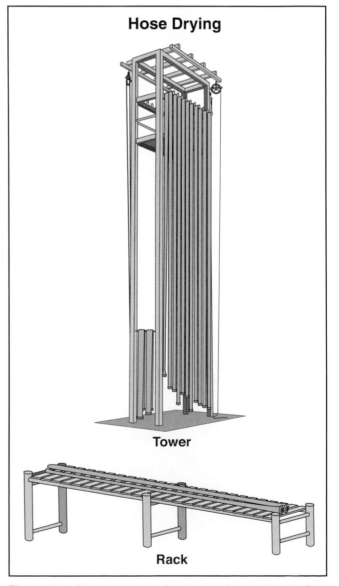
Figure 9.10 Hose towers and racks can be used to dry fire hose.

- Secure coupling ends when hose is hung in an area with directional airflow. Swinging couplings can collide with each other or with tower supports, resulting in mechanical damage.
- Cover male threads with precut sections of tubing to provide additional protection.
- Incline drying racks enough to allow water to drain from the hose during drying.
- Avoid placing hose sections too closely together or allowing them to touch, which can slow the drying process.

Storing Hose

After fire hose has been washed and dried, roll and store it in racks in a manner that protects the rolls from damage. Hose storage racks may be mounted to walls and floors or freestanding on the floor. Mobile hose racks can be used to both store and move hose from storage rooms to apparatus for loading **(Figure 9.11)**. Hose stored in the fire apparatus room/bay may be exposed to airborne contaminants such as:

- Cleaning solvents
- Lubricants
- Oils
- Gasoline
- Diesel fumes

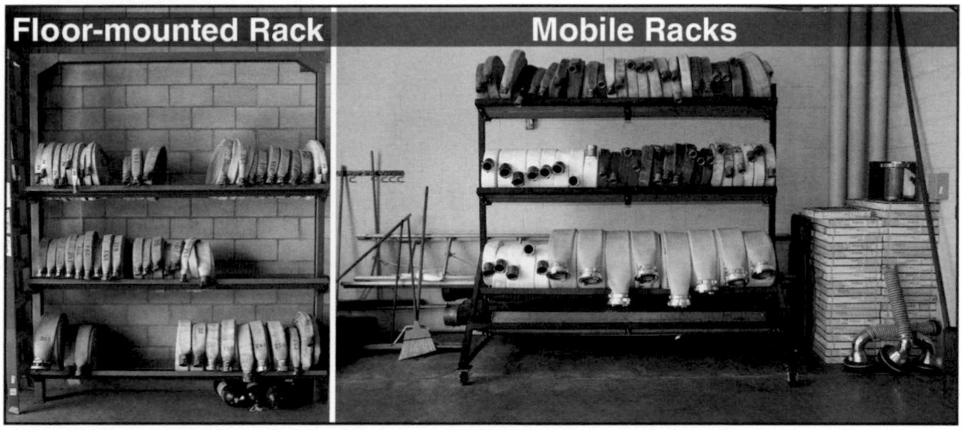

Figure 9.11 Fire hose can be stored on floor- or wall-mounted racks or on mobile hose racks.

NOTE: If hose must be stored in the fire apparatus room/bay, inspect and clean it more frequently than fire hose that is stored in a separate space.

CAUTION: Never store solvents, petroleum products, or other chemicals close to fire hose and couplings.

Take the following precautions to prevent damage to hose stored in racks:

- Locate hose racks in a clean, well-ventilated room that is easily accessible to the apparatus room/bay.
- Store hose where it is not exposed to direct sunlight. The sun's ultraviolet rays break down the natural or synthetic fabric of the hose, reducing its expected service life.
- Pack cotton fabric hose loosely so that air circulates around it. Synthetic and rubber-jacketed hose can be stored in tight rolls after normal cleaning procedures.
- Store hose in a rack so that couplings are not in walkways and will not come into contact with equipment or passing personnel.
- Roll the hose with the male end inside the roll to protect the male coupling threads.
- When it is necessary to store fire hose with the male coupling on the outside of the roll, it is recommended that the exposed threads be protected with a cap or other protective device.
- Place two-way couplings in a storage rack in a way that prevents dirt or other foreign objects from collecting in their ramp grooves. These contaminants can interfere with their ability to securely lock into place.

Preventing Damage to Hose

The types of damage that can occur to the exterior covering and the inner lining of fire hose include:

- **Mechanical damage** — Abrasions, cuts, and tears
- **Thermal damage** — Exposure to fire, high heat, or freezing temperatures
- **Organic damage** — Mold and mildew
- **Chemical damage** — Deterioration due to solvent action on synthetic materials and natural fibers
- **Corrosion** — Oxidation of metal couplings
- **Age deterioration** — Cracking at points where hose is folded, and separation of inner liner from exterior covering

Mechanical Damage

Mechanical damage occurs when contact with an object or surface causes **(Figure 9.12)**:

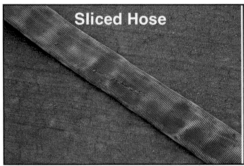

Figure 9.12 Cuts/slices and crushed couplings are two examples of mechanical damage that can be done to fire hose.

- Slices
- Abrasions on the exterior covering
- Cracked inner linings
- Rips
- Crushed or damaged couplings

The following practices are recommended to help prevent mechanical damage:

- Avoid laying or pulling a hose over rough, sharp edges or objects, such as:
  - Corners
  - Broken glass
  - Windowsills
  - Structural steel
  - Parapets
- Use a hose roller or place a folded salvage cover over sharp edges.
- Clear windowsills of broken glass fragments.
- Provide traffic control measures to prevent vehicles from driving over hose.
- Use hose ramps or bridges to protect hose from vehicles driving over it when traffic cannot be rerouted.
- Open and close nozzles, valves, and hydrants slowly to limit excessive stress and prevent water hammer.
- Provide **chafing blocks** to prevent abrasion to hose when it vibrates near the pumper.
- Avoid excessive pump pressure on hoselines.
- Deploy hoselines away from debris, or clear debris from the path of hose during overhaul operations.
- Change position of folds in hose when reloading it on apparatus.
- Clean hose before reloading it to prevent abrasions from dirt or grit.

Thermal Damage

Thermal damage to fire hose can result from excessive heat exposure or cold temperatures. Inner linings can also be dehydrated when hose is hung to dry in a drying tower or rack longer than necessary or when it is dried in direct sunlight. Mechanical hose dryers eliminate this concern, but extend the time required to dry large amounts of hose because of their limited capacity. To prevent thermal damage, follow these recommended practices:

- Protect hose from exposure to excessive heat or fire when possible.

- Remove hose from any heated area as soon as it is dry.

- Use moderate temperature settings for mechanical drying since warm air is much better than hot air.

- Keep the outside of woven-jacket hose dry when not in use.

- Run water through hose that has not been used for some time to keep the liner soft.

- Avoid laying fire hose on hot pavement to dry.

- Roll dry hose in a straight roll for storage to keep the liner from drying out.

- Prevent hose from coming in contact with, or being placed close to, vehicle exhaust systems.

- Use hose bed covers on apparatus to shield the hose from the sun.

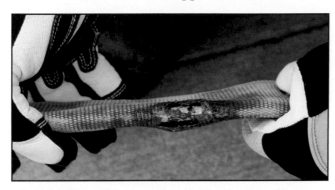

Figure 9.13 This section of fire hose was charred and melted during a fire.

Excessive heat exposure or direct flame contact can cause **(Figure 9.13)**:

- Charring

- Melting

- Weakening the outer jacket

- Dehydrating the rubber lining

Cold damage occurs when water on the inside and/or the outside of fire hose freezes. Fire departments located in regions that experience extreme cold temperatures should use special cold-resistant hose designed for use at temperatures down to -65°F (-54°C). Cold-resistant hose should perform with the same reliability as regular fire hose while withstanding the rigors of freezing and thawing. Regardless of the type of fire hose used in extreme cold temperatures, allow some water to flow through the nozzle to prevent water from freezing inside the hose during intermittent use at fires.

Use the following guidelines to help prevent hose from freezing:

- Circulate water from a hydrant through the fire pump, discharging it through a drain-off hose that routes water down a gutter or to a place away from the pumping apparatus.

- Immediately drain and roll hose that is no longer needed for fire fighting operations.

- Tighten all hose connections to prevent couplings from leaking and freezing.

Figure 9.14 Mold has begun eating at the fibers of this section of fire hose.

Organic Damage

Mildew and mold are living organisms (fungus) that can rot natural fibers **(Figure 9.14)**. When hose with a woven-jacket of cotton or other natural fiber is stored wet, rot may weaken the jacket, which can lead to ruptures under pressure. The outer jacket of some woven-jacket fire hose is made of synthetic fibers such as Dacron™ polyester that can resist organic damage. The outer jacket of some natural fiber hose has been chemically treated to resist mildew and mold, but such treatment is not always effective. Rubber-jacket hose is not subject to organic damage.

Some methods of preventing mildew and mold on fire hose include:

- Remove all wet hose from the apparatus after use and replace with dry hose or dry the wet hose thoroughly before reloading it on the apparatus.

- Inspect, wash, and dry hose that has been contaminated in any way.

- Remove, inspect, sweep, and reload hose that has not been unloaded from the apparatus in six months. Make sure that the hose is folded in different places than when previously loaded.

- Inspect and test hose annually and after possible damage or freezing.

- Ensure that cotton or cotton-blend fire hose is dry before storing or loading.

- Cover hose beds with water repellant covers to keep hose loads dry during inclement weather.

- Inspect fire hose in storage racks and hose beds periodically.

- Remove and rotate hose periodically. Even if mildew is not visible, a musty smell is often an indicator that rot is hidden somewhere within the hose.

- Ventilate all areas where fire hose is kept, including pumping apparatus hose beds and compartments.

- Wash hose immediately whenever mildew is discovered. The steps include:

    — Scrub the cover jacket with a mild soap or manufacturer recommended cleaning solution.

    — Rinse well.

    — Dry completely or to the point recommended in the manufacturer's instructions.

    — Inspect the hose section within the next few days for the reappearance of mildew.

Chemical Damage

Certain chemicals and chemical vapors can damage the outer jacket on fire hose or cause the rubber lining to separate from the inner jacket. Common examples of chemical damage to fire hose include:

- Exposure to petroleum products, paints, acids, or alkalis may weaken hose to the point of bursting under pressure:

    — Motor oil from contact with streets and highways will penetrate the woven outer cover and cause a reaction that separates the inner lining of the hose.

    — Gasoline contact will also react to separate the inner lining of the hose, but has a much quicker and more severe reaction.

- Battery acid can destroy hose jacket fibers.

- Runoff water from a fire may carry foreign materials that can cause chemical damage to fire hose.

- After exposure to chemicals or chemical vapors, hose should be cleaned as soon as it is practical.

Some recommended practices include:

- Avoid laying fire hose against curbs where oil, gasoline, and battery acid may accumulate or pool from parked automobiles. Hose laid in gutters may also come in contact with fire fighting runoff water that could contain harmful chemicals. Even though some types of fire hose are constructed from materials that chemical exposure does not affect, other hose types are still used.

- Avoid exposing fire hose to hazardous materials spills.

- Avoid exposing fire hose to spills of foam concentrate, which is mildly corrosive and can deteriorate the hose lining or cover material if it remains on the hose.

- Rinse fire hose suspected of having contacted acid or other caustic chemicals with copious amounts of water. Remove the hose from service and contact the manufacturer for further maintenance procedures.

- Periodically remove hose from the apparatus, wash it with clean water, and dry it thoroughly.

- Test hose thoroughly if there is any suspicion of damage (see Service Testing Fire Hose section).

- Dispose of hose according to departmental SOPs if it has been exposed to hazardous materials and cannot be decontaminated.

Corrosion

Corrosion is a chemical process in which a metal is attacked by some substance in its environment and converted to an unwanted compound that gradually weakens or destroys the metal. The most common fire hose coupling metals are made of brass or an aluminum alloy, such as Pyrolite. Each of these metals possesses a high resistance to corrosion, but each will receive some deterioration when exposed to certain conditions.

Brass is highly resistant to corrosion. Over time, however, a brass coupling will corrode when it is in contact with moist organic materials or earth. The metal will darken and turn green as copper oxides are formed. Although these copper oxides are usually found only on exposed surfaces, they can form on the interior of female swivels or inside nozzle surfaces, reducing the ease of the device's operation. Normal cleaning removes most of the surface corrosion; however, the only way to free the swivels or operating mechanisms is to lubricate moving parts according to the manufacturer's recommendations.

Aluminum couplings develop a layer of corrosion (aluminum oxide) that "seals" the metal against further oxidation. This protective layer can be scratched or abraded during normal use, resulting in a new layer being formed.

 Couplings with Dissimilar Metals

When brass and aluminum couplings are threaded together, **galvanic corrosion** may occur where the threads meet. This corrosion can prevent the couplings from being loosened or tightened without the use of tools. There are two basic methods to avoid the formation of such corrosion:

- Do not join two lengths of hose equipped with couplings made of dissimilar metals

- Disconnect the couplings routinely and coat the coupling threads with a petroleum-based lubricant that is resistant to galvanic corrosion

Age Deterioration

Hose near the top of the hose bed is deployed most often. In contrast, lower layers may seldom be removed. When fire hose is left in an apparatus bed for extended periods of time, the hose can deteriorate and crack because of sharp folds in a tightly packed hose load. To prevent this deterioration, hose loads that are not routinely used should be removed and repacked on a regular schedule. When reloading the hose, pack the hose loosely and fold the hose in places that were not previously folded. Because fire hose that is loaded on edge wears more quickly, manufacturers recommend using a flat load.

Fire hose will also deteriorate if it is left hanging in a hose tower for extended periods of time. The inner lining of hose can become weakened at the point where it hangs over the support peg. Reinforced jacketed fabric hose may undergo a separation of the rubber or plastic lining from the inner reinforcement, reducing the strength of the hose at the point of the separation. To prevent this damage, remove the hose from the tower as soon as it is dry. If fire hose must remain in a tower for prolonged periods, periodically change the hose/peg contact point.

NOTE: Always follow the manufacturer's instructions and department SOPs for hose care and maintenance.

Cleaning Nozzles

Fire brigade members should inspect nozzles periodically and after each use to make sure that they are in proper working condition. This inspection includes the following:

- Check the swivel gasket for damage or wear. Replace worn or missing gaskets

- Look for external damage to the nozzle. If the nozzle has spinning teeth, ensure no teeth are missing and that they spin freely.

- Look for internal damage and debris. When necessary, thoroughly clean nozzles with soap and water, using a soft bristle brush **(Figure 9.15)**.

- Check the ease of operating the nozzle parts. Clean and lubricate any moving parts that appear to be sticking according to manufacturer's recommendations.

- Check to make sure that the pistol grip (if applicable) is secured to the nozzle.

- Ensure nozzles are stored with the bales closed.

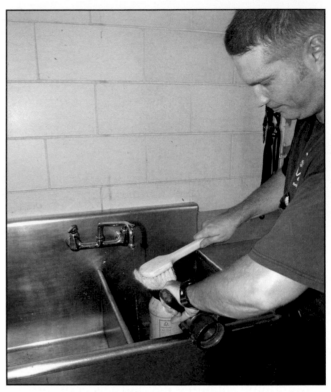

Figure 9.15 A soft bristle brush can be used with soap and water when cleaning fire nozzles.

Service Testing Fire Hose

NFPA 1962, *Standard for the Inspection, Care, and Use of Fire Hose, Couplings, and Nozzles and the Service Testing of Fire Hose*, provides guidelines for service testing of fire hose. Service tests are performed annually, after repairs have been made, and after a vehicle has run over the hose.

Before being service tested, examine the hose for excessive wear or damage to the jacket, coupling damage, and defective or missing gaskets. If any defects are found, tag the hose for repair. If damage is unrepairable, remove the hose from service.

Test Site Preparation

Hose should be tested in a paved area with enough room to lay out the hose in straight lines, free of kinks, bends, or twists. The site should be protected from vehicular traffic. If testing is conducted at night, the area should be well lighted. The test area should be smooth and free from rocks and debris. A slight grade to aid water drainage is helpful. A water source sufficient for charging the hose is necessary.

The following equipment is needed to service test hose:

- Hose-testing machine, portable pump, or fire department pumper equipped with gauges certified as accurate within one year before testing

- **Hose-test gate valve**

- Means of recording the hose numbers and test results

- Tags or other means to identify sections that fail

- Nozzles with shutoff valves

- Means of marking each length with the year of the test to easily identify which lengths have been tested and which have not without looking in the hose records

Service Test Procedure

Exercise care when working with hose, especially when it is under pressure. Pressurized hose is potentially dangerous because of its tendency to whip back and forth if a rupture occurs or a coupling pulls loose. To prevent this reaction, use a specially designed hose test gate valve. These valves have a ¼-inch (6 mm) hole in the gate that permits pressurizing the hose but does not allow water to surge through the hose if it fails. Even when using the test gate valve, stand or walk near the pressurized hose only as necessary.

> **CAUTION:** The number of personnel in the test area should be limited and all personnel operating in the area of the pressurized hose should wear appropriate PPE as a safety precaution.

When using a pumping apparatus, connect the hose to discharges on the side of the apparatus opposite the pump panel. Close all valves slowly to prevent water hammer in the hose and pump. Test lengths of hose should not exceed 300 feet (100 m) because it is difficult to purge air from longer lengths of hose.

Laying large-diameter hose flat on the ground before charging it helps to prevent unnecessary wear on the edges. Stand away from the discharge valve connection when charging because the hose has a tendency to twist when it is filled with water and pressurized; this twisting could cause the connection to loosen.

Keep the hose testing area as dry as possible when filling and discharging air from the hose. During testing, this air aids in detecting minor leaks around couplings.

Indicators of Removal from Service. While service testing fire hose, you should watch for damage or failure indicators that would require a section of hose to be removed from service. These indicators may include:

- Leaks
- Couplings loosening or separating from the hose
- Hose rupturing/bursting
- Couplings separating from the hose

NOTE: Some damage to fire hose may not require removal from service. If a coupling has become loosened or a leak occurs close to a coupling, the hose may be cut to remove the damaged location and a new coupling attached (also called recoupling).

Recording Procedures. Fire hose records can be kept on cards, log sheets, or computers. These records should include the following:

- Information on the date of purchase
- Date and results of periodic testing
- Date and type of repairs performed
- Causes of failure, if any
- Manufacturer's name
- Remarks concerning testing
- Unusual features

These records are kept as part of the fire agency's or individual company's complete equipment inventory. These records indicate the disposition of the hose and its assigned location, engine, engine compartment, and rack storage.

After a section of hose has been service tested, the test results should be documented according to the AHJ's SOPs. Any damage and/or repairs made to the hose or if the hose is removed from service should be clearly and concisely documented.

Inspection, Maintenance, and Cleaning of Rope and Webbing

NFPA 1081 (2018): 4.1.2.4

Fire brigade members must maintain (inspect, clean, and store) all rope so that it is ready for use when needed. A log must be kept for personnel to record the rope's use and maintenance history.

Inspecting Rope

Personnel should inspect all ropes after each use and inspect unused rope at least once a year. Document inspections in the rope log. If any of the following damage is found, remove the rope from service and have it destroyed:

- Imbedded shards of glass
- Metal shavings
- Wood splinters
- Foreign objects that can damage the fibers

Kernmantle Rope

Inspecting **kernmantle rope** for damage is somewhat difficult because the damage may not be obvious. When inspecting, put a slight tension on the rope while feeling for lumps, depressions, or soft spots. Knots or bends cause soft spots, but they may not be signs of permanent damage to the core because core fibers may only be temporarily misaligned. If you feel a soft spot, inspect the outer sheath. If the sheath is damaged, the core is probably damaged as well. However, the core of a kernmantle rope can be damaged without visible evidence on the outer sheath. If there is any doubt about the rope's integrity, it should be removed from service, downgraded for use as **utility rope**, or destroyed.

In addition to inspecting for damage to the core and sheath, note features such as:

Figure 9.16 This section of rope was contaminated by contact with motor oil during an incident.

- Irregularities in shape or weave
- Foul smells
- Discoloration from chemical contamination **(Figure 9.16)**
- Roughness
- Abrasions
- Deterioration (fuzziness)

NOTE: Some deterioration is normal, but rope that is excessively fuzzy in one spot or overall should be removed from service.

Laid Rope

Fire brigade members should untwist synthetic **laid rope** so they can inspect all sides of each strand. In synthetic rope, mildew is not necessarily a problem because the fiber resists rotting and molding. However, personnel must remove mildew and then clean and reinspect the rope. When inspecting synthetic rope, look for the following:

- Soft, crusty, stiff, or brittle spots
- Cuts, nicks, or abrasions
- Dirt or grease

- Excessive stretching
- Chemical damage
- Other obvious flaws

Natural fiber laid rope deteriorates with age. When it reaches the end of its manufacturer's recommended service life, personnel must remove it from service. The rope's age can be determined from the rope log. When inspecting natural rope, look for the following signs of damage:

- Ruptured fibers and powdering between strands indicates internal wear or that the rope has been overloaded.
- Dark red, brown, or black spots between the strands, along with a sour, musty, or acidic odor indicate rot and mildew.
- Brittle or ruptured fibers, salt incrustation, or swollen areas indicate chemical damage.
- Rust spots, which occur on ropes in prerigged pulley systems or ropes that are stored with other metal devices, indicate weakened fibers and reduced holding power.
- Accumulations of heavy, greasy materials indicate adverse effects on rope strength and reduced holding power.

Rot will quickly spread from a rotten rope to a new rope if they are stored next to one another. When rot is discovered, the rotten rope and any surrounding ropes must be immediately removed from service, cleaned, and reinspected. The storage area should be cleaned, dried, and ventilated before putting the rope back into it.

Braided Rope

Visually inspect **braided rope** for exterior damage, such as nicks, cuts, heat sears (whether from friction or fire), and excessive or unusual fuzziness. Feel and squeeze the surface of the rope to inspect for permanent mushy spots or other deformities.

Braid-on-Braid Rope

Visually inspect **braid-on-braid rope** for:

- Heat sears
- Nicks
- Cuts

Feel for lumps, which indicate core damage. If the rope's diameter has shrunk, this result may indicate a break in the core. If there is any damage or questionable wear on the sheath, carefully examine it. Check to see if the sheath slides on the core. If it does, cut the end of the rope, pull off the excess material, and then seal the end.

Maintaining Rope

If not properly maintained, synthetic and natural fiber ropes can be easily damaged. In addition to the manufacturer's instructions, the following guidelines can help to ensure that ropes remain in good condition:

- **Avoid abrasion and unnecessary wear** — Rope can be weakened from constant vibration against apparatus compartment surfaces, compression when stored in tight spaces, and surface damage due to chafing or dragging over splintered, rough, or gritty surfaces.
- **Avoid sharp angles, bends, and knots** — Sharp angles, bends, and knots can reduce strength by as much as 50 percent.
- **Protect ends from damage** — Whip or tape cut ends to prevent unravelling.
- **Avoid sustained loads** — Natural fiber ropes have less ability to bear sustained loads than synthetic fiber ropes. If they are subjected to heavy loads for long periods of time, they can break well below the rated load limit. Never exceed the load limit of any rope, or subject it to sustained loads for more than two days.

- **Avoid rust** — Keep all synthetic or natural fiber ropes away from rust, which can weaken rope in as little as one to two weeks. If ropes become rust-stained, inspect the extent of the stain. If rust shows halfway through the rope, then the rope may have lost as much as half of its strength. The rope should be removed from service and destroyed.

- **Prevent contact with chemicals** — Natural fiber rope is vulnerable to chemicals and solvents. Synthetic rope is not entirely resistant to damage from oils, gasoline, paint, and chemicals. Do not let rope contact storage battery solution, washing compounds or solutions, or animal waste. Strong acids, alkalis, and solvents can also damage any rope.

- **Reverse ends of the rope periodically** — Uncoil the rope and recoil it with the location of the ends changed. This action will ensure even wear along all portions of the rope.

- **Do not walk on rope** — Walking on rope grinds dirt and debris into the strands and compresses (bruises) the strands.

- **Schedule regular inspection and maintenance** — The AHJ should establish a schedule and include it in its SOPs.

Cleaning Rope

After use, visually inspect the rope to determine if it has been contaminated or soiled. Use a stiff bristled brush to remove loose surface debris and grime. If additional cleaning is needed, follow the manufacturer's instructions and consult the general cleaning guidelines in the following section.

Synthetic Fiber Ropes

To loosen imbedded dirt particles, wash synthetic fiber ropes with a mild detergent or fabric softener added to lukewarm or warm water. Do not use bleaches or strong cleansers. The following three methods are used for cleaning synthetic rope **(Figure 9.17)**:

Figure 9.17 Ropes can be washed by hand or by being placed in a rope bag and then placed into a washing machine.

- **Washing by hand** — Place the rope into a utility sink filled with water and detergent. Scrub the rope with a bristle brush. You can also place the rope in a mesh bag, allow it to soak in the sink, and then agitate it by hand to remove grit. When the rope is clean, rinse it thoroughly in clean water to remove detergent.

- **Rope-washing device** — Commercial rope-washing devices consist of a bristle-lined plastic tube that has a garden hose connection on one side. The rope is manually fed through the device, and multidirectional streams of water clean all sides of the rope at the same time. These devices remove mud and other surface debris; however, these devices cannot be used with detergent and do not address deeper cleaning concerns.

- **Washing machine** — Front- or top-loading clothes washers without center agitators can be used to clean rope. Place the rope in a mesh bag to protect the exterior from abrasion. Set the washer on the coolest wash/rinse temperature available, and use only a small amount of mild detergent. A washing machine can also rinse a rope that has been cleaned with a high-pressure washer.

After you have washed and rinsed the rope, you must dry it immediately. To dry the rope, you can spread it out on a hose drying rack, suspend it in a hose tower, or loosely coil it in a hose dryer. Never place it near a heat source or use a heated dryer because heat can reduce the rope's tensile strength. Avoid drying or storing in direct sunlight, as ultraviolet light can also weaken the rope.

Natural Fiber Ropes

Wipe or gently brush the rope to remove as much of the dirt and grit as possible. Do not use water. Water initially strengthens natural fiber rope, but over time it damages and weakens the fiber. If the rope gets wet during use, dry it thoroughly using the same method described for synthetic rope.

> **CAUTION:** Contact with water will ultimately weaken natural fiber ropes.

Maintaining a Rope Log

Keep a **rope log** for every life safety rope throughout each rope's working life. The log must include:

- Product label and manufacturer's instructions
- Information regarding purchase date, use, maintenance, and inspection
- Incidents that result in impact loading
- Inspector's signature and inspection date

In addition to recording visual inspections and known failures, maintenance log information helps determine when the rope should be removed from service. You may store the log at the station or in the rope storage bag. Rope logs are not required for utility ropes.

Cleaning and Maintaining Webbing

Care, cleaning, and maintenance of **webbing** follow the same guidelines used for synthetic rope. Follow the manufacturer's instructions, especially for life safety harnesses and ladder belts.

Other Fire Fighting Tools and Equipment

NFPA 1081 (2018): 4.1.2.4

Fire brigade members frequently use hand tools, power plants, electrical generators, and other powered equipment in the course of their duties. Tools and equipment require regular maintenance and testing to ensure that they will function properly when needed. This upkeep ultimately reduces replacement costs to the fire brigade. Each fire brigade should establish equipment and hose maintenance and testing programs.

Read the manufacturer's recommended maintenance guidelines for all tools, especially power tools. Follow your department's procedures to report any tools or equipment that need repairs. Tools that are damaged or excessively worn should be removed from service, tagged, and sent to the proper authority for repair or replacement.

The following sections will address maintenance of:

- Hand tools
- Power equipment

Hand Tools

Fire brigade members may use common hand tools, including:

- **Axes**
- **Pike poles**
- **Prying tools** (such as **Halligan tools**, pry axes, **crowbars**, and pry bars)
- Hammers

Many of these tools have wooden or fiberglass handles, cutting edges, and plated or unprotected metal surfaces. Each of these tool components require specific care and maintenance procedures, which the following sections describe.

Wooden Handles

Care and maintenance of wooden handles includes **(Figure 9.18)**:

- Inspecting the handle for cracks, blisters, or splinters.
- Sanding the handle if necessary to eliminate splinters.
- Washing the handle with mild detergent, rinsing, and wiping dry. Do not soak the handle in water because it will cause the wood to swell.
- Applying a coat of boiled linseed oil to the handle to preserve it and prevent roughness and warping. Do not paint or varnish the handle.
- Checking the tightness (secure attachment) of the tool head.
- Limiting the amount of surface area used for tool marking. Unit designations can be applied on strips of tape or self-adhesive bar codes on the handle.

NOTE: Dispose of the used cleaning materials in accordance with the fire brigade's SOPs.

Fiberglass Handles

Fiberglass handles are easier to maintain than wood handles. Care includes **(Figure 9.19)**:

- Washing the handle with mild detergent, rinsing, and wiping dry
- Checking for damage or cracks
- Checking the tightness of the tool head

Figure 9.18 Occasionally, wooden axe handles require sanding and the application of a coat of boiled linseed oil.

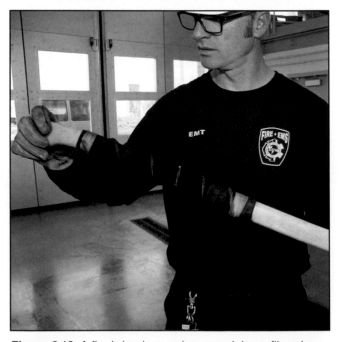

Figure 9.19 A fire brigade member examining a fiberglass axe handle.

Cutting Edges

Cutting edges on axes require the following care and maintenance:

- Inspecting the cutting edge for chips, cracks, or spurs.

- Replacing the axe head when required.

- Filing the cutting edges by hand; grinding weakens the tool.

- Sharpening blade as specified in departmental SOPs.

How well an axe head is maintained directly affects how well it will perform. If the blade is sharp and ground too thin, pieces of the blade may break when cutting gravel roofs or striking nails and/or screws in doors, walls, roof decking, or flooring. If the blade is too thick, regardless of its sharpness, personnel will have difficulty driving the axe head through ordinary objects.

NOTE: Never apply paint to the cutting surface of an axe head since it may cause the cutting surface to stick and bind.

Plated Surfaces

Protection of plated surfaces comes from chromium or an electro-plating process that applies another metal. Wipe plated surfaces clean, or wash them using mild detergent and water, rinse, and wipe dry. Inspect these surfaces for damage.

Unprotected Metal Surfaces

Unprotected metal surfaces are the blades, wedges, pikes, handles, and other tool components that have not been electroplated to protect them from corrosion. Instructions for care are as follows:

- Use an emery cloth or steel wool to remove dirt and rust.

- Use a metal file to remove burrs from the cutting edge and body.

- Do not make the blade edge too sharp since this may cause the blade to chip or break.

- Do not use a mechanical grinder to sharpen the blade edge because it may cause a loss of temper through overheating.

- Oil the metal surface lightly. Light machine oil works best.

- Do not apply oil to the striking surface of tools.

- Do not paint metal surfaces since paint hides defects.

- Inspect the metal for chips, cracks, burrs, or sharp edges, and file them off when found.

Power Equipment

The various types of power equipment must be ready to perform at their optimal performances when needed. An established maintenance program includes intervals ranging from daily, bimonthly, monthly, quarterly, semi-annual, or annually, including after use. When cleaning some of the tools, different types of solvent may have to be used. For example, after the operation of a chainsaw, the lubricant for the chain will require a strong solvent, such as mineral spirits, that can be used in the housing and arm of the blade to remove excess oil from these areas. Other equipment will require only the use of a mild soap. Before performing any maintenance, fire brigade members must refer at the manufacturer's user manual and the **safety data sheet (SDS)** of any solvent used.

Fire brigade members should follow department equipment inspection and maintenance policies and procedures as well as manufacturers' recommended procedures. When in doubt, you should refer to the appropriate policy or procedure.

The following sections will address maintaining:

- Power plants and electrical generators
- Power tools
- Portable lighting equipment

Maintaining Power Plants and Electrical Generators

All portable generators and lighting equipment must receive regular inspections and maintenance. Follow these guidelines:

- Review the manufacturer's service manual for specific directions.

- Inspect hydraulic power plants and electrical generators periodically and after each use.

- Inspect spark plugs for damage, visible corrosion, carbon accumulation, or cracks in the porcelain. Make sure the spark plug wire is tight.

- Replace the spark plug if it is damaged or the service manual recommends replacement. Ensure the gap between the spark plug electrodes is properly set prior to installing. Any plug indicating the presence of carbon soot around the ground electrode, or shows signs of arcing, should be replaced.

- Check the power plant/generator's carburetor and identify any signs of fuel leaks.

- Ensure that fuel is fresh. A fuel mixture may separate or degrade over time.

  NOTE: Consult the manufacturers' recommendations regarding the proper fuels to be used.

- Check the fuel level and refill it as needed **(Figure 9.20)**.

- Visually inspect the fuel in the tank to ensure that it is not contaminated. Discard contaminated fuel in an approved manner.

- Check the oil level and refill it as needed.

- Start the power plant/generator and run any tests required in the service manual. If a problem is found with the power plant/generator, consult the manual to determine the proper action. Only qualified service personnel or a licensed electrician should perform repair work on the generator.

- Avoid starting a power plant/generator while under a load (lighting or other equipment turned on and plugged in). Starting a power plant/generator while under a load can damage the system.

- Do not run the power plant/generator for a long period of time without a load. This action will overheat and damage the generator.

- Clean the work area and return all tools and equipment to the proper storage areas.

- Document the maintenance on the appropriate forms or records.

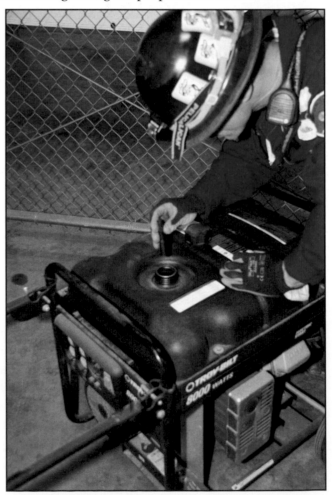

Figure 9.20 Fire brigade members must check the fuel levels of gasoline- or diesel-powered equipment.

> **CAUTION:** Always start and operate all gas- or diesel-powered equipment in a well-ventilated area.

Some types of equipment and some kinds of maintenance are not your responsibility. The driver/operator typically inspects and maintains apparatus electrical systems and apparatus-mounted lights and generators. Qualified technicians must perform detailed maintenance and modification of any lighting equipment.

Maintaining Power Rescue Tools

To inspect, care for, and maintain power rescue tools, you should follow the manufacturer's recommendations and departmental SOPs. Follow these general guidelines:

- Review the manufacturer's service manual for specific directions.
- Inspect power tools according to the fire brigade's SOPs.
- Make sure that all parts and support items are accessible.
- Keep battery packs fully charged.
- Keep pneumatic air cylinders fully charged.
- Check all fluid levels.
- Use only the recommended types of lubricants, hydraulic fluids, and fuel grades.
- Inspect saw, chisel, and cutter blades on a regular basis **(Figure 9.21)**. Replace blades that are worn or damaged.

Figure 9.21 A fire brigade member inspecting a power saw blade for damage including bent or missing teeth.

- Check all electrical components, such as cords and portable receptacles, for cuts or other damage.
- Make sure that all protective guards are functional and in place.
- Inspect hydraulic supply hoses for damage.
- Inspect hydraulic hose couplings (quick disconnect fittings) to ensure that they are clean and functional.
- Inspect pneumatic supply hoses for damage.
- Inspect pneumatic hose couplings (quick disconnect fittings) to ensure that they are clean and functional.
- Clean the work area and return all tools and equipment to the proper storage areas.
- Document the maintenance on the appropriate forms or records.

Maintaining Portable Lighting Equipment

Maintaining portable lighting includes all of the following:

- Inspect all electrical cords for damaged insulation, exposed wiring, or missing or bent prongs.

- Test the operation of the lighting equipment. Connect each light to the generator one light at a time to prevent overloading **(Figure 9.22)**. Avoid looking directly into the lights when they are powered.

- Replace lightbulbs as necessary. Shut off the power and allow the bulb to cool before replacing. If the bulb must be replaced immediately, wear leather gloves to prevent being burned. Discard faulty bulbs in an approved manner.

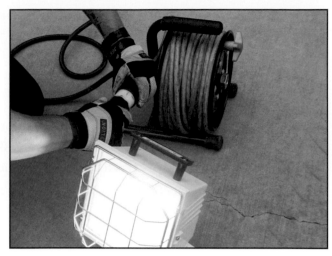

Figure 9.22 Portable lights should be connected one at a time during inspection.

Chapter Review

1. What should be checked when inspecting ground ladders?

2. What procedures should be part of every fire extinguisher inspection?

3. What precautions should be taken when drying hose?

4. What guidelines should be followed in order to ensure rope remains in good conditions?

5. What should be included in the care and maintenance of wooden handles?

Key Terms

Axe — Forcible entry tool that has a pick or flat head and a blade attached to a wood or fiberglass handle. *Also known as* Firefighter's Axe.

Beam — Main structural member of a ladder supporting the rungs or rung blocks. *Also known as* Rail *or* Side Rail.

Braid-on-Braid Rope — Rope that consists of a braided core enclosed in a braided, herringbone patterned sheath.

Braided Rope — Rope constructed by uniformly intertwining strands of rope together (similar to braiding hair).

Chafing Block — Blocks placed under hoselines to protect the hose covering from damage due to rubbing against the ground or concrete.

Crow Bar — Prying tool with a blade at either end; one end is significantly curved to provide additional mechanical advantage.

Galvanic Corrosion — An electrochemical process in which two dissimilar metals corrode when brought into electrical contact with each other in the presence of an electrolyte solution such as water.

Guide — Device to hold sections of an extension ladder together while allowing free movement.

Halligan Tool — Prying tool with a claw at one end and a spike or point at a right angle to a wedge at the other end. *Also known as* Hooligan Tool.

Halyard — Rope used on extension ladders to extend the fly sections. *Also known as* Fly Rope.

Heat Sensor Label — Label affixed to the ladder beam near the tip to provide a warning that the ladder has been subjected to excessive heat.

Hose Test Gate Valve — Special valve designed to prevent injury caused by a burst hoseline during hose testing.

Hose Tower — Part of a fire station or building designed so that fire hose can be hung vertically to drain and dry.

Kernmantle Rope — Rope that consists of a protective shield (mantle) over the load-bearing core strands (kern).

Laid Rope — Rope constructed by twisting several groups of individual strands together.

Maintenance — Keeping equipment or apparatus in a state of usefulness or readiness.

Pawls — Devices attached to the inside of the beams on fly sections; used to hold the fly section in place after it has been extended. *Also known as* Dogs *or* Ladder Locks.

Pike Pole — Sharp prong and hook of steel, on a wood, metal, fiberglass, or plastic handle of varying length, used for pulling, dragging, and probing.

Prying Tools — Hand tools that use the principle of leverage to allow the rescuer to exert more force than would be possible without the tool; typically long, slender, and constructed of hardened steel.

Pulley — Small, grooved wheel through which the halyard is drawn on an extension ladder.

Repair — To restore or put together something that has become inoperable or out of place.

Roof Ladder — Straight ladder with folding hooks at the top end; the hooks anchor the ladder over the roof ridge.

Rope Log — Record of all use, maintenance, and inspection throughout a rope's working life; also includes the product label and manufacturer's recommendations.

Rung — Step portion of a ladder running from beam to beam.

Safety Data Sheet (SDS) — Reference material that provides information on chemical that are used, produced, or stored at a facility. Form is provided by chemical manufacturers and blenders; contains information about chemical composition, physical and chemical properties, health and safety hazards, emergency response procedures, and waste disposal procedures. *Also known as* Material Safety Data Sheet (MSDS) *or* Product Safety Data Sheet (PSDS).

Service Test — Series of tests performed on apparatus and equipment in order to ensure operational readiness of the unit; should be performed at least yearly, or whenever a piece of apparatus or equipment has undergone extensive repair.

Utility Rope — Rope designed for any use except rescue; can be used to hoist equipment, secure unstable objects, or cordon off an area.

Webbing — Device used for creating anchors and lashings, or for packaging patients and rescuers; typically constructed from the same material as synthetic rope.

Woven-Jacket Hose — Fire hose constructed with one or two outer jackets woven on looms from cotton or synthetic fibers.

Skill Sheet List

The following skill sheets should be used to evaluate the skills described in this chapter:

NOTE: Students should wear the PPE appropriate to the NFPA 1081 level (Incipient, Advanced Exterior, Interior Structural, etc...) being evaluated.

Common Advanced Exterior and Interior Structural Facility Fire Brigade Member Training Requirements

Chapter Contents

JPRs addressed in this chapter

This chapter provides information that addresses the following job performance requirements of NFPA 1081, *Standard for Facility Fire Brigade Member Professional Qualifications (2018)*.

5.1.2.1	5.3.7	6.2.7	6.3.9
5.1.2.2	6.1.2.3	6.3.1	

1. Review the basics of fire detection systems. [5.1.2.1, 5.3.7, 6.1.2.3, 6.3.1]

2. Describe the methods for receiving and interpreting alarm conditions. [5.3.7, 6.3.1]

3. Identify the components of a preincident plan. [5.1.2.1, 6.1.2.3]

4. Identify the other important preincident data. [5.1.2.1, 6.1.2.3]

5. Describe the various plans that may be used at an incident. [5.1.2.1, 6.1.2.3]

6. Explain how incident plans should be utilized. [5.1.2.1, 6.1.2.3]

7. Describe the procedures for interfacing with mutual aid organizations. [5.1.2.2, 6.2.7, 6.3.9]

Chapter 10
Utilizing the Preincident Plan

In Chapter 1 of this manual, you learned about the National Incident Management System – Incident Command System and how it impacts fire brigade emergency operations. This chapter describes topics and skills related to utilizing the preincident plan to include:

- Interpreting alarm conditions
- Components of preincident plans
- Utilizing incident plans
- Interface with mutual aid organizations

Review Section: Fire Detection Systems

NFPA 1081 (2018): 5.1.2.1, 5.3.7, 6.1.2.3, 6.3.1

Fire detection systems identify the presence of the fire or fire gases within a facility and initiate some type of alarm and/or activate fire suppression systems. These systems are used in hospitals, warehouses, manufacturing, refineries, and many other types of facilities. Fire brigade members must be familiar with the fire detection systems found at their facilities and be able to interpret fire alarm system conditions during an emergency.

The basic categories of fire alarm systems include:

- **Protected Premises (Local) Systems** — Provide notification only to building occupants. There are no provisions for automatic off-site reporting.
- **Auxiliary Fire Alarm Systems** — Usually connect to a municipal fire alarm system where the appropriate response agencies are dispatched to the alarm.
- **Supervising Station Alarm Systems** — Monitor remote locations to report supervisory, trouble, or alarm signals to the appropriate authorities.

Common fire detection system components include the:

- Fire alarm control unit (FACU)
- Initiating devices
- Auxiliary services
- Power supplies
- Notification appliances

Fire detection systems can generate three types of alerts. An alarm indicates the presence of a fire or other emergency. A trouble alert indicates the system or one of its components is malfunctioning. Supervisory alarms may also indicate a problem with one or more components of a fire detection system.

Interpreting Alarm Conditions

NFPA 1081 (2018): 5.3.7, 6.3.1

Most facilities are equipped with some type of fire alarm and notification system, whether designed to work locally (within a structure or throughout a site) or send a signal to an outside agency. Fire brigade members must be aware of the types of system(s) at their site, their purposes, and the process of interpreting alarm conditions (signals) from these systems in order to facilitate an emergency response. This section will describe the following:

- Fire command/control centers
- Receiving and interpreting notifications from alarm systems

Review Section: Fire Command/Control Centers

Many large facilities incorporate a **fire command center** (FCC, sometimes called a fire control room or station) that consolidates the fire protection system controls in one location. A central location allows the various fire protection systems in the structure to be conveniently monitored and controlled as needed. Items contained in the FCC can include **(Figure 10.1)**:

- **Fire alarm control unit (FACU)**
- Smoke-control station
- Fire pump status indicators
- Emergency elevator controls
- Emergency communication systems
- Spare sprinklers and fusible links
- Building plans and system diagrams

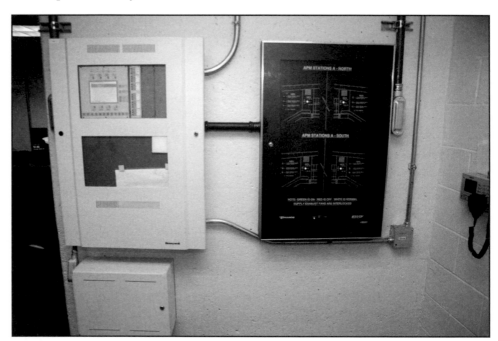

Figure 10.1 This fire alarm control unit is an important part of the facility's fire command center.

Review Section: Receiving and Interpreting Notifications from Alarm Systems

When a fire detection device activates, it sends a signal to the fire alarm system. Fire brigade members must know the various ways that they can receive alarm system notifications, prompting them to take appropriate action. Each facility will outline response requirement in the facility's SOPs. Personnel may receive alarm notifications by:

- Telephone or cellphone calls
- Alarm system printouts

Figure 10.2 Fire brigade personnel can receive alarm notifications from alarm panel display screens.

- Alarm panel display screens **(Figure 10.2)**

  Alarm conditions or notifications may come in the following forms:

- Supervisory/tamper alarms
- System trouble alarms
- Fire suppression system activations
- Localized fire alarms
- Hazardous release alarms
- Fire alarms from specific zones/locations

  After receiving an alarm notification, personnel may take the following actions:

- Acknowledging the alarm and identifying the alarm type and location
- Relaying information to fire brigade personnel to initiate a response
- Contacting facility management as well as local fire and emergency services agencies
- Notifying appropriate fire alarm maintenance personnel

Components of a Preincident Plan
NFPA 1081 (2018): 5.1.2.1, 6.1.2.3

NFPA 1620, *Standard for Pre-Incident Planning*, outlines requirements for **preincident planning**. During this process, facility fire brigades should identify the target hazards (areas with the highest potential for the loss of lives or property) in their response area. The information gathered should include:

- Life risk
- Property and equipment in the facilities or areas
- Any extraordinarily hazardous materials or processes
- Any impediments to access/egress
- Any built-in fire protection devices or systems
- Anything that would affect fire behavior or fire suppression and/or rescue efforts

Personnel should analyze the data that they gather during the preincident survey and translate it into preincident plans for the facilities. Preincident plans should include sketches, diagrams, maps, or photographs of key features of the facility **(Figure 10.3)**. This information can assist fire brigade personnel with any of the following:

- Locating and controlling a fire
- Locating occupants
- Determining potential hazards
- Improving emergency operations and safety for occupants and fire brigade members

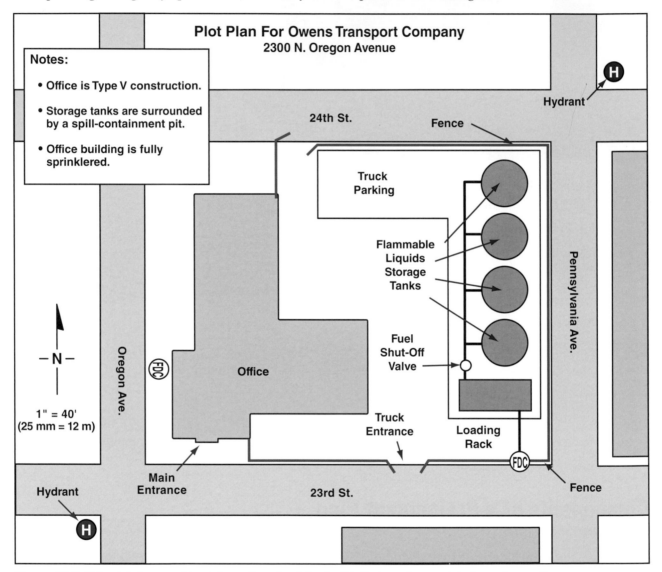

Figure 10.3 This plot plan provides information about the facility that can be used during a fire or other emergency.

Preincident plans should include the following details about a facility in their maps, drawings, photographs, and written notes **(Figure 10.4)**:

- Construction type
- Floor plan or layout
- Contents
- Occupancy type

Preincident Plan

Building: 221B

Dimensions

Length: 100 ft
Width: 90 ft
Floors: 3
Sq Ft: 27,000

Building Informaion

Construction: Type II
Classification: Manufacturing

Fire Alarm System

Make: FireSafe
Model: FS-101-XL
Location: Lobby
Mechanical Room

Fire Hydrants

NE corner @ 52 ft
SE corner @ 67 ft

Fire Pumps

QTY: 2
Make: Kente
Capacity: 2,500 GPM
Auto/Manual: Yes

FDC

QTY: 1
Type: Siamese wall mount
Location: NE side of building
near Door B4

Elevators

QTY: 2
Make: Upzendowner
Service: Smith Co.
(405) 555-1010

Emergency Generator

QTY: 1
Make: Northern CAT
Output: 480 Kw
Location: SE corner

Uninterrupted Power Supply (UPS)

Location: Room 1001C3

Communications

Public Address System
Elevator Phone

Roof Access

Inside: 3rd floor
Room 303M5

Sprinkler System (WET)

Door B4

Utility Shut-Offs

Natural Gas

Location: NE side of building
near Door B4

Water Mains

Location: NE side of building
near Door B4

Electrical

Location: Building 221A
Generator
UPS

Known Chemical Hazards Within Building

Figure 10.4 An example of a preincident plan that contains information the Incident Commander needs during a fire or other emergency.

- Hazardous materials storage and warning placards and signage
- Special processes
- Fuel loading
- Fences and gates surrounding the property that may obstruct access
- Site specific hazards

Fire brigade members must be familiar with their facility's preincident plans in order to:

- Become familiar with structures in their facility, their uses, and their associated hazards.

- Recognize existing hazards.

- Be prepared to follow the emergency operational procedures for various types of incidents that may occur at the facility.

- Visualize how standard tactics may apply in various occupancies.

- Develop new tactics, if necessary.

- Determine whether occupants may have disabilities or medical conditions that affect or limit self-evacuation, areas of refuge, or safe havens.

- Determine if any occupants with language barriers may require translators.

Fire brigade members should regularly review preincident plans to identify any changes to buildings, facilities, processes, or emergency procedures at their site. Changes in floor plans, uses or processes, access, and occupancy status can significantly affect emergency response.

Other Important Preincident Data

In order to operate within a preincident plan, fire brigade members need the following data:

- **Locations of water supply sources** — The locations of water supply sources at the facility and the volume of water found at each source. The list of water supply sources at or near the facility should include:
  - Fire hydrants and/or water manifolds
  - Elevated water tanks
  - Drafting sources such as reservoirs, ponds, lakes, and rivers

- **Location of other extinguishing agents** — The locations of and procedures for accessing these extinguishing agents and delivering to the area where they will be used. These agents may include:
  - Foam concentrates
  - Dry chemical agents
  - Dry powder agents
  - Clean agents (such as Halons, Halotron™, FE-200™, and FE-13™ and Inergen™)

- **Site Specific Hazards** — The site specific hazards or hazardous processes found at a facility. Site hazards may include (**Figure 10.5**):
  - Chemical storage tanks, piping, and facilities
  - Chemical refining processes
  - Pits and confined spaces
  - Commercial cooking equipment
  - Industrial furnaces and ovens
  - Large stockpiles of combustible materials such as wood, cardboard, and paper
  - Hazardous processes such as welding, cutting, grinding, or painting
  - Hazardous chemicals or energy sources

- **Fire Suppression and Detection Systems within the Facility** — The types, locations, operating procedures, and emergency response procedures for fire suppression and detection systems. Fire brigade members should be familiar with the fire suppression and detection systems used at their facility, how the systems work, and how to interpret the signals received from detection systems.

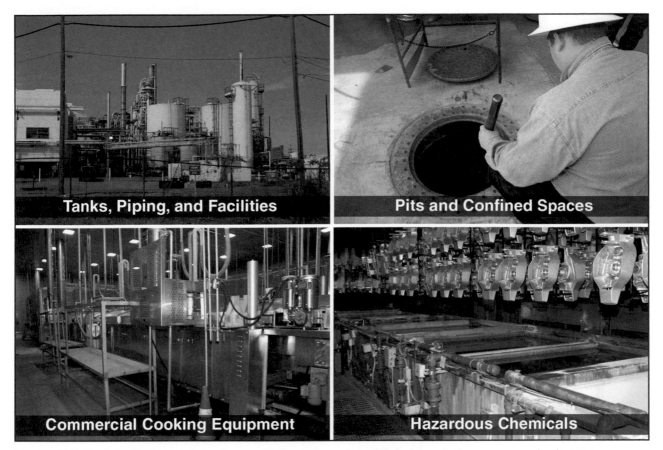

Figure 10.5 Each facility has certain site specific hazards such as those shown in the accompanying images.

- **Symbols Used in Preincident Plan Illustrations** — Common map and construction symbols, such as those found in NFPA 170, *Standard for Fire Safety and Emergency Symbols*. Some sites develop special symbols for their maps and sketches that identify the locations of special hazards, hazardous materials, and other locally important items. Some fire brigades use computerized geographic information system (GIS) or other electronic mapping programs to ensure accuracy of the data included on their site maps and facility floor plans. Laptop computers, notebooks, and tablet devices are also useful for recording notes and drawing site and floor plans. **Figure 10.6, p. 312** shows common map and construction symbols and their meanings. These symbols are used to identify the following:

  — Locations of:

    • Site structures in relation to one another

    • Fire protection systems

    • Water mains

    • Automatic sprinkler control valves

    • Fire hydrants and/or manifolds

    • Electrical and gas utilities

    • Prestaged fire brigade equipment

  — Construction features that include:

    • Type of construction

    • Partitions

    • Roof types

    • Other important features

    • Thickness of walls

    • Openings

    • Parapets

Common Map Symbols

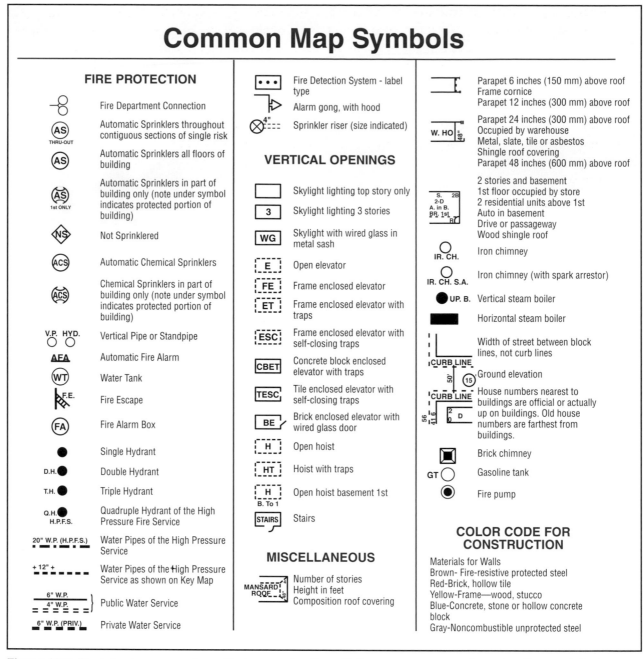

Figure 10.6 Fire brigade personnel need to become familiar with the common map and construction symbols that may be used in preincident plans.

Other Incident Plans

During an incident, the information found in the preincident plan, along with size-up of the situation, provide the groundwork for other incident plans. These other plans include:

- Operational plans
- Incident action plans (IAP)
- Strategic goals
- Tactical objectives
- Incident safety plan

Operational Plans

Operational plans are used to identify the following:

- Resources needed to mitigate a hazard
- Resource assignments
- Safety factors relating to incident control

Operational plans identify the specific resources and procedures needed to successfully deal with a variety of hypothetical incidents at that particular facility or site. The incident scenarios are considered to be the most likely to occur at the location in question. For example, if a facility uses or stores large quantities of toxic or highly flammable materials, personnel should create response plans involving these materials. Plans for evacuating large numbers of employees to areas of safe refuge should also be created. This process should be applied to all areas in the facility.

Operational plans include possible resource deployments. In the most likely scenarios, possible options for deploying the initial alarm resources are identified, as well as options for the deployment of those secondary resources that would respond to the incident. Scenarios based on increasingly larger and more complex hypothetical incidents help planners to identify the resources that may be needed and how they can be deployed to the best advantage.

Operational plans may often include provisions for a number of possible contingencies. Typical contingencies include the potential for unusually severe weather conditions that increase the spread of fires or hazardous materials. Considering these variables, an operational plan might specify an increase in the initial alarm resources at certain points on the **daily burning index**.

Operational plans may specify different initial alarm resource levels for a given occupancy if the number of people normally in the building or facilities varies at different times of the day or night. For example, the operational plan for an administrative building may specify that the initial alarm assignment be doubled if an alarm is received during hours of operation. The operational plans for occupancies that store large quantities of flammable liquids may specify that a bulk foam transport be a part of the initial alarm assignment so that large quantities of foam are immediately available, if needed **(Figure 10.7)**.

Figure 10.7 A foam tender that can provide large volumes of foam concentrate as called for in some operational plans. *Courtesy of Ron Jeffers, Union City, NJ.*

Fire brigade members use the data that they gather regarding any particular target hazard to project the strategic and tactical possibilities and probabilities at that location. Based on these scenarios, the resources needed are compared to the resources available. If required resources are more than or different from what the facility has available, planners can recommend the purchase of the necessary resources or the development of mutual aid or automatic aid agreements with nearby facilities or departments that have those resources.

Incident Action Plans (IAP)

Using the information obtained in the initial size-up and any other information available in an operational plan, the IC can devise a plan for the safe and efficient disposition of an incident. On relatively small, routine incidents, the plan does not need to be in writing, but must be communicated throughout the on-scene organization. On larger, more complex incidents covering multiple operational periods, the plan should be in writing and it must be distributed to the leaders of all units assigned to the incident and communicated to all incident personnel. ICS Form 201 can serve as a template for a written IAP. **Appendix C** contains an example of a completed ICS Form 201. Personnel should practice, evaluate, and update the plan as necessary both to ensure proper response and to record actions taken in case of subsequent litigation.

NOTE: Regardless of the size of the incident, an incident action plan must be communicated to all responders.

Strategic Goals

Strategic goals are broad, general statements of the overall outcomes to be achieved. Before an incident occurs, strategic goals should be translated into fire brigade SOPs. The four overall priorities that dictate these goals are the following, in order of importance:

- Life safety
- Property/environmental conservation
- Incident stabilization
- Facility restoration

These priorities should guide the development of the IAP. Deciding how to meet these priorities dictates the tactical objectives for the incident. Strategic goals and tactical objectives must be constantly evaluated/reevaluated. The continual process of size-up ensures that these goals and objectives are being accomplished. Fire brigade members should see the incident change as they meet their goals and objectives. Their priorities will also change as a result. Brigade leaders must be flexible enough to cope with a rapidly changing situation.

Tactical Objectives

Tactical objectives are measurable outcomes that are more specific than strategic goals. The following are examples of some common tactical objectives:

- Provide for the safety of fire brigade members, occupants, and others.
- Contain the incident to a specified geographic area.
- Mitigate the problem.
- Restore the scene.

NOTE: The implementation of the plan determines how personnel achieve these objectives.

Incident Safety Plans

The Incident Safety Officer (ISO) must develop an incident safety plan that is based upon the IC's strategies and tactics outlined in the incident action plan. The incident safety plan varies according to the type of incident. It is based on the risk management model and takes into consideration the potential hazards and the risks involved.

Utilizing Incident Plans

NFPA 1081 (2018): 5.1.2.1, 6.1.2.3

Each facility will outline the specific procedures for utilizing a preincident plan in the facility's SOPs. Advance exterior and interior fire brigade members must work within the incident plans utilized at their facility during an emergency. Once an emergency occurs, the fire brigade leader will access the appropriate preincident plan and review the data it contains. This review includes identifying:

- Components of the preincident plan, such as fire suppression and detection systems
- Structural features
- Site-specific hazards
- Response considerations

Additionally, the fire brigade leader will conduct a size-up of the emergency to identify specific situational conditions. The fire brigade leader then merges the information from the preincident plan and the size-up to create one or more incident plans tailored to the emergency.

Once these incident plans have been developed, the leader will assign specific tasks to fire brigade members to meet strategic and tactical goals **(Figure 10.8)**. Fire brigade members must work within those specific assignments and do the following:

- Wear appropriate PPE and SCBA.

- Follow the incident safety plan.

- Follow standardized communications procedures.

- Accomplish assignments in accordance with the IAP.

- Provide updated information to the fire brigade leader about changing conditions on the scene.

- Report completion of assignments to the fire brigade leader.

- Conduct postincident field decontamination of personnel, tools, equipment, PPE, and SCBA to reduce cancer or secondary cross-contamination risks.

Figure 10.8 A fire brigade leader assigning tasks to a fire brigade team.

Interface with Mutual Aid Organizations

NFPA 1081 (2018): 5.1.2.2, 6.2.7, 6.3.9

When facility fire brigades interact with outside agencies, they may create a unified command. Under this framework, the involved agencies agree to share the incident command responsibility. This interaction may be the result of formal mutual aid agreements with other local emergency response organizations. Fire brigade personnel may interact with the following agencies:

- Fire brigades (mutual or automatic aid) from nearby facilities

- Municipal fire departments

- Specialty emergency response teams (hazardous materials, confined space, and technical rescue)

- Emergency medical services (EMS)

- Local law enforcement agencies

- Outside contractors
- **Local Emergency Planning Committee (LEPC)** for preincident planning
- Government agencies
- News media (generally interact with specially trained management personnel)
- Medical facilities

Personnel must develop an effective working relationship with outside agencies before an incident occurs. All parties must agree upon the designated roles and responsibilities they will perform during an emergency. Mutual and automatic aid agreements must be regularly reviewed and maintained to ensure an adequate response to the facility when needed. The development of this relationship can begin with outside agencies visiting the site and performing a full review of potential hazards. With the assistance of the facility fire brigade, local fire and EMS officials can develop a preincident plan for the facility. With this assistance, law enforcement agencies can develop a contingency plan to handle wide area evacuations. The preincident planning should indicate all external agencies that may be involved during an incident. Without this type of cooperation and planning, the ability of agencies to effectively work together in an emergency could be impaired.

Regardless of how carefully considered and how well written the operational plan may be, it must be tested in one or more joint training exercises. Several full-scale exercises may be needed before all personnel can feel comfortable that the plan will function as intended. After each exercise, conduct a comprehensive, subjective, nonthreatening critique of the exercise. Review all aspects of the plan and correct any deficiencies that emerge. Once the plan has been found to be fully functional, it should then be tested at least annually. Annual testing will allow the plan to be updated as necessary, to accommodate changes in organizations, to refresh personnel on their roles and responsibilities, and to train new personnel in the plan's requirements.

Mutual aid agreements provide reciprocal assistance from one agency to another during an emergency based upon a prearrangement between the agencies involved and generally made upon the request of the receiving agency. In contrast, automatic aid agreements are often established between two or more agencies to automatically dispatch predetermined resources to any fire or another emergency reported in the geographic area that the agreement covers **(Figure 10.9)**. These areas are generally where the boundaries between jurisdictions meet or where jurisdictional "islands" exist.

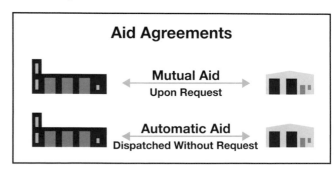

Figure 10.9 Illustrating the difference between mutual and automatic aid agreements.

Mutual and automatic aid agreements can prove highly beneficial to all parties. For example, agreements between organizations with similar fire response capabilities can provide additional resources (fire fighting apparatus, extinguishing agents, and personnel) in the event of a catastrophic incident. Mutual and automatic aid agreements can make available specialized extinguishing agents, equipment, and personnel trained to use those resources in the event that a nonindustrial facility experiences an emergency involving materials related to a particular industry.

Mutual and automatic aid agreements must be written documents that establish the roles and responsibilities of all agencies identified. The agreement should identify who will be in charge of an incident and who will provide what types of services or support so that no confusion arises during an emergency. A mutual or automatic aid agreement should address the following:

- Procedures to be followed
- Organizational structure
- On-site standard operating procedures
- Incident management system
- Communication protocols
- Integration of operational personnel into teams under a unified command structure

Once a mutual or automatic aid agreement is reached, joint training sessions and drills should be scheduled and conducted for the facility fire brigade and personnel from mutual aid agencies. These personnel should receive familiarization training on the facility or site to include:

- Access to the site and facilities
- Available water sources
- Layout and hazards
- Apparatus, personal protective equipment, and tools and equipment
- Standard operating procedures
- Specialized extinguishing agents available on site
- Specialized fire fighting tools and equipment available on site
- Communications equipment and procedures

Joint training sessions and drills between facility fire brigades and local municipal fire departments develop more than just their fire fighting and emergency response skills. They also develop a cooperative attitude that lays the foundation for successful joint emergency operations.

Chapter Review

1. What are the three basic types of fire alarm systems?

2. What are some items that may be contained in a fire command center?

3. What types of information should be gathered for a preincident plan?

4. What information should be gathered about the locations of water supply sources?

5. What is the difference between strategic goals and tactical objectives?

6. What data should the fire brigade leader review from the preincident plan when an emergency occurs?

7. What subjects should a mutual aid agreement address?

Discussion Question

1. With what agencies does your facility have mutual or automatic aid agreements?

Key Terms

Daily Burning Index (DBI) — A number related to the contribution of fire behavior to the effort of containing a fire during a 24-hour period. The difficulty of fire control is derived from a combination of how fast fire will spread how much energy will be produced.

Fire Alarm Control Unit (FACU) — The main fire alarm system component that monitors equipment and circuits, receives input signals from initiating devices, activates notification appliances, and transmits signals off-site.

Fire Command Center — Designated room or area in a structure where the status of the fire detection, alarm, and protection systems is displayed and the systems can be manually controlled; may be staffed or unstaffed and can be accessed by the fire department.

Local Emergency Planning Committee (LEPC) — Community organization responsible for local emergency response planning. Required by SARA Title III, LEPC's are composed of local officials, citizens, and industry representatives with the task of designing, reviewing, and updating a comprehensive emergency plan for an emergency planning district; plans may address hazardous materials inventories, hazardous material response training, and assessment of local response capabilities.

Preincident Planning — Act of preparing to manage an incident at a particular location or a particular type of incident before an incident occurs. *Also known as* Prefire Inspection, Prefire Planning, Pre-Incident Inspection, Pre-Incident Survey, *or* Preplanning.

Strategic Goals — Broad statements of desired achievement to control an incident; achieved by the completion of tactical objectives.

Tactical Objectives — Specific operations that must be accomplished to achieve strategic goals; objectives must be both specific and measurable.

Skill Sheet List

The following skill sheets should be used to evaluate the skills described in this chapter:

NOTE: Students should wear the PPE appropriate to the NFPA 1081 level (Incipient, Advanced Exterior, Interior Structural, etc...) being evaluated.

Common Advanced Exterior and Interior Structural Facility Fire Brigade Member Training Requirements

Chapter Contents

JPRs addressed in this chapter

This chapter provides information that addresses the following job performance requirements of NFPA 1081, *Standard for Facility Fire Brigade Member Professional Qualifications (2018)*.

5.2.1	5.2.4	5.3.10	6.1.2.2	6.2.10
5.2.2	5.2.9	6.1.2.1	6.2.8	6.3.7

Learning Objectives

1. Explain the purpose of different components of PPE. [5.2.1, 5.2.9, 6.1.2.1, 6.2.10]

2. Identify the different types of protective clothing. [5.2.1, 5.2.9, 6.1.2.1, 6.2.10]

3. Describe the safety considerations for PPE. [5.2.1, 5.2.9, 6.1.2.1, 6.2.10]

4. Explain the methods for maintaining PPE. [5.2.1, 5.2.9, 6.1.2.1, 6.2.10]

5. Describe the methods for using personal safety alert systems. [5.2.1, 5.2.9, 6.1.2.1, 6.2.10]

6. Describe the types of respiratory protection equipment. [5.2.2, 5.2.4, 6.1.2.2, 6.2.8]

7. Explain the methods for facepiece fit testing. [5.2.2, 5.2.4, 6.1.2.2, 6.2.8]

8. Identify different respiratory hazards. [5.2.2, 5.2.4, 6.1.2.2, 6.2.8]

9. List the components of SCBA. [5.2.2, 5.2.4, 6.1.2.2, 6.2.8]

10. Describe the protection limitations of SCBA. [5.2.2, 5.2.4, 6.1.2.2, 6.2.8]

11. Explain proper storage methods for SCBA. [5.2.2, 5.2.4, 6.1.2.2, 6.2.8]

12. Describe the procedures for donning and doffing of breathing apparatus. [5.2.2, 6.1.2.2]

13. Explain inspection and maintenance procedures of respiratory equipment. [5.2.2, 5.3.10, 6.1.2.2, 6.3.7]

14. Describe the methods for using respiratory protection equipment. [5.2.1, 5.2.2, 5.2.4, 6.1.2.2, 6.2.8]

Chapter 11
Personal Protective Equipment and Respiratory Protection

All fire brigade members above the incipient level are required to wear NFPA-compliant or equivalent fire fighting personal protective equipment (PPE) because of the hostile environment in which they may perform their duties. NFPA standards that reference required equipment are indicated in this chapter.

Providing and using protective equipment will not necessarily guarantee fire brigade member safety; however, injuries can be reduced and prevented if protective equipment and respiratory protection are used properly. All protective equipment has inherent limitations that fire brigade members must recognize so that they do not overextend the item's range of protection.

Fire brigade personnel participating in offensive operations in the hazard area must wear full protective equipment. The following sections discuss:

- Personal protective equipment
- Donning and doffing breathing apparatus
- Using respiratory protection equipment
- Respiratory protection
- Inspection and maintenance of respiratory equipment

Personal Protective Equipment
NFPA 1081 (2018): 5.2.1, 5.2.9, 6.1.2.1, 6.2.10

You should properly wear all **personal protective equipment (PPE)** with all closures fastened, self-contained breathing apparatus (SCBA) facepiece in place, and air cylinder activated before entering the structure. Your helmet's face shield, if so equipped, provides a secondary layer of eye protection. Your supervisor, incident safety officer, or another fire brigade member should perform a quick inspection to make sure your PPE is properly donned and operational before you enter the structure **(Figure 11.1)**.

NOTE: Fire brigade members should understand that the extra weight that personal protective equipment adds can limit the amount of time they can safely function in a hostile environment.

Figure 11.1 Fire brigade personnel checking each other's PPE prior to entering a hazard environment.

WARNING: Always wear the correct PPE that is designed to protect you from the specific type of hazard(s) that the incident presents.

PPE is designed to protect you from hazards and minimize the risk of injury or fatality. PPE usually consists of the following:

- Respiratory protection equipment
- **Personal alert safety system (PASS)**
- **Helmets**, coats, trousers, boots, **protective gloves**, and **protective hoods**
- Eye protection
- **Hearing protection**

 Standards for PPE

A number of standards mandate PPE design, construction, maintenance, and use, including the following:

- **PPE design and construction** — NFPA 1971, *Standard on Protective Ensembles for Structural Fire Fighting and Proximity Fire Fighting*, and NFPA 1500™, *Standard on Fire Brigade Occupational Safety and Health Program*

- **PPE care and maintenance** — NFPA 1851, *Standard on Selection, Care, and Maintenance of Protective Ensembles for Structural Fire Fighting and Proximity Fire Fighting*

- **Liquid splash-protective ensembles and clothing for hazardous materials emergencies** — NFPA 1991, *Standard on Vapor-Protective Ensembles for Hazardous Materials Emergencies*; NFPA 1992, *Standard on Liquid Splash-Protective Ensembles and Clothing for Hazardous Materials Emergencies*; and NFPA 1994, *Standard on Protective Ensembles for First Responders to CBRN Terrorism Incidents*

- **Wildland fire fighting protective clothing** — NFPA 1977, *Standard on Protective Clothing and Equipment for Wildland Fire Fighting*

- **Station/work uniforms** — NFPA 1975, *Standard on Station/Work Uniforms for Emergency Services*

- **SCBA** — NFPA 1981, *Standard on Open-Circuit Self-Contained Breathing Apparatus (SCBA) for Emergency Services*

- **PASS devices** — NFPA 1982, *Standard on Personal Alert Safety Systems (PASS)*

- **Safety glasses** — American National Standards Institute (ANSI) Standard Z87.1, *Occupational and Educational Personal Eye and Face Protection Devices*, or Canadian Standards Association (CSA) Standard Z94.3-M1982 in Canada

- **Goggles for wildland fire fighting** — ANSI Z87.1, *Occupational and Educational Personal Eye and Face Protection Devices*

- **PPE used by facility fire brigade members** — NFPA 600, *Standard on Facility Fire Brigades* and NFPA 1081, *Standard for Facility Fire Brigade Member Professional Qualifications*

Some emergency situations require hazard-specific protection, including respiratory protection, while other situations require only protective clothing. Types of PPE include **(Figure 11.2)**:

- Station and work uniforms
- **Structural fire fighting protective clothing**
- Wildland fire fighting protective clothing
- Roadway operations protective clothing

Figure 11.2 Examples of PPE used by fire brigade personnel: flame resistant coveralls (left), structural protective clothing and SCBA (center) and chemical protective clothing (right).

- Emergency medical protective clothing

- Special protective clothing such as chemical protective clothing

NOTE: Emergency medical protective clothing and special protective clothing are beyond the scope of this chapter. You will likely learn about emergency medical protective clothing when you are trained to your AHJ's level of emergency medical services training. Special protective clothing is taught during hazardous materials awareness and operations training.

Thermal PPE

All PPE designed for structural and **proximity fire fighting** must meet the requirements of NFPA 1971. This standard addresses the requirements for:

- Helmets
- Trousers
- Eye protection
- Protective hoods
- Coats
- Boots
- Protective gloves

NFPA 1971 requires that all components must include a permanent label that shows compliance with the standard. Labels must include the following information:

- Manufacturer's name, identification, or designation

- Manufacturer's address

- Country of manufacture

- Manufacturer's lot or serial number

- Month and year of manufacture

- Model name, number, or design

- Size or size range

- Principal materials of construction

- Footwear size and width (where applicable)

- Cleaning precautions

PPE components must be compatible with each other to provide the level of protection. Each component is designed to protect you from specific hazards and may not protect you from other hazard types. For instance, structural PPE offers no protection against many types of hazardous materials.

Fire brigade members should never alter their protective clothing. Changing, adding, or removing components may endanger your life, void the manufacturer's warranty, and/or affect your workers' compensation benefits. Alterations include:

- Removing the moisture barrier or liner of coats and trousers
- Sewing hooks, loops, or clasps to the outer shell
- Adding combustible decals to the helmet

WARNING: Unauthorized alteration of your PPE may expose you to fire scene hazards and endanger your life.

Structural PPE is designed to cover all portions of your skin when you are reaching, bending, or moving. It also prevents heat transfer from the fire to your body. During heat exposure, the clothing absorbs the heat, preventing transfer to the skin, but there are limits to how much heat the structural protective clothing can absorb. The clothing will become hot enough to cause contact burns when trapped heat permeates the fire brigade member's underclothing, or bare skin touches the material. The usual temperature limit is above 400° F (200° degrees C). The amount of time until the protective clothing reaches a dangerous absorption limit varies based upon the heat transfer rate. The lower the heat transfer rate, the longer the protective clothing will protect you and stay within tolerable limits.

Since protective clothing absorbs and stores heat, it can take longer than expected to cool. Simply leaving a hot environment for a short period of time may not be long enough to cool the clothing to safe levels for reentry into a fire environment. You may experience contact burns or heat stress even after leaving a heated environment if you do not follow rehab protocols that allow enough time for the clothing to cool.

Protective clothing also prevents heat from being transferred *away* from your body. Usually your body sweats to cools itself, but the protective clothing traps body heat and moisture inside the clothing barriers **(Figure 11.3)**. This feature may increase the following conditions:

- Breathing and heart rate
- Skin temperature
- Core temperature
- Physiological stress

If environmental conditions allow, open your protective clothing to permit air flow around your body during authorized breaks or trips to rehabilitation facilities. This practice will lessen heat stress and reduce your heart rate.

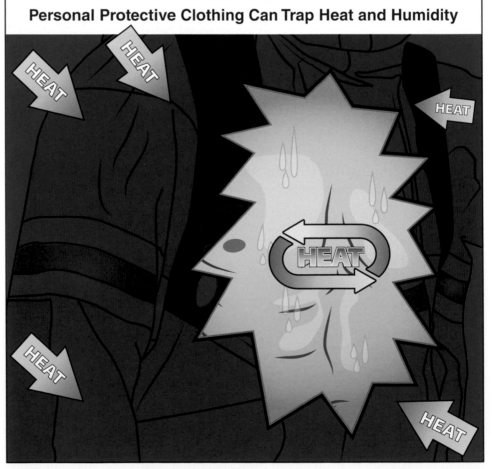

Figure 11.3 Illustrating how protective clothing can prevent heat from being transferred *away* from a fire brigade member's body.

Helmets

Head protection is one of the primary concerns for fire brigade members. Helmets, which are manufactured in a wide variety of designs and styles, provide multiple benefits during **structural fire fighting** operations, including:

- Preventing heated or scalding water and embers from reaching the ears and neck
- Protecting the head from impact injuries caused by objects or falls
- Protecting from heat and cold

Helmets can also help identify personnel. Shell color may indicate the fire brigade member's rank, other markings can indicate the unit, and removable identification labels are used for accountability on an incident scene. The fire brigade's standard operating procedures (SOPs) should identify these uses as they pertain to the specific fire brigade.

To ensure proper protection, you must correctly wear your helmet. Place the helmet on your head, and secure the chin strap under your chin and tighten it. If so equipped, fold the ear flaps down to cover your ears and neck, even if you are wearing a protective hood. Some helmets have a ratchet at the back of the headband to allow fit adjustment.

Eye Protection

Eye injuries are fairly common at emergency incidents, but they are sometimes unreported because they are not always debilitating. Eye injuries are often easy to prevent. Eye protection comes in many forms, including **(Figure 11.4)**:

- SCBA facepieces
- Helmet-mounted faceshields
- Goggles
- Safety glasses

Figure 11.4 This figure shows the various devices used for eye protection.

Helmets must come equipped with faceshields, or accommodate goggles. Faceshields alone do not provide adequate protection from flying particles or splashes and should be used in combination with a primary form of eye protection such as goggles or safety glasses. NFPA 1500™, *Standard on Fire Department Occupational Safety and Health Program*, requires that fire brigade personnel wear goggles or other appropriate primary eye protection when they participate in operations where protection from flying particles or chemical splashes is necessary. When responding to an incident requiring SCBA, the facepiece is your primary eye protection.

In other situations, you will need eye protection when respiratory protection is not required. Some of these situations include:

- Emergency medical responses where exposure to body fluids is possible
- Vehicle extrication operations
- Industrial occupancy inspections
- Station maintenance

These situations call for safety glasses or goggles, which protect against most eye hazards. Several styles of safety glasses or goggles are available, including some that fit over prescription glasses. Prescription safety glasses are another option, although they must have frames and lenses that meet ANSI or CSA standards for safety glasses. In fire brigade facilities and maintenance areas, you should be aware of warning signs posted near power equipment requiring the use of eye protection. Follow your department's safety policies and procedures regarding appropriate eye protection.

Protective Hoods

Protective hoods are fire-resistant fabric coverings that protect your ears, neck, and face from exposure to heat, embers, and debris. They cover areas that the SCBA may not protect, such as:

- Around the facepiece
- Under the helmet
- Under the ear flaps
- Under the coat collar

Figure 11.5 A fire brigade member adjusting the fit of his protective hood.

The protective hood's face opening has an elastic edge that fits tightly to the SCBA facepiece, forming a seal. Hoods are available with long or short skirts and are designed to fit inside the protective coat, forming a continuous layer of protection **(Figure 11.5)**.

Pull the hood on before the protective coat to help keep the hood's skirt under the coat. To ensure a secure seal between the hood and the SCBA facepiece, secure the facepiece before pulling up the hood. This technique ensures that you will not compromise the facepiece-to-face seal.

Protective Coats

NFPA 1971 requires that all structural fire fighting **protective coats** be made of three components **(Figure 11.6)**:

- Outer shell
- Moisture barrier
- Thermal barrier

Figure 11.6 The three component layers of a protective coat include the a) thermal barrier, b) moisture barrier, and c) outer shell.

These barriers absorb heat and trap insulating air that prevents heat transfer from the fire to your body. Removing the liner and wearing only the shell compromises the design of the coat, increasing the likelihood of injuries or death. Protective barriers also provide limited protection from:

- Direct flame contact
- Hot water
- Steam
- Cold temperatures
- Other environmental hazards

WARNING: All layers of the protective coat must be in place during a fire fighting operation. Failure to wear the entire coat and liner system during a fire may expose you to severe heat, resulting in serious injury or death.

Protective coats have many design features that provide protection and convenience. Design features that NFPA 1971 requires include **(Figure 11.7)**:

Figure 11.7 Common design features of modern fire coats. *Courtesy of Assistant Chief Brandon LeMay and the South Bay Fire Department, Olympia (WA).*

- **Retroreflective trim** — Strips of reflective trim on the torso and sleeves that make the coat more visible at night or in low light conditions.

- **Wristlets** — Fabric interface between a sleeve's end and a fire brigade member's palm that protects the wrist from water, embers, and other debris. Keeps coat sleeves from riding up when reaching.

- **Collar** — Protects the neck from water, embers, and other debris. The collar must be turned up under the helmet ear flap.

- **Closure system** — Snaps, clips, zippers, or Velcro® fasteners that secure the coat's front.

- **Drag rescue device (DRD)** — Harness and hand loop at the back of the neck that enables a rescuer to grab and drag a downed fire brigade member.

Coats typically contain reinforcement in high compression areas, such as the shoulders, and areas prone to wear, such as the elbows. Coats may also have cargo, radio, or SCBA facepiece pockets.

Protective Trousers

Protective trousers are constructed from the same fabric, moisture barrier, and thermal layering used in protective coats **(Figure 11.8)**. Much like the coats, high compression areas and areas prone to wear contain reinforcement, and cargo or patch pockets may be attached for carrying gloves and small tools. Heavy-duty suspenders hold up the trousers. Closure systems are the same as those found on the protective coat. NFPA 1971 also requires retroreflective trim on protective trousers.

Protective Gloves

Protective gloves protect hands and wrists from heat, steam, or cold penetration, and resist cuts, punctures, and liquid absorption. Gloves must allow enough dexterity and tactile feel for you to effectively perform your job. For instance, gloves must permit you to grasp tools and nozzles or manipulate small objects such as control knobs on portable radios. Properly worn, gloves cover the wristlet of the protective coat to form a complete seal **(Figure 11.9)**. Gloves worn for structural fire fighting must be NFPA-compliant for this type of activity.

Figure 11.8 A fire brigade member donning protective trousers.

Figure 11.9 Two views of a fire brigade member's glove. *Courtesy of Shad Cooper/Sublette County Unified Fire.*

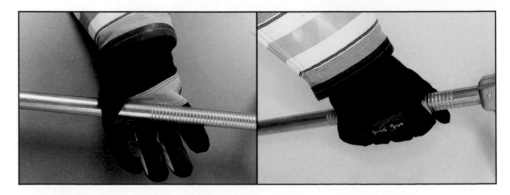

Fire Boot Construction

Boot Loops

Foam Cushioning

Water-Proof Rubber or
Water-Resistant Leather

Reflective
Material

Moisture
Barrier

Foam Cushioning

Inner
Liner

Heel Stabilizer

Reflective
Material

Reflective
Material

Insole

Rubber
Cap

Steel Toe
Cap

Puncture-Resistant
Stainless Steel Midsole

Chemical-Resistant
Rubber Sole

Cushioning Material

Figure 11.10 Two common types of fire fighting boots and a cutaway view of fire boot components. *Photos courtesy of Shad Cooper/Sublette County Unified Fire.*

Figure 11.11 A stand-alone PASS device (left) and an integrated PASS device (right).

Protective Footwear

Fire fighting boots are available in a variety of styles and materials and should meet the requirements of NFPA 1971. They protect the foot, ankle, and lower leg from:

- Puncture wounds to the sole
- Crushing wounds to the toes and instep
- Scalding water or contaminated liquids
- Burns from embers and debris

Fire fighting boots, which have a steel inner sole and a steel or reinforced toe cap, must be high enough to protect the lower leg. The outer shell may be made of rubber, leather, or another water-resistant material. Thermal, physical, and moisture barriers are required inside the shell **(Figure 11.10)**. Boot tops fit inside the trouser legs, providing a complete barrier even when you kneel.

Personal Alert Safety Systems (PASS)

PASS emit a loud alarm to alert other personnel that a fire brigade member is in danger. The alarm activates when a fire brigade member is motionless for more than 30 seconds, or when a fire brigade member presses the emergency button. In some models, the system may activate when the temperature exceeds a preset limit. The alarm must sound at a minimum of 95 decibels (dBA) and go off continuously for at least one hour.

PASS devices assist rescuers trying to locate trapped, unconscious, or incapacitated fire brigade members. They are useful in:

- Total darkness
- Dense smoke
- Confined spaces

Some devices are stand-alone, manually activated units. Other devices are integrated units connected to the SCBA regulator that activate automatically when the main air supply valve is opened **(Figure 11.11)**. Fire brigade personnel can also activate SCBA-mounted devices without opening the cylinder valve.

PASS devices have at least three settings: *off*, *alarm*, and *sensing*. They also have a pre-alarm mode that activates if you are motionless for 30 seconds. This pre-alarm tone is different from the full alarm tone and is intended to prevent false alarms.

You must learn how to turn the unit from *off* to *sensing* (on) and to manually activate the alarm. You are also responsible for testing, maintaining, and activating your PASS device according to your department's SOPs, manufacturer's instructions, NFPA 1500™, and NFPA 1982.

Hearing Protection

Fire brigade members are exposed to a variety of loud noises in the fire station, during training, en route to incidents, and at the emergency scene. Hearing protection devices guard against temporary and permanent hearing loss.

NFPA 1500™ requires hearing protection devices. To comply with this standard, departments must protect fire brigade members from the effects of harmful noise. Eliminating or reducing noise is the best solution, but sometimes this option is not possible. In these cases, departments must provide hearing protection devices and establish a hearing conservation plan **(Figure 11.12)**.

Figure 11.12 Fire brigade members may wear different types of hearing protection to include ear plugs, communications headsets, and ear muffs.

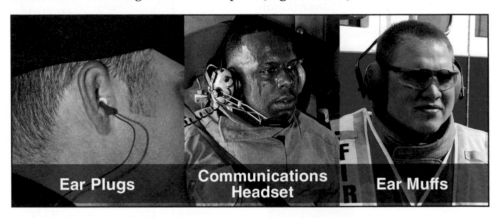

Ear Plugs — Communications Headset — Ear Muffs

Fire brigade members should use hearing protection when riding on an apparatus where the noise exceeds maximum noise exposure levels (90 decibels in the U.S., 85 decibels in Canada). Intercom/ear protection systems are most effective for this purpose. They also allow the crew to communicate with each other or monitor radio communications.

You must also wear hearing protection when operating:

- Power tools
- Apparatus pump
- Generators
- PASS device tests

In some situations, standard hearing protection is impractical and may even be dangerous. For example, during structural fire fighting, it prevents you from:

- Communicating with other fire brigade members
- Hearing changes in fire behavior
- Hearing radio transmissions
- Hearing calls from a trapped victim

Other Types of Protective Clothing

Depending upon the hazards found at a facility, fire brigade members may be required to wear other types of protective clothing such as:

- Proximity protective clothing
- Wildland protective clothing
- Chemical protective clothing
- High visibility/reflective clothing

Proximity Protective Clothing

NFPA 1976, *Standard on Protective Ensemble for Proximity Fire Fighting*, provides information on proximity protective clothing. Proximity suits are designed for close proximity exposures to high radiant heat. Proximity clothing has a reflective outer covering designed to reflect radiant heat. With the addition of one or more layers of thermal barrier, they also can withstand exposure to steam, liquids, and some weaker chemicals. Modern proximity suits consist of a helmet or hood, coat, trousers, and gloves used in conjunction with standard flash hoods and fire fighting boots **(Figure 11.13)**. The helmet or hood generally has a visor that contains a gold-plated shield to reflect heat from the fire away from the wearer's face.

Figure 11.13 Many airport fire brigades have their personnel wear proximity protective clothing.

Some fire brigades require the use of proximity protective clothing during fire control activities at their locations, while other brigades do not. Proximity protective clothing is not designed for use in normal structural fire control operations.

Chemical Protective Clothing

Structural fire fighting PPE is not intended for chemical emergencies. Pre-emergency plans should identify all chemicals on site and specify protective clothing to be worn at emergencies involving those chemicals. There are four levels of chemical protective clothing that are identified as Level A, B, C and D.

- *Level A protection* — Worn when the highest level of respiratory, skin, eye, and mucous membrane protection is needed; consists of positive-pressure self-contained breathing apparatus and fully encapsulating chemical-resistant suit.

- *Level B protection* — Worn when the highest level of respiratory protection is needed with a lesser level of skin and eye protection; consists of positive-pressure self-contained breathing apparatus and a chemical-resistant coverall or splash suit. The Level B ensemble is the minimum level recommended for initial-site entries until the health and safety officer defines the hazards via monitoring, sampling, and other reliable methods of analysis.

- *Level C protection* — Worn when the type of airborne substance is known, the concentration has been measured, criteria for using air purifying respirators is met, and skin and eye exposure are unlikely; consists of air purifying respirator and chemical-resistant coverall or splash suit. Periodic air monitoring is required.

- *Level D protection* — Consists of common work uniforms, street clothing, or coveralls. Level D protection can be worn only when no atmospheric hazards exist.

Wildland PPE

Structural fire fighting PPE is generally too bulky, heavy, and hot to be practical for wildland fire fighting. NFPA 1977 contains the specifications for wildland fire fighting PPE and equipment. Wildland PPE and equipment includes:

- **Gloves** — Made of leather or inherently flame-resistant materials. They protect the hand and wrist from sharp or hot objects, temperature extremes, and scalding water.

- **Goggles** — Protect the eyes from ash, embers, dust, and other **particulates**.

- **Jackets** — Made of high-strength, flame-resistant fabric, such as aramid or treated cotton and may have a thermal liner for use in cold climates. The cuffs close snugly around the wrists, and the front of the jacket must close completely from hem to neck.

- **Trousers** — Made of the same material and design as the jackets. The leg cuffs must close securely around the boot tops.

- **One-piece jumpsuits** — One-piece protective garments are similar in design to the two-piece jacket and trousers ensemble.

- **Long-sleeve shirts** — Protective shirts are worn under the jackets.

- **Helmet** — A lightweight helmet with chin straps that provides impact, penetration, and electrical insulation protection.

- **Face/neck shrouds** — Flame-resistant fabric that attaches to the helmet and protects the face and neck.

- **Footwear** — Typically lace-up safety boots with lug or grip-tread soles. Must protect the lower leg. Because the steel toes in ordinary safety boots absorb and retain heat, they are not recommended for wildland fire fighting.

- **Fire shelter** — Fire-resistant aluminized fabric covers that protect the fire brigade member from convected and radiant heat. NFPA 1500™ requires its use, and its design must meet the United States Department of Agriculture (USDA) Forest Service Specification 5100-606.

- **Load-carrying or load-bearing equipment** — Belt and suspender systems that distribute the weight of equipment that a fire brigade member might carry.

- **Respiratory protection** — Beginning in 2011, NIOSH certified, NFPA approved **air-purifying respirators (APR)** and **powered air-purifying respirators (PAPR)** are available for wildland fire fighting.

- **Chain saw protection** — Chaps, leggings, or protective trousers made of ballistic nylon fibers that protect the legs.

In addition, most wildland fire agencies provide fire brigade members with a canteen or bottled water and a backpack or web belt for carrying extra gear. Fire brigade members carry **fusees**, extra food, water, clean socks, and other items in these packs.

Wildland protective garments will not protect you from extreme heat or provide vapor protection. As with structural fire fighting gear, you should never wear underclothing made of or including synthetic materials, such as nylon, polyester, iron-on patches, or transfer decals, when fighting a wildland fire. These materials melt when heated and can stick to your skin, causing serious burns. Refer to your department's policies on what underclothing is approved at wildfire incidents.

> **WARNING:** Wildland PPE is not designed, certified, or intended for interior structural fire fighting.

In the absence of full, wildland fire fighting gear, NFPA 1500™ specifies the minimum PPE for fire brigade members to participate in ground cover fire fighting. This standard requires fire brigade members to be equipped with the following:

- Helmet with eye protection and neck shroud
- Flame retardant shirt and pants (or one-piece jumpsuit)
- Protective footwear (sturdy boots without steel toes)
- Gloves
- Fire shelter (in crush-resistive case)

High Visibility/Reflective Clothing

Emergency operations along roadways are dangerous for fire brigade members and other emergency responders. Each year, emergency workers are injured and killed while working around roadways. The best protection is to be visible to motorists and to work behind a barrier such as your apparatus.

U.S. Department of Transportation (DOT) regulations require all personnel at roadway incidents to wear high-visibility vests. At a minimum, these vests should meet ANSI standards. They must have reflective trim and five-point breakaway fasteners at the shoulders, side, and waist to meet NFPA safety standards in the U.S. and Canada regulations. Reflective trim on structural PPE does not provide enough visibility to meet these standards. You should wear vests over your PPE if possible, but not while performing fire fighting or hazardous materials activities at the scene. Don the vest only after you have completed these activities or if you have been assigned duties other than fire fighting or hazardous materials control.

Other types of high visibility clothing may include:

- Coveralls
- Hard hats
- Gloves

 Training and Other Resources

Fire brigade members who are expected to work in or around active roadways should have additional training and follow their agencies SOPs. The U.S. Fire Administration's *Traffic Incident Management System* handbook is a source for additional information.

Safety Considerations for PPE

PPE is designed to create a protective barrier between you and your work environment. However, this barrier can also isolate you, preventing you from being aware of environmental changes and making you overconfident of your own safety **(Figure 11.14)**.

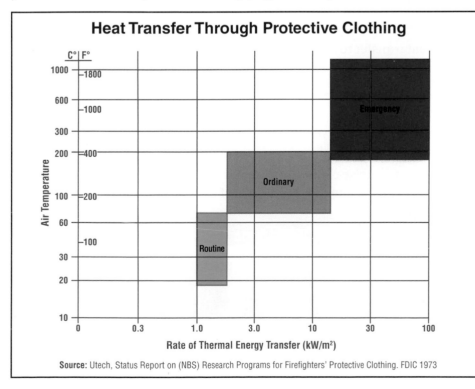

Figure 11.14 PPE protects fire brigade members from high temperature environments.

The following safety considerations relate to your personal protective equipment:

- Wear fire resistant personal clothing under your protective clothing. Avoid wearing clothing with screen-printed decals and tranfers that may conduct heat to the skin's surface.

- Consider the design and purpose of your protective clothing, and be especially aware of each garment's limitations.

- Moisture in the shell and liner material can rapidly transfer heat, resulting in serious steam burns. Ensure that the garment is dry before wearing it into a fire.

- PPE insulates you from the heat of a fire, but it will also delay your awareness of temperature increases.

- Never wear protective clothing that does not fit because it will provide reduced protection. Tight clothing will not close properly, leaving gaps in the protective materials. Loose clothing can hinder mobility and dexterity by bunching up at shoulders, elbows, and knees. Loose articles can also:
  - Snag on debris
  - Absorb contaminants
  - Create a tripping hazard
  - Reduce thermal protection

- Make sure that the overlap between coat and trousers is a minimum of 2 inches (50 mm) at the waist when you bend over at a 90-degree angle.

- Donning standard protective clothing will impair your balance and gait (manner of walk).

- Thermal burns may occur at compression points (where the garment layers are pressed together), such as under the SCBA shoulder harness, along sleeves in contact with hoselines, and on knees when kneeling on hot debris and embers.

- The thermal environment will heat the exterior of the PPE, resulting in thermal saturation that can cause contact burns. If you feel contact burns developing, immediately withdraw from the area.

- Prolonged exposure to hot environments will cause your body to sweat in order to cool itself. The protective clothing liner will retain the moisture, which may cause heat stress or burns. When you feel the symptoms of heat exhaustion, including weakness, dizziness, rapid pulse, or headache, move to a cool, safe area, remove your PPE, and follow established rehabilitation procedures.

- PPE is designed to protect you, but it cannot protect against fire conditions such as explosions, back-draft, flashover, or other rapid fire development.

- PPE absorbs heat, which delays heat transfer to the wearer. This heat can build until the PPE is hotter than the ambient temperature.

- Heating of PPE's Velcro® fasteners can fuse the Velcro® components together. In such cases, the PPE will need to be cut open to remove it from you.

- The buildup of heat will penetrate through all layers of the PPE and can cause burns and raise your temperature.

- RIC, rescue, and rehab personnel must exercise caution and wear their fire fighting gloves when trying to remove super-heated PPE from fire brigade members. The heat of the PPE can burn rescuers' hands.

> **WARNING:** If your PPE and/or SCBA are damaged during fire fighting operations, you should evacuate the structure.

> **WARNING:** Burns are a result of time and temperature. The longer the exposure and the higher the temperature, the greater the severity of a burn. First-degree burns start when skin temperature reaches 118°F (48°C). Second-degree burns start at 131°F (55°C), and third-degree burns start at 152° F (67°C).

Care of PPE

Your PPE is your primary barrier protecting you from injury and illness. However, it can also cause injury or illness if it is not properly maintained. Hydrocarbon contamination will reduce the fire resistance of your PPE. Chemicals, oils, and petroleum products in or on the outer shell can ignite when exposed to fire. Some contaminants can reduce the effectiveness of retroreflective trim, and soot can obscure its visibility. Hydrocarbons, body fluids, and toxins that contaminate PPE can be inhaled, ingested, or absorbed, causing serious and sometimes fatal illness.

You are responsible for the inspection, cleaning, and condition of the PPE assigned to you. You can find procedures for the care of your PPE in your organization's SOPs, the manufacturer's instructions, and NFPA 1851.

Inspecting PPE for Damage or Contamination

You should frequently inspect your PPE. Inspection periods should occur:

- At the start of your work shift
- After washing, repair, or decontamination
- After every use
- On a periodic basis, such as weekly or monthly

Conditions that you should look for during a routine inspection include (**Figure 11.15**):

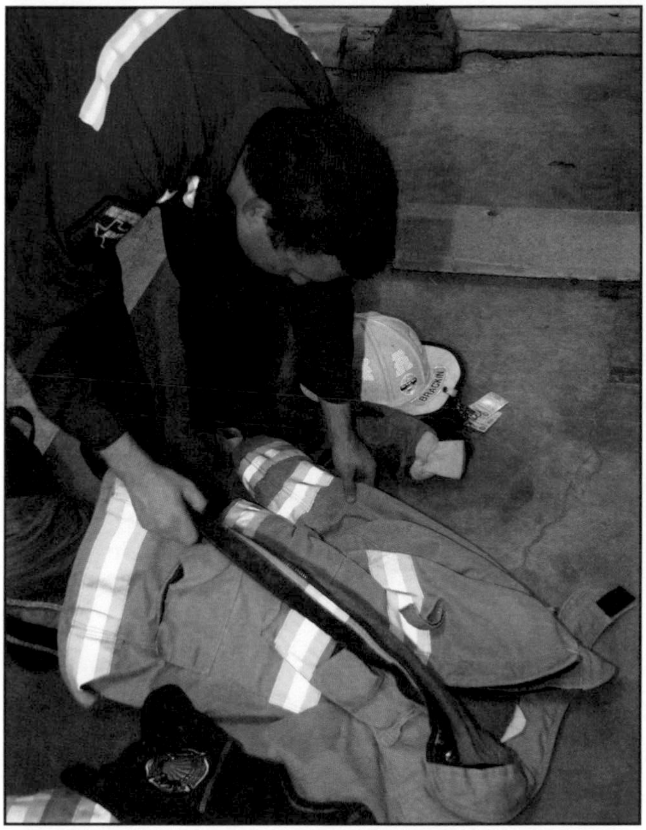

Figure 11.15 A fire brigade member inspecting his PPE at the start of his work shift.

- Soiling
- Contamination
- Missing or damaged hardware and closure systems
- Physical damage, including rips, tears, fraying hems and cuffs, and damaged stitching on seams
- Wear due to friction under arms, in the crotch, and at knee and elbow joints
- Thermal damage, including charring, melting, discoloration, and burn holes
- Shrinkage
- Damaged or missing retroreflective trim or reinforcing trim
- Loss of reflectivity of shell on proximity equipment
- Cracks, melting, abrasions, or dents in helmet shell
- Missing or damaged faceshield or hardware
- Missing or damaged earflaps or neck shroud
- Loss of watertight integrity in footwear
- Damage to or faulty installation of DRD
- Date of manufacture to determine time in service

If your protective clothing requires only routine cleaning that will not cause the item to be removed from service, you should perform the cleaning yourself. If you determine that your PPE requires advanced cleaning or decontamination, repairs, or replacement, immediately report such to your supervisor. A fire brigade member who is trained in advanced inspection requirements, such as the brigade's Health and Safety Officer (HSO), should perform an annual inspection.

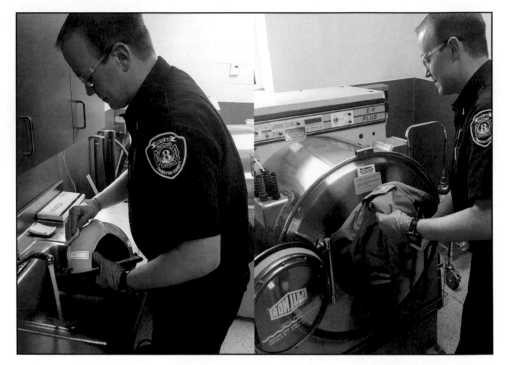

Figure 11.16
Demonstrating routine cleaning (left) and advanced cleaning (right). *Photos courtesy of Assistant Chief Brandon LeMay and the South Bay Fire Department, Olympia (WA).*

Cleaning PPE

NFPA 1851 defines two levels of cleaning for PPE **(Figure 11.16)**:

- Routine cleaning
- Advanced cleaning and decontamination

   NOTE: Follow the manufacturers' directions for the proper cleaning, care and maintenance of your PPE.

   The amount and type of contamination and whether the equipment must be removed from service determines the type of cleaning. Many fire brigades provide spare sets of PPE to replace units removed from service for cleaning, decontamination, or repairs. NFPA standards recommend that each fire brigade member be issued two sets of structural fire fighting PPE. Having two sets of gear ensures that one set of gear can be laundered immediately following an incident while the spare set can be donned in case there is an incident before the first set is cleaned. Wearing uncontaminated PPE is a preventative measure against the risk of cancer later in life.

   Routine cleaning. Routine cleaning does not require that the clothing be removed from service. At an incident scene, the process for routine cleaning includes:

- Brushing off loose debris with a broom or soft bristle brush
- Using a gentle spray of water to rinse off debris and soil

   To remove heavy soil, you should perform cleaning in a utility sink, in the designated cleaning area at the fire station. Whether you are at the scene or in the station, follow the manufacturer's recommendations and wear appropriate gloves and eye protection.

   Advanced cleaning. Personnel trained in the care and cleaning of protective clothing should perform advanced cleaning. They should use a washing machine that can handle heavy loads and is dedicated to cleaning protective clothing.

WARNING: Do not wash contaminated protective clothing in washing machines used for other garments or items, such as your home washing machine or a public laundry. This may expose you, your family, or others to dangerous contaminants.

Specialized cleaning. Specialized cleaning is required when clothing is contaminated with hazardous materials or body fluids that routine or advanced cleaning cannot remove. A trained department member or an outside contractor may perform the cleaning.

> **WARNING:** Do not take contaminated protective clothing into the living or sleeping quarters of the fire station or your residence.

> **WARNING:** PPE should not be stored where it can come in contact with vehicle exhausts.

> **CAUTION:** PPE that is regularly carried in facility vehicles should be placed in closable garment bags to protect it from sunlight degradation.

Repairing PPE

The manufacturer, an approved repair facility, or a trained department member must remove damaged protective clothing from service immediately. Clothing damaged beyond repair must be removed from service and destroyed. Some damaged clothing may be marked "for training use only" and used in training that does not involve fire or hazardous materials.

> **WARNING:** Remove damaged protective clothing from service immediately when it is recognized as damaged.

Figure 11.17 Examples of well-ventilated PPE lockers at a facility.

Storing Personal Protective Clothing

The care of structural fire fighting clothing includes the proper storage of garments both at the fire brigade office/station and on the apparatus. Protective clothing can be damaged by physical contact with the apparatus, in compartments, and near loose equipment. Personal protective clothing is also susceptible to damage from the sun. Ultraviolet light can deteriorate the fabric and cause damage to the seams of the outer shell and inner liner. Clothing should be dried and stored out of direct sunlight. When stored at the office/station between shifts, the clothing should be in a well-ventilated locker outside the living quarters **(Figure 11.17)**. This ventilation helps to prevent mildew and mold from growing on the garments and keeps contamination out of the living or dorm areas.

Retiring Personal Protective Clothing

Structural fire fighting clothing that is damaged or contaminated to the point that the organization determines that it is not possible or cost effective to repair should be retired as outlined in NFPA 1851. Structural fire fighting clothing that is not in compliance with the appropriate NFPA standard edition that was in effect when the component(s) were manufactured must also be retired.

Many manufacturers of protective clothing recommend a 7- to 10-year service life for their products. Under this recommendation, barring damage or contamination, the clothing would get seven years of active service and then spend three years in reserve status before being retired.

Using Personal Alert Safety Systems

NFPA 1500™ mandates that all fire brigade members and rescuers use PASS devices. The acronym PAD (personal alert device) is also used. A downed or disoriented fire brigade member inside a structure or hazardous area poses a severe rescue challenge. PASS devices assist rescuers attempting to locate the individual, even in dense smoke. The device, about the size of a portable transistor radio, is worn on the fire brigade member's self-contained breathing apparatus or coat. Personnel fire brigade personnel should insure they activate their PASS devices before entering a structure or hazardous area. If the individual should remain motionless for approximately 30 seconds, the PASS device will trigger, emitting a loud, pulsating shriek. The fire brigade member can also manually trigger the alarm **(Figure 11.18)**. Rescuers can follow the sound to locate the lost or downed fire brigade member. Some SCBA manufacturers have integrated a distress alarm system into the SCBA air circuit. Once the cylinder valve is opened, the distress alarm system is automatically activated. The alarm on this type of system is triggered in the same manner as stand-alone PASS devices.

Figure 11.18 A fire brigade member manually activating his PASS device.

PASS devices can save lives, but they must be properly used and maintained. The user must remember to turn on and test the device before entering a structure. Training classes should be conducted on techniques that fire brigade personnel should use when attempting rescue of a lost fire brigade member. Locating even the loud shriek of a PASS device in poor visibility conditions can be more difficult than expected because the sound reflects off walls, ceilings, and floors. Rescuers should not sidestep established search procedures, even when they think they can tell the location of the alarm sound. Noise from SCBA operation and muffled hearing because of protective hoods also adds to the difficulty of accurately determining the sound's origin. Recommendations for use of PASS devices include the following:

- Make sure that the system selected meets the requirements of NFPA 1982, *Standard on Personal Alert Safety Systems (PASS) for Fire Fighters.*

- Test the PASS at least weekly and maintain in accordance with manufacturer's instructions.

- Conduct practical training with the PASS under realistic conditions to teach fire brigade personnel to react appropriately to PASS alarm activations.

- Retrain every six months with PASS devices.

- Train fire brigade personnel to turn on and test the device before entering a hazardous atmosphere.

- Train rescuers to stop in unison, control breathing, and lift hood or earflaps away from ears to improve their chances of hearing the distress sound.

- Turn off the PASS device to facilitate communications when a downed fire brigade member is located.

Respiratory Protection

NFPA 1081 (2018): 5.2.2, 5.2.4, 6.1.2.2, 6.2.8

Respiratory protection is crucial to the well-being of the industrial fire brigade member. Failure to use this equipment could lead to failed rescue attempts, injuries, or fatalities. Fire brigade managers should establish respiratory protection programs and ensure that their members are trained on the following considerations involving respiratory protection at an emergency incident:

- **Respiratory hazards**
- Requirements for wearing respiratory protection
- Procedures for donning and doffing equipment
- Proper care and maintenance of equipment
- Command and control procedures

Inhalation of smoke and other products of combustion poses short-term, long-term, and even fatal health hazards. Wearing appropriate respiratory protection is the most effective way to protect your health. The use of SCBA is a required skill for fire brigade members according to NFPA 1081. Operations requiring SCBA protection include any activities that may take place in or near a potentially immediately dangerous to life and health (IDLH) environment as defined by NFPA, OSHA, or the AHJ's policies. Research also indicates that fire brigade members should wear SCBA during overhaul operations (Horn, et al. 2016). Byproducts of combustion present during overhaul can cause long-term health risks such as cancer or respiratory disease.

 Other Operations Requiring Respiratory Protection

Numerous other response operations require respiratory protection, which may be different from SCBA:

- Wildland fires, which produce smoke and other products of combustion
- Medical responses, which may expose you to airborne pathogens
- Confined-space search, rescue, and recovery, which may take place in toxic or low oxygen atmospheres
- Repair work that generates fine particulates such as dust, paint, or metal shavings

Always wear respiratory protection equipment that is appropriate for the type of hazard. Use the equipment properly so that you are not exposed to respiratory hazards.

Types of Respiratory Protection Equipment

The two primary categories of respiratory protection equipment are **atmosphere-supplying respirators (ASRs)** and air-purifying respirators (APRs). ASRs provide breathable air for working in oxygen-deficient, toxic, or gas-filled atmospheres, while APRs only filter particulates out of the surrounding air. The primary type of respiratory protection that you will use in the fire service is the ASR.

Open-Circuit Self-Contained Breathing Apparatus

One type of ASR is an **open-circuit SCBA**. Several companies manufacture open-circuit SCBA, each with different design features or mechanical construction **(Figure 11.19, p. 340)**. Open-circuit SCBA vents exhaled breath into the atmosphere.

It is not a recommended practice to interchange parts between different brands of SCBAs. While certain parts, such as cylinders and backpacks, may be interchangeable, such substitution voids NIOSH and Mine Safety and Health Administration (MSHA) certification. Substituting different parts may also void warranties and leave the fire brigade or individual members liable for any injuries incurred. The common components of this type of breathing apparatus will be described in detail later in this chapter.

Figure 11.19 A front and back view of an open-circuit SCBA as it is being worn.

CAUTION: Do not interchange parts between different brands of SCBAs.

Open-Circuit Supplied Air Respirators (SAR)

Incidents involving hazardous materials or confined space rescues often require a longer air supply than fire brigade personnel can obtain from standard open-circuit SCBA. In these situations, fire brigade members may use an open-circuit **supplied air respirator (SAR)**. The supplied air respirator or airline respirator is an atmosphere-supplying respirator where the user does not carry the breathing air source. The apparatus usually consists of **(Figure 11.20)**:

- A facepiece
- A belt- or facepiece-mounted regulator
- A voice communications system
- Up to 300 feet (90 m) of air supply hose
- An emergency escape pack or emergency escape breathing support system (EEBSS)
- A breathing air source (either cylinders mounted on a cart or a portable breathing air compressor)

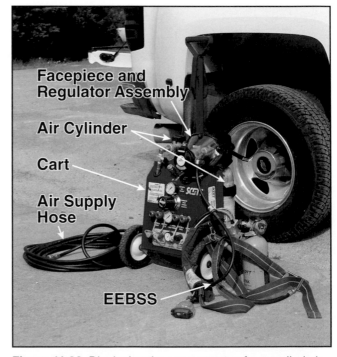

Figure 11.20 Displaying the components of a supplied air respirator system.

Due to the potential for damage to the air supply hose, the EEBSS provides enough air, usually 5, 10, or 15 minutes' worth, for the user to escape the hazardous atmosphere. SAR apparatus are not intended or certified for fire fighting operations because of the potential damage to the airline from heat, fire, or debris.

Closed-Circuit Self-Contained Breathing Apparatus

Within the fire service, personnel use open-circuit breathing apparatus more often than **closed-circuit self-contained breathing apparatus**. However, closed-circuit apparatus are sometimes needed for hazardous materials incidents because of their longer air supply duration **(Figure 11.21)**. In contrast to open-circuit SCBA, closed-circuit SCBA filters and reoxygenates exhaled breath, and feeds it back to the user.

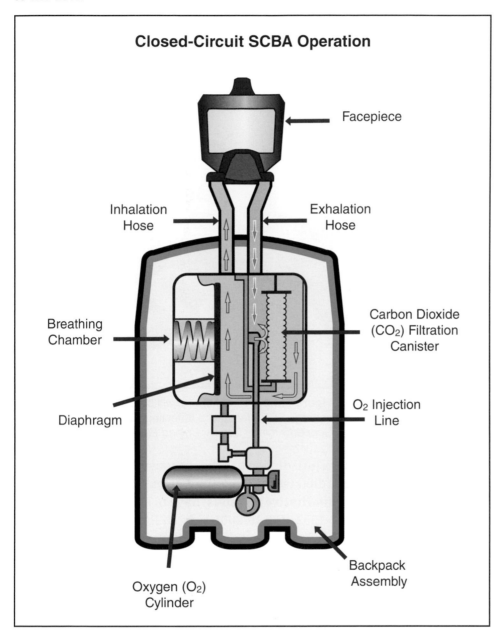

Closed-Circuit SCBA Operation

Facepiece

Inhalation Hose

Exhalation Hose

Breathing Chamber

Carbon Dioxide (CO$_2$) Filtration Canister

Diaphragm

O$_2$ Injection Line

Oxygen (O$_2$) Cylinder

Backpack Assembly

Figure 11.21 Illustrating the operation of a closed-circuit SCBA.

Closed-circuit SCBA are available with durations ranging between 30 minutes and 4 hours, and usually weigh less than open-circuit units of similarly rated service time. They weigh less than an open-circuit SCBA because they use one small cylinder containing pure oxygen instead of a larger cylinder containing compressed breathing air. Common components of include:

- Backpack and harness assembly
- Air regeneration assembly (filters and oxygen cylinder)
- Regulator assembly
- Facepiece assembly

Facepiece Fit Testing

Since the proper function of respiratory protection equipment depends on a full and complete seal between the facepiece and the wearer, facepiece fit testing is essential to the respiratory protection program established by the AHJ. The primary purpose of fit testing is to determine that the make, model, and size of respirator facepiece provides a full and complete seal for a particular individual. The sections that follow discuss the test procedures, test protocols, and record keeping of the facepiece fit-test program.

Test Procedures

OSHA and NFPA require facepiece fit testing when an employee is hired or transferred into a position that will expose the employee to hazardous atmospheres. All individuals who use respiratory protection equipment must undergo a medical evaluation/examination to be certified physically fit to perform the tasks that require the equipment. Once a physician/licensed health-care professional certifies an individual, the employee undergoes an entry-level facepiece fit test using the type or types of respiratory protection equipment that he or she will wear **(Figure 11.22)**.

Annual retests are required to ensure that no changes have occurred that may compromise the fit of the facepiece. Potential changes that would require retesting could include weight gain or loss, major dental work, facial injuries, a change in facepieces, or a change in respiratory hazards. Along with the fit test, an employee must get an annual medical evaluation.

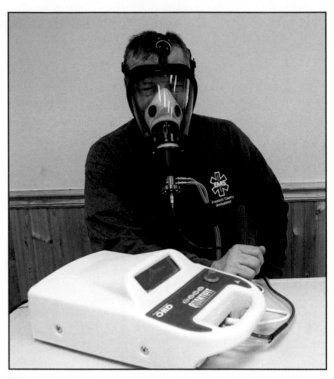

Figure 11.22 Personnel who will be using SCBA must undergo SCBA facepiece fit-testing. *Courtesy of Shad Cooper/Sublette County Unified Fire.*

Test Protocols

Although NFPA 1500™ states that the authority having jurisdiction has the responsibility for establishing the facepiece fit-testing protocol, OSHA regulations dictates the guidelines given in that standard. Two options for fit-testing protocols (**quantitative** and **qualitative** methods) have been approved by OSHA Title 29 *CFR* 1910.134, CSA Z94.4-1993, ANSI Z88.2-1992, Z88.10-2001, and NFPA 1500™. Both options measure the amount of leakage through the respirator facepiece seal. Quantitative fit testing is the most accurate of the two options because it measures the concentration of test agent within the mask. The qualitative fit-test method relies on the wearer's senses to detect any leakage.

Record Keeping

Fit-test records must be maintained in the member's personnel file or in a separate facepiece file and made available to the individual. Fit-test records should include:

- Test subject's name
- Overall fit factor
- Model of facepiece/respirator
- Size of facepiece/respirator
- Test results
- Type of fit test performed (quantitative or qualitative)
- Manufacturer of facepiece/respirator
- Style of facepiece/respirator
- Date of test

Additional information may include any difficulties encountered while giving the test, such as interface with protective clothing and equipment or personal fit problems. The name of the person administering the test may also be included in the records. Records on all subsequent retests, whether required annually or due to a change in the work environment, and the subject's physical characteristics, are also included in this file.

Respiratory Hazards

Respiratory hazards are commonly found in IDLH atmospheres that produce immediate, irreversible, and debilitating effects on a person's health and may result in death. Before entering a potentially IDLH structure or area, you must don the correct level of PPE and respiratory protection.

Common respiratory hazards include:

- Oxygen deficiency
- Particulate contaminants
- **Airborne pathogens**
- Elevated temperatures
- Gases and vapors

Oxygen Deficiency

Both NFPA and OSHA define an **oxygen-deficient atmosphere** as containing less than 19.5 percent oxygen. When oxygen concentrations fall below 18 percent, the respiratory rate increases. As less oxygen reaches body tissues, **hypoxia** occurs. **Figure 11.23** illustrates the physiological effects of hypoxia.

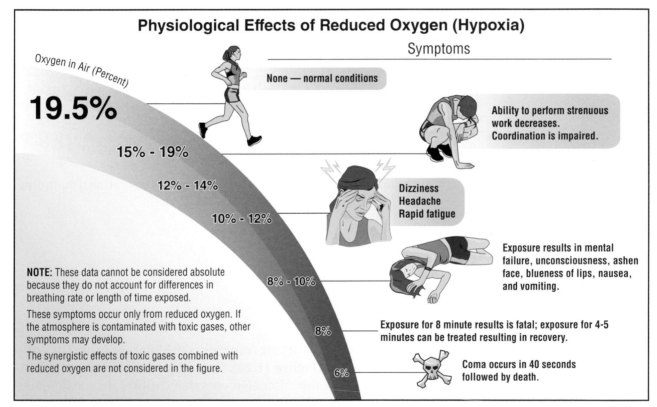

Figure 11.23 Oxygen deficiency has increasingly severe effects depending on the level of oxygen reduction and the amount of time it is endured.

Combustion is the most common cause of oxygen-deficient atmospheres. Fire consumes oxygen and produces toxic gases, which physically displace oxygen or dilute its concentration. Oxygen-deficient atmospheres are also found in compartments where carbon dioxide (CO_2) total-flooding extinguishing systems have discharged.

Other environments with oxygen-deficient atmospheres include confined spaces, such as:

- Sewers
- Grain bins
- Chemical storage tanks
- Underground caverns

Some fire brigades have instruments to monitor atmospheres and measure oxygen levels or the presence of toxic gases. Where monitoring is not possible or monitor readings are questionable, fire brigade members should not enter unknown atmospheres without wearing SCBA.

Elevated Temperatures

Breathing air that has been heated to temperatures normally found during a structure fire can damage the respiratory tract. The damage can be much worse when the air is moist. Excessive heat inhaled quickly into the lungs can cause a decrease in blood pressure and failure of the circulatory system. Inhaling heated gases can cause **pulmonary edema** which can cause asphyxiation. Introducing fresh, cool air will not immediately reverse tissue damage. The condition requires prompt medical treatment.

WARNING: Inhaling air that has been heated to flame temperatures can cause serious injury or death.

Particulate Contaminants

Particulate contaminants are small pieces of matter that may be suspended in the air and are harmful to the respiratory system. Particulates are especially dangerous in the short term when they are smaller than one micrometer [0.001 mm] because the nasal membranes cannot keep the smaller particulates from entering the lungs. Sources of smaller particulates include:

- Vehicle exhaust emissions
- Heated metals or metal compounds
- Chemical reactions
- Combustion

Exposure to particulate contaminants can cause the following:

- Asthma
- Cardiovascular disease
- Premature death
- Lung cancer
- Chronic obstructive pulmonary disease (COPD)

Fire brigade members may encounter contaminated atmospheres in a variety of operations, including:

- Wildland fires
- Operation of fire apparatus and small engines
- Operations following an explosion or building collapse
- Structural fires, especially during the overhaul phase
- Rescue operations
- Hazardous materials incidents

Air-purifying respirators (APRs) and powered air-purifying respirators (PAPRs) are generally sufficient to protect you from particulate contaminants **(Figure 11.24)**. Cartridge and canister type APR/PAPRs have half or full facepiece units with replaceable filter elements that capture the particulates. APR/PAPRs are approved for wildland fire fighting but do not protect against toxic gases, or heated or oxygen-deficient atmospheres. APR canisters or cartridges exposed to increased levels of oxygen (above 23 percent) may yield unknown, adverse reactions.

WARNING: Evacuate an atmosphere if your respiratory equipment yields atypical or malfunctioning reactions.

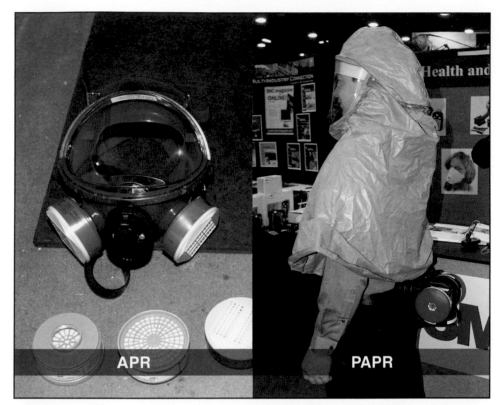

Figure 11.24 An air-purifying respirator (APR) on the left and a powered air-purifying respirator (PAPR) on the right.

Air-Purifying Respirators (APRs)

Air-purifying respirators (APRs) pass ambient air through a single-use filter, canister, or cartridge as the wearer breathes. These filters/canisters/cartridges are color-coded for a specific hazard to help the users select proper protection. As the air moves through the filter, contaminants are removed. APRs may have full facepieces that provide a complete seal to the face and protect the eyes, nose, and mouth, or half facepieces that provide a complete seal to the lower part of the face and protect the nose and mouth. APR filters are mounted on one or both sides of the facepiece. When using a half facepiece mask, eye protection is required.

Particulate filters are used primarily at emergency medical incidents to protect against airborne diseases. They are also appropriate for:

- Investigations or inspections involving body recovery
- Bird, bat, or rodent excrement
- Agricultural and industrial accidents
- Particulate-producing tools (sanders and paint sprayers)

Limitations of the APR include:

- Limited life of the filters, canisters, and cartridges
- Constant monitoring of the contaminated atmosphere
- Normal oxygen content of the atmosphere before use

Usage should be restricted to the hazards for which the APR is certified. Fire brigade members should regularly inspect APRs and clean them following each use. Discard filters, canisters, and cartridges following use and when they have passed their end of service life date.

Gases and Vapors

Gases and vapors may be present at both fire and nonfire incidents. Gases exist at standard temperature and pressure, while vapors result from temperature or pressure changes that affect a solid or liquid. For example, natural gas is commonly found in a gaseous state, while steam is a vapor created when water is heated.

Gases and vapors can be inhaled, ingested, or absorbed into the body, resulting in illnesses and death. Exposure may cause:

- Cancer
- Thyroid damage
- Eye irritation
- Cardiovascular disease
- Respiratory problems

Fire gases and vapors. Combustion creates harmful gases and vapors that may include:

- Carbon monoxide (CO)
- Hydrogen cyanide (HCN)
- Hydrogen sulfide
- Phosgene
- Ammonia
- Radionuclides
- Carbon dioxide (CO_2)
- Hydrogen chloride
- Nitrous gases
- Sulfur dioxide
- Formaldehyde

Since the products of combustion are potentially deadly, fire brigade members must use SCBA when operating in or near toxic atmospheres. Although smoke volume and density diminish during overhaul, the respiratory hazard remains above short-term exposure limits. In many cases, the hazards from smoke increase as the size of the particulates decreases. You are less likely to see the particulates that can penetrate the deepest into your lungs. Hazardous concentrations may also be present in areas outside the structure.

Hazardous gases and vapors. Hazardous materials can produce potentially hazardous gases and vapors in nonfire emergencies, such as:

- Incidents involving industrial, commercial, or warehouse occupancies
- Spills resulting from transportation accidents
- Leaks from storage containers or pipelines

At any hazmat incident, fire brigade members should remain at a safe distance (upwind, uphill, upstream) until the completion of a risk analysis. You should consider the atmosphere at these incidents dangerous, so wear your SCBA until air monitoring demonstrates that the atmosphere is safe.

Hazardous nonfire gases and vapors are a possibility at transportation incidents and in storage and manufacturing facilities. Common nonfire gas and vapor types may include:

- Carbon dioxide
- Sulfur dioxide
- Pesticides
- Ammonia
- Chlorine
- Hydrogen sulfide

Toxic gases may also be found in:

- Sewers
- Caves
- Storage tanks
- Bins
- Storm drains
- Trenches
- Tank cars
- Other confined spaces

The atmosphere in these areas may also be oxygen-deficient and potentially deadly. Fire brigade members performing search, rescue, and recovery in these areas must use SCBAs.

Figure 11.25 High-efficiency particulate air (HEPA) filter masks provide protection against airborne pathogens.

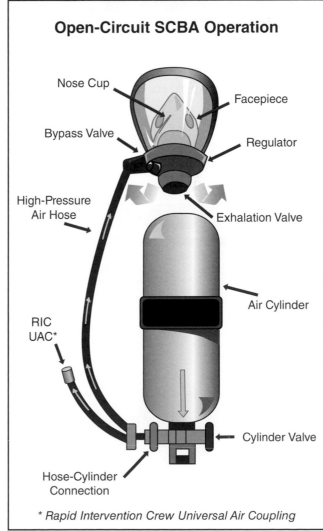

Open-Circuit SCBA Operation

Nose Cup

Facepiece

Bypass Valve

Regulator

High-Pressure Air Hose

Exhalation Valve

Air Cylinder

RIC UAC*

Cylinder Valve

Hose-Cylinder Connection

Rapid Intervention Crew Universal Air Coupling

Figure 11.26 An open-circuit SCBA vents exhaled air to the outside environment.

Airborne Pathogens

Airborne pathogens, which are disease-causing microorganisms (viruses, bacteria, or fungi) suspended in the air, cause infection through inhalation or direct contact. You may encounter them during:

- Medical responses
- Vehicle extrications
- Rescue and recovery operations
- Terrorist attacks

Protection against airborne pathogens includes **high-efficiency particulate air (HEPA) filters**, APR/PAPRs, and SCBA. HEPA filter masks are single-use masks **(Figure 11.25)**. Surgical masks are not approved for use against airborne pathogens but may prevent patients who are wearing them to spread diseases by exhaling, sneezing, or coughing.

SCBA Components

SCBA is a type of atmosphere-supplying respirator that provides air in a cylinder. There are two main types of SCBA: open-circuit SCBA, which use compressed air, and closed-circuit SCBA, which use compressed oxygen. In open-circuit SCBA, exhaled air is vented to the outside atmosphere **(Figure 11.26)**. In closed-circuit SCBA (also known as a "rebreather" apparatus), exhaled air stays within the system for reuse. Closed-circuit SCBA are much less common and are mainly used at:

- Shipboard operations
- Extended hazardous materials incidents
- Some rescue operations
- Mine rescue operations
- Industrial facilities

Open-circuit SCBA consists of four basic components **(Figure 11.27, p. 348)**:

- Backplate and harness assembly
- Air cylinder assembly
- Regulator assembly
- Facepiece assembly

NOTE: SCBA may also have a number of other components unique to that manufacturer's design.

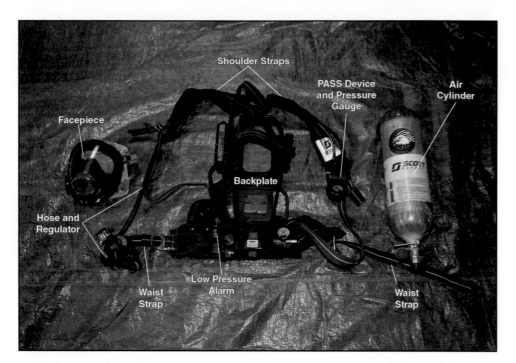

Figure 11.27 The components of an open-circuit SCBA.

Backplate and Harness Assembly

A rigid frame with adjustable straps holds the breathing air cylinder on the backplate, and onto the fire brigade member's back. The straps stabilize the unit, carry part of its weight, and provide a secure and comfortable fit. An adjustable waist strap also distributes some of the apparatus' weight to the hips.

Air Cylinder Assembly

The air cylinder, which contains breathing air under pressure, may be constructed of steel, aluminum, aluminum wrapped in fiberglass, or a Kevlar®/carbon composite material. **Table 11.1** shows common cylinder sizes.

Table 11.1 Breathing Air Cylinder Capacities		
Rated Duration	**Pressure**	**Volume**
30-minute	2,216 psi (15 290 kPa)	45 ft³ (1 270 L) cylinders
30-minute	4,500 psi (31 000 kPa)	45 ft³ (1 270 L) cylinders
45-minute	3,000 psi (21 000 kPa)	66 ft³ (1 870 L) cylinders
45-minute	4,500 psi (31 000 kPa)	66 ft³ (1 870 L) cylinders
60-minute	4,500 psi (31 000 kPa)	87 ft³ (2 460 L) cylinders

• Rated duration does not indicate the actual amount of time that the cylinder will provide air.

Depending on size and construction materials, cylinders weigh from approximately 8 to 20 pounds (4 to 9.5 kg). This weight significantly increases physical stress during emergency operations.

The cylinder has a control valve, threaded stem and/or quick-connect fitting, and a pressure gauge attached to one end **(Figure 11.28)**. When the cylinder is in operation, the wearer fully opens the control valve to permit air into the system. The high-pressure hose attaches to the stem and connects the cyl-

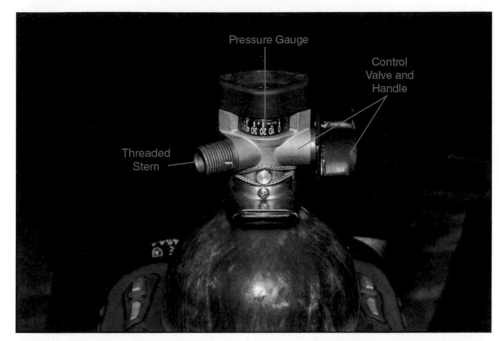

Figure 11.28 The parts of a SCBA air cylinder control valve assembly.

inder to the regulator assembly. Air from the cylinder travels through the high-pressure hose to the regulator. The pressure gauge displays an estimate of the amount of air in the cylinder in pounds per square inch (psi) (kilopascal [kPa]).

Regulator Assembly

The regulator reduces the high pressure of the cylinder air to slightly above atmospheric pressure and controls air flow to the wearer. When the wearer inhales, a pressure differential occurs in the regulator. The apparatus diaphragm moves inward, tilting the admission valve so that low-pressure air can flow into the facepiece. The regulator diaphragm is then held open, which creates the positive pressure. Exhalation moves the diaphragm back to the "closed" position. The regulator may be located on the facepiece, the shoulder harness, or the waist belt harness **(Figure 11.29)**.

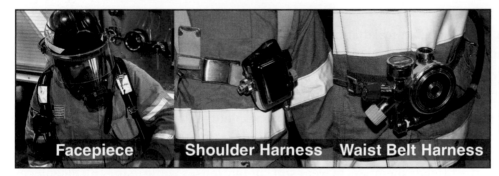

Figure 11.29 On modern SCBAs, the regulator attaches to the facepiece while on older models it was located on the shoulder harness or waist belt harness.

Depending on the SCBA model, the regulator will have two control valves for normal and emergency operations: the mainline valve and the bypass valve. On models equipped with both valves, the mainline valve locks in the open position during normal operations and the bypass valve is closed. On some SCBA, the bypass valve controls a direct air line from the cylinder in the event that the regulator fails. Once the valves are set in their normal operating position, they should not be changed unless the wearer needs the emergency bypass function. The current generation of regulators includes only the bypass valve.

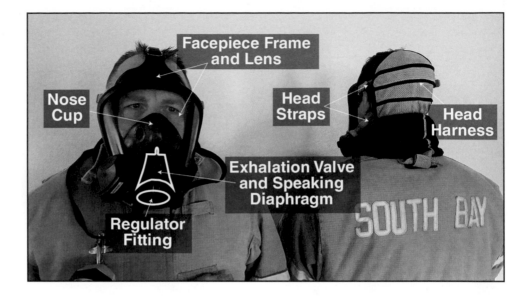

Figure 11.30 The components of the facepiece assembly. *Courtesy of Assistant Chief Brandon LeMay and the South Bay Fire Department, Olympia (WA).*

Facepiece Assembly

The facepiece assembly provides fresh breathing air while protecting the eyes and face from injury. To accomplish these functions, the facepiece must fit tightly to the face. The facepiece assembly consists of **(Figure 11.30)**:

- **Facepiece frame and lens** — The lens is made of clear safety plastic and mounted in a flexible rubber facepiece frame. According to NFPA 1981, all new SCBA facepieces must be equipped with a heads-up display (HUD). This feature displays a series of lights on the inside of the facepiece lens indicating the approximate amount of air remaining in the cylinder.

- **Head harness and straps** — A harness, with adjustable straps, net, or some other arrangement, holds the facepiece snugly against the face.

- **Exhalation valve** — A simple, one-way valve that releases exhaled air without admitting any of the contaminated outside atmosphere.

- **Nose cup** — The nose cup deflects exhalations away from the lens, reducing fogging or condensation on the lens.

- **Speaking diaphragm** — This mechanical diaphragm grants the wearer limited communication. An electronic speaking diaphragm connected to a portable radio may replace it.

- **Regulator fitting or hose connection** — The regulator fitting or hose connection permits the regulator or hose to be attached to the facepiece frame.

NFPA 1500™ prohibits beards or facial hair that prevents a complete seal between the facepiece and the wearer's face. Wearing eyeglasses is also prohibited if the side frames pass through the seal area. Eyeglass kits are provided with all full facepiece masks. Both NFPA 1500™ and *Code of Federal Regulations (CFR)* 1910.134 allow fire brigade members to wear soft contact lenses while using full facepieces if the fire brigade member has demonstrated successful long-term (at least 6 months) use of contact lenses without any problems.

 NFPA Safety Alert Issued for SCBA Facepiece Lenses

On July 2, 2012, the National Fire Protection Association issued the following safety alert:

Exposure to high temperature environments, which fire brigade members can encounter during fires they are attempting to extinguish, can result in the thermal degradation or melting of a Self-Contained Breathing Apparatus (SCBA) facepiece lens, resulting in elimination of the protection meant for the user's respiratory system and exposing the user to products of combustion and superheated air.

This alert was based on data the National Institute for Occupational Safety and Health (NIOSH) while investigating firefighter line of duty deaths between 2002 and 2011. The investigations into three fatalities indicated that fire brigade members encountered thermal conditions that exceeded the level of protection the facepiece lenses were designed to withstand. At the same time, investigations determined that the facepiece lens offered the lowest level of thermal protection of any part of the personal protective ensemble. The degradation of the lens resulted in the inhalation of products of combustion and thermal injuries to the fire brigade member's respiratory system.

After the investigations, the NFPA recommended the following:

- SCBA facepieces should be inspected before and after each use in accordance with NFPA 1852, *Selection, Care, and Maintenance of Open-Circuit Self-Contained Breathing Apparatus.*

- SCBA facepieces that exhibit evidence of exposure to intense heat, such as cracking, crazing, bubbling, discoloration, deformation, or gaps between the lens and frame must be removed from service and repaired or replaced.

- Fire brigade training programs must contain information on the limitations of respiratory protection, the effects on the facepiece of prolonged or repeated exposures to intense heat, and ways to respond to problems that may occur when the facepiece is exposed to intense heat.

- When fire brigade members and fire officers evaluate structure fires, they must consider the potential for facepiece failure during an interior fire attack. Situational awareness and an understanding of fire behavior are essential to preventing facepiece failure.

- When interior conditions deteriorate, fire brigade members must recognize the change in conditions and withdraw or seek a safe refuge.

In response to this safety alert, NFPA has included lens radiant heat testing to the latest edition of NFPA 1981. The test measures the inhalation and exhalation performance of the facepiece assembly while under radiant heat. The facepiece must maintain air pressure specified in the standard under radiant heat conditions typical for a structure fire for 24 minutes. The updated requirement in NFPA 1981 is intended to provide manufacturers with a benchmark for creating SCBA facepieces that are more resistant to heat and less likely to fail unexpectedly.

Additional SCBA Components

Manufacturers of SCBA varies depending upon the features included in their designs. Many of the components in this section have become standard on newer model SCBA and are included in NFPA 1981 for testing and specifications. Older but still serviceable SCBA may not include these components.

Remote pressure gauge. A **remote pressure gauge** must be mounted in a visible position to display the air pressure within the cylinder **(Figure 11.31)**. Pressure readings are most accurate at or near the upper range of the gauge's rated working pressures. Low pressure is measured less accurately, so the readings at this low end of the scale may not match the reading on the regulator gauge. When the readings differ occurs, assume that the lowest reading is correct. Check that the equipment is in working order before using it again.

Figure 11.31 A fire brigade member checking his SCBA's remote pressure gauge.

End-of-service-time indicator (EOSTI). NFPA and NIOSH require that all SCBAs have two end-of-service-time indicators (EOSTI) or redundant low-pressure alarms installed. The EOSTI's alarm warns the user that the system is reaching the end of its air supply, typically when it reaches 33 percent of the cylinder's capacity **(Figure 11.32)**. The EOSTI has both an audible alarm (such as a bell, electronic beep, or high-pitched siren) and a flashing light or physical vibration. The alarm cannot be turned off until the air cylinder valve is closed and the system is bled of all remaining pressure.

Figure 11.32 Two types of low-pressure alarms: a visual indicator on the SCBA regulator that is visible to the wearer and a low-pressure alarm bell.

Rapid Intervention Crew Universal Air Coupling. All NFPA-compliant SCBA manufactured since 2001 are equipped with a rapid intervention crew universal air coupling (RIC UAC) located within 4 inches (100 mm) of the cylinder outlet. This coupling allows any cylinder that is low on air to be trans-filled from another cylinder, regardless of its manufacturer **(Figure 11.33)**. When the cylinders are connected, the air supply equalizes between them. Older SCBA can be retrofitted with the RIC UAC, but this modification is not required. The use of this feature requires thorough training.

Figure 11.33 A close up of a RIC UAC on a SCBA.

Emergency Escape Breathing Support System (EEBSS). EEBSS allows two fire brigade members to share air from one cylinder without removing their facepieces. The fire brigade member with a malfunctioning SCBA can connect his or her regulator to the buddy breathing output on the working SCBA **(Figure 11.34)**. As both fire brigade members use the same air, they should make their way out of the dangerous environment toward the nearest means of emergency egress or the nearest safe haven.

Figure 11.34 A fire brigade member can connect his air cylinder to a fallen fire brigade member's SCBA using a buddy breathing system.

Figure 11.35 The lights of this SCBA facepiece's heads-up display provide a constant reminder of the available air pressure in an air cylinder. *Courtesy of Arlington (TX) Fire Department. Photograph by Jason Arias.*

Integrated PASS Control Module. PASS control modules contain analog or digital displays to provide information about the operation of the SCBA and PASS device. The displays are required to show remaining breathing air cylinder content. Manufacturers may also include other vital information, such as:

- Cylinder pressure
- Remaining battery life
- Alarms
- Estimates for remaining operational time

Heads-up Display (HUD). Heads up displays show vital equipment information on the inside of the facepiece **(Figure 11.35)**. HUDs may be integrated into the facepiece or mounted on the shoulder and projecting an image to the facepiece. According to NFPA 1581, the HUD must display the breathing cylinder content at least in 100, 75, 50, and 33 percent increments. The display should also flash at one-percent increments to indicate to the wearer the rate at which air is being used. Manufacturers may also include other information as part of the display depending upon their designs.

Alert Lighting Systems. All PASS devices emit an alarm when they activate. Some manufacturers have also included a lighting system into the SCBA harness that flashes emergency signals when the PASS device activates. The intention is for rescuers to receive both a visual and audio signal to follow when searching for a downed fire brigade member.

Voice Communications Systems. Some manufacturers integrate voice communication systems into SCBA to supplement radio communications. Fire brigade members can turn the systems on or off as needed, and NFPA 1581 allows the systems to have a volume control. Some systems are voice activated, providing hands-free communications. The systems may also use a wired or wireless interface to connect to the fire brigade member's radio rather than operate as a standalone replacement for a radio.

Built-in Thermal Imagers. Some manufacturers have integrated thermal imagers (thermal imaging cameras) into their SCBA facepieces. These imagers can aid fire brigade personnel in locating victims and fires that smoke obscures or within walls.

SCBA Protection Limitations

All respiratory protection equipment has limitations. You must be aware of these limitations to operate safely and effectively in hazardous atmospheres. The wearer or the equipment itself may create limitations.

Wearer Limitations

The limitations that you have the greatest control over include:

- **Lack of physical condition** — If you are not in good physical condition or if you are overweight, you may rapidly deplete your air supply.

- **Lack of agility** — If you are not sufficiently agile, the weight and restriction of the equipment will make you less so, thus making it difficult to accomplish your assigned tasks.

- **Impaired balance** — Donning SCBA will impair your balance and gait (manner of walk).

- **Inadequate pulmonary capacity** — You must have sufficient lung capacity to inhale and exhale sufficient air while wearing respiratory protection equipment.

- **Weakened cardiovascular ability** — You must have a strong enough heart to prevent heart attacks, strokes, or other health-related problems while performing strenuous activity.

- **Psychological limitations** — You must be able to overcome stress, fear, and feelings of claustrophobia while wearing respiratory protection equipment.

- **Unique facial features** — The shape and contour of the face can affect the ability to get a complete facepiece-to-face seal. Weight loss or gain can alter the facepiece seal.

You can offset these limitations through constant training with each type of respiratory protection equipment you use, periodic medical evaluations, and proper fit testing of respiratory protection facepieces. Training will help you develop confidence and skill while wearing respiratory protection equipment.

Equipment Limitations

SCBA units have limitations, including:

- **Limited visibility** — The full facepiece can reduce peripheral vision, and facepiece fogging can reduce overall vision.

- **Decreased ability to communicate** — The facepiece can hinder voice communication unless it has built-in voice amplification or a microphone connection.

- **Decreased endurance** — The weight of SCBA units, averaging between 25 and 35 pounds (12.5 and 17.5 kg), makes you tire more quickly.

- **Decreased mobility** — The increase in weight and restrictions from the harness straps can reduce your mobility.

- **Poor condition of apparatus** — Minor leaks and poor valve and regulator adjustments can result in excess air loss.

- **Low air cylinder pressure** — If the cylinder is not filled to capacity, the amount of working time is reduced proportionately.

You have some control over these limitations through frequent and proper inspections, care, and maintenance. Training with the units that you will use at an incident can also help you overcome the weight and mobility factors.

Storing Respiratory Protective Equipment

Methods of storing respiratory protection equipment vary among fire brigades. Each fire brigade should use the most appropriate method to facilitate quick and easy donning. When stored at fixed facilities, the SBCA may be kept in storage cases or mounted on brackets along walls. If the SCBA is stored on

Figure 11.36 SCBA may be stored in apparatus compartments, apparatus seats, or special cabinets located around a facility.

Compartment Mounts   Seat Mounts   Cabinets

fire brigade vehicles or fire apparatus, fire brigade members can place it in seat mounts, side mounts, and compartment mounts. Personnel can also store it in cases or even in special cabinets at designated locations at the industrial site **(Figure 11.36)**. If the SCBA is placed in seat mounts, a fire brigade member should arrange it so that it may be donned without having to remove the seat belt. In all cases, respiratory protection equipment should be stored out of direct sunlight, which can be damaging to equipment components.

Donning and Doffing Breathing Apparatus

NFPA 1081 (2018): 5.2.2, 6.1.2.2

Fire brigade members should be trained on and competent in the donning and doffing procedures for the SCBA and/or SAR that their brigade uses. The following sections cover the general procedures for donning and doffing SCBA and SAR.

Donning and Doffing SCBA

Fire brigade members can use several methods to don an SCBA, depending on how it is stored. Each method requires different steps. The most common methods include **(Figure 11.37)**:

- Over-the-head method
- Coat method
- Donning from a seat
- Donning from a side/rear external mount or backup mount

Figure 11.37 These photos demonstrate the four common methods of donning SCBA.

Over-the-Head   Coat   Seat   Side Mount

Different brands and models also require different steps for securing the SCBA to the wearer. Rather than listing the procedures for each manufacturer's model, this section provides only a general description of the four donning techniques. Make sure to follow the manufacturer's instructions and local SOPs for the particular SCBA assigned to you.

General Donning Considerations

Fire brigade members with daily shift changes should perform a daily inspection and operational check at the start of their shifts, then return the SCBA to the apparatus-mounted storage rack or the storage case. Departments that are unable to make daily inspections should perform the following checks immediately prior to donning the SCBA:

- Check the air cylinder gauge to make sure the cylinder is full. NFPA 1852, *Standard on Selection, Care, and Maintenance of Open-Circuit Self-Contained Breathing Apparatus (SCBA)*, recommends no less than 90 percent of cylinder capacity **(Figure 11.38)**.

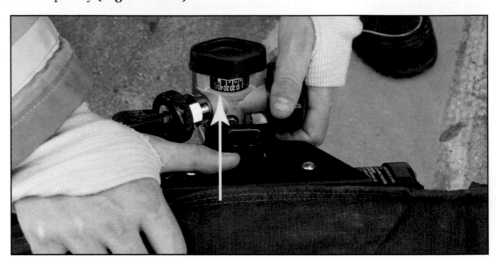

Figure 11.38 Fire brigade members should check the air cylinder gauge as they open the cylinder valve.

- Check the remote gauge and cylinder gauge to ensure that they read within the manufacturer's recommended limits.

- Check the harness assembly and facepiece to ensure that all straps are fully extended.

- Operate all valves to ensure that they function properly and are left in the correct position.

- Test the low-pressure alarm.

- Test the PASS device to ensure that it is working.

- Check all battery-powered functions.

Refer to manufacturer's instructions regarding any variations in SCBA use. For example, on some SCBA, the audible alarm does not sound when the cylinder valve is opened and not all facepieces are designed for a seal check without the regulator being attached and activated.

Donning an Unmounted SCBA

Fire brigade members can don SCBA stored in cases using the over-the-head method or the coat method. In both methods, position the SCBA on the ground in front of the fire brigade member (either in or out of the case) with all straps extended, ready to don.

Donning from a Seat Mount

Seat-mounted SCBA permit fire brigade members to don the unit while seated in the apparatus. You should use this method only if you can do so without removing the apparatus seat belt. Even with a seat mount, jurisdictions may still have policies dictating when SCBA can be donned — before departure, in-transit, or after arrival.

NFPA 1901, *Standard for Automotive Fire Apparatus*, requires that a mechanical latching device hold the SCBA in place. A wide variety of mounting brackets are available that meet this requirement. The facepiece should be stored in a drawstring or other quick-opening bag, or in a pouch on your protective coat. This measure will keep it clean and protect it from dust and scratches.

NOTE: Do not keep the facepiece connected to the regulator during storage. These parts must be kept separate in order to check for proper facepiece seal.

> **CAUTION:** Never connect the regulator and breathe cylinder air when seated in the apparatus. Doing so will deplete your air supply before you arrive at the incident.

> **WARNING:** Never stand to don SCBA while the apparatus is moving. NFPA 1500TM requires fire brigade members to remain seated and belted at all times while the apparatus is in motion.

The air cylinder's position in the seat back should match the proper wearing position for the fire brigade member. A seat-mounted SCBA allows personnel to check the equipment more frequently and makes conducting safety checks more convenient.

Carefully exit the apparatus while maintaining three points of contact because the extra weight of the SCBA on your back can make slips and falls more likely. Be sure to adjust all straps for a snug and comfortable fit.

Donning from a Side or Rear External Mount

Side- or rear-mounted SCBA are mounted on the exterior of the apparatus. Although this type of mount does not permit donning en route and requires more time for donning than seat-mounted SCBA, it reduces the chances of slips and falls. It is also faster than donning an SCBA stored in a carrying case within an apparatus compartment. Disadvantages of exterior mounting include exposing the SCBA to weather and other physical hazards, though waterproof covers will minimize the risk of damage.

When SCBA are mounted at the correct height, fire brigade members can don them with little effort. Having the mount near the running boards or tailboard allows the fire brigade member to don the equipment while sitting on the running board or tailboard. The donning steps are similar to those for seat-mounted SCBA.

Donning from a Backup Mount

Backup mounts located inside a compartment are protected from the weather and provide the same advantages as side- or rear-mounted equipment. The backup mount provides quick access to SCBA. However, some compartment doors may interfere with donning SCBA. Other compartments may be located too high on the apparatus, making donning more difficult.

One type of compartment mount has a telescoping frame that extends the equipment outward. Some of these mounts also telescope upward or downward so that a standing fire brigade member can don the SCBA more quickly.

The procedure for donning SCBA using the backup method is similar to the method used for seat-mounted SCBA. In some instances, fire brigade personnel will need to remove some high-mounted SCBA, and don using the over-the-head or coat method.

Donning the Facepiece

Most SCBA facepieces are donned using similar steps regardless of manufacturer. One significant difference is in the adjustment of straps to secure the facepiece in place. For example, some facepieces use a rubber harness and others have a mesh skullcap. Both types have adjustable straps, although some models have more straps than others.

The regulator's location is another difference. On some units, the regulator attaches to the facepiece while on other units it is mounted on the waist belt or shoulder harness. The shape and size of facepiece lenses may also differ. Despite these differences, donning procedures for facepieces are essentially the same.

The following are general considerations for donning all SCBA facepieces:

- Fully extend all straps.
- Ensure that no hair is between the skin and the facepiece sealing surface.
- Center the chin in the chin cup and the harness at the rear of the head.
- Tighten the facepiece straps by pulling opposing straps evenly and simultaneously to the rear. Pulling the straps outward, to the sides, may damage them and prevent proper engagement with the adjusting buckles. Tighten the lower straps, then the temple straps, and finally the top strap, if there is one.
- Check that the facepiece is completely sealed to the face, the exhalation valve is functioning, and all connections are secure. If there is a donning mode switch, check that it is in the proper position.
- Ensure that the protective hood is over the facepiece harness or straps. Ensure that the hood is covering all exposed skin, that your vision is unobscured, and that no portion of the hood is between the facepiece and your face.
- Wear the helmet with the chin straps secured. Adjust helmets equipped with a ratchet adjustment so that the helmet fits properly.

Doffing SCBA

Doffing (removal) techniques differ for the various types of SCBA, but have some similarities. The following actions apply when doffing any brand or model:

- Make sure you are outside the contaminated area and that the SCBA is no longer required.
- Discontinue the flow of air from the regulator to the facepiece.
- Disconnect the regulator from the facepiece and secure it.
- Remove the protective hood or pull it down around your neck.
- Remove the facepiece by loosening the straps and lifting it from your chin.
- Remove the backpack assembly while protecting the regulator.
- Close the cylinder valve.
- Relieve pressure from the regulator according to the manufacturer's instructions.
- Turn off the PASS device and/or control module.
- Extend all facepiece and harness straps.
- Check the air pressure to determine if the air cylinder needs to be refilled or replaced.
- Clean and disinfect the facepiece.
- Clean the SCBA backplate and harness, if necessary.
- Secure the unit in its case, seat bracket, or storage bracket.

Donning and Doffing Supplied-Air Respirators

The manufacturer provides the specific procedures for operating, donning, and doffing SAR systems, and fire brigades should base their training on these procedures. The following are general procedures for donning and doffing SAR.

Donning Supplied-Air Respirators

In general, some of the donning procedures for SAR are the same as those listed for SCBA units:

- Remove the portable supplied-air respirator system from the apparatus and locate it near the entrance to the incident. If the air supply is permanently mounted on the apparatus, locate the vehicle so that the air-supply hoses are protected from traffic or other sources of damage.

- Check the air-supply source to ensure that it is operating properly and that the cylinders are full.

- Extend the air-supply hoses and attach them to the air-supply source.

- Don the harness, regulator, and EEBSS and pull the harness straps snugly to prevent movement of the harness.

- Check the EEBSS cylinder for proper operation and ensure that the cylinder is full.

- Don the facepiece using the method described for the SCBA facepiece or the manufacturer's recommended method.

- Connect the facepiece to the air-supply hose or regulator.

- Don the hard hat, helmet, or other protective equipment.

- Attach the tag line.

Fire brigade personnel who are assigned to monitor a SAR team should remain with the air-supply equipment and ensure that air-supply hoses do not become snared on obstacles. They must also maintain communications with the team either through radio or physical tag lines. These individuals may also perform the function of the rapid intervention crew (RIC). As such, they must be fully equipped with protective clothing, respiratory protection (SCBA), and forcible-entry tools.

Doffing Supplied-Air Respirators

When the fire brigade member determines that it is safe to doff the SAR, follow the manufacturer's recommendations. In general, they include the following procedures:

- Remove the helmet, and pull the protective hood down around the neck.

- Close the air-supply valve on the regulator, disconnect the low-pressure hose from the regulator, or place the regulator in the donning mode.

  — Loosen the facepiece harness strap buckles and remove the facepiece.

  — Extend the facepiece harness straps.

- Place the facepiece in the case, the carrying bag, or some other protected area while doffing the rest of the system. The facepiece is not stored until it has been inspected and cleaned.

- Turn off the air supply at the source, bleed the air-supply line, and disconnect it from the regulator.

- Loosen the shoulder and waist harness, extend the straps completely, and remove the harness assembly, setting it on the ground.

- Inspect the system, replace the EBSS if used, replenish the air-supply cylinders, clean the system, and store it properly.

Inspection and Maintenance of Respiratory Equipment

NFPA 1081 (2018): 5.2.2, 5.3.10, 6.1.2.2, 6.3.7

Fire brigade members inspect their SCBA and SAR on an organizational schedule based on NFPA, OSHA, and manufacturer requirements. Fire brigade members should perform inspections daily, weekly, or whenever they report for duty. The period between inspections must not exceed one week. Qualified SCBA and SAR repair technicians must inspect the units annually and after any repairs have been completed.

SCBA/SAR Inspection and Care

Your SCBA requires ongoing inspection and maintenance to protect you. You must clean and inspect it:

- After each use
- At the start of every duty shift
- Every week

If repairs are necessary, report them immediately. Extensive repairs and cleaning may require that the unit be taken out of service and replaced by a reserve unit.

SCBA Inspections

Each fire brigade should establish a daily/weekly SCBA inspection policy and program. A daily/weekly inspection should include the following SCBA components:

- Facepiece (**Figure 11.39**)
- Backplate and harness assembly
- Breathing air cylinder assembly
- Hoses
- Low-pressure alarm
- Regulator
- Pressure indicator gauges
- Integrated PASS

These inspections can help identify wear and tear, damage, and potential problems before they result in failure during an emergency. Fire brigade personnel should document SCBA/SAR inspections to record the findings, report problems, and show trends.

NOTE: During the inspection, the inspector should check the hydrostatic test date label on the air cylinder to see if the cylinder is due for hydrostatic testing to check for flaws and leaks.

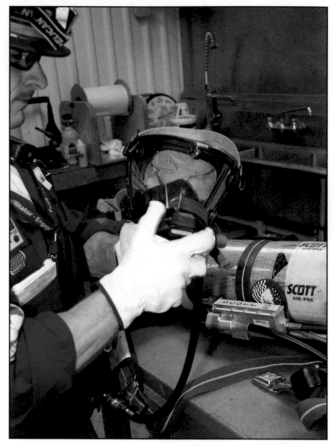

Figure 11.39 A fire brigade member inspecting a SCBA facepiece.

SCBA/SAR Care

You should clean and sanitize the SCBA/SAR facepiece after each use to prevent debris from collecting in the exhalation valve and regulator fitting. Dirt or other foreign materials can cause the exhalation valve to malfunction and allow cylinder air to escape, depleting the air supply. Debris can also prevent the regulator from fitting securely to the facepiece. Soot and scratches on the facepiece lens can reduce visibility.

Wash the facepiece thoroughly with warm water containing a mild commercial disinfectant and then rinse with clear, warm water. After cleaning, take special care to ensure proper operation of the exhalation valve. If it does not operate correctly, either repeat cleaning to identify the problem or report the facepiece as damaged and out-of-service. Dry the facepiece with a lint-free cloth or air dry it. Do not use paper towels to dry the facepiece because they will scratch the facepiece lens. Specialized respiratory drying equipment is also available.

You must not submerge regulators and low-pressure hoses in water for cleaning. Sanitize the facepiece seal and its interior to prevent you from inhaling or coming in contact with contaminants, especially if you share the facepiece with other personnel. Refer to the manufacturer's instructions on proper facepiece care and maintenance.

Facepiece lenses can also fog up internally due to the difference between the inside and outside temperatures or a defective or missing nose cup. To prevent fogging, some SCBA facepieces are permanently treated with an antifogging chemical. Fire brigade personnel can also apply manufacturer recommended antifogging chemicals to the facepiece lens following cleaning.

Fire brigades often issue each fire brigade member an individual facepiece that is not shared with other fire brigade members. This practice eliminates the risk of spreading germs from one wearer to the next and ensures that the mask is the correct size, providing a complete seal. Even if you are assigned your own facepiece, clean it after each use. After the facepiece is clean and dry, store it in a case, a bag, or coat pocket. Leave the facepiece straps fully extended to facilitate donning.

Annual SCBA/SAR Inspection and Maintenance

In accordance with manufacturer's recommendations, specially trained, factory qualified technicians must perform annual inspection and maintenance. These technicians may be trained fire brigade personnel or certified maintenance contractor employees.

Refilling SCBA/SAR Cylinders

Fire brigade members may use three breathing air systems to refill depleted SCBA/SAR air cylinders:

- **Stationary fill systems** — Systems permanently installed within the fire brigade's station or facility **(Figure 11.40)**

Figure 11.40 A fire brigade member using a stationary fill station to reservice a SCBA air cylinder.

- **Mobile fill systems** — Systems mounted on apparatus or trailers

- **Firefighter Breathing Air Replenishment Systems (FBARS)** — Systems installed in high-rise buildings; might also be referred to as a Firefighter Air Replenishment Systems (FFARs).

Each source must provide Type 1 Grade D quality air, as OSHA and Canadian government requirements specify.

The following safety precautions apply when refilling an SCBA/SAR cylinder:

- Check the hydrostatic test date of the cylinder.

- Perform required inspection of cylinders before filling.

- Check the working pressure.

- Wear the required hearing and eye protection during fill operations.

- Place the cylinder in a shielded fill station.

- Fill the cylinder slowly to prevent it from overheating.
- Ensure that the cylinder is full but not overpressurized (overfilled).
- Allow only trained personnel to operate the fill equipment.

> **CAUTION:** Do not fill cylinders if hydrostatic testing is out of date or if the cylinder is damaged.

Filling unshielded cylinders while a fire brigade member is wearing the SCBA is prohibited. However, a rapid intervention crew (RIC) rescuing a trapped or incapacitated fire brigade member may be granted an exception to this rule. The following criteria must be met before filling a worn SCBA:

- NIOSH-approved RIC Universal Air Connection (UAC) fill options are used.
- A risk assessment has been conducted to limit safety hazards and ensure that necessary equipment is fully operational.
- There is an imminent threat to the safety of the downed fire brigade member, and immediate action is required to prevent loss of life or serious injury.

Stationary Fill Stations

SCBA/SAR breathing air cylinders are filled from a **cascade system** or directly from a compressor air purification system. Both systems connect to a fill station that holds the SCBA/SAR cylinders in rupture-proof sleeves during the filling process. If your department fills its own SCBA/SAR cylinders, you will receive training on how to safely use the system. Filling procedures should be posted on the fill station and must follow the fill station manufacturer's recommendations to avoid excessive overheating in the cylinder. Some departments do not fill their own cylinders, and contract the process out to a qualified breathing air supplier.

A third-party testing facility must regularly test breathing air, and the department must document the testing results. The department's health and safety officer is usually responsible for monitoring the testing and maintaining the documentation.

An **auto-cascade system** is a type of automated stationary fill station. When fire brigade members place cylinders in the system, valves automatically open and close to complete the fill process. Auto-cascade systems fill cylinders to a programmable desired pressure. These systems may be retrofitted to existing, manual cascade systems as add-on modules.

Mobile Fill Systems

Mobile breathing air fill systems are designed to refill air cylinders at emergency incidents. They typically consist of a fill station equipped with a breathing-air compressor or cascade fill station and are mounted on a trailer or the apparatus chassis.

System operations are similar to the stationary systems previously mentioned. The system may also support a SAR system or a firefighter breathing air replenishment system (FBARS) installed in a high-rise structure.

Firefighter Breathing Air Replenishment Systems (FBARS)

To fight fires in tall structures more effectively and avoid the need to carry full SCBA cylinders to upper floors, fire brigades need a way to refill SCBA cylinders on upper floors. In many municipalities now require that all newly constructed buildings taller than 75 feet (25 m) install FBARS. FBARS provide an endless source of breathing air to any floor within the structure from a ground level connection. These systems can also be used in industrial or other facilities. FBARS typically consist of:

- An air connection panel, containing connection fittings, control valves, and gauges, located on the exterior of the structure
- An Emergency Air Storage (EAS) system that provides breathing air if a mobile system is unavailable to supply the external connection

- Remote air fill panels, containing a certified rupture-proof containment fill station, connection and control valves, and gauges, located in protected stairwells on specific floors
- Interconnected piping certified to carry breathing air under pressure throughout the system
- Low air pressure monitoring switches and alarms, used to maintain a minimum air pressure and warn of pressure loss or system failure

Not all high-rise buildings have these systems, but their installation and use is increasing. Fire brigade members should know which structures in their jurisdiction have these systems and know how to use them.

Figure 11.41 One fire brigade member changing out the air cylinder of another fire brigade member's SCBA.

Exchanging SCBA Cylinders

SCBA backplates are designed for easy removal and exchange of breathing air cylinders. You may be required to exchange the breathing air cylinder under the following circumstances:

- During the daily/weekly inspection, if the cylinder contains less than 90 percent of its capacity
- During training exercises
- During long-duration emergency operations
- After any emergency operations

Changing SCBA breathing air cylinders can be either a one- or two-person task **(Figure 11.41)**. If only one fire brigade member is available to replace the cylinder, the fire brigade member will doff the SCBA in order to replace it.

When two people are present, the fire brigade member with an empty cylinder simply positions the cylinder so that the other fire brigade member can easily change it. The fire brigade member changing the cylinder should report the pressure in the new cylinder to the wearer after exchanging the cylinders. The fire brigade member who can accomplish the tasks most easily should complete the steps.

Keep empty cylinders separate from full cylinders that have been serviced and are ready for use. Clearly mark damaged cylinders and keep them separate from both empty and full cylinders.

Using Respiratory Protection Equipment

NFPA 1081 (2018): 5.2.1, 5.2.2, 5.2.4, 6.1.2.2, 6.2.8

Properly worn, maintained, and inspected respiratory protection equipment will prevent exposure to airborne hazards. Specially trained, factory-qualified technicians must perform annual inspection and maintenance in accordance with manufacturer's recommendations.

Fire brigade members must be aware of additional safety concerns, such as:

- Fatigue
- Regulating air supply
- Proper exit procedures

Safety Precautions for SCBA Use

When using SCBA, you should follow these safety precautions:

- Only enter an IDLH atmosphere if you are certified to wear SCBA and have been properly fit-tested for the facepiece.

- Closely monitor how you feel while wearing the SCBA. If you become fatigued, notify your supervisor and take a rest before returning to work.

- Remember that your air supply duration can vary, depending on:
  - Air cylinder size and beginning pressure
  - Your physical conditioning
  - The task being performed
  - Your level of training
  - The operational environment
  - Your level of stress
  - Air management techniques

- Before entering the IDLH atmosphere, check cylinder pressure and estimate your **point of no return** based upon your air supply, pressure, and mission objective.

- Use your training to establish a personal baseline for your individual air usage as a means of understanding how long you can work while on air.

- After entering an IDLH atmosphere, keep your SCBA on and activated until you leave the contaminated area. Improved visibility does not ensure that the area is free of contamination. Before removing your SCBA, the atmosphere must be tested with properly calibrated instruments and found to be safe.

- In any IDLH atmosphere, work in teams of two or more. Team members must remain in physical, voice, or visual contact with each other while in the hazardous area. Radio contact is insufficient. If available, a thermal imager (TI) can help maintain contact.

- While in the IDLH atmosphere, frequently check your air supply status.

- Exit the IDLH atmosphere before the low air alarm activates to avoid using the reserve air supply.

> **WARNING:** Radio contact is insufficient communication between team members in any IDLH atmosphere.

Special SCBA Procedures

The industrial fire brigade member must operate effectively in areas of obscured vision and negotiate tight passages without having to completely shed the breathing apparatus. The following sections address techniques for accomplishing these tasks.

Operating in Areas of Obscured Visibility

In many instances where protective breathing apparatus is required, fire brigade members will operate in an area of obscured visibility. Most interior fire attacks and many exterior attacks present fire brigade personnel with heavy smoke conditions that may reduce visibility to zero. Fire brigade personnel must learn techniques for moving about and performing critical tasks when vision is diminished.

Crawling is the primary method of moving about in areas of obscured visibility. It allows fire brigade members to remain close to the floor and avoid the higher heat found closer to ceiling level. It also allows fire brigade members to feel in front of themselves as they move along. This technique prevents them from running into objects in front of them or falling down stairs, elevator shafts, and holes burned in the floor. Crawling also allows fire brigade personnel to feel for furniture or victims who may be lying on the floor. If fire brigade members can see the floor, they may be able to move about using a crouched or "duck" walk. This method is slightly faster than crawling but is more dangerous unless fire brigade members can clearly see the floor in front of them.

When entering an area of obscured visibility, facility fire brigade personnel must operate in teams of at least two, and they should have some sort of guideline that leads them back to the point of entrance if necessary. The guideline may be a hoseline, rope, or electrical cord. In the event they must evacuate the structure in a hurry, the fire brigade members can turn around and follow the guideline to safety. If the team does not have a guideline or becomes separated from it, they should proceed to a wall and follow it until a door or window is found.

Exiting Areas with Restricted Openings Under Emergency Circumstances

In an emergency, facility structural fire brigade members may need to exit an opening that is too small to allow them to pass through in a normal manner while wearing SCBA. They may need to loosen parts of the SCBA harness or doff the backpack, exit the restricted area, and resecure or redon the backpack. Removing the SCBA should be limited only to the extent to which it is necessary to exit the area. The type of apparatus determines the procedures the fire brigade member uses for removing the SCBA and maneuvering through an opening. Fire brigade members should be familiar with their particular SCBA equipment. Some factors to keep in mind include:

- Maintain contact with the regulator.
- Loosen straps as necessary to reduce your profile.
- Remove one or both backpack harness straps if necessary to reduce your profile further.
- Push the SCBA in front of you as necessary, maintaining control of the SCBA at all times.

Exit Indicators

Your team should be prepared to make a rapid exit or withdrawal if the environment becomes more hazardous. If conditions deteriorate or team members experience equipment failure, the team should withdraw as a team. Nonemergency exit procedures should be the most common, and used at the majority of incidents. Emergency exit procedures, though not as common, should also be considered. These procedures are used in life-threatening situations, such as SCBA failures and catastrophic changes during the incident.

Practice exit techniques during training, and follow them during emergency incidents. The following sections cover nonemergency exit procedures. Many circumstances exist in which fire brigade members must exit contaminated or hazardous areas. Situations or events that signal the need for exit are called exit indicators.

Nonemergency exit indicators occur when:

- The situation is stabilized.
- There is a change in operational strategy.
- It is necessary to replace an air cylinder.
- The Incident Commander (IC) orders a nonemergency withdrawal.
- The assignment is completed.

Emergency exit indicators include:

- Activation of SCBA low-pressure air alarm.
- SCBA failure.
- Withdrawal orders issued by the IC or Safety Officer.

- Changes in environmental conditions, such as temperature, wind direction and speed, and water level and speed, either within or around the site of the incident.

- Changes in oxygen level.

- Indications of new hazards.

At an incident, the IC is responsible for having the environment monitored constantly. When monitoring reveals a potential hazard, such as chemical concentrations that approach the permissible exposure limit (PEL), the IC issues orders to change the required level of respiratory protection or withdraw from the area.

Fire brigade members may detect a change in oxygen level, especially oxygen deficiency. If you experience any of the following symptoms of oxygen deficiency, immediately report this information to the IC and evacuate the area:

- Light-headedness

- Disorientation

- Loss of coordination

- Increased breathing rates

- Rapid fatigue

Mayday Procedures

When breathing apparatus malfunctions, the resulting emergencies can be overcome in several ways. Regardless of other considerations, the conservation of air and immediate withdrawal from the hazardous atmosphere are of the utmost importance. The following list of suggestions can effectively resolve an emergency situation:

- Do not panic! Panicking causes rapid breathing that uses more valuable air.
  — Control breathing while crawling.
  — Communicate with other team members.

- Stop and think. How did you get to where you are? Downstairs? Upstairs? Left turns?

- Listen:
  — For noise from other personnel
  — For hose and equipment operation
  — For sounds that indicate the location of fire

- Use the portable radio to announce your last known location.

- Activate your PASS device.

- Place a flashlight on the floor with the light shining toward the ceiling.

- Remember the different methods to find a way out:
  — Follow the hoseline out if possible (male coupling is closest to exit, female is closest to the fire).
  — Follow search lines or taglines if available.
  — Crawl in a straight line (hands on floor, move knee to hand).
  — Crawl in one direction (all left-hand turns, all right-hand turns) once in contact with the wall.
  — Call for directions, call out, or make noise for other fire brigade members to assist you.
  — Break a window or breach a wall to escape, if possible.

- Lie flat on the floor close to a wall so that you will be easier to find if you are exhausted or feel you may lose consciousness.

Equipment Malfunctions

Fire brigade members need to be aware of types of SCBA equipment failures and the procedures for dealing with them. Common equipment malfunctions include:

- Low air supply
- Regulator malfunction
- Facepiece failure

Regulator Malfunction

Although a regulator usually works as designed, it can malfunction. One method of using SCBA when the regulator becomes damaged or malfunctions is to open the bypass valve to provide a flow of air into the facepiece. The bypass valve should be closed after the fire brigade member takes a breath and then opened each time the next breath is needed. Another option, if the air supply allows, is to keep the bypass valve open slightly to help ensure positive pressure in facepiece.

Facepiece Failure

If the facepiece fails, various extreme techniques may be available as emergency measures. A thorough knowledge of the fire brigade's SCBA is necessary. Fire brigade personnel should obtain this type of training based on their particular SCBA, following the manufacturer's recommendations and fire brigade's standard operating procedures. You may be able to cover the facepiece with a gloved hand as you and your buddy exit the facility. Your buddy should notify the IC to have RIC meet you en route to the exit.

Evacuation Signals

Evacuation signals are used when command personnel decide that all fire brigade members should be pulled from a burning building or other hazardous area because conditions have deteriorated beyond the point of reasonable safety. All fire brigade members should be familiar with their fire brigade's method of sounding an evacuation signal. This communication may be done in several ways. The two most common ways are to broadcast a radio message ordering them to evacuate, and to sound the audible warning devices on the apparatus at the fire scene for an extended period of time. The radio broadcast of an evacuation signal should be handled in a manner similar to that described for emergency traffic. The message should be broadcast several times to make sure that all personnel hears it. Both methods may need to be used to increase the success of alerting all personnel, depending on conditions at the scene. For example, radio signals may be disrupted by infrastructure. The use of audible warning devices on apparatus, such as sirens and air horns, works in small structures but may not be heard by fire brigade members working in a large building.

Nonemergency Exit Techniques

The Incident Command System (ICS) and the accountability requirements of NFPA 1500™ dictate nonemergency exit techniques including:

- Buddy system
- Controlled breathing
- Entry/egress paths
- Accountability systems

Buddy System

In all hazardous atmospheres or situations, fire brigade members work in teams of at least two members. Each team member is responsible for the safety of his or her buddy. At the first sign of any exit indicator (orders, low air alarm, or change in conditions), team members must leave as a group or in pairs. Individual members must never be left alone in the IDLH atmosphere. The only time a member may work alone is in a confined space where two members cannot fit. The second team member should remain outside the area monitoring the search line, ready to enter the space if the need for rescue arises.

Controlled Breathing

Controlled breathing techniques allow for efficient air use in IDLH atmospheres. In one method, fire brigade members inhale naturally through the nose, then forcefully exhale through the mouth, reducing air consumption.

Another controlled breathing method is the Reilly Emergency Breathing Method, which involves inhaling deeply through the nostrils, expanding the diaphragm to fill the lungs fully. When the lungs are full, the SCBA wearer hums while exhaling in a slow, consistent manner.

Practice controlled breathing methods in training until they become second nature. Conscious breathing slows the consumption of your breathing air cylinder. Controlled breathing is an important exit technique because it reduces air consumption during the time required to exit.

Entry/Egress Paths

When you exit an IDLH area, use the same path that you used to enter. This path will have familiar landmarks, and it may also be the most direct route. This method reduces the possibility that you will become lost or disoriented and allows you to calculate the time it will take to exit the area. Practice this technique during training to make it a habit at an incident.

You should also watch for other means of egress in case your entry route is blocked. Apply your situational awareness as you arrive at the scene of an incident and prepare to enter the structure. Look for other possible exit points, note any potential obstructions, and observe the fire conditions visible at the time you enter the IDLH area.

Accountability Systems

NFPA 1500™ requires the use of accountability systems to keep track of personnel in an IDLH environment. Individual fire brigades may have different accountability SOPs, but typically fire brigade members should check in with the accountability officer or IC before entering the IDLH area. All personnel, their locations, and their functions are then noted on a tracking board or some other tracking system. When fire brigade members leave the IDLH area, they check out with the accountability officer or IC so that they are not counted as missing.

Chapter Review

1. What are some situations in which eye protection is needed?
2. What is proximity protective clothing designed to protect users from?
3. What is a disadvantage of the safety barrier that PPE create?
4. What conditions should be looked for when inspecting PPE?
5. Why are personal alert safety systems important?
6. What is the primary type of respiratory protection used in the fire service?
7. Why is facepiece fit testing essential to respiratory protection?
8. What are some nonfire gases that can pose a respiratory hazard?
9. What additional components now exist on SCBA?
10. What are the wearer and equipment limitations of SCBA protection?
11. What basic guidelines should be followed when storing respiratory protective equipment?

12. Name and describe the common methods for donning SCBA.

13. What precautions should be taken when refilling a SCBA/SAR cylinder?

14. What actions may be taken during mayday procedures?

Discussion Question

1. What are some evacuation and mayday SOPs at your facility?

Chapter 11 End Notes

Horn, Gavin P.; Steve Kerber; Kenneth W. Fent; Bo Fernhall; Denise L. Smith, 2016. "Cardiovascular & Chemcial Exposure Risks in Modern Firefighting." Illinois Fire Service Institute – IFSI Research, University of Illinois at Urbana-Champaign. Accessed online.

Key Terms

Air-Purifying Respirator (APR) — Respirator that removes contaminants by passing ambient air through a filter, cartridge, or canister; may have a full or partial facepiece.

Airborne Pathogens — Disease-causing microorganisms (viruses, bacteria, or fungi) that are suspended in the air.

Atmosphere-Supplying Respirator (ASR) — Respirator that supplies the user with an air supply from a source independent of the ambient atmosphere.

Auto-Cascade System — Completely automated stationary fill station that fills air cylinders to a programmed pressure.

Cascade System — Three or more large, interconnected air cylinders, from which smaller SCBA cylinders are recharged; the larger cylinders typically have a capacity of 300 cubic feet (9 cubic meters).

Closed-Circuit Self-Contained Breathing Apparatus — SCBA that recycles exhaled air; removes carbon dioxide and restores compressed, chemical, or liquid oxygen. Not approved for fire fighting operations.

Code of Federal Regulations (CFR) — Rules and regulations published by executive agencies of the U.S. federal government. These administrative laws are just as enforceable as statutory laws (known collectively as federal law), which must be passed by Congress.

Emergency Escape Breathing Support System (EEBSS) — Feature installed on some SCBA which allows two firefighters to breath from one cylinder without removing their facepieces.

End-of-Service-Time Indicator (EOSTI) — Warning device that alerts the user that the respiratory protection equipment is about to reach its limit and that it is time to exit the contaminated atmosphere; its alarm may be audible, tactile, visual, or any combination thereof.

Fire Fighting Boots — Protective footwear meeting the design requirements of NFPA, OSHA, and CAN/CSA Z195-02 (R2008).

Firefighter Breathing Air Replenishment Systems (FBARS) — A standpipe for air permanently installed within a high-rise building or a large horizontal structure. Air is pumped into the system by a fire department's mobile air truck on the ground, providing an immediate and continuous supply of breathing air to the responders. Air bottles can then be refilled in a matter of seconds at fill stations located throughout a high-rise building.

Fusee — Colored flare designed as a roadway or railway warning device used to ignite backfires and other prescribed fires.

Hearing Protection — Device that limits noise-induced hearing loss when firefighters are exposed to extremely loud environments, such as apparatus engine noise, audible warning devices, and the use of power tools and equipment.

Helmet — Headgear worn by firefighters that provides protection from falling objects, side blows, elevated temperatures, and heated water.

High-Efficiency Particulate Air (HEPA) Filter — Respiratory filter that is certified to remove at least 99.97 % of monodisperse particles of 0.3 micrometers in diameter.

Hypoxia — Potentially fatal condition caused by lack of oxygen.

Open-Circuit Self-Contained Breathing Apparatus — SCBA that allows exhaled air to be discharged or vented into the atmosphere.

Oxygen-Deficient Atmosphere — Atmosphere containing less than the normal 19.5 percent oxygen. At least 16 percent oxygen is needed to produce flames or sustain human life.

Particulate — Very small particle of solid material, such as dust, that is suspended in the atmosphere.

Personal Alert Safety System (PASS) — Electronic lack-of-motion sensor that sounds a loud alarm when a firefighter becomes motionless; can also be manually activated.

Personal Protective Equipment (PPE) — General term for the equipment worn by fire and emergency services responders; includes helmets, coats, trousers, boots, eye protection, hearing protection, protective gloves, protective hoods, self-contained breathing apparatus (SCBA), personal alert safety system (PASS) devices, and chemical protective clothing. When working with hazardous materials, bands or tape are added around the legs, arms, and waist.

Point of No Return — Point at which air in the SCBA will last only long enough to exit a hazardous atmosphere.

Powered Air-Purifying Respirator (PAPR) — Motorized respirator that uses a filter to clean surrounding air, then delivers it to the wearer to breathe; typically includes a headpiece, breathing tube, and a blower/battery box that is worn on the belt.

Protective Coat — Coat worn during fire fighting, rescue, and extrication operations.

Protective Gloves — Protective clothing designed to protect the hands.

Protective Hood — Hood designed to protect the firefighter's ears, neck, and face from heat and debris; typically made of Nomex®, Kevlar®, or PBI®, and available in long or short styles.

Protective Trousers — Trousers worn to protect the lower torso and legs during emergency operations.

Proximity Fire Fighting — Activities required for rescue, fire suppression, and property conservation at fires that produce high radiant, conductive, or convective heat; includes aircraft, hazardous materials transport, and storage tank fires.

Pulmonary Edema — Accumulation of fluids in the lungs.

Qualitative Fit Test (QLFT) — Respirator fit test that measures the wearer's response to a test agent, such as irritant smoke or odorous vapor. If the wearer detects the test agent, such as through smell or taste, the respirator fit is inadequate.

Quantitative Fit Test (QNFT) — Fit test in which instruments measure the amount of a test agent that has leaked into the respirator from the ambient atmosphere. If the leakage measures above a pre-set amount, the respirator fit is inadequate.

Remote Pressure Gauge — Pressure gauge that is not mounted on the regulator but can be seen by the SCBA wearer; commonly found on SCBA that have facepiece-mounted regulators.

Respiratory Hazards — Conditions that create a hazard to the respiratory system, including products of combustion, toxic gases, and superheated or oxygen-deficient atmospheres.

Retroreflective Trim — Surfaces such as those used on road signs, emergency vehicle markings, protective clothing, or safety vests which are designed to reflect light along multiple planes at once, giving the surface the appearance of illumination.

Structural Fire Fighting — Activities required for rescue, fire suppression, and property conservation in structures, vehicles, vessels, and similar types of properties.

Structural Fire Fighting Protective Clothing — General term for the equipment worn by fire and emergency services responders; includes helmets, coats, pants, boots, eye protection, gloves, protective hoods, self-contained breathing apparatus (SCBA), and personal alert safety system (PASS) devices.

Supplied Air Respirator (SAR) — Atmosphere-supplying respirator for which the source of breathing air is not designed to be carried by the user; not certified for fire fighting operations.

Skill Sheet List

The following skill sheets should be used to evaluate the skills described in this chapter:

NOTE: Students should wear the PPE appropriate to the NFPA 1081 level (Incipient, Advanced Exterior, Interior Structural, etc...) being evaluated.

Common Advanced Exterior and Interior Structural Facility Fire Brigade Member Training Requirements

JPRs addressed in this chapter

This chapter provides information that addresses the following job performance requirements of NFPA 1081, *Standard for Facility Fire Brigade Member Professional Qualifications (2018)*.

5.2.4   5.2.9   6.2.8   6.3.7

5.2.6   5.3.10   6.2.10

Learning Objectives

1. Identify the importance of familiarity with tool and equipment storage. [5.2.4, 5.3.10, 6.2.8, 6.3.7]

2. Describe the types of rope and their uses. [5.2.4, 5.3.10, 6.2.8, 6.3.7]

3. Explain the different materials used to create ropes. [5.2.4, 5.3.10, 6.2.8, 6.3.7]

4. Describe the different constructions of ropes. [5.2.4, 5.3.10, 6.2.8, 6.3.7]

5. Explain the proper methods for storing rope. [5.2.4, 5.3.10, 6.2.8, 6.3.7]

6. Identify the materials and construction of webbing and its uses. [5.2.4, 5.3.10, 6.2.8, 6.3.7]

7. Describe the different elements and types of knots. [5.2.4, 5.3.10, 6.2.8, 6.3.7]

8. Describe the methods for hoisting various tools and equipment. [5.2.4, 5.3.10, 6.2.8, 6.3.7]

9. Identify the various uses for rope and webbing at an emergency scene. [5.2.4, 5.3.10, 6.2.8, 6.3.7]

10. Describe the different types of hand tools and the processes of using them. [5.2.4, 5.3.10, 6.2.8, 6.3.7]

11. Describe the different types of power tools and the processes of using them. [5.2.4, 5.3.10, 6.2.8, 6.3.7]

12. Describe the different types of emergency scene lighting equipment tools and the processes of using them. [5.2.4, 5.2.6, 5.3.10, 6.2.8, 6.3.7]

13. Identify the uses of thermal imagers. [5.2.4, 5.2.6, 5.3.10, 6.2.8, 6.3.7]

14. Describe the uses of air monitoring equipment. [5.2.4, 5.2.9, 5.3.10, 6.2.8, 6.2.10, 6.3.7]

Chapter 12
Fire Brigade Tools and Equipment

Fire brigade members must have the appropriate tools, equipment, and training on how to properly use them at a fire or rescue operation. This chapter will describe:

- Tools and equipment storage
- Ropes and webbing
- Hand tools
- Power tools
- Emergency scene lighting equipment
- Thermal imagers
- Air monitoring equipment

Tools and Equipment Storage

NFPA 1081 (2018): 5.2.4, 5.3.10, 6.2.8, 6.3.7

Fire brigade members should be familiar with the location of each tool or piece of equipment they may use at their facility. Each fire brigade must establish how the tools and equipment will be stored in a state of readiness for use during an emergency. The storage methods will depend on the type of facility and fire brigade. Tool and equipment storage methods may include:

- Centrally located storage rooms
- Dispersed cabinets
- Apparatus compartments
- Specialized equipment trailers and pods for rescue, hazardous materials, and communications

After each use, tools and equipment should be inspected, maintained, and returned to their appropriate storage location. These steps ensure that the tools and equipment are returned to service and available for future incidents.

NOTE: The specific skills for maintaining tools and equipment were covered in Chapter 9, Equipment Inspection, Testing, and Maintanance.

Rope and Webbing

NFPA 1081 (2018): 5.2.4, 5.3.10, 6.2.8, 6.3.7

Fire brigade members regularly use rope. You may be trained to use rope in a variety of applications, including:

- Rescues
- Hoisting tools
- Securing unstable objects
- Cordoning off areas
- Gaining access to areas above and below ground level

You must know the different types of ropes, what they are made from, and how they are constructed. You must also train on the methods to inspect, clean, store, and maintain them, ensuring that accurate records of their use are kept.

Types and Usage

Fire brigades use different types of rope and webbing. The following sections describe each type, its construction, and its capabilities during an emergency.

Life Safety Rope

Life safety rope is designed and manufactured to be used only for rescue operations in order to raise, lower, or support victims and/or fire brigade members **(Figure 12.1)**. It should not be used for utility purposes. NFPA 1983, *Standard on Life Safety Rope and Equipment for Emergency Services*, specifies that only rope of **block creel construction** using continuous filament virgin fiber for load-bearing elements is suitable for life safety applications.

NFPA 1983 requires manufacturers to provide information regarding proper use, inspection, and maintenance procedures and criteria for retiring life safety rope from service. Under this standard, ropes should pass field inspections in accordance with manufacturer and AHJ requirements. In order to be reused in life safety situations, the standard also requires that rope meet the following criteria:

- No abrasions or visible damage
- No exposure to heat or direct flame
- No exposure to any **impact load**
- No exposure to the liquids, solids, gases, mists, or vapors of any chemical or other material that can deteriorate rope

Figure 12.1 Technical rescuers using life safety rope raise a "victim" during a training exercise.

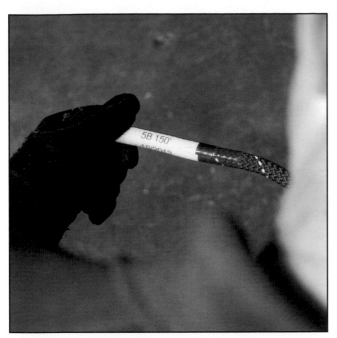

Figure 12.2 A printed label can be sealed to the end of a rope to provide the unit number and date the rope entered service.

Figure 12.3 Utility rope can be used to hoist equipment.

The manufacturer's recommended regularly scheduled inspections cannot detect impact loading. Start and keep a rope log throughout the rope's working life. Maintaining accurate rope logs ensures that life safety ropes remain a reliable source of protection for rescuers and victims.

When life safety rope is purchased, it must be permanently identified. Departments often have personnel mark the ends of new ropes with the unit number and the date that the rope was placed in service. Marking the ends of new ropes can be done with a printed label sealed to the rope ends with a liquid compound made for this purpose **(Figure 12.2)**.

Remove a life safety rope from service if it has been subjected to an impact load or fails inspection, been used only as utility rope, or is marked for destruction. You must alter the rope in some way so that it cannot be mistaken for a life safety rope and unintentionally used again for that purpose. You can discard the rope or remove the manufacturer's label, cut the rope into shorter lengths, and clearly mark it as utility rope. Life safety rope that has been converted to utility rope is referred to as *downgraded*. Refer to your jurisdictional policy regarding reclassification of life safety rope as utility rope.

Utility Rope

Fire brigade members rely on utility rope to hoist equipment, secure unstable objects, or cordon off an area **(Figure 12.3)**. Unlike the rope industry, NFPA does not have standards addressing the properties, care, and capabilities of utility rope. Downgraded life safety rope may be used as utility rope if it is still in good condition. Inspect utility rope regularly to see if it is damaged.

> **CAUTION:** Ensure that downgraded life safety rope is clearly marked as utility rope. Ensure that utility rope is not stored with life safety rope to avoid confusion.

Rope Materials

Fire service rope can be constructed from synthetic fibers (life safety and utility ropes) or natural fibers (only utility ropes). The main difference between synthetic and natural fiber ropes is the material used in the construction, which affects the capabilities and longevity of each type of rope. Synthetic ropes are becoming more popular as utility ropes because natural fiber ropes lose their strength when they get wet, and rot rapidly.

Synthetic Fiber Rope

Synthetic fibers include:

- Polypropylene
- Nylon
- Kevlar™

- Polyester
- Polysteel®
- Spectra®

A disadvantage of some synthetic fibers is that they will melt when exposed to heat. In contrast, **synthetic fiber rope** has the following advantages:

- Excellent resistance to water, mildew, mold, rotting, and shrinkage
- Longer life span than natural fiber rope
- Lightweight yet strong
- Easy to maintain

Natural Fiber Rope

Most **natural fiber rope** is made from plant fibers such as:

- Manila
- Hemp

- Sisal
- Cotton

Natural fiber ropes should not be used for life safety applications. Natural fiber rope is prone to mildew and mold, deteriorates when exposed to chemicals, and burns when in contact with embers or open flame.

Generally, synthetic rope has more advantages than natural fiber rope. However, natural fiber rope has the following advantages:

- More resistant to sunlight than synthetic rope
- Chars rather than melts (fails) when exposed to heat

Rope Construction

The most common types of rope construction are **(Figure 12.4)**:

- Kernmantle
- Laid (twisted)
- Braided
- Braid-on-braid

Kernmantle Rope

Kernmantle rope is a jacketed synthetic rope composed of a braided covering or sheath (mantle) over a core (kern) of the main load-bearing strands. The core strands run parallel with the rope's length and work in conjunction with the covering to increase the rope's stretch resistance and load characteristics. The core is made of high-strength fibers, usually nylon, which accounts for most of the total strength of the rope. The sheath provides the rest of the rope's overall strength and protects the core from abrasion and contamination. Kern-

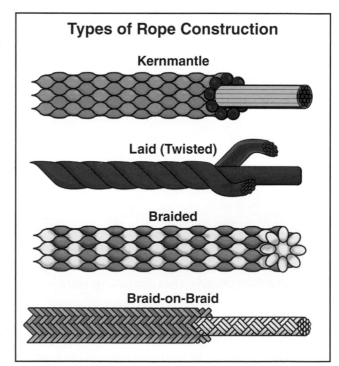

Figure 12.4 Illustrating the most common types of rope construction.

mantle construction is best suited for life safety rope; all of the other types of rope construction are used for utility ropes.

Kernmantle rope comes in both dynamic (high-stretch) and static (low-stretch) types. **Dynamic rope** is optimal for situations when the threat of long falls is a possibility. To reduce the shock of impact in falls, dynamic rope is designed to stretch without breaking. Because this elasticity hinders trying to raise or lower heavy loads, fire bridge personnel should avoid utilizing dynamic rope for rescue or hoisting applications.

Static rope, designed for low stretch without breaking, works for most rope-rescue operations. According to NFPA 1983, low-stretch rope must not elongate more than 10 percent when tested under a load equal to 10 percent of its breaking strength. Static rope is used for rescue, rappelling, and hoisting, and where either falls are unlikely to occur or only short falls are possible.

Laid (Twisted) Rope

Laid ropes are constructed by twisting fibers together to form strands, then twisting the strands (typically three) together to make the final rope. Most natural fiber ropes and some synthetic ropes are this type of rope. Laid ropes are used solely as utility ropes, and their strand exposure make them easy to inspect after an incident.

Laid ropes are susceptible to abrasion and other physical damage. Damage also immediately affects the rope's strength because such a large proportion of the load-bearing strands are exposed.

Braided Rope

Braided rope is constructed by uniformly intertwining strands of rope together in a diagonally overlapping pattern. Braided rope is less likely to twist during use than laid rope, but its load-bearing fibers are still vulnerable to direct abrasion and damage. Most braided ropes are synthetic, although some use natural fibers. Braided rope is most commonly used as utility rope.

Braid-On-Braid Rope

Braid-on-braid rope, also known as *double-braided rope*, consists of a braided core enclosed in a braided sheath. It is sometimes confused with kernmantle rope because both types are jacketed. Kernmantle rope has a core rope strand running the length of the rope while braid-on-braid rope has a braided core running the length of the rope. Braid-on-braid rope does not resist abrasion as well as kernmantle rope.

Braid-on-braid rope is strong, with its strength split evenly between the sheath and the core. However, the sheath may slide along the inner core of the rope. Braid-on-braid rope is most often used as a utility rope.

Rope Storage

Proper rope storage helps ensure that a rope maintains its condition and rated load strength and reaches its life expectancy. Whether stored in a fire brigade storage cabinet or on an apparatus, the rope should be in a clean, dry, unheated area with freely circulating air currents. All rope must be protected from the weather, stored out of direct sunlight, and kept away from chemicals, fumes, and vapors. Fire brigade personnel should not store ropes in the same compartments as gasoline-powered tools or fuel containers. New rope is generally stored on reels until it is placed into service.

The best method for storing rope is to place it into a nylon or canvas storage bag **(Figure 12.5, p. 380)**. The bag makes the rope easy to transport and protects it from abrasion and contamination. Mark the bag to indicate the type, diameter, and length of rope and the unit to which it has been assigned. You can also attach the rope log to the bag. Ropes stored in bags can be quickly deployed by holding the end of the rope and dropping or throwing the bag. The weight of the rope inside the bag carries the bag toward the target, and the rope unravels from the bag as it travels through the air. The bag may have a drawstring and shoulder straps to make carrying easier.

NOTE: Do not drop or throw rope bag if there is a chance of it hanging up onto overhead obstructions.

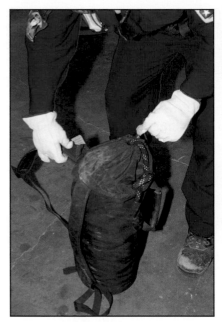

Figure 12.5 A fire brigade member storing rope in a rope bag.

Figure 12.6 Webbing being used in life safety (left) and utility applications (right).

Webbing

Webbing works in conjunction with rope for both life safety and utility applications **(Figure 12.6)**. Webbing comes in the following forms:

- Piece of material
- Ladder belt
- Loop
- Rescue harness

Materials and Construction

Webbing is constructed from the same materials used to make synthetic rope. Lengths of webbing can be flat or tubular, in either a spiral-weave or chain-weave design **(Figure 12.7)**. One-inch (25 mm) webbing is the most commonly used in the fire service, although webbing for other applications may be larger. Any webbing utilized for life safety applications must be NFPA 1983 compliant.

Flat Webbing. Flat webbing is constructed of a single layer of material that resembles an automobile seat belt. While it is less expensive than tubular webbing, it is stiffer and more difficult to tie into knots. In rescue applications, it is mainly used for straps and harnesses.

Tubular Webbing. Tubular webbing is commonly used for rescue applications since it is easier to tie than flat webbing. The two types of tubular webbing are edge-stitched and spiral weave. Edge-stitched webbing is formed by fold-

Figure 12.7 Examples of flat (left) and tubular (right) webbing.

ing a piece of flat webbing lengthwise and sewing the edges together. Spiral weave tubular webbing, also known as *shuttle-loom construction*, is preferred for rescue work.

Figure 12.8 Fire brigade members often carry a section of webbing tied into a loop.

Figure 12.9 An example of daisy-chained webbing.

Running End

Standing Part

Working End

Tag Line

Figure 12.10 Illustrating the parts of a rope being used to raise a ladder.

Storage of Webbing

Fire brigade members often carry 20 to 30 feet (6 to 9 m) of utility webbing in a pocket of their protective coat or trousers (**Figure 12.8**). You can quickly tie utility webbing into a loop, attach it to a piece of rope hardware, or wrap it around an object. Roll or daisy-chain long lengths of webbing for storage (**Figure 12.9**).

Knots

Knots can join ropes and webbing together, secure them to people and objects, and form loops. Improperly tied knots can be hazardous to both rescuers and victims.

When tying knots, a rope is divided into the following three parts (**Figure 12.10**):

- The **working end** is used to tie the knot or **hitch**.
- The **running part** is the free end that is used for hoisting or pulling.
- The **standing part** is the section between the working end and the running part.

Tighten knots until snug. After tying, all slack should be removed in a process known as *dressing*. Even dressed knots can loosen or fail because of repeated loading and unloading of the rope.

To prevent such failures, tie an **overhand safety knot** in the tail of the working end. Tying this knot is addressed in a later section of this chapter. Another type of safety knot is a hitch, which is a temporary knot that can be undone by pulling against the strain that holds it.

Elements of a Knot

To be suitable for use in the fire service, a knot must be easy to tie and untie, remain secure under load, and reduce the rope's strength as little as possible. A rope's strength is reduced whenever it is bent; the tighter the bend, the more strength is lost. Some knots create tighter bends than others, reducing the rope's strength.

Bight, *loop*, and *round turn* are names for the bends that a rope undergoes when tying a knot or hitch. Knots and hitches are a combination of bights, loops, and round turns. Combine these forms so the tight part of the rope bears weight on the working end and holds it in place. Each of these formations is shown in the following figures **(Figure 12.11)**:

- Form a bight by bending the rope back on itself while keeping the sides parallel.
- Make a loop by crossing the side of a bight over the standing part.
- Make a round turn by further bending one side of a loop.

Figure 12.11 Examples of a bight, a loop, and a round turn.

Types of Knots and Hitches

The most common types of knots and hitches used in the fire service include **(Figure 12.12)**:

- Overhand safety
- **Bowline knot**
- **Clove hitch**
- **Figure-eight knot**
- Figure-eight on a bight
- Figure-eight follow through
- Water knot

Overhand Safety Knots. As an added measure of safety, an overhand safety knot (simply called a *safety*) can be used when tying any type of knot. Although any properly tied knot should hold, it is best to provide the highest level of safety possible. Use of the overhand safety knot eliminates the danger of the running end of the rope slipping back through the knot and causing it to fail.

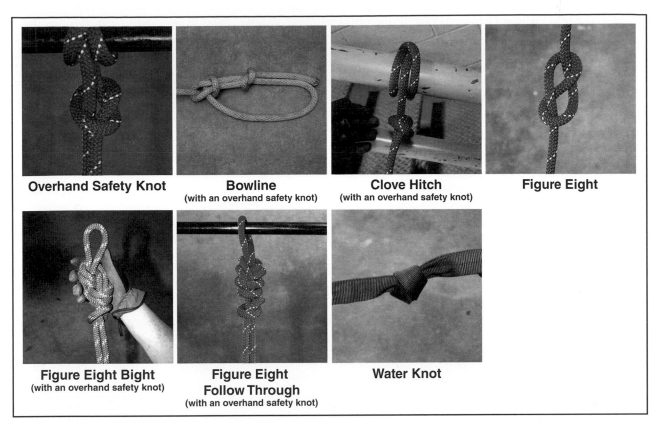

Overhand Safety Knot

Bowline
(with an overhand safety knot)

Clove Hitch
(with an overhand safety knot)

Figure Eight

Figure Eight Bight
(with an overhand safety knot)

**Figure Eight
Follow Through**
(with an overhand safety knot)

Water Knot

Figure 12.12 Examples of common knots and hitches.

Bowline Knot. The bowline is easily tied and untied while forming a single loop that will not constrict. Fire brigade members should be able to tie a bowline in the open as well as around an object.

Clove Hitch. The clove hitch essentially consists of two half-hitches. The clove hitch may be formed anywhere in the rope, from either end or the middle. If a clove hitch is used for utility applications and will be subjected to repeated loading and unloading, an overhand safety knot should be tied as well. Its principal use is to attach a rope to an object, such as a pole, post, or hoseline. This knot is ineffective for life safety applications because repeated loading and unloading will cause it to fail.

Figure-Eight Knot. The figure-eight is the foundation knot for an entire family of figure-eight knots. It can also be a stopper knot so that the rope will not pass through a rescue pulley or the grommet of a rope bag.

Figure-Eight Bend. The figure-eight bend is used primarily on life safety rope to tie ropes of equal diameters together. **Figure 12.13** illustrates how to tie a figure-eight bend.

Figure 12.13 An example of a figure-eight bend knot.

Figure-Eight on a Bight. The figure-eight on a bight is an effective way to tie a closed loop. To tie a figure-eight on a bight, form a bight in the rope and then tie a simple figure-eight with the bight in the doubled part of the rope.

Figure-Eight Follow Through. The figure-eight follow through is used to secure objects. It is basically a figure-eight on a bight that is around the object.

Water Knot. The water knot is preferred for joining two pieces of webbing or the ends of the same piece when a loop is needed. Because the water knot has a tendency to slip, dress the knot properly and have the webbing as flat as possible when forming the knot. Allow at least 3 inches (75 mm) for the tail.

Hoisting Tools and Equipment

Rope and webbing are frequently used to raise or lower tools and equipment, with one notable exception. For safety reasons, the Occupational Safety and Health Administration (OSHA) prohibits hoisting pressurized cylinders, such as SCBA cylinders.

> **WARNING:** Never hoist pressurized cylinders. If accidently dropped, an explosion may occur.

Using proper knots and securing procedures can prevent equipment from being dropped, preventing damage to the equipment and injury to personnel below. A separate **tag line** may be tied to the equipment, or part of the hoisting line may also serve as a tag line. Tag lines are non-load-bearing and help prevent tools from spinning or snagging while being hoisted. Fire brigade members on the ground use the tag line to prevent the equipment from striking the structure or other objects **(Figure 12.14)**. When one rope serves as both the tag line and the hoisting line, the knot or hitch-tying methods and methods of hoisting may vary.

Figure 12.14 A fire brigade member beginning to play out a tag line attached to a ladder.

Carabiners and pulleys are common types of hardware in hoisting. A carabiner is a snap link made from aluminum, titanium, or steel, with a spring or screwed gate that connects ropes to other mechanical gear. A pulley is a simple device that creates a **mechanical advantage** or a change in direction **(Figure 12.15)**. It consists of a grooved wheel through which a rope can run to change the direction or point of application of a force applied to the rope.

When hoisting tools or equipment, safety is your primary consideration. Always use the following general safety guidelines:

- Be sure that you are balanced and standing firmly on the ground before starting a hoisting operation.

- Use the hand-over-hand method to maintain control of the rope.

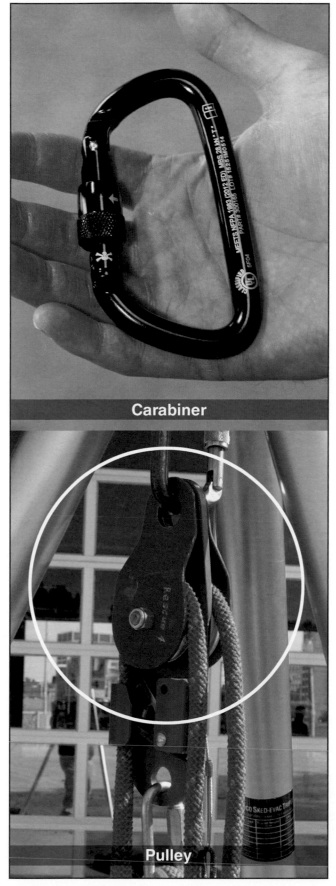

Figure 12.15 Common hoisting hardware includes carabiners and pulleys.

- Use an edge roller or padding to protect rope from physical damage when pulling it over sharp edges, such as cornices or parapet walls.
- Use a pulley system to provide mechanical advantage for lifting heavy objects.
- Work in teams when operating at heights.
- Make sure that all personnel are clear of the hoisting area.
- Avoid hoisting operations near electrical hazards or use extreme caution if electrical hazards are unavoidable.
- Secure the nozzles of any charged hoselines to prevent accidental discharge.
- Use a tag line to help control the hoisted object.
- Avoid hoisting tools and equipment if it is safer to hand-carry them up stairs, a ladder, or an aerial device.

Hoisting an Axe

The procedure for attaching and hoisting is the same for either a pick-head axe or a flat-head axe. The hoisting rope can also be used as the tag line.

Hoisting a Pike Pole

Pike poles should be hoisted with the pike pointing up. Tie a clove hitch near the butt end of the handle, followed by a half-hitch in the middle of the handle and another half-hitch around the head.

Hoisting a Ladder

Tie a figure-eight on a bight and slip it through two rungs of the ladder, about one-third of the way from the top of the ladder. Pull the loop through and slip it over the top of the ladder. Secure a tag line to the ladder near the foot.

Hoisting Hoselines

Use caution to avoid damaging the nozzle or coupling when hoisting hoselines to upper floors. Fire brigade members can hoist charged hoselines, but it is safer and easier to hoist a dry hoseline.

Hoisting a Power Saw

To hoist a rotary saw or chainsaw, tie a figure-eight on a bight through the closed handle, then attach a tag line through the handle.

Other Emergency Scene Uses

In addition to hoisting and lowering tools and equipment, personnel may use utility rope and webbing in other applications. The most common applications are designating control zones, establishing a search lifeline, and stabilizing objects.

Rescue Uses

Personnel should never use utility rope during rescue operations. Instead, life safety rope is recommended for:

- Rappelling

- Lifting victims and rescuers

- Removing victims from ice and swift water situations

These operations require specialized training beyond the basically trained fire brigade levels, but you may be required to assist technical rescue personnel in these operations. You must recognize and know your department's policy on life safety ropes, hardware, and equipment.

Control Zone Perimeter

Personnel have traditionally used utility rope to establish the perimeter to control access to required control zones. Clove hitches with half-hitch overhand safety knots are used to tie the rope to trees, sign posts, or other stationary objects.

Search Lines

Search lines can assist search teams working in dark, smoke-filled, or confined spaces. They allow team members to remain in contact with each other and fire brigade members at the line's entry point. They also provide a physical means of finding an exit route. Branch lines are sometimes attached to the main search line, allowing team members to search larger areas away from the search line while still remaining in contact with the team (**Figure 12.16**).

The use of a search rope can be difficult due to the amount of equipment or materials staged for work. The use of search rope generally works best in large open areas. If you are expected to work with a search rope during an emergency, your fire brigade should train regularly with this type of operation to help ensure proficiency.

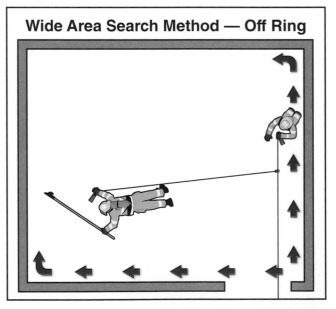

Figure 12.16 Illustrating how ropes can be used as search lines.

Object Stabilization

Utility rope and webbing may be used to stabilize an object. For example, they may be used to prevent a vehicle from falling after it has rolled on its side or is suspended over an edge. The rope or webbing is secured to an anchor point (a strong stationary object) and then tied to the object to be stabilized. Wire rope or cable from a winch may also be used for this operation. Before any work is performed around the object, you must be certain that:

- The rope or webbing and the anchor point are strong enough to hold the object's weight.

- The knots are tight and safety knots are in place.

- The attachment points at both ends are secure and will not pull free.
- Personnel are clear from the stabilizing line in case it breaks and snaps back.

Hand Tools

NFPA 1081 (2018): 5.2.4, 5.3.10, 6.2.8, 6.3.7

Fire brigade members may rely on a variety of hand tools during fire fighting, rescue, or extrication operations. The following sections describe these types of tools and their usage.

Portable/Hand Lights

Fires and other emergencies can happen at night or in darkness such as inside confined spaces, which can limit a fire brigade member's vision. To compensate, fire brigade members may use portable or handheld lights. These devices are usually battery operated and should be checked on a routine basis and after each use to ensure the batteries are fully charged. These lights should be intrinsically safe (vapor proof) to prevent the possibility of flammable vapors entering a unit, forming a flammable mixture, and being ignited by the device when it is turned on or off. These devices may include:

- Handheld flashlights
- Helmet-mounted flashlights
- Flashlights that clip onto the fire brigade member's coat

Cutting Tools

Cutting tools are often specific to the types of materials they can cut and how fast they can cut them. No single cutting tool will safely and efficiently cut all materials. Using a cutting tool on materials for which it was not designed can damage the tool and endanger the operator.

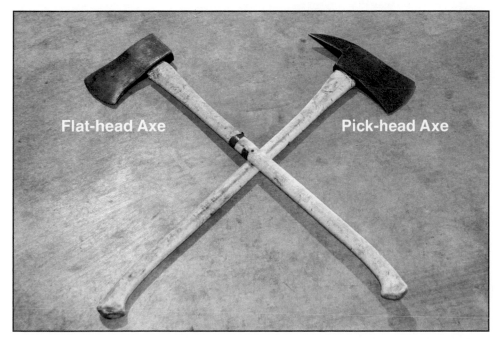

Figure 12.17 This photo shows the flat-head and pick-head axes.

Axes

Axes are the most common types of cutting tools that fire brigade members use. The two basic types of axes are the pick-head axe and the flat-head axe **(Figure 12.17)**. Smaller axes and hatchets may be used in salvage and overhaul operations, but they are usually too lightweight and inefficient for effective use in forcible entry operations.

Pick-head axe. The pick-head axe is a versatile forcible entry tool that can be used for cutting, prying, and digging during structural fire fighting operations. It is available with either a 6-pound or an 8-pound (2.7 kg or 3.6 kg) head. The head is made of hardened steel and the handle is made of either wood or fiberglass of varying size. The pick-head axe is effective for chopping through:

- Wooden structural components
- Aluminum siding
- Natural and lightweight materials
- Shingles
- Roof coverings

The pick end can be used to penetrate materials that the blade cannot cut easily or to make a quick inspection hole prior to opening an area. The side of the axe blade can be used as a striking tool to break windows or as a prying tool to force some doors.

Flat-head axe. The flat-head axe is the same as the pick-head axe in size, design, and construction, except that a flat striking face replaces the pick end. The blade of the flat-head axe can be used for all the same purposes as that of a pick-head axe. Unlike the pick-head axe, the striking face of flat-head axe can be used to strike another tool, forcing the bit end into a doorjamb or windowsill. The flat-head axe is versatile enough for both structural and ground cover fire fighting operations.

Metal Cutting Devices

Metal cutting devices are used to cut through heavy-duty locks, metal-clad doors, and window security bars and grilles, and similar items. The devices include **(Figure 12.18)**:

- Bolt cutters
- Cutting torches
- Rebar cutters

Figure 12.18 Examples of three types of metal cutting devices.

Bolt Cutters. Bolt cutters are used to cut:

- Bolts
- Pins
- Hasps
- Certain padlock shackles
- Iron bars
- Cables
- Chains

Manual bolt cutters are less effective than they once were because they cannot cut modern high-security chains, hasps, and padlock shackles. These materials shatter the bolt cutter blades or cause the handles to fail should the operator exert enough pressure. Certain other locks are designed to prevent bolt cutters from being inserted into the shackle.

When using bolt cutters, always wear face shields and eye protection to prevent fragments of the cut material from striking your face. Do not use bolt cutters to cut case-hardened materials found in locks and other security devices. Avoid using bolt cutters to cut any energized cables unless the cutters are insulated and designed for that task.

Cutting torches. A cutting torch may be used to cut:

- Security bars
- Gates
- Grilles
- Rebar

Fire brigade members commonly use:

- Oxyacetylene cutting torches
- Burning bars
- Oxy-gasoline cutting torches
- Plasma cutters

Training based on the manufacturer's recommendations specific to each cutting and burning device is necessary for safe and efficient operation. A charged hoseline must be in place during the cutting operation to cool the metal and control any sparks that are generated.

Do not use cutting torches in or near a flammable or explosive environment. Sparks, the exposed flame of the torch, or hot fragments (slag) can ignite a fire or cause an explosion.

CAUTION: Ignition sources should not be introduced into the area with the possibility of having a combustible/flammable atmosphere.

Rebar cutters. These hydraulic cutting tools are available in both powered and manual versions. The manual version requires more energy to use than the powered version, but it can be used in areas beyond the reach of the hydraulic supply hose on powered units. Fire brigade members can use rebar cutters to cut steel reinforced bars (rebar) in concrete walls or to cut door or window security bars.

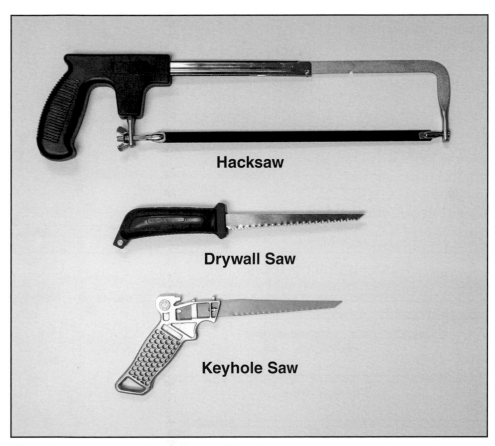

Figure 12.19 Examples of three types of handsaws.

Handsaws

Handsaws may be useful when power saws are unavailable or the work space around the location of the cut is limited. Hacksaws, drywall saws, and keyhole saws are the most common handsaws in use **(Figure 12.19)**. Fire brigade members should know which saw is best suited to the job and should maintain good handsaw technique.

Manual Prying Tools

Prying tools are useful for:

- Opening doors, windows, and locks
- Moving heavy objects

Pry bars and other manually operated prying tools use the principle of the lever and fulcrum to provide mechanical advantage. Force applied to the tool's handle is multiplied at the working end based upon the distance between the fulcrum and the working end. Prying tools with longer handles produce greater force at the working end.

The most common manual prying tools used in the fire service are as follows **(Figure 12.20, p. 390)**:

- Crowbar
- Pry (pinch) bar
- Halligan tool
- **Hux bar**

- Claw tool
- Kelly tool
- Pry axe
- Flat bar (nail puller)
- Rambar

Most manual pry tools are constructed from a single piece of high-carbon steel, approximately 30 to 36 inches (760 to 900 mm) in length. These tools usually have one end that is beveled into a single wedge or fork. The opposite end may include a hook, pike tip, or adz. A rambar has a sliding weight on the shaft that can drive the wedge or fork into an opening. Miniature versions of manual pry tools are also available with accompanying sheaths for carrying the tool.

Certain prying tools can also be utilized as striking tools while others cannot. You need to be familiar with the capabilities and limitations of each manual prying tool, such as knowing which surfaces are used for prying and which surfaces may be used for striking.

Pushing/Pulling Tools

Pushing and pulling tools have limited use in forcible entry, but in certain instances, such as breaking glass and opening walls or ceilings, they are the tools of choice. This category of tools includes the following **(Figure 12.21)**:

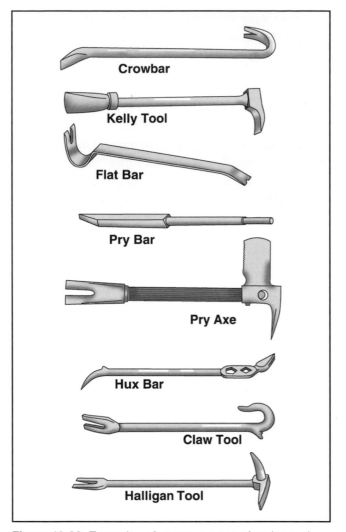

Figure 12.20 Examples of common types of prying tools.

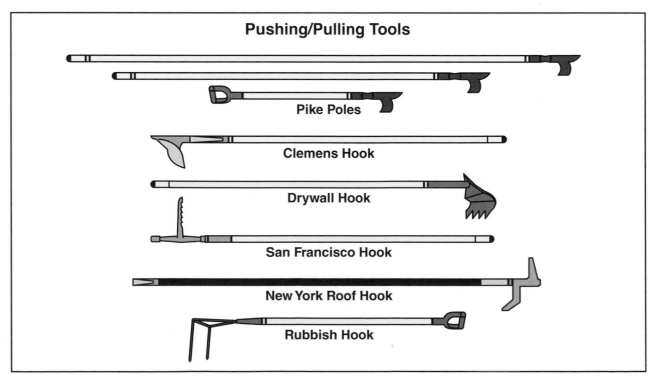

Figure 12.21 Examples of common pushing/pulling tools.

- Pike pole
- Plaster hook
- San Francisco hook
- New York roof hook

- Clemens hook
- Drywall hook
- Multipurpose hook
- Rubbish hook

Pike poles and hooks, which are available in various lengths, give fire brigade members a reach advantage when performing certain tasks. The plaster hook has two knifelike wings that depress as the head is driven through a ceiling or other obstruction and reopen or spread outward under the pressure of self-contained springs.

Use pike poles and hooks (with the exception of the all-metal, New York roof hook) for pushing or pulling, never prying. If a lever is needed, select the appropriate prying tool. The wooden or fiberglass handles of pike poles and hooks may break if used as a lever.

Striking Tools

A striking tool consists of a weighted head attached to a handle. The following are examples of common striking tools **(Figure 12.22)**:

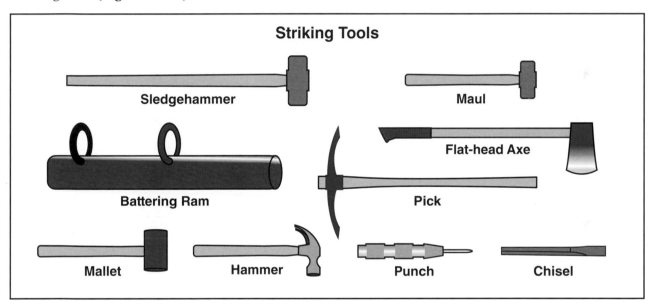

Figure 12.22 Examples of common striking tools.

- Sledge hammer (8, 10, and 16 pounds [3.5, 4.5, and 7.5 kg])

- Maul
- Pick
- Mallet
- Punch

- Battering ram
- Flat-head axe
- Hammer
- Chisel

In some cases, a fire brigade member can accomplish a task with just a striking tool. In other situations, the striking tool is used with another tool to gain entry. When striking tools are dropped or used improperly, they can crush fingers, toes, and other body parts. Poorly maintained striking surfaces may cause metal chips or splinters to fly into the air. Therefore, proper eye protection (safety glasses or goggles in addition to the helmet faceshield) must be worn when using striking tools.

Tools Used in Combination

No single forcible entry tool provides fire brigade members with the needed force or leverage to handle all forcible entry situations. In some cases, fire brigade members must combine two or more tools to accomplish a task, such as a flat-head axe and a Halligan tool to form what is commonly known as "irons" **(Figure 12.23)**. The types of tool combinations carried vary, depending on building construction, security concerns, tool availability, and other factors within a fire brigade and the area served.

Figure 12.23 A fire brigade member carrying a set of irons.

Fire brigade members should select the appropriate tools to accomplish the job. Using tools in situations for which they are not designed can be dangerous. Preincident surveys will help determine which tools will be required to force entry into a building or through a particular door, window, or wall in that building.

Tool Safety

Improper use of power and hand tools can result in:

- Strains
- Fractures
- Lacerations

- Sprains
- Abrasions

To prevent these injuries you must:

- Wear appropriate PPE.
- Use undamaged tools.
- Select the right tool for the type of opening to be made.
- Use tools for their intended purpose only.
- Position yourself so that your weight is balanced on both feet.
- Ensure that you have room to properly operate the tool.
- Be aware that there will be a sudden release of energy when the door, window, or wall is opened.
- Ensure that other personnel are out of the immediate area.
- Be aware of the environment to prevent possible gas or vapor ignitions.

You must become familiar with all the tools you will use, which includes reading and following all the manufacturer's guidelines as well as your department SOPs on tool safety. When tools are not in use, they should be kept in properly designated places on the apparatus. Check the location of tools carried on the apparatus and make sure they are secured in their brackets. Immediately repair or replace damaged tools.

As with other tools, using prying tools incorrectly creates a safety hazard. If a job cannot be completed with a particular tool, do not strike the handle of the tool; use a larger tool. A prying tool should not be used as a striking tool unless it has been designed for that additional purpose.

Unacceptable Practice: Cheater Bars

A cheater bar is a piece of pipe slipped over the handle of a prying tool to lengthen it in order to provide more leverage. Use of a cheater exerts forces on the tool that are greater than the tool was designed to withstand. The additional force can cause the tool to slip, break, or shatter, causing serious injury to a fire brigade member and/or damage to the tool. A fire brigade member should select a prying tool that is large enough to complete a specific job.

To prevent injury, use care with rotary saws, power saws, and chain saws as follows:

- Match the saw and saw blades to the task and material to be cut.

- Never force a saw beyond its design limitations.

- Always wear full PPE, including gloves, hearing protection, and eye protection.

- Fully inspect the saw before and after use.

- Do not use any power saw when working in a flammable atmosphere or near flammable liquids.

- Maintain situational awareness.

- Keep unprotected and nonessential people out of the work area.

- Follow the manufacturer's guidelines for proper saw operation.

- Keep blades and chains sharpened since a dull saw is more likely to cause an accident than a sharp one.

- Be aware of hidden hazards, such as electrical wires, gas lines, and water lines.

- Remember that the rotating blade on a rotary saw continues to spin after the throttle has been released.

- Use only blades that are manufacturer-approved for your saw; blades from different manufacturers may not be interchangeable.

- When making cuts, account for the twisting (gyroscopic or torsion effect) of a rotary saw blade in order to maintain control of the saw.

- Start all cuts at full revolutions per minute (rpm) to prevent the blades from binding into the material.

- Store blades in a clean, dry environment.

- Store composite blades in compartments where gasoline fumes will not accumulate because hydrocarbons can attack the bonding material in these blades, causing them to deteriorate and shatter during use.

Carrying Tools

You must carry forcible entry tools in the safest manner possible to protect yourself, other fire brigade members, and bystanders. When lifting heavy tools or other objects, always lift with your legs and not your back. Get help when transporting heavy tools. Avoid running with tools. Some recommended safety practices for carrying specific tools are as follows (**Figure 12.24**):

Figure 12.24 Fire brigade members should follow safe practices when carrying forcible entry tools.

- **Axes** — If not in a scabbard, carry the axe with the blade away from the body. With pick-head axes, grasp the pick with a hand to cover it. Never carry an axe on the shoulder.

- **Prying tools** — Carry these tools with any pointed or sharp edges away from the body. This task can be difficult when carrying tools with multiple cutting or prying surfaces, such as a bit on one end and an adz on the other.

- **Combinations of tools** — Strap tool combinations together. Halligan tools and flat-head axes can be nested together and strapped.

- **Pike poles and hooks** — Carry these tools with the tool head down, close to the ground, and ahead of the body when outside a structure. When entering a building, carefully reposition the tool and carry it with the head upright close to the body to facilitate prompt use. These tools are especially dangerous because they are somewhat unwieldy and can injure anyone accidentally jabbed with the working end of the tool.

- **Striking tools** — Keep the heads of these tools close to the ground. Maintain a firm grip. Heavy mauls and sledgehammers may slip from your grasp.

- **Power tools** — Never carry a power tool in operation more than 10 feet (3 m); running power tools are potentially lethal weapons. Transport the tool to the area where the work will be performed and start it there. Carry the saw with the blade forward and toward the ground. To prevent fuel from leaking, ensure that the gas cap is tight and the gasket is in place.

Power Tools

NFPA 1081 (2018): 5.2.4, 5.3.10, 6.2.8, 6.3.7

Fire brigade members may use a variety of power tools during fire fighting, rescue, or extrication operations. The following sections describe these types of tools and their usage.

Powered Rescue Tools

There are four basic types of powered rescue tools (**Figure 12.25**):

- Spreaders
- Combination spreader/shears
- Shears (cutters)
- Extension rams

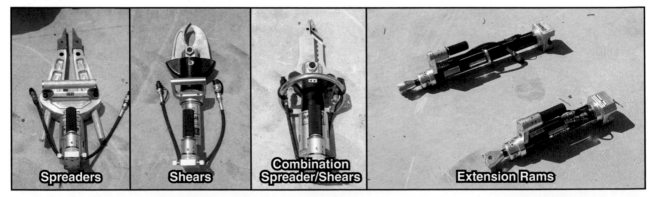

Figure 12.25 Examples of the four basic types of powered rescue tools.

Spreaders

Powered hydraulic spreaders were the first powered hydraulic tools used in the fire service. When combined with chains and adapters, they are used for pushing and pulling. Spreaders produce tremendous force at their tips, which may spread as much as 32 inches (800 mm) apart.

Shears (Cutters)

Hydraulic shears or cutters can cut almost any metal object that fits between the blades. They can also cut plastics, wood, and other materials. The blades typically have an opening spread of approximately 7 inches (175 mm).

Combination Spreader/Shears (Cutters)

This tool has the ability to perform both cutting and spreading operations. It is efficient for a small rapid-intervention vehicle or for departments with limited resources. The combination tool is versatile, but it cannot cut or spread as forcefully as the individual units.

Extension Rams

Extension rams are designed primarily for pushing, but they can also be used for pulling. They are typically used when objects must be pushed farther than the maximum opening distance of hydraulic spreaders, such as when displacing the dashboard of a vehicle, which is referred to as a dash rollover or dash roll-up. The largest of these tools can extend from a closed length of 3 feet (1 m) to an extended length of nearly 5 feet (1.5 m). Their opening force (used for pushing) is about twice as powerful as their closing force (used for pulling).

Cutting Tools

Cutting tools cut material away from a trapped victim. Most cutting tools are power saws, which are faster and easier to handle than powered shears. Saws are also more powerful than shears, capable of cutting through even exotic metals. Saws can be gasoline-, electric-, or battery-powered. The most common types of saws are **(Figure 12.26)**:

- Reciprocating
- Rotary
- Circular
- Whizzer

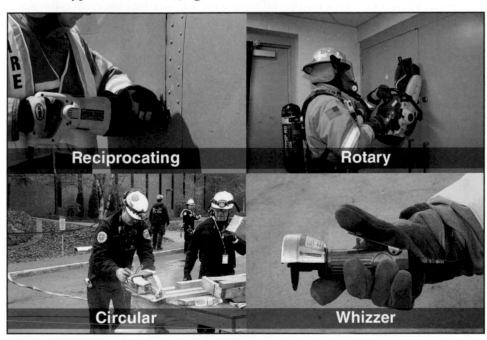

Figure 12.26 Examples of common power saws.

Reciprocating Saw

The reciprocating saw is a powerful, versatile, and controllable saw with a short, straight blade that moves in and out like a handsaw. It can use a variety of blades for cutting materials. When equipped with a metal-cutting blade, it is ideal for cutting sheet metal body panels and structural components on vehicles.

> **CAUTION:** Do not force the saw beyond its design limits; you may be injured and the saw may be damaged. Follow manufacturer's safety recommendations and departmental SOPs.

Rotary Rescue Saw

Rotary rescue saws used in the fire service are typically gasoline powered, with different blades for cutting wood, metal, or masonry. Large-toothed blades can make quick, rough cuts, while fine-toothed blades are used for precision cutting. Blades with carbide-tipped teeth are superior to standard blades because they are less prone to dulling.

Circular Saw

Electric circular saws are versatile, lightweight, and easy to handle. Small battery-powered circular saws are also available. Electrically or battery-operated circular saws used in vehicle extrication are usually the same as those saws used in construction. They are primarily designed for cutting wood and can be useful when cutting shoring material on site. When equipped with a metal-cutting blade, circular saws can make straight-line cuts in metal.

Lifting Tools

Lifting tools are used to lower rescuers, remove an object from a trapped victim, or lift a victim out of a hole or confined space. Commonly used rescue tools include tripods and pneumatic lifting bags **(Figure 12.27)**.

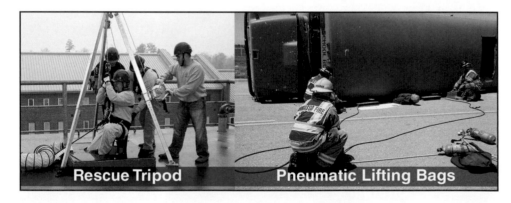

Figure 12.27 Rescue tripods (left) and pneumatic lifting bags (right) are two types of common rescue tools.

Tripods

Rescue tripods are used to create an anchor point above a manhole or other opening. This feature allows rescuers to be safely lowered into confined spaces and rescuers and victims to be hoisted out of them.

Pneumatic Lifting Devices

Pneumatic lifting devices are air-pressurized devices that give rescuers the ability to lift or displace objects that cannot be lifted with other rescue equipment. The three basic types of **pneumatic lifting bags** are high-pressure, medium-pressure, and low-pressure.

High-pressure bags. High-pressure bags are constructed from a tough, neoprene or butyl rubber exterior reinforced with steel wire or Kevlar™ Aramid fiber. When deflated, the bags lie flat and are about one half to 1 inch (13 to 25 mm) thick. Their surface area ranges from 6 x 6 inches (150 mm by 150 mm) to 36 x 36 inches (900 mm by 900 mm), and they inflate up to a height of 20 inches (500 mm). As this type of bag inflates, it loses stability and lifting power.

Medium- and low-pressure cushions. Medium- and low-pressure cushions are considerably larger than high-pressure bags and can inflate to a greater height, up to 6 feet (2 m). They can lift and stabilize large vehicles or objects. They are most stable when fully inflated.

Lifting device safety rules. Operators should follow these safety rules when using pneumatic lifting bags:

- Plan the operation before starting the work.
- Follow the manufacturer's recommendations for the specific system used.
- Keep all components in good operating condition and all safety seals in place.
- Remember that fuel and other petroleum products can weaken the bags and shorten their working life. Never store, use, or place a bag in an area where contact may occur.
- Make sure you have an adequate air supply and sufficient cribbing materials.
- Be familiar with the equipment's operating principles, methods, capabilities, and limitations.
- Keep all components in good operating condition.
- Make sure all safety seals are in place.
- Position the devices on or against a solid surface.
- Keep sharp objects away from the devices as they inflate.
- Never inflate a device without a load.
- Inflate slowly and continually monitor the load for signs of shifting.
- Never work underneath a load that is supported only by pneumatic lifting devices.
- Interrupt the process frequently to increase shoring or cribbing — lift an inch, crib an inch.
- Use enough cribbing to support the load in case of device failure.
- Use at least three pieces of cribbing per layer and make sure the top layer is solid. Openings in the center of the cribbing may cause a device to shift or rupture.
- Ensure that the top tier is solid when using box cribbing and that a protective mat is used.
- Never let the device contact materials hotter than 220°F (104°C).
- Stack devices, as necessary, in accordance with manufacturer's recommendations.
- When stacking devices, inflate the bottom device first and put the smaller device on top. Never stack more than two devices. Single, multicell devices are more effective.

NOTE: Manufacturers do not recommend placing a piece of material between the bag and the object to be lifted. Lifting bags are created with a gripping surface to prevent slippling, so the surface of the bag is the best contact point.

> **CAUTION:** Pneumatic lifting bags should be tested and inspected according manufacturer's recommendations. If there are any signs of damage or deterioration, immediately remove the bag from service.

> **WARNING:** If you place anything between the bag and the lifted object, it must be made of pliable material, such as a folded salvage cover. Plywood or another rigid material can be forcefully ejected if the bag distorts under pressure.

Pulling Tools

Pulling tools can separate vehicle components, remove objects from trapped victims, or stabilize vehicles that are resting over an edge. Typical pulling tools include **(Figure 12.28)**:

- **Winches**
- **Come-alongs**
- Chains

Figure 12.28 Illustrating three types of pulling tools.

Winches

Winches are typically mounted on the front, rear, or side of a vehicle. Compared to other pulling devices, they are stronger, faster to deploy, and have a greater travel or pulling distance. An electric or hydraulic motor or a PTO system often provides power to winches. They are used in conjunction with chains and/or cables.

Winch cables are made from steel or synthetic fiber. Steel cable is made from thin strands of wire wound together. Steel is durable and long lasting, but heavy and rigid, making it difficult to handle. Synthetic fiber cable is lighter and stronger than steel, floats in water, and resists ultraviolet light. Non-extreme temperature variations have no effect on these cables.

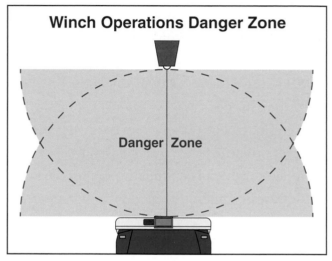

Figure 12.29 Winch operators and other personnel need to stay outside the winch cable's danger zone.

Position the winch as close as possible to the object being pulled. With less cable deployed, personnel, and equipment are less likely to be struck by the recoiling cable. Handheld remote-control devices allow the winch operator to stand outside the danger zone where the cable can whip around if it breaks **(Figure 12.29)**.

Winch cables should be inspected regularly because they develop memory on the coil, returning to the coiled form it had on the winch after it is stretched out. Vehicle vibrations can fray the cable over time.

 Reducing Danger During Winch Operations

There is a risk of injury or death if the cable, hooks, or straps fail while the winch and cable are under tension. To reduce the chance of injury, you should:

- Always follow the winch/cable manufacturer's operating instructions.
- Inspect the winch/cable regularly and prior to each use. Immediately replace any frayed, kinked, or damaged cable.
- Inspect winch mounting and ensure that mounting bolts are tight before every use.
- Never exceed the rated load capacity of the winch/cable.
- Never operate the winch when there are fewer than five wraps of cable around the winch drum.

- Use mechanical advantage to reduce the load on the cable when pulling objects at or near the winch's rated capacity.

- Never wrap the cable around an object and hook it back onto itself. This will damage the cable.

- Place the hook so its back is either facing the ground or facing away from the winch operator. In the event of a hook failure under a load, the broken hook will move in the direction of the hook's back.

- Keep the duration of winching pulls as short as possible. Do not pull for more than one minute when operating at or near the rated load capacity of the winch/cable.

- Never step over or stand near a cable that is under tension.

- Keep yourself and other individuals at a safe distance to the side of the cable under tension. Ensure that no one is standing in front of or behind the winch or the anchor point.

- Use heavy-duty gloves to protect your hands when handling the cable. Never let the cable slide through your hands.

- Drape a blanket, coat, or tarp over the cable approximately 5 to 6 feet (1.5 to 1.8 m) from the hook. This technique makes the cable more visible to nearby personnel and reduces the recoil force of the cable if it breaks.

Come-Alongs

Come-alongs are portable cable winches that a manual ratchet lever operates. A come-along must be attached to a secure anchor point, after which its cable, chain, or webbing is connected to the object that must be pulled. The ratchet lever is then used to rewind the cable, pulling the object back toward the anchor point. Come-alongs typically have a load capacity ranging from 1 to 10 tons (0.9 t to 9.1 t).

WARNING: Use only the operating handles that the come-along's manufacturer provides. These handles are designed to fail before the cable. Never use a prybar or another tool as a replacement.

Chains

Chains are used with both winches and come-alongs. The two main chain types are alloy steel chain and proof coil chain, also known as *common* or *hardware chain*. Only alloy steel chain should be used in rescue operations since it resists abrasion, corrosion, and effects of hazardous atmospheres.

Emergency Scene Lighting Equipment

NFPA 1081 (2018): 5.2.4, 5.2.6, 5.3.10, 6.2.8, 6.3.7

Emergency scene lighting equipment includes electrical **generators**, lights, and auxiliary electrical equipment **(Figure 12.30)**. The following sections address each of these types of equipment.

Electric Generators

Emergency services personnel often use generators as a power source. Emergency scene lighting and portable rescue equipment are powered by portable electric generators, apparatus-mounted generators, or the apparatus' electrical system.

Figure 12.30 A fire brigade member inspecting emergency scene lighting equipment.

Small gasoline or diesel engines power portable electric generators, which have 110- and/or 220-volt capacity outlets. Most of these generators are light enough that two people can carry them. They are useful when vehicle-mounted electrical systems are unavailable.

Vehicle-mounted generators produce more power than portable units. They can be powered via gasoline, diesel, or propane gas engines, or by hydraulic or power take-off (PTO) systems.

The apparatus' electrical system may also provide direct power to portable lights and equipment. If small amounts of power are needed to operate lights and tools, an inverter is used to convert the vehicle's 12- or 24-volt direct current (DC) into 110- or 220-volt alternating current (AC). The advantages of this method include fuel efficiency and minimal noise. Disadvantages include constant apparatus exhaust, limited power supply, and limited mobility.

Lighting Equipment

Lighting equipment can be divided into two categories: portable and fixed. Portable lights are used to illuminate building interiors or remote areas. Some portable lights are mounted on telescoping stands, which allow them to be raised and directed more effectively.

Fixed lights are mounted on a vehicle and wired directly to the vehicle-mounted generator or apparatus' electrical system. They can provide overall lighting of the emergency scene. These lights are usually mounted on telescoping poles that can be raised, lowered, or rotated. Some units consist of large banks of lights mounted on hydraulically operated booms. The amount of power the vehicle-mounted generator or apparatus electrical system can produce dictates the number of fixed light units.

Auxiliary Electrical Equipment

Auxiliary electrical equipment consists of the following:

- Electrical cables
- Receptacles
- Junction boxes
- Adapters
- Extension cords
- Connectors
- Ground fault circuit interrupter (GFCI) devices

> **CAUTION:** The temporary electrical equipment selected for use should be compatible with the area's hazardous electrical classification, as applicable.

All auxiliary equipment must be waterproof, intrinsically safe, and designed for the amount of electrical current it is intended to carry. Electrical cables and extension cords can only carry a limited amount of electricity. Cords may be stored in coils, on portable cord reels, or on apparatus-mounted automatic rewind reels. Electrical cables and extension cords should also have adequate insulation and no exposed wires. Twist-lock receptacles and connectors equipped with grounding wires provide secure, safe connections as long as they are not immersed in water.

Junction boxes, which provide multiple outlets or connections, are supplied through one inlet from the power source. All outlets must be equipped with ground fault circuit interrupter devices and meet the requirements outlined in NFPA 70E, *Standard for Electrical Safety in the Workplace*®.

Adapter connections are used to permit different types of plugs and receptacles to be connected. Adapters allow mutual aid departments to operate electrical lights and tools off each other's generators and power sources. Adapters allow fire brigade lights and power tools to be plugged into standard electrical outlets inside structures.

Safety Considerations for Emergency Scene Lighting

Emergency scene lighting equipment should be used with caution. Safety guidelines should be followed when deploying and using emergency scene lighting equipment:

- Assign two personnel to safely carry portable generators to their setup position.
- Ensure portable generators are positioned downwind so that exhaust fumes do not present an ignition or contamination hazard.
- Wear hearing protection when operating portable generators if needed.
- Be aware that generator noise can make communications near these devices difficult.
- Always adjust lights to a height that allows them to be directed toward the scene, but not into the eyes of approaching drivers.
- Remove damaged cords with faulty insulation or exposed wires from service.
- Do not immerse power cords and connections in water.
- Never connect more lights than the power source can support.

Overtaxing a power source results in poor lighting and possible damage to the lights, generator, or electrical system. It may also restrict the operation of other tools using the same power source. Some lighting units produce extreme heat and can cause burns or melt paint and plastics on apparatus. Be careful when moving lights or turning them off.

Placement of Emergency Scene Lighting

When ordered to set up emergency scene lighting, you will select the appropriate equipment from the apparatus. If the generator is apparatus-mounted, you will gather the lights, cords, and adapters and carry them to the setup location(s). If the generator is portable, you will need to carry it to a safe location.

Thermal Imagers

NFPA 1081 (2018): 5.2.4, 5.2.6, 5.3.10, 6.2.8, 6.3.7

Thermal imagers (TIs) allow fire brigade members to see sources of heat through darkness and thick smoke. They are also used to locate victims and hidden fires **(Figure 12.31)**. TIs identify temperature differentials on surfaces. Contrary to the way they are often described, TIs cannot "see through" objects.

They can tell you if a surface or area is hotter than the surrounding area. For example, if a TI shows that a wall is hot, then heat has spread into that wall. There could be a fire behind the wall generating this heat or a fire within the wall.

Using TIs during search and rescue or fire fighting operations has the following advantages:

Handheld TI

TI Integrated into SCBA Air Gauge

Figure 12.31 Thermal imagers being used to locate hidden fires, a handheld TI (left) and a TI that is integrated into a SCBA remote air gauge (right).

- Enhances situational awareness.
- Improves visibility in an obscured environment.
- Provides additional information during search.
- May be useful in locating victims, the seat of the fire, or hidden fires.

  TIs have some limitations:
- They cannot detect a person under or behind furniture, boxes, or crates or on the opposite side of a wall.
- They cannot "see" through water, glass, or other reflective surfaces.
- TIs may be unable to detect fire on lower floors through padded floor coverings such as carpet.

You should be properly trained on the use of your fire brigade's TI, including the interpretation of data. When in doubt, refer to the manufacturer's documentation for proper use. In addition, two NFPA standards include information about the use and requirements for TIs:

- NFPA 1408, *Standard for Training Fire Service Personnel in the Operation, Care, Use, and Maintenance of Thermal Imagers*
- NFPA 1801, *Standard on Thermal Imagers for the Fire Service*

Inspect TIs after every use, following the manufacturer's instructions. Replace batteries as needed, clean them regularly, and make sure they are properly stored. Immediately report damage and/or malfunction.

TIs are valuable tools but should not be relied upon to provide all of the information about a fire or about the locations of victims. They are not a replacement for your senses or observations, and like other tools, TIs may fail under fire conditions. However, TIs still provide helpful information about interior conditions at a scene.

Air Monitoring Equipment

NFPA 1081 (2018): 5.2.4, 5.2.9, 5.3.10, 6.2.8, 6.2.10, 6.3.7

Detection and monitoring devices allow facility fire brigade members to detect, identify, and measure hazardous materials. One device may measure radiation while another device determines the percentage of flammable vapors in the air. No single device or instrument will detect, identify, and measure all hazardous materials, and all devices and instruments have their strengths and limitations. With proper training, fire brigade members may perform air monitoring and sampling missions at hazardous materials and weapons of mass destruction (WMD) incidents under the direction of qualified experts (such as a hazmat technician or allied professional) or written guidance such as SOPs.

Air monitoring and sampling can be an important aspect of mitigation, assisting in the following tasks:

- Identifying hazards (what materials are involved in the incident and the concentrations present)
- Determining appropriate PPE, tools, and equipment
- Determining perimeters and the scope of the incident (how far the materials have traveled, areas that have been contaminated, and/or areas that are free of contamination and may be safe)
- Checking the effectiveness of defensive operations
- Ensuring that decontamination operations are effective
- Detecting leaks from containers or piping systems
- Monitoring decon runoff for contamination levels
- Determining when the scene is safe for non-fire brigade members following a fire or emergency

Most agencies that use air detection and monitoring devices will have a variety of equipment available to detect different materials and hazards in the air. If fire brigade members do not understand how to use the devices or interpret the information provided, they could easily jeopardize their safety and

Figure 12.32 A fire brigade member using air monitoring equipment at a facility.

the safety of other individuals. For example, a device could take several seconds to draw in a sample and analyze it (known as the instrument reaction time). If fire brigade members move too quickly, they may find themselves in a situation where the concentration of the hazardous material is much higher than what the meter is telling them because they have moved beyond the area where their meter took the sample.

Fire brigade members must use their understanding of the behavior of hazardous materials coupled with an understanding of the detection device in order to be successful in their mission. Most gases are heavier than air. Detection and monitoring then, must be conducted at different heights and levels.

Fire brigade members assigned to detecting, monitoring, and sampling duties must be trained to correctly use the instruments available to them. They must understand the capabilities and limitations of each device. They must be able to accurately interpret the data provided to them as well as maintain, field test, and calibrate the devices according to manufacturers' instructions. Finally, they must use the devices in accordance with predetermined procedures. These procedures are based on the availability, capabilities, and limitations of personnel, appropriate personal protective equipment, and other resources available at the incident **(Figure 12.32)**. If possible, monitoring and sampling results should be verified using more than one sampling method and form of technology.

> **WARNING:** All personnel assigned to conduct detection, monitoring, and sampling must have proper training. They must also wear appropriate PPE when operating in potentially hazardous areas.

Chapter Review

1. What are some potential storage methods?

2. What is life safety rope exclusively used for?

3. What are the disadvantages of synthetic fiber rope?

4. Name the different constructions of rope.

5. What is the best method for storing rope?

6. What are the different uses of flat and tubular webbing?

7. Name and describe three different knots.

8. What safety guidelines should be followed when hoisting a tool?

9. Name the different uses of rope at an emergency scene.

10. What should be done to prevent injuries when using hand tools?

11. What different types of hazards are present when operating power tools?

12. What safety considerations should be taken using emergency lighting?

13. What are the limitations of thermal imagers?

14. What tasks can air monitoring assist with?

Discussion Question

1. What types of powered tools do you use at your facility?

Key Terms

Block Creel Construction — Method of manufacturing rope without any knots or splices; a continuous strand of fiber runs the entire length of the rope's core.

Bowline Knot — Knot used to form a loop; it is easy to tie and untie, and does not constrict.

Clove Hitch — Knot that consists of two half hitches; its principal use is to attach a rope to an object such as a pole, post, or hose.

Come-Along — Manually operated pulling tool that uses a ratchet/pulley arrangement to provide mechanical advantage.

Dynamic Rope — Rope designed to stretch under load, reducing the shock of impact after a fall.

Extension Ram — Powered hydraulic tool designed for straight pushing operations.

Figure-Eight Knot — Knot used to form a loop in the end of a rope; should be used in place of a bowline knot when working with synthetic fiber rope.

Generator — Portable device for generating auxiliary electrical power; generators are powered by gasoline or diesel engines and typically have 110- and/or 220-volt capacity outlets.

Hitch — Temporary knot that falls apart if the object held by the rope is removed.

Hux Bar — Multipurpose forcible entry tool that can also be used to open a hydrant.

Impact Load — Dynamic and sudden load placed on a rope, typically during a fall.

Life Safety Rope — Rope designed exclusively for rescue and other emergency operations; used to raise, lower, and support people at an incident or during training.

Mechanical Advantage — Advantage created when levers, pulleys, and other tools are used to make work easier during rope rescue or while lifting heavy objects.

Natural Fiber Rope — Utility rope made of manila, sisal, or cotton; not accepted for life safety applications.

Overhand Safety Knot — Supplemental knot tied to prevent the primary knot from failing; prevents the running end of the rope from slipping back through the primary knot.

Pneumatic Lifting Bag — Inflatable, envelope-type device that can be placed between the ground and an object and then inflated to lift the object; it can also be used to separate objects. Depending on the size of the bag, it may have lifting capabilities in excess of 75 tons (68 040 kg).

Running Part — Free end of the rope used for hoisting, pulling, or belaying.

Standing Part — Middle of the rope, between the working end and the running part.

Static Rope — Rope designed not to stretch under load.

Synthetic Fiber Rope — Rope made from continuous, synthetic fibers running the entire length of the rope; it is strong, easy to maintain, and resists mildew and rotting.

Tag Line — Non-load-bearing rope attached to a hoisted object to help steer it in a desired direction, prevent it from spinning or snagging on obstructions, or act as a safety line.

Thermal Imager — Electronic device that forms images using infrared radiation. *Also known as* Thermal Imaging Camera.

Winch — Pulling tool that consists of a length of steel chain or cable wrapped around a motor-driven drum; most commonly attached to the front or rear of a vehicle.

Working End — End of the rope used to tie a knot.

Skill Sheet List

The following skill sheets should be used to evaluate the skills described in this chapter:

NOTE: Students should wear the PPE appropriate to the NFPA 1081 level (Incipient, Advanced Exterior, Interior Structural, etc...) being evaluated.

Common Advanced Exterior and Interior Structural Facility Fire Brigade Member Training Requirements

JPRs addressed in this chapter

This chapter provides information that addresses the following job performance requirements of NFPA 1081, *Standard for Facility Fire Brigade Member Professional Qualifications (2018)*.

5.2.4   5.3.11   6.3.8

5.3.2   6.2.8

Learning Objectives

1. Identify the different parts of a ladder. [5.2.4, 5.3.2, 5.3.11, 6.2.8, 6.3.8]

2. Describe the different types of ladders. [5.2.4, 5.3.2, 5.3.11, 6.2.8, 6.3.8]

3. Explain the safety precautions when using and raising ladders. [5.2.4, 5.3.2, 5.3.11, 6.2.8, 6.3.8]

4. Describe the methods for carrying ladders. [5.2.4, 5.3.2, 5.3.11, 6.2.8, 6.3.8]

5. Explain the methods for properly placing ground ladders. [5.2.4, 5.3.2, 5.3.11, 6.2.8, 6.3.8]

6. Describe the methods for properly securing ground ladders. [5.2.4, 5.3.2, 5.3.11, 6.2.8, 6.3.8]

7. Explain the methods for raising ladders. [5.2.4, 5.3.2, 5.3.11, 6.2.8, 6.3.8]

8. Describe the methods for working from ladders. [5.2.4, 5.3.2, 5.3.11, 6.2.8, 6.3.8]

Chapter 13
Ground Ladders

Fire service ground ladders can be an important part of the equipment at emergency incidents. Many fire brigades use fire service ground ladders at their facilities, depending on the conditions and hazards at their facility. These ladders may be stored ready for use at predesignated locations around the facility, carried on fire brigade vehicles such as pickups, or carried on fire brigade pumpers or aerial ladder apparatus.

Depending on ladder length, ground ladders require from one to six fire brigade members to carry and raise into position. While primarily used to access upper stories and roofs of buildings, ground ladders can also be used to reach areas, such as storm drains, trenches, and pits, below ground level.

Fire brigade members must know the following about ground ladders:

- Parts of a ladder
- Ladder safety
- Placing ground ladders
- Ladder raises

- Ladder types
- Carrying ladders
- Securing ground ladders
- Working from a ladder

Parts of a Ladder

NFPA 1081 (2018): 5.2.4, 5.3.2, 5.3.11, 6.2.8, 6.3.8

The following terms are used to describe the parts of fire service ladders **(Figures 13.1 and 13.2, p. 410-411)**:

- **Beam** — Main structural member of a ladder supporting the rungs or rung blocks.

- **Bed section (also called the *base section* or *main section*)** — Lowest and widest section of an extension ladder; while the ladder is being raised or lowered, this section always maintains contact with the ground or other supporting surface.

- **Butt (also called *heel* or *base*)** — Bottom end of the ladder; the end placed on the ground or other supporting surface when the ladder is positioned.

- **Butt spurs** — Metal plates, spikes, or cleats attached to the butt end of ground ladder beams to prevent slippage.

- **Fly Section** — Upper section(s) of extension or some combination ladders; the section that moves.

- **Footpads (also called *shoes*)** — Swivel plates attached to the butt of the ladder; usually have rubber or neoprene bottom surfaces.

- **Guides** — Wood or metal strips, sometimes in the form of slots or channels, on an extension ladder that guide the fly section while being raised.

- **Halyard** — Rope or cable used for hoisting and lowering the fly sections of an extension ladder; also called fly rope.

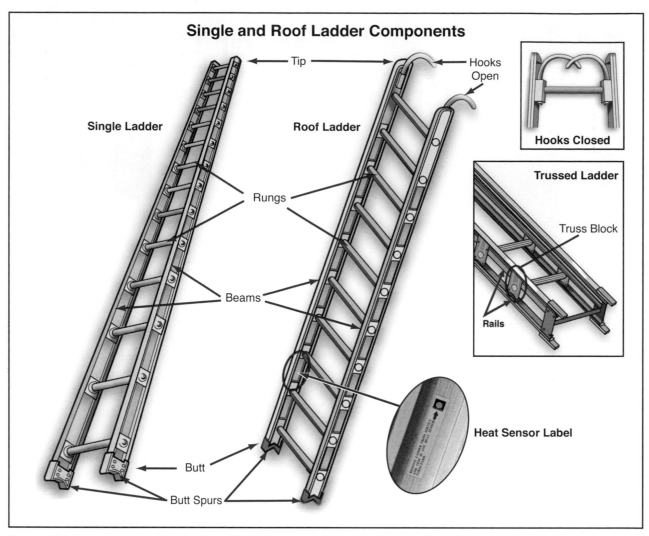

Figure 13.1 Components of single and roof ladders.

- **Heat Sensor label** — Label affixed to the inside of each beam of each ladder section; a color change indicates that the ladder has been exposed to a sufficient degree of heat and should be tested before further use.

- **Hooks** — Curved metal devices installed near the top end of roof ladders to secure the ladder to the highest point on a peaked roof of a building.

- **Pawls (also called *dogs* or *ladder locks*)** — Devices attached to the inside of the beams on fly sections used to hold the fly section in place after it has been extended.

- **Protection plates** — Strips of metal attached to ladders at chafing points, such as the tip, or at areas where it comes in contact with the apparatus mounting brackets.

- **Pulley** — Small, grooved wheel through which the halyard is drawn on an extension ladder.

- **Rails** — The two lengthwise members of a trussed ladder beam that are separated by truss or separation blocks.

- **Rungs** — Cross members that provide the foothold for climbing; the rungs extend from one beam to the other.

- **Stops** — Wooden or metal pieces that prevent the fly section from being extended too far.

- **Tie rods** — Metal rods located beneath rungs extending from one beam to the other of a wooden ladder.

- **Tip (top)** — Extreme top of a ladder.

- **Truss block** — Spacers set between the rails of a trussed ladder; may support rungs.

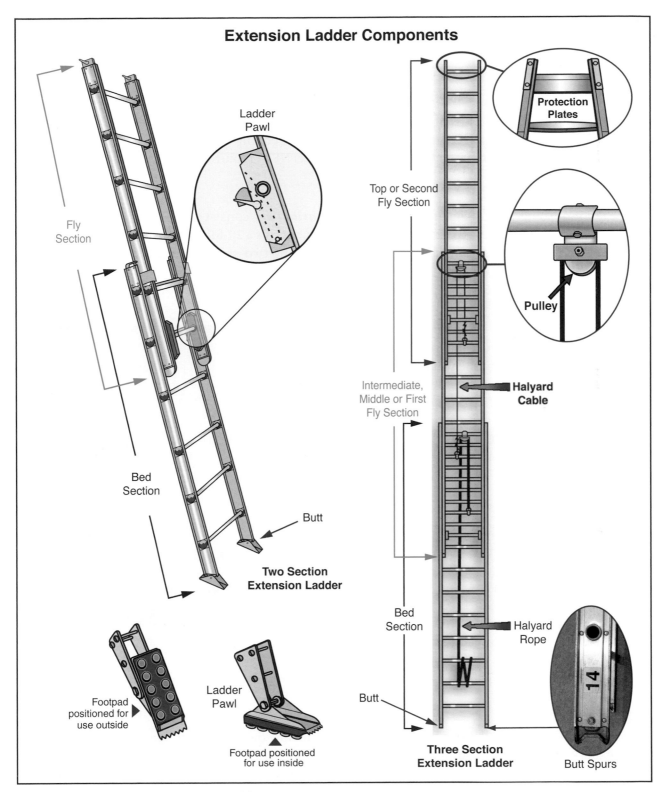

Figure 13.2 Components of extension ladders.

Ladder Types

NFPA 1081 (2018): 5.2.4, 5.3.2, 5.3.11, 6.2.8, 6.3.8

Fire brigades may use any of these four common types of ground ladders:

- Single ladders
- Folding ladders
- Roof ladders
- Extension ladders

Depending on local requirements, the fire brigade may use commercial ladders, such as stepladders for some functions. However, commercial ladders may not meet NFPA requirements for emergency operations.

Single Ladders

Single ladders, sometimes called *wall ladders* or *straight ladders*, consist of one section of a fixed length. The length of the beams is used to identify single ladders, such as a 20-foot (6 m) straight ladder. They are often used for quick access to windows and roofs on one- and two-story buildings. Some single ladders are of the trussed type, a design intended to maximize strength while reducing weight. Lengths of single ladders vary from 6 to 32 feet (2 to 10 m) with the more common lengths ranging from 12 to 24 feet (4 to 7 m).

Roof Ladders

Roof ladders are single ladders equipped with folding hooks that anchor the ladder over the ridge of a pitched roof or some other roof part. In position, roof ladders generally lie flat on the roof surface so that a fire brigade member can stand on it while working. The ladder distributes the fire brigade member's weight and helps prevent slipping. Roof ladders may also be used as wall or straight ladders. Their lengths range from 12 to 24 feet (4 to 7 m).

Figure 13.3 A fire brigade member checking the operation of a folding ladder.

Folding Ladders

Folding ladders are single ladders that are often used for accessing limited spaces. When folded on their hinged rungs, they can be carried in narrow passageways and used in attic scuttle holes, small rooms or closets. Folding ladders are commonly found in lengths from 8 to 16 feet (2.5 m to 5 m) with the most common being 10 feet (3 m). NFPA 1931 requires folding ladders to have footpads attached to the butt to prevent slipping on floor surfaces. Always wear gloves when closing a folding ladder to protect hands and fingers from being pinched between the moving metal parts **(Figure 13.3)**.

Extension Ladders

An **extension ladder** consists of a base or bed section and one or more fly sections that travel in guides or brackets to permit length adjustment. The full length to which it can be extended indicates its size. Extension ladders can be adjusted incrementally to the specific length needed to access windows and roofs. Extension ladders generally range in length from 12 to 39 feet (4 to 11.5 m).

Combination Ladders

Combination ladders can be used as self-supporting stepladders (A-frame) and as single or extension ladders. Lengths range from 8 to 14 feet (2.5 m to 4.3 m) with the most common length being 10 feet (3 m). These ladders must be equipped with positive locking devices to hold the ladder in the open position.

Ladder Safety

NFPA 1081 (2018): 5.2.4, 5.3.2, 5.3.11, 6.2.8, 6.3.8

Exercise caution when lifting, carrying, and raising a ladder, otherwise you risk possible injury or death. The following sections provide general guidelines for ladder safety.

General Guidelines for Ladder Safety

To be able to safely carry, raise, lower, and work on ladders, fire brigade members should (**Figure 13.4, p. 414**):

- Develop and maintain adequate upper body strength.
- Wear a full body harness with safety line when training on ladders.
- Operate ladders according to departmental training and procedures.
- Wear full personal protective equipment, including gloves and helmet, when handling and working with ladders.
- Choose the correct ladder for the assigned task.
- Use leg muscles, not back or arm muscles, when lifting ladders below the waist.
- Use an adequate number of fire brigade members for each carry and raise.
- Do not raise any ladders to within 10 feet (3 m) of electrical wires.

WARNING: Ladders coming in contact with power sources may result in electrocution of anyone in contact with the ladder.

- Avoid positioning the ladder on ice or other slippery surfaces.
- Secure the tip and anchor the foot of the ladder when in use during training or emergency incidents.
- Grasp extension ladder beams when extending or retracting to prevent fingers from being pinched or caught between sections.
- Ensure the hooks of the pawls are seated over the rungs.
- Ensure the ladder is stable before climbing (both butt spurs in contact with a stable surface, with the ground/roof ladder hooks firmly set).
- Use caution when moving ladders sideways.
- Climb smoothly and rhythmically.
- Never overload the ladder (one fire brigade member every 10 feet [3 m] or one per section).
- Use a leg lock or ladder belt when working from a ground ladder.
- Relocate a positioned ladder only when ordered to do so.
- Use ladders for their intended purposes only.
- Inspect ladders for damage and wear after each use.
- Secure the foot of unattended ladders to a stationary object using ropes.

WARNING: Sliding down a ladder either feet first or head first – even in an emergency – is unsafe and may result in serious injury or death.

Figure 13.4 Examples of common ladder safety guidelines.

PPE

Lift with Legs

Leg Lock

Ladder Belt

Because speed is often required, movements when carrying, raising, or lowering ladders should be smooth and controlled. Teamwork is important when moving ladders. Individual and team proficiency in handling ladders gets developed and maintained through training. To prevent injuries, use the following proper lifting and lowering techniques when handling ground ladders:

- Assign the correct number of fire brigade members for the length and type of ladder to be lifted.

- Bend your knees, keeping your back as straight as possible, and lift with your legs, *not with your back or arms.*

- Lift on the command of a fire brigade member who can see the other members of the team.

- Make it known immediately if you are not ready to lift a ladder when working with a team; lifting should occur in unison.

- Reverse the procedure for lifting when it is necessary to place a ladder on the ground before raising it as follows:
  - Lower the ladder using your leg muscles.
  - Keep your body perpendicular to the ladder and your feet parallel to the ladder so that when the ladder is placed, it does not rest on your toes.

Safety When Raising Ladders

Before raising a ladder, consider the precautions you must take. Some of the more important ones are electrical hazards, the position of the extension ladder fly section, and tying the halyard.

Electrical Hazards

People climbing ladders that come in contact with live electrical wires can result in electric shock, severe injury, and death. Before making the final selection on where to place a ladder or what method to use for raising it, use the following guidelines to avoid electrical contact hazards:

- Look up to check for overhead electrical wires or equipment.
- Look up AGAIN before raising the ladder.
- Keep a distance of at least 10 feet (3 m) from all energized electrical lines or equipment; the Occupational Safety and Health Administration (OSHA) refers to this distance as the "Circle of Safety" in its regulations and worker safety documentation.
- Maintain this distance while raising the ladder, using the ladder, and lowering the ladder.
- Use an alternate method for raising the ladder if the ladder may come to rest a safe distance from electrical equipment but come too close to the equipment during the actual raise. Another method could be to raise the ladder using a beam raise parallel to the structure as opposed to perpendicular **(Figure 13.5)**.

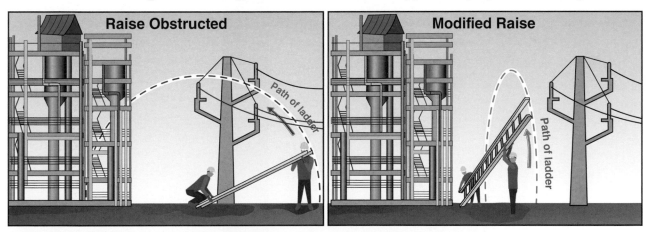

Figure 13.5 Ladder raises should be adapted to the clearances available at the location.

> **WARNING:** All ladders will conduct electricity, especially when wet, regardless of their construction material.

Position of the Fly Section on Extension Ladders

Ladder placement is based on the ladder design, construction materials, and the fly position at which the manufacturer's tests show it to be strongest. Failure to follow this recommendation could void the ladder's warranty if failure or damage occurs.

Most modern metal and fiberglass ladders are designed to be used with the *fly out*. Wooden ladders that are designed with the rungs mounted in the top truss rail are intended to be used with the *fly in* (**Figure 13.6**). A new type of extension ladder can be used with the fly in or out. Consult departmental SOPs or the ladder manufacturer to determine the correct fly position.

Some departments have ladders that are intended to be used with the fly out but prefer that the fire brigade member extending the halyard be on the outside of the ladder. In this case, fire brigade members will need to pivot or roll the ladder 180 degrees after it has been extended.

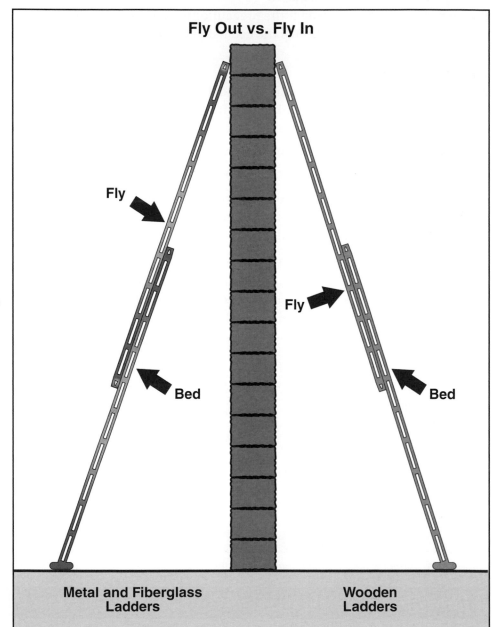

Figure 13.6 Illustrating the concepts of FLY OUT and FLY IN.

Securing the Halyard

Once an extension ladder is resting against a structure and before it is climbed, the excess halyard should be secured (tied off) to prevent anyone from becoming tangled in the rope when ascending or descending the ladder. Some halyards (closed halyards) are tied as a feature of the ladder.

Carrying Ladders

NFPA 1081 (2018): 5.2.4, 5.3.2, 5.3.11, 6.2.8, 6.3.8

Fire brigade members must safely and quickly carry ground ladders from the apparatus to where they will be used. After selecting a ladder for a purpose, remove the ladder from the apparatus. On pumping apparatus, one or two fire brigade members should be able to remove the ladder. On aerial apparatus, three or four fire brigade members may be required. Because there are different types of apparatus and means of mounting ladders, all carries in this section are demonstrated from the ground. In most cases, the ladders are carried butt end forward.

Selecting the Correct Ladder

The Incident Commander (IC) or supervisor at an incident will usually indicate which ladder to use and/ or where to place the ladder. In the absence of those orders, you must be able to select an appropriate ladder and a safe location for its placement.

When personnel are working on a roof or upper stories, there must be at least two means of escape with at least two ladders at two remote locations. Ground ladders or aerial devices may provide escape routes.

Selecting a ladder to reach a specific point requires the ability to judge distance. Depending upon the height of the foundation and other factors, a residential story averages about 10 feet (3 m), and the distance from the floor to a windowsill averages about 3 feet (1 m). A commercial story averages 12 feet (4 m) from floor to floor, with a 4-foot (a little more than 1 m) distance from the floor to windowsill. **Table 13.1** is a guide that can be used in selecting ladders for specific locations.

Table 13.1
Ladder Selection Guide

Working Location of Ladder	Ladder Length
First story roof	16 to 20 feet (5 m to 6.0 m)
Second story window	20 to 28 feet (6.0 m to 8.5 m)
Second story roof	28 to 35 feet (8.5 m to 11 m)
Third story window or roof	40 to 50 feet (12 m to 15 m)
Fourth story roof	over 50 feet (over 15 m)

Fire brigade members should be able to determine how far ladders will reach based on their designated length. The designated length is a measurement of the total length of a single section ladder and the maximum extended length of an extension ladder. The designated length will be less than the ladder's reach because ladders are set at angles of approximately 75 degrees for climbing.

Single, roof, and folding ladders meeting NFPA 1931 are required to have a measured length equal to the designated length. In the case of extension ladders, however, the maximum extended length may be as much as 6 inches (150 mm) *less* than the designated length.

Once you understand the concept of designated length and estimating heights on a structure, you should be able to select the correct ladder lengths for ladder placements such as the following:

- Extending a ladder a minimum of three to five rungs beyond the roof edge to provide a footing and a handhold for anyone stepping on or off the ladder **(Figure 13.7a, p. 418)**.

- Placing the tip of a ladder even with the top of the window and to the windward (upwind) side of it to gain access to a narrow window or for opening the window for ventilation **(Figure 13.7b, p. 418)**.

- Placing the tip of a ladder just below the windowsill when performing rescue from a window opening **(Figure 13.7c, p. 418)**.

NOTE: Building walls or parapets that extend more than 6 feet (2 m) above the roof may require the use of an additional ladder to reach the roof deck. Place a roof or straight ladder on the roof side of the parapet and next to the extension ladder to assist fire brigade members to and from the roof.

Figure 13.7a A ladder extended for roof access.

Three to Five Rungs

Figure 13.7b Ladder placement for either a narrow window or for opening a window to ventilate the structure.

Figure 13.7c A ladder positioned below a windowsill for rescue purposes.

Table 13.2 Maximum Working Heights for Ladders Set at Proper Climbing Angle	
Designated Length of Ladder	**Maximum Reach**
10 foot (3.0 m)	9 feet (2.5 m)
14 foot (4 m)	13 feet (3.5 m)
16 foot (5 m)	15 feet (4.5 m)
20 foot (6 m)	19 feet (5.5 m)
24 foot (7 m)	23 feet (6.5 m)
28 foot (8.5 m)	27 feet (8 m)
35 foot (11m)	34 feet (10.5 m)
40 foot (12 m)	38 feet (11.5 m)
45 foot (14 m)	43 feet (13 m)
50 foot (15 m)	48 feet (14.5 m)

Table 13.2 provides information on the maximum working heights of various ground ladders when placed at the proper climbing angle. Note the following measurements when considering the information in this table:

- For lengths of 35 feet (11 m) or less, reach is approximately 1 foot (300 mm) less than the designated length.
- For lengths over 35 feet (11 m), reach is approximately 2 feet (600 mm) less than the designated length.

Removing Ladders from the Apparatus

Ground ladders are mounted on pumpers, aerial ladder apparatus, quints, and specialized apparatus. They are carried on pumper apparatus and may be mounted in the following ways:

- Hanging on a beam in racks on the side of the apparatus
- Standing on the lower beam in a compartment between the hose bed and the vehicle's body, accessed from the rear
- Flat in a compartment under the hose bed, accessed from the rear of the apparatus
- In a mechanically operated rack that lowers the ladder from the top of the hose bed to the side of the vehicle

On aerial and quint apparatus, the ladders may be mounted vertically on the left or right side of the apparatus bed or in racks within the bed, which are accessed from the rear of the apparatus. Specialized apparatus, such as mobile water supply apparatus and aircraft rescue and fire fighting apparatus, generally carry ladders vertically on the outside of the apparatus body.

When using the ground ladders mounted on your apparatus, you must know the following:

- Types, length, and location of ladders carried on the apparatus
- How the ladders are stored, either with the butt toward the front or the rear of the apparatus
- How the ladders are nested together
- How one nested ladder can be removed leaving the other securely in place
- The order in which nested ladders are stored
- Whether the extension ladder's fly is located on the inside or the outside when it is stored on the side of the apparatus
- The method used to secure ladders in place
- The location at which mounting brackets extend through vertically mounted ladders (A good practice is to mark ladders to indicate which rungs go in or near the brackets.)

The procedures for removing ground ladders from the apparatus when the ladders are mounted on the side or top differ from those used when they are mounted in a flat position. To remove mounted ladders, first unlatch the securing devices and lift the ladder off the bracket and into the correct carrying position. Remove any equipped ladder protective covers.

To remove ladders that are stored internally in compartments, open the compartment access panel (if there is one) and then slide the ladder out to the proper carrying point. When multiple fire brigade members are required to carry the ladder, they stand on either side of the horizontally racked ladder and take their assigned position as the ladder is pulled out. Once the ladder has been removed from the apparatus, fire brigade members should reposition on the same side of the ladder for carrying.

Safety When Carrying Ladders

Safety considerations when carrying ground ladders include:

- Maintain situational awareness of other fire brigade members at the scene.
- Lift the ladder with your legs rather than with your back.

- Look ahead, scanning for obstructions, other people, and trip hazards.

- Use an appropriate number of personnel to carry the ladder based upon the conditions at the scene and the length of the ladder **(Figure 13.8)**.

- Work and communicate as a team.

- Identify one member of your lift team as a leader.

- Carry roof ladders with the hooks closed.

- Carry ladders with the butt end first to facilitate transition from a ladder carry to a ladder raise, if needed.

Figure 13.8 Two fire brigade members carrying an extension ladder.

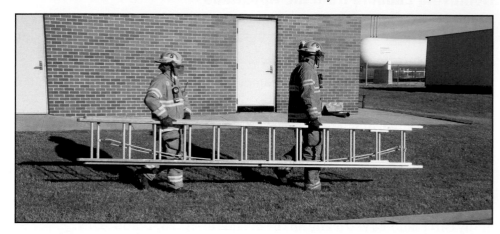

CAUTION: Carrying the forward end of a ladder at eye level impedes the carrier's balance and visibility and increases the risk of the butt spurs striking someone else in the head.

 Three or More Fire Brigade Member Ladder Carries

If needed for safety of the crew or speed of deployment, three or more fire brigade members may be tasked to complete these same carries. In the case of three fire brigade members, add a fire brigade member at the mid-length of the ladder. If four fire brigade members are needed, two fire brigade members are positioned at the butt of the ladder, and two at the tip of the ladder.

Placing Ground Ladders

NFPA 1081 (2018): 5.2.4, 5.3.2, 5.3.11, 6.2.8, 6.3.8

Proper placement of ground ladders helps ensure the safety and efficiency of fireground operations. The following sections contain basic considerations and requirements for ground ladder placement.

Situational Awareness: Ladder Assignments

Communicating your observations when assigned a task is essential for safety. Observe and communicate to crew members and/or your supervisor the following conditions specific to ground ladders:

- Presence of overhead electrical wires and obstructions

- Ground conditions: muddy, icy, and/or uneven terrain

- Building structural integrity: condition of the wall and windows where the ladder will be raised

- Wind direction and speed

- Appropriateness of the chosen ladder: length, single or extension, correct for the task

- Structural features such as the type of roof, wall height, and presence of overhangs

Factors Affecting Ground Ladder Placement

While a fire brigade leader may designate the general location where the ladder is to be placed and the task to be performed, the personnel carrying the ladder must assess the location for hazards and decide the safest place to place the butt of the ladder for raising. Usually, the fire brigade member nearest the butt is the logical person to make this decision. When two fire brigade members are at the butt, the one on the right side is usually the one responsible for placement. Because this guideline may vary from one department to another, fire brigade members must follow their department SOPs.

Two objectives are to be met when placing ground ladders:

1. Position the ladder properly for its intended use.

2. Place the butt the proper distance from the building for safe and easy climbing.

Many factors dictate the exact place to position the ladder. If you are using a ladder for positioning a fire brigade member to break a window for ventilation, place it alongside the window to the windward (upwind) side. The tip should be even with the top of the window. Use this position when fire brigade members need to climb in or out of narrow windows or direct hose streams into them.

If you use a ladder for entry or rescue from a window, place the ladder tip slightly below the sill. If the sill projects out from the wall, wedge the ladder tip under the sill for additional stability. If the window opening is wide enough to permit the ladder tip to project into it and allow room beside it to facilitate entry and rescue, place the ladder so that two or three rungs extend above the sill.

Other ladder placement guidelines include the following:

- Place ladders at two or more points on different sides of the building.

- Avoid placing ladders over openings (such as windows and doors) where they might be exposed to heat or direct flame contact.

- Take advantage of strong points (such as the corners) in building construction when placing ladders.

- Raise the ladder directly in front of the window when it is to be used as a support for a smoke ejector removing cold smoke after a fire has been extinguished. Place the ladder tip on the wall above the window opening.

- Avoid placing ladders where they may come into contact with overhead obstructions such as wires, tree limbs, or signs.

- Avoid placing ladders on uneven terrain or on soft spots.

- Avoid placing ladders in front of doors or other paths of travel that fire brigade members or evacuees will need to use. Instead, place the ladder to the side of the opening.

- Avoid placing ladders on top of sidewalk elevator trapdoors or sidewalk deadlights. These areas may give way under the added weight of fire brigade members, their equipment, and the ladder.

- Do not place ladders against unstable walls or surfaces.

The distance of the butt from the building establishes the angle between the ladder and the ground. If the butt is placed too close to the building, its stability is reduced because the weight of the person climbing tends to cause the tip to pull away from the building. With the exception of certain rescue situations, when the ladder has been raised into place, the desired angle of inclination is approximately 75 degrees **(Figure 13.9, p. 422)**. A 75-degree angle provides the following benefits:

- Good stability

- Less stress placed on the ladder

- Optimal climbing angle

- Easiest climbing position: the climber can stand perpendicular to the ground, at arm's length from the next rung at shoulder level

Figure 13.9 A climbing angle sticker (left) and a fire brigade member checking the climbing angle of a ladder he has raised (right).

If the butt of the ladder is placed too far away from the building, the load-carrying capacity of the ladder is reduced, and it has more of a tendency to slip. If placement at wider angles becomes necessary, either tie in or heel (steady) the bottom of the ladder at all times. (See Securing the Ladder section for tying in and heeling instructions.)

An easy way to determine the proper distance between the butt of the ladder and the building is to divide the working length (length actually used) of the ladder by 4. For example, if you need 20 feet (6 m) of a 28-foot (8.5 m) ladder to reach a window, place the butt end 5 feet (1.5 m) from the building (20 feet divided by 4 [6 m divided by 4]). In this calculation, only the length of the ladder to reach the window is used and not the ladder's overall length. Exact measurements are unnecessary at the fire scene.

Experienced fire brigade members develop the ability to visually judge the proper positioning for the ladder. When the ladder is at the proper angle, a fire brigade member standing straight up on the bottom rung should be able reach straight ahead and grasp a rung directly in front of him or her. Ladders are also equipped with an inclination marking on the outside of the beam that aligns vertical and horizontal when the ladder is properly set.

Securing Ground Ladders

NFPA 1081 (2018): 5.2.4, 5.3.2, 5.3.11, 6.2.8, 6.3.8

Ground ladders must be secured whenever fire brigade members climb or work from them. Two methods are used for securing a ladder: heeling and tying in. The process of securing a ground ladder may include:

- Lock the extension ladder locks in place before the ladder is placed against the structure.

- Tie the halyard with a clove hitch and an overhand safety (extension ladder only).

- Heel and/or secure the ladder with a rope to a nearby, firm object to prevent ladder movement.

> **CAUTION:** Raised ladders that must be left unattended should be secured to prevent the ladders from toppling.

Heeling

One way of preventing movement of a ladder is to properly heel it. Several methods are used for properly heeling, also known as *footing*, a ladder **(Figure 13.10)**. Regardless of the method used, fire brigade members should adhere to the following guidelines:

Figure 13.10 These photos show three methods of heeling or footing a ladder.

- Wear full PPE with helmet faceshield deployed when heeling the ladder.

- Be alert for falling objects or debris.

- Stay alert for fire brigade members descending the ladder

  When heeling the ladder from beneath the ladder:

- Stand beneath the ladder with feet about shoulder-width apart (or one foot slightly ahead of the other).

- Grasp the ladder beams, not the rungs, at about eye level and pull the ladder backward toward the building.

- Look forward, not up, when someone is climbing the ladder.

  When heeling a ladder from outside (not under) the ladder:

- Stand on the outside of the ladder and chock the butt end with one foot.

- Place your toes against the butt spur or place one foot on the bottom rung.

- Grasp the beams and press the ladder against the building.

  NOTE: Heeling a ladder from outside provides maximum situational awareness and is the preferred method.

Tying In

Whenever possible, a ladder should be tied securely to a fixed object. Tying in a ladder is simple, can be done quickly, and is strongly recommended to prevent the ladder from slipping or pulling away from the building. Tying in also frees personnel who would otherwise be holding the ladder in place. A **rope hose tool** or safety strap can be used between the ladder and a fixed object **(Figure 13.11)**.

Ladder Raises

NFPA 1081 (2018): 5.2.4, 5.3.2, 5.3.11, 6.2.8, 6.3.8

To be most effective, teamwork, smoothness, and rhythm are necessary when raising and lowering fire brigade ladders. There are many ways to safely raise ground ladders. These methods vary depending on the ladder's type and size, number of personnel available to perform the raise, and weather and topography considerations. The raises described here are some of the more commonly used methods. The sections that follow begin with general procedures to follow before raising a ladder.

NOTE: The following sections only contain step-by-step information for raising ladders. In every case, the procedure for lowering the ladder is to reverse the listed steps in the given order.

Transition from Carry to Raise

The methods and precautions for raising single-section and extension ladders are much the same. It is not necessary to place the ladder flat on the ground prior to raising it; only the butt needs to be placed on the ground. The transition from the carrying position to the raise can and should be done in one smooth and continuous motion.

One-Fire Brigade Member Raise

One fire brigade member may safely raise single ladders and small extension ladders. The following procedures should be used to perform these raises.

One-Fire Brigade Member Single Ladder Raise

Figure 13.11 Webbing can be used to tie off the tip of a ladder.

Figure 13.12 A fire brigade member placing the butt end of a ladder on the ground at the point where the ladder will be raised. *Courtesy of Shad Cooper/Sublette County Unified Fire.*

Single and roof ladders are generally light enough that one fire brigade member can place the butt end at the point where it will be located for climbing without steadying it against the building or another object before raising **(Figure 13.12)**.

Figure 13.13 A fire brigade member placing the butt end of a ladder against a building to prevent it from slipping while the ladder is raised.

One-Fire Brigade Member Extension Ladder Raise

One method of raising extension ladders with one fire brigade member is from the low-shoulder carry; however, a different procedure for placing the ladder butt is used. When using the one-fire brigade member raise from the low-shoulder carry, a building is used to heel the ladder to prevent the ladder butt from slipping while the ladder is brought to the vertical position **(Figure 13.13)**.

Two-Fire Brigade Member Raises

Whenever two or more fire brigade members are involved in raising a ladder, the fire brigade member at the butt end, called the heeler, is responsible for placing it at the desired distance from the building and determining whether the ladder will be raised parallel with or perpendicular to the building. During the operation, the heeler also gives commands. Space permitting, it makes little difference if a ladder is raised parallel with or perpendicular to a building. If raised parallel with the building, the ladder must be pivoted after it is in the vertical position. There are two basic ways for two fire brigade members to raise a ladder: the flat raise and the beam raise **(Figure 13.14)**.

Flat Raise

Beam Raise

Figure 13.14 Fire brigade members demonstrating the flat and beam raises.

Three-Fire Brigade Member Raises

As a general rule, a longer extension ladder will weigh more and require additional personnel to raise, compared to shorter ladders longer extension ladders. Typically, at least three fire brigade members should raise ladders of 35 feet (11 m) or longer.

To raise a ladder with three fire brigade members, follow the same procedures for the two-fire brigade member flat raise. Position the third fire brigade member along the beam. One fire brigade member heels the butt end while a second fire brigade member begins raising the tip. The third fire brigade member can assist the second at the tip or step underneath to assist in walking. the ladder upright **(Figure 13.15)**.

Four-Fire Brigade Member Flat Raise

When available, four fire brigade members can better handle the larger and heavier extension ladders. A flat raise is normally used, and the procedures for raising the ladder are similar to the three-fire brigade member raise except for the placement of personnel. A fire brigade member at the butt is responsible for placing the butt at the desired distance from the building and determining whether the ladder will be raised parallel with or perpendicular to the building.

Moving a Raised Ladder

In some cases, the basic ladder-raising procedures are insufficient to get the ladder into its final position for use. In these situations, it will be necessary to move the ladder slightly after it has been extended.

Pivoting Ladders with Two Fire Brigade Members

Occasionally, an extension ladder is raised with the fly in the incorrect position for deployment. When this happens, it is necessary to pivot the ladder. Any ladder flat-raised parallel to the building also requires pivoting to align it with the wall upon which it will rest. Pivot the ladder on the beam closest to the structure. Whenever possible, pivot the ladder before it is extended **(Figure 13.16)**.

The two-fire brigade member pivot may be used on any ground ladder that two fire brigade members can raise. The same procedure is used for positioning a ladder that was flat-raised parallel to the building. In this case, the beam nearest the building is used to pivot the ladder 90 degrees.

Shifting Raised Ground Ladders

Circumstances may require that ground ladders be moved while vertical. Because they are hard to control, shifting a ladder that is in a vertical position should be limited to short distances such as aligning ladders perpendicular to a building or to an adjacent window.

One fire brigade member can safely shift a single ladder that is 20 feet (6 m) long or less. Be-

Figure 13.15 Three fire brigade members raising an extension ladder.

Figure 13.16 Fire brigade members practicing a ladder pivot operation.

cause of their weight, extension ladders require two fire brigade members for the shifting maneuver. Another way to shift a ladder a short distance from side to side is to place the ladder against the building, slide the top of the ladder sideways, and then pick up the butt and move it into position.

Working from a Ladder

NFPA 1081 (2018): 5.2.4, 5.3.2, 5.3.11, 6.2.8, 6.3.8

To operate on a ladder, you need to know how to:

- Climb the ladder
- Work from the ladder
- Descend ladders safely
- Lock into the ladder
- Carry tools and equipment up and down

During ladder operations, you may need to work from the ladder to accomplish tasks such as:

- Opening or ventilating windows
- Assisting victims down a ladder
- Operating a hoseline from a ladder

Figure 13.17 A fire brigade member demonstrating proper ladder climbing techniques.

Climbing Ladders

Ladder climbing should be done smoothly the least possible amount of bounce and sway. This smoothness is accomplished if your knee is bent to ease the weight on each rung. Balance on the ladder will come naturally if the ladder is properly spaced away from the building to create an optimum climbing angle that puts your body perpendicular to the ground (usually a 75-degree angle).

The climb starts after the climbing angle has been checked and the ladder is properly secured. To begin your climb, follow these instructions:

- Focus your eyes forward, with an occasional glance at the tip of the ladder.
- Keep your arms straight (horizontal) during the climb; this keeps your body away from the ladder and permits free knee movement.
- Place your hands on the rungs when no equipment is being carried.
- Grasp the rungs with palms down and thumbs beneath the rungs.
- Grasp alternating rungs while climbing.
- Coordinate hand and foot movement so that the right hand and left foot are in contact with the ladder as you move the opposite hand and foot to the next rungs **(Figure 13.17)**.

- Place your feet near the beams with the halyard tied in the center of the rung. If your feet should slip, your arms and hands are in a position to stop the fall.

- Climb using your leg muscles and not your arm muscles. Your arms and hands should not reach above your head while climbing because that will bring your body too close to the ladder.

- Practice climbing slowly to develop form rather than speed. Speed develops with repetition after the proper technique is mastered. Whether from excessive speed with good form, or improper form, quick movements or jerky movements cause the ladder to bounce and sway.

Securing to the Ladder

Fire brigade members must sometimes work with both hands while standing on a ground ladder. Ideally, a ladder belt should be used when a fire brigade member operates from a ladder however a leg lock can be used if a harness is not available.

> **WARNING:** Do not exceed the rated load capacity of the ladder. To avoid overloading the ladder, allow only one fire brigade member on each section of a ladder at the same time. Be careful about stressing ladders laterally.

If a **ladder belt** is used, strap it tightly around the waist. The hook may be moved to one side, out of the way, while you are climbing the ladder. After reaching the desired height, slide the hook to the center of your body and attach it to a rung. According to NFPA 1983, *Standard on Life Safety Rope and Equipment for Emergency Services*, a ladder belt is rated only as a positioning device for use on a ladder and does not meet the requirements of life safety harnesses.

> **WARNING:** Never use a leg lock on an aerial ladder as extending or retracting the ladder could result in serious injury.

Carrying Tools Up and Down Ladders

At an incident, you may have to carry a tool, such as an axe or saw, up and down a ladder. Carrying tools up and down a ladder disrupts the natural climbing motion because of the added weight and the need to use one hand to hold the tool (**Figure 13.18**). If a tool is carried in one hand, it may be preferable to slide the free hand under the beam rather than on the rungs while making the climb. This method permits constant hand contact with the ladder. Whenever possible, use a utility rope to hoist tools and equipment rather than carrying them up a ladder.

Deploying a Roof Ladder on a Pitched Roof

Before deploying a roof ladder, it must be carried up a ground ladder to the roof. First, use a low-shoulder carry to carry the roof ladder (hooks closed) to where the extension ladder has been placed for climbing. Because roof ladders are deployed so that the hooks can attach to the roof peak, they may be carried either butt first or tip first. Heel the roof ladder at the base of the extension ladder. Set the ladder down, walk back to the tip and open the hooks. Raise the ladder and rest it against the extension ladder beam with the hooks on the top end, right. To carry the roof ladder up while climbing the extension ladder you can either:

Figure 13.18 A fire brigade member demonstrating how carry an axe while climbing a ladder.

1. Shoulder the roof ladder before mounting the extension ladder and then climb.

2. Climb a short distance up the extension ladder, then reach through the roof ladder and shoulder it before climbing the rest of the extension ladder.

There are numerous ways to deploy a roof ladder on a pitched roof. Once the roof ladder has been carried to the roof, lock in with one leg or connect a ladder belt to an appropriate rung. Remove the ladder from the shoulder and slide it on the beam, hooks out, up to the peak. When the hooks are over the peak, turn the ladder onto both beams, hooks over the peak and pull down to ensure the hooks have engaged the roof. Sliding the roof ladder on both beams until the hooks engage the peak is an alternate method for deploying a roof ladder **(Figure 13.19)**.

Figure 13.19 A fire brigade member practicing how to slide a roof ladder up a roof.

Figure 13.20 A fire brigade member assisting a "victim" down a ladder during a training exercise.

Assisting a Victim Down a Ladder

When using a ground ladder for rescue through a window, the ladder tip is raised to just below the sill. This makes it easier for a conscious victim to climb onto the ladder or for fire brigade members to lift an unconscious victim onto the ladder. The ladder is heeled and all other loads and activity removed from it during rescue operations. Because conscious victims may be unaccustomed to climbing down a ladder, they must be protected from slipping and falling. To bring victims down a ground ladder, at least four fire brigade members are needed: two inside the building, one or two on the ladder, and one to heel the ladder. The following methods can be used to assist a victim down a ladder set at the normal climbing angle; but these methods work better if the ladder is set at a slightly steeper angle.

The method chosen for assisting a victim down a ladder depends upon whether the victim is conscious or unconscious. Conscious victims are usually the easier of the two because they are able to assist with climbing onto and down the ladder **(Figure 13.20)**. They can be lowered feet first (facing the building) onto a ladder.

An unconscious victim is unable to assist with climbing onto or down the ladder. This can create additional difficulties in moving the victim and safety concerns for the rescue personnel involved. The victim can be held on a ladder in the same way as a conscious victim except that the victim's body rests on the rescuer's supporting knee. The victim's feet must be placed outside the rails to prevent entanglement. The rescuer grasps the rungs to provide a secure hold on the ladder and help to protect the victim's head from hitting the ladder.

Methods for assisting unconscious victim include **(Figure 13.21)**:

Figure 13.21 Unconscious victims can be brought down a ladder using one of these three methods: the on-the-knee method, the cross-body method, or the modified cross-body method.

 Assisting an Unconscious Victim

An unconscious victim who regains consciousness while being rescued down a ladder may grab the ladder or the rescuer. This sudden reaction from the victim may cause the fire brigade member to lose his/her grip or footing and increase the risk of falling off the ladder, especially if the victim is facing the fire brigade member. It is critical that any fire brigade member assisting an unconscious victim down a ladder observe the victim and be prepared to respond if the victim regains consciousness.

- **On-the-knee** — The victim is rested on the fire brigade member's knee between the fire brigade member's body and the ladder.

- **Cross-body method** — The victim is carried horizontally facing the fire brigade member. The fire brigade member has one arm between the victim's legs and the other arm under the victim's lowest arm at the armpit. The fire brigade member's hands maintain contact with the ladder rails to keep the victim in place on the way down the ladder.

- **Modified cross-body method** — The modified method is basically the same as the cross-body method except that the victim is facing the ladder rather than the fire brigade member. While it is recommended that the victim face the fire brigade member, there may be instances where that position protects the victim better than the normal position. For example, a victim's injuries might prevent carrying him or her in the regular position.

A victim's size also plays a factor in lowering him or her down a ladder. Large victims require more personnel to move and may require more equipment as well. Removing extraordinarily heavy victims requires two rescuers. Two ground ladders are placed side by side. One rescuer supports the victim's waist and legs. A second rescuer on the other ladder supports the victim's head and upper torso **(Figure 13.22)**. Small children who must be brought down a ladder can be cradled across the rescuer's arms.

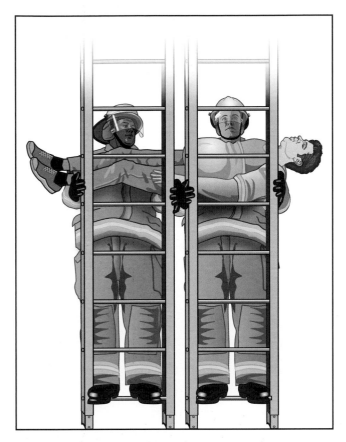

Figure 13.22 Two fire brigade members and ladders may be needed to bring large or obese victims down a ladder.

Chapter Review

1. Name and describe five parts of a ladder.

2. What keeps roof ladders in place?

3. What safety guidelines should be followed to avoid electrical hazards while raising ladders?

4. What must fire brigade members know when removing a ladder from the apparatus?

5. What are the two objectives when placing ground ladders?

6. What guidelines should be followed while heeling a ladder?

7. What methods can be used to move a raised ladder?

8. Name and describe the methods for helping a victim down a ladder.

Key Terms

Bed Section — Bottom section of an extension ladder.

Butt — Heel (lower end) of a ladder.

Butt Spurs — Metal safety plates or spikes attached to the butt end of ground ladder beams.

Extension Ladder — Variable-length ladder of two or more sections that can be extended to a desired height.

Fly Section — Extendable section of ground extension or aerial ladder.

Folding Ladder — Single-section, collapsible ladder that is easy to maneuver in restricted places such as access openings for attics and lofts.

Hooks — Curved metal devices installed on the tip end of roof ladders to secure the ladder to the highest point on the roof of a building.

Ladder Belt — Belt with a hook that secures the firefighter to the ladder.

Rails — The two lengthwise members of a trussed ladder beam that are separated by truss or separation blocks.

Rope Hose Tool — Piece of rope spliced to form a loop through the eye of a metal hook; used to secure hose to ladders or other objects.

Single Ladder — One-section nonadjustable ladder.

Stops — Wooden or metal pieces that prevent the fly section from being extended too far.

Tip (top) — Extreme top of a ladder.

Truss Block — Spacers set between the rails of a trussed ladder; may support rungs.

Skill Sheet List

The following skill sheets should be used to evaluate the skills described in this chapter:

NOTE: Students should wear the PPE appropriate to the NFPA 1081 level (Incipient, Advanced Exterior, Interior Structural, etc...) being evaluated.

Common Advanced Exterior and Interior Structural Facility Fire Brigade Member Training Requirements

Chapter Contents

JPRs addressed in this chapter

This chapter provides information that addresses the following job performance requirements of NFPA 1081, *Standard for Facility Fire Brigade Member Professional Qualifications (2018)*.

5.3.2   6.2.2
5.3.10   6.3.7

1. Describe the basics of forcible entry. [5.3.2, 5.3.10, 6.2.2, 6.3.7]

2. Recognize the challenges of gaining access to the property. [5.3.2, 5.3.10, 6.2.2, 6.3.7]

3. Identify the different basic types of locks and locking devices. [5.3.2, 5.3.10, 6.2.2, 6.3.7]

4. Recognize the importance of coordinating forcible entry and maintaining door control. [5.3.2, 5.3.10, 6.2.2, 6.3.7]

5. Identify the considerations for breaking door glass. [5.3.2, 5.3.10, 6.2.2, 6.3.7]

6. Describe the methods for forcing swinging and sliding doors. [5.3.2, 5.3.10, 6.2.2, 6.3.7]

7. Explain the methods for forcing high security access area doors and gates and padlocks. [5.3.2, 5.3.10, 6.2.2, 6.3.7]

8. Describe the methods for forcing overhead and fire doors. [5.3.2, 5.3.10, 6.2.2, 6.3.7]

9. Describe the methods for forcing entry though windows. [5.3.2, 5.3.10, 6.2.2, 6.3.7]

10. Explain the methods for breaching walls. [5.3.2, 5.3.10, 6.2.2, 6.3.7]

Chapter 14
Forcible Entry

Fire brigades may not need to perform forcible entry as often as municipal fire departments because facilities may have security personnel on duty or the fire brigade may have access keys or cards to facility locations. However, there may be times when fire brigade personnel must move quickly to gain access into an area can require fire brigade members to force locks, doors, windows, or other barriers. The sooner that entry can be made, the faster fire brigade members can control the emergency. Forcible entry requires knowledge of building construction, fire behavior, and property conservation. To gain entry, fire brigade members must use the correct location and the proper technique. Effective size-up and situational awareness are essential during forcible entry. The characteristics of various types of barriers and the forcible entry procedures used to gain entry through them are discussed in this chapter.

Basic Principles of Forcible Entry

NFPA 1081 (2018): 5.3.2, 6.2.2

Forcible entry refers to the techniques used to gain access into a compartment, structure, facility, or site when the normal means of entry is locked or blocked. Forcible entry techniques do minimal damage to the structure or structural components, and provide quick access to the emergency. Do not use forcible entry when normal means of access are available. These techniques can also be applied to:

- Vehicles
- Aircraft
- Railway passenger cars
- Ships

The Incident Commander (IC) or your supervisor will determine where to force entry based upon the following factors:

- Tactics that must be fulfilled
- Location of the fire or hazard
- Stage of the fire
- Effect on ventilation
- Effort required to force entry

Each forcible entry operation requires the fire brigade personnel to size up the situation. Fire brigade personnel must be aware of and properly trained in order to safely gain access into facility locations. They should know where these locations are and what procedures must be followed when dealing with emergencies involving these locations. Access into these locations may be through areas with low overhead clearances or along roadways with weight/load restrictions. Water supplies within these locations may be limited and fire brigade personnel need to know where those supplies are located and how to access them. Fire brigade personnel should wait to be ordered to force entry before doing so.

Additionally, each facility may have certain unique hazards. Examples of such hazards may include:

- Hazardous process units
- Railcar movement areas
- Dangerous equipment locations
- Electrical substations and other electrical equipment
- Radiation hazard areas
- Classified/secured areas
- Areas that require specialized safe shutdown mode procedures

Site drawings can be used to help identify potential access/forcible entry points. These site drawings identify hazards, normal entry points, emergency exits and forcible entry points, suppression systems, fences, and other locally required information. Fire brigade personnel must be able to read these drawing to assist with forcible entry operations.

It may be easier to force a basement window to apply water on a fire than to force entry through a door and advance a hoseline down an interior stairway. The location of an opening that adds fresh air to a ventilation-controlled fire can drastically affect fire behavior. Any entry into a structure is a form of ventilation, allowing an exchange of fresh air and products of combustion. Control doors and windows to limit the amount of fresh air from entering the structure which can intensify the fire.

At every door or window, remember to first "try before you pry" **(Figure 14.1)**. The door or window may be unlocked and can be opened in a normal manner. Second, especially on commercial and industrial occupancies, look for a lock box near the main entrance. Using a door key or numeric keypad combination from inside a lock box reduces property damage and may allow quicker entry than having to force a door or window **(Figure 14.2)**. Lock box information may be stored in building preincident plans and/or computer-aided dispatch (CAD) data to speed access during incident operations.

Figure 14.1 Fire brigade members should always try to open doors and windows normally before trying to pry them.

Figure 14.2 An example of a key lockbox located to the left of this warehouse door.

General considerations for forcible entry are as follows:

- **Doors and locks** — Construction, direction of opening (inward or outward), type of frame, type of lock, and mounting of the lock.
- **Proper tools** —Knowing and using the correct tools needed to do a particular job; adjusting entry activity based upon available tools.
- **Security barriers** — Could include bars, grilles, Lexan® windows, and others; require specialized training, tools, and knowledge to force; block escape routes for both fire brigade members and occupants; may necessitate making multiple openings for entry.

NOTE: The tools described in this chapter are not intended to be a comprehensive list of all tools that may be available.

Fire brigade members must know the capabilities and limitations of the forcible entry tools available to them. Selecting the proper tool can make the difference in overcoming a barrier. This section describes the various forcible entry tools and provides information on their use, care, and maintenance. When using any forcible entry tools, always wear appropriate personal protective equipment (PPE), especially hand, eye, and hearing protection.

> **CAUTION:** Always wear appropriate PPE when using forcible entry tools.

Forcible entry tools can be divided into four basic categories:

- Cutting tools
- Prying tools
- Pushing/pulling tools
- Striking tools

NOTE: These tools were previously discussed in Chapter 12, Fire Brigade Tools and Equipment.

Forcing Entry Through Doors

NFPA 1081 (2018): 5.3.2, 5.3.10, 6.2.2, 6.3.7

Forcing entry through doors is the most conventional method used in the fire service. A fire brigade member can perform forcible entry, if necessary, once he or she has sized-up a door. Determining the type of forcible entry to use depends on the fire brigade member's knowledge of door construction and locks.

Begin the decision making process with a focus on producing the least amount of damage to maximum amount. Determine the severity of the emergency and the speed with which entry must be gained. For example, destroying or removing the door during forcible entry eliminates the ability to open and close it to maintain door control. Consider the following ways to reduce the amount of damage that will result from forcible entry:

- Try to open the door in the normal fashion. If that does not work, look for a lock box. A lock box may contain a key or means of opening the door.
- Look for a door window or side light panel that you can break to provide access to the lock on the interior.
- Determine if it is quicker to:
  - Force the lock.
  - Remove hinge pins.
  - Force the door.
  - Pry the door from the jamb.

Rapid-entry lock box systems provide a means to open locked doors without forcing entry because the lock box holds all necessary keys or numeric keypad combinations to unlock the building, storage areas, gates, and elevators. The lock box is mounted at a high-visibility location on the building's exterior. Unauthorized duplication of the master key is prevented because the special key blanks are not available to locksmiths and cannot be duplicated with conventional equipment. Only the fire brigade possesses a master key that opens all boxes in its jurisdiction.

During forcible entry, it is critical to maintain control of the door. The structure's ventilation profile will change if you open a door, and it may have an adverse effect on fire behavior. If the door will be damaged to the point that it cannot be closed, take steps to deal with subsequent changes in fire behavior. Station a fire brigade member at the door to maintain control of the door to block the flow path from the exterior and control air flow into the structure during interior fire fighting operations. This fire brigade member can help drag hose into the structure as needed **(Figure 14.3)**. He or she can also prevent the entry door from closing on a hoseline. Propping a door open is an option, but only if the door's closing would block a means of egress.

Figure 14.3 If a forced door won't close or stay closed, a fire brigade member may be stationed at the door to control it.

Gaining Access to the Property

Fire brigade members may need to force their way through a fence or gate in order to reach the door to be opened. Property owners often install security fences and gates to prevent unauthorized access. Preincident surveys can provide information on the type of security used and location of lock boxes.

Fences can be made of:

- Wood
- Masonry
- Chain-link
- Ornamental metal
- Plastic
- Barbed wire
- Wire fabric

Some fences are topped with barbed wire or razor ribbon **(Figure 14.4)**. Fences may also be used to contain livestock, pets, or guard dogs for security. Adequate size-up and using the most efficient tools and techniques are crucial when forcing entry through fences and gates.

Fire brigade members may sometimes encounter electrified fences. Take care when cutting these fences to prevent electrical shocks. If possible, deenergize the fence before cutting; if not, take insulation precautions to avoid electric shock or find other means of entry.

CAUTION: Electric shock may result if you cut electrified fences before deenergizing them.

Figure 14.4 The razor wire atop this fence can impede intruders and fire brigade personnel alike.

Figure 14.5 This gate is secured with a chain and padlock.

Fencing material that is stretched tight can recoil when it is cut, inflicting injuries to fire brigade members. Stand beside the fence post and cut the wire where it joins the post. When it is cut, it will recoil in the direction of the next post. Cut wire fences near posts to facilitate repair after the incident, provide adequate space for fire apparatus access, and reduce the danger of injury from the recoil of wires when they are cut. Alternatively, cut the wire bands holding the fence material to the posts and lay the material on the ground.

Various fences can be forced in several ways:

- Cut barbed wire fences with bolt cutters.

- Cut chain-link fences with a rotary saw; bolt cutters may be used as well but are slower.

> **CAUTION:** Wire will recoil in the direction of the next post on the fence when it is cut.

In the case of masonry and ornamental metal fences, it may be easier and faster to go over the fence than through it. A-frame ladders can be used to bridge these fences.

Security fences will have access points with locked or controlled gates. Security gates are used for:

- Residential housing complexes
- Industrial sites
- Construction sites
- Agricultural sites

Where continuous access is needed, gates may be staffed during operations hours. In other situations, the gates may be locked with chains and padlocks or other locking devices. In some industrial complexes, electronic locks activated by a remote opener (similar to a garage door opener), barcode reader, or a keypad usually control gates. There may also be a lock box near the gate that contains an opener or keypad code.

If necessary, and if allowed by the fire brigade's SOPs, fire brigade members may force entry by prying the gate open or by using the apparatus bumper to force the gate. Fence gates are often secured with padlocks or chains and can be accessed using the techniques described previously **(Figure 14.5)**. Gates used to secure patios, swimming pools, or backyards will usually have internal key-operated deadbolt locks. These gates are best accessed using through-the-lock and rim lock techniques. Prying or cutting the gate should be the last method chosen because of the amount of damage that will be done to the gate and fence.

NOTE: Some gates on commercial sites may be provided with special padlocks and/or electronic key switches that are operated with the same key used to access lock boxes.

Door Locks/Latches

Locks and latches are part of the hardware normally found on all exterior doors and many interior doors. Door latches keep the door closed and consist of a handle on both sides of the door and a spring-loaded bar that extends into a receiver in the doorframe. It may or may not have a lock as part of the assembly. Locks can be divided into four basic types:

- Mortise latch and lock
- Rim lock
- Cylindrical lock
- High security locks

Mortise Latch and Lock

The **mortise latch and lock** assembly is mounted in a cavity in the door edge. Older mortise assemblies have only the latch to hold the door closed, while newer units consist of both a latch and a key-operated deadbolt **(Figure 14.6)**. When the mechanism is in the locked position, the bolt protrudes from the lock into a receiver that is in the jamb. The latch may be operated with a doorknob or lever. Mortise locks are used on exterior wood and metal doors and can be found on:

- Private residences
- Commercial buildings
- Industrial buildings

Figure 14.6 A cutaway illustration of a mortise latch and lock assembly.

Cylindrical Lock

Cylindrical locks are the most common type of lockset found in residential applications. Their installation involves boring two holes at right angles to one another: one through the face of the door to accommodate the main locking mechanism and the other in the edge of the door to receive the latch or bolt mechanism. The two types of cylindrical locks are the key-in-knob lock and the tubular deadbolt lock.

The key-in-knob lock has a keyway in the outside doorknob; the inside knob may contain either a keyway or a button **(Figure 14.7)**. The

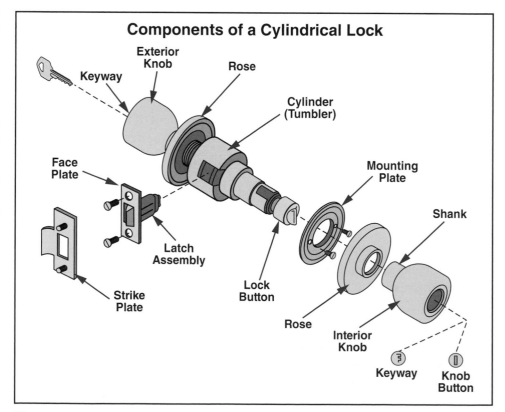

Figure 14.7 An exploded view of a key-in-knob cylindrical lock assembly.

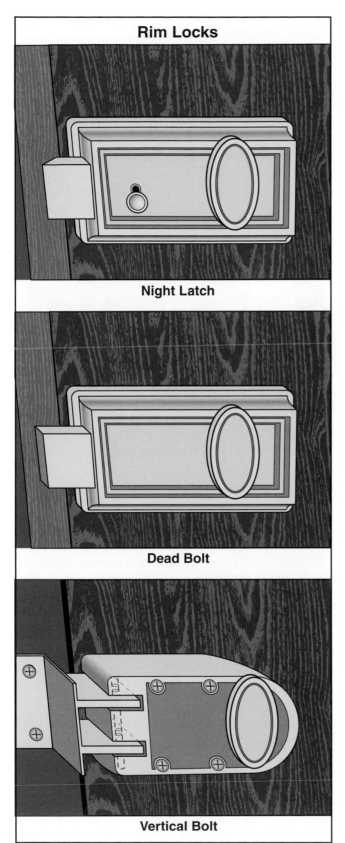

Rim Locks

Night Latch

Dead Bolt

Vertical Bolt

Figure 14.8 Three types of rim locks.

button may be a push button or a push-and-turn button. Key-in-knob locks are equipped with a latch mechanism that locks and unlocks using both the key and, if present, the knob button. In the unlocked position, a turn of either knob retracts the spring-loaded beveled latch bolt, which is usually no longer than ¾-inch (19 mm). Because of the relatively short length of the latch, key-in-knob locks are some of the easiest to pry open. If the door and frame are pried far enough apart, the latch clears the strike and allows the door to swing open.

The tubular deadbolt lock is mounted above the doorknob and may have a single cylinder or double action cylinder. The single cylinder deadbolt has a keyway on the outside of the door and a thumb turn knob on the inside. The double cylinder lock has a keyway on both sides of the door.

NOTE: The easiest way to breach modern deadbolts in a wood residential door is to force the door itself.

Rim Lock

A **rim lock** is mounted on the interior door surface and is used as a supplemental lock for doors that may or may not have other types of locks. Turning a thumb-turn knob on the inside of the door operates rim locks.

Although some rim locks have a keyway in a cylinder on the exterior of the door, not all do, making it difficult to recognize their presence. A variety of rim locks are currently available including the following **(Figure 14.8)**:

- **Night latch** — This rim lock has a spring-loaded bolt with a beveled edge facing the doorframe. This feature allows the door to lock when it is closed.

- **Deadbolt** — This rim lock has a rectangular bolt that you must manually retract before the door can be closed and the bolt engaged with the receiver. If the bolt is extended, the door cannot be closed.

- **Vertical deadbolt** — This rim lock has a bolt that slides vertically into the receiver and does not cross the door opening and makes it impossible to open by spreading the door from the doorjamb.

High Security Locks

High security locks include **(Figure 14.9)**:

- **Multiple bolt locks** — The multiple bolt or multilock is a deadbolt lock that, when engaged, projects bolts 1 inch (25 mm) into two or more points on one edge of the door. Some versions extend hardened steel bolts into all four edges of the doorframe. The lock may have a thumb turn knob or keyway on the inside of the door as well as a keyway on the exterior. A surface-mounted version may also be encountered.

Figure 14.9 High security lock systems include: multiple bolt locks, electronic key locks, and electromagnetic locks.

- **Electronic keyless locks** — Found on both exterior and interior doors, keyless or digital locks may have a:

  — Keypad

  — Card reader

  — Fingerprint-activated screen

NOTE: The locks are generally battery powered. Some keypads may also have a keyway. They are used for areas that require continuous security and controlled access.

- **Electromagnetic locks** — The electromagnetic or magnetic lock consists of an electromagnet attached to the doorframe and an armature plate mounted on the door. An electric current passing through the electromagnet and the armature plate holds the door shut. Shutting off the power will release the door.

NOTE: These types of locks are generally difficult to open using hand tools.

Locking Devices

Locking devices may be supplemental to the door lock or used in place of it. The best example of locking devices are padlocks. Other devices, such as door chains or drop bars, impede entry but are not locks in the traditional sense.

Padlocks are portable or detachable locking devices. There are two basic types of padlocks: standard and heavy-duty. Standard padlocks have shackles of ¼ inch (6 mm) or less in diameter and are not case-hardened steel. Heavy-duty padlocks have case-hardened steel shackles more than ¼ inch (6 mm) in diameter. Many heavy-duty padlocks have what is called "toe and heel locking" where both ends of the shackle are locked when depressed into the lock mechanism. These shackles will not pivot if one side of the shackle is cut. To remove the lock, cut both sides of the shackle. Padlocks may be key or combination operated.

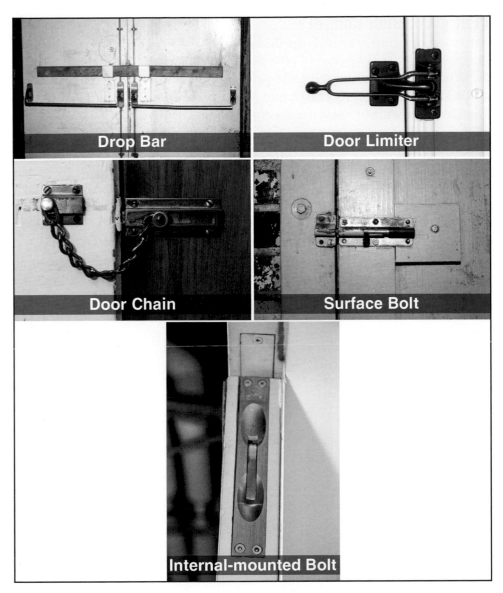

Figure 14.10 Other types of locking devices.

Other locking devices include the following **(Figure 14.10)**:

- **Drop bar** — Brackets are bolted or welded to the door and a wood or metal bar rests in the brackets and extends across the doorframe.

- **Door chain** — The door chain is a supplemental locking device for residential doors. A chain permits the door to be opened enough for a person within a residence to see and speak to a visitor but still restrict access.

- **Door limiter** — Restricts the opening of the door and is similar to the supplemental security locks found in hotel rooms. The door limiter consists of a frame-mounted plate with a shaft and knob and a hinged U-shaped shackle that mounts on the door.

- **Surface bolt** — Manually operated supplemental locking devices that can be mounted on most doors and some windows.

- **Internal-mounted bolt** — Flush bolts are installed in the edge of one side of a set of double doors. This permits one side to remain locked while the other door is used for entry and exit. When desired, the bolts can be retracted and both doors opened.

With the exception of the drop bar and the internally mounted bolts, the remainder of the locking devices may be easy to force depending on the tool that you use. It will also be difficult to tell if any of these types of devices are mounted and in use before attempting to force entry.

Coordinating Forcible Entry and Door Control

Forcible entry creates a ventilation opening in a structure and changes the flow path of hot fire gases. Forcing entry also introduces a new source of oxygen to the fire in the structure. As a result, forcible entry must be coordinated with whatever interior activities require entry. Before forcing entry, personnel should be prepared to enter a structure to conduct search and rescue or interior fire attack. The longer the time period between forcing an opening or breaking glass and the beginning of interior fire attack or search and rescue, the more time the fire has to entrain new oxygen and grow.

A door may not close properly once it is forced. You or another fire brigade member should be assigned to monitor the door to control the flow path and to keep the door closed unless coordinated tactics require it to be open.

Breaking Door Glass

One of the fastest and least destructive techniques for forcing locked doors is to break the glass in the door or the sidelight next to it. Once the glass is broken, the fire brigade member can reach inside and unlock the door. In some situations, breaking the glass (or what appears to be glass) may be more difficult and costly. Tempered glass is expensive and Plexiglas™, Lexan®, and wire glass may resist being broken with conventional hand tools.

Ordinary window glass will shatter into sharp fragments when broken. Fire brigade members should wear full protective equipment, especially hand and eye protection, to prevent injuries from shattered glass. If fire brigade members are breaking the glass to gain access into a burning building, they should wear SCBA and have a charged hoseline in place, ready to attack the fire. The techniques used for breaking both door glass and window glass are similar.

Consider that glass doors or glass in doors are part of the barrier to ventilation of the door. Breaking the glass will have the same effect on the flow path as opening the door; however, the glass cannot be "unbroken." Once the glass is broken, that doorway is a ventilated opening to the fire for the remainder of the operation **(Figure 14.11)**.

Figure 14.11 If this glass door is broken, fresh air will continue to enter the structure even as some heat and smoke escape.

Forcing Swinging Doors

The most common type of door is one that swings at least 90 degrees to open and close. Most swinging doors have hinges mounted on one side that permit them to swing in one or both directions; others swing on pivot pins at the top and bottom of the door. Swinging doors can be either inward- or outward-swinging or both. Double-acting swinging doors are capable of swinging 180 degrees. An easy way to recognize which way a door swings is to look for the hinges. If you can see the hinges of the door, it swings toward you. If you cannot see the hinges, the door swings away from you. Forcing entry through swinging doors involves basic skills and requires practice to master.

Figure 14.12 One fire brigade member can attempt to force a door using a rambar but using a Halligan tool and a striking tool requires two fire brigade members.

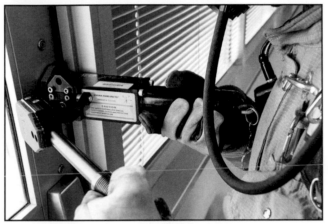

Figure 14.13 A fire brigade member uses a rabbit tool to force a metal door in a metal frame.

Inward-Swinging Doors

Forcible entry of single inward-swinging doors requires one or two skilled fire brigade members, depending upon the tool or tools used. For example, a single fire brigade member using a rambar can open most standard swinging doors; however, if a Halligan tool and flat-head axe are used, two fire brigade members are required **(Figure 14.12)**.

If the swinging door is metal or metal-clad in a metal frame set in a concrete or masonry wall, you may need other forcible entry techniques. In some cases, you can use a hydraulic door opener (often called a **rabbit tool**) to force the door open **(Figure 14.13)**. In other cases, doors resist being pried open, so it is necessary to cut around the lock in either of two ways. First, you can use a rotary saw with a metal cutting blade to make two intersecting cuts that isolate the locking mechanism and allow the door to swing. A second method using three intersecting cuts can also produce the same result.

Outward-Swinging Doors

Because the hinges on outward-swinging doors are mounted on the outside, it is often possible to use a nail set and hammer to drive the pins out of the hinges and simply remove the door. If the hinge bottoms are solid and the pins cannot be driven out, it may be possible to break off the hinges with a rambar or Halligan. It may be possible to cut off the hinges with a rotary saw or a cutting torch **(Figure 14.14)**. You can also insert the blade of a rambar or Halligan into the space between the door and the doorjamb and pry that space open wide enough to allow the lock bolt to slip from its keeper.

Figure 14.14 Two methods of forcing a door are by breaking or prying the hinges off or by using a rotary saw to cut them.

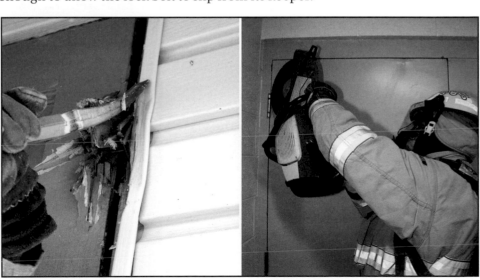

Double-Swinging Doors

Double-swinging doors can present a problem depending on how they are secured. If only a mortise lock secures the doors, you can insert the blade of a rambar or wedge of a Halligan between the doors to pry them far enough apart for the bolt to slip past the receiver. You can insert a metal-cutting blade of a rotary saw into the space between the doors to cut the deadbolt **(Figure 14.15)**. Some double doors have a security molding or weather strip over the space between the doors. Remove this molding or cut away a section to allow the blade of the forcible entry tool to be inserted.

Figure 14.15 A rotary saw can be used to cut the deadbolt of a set of double doors.

Doors with Drop Bars

If a single- or double-swinging door is locked with a drop bar, try one of the following methods to force entry:

- Use a rambar or Halligan tool to spread the space between the double doors. Insert a handsaw blade or other narrow tool through the opening and lift the bar up and out of the stirrups.

- Use a rotary saw to cut the exposed bolt heads that are holding the stirrups on the outside of the door. This will allow the drop bar to fall away and the door to be opened.

- Insert a rotary saw blade through the space between the double doors and cut the security bar.

Tempered Plate Glass Doors

In commercial, light industrial, and institutional occupancies, fire brigade members may be faced with metal-frame doors with **tempered plate glass** panels. These doors are heavy and very expensive. Tempered glass mounted in a metal doorframe can be very difficult to break. Unlike regular plate glass, tempered glass resists heat; when broken, it shatters into thousands of tiny cubelike pieces.

Only as a last resort should you break tempered plate glass doors. If a tempered plate glass door must be broken, use the following guidelines:

- Use the pick end of a pick-head axe and strike the glass at a bottom corner.

- Wear complete PPE including a helmet-mounted faceshield or goggles to protect against eye injury.

- Place a salvage cover against the glass and strike through the cover to shatter the glass **(Figure 14.16)**.

- Scrape any remaining glass from the frame.

NOTE: If you want to avoid breaking the glass, you can also use the through-the-lock method to open tempered plate glass doors.

Figure 14.16 Fire brigade members practicing a method for breaking tempered glass.

Forcing Sliding Doors

Sliding doors consist of one or more panels that slide in or on a track on guide wheels or rollers. These doors may be operated manually or by some type of mechanism. Sliding doors may be found in hospitals, combustible/flammable liquid storage rooms, boiler rooms, separating process areas, confinement/ prison cells, aircraft hangars, and other facilities. Locking devices include latches on the inside of the door and security bars placed in the track. Forcible entry techniques include breaking the glass with an axe, cutting through a panel, or on smaller sliding doors, lifting the sliding panel up and out of its track. Attempting to spread a glass-type sliding door from the frame will result in the door shattering uncontrollably.

Aircraft hangars are equipped with large sliding doors usually with steel framing and aluminum or steel siding. Hangar doors are usually equipped with smaller personnel doors in one or more panels **(Figure 14.17)**. Some facilities are equipped with sliding fire doors to help isolate different portions of a structure during a fire.

Figure 14.17 An aircraft hangar equipped with numerous sliding doors and a personnel door (inside the circle).

Forcing High Security Area Access Doors and Gates

Fire brigade members will encounter security doors and gates in a number of forms including:

- Rollup doors, both manual and power operated
- Doors with open steel bars
- Doors that consist of multiple slats that can be closed to form a solid panel

High security area access doors or gates will delay entry and will require planning to determine the most efficient form of entry. Some doors may have padlocks on the outside while others may have locks on the inside. If the lock is inside, there is usually a second means of entry into the structure. Forcible entry techniques include cutting off the padlock, using a rotary saw to make an opening near the lock, or cutting out a section of the door. You should know the specific types of security doors and gates in your response area and practice the correct procedure for each.

Forcing Padlocks

Fire brigade members must be capable of forcing either the padlock itself or the device to which it is fastened. Fire brigade members can use conventional forcible entry tools to break a padlock or detach the hasp to gain access. The following tools are available to make forcible entry through padlocks easier:

- **Duck-billed lock breaker** — Wedge-shaped tool that will widen and break the shackles of padlocks, much like using the hook of a Halligan-type tool. Insert this tool into the lock shackle, and strike the tool with a maul or flat-head axe until the padlock shackles break.

- **Hammerhead pick** — Has a pick on one end of the tool head and a hammerhead or striking surface on the other. Insert the pick into the padlock shackle and strike the tool with a maul or flat-head axe until the padlock shackles break.

- **Locking pliers and chain** — Lock the locking pliers firmly onto the body of the padlock. To keep the padlock stable, hold onto the chain. To cut both shackles, another fire brigade member uses a power saw or torch.

- **Hockey puck lock breaker (pipe wrench)** — Adjust the pipe wrench to grip the hockey puck lock firmly. Apply downward pressure to the end of the wrench's handle to twist the lock and break its interior mechanism.

If these techniques fail to break the padlock, break the hasp or detach it from the doorframe. If the shackle of the padlock exceeds ¼ inch (6 mm) and the lock, including the body, is case-hardened, the fire brigade member faces a more difficult forcible entry task.

NOTE: This method will not work on some high-security locks. These locks have a case-hardened retaining ring in the lock body that prevents the lock cylinder from being removed.

Using a rotary saw with a metal-cutting blade or a cutting torch may be the quickest method for removing some padlocks **(Figure 14.18)**. High-security padlocks are designed with heel and toe shackles. These shackles will not pivot if only one side of the shackle is cut. Cutting padlocks with a power saw or torch can be somewhat dangerous. Use the following techniques for removing this type of padlock:

- Stabilize the lock with a set of locking pliers.

- Attach a chain to the lock and pull it straight away from the hasp.

- Request a second fire brigade member to cut both sides of the padlock shackle with the saw or torch.

Figure 14.18 A fire brigade member practicing cutting a padlock with a rotary saw.

Forcing Overhead Doors

Forcing overhead doors can be labor intensive and in the facility environment, may not be the method of choice. However, if it is necessary to force an overhead door, use a rotary saw to cut a square or rectangular opening about 6 feet (2 m) high and nearly the full width of the door. Once you have access to the interior, use the lift mechanism to open the door fully. Use cribbing or shoring blocks to prevent overhead doors from closing unintentionally. Attach a pair of vice grips (locking pliers) to the overhead door rail above head height to keep the door from closing **(Figure 14.19)**.

> **WARNING:** Block all overhead doors in the up or open position to prevent injury to fire brigade members if the built-in control device fails.

Forcing Fire Doors

Fire doors are movable assemblies designed to cover doorway openings in rated separation walls to prevent the spread of fire from one part of a building to another. Types of standard fire doors include, sliding, swinging, and overhead rolling varieties. Fire doors are normally found on the inside of structures, separating one area from another, enclosing a hazardous process or storage area, or protecting a means of egress (exit path such as a protected stairway).

Cut Opening

Lift Door

Attach Vice Grips to Rail

Figure 14.19 Illustrating one method for forcing overhead doors.

Exterior fire doors are usually found where a structure must be protected from an adjacent exposure. Because the door is on the outside of the structure, it will probably be locked. Forcible entry should be similar to any other overhead or sliding door.

Interior fire doors will have been activated manually or automatically when the fire was detected. Because these doors only operate when there is a fire, they will not lock in place when closed. When passing through an opening that a fire door protects, block the door open to prevent it from closing and blocking a means of egress or cutting off the hoseline water supplies.

Fire doors are a part of the protection system in the structure; however, there may be times when you may need to force fire doors. They are positioned to create separations with higher than normal fire-resistance ratings. Leaving fire doors in place is preferable — much like not interfering with sprinkler systems. Use caution when propping these doors open or forcing them because it also changes the flow path.

Forcing Entry Through Windows

NFPA 1081 (2018): 5.3.2, 5.3.10, 6.2.2, 6.3.7

Windows are sometimes easier to force than doors even though they are not the best entry point into a burning building. Entry can be made through a window to open a locked door from the inside. As with doors, size-up of windows is critical to a successful forced entry. Forcing open the wrong window may also disrupt ventilation efforts, intensify fire growth, and draw fire to uninvolved sections of the building.

Breaking Window Glass

The most common forcible entry technique used is breaking the glass, but it creates the following hazards and obstacles:

- Slows entry into the structure while fire brigade members clear the glass shards from the frame.

- Creates flying glass shards that may travel great distances from windows on upper floors.

- Covers floors in glass shards which can make footing treacherous for fire brigade members advancing charged hoselines.

- Could shower glass on victims inside the structure causing additional injury.

- Changes the flow path.

- Cannot be undone once the glass is broken.

NOTE: When using a pike pole to break a window, position yourself upwind and higher than the window so that falling glass will not slide down the handle toward you.

Wire glass is more difficult to break and remove than ordinary window glass because the wire prevents the glass from shattering and falling out of the frame. Use a sharp tool, such as the pick of an axe, to chop wire glass out of its frame.

Safety film is a product often applied to windows in high-rises, schools, or larger structures. The film acts as an adhesive that prevents particles or shards of glass from falling when the glass breaks. Safety film can be an impediment to breaking windows during operations. Where the safety film is present, cutting tools rather than striking tools may be required to break the windows.

Because windows containing two and three layers of glass are expensive, fire brigade members must decide if the benefits of breaking the window outweigh the expense of replacing the windows. Multipane windows are also time-consuming to remove because the glass is held in place by a rubber cement that makes shard removal difficult.

Forcing Windows

Forcible entry through windows can be made using a variety of approaches depending upon the window's construction. Forcible entry approaches to various window constructions include:

- **Fixed Windows** — Force fixed windows or block window walls only as a last resort. These walls are 2 to 4 inches (50 to 100 mm) thick and may be individual blocks held together with mortar or vinyl strips or manufactured panels of blocks up to 47 inches (1 190 mm) square. To break these windows, you may need a sledge hammer or battering ram.

- **Double-Hung Windows** — Forcible entry techniques for double-hung windows depend on how the window is locked and the material of which the sash frames are made. Metal-frame windows are more difficult to pry. The lock mechanism will not pull out of the sash and may jam, creating additional problems. Use the same technique given for a woodframe window, but if the lock does not yield with a minimal amount of pressure, it may be quicker to break the glass and open the lock manually.

- **Single-Hung Windows** — Single-hung windows are identical to double-hung windows with the exception that only the bottom panel moves. Locks and locking devices are the same as those found on the double-hung windows. Forcible entry procedures are also the same as those used on the double-hung window.

- **Casement Windows** — To force open a single-casement window, break the lowest pane of glass and clear shards from the frame. Cut open the window screen behind in the same area. Reach in and unlock the locking mechanism, operate the crank to open the window frame, and then remove the screen completely. If the window has one full pane of glass, break it, clear the shards from the frame, and remove the screen. It will be unnecessary to crank it open once the glass is removed.

- **Horizontal Sliding Windows** — The technique for forcing entry through a horizontal sliding window is the same as that used with the sliding door.

- **Awning Windows** — Forcible entry through awning windows requires that you either break the glass or pry the window up from the frame.

- **Jalousie Windows** — You must remove several panes to enter through these windows. Because most awning and jalousie windows are relatively small, they offer very restricted access even when all of the glass is removed. As an alternative, if you must enter through a jalousie window, it may be faster and more efficient to cut through the wall around the entire window assembly and remove it.

- **Projecting Windows** — Forcing entry through projecting windows may be limited to breaking the glass or cutting the window panel out of the frame.

- **Pivoting Windows** — Forcing entry through these windows follows the same procedure as the projecting window.

- **Barred Windows** — If there are sufficient resources available, remove all security bars from the building to allow for emergency egress when crews are operating inside the building. Security grilles or screens may be permanently fixed, hinged at the top or side, or fitted into brackets and locked securely. Security grilles or screens that are hinged can be opened easily if the lock is accessible and can be cut from the frame. If not, you can cut the screen fabric with a rotary saw. Once you remove the screen, the window must be forced as previously described.

Secure or More Structurally Sound Windows

Some windows are intentionally designed to be more secure or more structurally sound. Such windows may be constructed with materials that cannot be cut or forced. Others may require special tools and equipment to force. Your local jurisdiction should provide you with training and tools to force these windows. The jurisdiction should also identify buildings that are so secure that the windows cannot be forced and have special fire incident plans for these structures in case of emergencies. In the absence of proper tools, training, or accurate knowledge of the locations of these features, it is preferable to explore other options for gaining entry into the structure rather than attempting to identify a method for forcing the secure window.

Breaching Walls

NFPA 1081 (2018): 5.3.2, 5.3.10, 6.2.2, 6.3.7

In situations where doors and windows are inaccessible or heavily secured, it may be faster and more efficient to gain access through the structure's wall. Creating a hole in a wall is known as **breaching**. Breaching requires a thorough knowledge of building construction, accurate size-up of the situation, and determination that breaching a particular wall is safe and will accomplish the purpose. Exterior walls will be more difficult to breach than interior walls as described in the following sections.

Depending on the type of structure and its design, interior walls may be load-bearing or nonload-bearing. Construction materials may be:

- Plaster or Gypsum Partition Walls
- Reinforced Gypsum Walls

The walls may contain electrical wires, water or gas pipes, or heating and cooling ducts. Your supervisor must determine what effect breaching the wall will have on the structural integrity prior to making the opening. The methods for breaching masonry, concrete, and glass block walls were described previously.

Figure 14.20 A fire brigade member using a Halligan tool to breach an interior wall during a training exercise.

Plaster or Gypsum Partition Walls

Both load-bearing and nonload-bearing interior walls are designed to limit fire spread. Covering the wall with a variety of materials, including gypsum wallboard or lath-and-plaster over wooden or metal studs and framing, provides fire resistance. Both lath-and-plaster and gypsum wallboard are often relatively easy to penetrate with forcible entry striking hand tools or rotary and chain saws **(Figure 14.20)**.

Reinforced Gypsum Walls

In some newer buildings, the interior walls in public access areas such as hallways, lobbies, and restrooms are covered with gypsum wallboard that is reinforced with Lexan®. Like other wallboard, reinforced wallboard is attached to the wall frame using drywall nails or screws. Reinforced wallboard looks identical to other wallboard because the Lexan® reinforcement is installed on the back of the wallboard. This wallboard is designed to resist breaching using conventional forcible entry hand tools. If fire brigade members are to breach this material in a timely fashion, they must know that they are not dealing with ordinary wallboard and must bring power saws with them when they enter the building. The only way they will know that the wallboard is reinforced is if the preincident planning survey identifies the wallboard material.

Chapter Review

1. What factors will help the IC determine where to force entry?

2. What ways can be used to force fences?

3. Where can mortise latch and lock be found?

4. Name and describe three other locking devices.

5. Why must forcible entry be coordinated with whatever interior activities that require entry?

6. What PPE should be worn when breaking door glass?

7. What methods can be used to force swinging doors locked with a drop bar?

8. Name and describe two types of tools that can be used to force padlocks.

9. What should be done when passing through the opening that an interior fire door protects?

10. What obstacles can be created when breaking window glass?

11. What type of walls require power tools when breaching?

Discussion Questions

1. What types of locks and locking devices are present in your facilities?

2. What type of windows are found in your facilities?

Key Terms

Breaching — The act of creating a hole in a wall or floor to gain access to a structure or portion of a structure.

Cylindrical Lock — Lock having the lock cylinder contained in the knob.

Forcible Entry — Techniques used by fire personnel to gain entry into buildings, vehicles, aircraft, or other areas of confinement when normal means of entry are locked or blocked.

Mortise Latch and Lock — Lock assembly mounted in a cavity in a door's edge.

Rabbit Tool — Hydraulic spreading tool that is specially designed to open doors that swing inward.

Rim Lock — Type of auxiliary lock such as a deadbolt mounted on the interior surface of a door.

Tempered Plate Glass — Type of glass specially treated to become harder and more break-resistant than plate glass or a single sheet of laminated glass.

Skill Sheet List

The following skill sheets should be used to evaluate the skills described in this chapter:

NOTE: Students should wear the PPE appropriate to the NFPA 1081 level (Incipient, Advanced Exterior, Interior Structural, etc...) being evaluated.

Common Advanced Exterior and Interior Structural Facility Fire Brigade Member Training Requirements

Chapter Contents

JPRs addressed in this chapter

This chapter provides information that addresses the following job performance requirements of NFPA 1081, *Standard for Facility Fire Brigade Member Professional Qualifications (2018)*.

5.2.4   6.2.8

5.2.9   6.2.10

1. Describe the safety precautions to take when conducting search and rescue operations. [5.2.4, 6.2.8]

2. Explain the different methods for conducting search and rescue methods. [5.2.4, 6.2.8]

3. Describe the methods for conducting rescues. [5.2.4, 6.2.8]

4. Identify the equipment that may be needed to power and light a rescue scene. [5.2.4, 6.2.8]

5. Explain the importance of preparing for special rescue situations and extractions. [5.2.4, 6.2.8]

6. Describe rapid intervention crew (RIC) operations. [5.2.9, 6.2.10]

Chapter 15

Search and Rescue and Rapid Intervention Crew (RIC) Operations

Because they may deal with life-threatening situations, facility fire brigade members must be thoroughly prepared for any potential search, rescue, and/or extrication situation they encounter at their facility site. IFSTA makes a definite distinction between rescue and extrication. *Rescue* incidents involve the removal and treatment of victims from situations involving natural elements, structural collapse, elevation differences, or any other situation not considered to be an extrication incident. *Extrication* incidents involve the removal and treatment of victims who are trapped by some type of man-made machinery or equipment.

Prior to committing personnel to a rescue operation, the Incident Commander (IC) should conduct a basic "Risk vs. Hazards" analysis. Because these situations are very dynamic and vary greatly, this analysis should include identifying: Is the victim(s) viable? What resources are on hand? What is the experience and skill level of the FBMs on hand? How far is the travel distance to reach the victim(s)? Any additional hazards? This basic "Risk vs. Hazards" analysis is critical. Many times rescuers have been severely injured and killed during rescue attempts for someone who has already perished.

Safety

NFPA 1081 (2018): 5.2.4, 6.2.8

While searching for victims in a fire, rescuers must always consider their own safety. Incident commanders also must consider the hazards to which rescuers may be exposed while performing search and rescue. Safety is the primary concern of rescuers because hurried, unsafe rescue attempts may have serious consequences for rescuers as well as victims.

Personnel must be properly trained and equipped with the necessary tools to accomplish a rescue in the shortest possible time. A rope is a typical search and rescue tool. A rope or hoseline extended into a room from the entry point may be used as a guideline to find the exit when conducting search and rescue operations in the dark or under extremely hazardous conditions **(Figure 15.1)**.

Figure 15.1 Fire brigade members can follow a hoseline to find their way out of a smoke-filled room.

Other search and rescue tools include marking devices (to indicate which rooms have already been searched), forcible entry tools (to aid in entry and egress and to enlarge the sweep area when searching), and thermal imagers (TIs), where available. Hoselines should be used to protect search teams. Not only do they afford the rescuer with protection from heat and fire, but they are a good way for personnel to find their way out of the fire area if they need to do so quickly.

Safety During Facility Searches

Every time a fire brigade member or rescuer responds to a fire, a human life may be in jeopardy. In order to assess the degree to which someone may be threatened, a search is initiated as soon as possible. While rescuers must work quickly, they must also operate safely and with sound judgment if they are to fulfill their assignment and avoid becoming victims themselves.

In some facilities, safely shutting down processes or operations to protect the community is the first priority over fire control and search and rescue. As others are evacuated, assigned employees may remain in specially designed enclosures, such as a control room, to safely shutdown critical operations. The location(s) of these critical areas should be noted during preplanning.

As personnel search a multistory structure, especially when visibility is limited because of smoke and/or darkness, they must always be alert for weakened or hazardous structural conditions, especially the floors. They should continually feel or sound the floor in front of them with their hands or a tool to ensure that the floor is still intact **(Figure 15.2)**. Otherwise, they may blindly crawl into an open elevator shaft, a stairway, an arsonist's trap, or a hole that may have burned through the floor. Personnel on or directly below the fire floor should also be alert for signs that the floor/ceiling assembly above them has weakened.

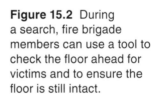

Figure 15.2 During a search, fire brigade members can use a tool to check the floor ahead for victims and to ensure the floor is still intact.

At a fire, fire brigade personnel should examine the situation and make an intelligent, informed decision based on the known events or circumstances. This data assists fire brigade personnel in determining if facility occupants in the hazardous environment can survive the fire and smoke conditions that are present and whether to commit personnel to life-saving and interior operations.

The environment within a structural fire can exceed 500° F (260° C) within three to four minutes with the potential for flashover (approximately 1,110° F [599° C]) to occur within five minutes. The upper human survivability limit is 212° F (100° C) according to the NFPA. While fire brigade members have personal protective equipment and SCBA to protect them under such conditions, facility occupants do not. Occupant survivability profiling is a type of size-up that should be employed to evaluate the potential of an occupant being alive within a fire environment. In conducting occupant survivability profiling, the fire brigade leader asks the following questions:

1. Are occupants suspected of or known to be trapped?

2. Is it reasonable to assume that the occupants are still alive?

If the answers to these questions are *no*, then the responders should take a different approach. They should stop what they are doing, analyze the bigger picture, and gather additional information on the situation. Fire brigade personnel should focus on fighting the fire first and search for victims later when it is safer to do so. This approach may contradict the instinct of fire brigade personnel to race into a hazardous environment to attempt rescue, but the use of occupant survivability profiling can be paramount to protecting the health and safety of fire brigade members.

When searching within a burning facility, fire brigade personnel should be very cautious when opening doors. Use a TI to check the door or spray with a short burst of water from a hose line. They should feel the top of the door and the doorknob with the back of a gloved hand to determine the heat level. If the door is excessively hot, it should not be opened until a charged hoseline is in position. Fire brigade members should not remain in front of the door while opening it. They should stay to one side, keep low, and slowly open the door. This can be assisted by using a rope to maintain control of the door as it opens. If there is fire behind the door, staying low allows the escaping heat and combustion products to pass over their heads.

NOTE: To prevent injury, fire brigades members should always keep on their gloves (and all other parts of the protective ensemble) when inside a burning facility.

If an inward-opening door is difficult to open, fire brigade members should not kick the door to force it open because a collapsed victim may be just inside the door. Kicking the door may injure the victim further, and it is neither a safe nor a professional way to force a door. The door should be slowly pushed open and the area behind it checked for possible victims.

Trapped or Disoriented Fire Brigade Members

Even with the best Incident Command and personnel accountability systems in place, unusual circumstances can lead to a fire brigade member, or a group of fire brigade members, becoming trapped or disoriented within a burning structure. Unexpected structural collapse, doors closing behind crews, or fire brigade members straying from a hoseline or search rope are all ways that this may occur.

If trapped or disoriented, fire brigade members should remain calm, call "**MAYDAY**," and activate their PASS device **(Figure 15.3)**. Fire brigade members have radios, and they should try to make radio contact as quickly as possible with other personnel on the emergency scene. They should try to describe their location as accurately as possible to narrow down the search area for rescuers.

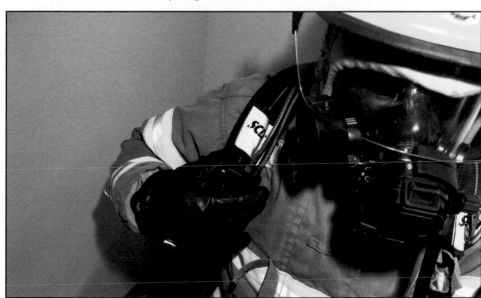

Figure 15.3 A disoriented fire brigade member activating his PASS device.

Becoming agitated can reduce a fire brigade member's ability to think and react quickly. Excitement or disorientation also causes members to expend their air supplies faster than normal. If possible, fire brigade members should try to retrace their steps to their original locations. If retracing is not possible, members should try to seek an exit from the facility or at least from the area that is on fire. Fire brigade members should shout for help periodically so that other personnel who may be in the area will hear them. If they do not have any success finding their way out, they should find a place of relative safety (a safe haven) and activate their PASS devices. If disoriented fire brigade members can locate a hoseline, they can crawl along it and feel the first set of couplings they come to in order to get their bearings. Hoselines into structural fires are generally forward lays with a female coupling at the exterior water supply source, and male couplings on the nozzle side. The male coupling has lugs on its shank; the female does not. Once the fire brigade members find a hoseline, they can follow the hoseline either to an exit point or to the nozzle team.

If fire brigade members find a window, they can signal for assistance with any of the following actions:

- Straddle the windowsill and activate the emergency alarm on their PASS devices and wave their flashlights out the window

- Yell and wave their arms

- Throw small objects out the window while being aware that personnel may be below the window

NOTE: Under no circumstances should fire brigade members throw their helmets or any other parts of their protective ensemble out of a window to attract attention.

Fire brigade members who become trapped by a structural collapse or suffer some sort of injury that prevents them from moving about are limited in their options compared to a disoriented member. These members should immediately activate the emergency alarms on their PASS devices and try to maintain composure to maximize their air supplies

If fire brigade members cannot find their way out of a building, they should attempt to stay close to a wall as rescuers normally search around the walls before making sweeps of large interior areas. If fire brigade members become exhausted or close to losing consciousness, they should assume a horizontal position on the floor next to an exterior wall, hallway, or doorway; this maximizes the audible effects of the PASS devices. This position also maximizes quick discovery by rescue crews. Disoriented members awaiting rescue should attempt to position their flashlights to shine toward the ceiling. This enhances the rescue crew's ability to see the lights and locate the members **(Figure 15.4)**.

Figure 15.4 A flashlight aimed towards the ceiling can help guide rescuers to a trapped or injured fire brigade member.

Rescuers searching for a fire brigade member should first try to quickly obtain an idea of the last location of the member. When performing the search, the rescuers should stop every so often and become perfectly quiet. This may allow the rescuers to hear calls for help or the downed fire brigade member's PASS device tone.

If it becomes necessary to remove a downed fire brigade member, the rescuers should use any safe means possible. In most cases, the need to exit the hostile atmosphere overrides the need to stabilize injuries before moving the member. If the fire brigade member has a functioning SCBA, carefully move the member so as not to dislodge the mask. If the fire brigade member does not have a functioning SCBA, is running out of air, or is low on air, either connect the mask to the Universal Rescue Connection (URC), if so equipped, on a rescuer's SCBA or simply quickly remove the victim from the hazardous atmosphere.

The best way for rescuers to avoid disorientation or the feeling of panic is through familiarity with both the search area and with search techniques in times of poor visibility. This can only be accomplished by training. Large or complex areas that are likely search areas should be visited often by the fire brigade so that they are familiar with the layout of these areas. Frequent drills should be held, searching these areas, with SCBA facepieces covered with waxed paper or commercially available vision obscuring devices, so that members become familiar with operating in poor visibility.

> **WARNING:** At no time should rescuers remove their facepieces or in any way compromise the proper operation of their SCBA in an attempt to share them with another fire brigade member or victim.

Safety Guidelines

The following is a list of safety guidelines that should be used by search and rescue personnel in any type of search operation within a building:

- Do not enter a facility in which the fire has progressed to the point where viable victims are not likely to be found.

- When backdraft conditions exist, only attempt entry after ventilation is accomplished.

- Work from a single operational plan. Crews should not be allowed to **freelance**.

- Maintain contact with command, which has control over search/rescue teams.

- Constantly monitor fire conditions that might affect search teams and individual fire brigade members.

- Have a RIC ready to help fire brigade members or teams in need of assistance.

- Always use the established personnel accountability system.

- Be aware of the secondary means of egress established for personnel involved in the search.

- Wear full personal protective equipment, including SCBA and PASS device.

- Work in teams of two or more and stay in constant contact with each other. Rescuers are responsible or themselves and each other.

- Search systematically to increase efficiency and to reduce the possibility of becoming disoriented.

- Stay low and move cautiously while searching.

- Stay alert — use all senses.

- Monitor continually the structure's integrity.

- Feel doors for excessive heat before opening them.

- Be aware of the potential flame spread through open gratings.

- Mark entry doors into rooms and remember the direction turned when entering the room. To exit the building, turn in the opposite direction when exiting the room.

- Maintain contact with a wall when visibility is obscured. Working together, search team members can extend their reach by using short section of ropes, webbing, or hand tools.

- Have a charged handline ready whenever possible when working on the fire floor (or the floor immediately below or above the fire) because it may be used as a guide for egress as well as for fire fighting.

- Coordinate with ventilation teams before opening windows to relieve heat and smoke during search.

- Close the door, report the condition, and follow the group/division supervisor's orders if fire is encountered during a search.

- Inform the group/division supervisor immediately of any room(s) that could not be searched, for whatever reason.

- Report promptly to the supervisor once the search is complete. Besides giving an "all clear" search report, also report the progress of the fire and the condition of the building.

Search and Rescue

NFPA 1081 (2018): 5.2.4, 6.2.8

Facility fire brigades must include search, rescue, and extrication situations in their pre-planning efforts. During pre-planning, the fire brigade can identify the various types of rescue or extrication situations that can occur at a given site and the resources (personnel, training, tools, and equipment) necessary to mitigate such situations. With this information, fire brigade leadership can determine the level of search, rescue, and extrication services needed for mitigation. This will also help leadership determine whether those services can be provided by the fire brigade or whether rescue should be contracted to another agency such as the local fire department or provided by mutual aid agreements. The costs in contracting may be considerably less than the costs of purchasing necessary rescue equipment and training for the fire brigade personnel.

If the fire brigade is to provide rescue, equipment must be purchased and proper training must be provided to the brigade members who will participate in rescue operations. If rescue services are to be contracted to an outside agency, then agreements must be made between the facility organization and the contracting agency to ensure proper protection and access is provided.

This chapter covers the basics of search, rescue, and extrication equipment and techniques as required by NFPA 1081. For more extensive information on extrication and rescue, see the IFSTA manuals **Fire Service Search and Rescue** and **Principles of Vehicle Extrication**.

Area Search

Regardless of how small an emergency situation may appear, the fire brigade must always conduct a thorough search. Even in relatively minor incidents (such as a contained, localized fire within a structure) there may be workers in the building who are incapable of exiting. Not locating a victim until after a "minor" emergency has been terminated or missing a victim entirely is unacceptable.

While size-up is initially the responsibility of the first-arriving fire brigade leader, all fire brigade members should look at the entire building and its surroundings as they approach the incident. Careful observation will give indications as to the size of the emergency, whether or not the building is likely to be occupied, the probable structural integrity of the building, and the general amount of time it will take to effectively search the structure. The initial exterior size-up will help maintain the fire brigade members' orientation within the building. Fire brigade members should identify alternate escape routes (windows, doors, fire escapes) and potential safe havens *before* they enter the building. Once inside, their specific location can sometimes be confirmed by looking out windows. They may also determine the location of the fire and its location in reference to their current position by looking out windows.

To obtain information about those who might still be inside and where they might be found, as well as to obtain information about the location and extent of the emergency situation, fire brigade members should first question workers who have escaped the emergency. If possible, all information should be verified; in any case, fire brigade members should not assume that all employees are safe until fire brigade personnel have searched the building. Because employees may be familiar with coworkers' habits and office or duty locations, they may be able to suggest where their coworkers are likely to be found. They may also have seen a fellow employee near a window or doorway prior to the fire brigade's arrival. Information on the number and location of victims should be relayed to the IC and all responding personnel.

Conducting a Search

There are two objectives of a building search: finding victims (searching for life) and obtaining information about the extent of the fire (searching for fire extension). In most structure fires, the search for life requires two types of searches: primary and secondary.

A **primary search** is a rapid but thorough search that is performed either before or during fire suppression operations. This type of search is often carried out under extremely adverse conditions, but it must be performed quickly and efficiently. During the primary search, fire brigade members must be sure to search the known or likely locations of victims as rapidly as conditions allow, moving quickly to search all affected areas of the structure as soon as possible. The search team(s) can verify that the fire conditions are as they appeared from the outside or report any surprises they may encounter.

A **secondary search** is conducted *after* the fire is under control and the hazards are somewhat abated. This type of search should be conducted by other than those who conducted the primary search. It is a very thorough, painstaking search that attempts to ensure that any remaining workers have been found.

NOTE: OSHA requires a **rapid intervention crew (RIC)** be in place prior to beginning a search in an immediate danger to life and health (IDLH) environment unless an imminent rescue situation is encountered where the presence of personnel in the structure is known or confirmed.

> **WARNING:** Neither interior nor exterior emergency operations should be attempted unless fire brigade members are wearing appropriate personal protective equipment and respiratory protection.

Primary Search

During the primary search, rescuers should always use the buddy system — working in teams of two or more **(Figure 15.5)**. By working together, the rescuers can conduct a search quickly while maintaining their own safety.

Primary search personnel should always carry forcible entry tools with them whenever they enter a building and throughout the search. Valuable time is lost if rescuers have to return to their equipment locker or apparatus to obtain this equipment. Also, forcible entry tools may be needed to open a way out of the building if rescuers become trapped.

Depending on conditions within the fire building, rescuers may be able to search while walking in an upright position, or they may have to crawl on their hands and knees. If there is only light smoke and little or no heat, walking is the most rapid means of searching a building. Searching on hands and knees (beneath the smoke and heat) can increase visibility and reduce the chances of tripping or falling into stairways or holes in floors. Move up and down stairs on hands and knees; ascend head first and descend feet first. Remember to account for the additional time needed to move this way.

Figure 15.5 A search team composed of three fire brigade members preparing to enter a structure.

When searching within a structure, rescuers should move systematically from room to room, maintaining constant contact with a wall or hoselines at all times searching each room completely, constantly listening for sounds from victims. Many fire brigades conduct their primary search from a hoseline. This allows them to provide fire suppression as well as a quick way to exit to safety, if needed. On the fire floor, fire brigade members should start their search as close to the fire as possible and then search back toward the entrance door. This procedure allows the search team to reach those in the most danger first — those who would be overtaken by any fire extension that might occur while the rest of the search was in progress. Personnel nearest the fire area are more likely to have been injured severely. In many cases, personnel at some distance from the fire area are able to self-rescue while teams conduct search operations. Because those who are a greater distance from the fire are in less immediate danger, they can wait to be reached as the team moves back toward safety.

Rescuers must search all areas such as offices, meeting rooms, break rooms, restrooms, computer rooms, storage and janitorial closets, attic areas, basements, walkways, crawl-ways, and any sheltered areas where disoriented victims may seek refuge. Rescuers should search the perimeter of each room and may need to extend their arms or legs or use the handle of a tool to reach completely under desks, tables, or other objects in areas of poor visibility. When the perimeter has been searched, they should then search the middle of the room.

During the primary search, visibility may be extremely limited, so rescuers may have to identify objects by touch. If rescuers are unfamiliar with a facility, touch may provide the only clue to what type of room or location the team is in. Visibility being obscured by smoke should be reported through channels to the IC because it may indicate a need for additional ventilation.

Rescue teams should maintain radio contact with their team leader and periodically report their progress and needs in accordance with fire brigade standard operating procedures **(Figure 15.6)**. Informing the IC of any areas that have not been completely searched is especially important so that additional search teams can be assigned to these areas if necessary.

During the primary search, negative information is just as important as positive information to ensure a complete search. If the search has to be aborted for any reason, the IC should be notified immediately and the search resumed as soon as possible.

Secondary Search

After the initial fire control and ventilation operations have been completed, personnel other than those who conducted the primary search are assigned to conduct a secondary search of the fire building. During the secondary search,

Figure 15.6 The leader of a search team giving a progress report over a portable radio.

speed is not as critical as thoroughness. The secondary search is conducted just as systematically as the primary search to ensure that no rooms or spaces are missed. As in the primary search, any negative information, such as the location where the fire is beginning to **rekindle**, is reported immediately.

Multistory Facilities

When searching in multistory facilities, the most critical areas are the fire floor, the floor directly above the fire, and the topmost floor. These floors should be searched immediately because this is where any remaining personnel will be in the greatest jeopardy due to rising smoke, heat, and fire. The majority of victims are likely to be found in these areas. Once these floors have been searched, the intervening floors should be checked.

During the primary search, doors to rooms not involved in fire should be closed to prevent the spread of fire into these areas. The exits, hallways, and stairs should be kept as clear as possible of unused hoselines and other equipment to facilitate the egress of building occupants and to reduce the tripping hazard.

In some cases, search and rescue personnel are advised to have a charged hoseline with them on all floors. Because advancing a charged hoseline during a search is a time-consuming process that may unnecessarily delay and impede the primary search, other fire brigades make this an option based on conditions. Fire brigade members must be guided by their fire brigade's SOPs.

Search Methods

Facility fire brigades may need to conduct searches within the interior of structures as well as around exterior process units. The following sections will describe the similarities and differences between the two types of searches.

Search Methods for Structure Interiors

When rooms, offices, or work spaces extend from a center hallway, teams should be assigned to search both sides of the hallway. If two teams are available, each can take one side of the hallway. If there is only one search team, they search down one side of the hallway and back up the other side.

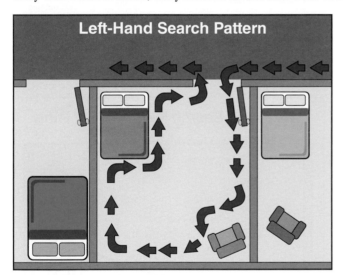

Figure 15.7 Illustrating a left-hand search pattern.

Entering the first room, the searchers turn right or left (a right or left hand search pattern) and follow the walls around the room until they return to the starting point. As rescuers leave the room, they turn in the same direction they used to enter the room and continue to the next room to be searched. For example, if they turned left when they entered the room, they turn left when they leave the room **(Figure 15.7)**. When removing a victim to safety or to exit the building, rescuers must turn opposite the direction used to enter the room. Rescuers must exit each room through the same doorway they entered to ensure a complete search. This technique may be used to search most buildings, from a one-story office or facility building to taller buildings and structures.

In most cases, the best method of searching small rooms is for one member to stay at the door while another member searches the room. The searcher remains oriented by maintaining a more-or-less constant dialogue with the member at the door. The searcher keeps the member at the door informed of the progress of the search. When the room search is completed, the two rejoin at the doorway, close and mark the door, and proceed to the next room. When searching the next room, the partners exchange their roles of searching the room and waiting at the door.

This last method reduces the likelihood of rescuers becoming lost within the room, which reduces some of the stress of the situation. When searching relatively small rooms, this technique is often quicker than when both members search together because the searcher can move along more quickly without the fear of becoming disoriented.

Search Methods for Exterior Process Units

Unlike traditional structural firefighters who may primarily conduct searches during emergencies inside of structures, fire brigade members often respond to fires and other emergencies in exterior areas, such as process units, where facility personnel work. Searching these areas requires additional caution and may require different techniques than searching inside of structures.

Some hazards that fire brigade members searching exterior process areas may encounter are:

- Equipment that is still operating and cannot be immediately shut down.

- Elevated or multi-level areas that are accessed by ladders or stairwells and/or pose fall hazards.

- Confined spaces.

- Areas that may not be immediately accessible due to extremely hazardous conditions.

Fire brigade members tasked with conducting search and rescue in exterior process areas will likely have to use different search techniques than firefighters searching the interior of a structure. Operating processes that can be made safe before or during search efforts should be isolated to protect fire brigade members operating in the area. Members may have to search from the outside of the process area toward the middle of the process, utilize search ropes, or simply scan inaccessible areas utilizing TIs or other devices.

- Searching from the outer edges of the process area, also known as triangulation, involves at least three search teams working from the outside boundaries of the search area toward the middle of the search area, then continuing past the other teams until they exit the area on the other side **(Figure 15.8)**.

- Brigade members can utilize search ropes to "fan" out across a wide search area. The searcher uses a rope marked with distance knots or rings and fixed to a stationary point to search the area in a side-to-side pattern. The searcher then moves to the next distance marker on the rope, and repeats the side-to-side search, until the entire area is covered **(Figure 15.9)**.

- Elevated areas, pre-existing confined spaces or collapsed areas, or areas that are inaccessible due to extreme hazards may not be immediately accessible to fire brigade members. In these cases, TIs or other devices may have to be utilized to scan the inaccessible areas from a safe location until brigade members can reach the area.

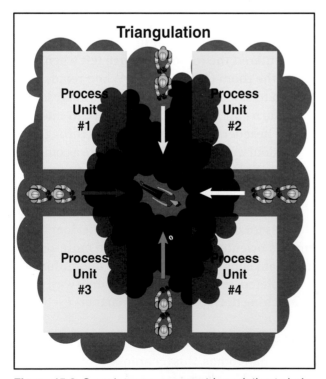

Figure 15.8 Search teams can use triangulation to help find trapped or disoriented facility personnel.

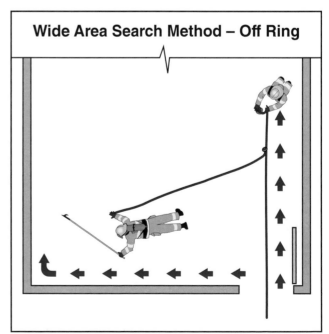

Figure 15.9 Illustrating the wide area search method.

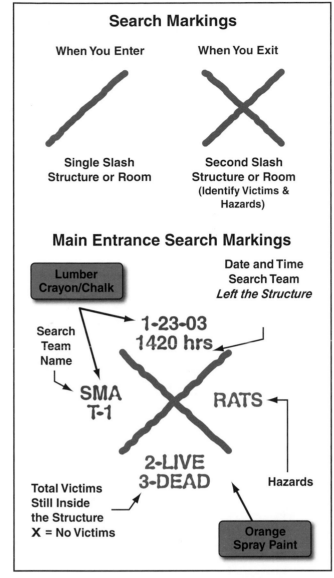

Search Markings

When You Enter

Single Slash
Structure or Room

When You Exit

Second Slash
Structure or Room
(Identify Victims &
Hazards)

Main Entrance Search Markings

Lumber
Crayon/Chalk

Date and Time
Search Team
Left the Structure

Search
Team
Name

1-23-03
1420 hrs

SMA
T-1

RATS

2-LIVE
3-DEAD

Hazards

Total Victims
Still Inside
the Structure
X = No Victims

Orange
Spray Paint

Figure 15.10 Examples of the Federal Emergency Management Agency's Urban Search and Rescue System search markings and their meanings.

Marking Systems

Fire brigades use several methods of marking searched rooms: chalk or crayon marks, masking tape, specially designed door markers, and latch straps over doorknobs. Latch straps made from rope or rubber also serve the secondary function of preventing a rescuer from being locked in a room. Methods that might contribute to fire spread (such as using furniture to block open doors) or methods that require subsequent searchers to enter the room to find the marker are not recommended. Standard operating procedures usually dictate the method of marking; however, any method used must be known and clearly understood by all fire brigade personnel who may participate in the search.

It is a best practice for search teams to use a two-part marking system. The team affixes half of the mark when entering the room and completes the mark when exiting the room **(Figure 15.10)**. This avoids duplication of effort by alerting other rescuers that the room is being or has been searched. If a search team becomes lost, this mark will serve as a starting point for others to begin looking for the team.

Rescue

NFPA 1081 (2018): 5.2.4, 6.2.8

Rescue involves removing a victim from an untenable or unhealthy atmosphere. This section discusses assisting victims to exit a hazardous location, emergency movement of victims, and rescue carries and drags.

An ambulatory or semiambulatory victim may only require help to walk to safety. One or two rescuers may be needed, depending on how much help is available and the size and condition of the victim.

Do not move a victim before treatment is provided unless there is an immediate danger to the victim or to rescuers. Emergency moves are necessary under the following conditions:

• There is fire or danger of fire in the immediate area.

• Explosives or other hazardous materials are involved.

• The victim is in an atmosphere that presents an IDLH hazard.

• It is impossible to protect the accident scene.

• It is impossible to gain access to other victims who need immediate life-saving care.

• The victim is in cardiac arrest and must be moved to a different area (a firm surface, for instance) so that rescuers can administer cardiopulmonary resuscitation (CPR).

The chief danger in moving a victim quickly is the possibility of aggravating a spinal injury. In an extreme emergency, however, the possible spinal injury becomes secondary to the goal of preserving life.

If it is necessary to perform an emergency move, the victim should be pulled in the direction of the long axis of the body — not sideways **(Figure 15.11)**. Jack knifing, or bending the victim from side to side, should also be avoided. If the victim is on the floor, pull on the victim's clothing in the neck or shoulder area. It may be easier to pull the victim onto a blanket and then drag the blanket.

Rescue Carries and Drags

It is always better to have two or more rescuers when attempting to lift or carry an adult. One rescuer may be able to safely carry a small, light adult, but two, three, or even four rescuers may be needed to safely lift and carry a large, heavier adult. An unconscious victim is always more difficult to lift; the victim is unable to assist in any way, and a relaxed body becomes "dead weight."

Inexperienced people may not be able to lift and carry a victim correctly. Their efforts may be uncoordinated, and they usually need close supervision to avoid further injury to the victim. Rescuers helping to carry a victim should guard against losing their balance. They should lift as a team and with proper technique to avoid jostling the victim unnecessarily.

Lifting incorrectly is also one of the most common causes of injury to rescuers. Rescuers should always keep their backs straight and lift with their legs, not their backs. If immobilization of a fracture is not feasible until the victim has been moved a short distance, one rescuer should support the weight of the injured body part while others move the victim. There are a number of carries and drags that may be used to move a victim from an area quickly; these are described in the following sections.

Cradle-in-Arms Lift/Carry

The cradle-in-arms lift/carry is effective for carrying children or very small adults if they are conscious **(Figure 15.12)**. This technique is usually not practical for carrying an unconscious adult because of the weight and relaxed condition of the body.

Figure 15.11 Two rescuers preparing to move a "victim" along the long axis of the victim's body.

Figure 15.12 A fire brigade member demonstrating the cradle-in-arms lift/carry.

Seat Lift/Carry

The seat lift/carry can be used with a conscious or an unconscious victim and is performed by two rescuers. The rescuers link their arms across the victim's back and under the victim's knees to form a seat.

Moving a Victim onto a Long Backboard or Litter

Occasionally, rescuers will have the advantage of being able to use some type of litter to remove a victim. There are many different types of litters such as the standard ambulance gurney, litter, scoop stretcher, basket litter, and long backboard. The long backboard is one of the most common types of litters used by rescue personnel. This section highlights the proper techniques for moving a victim onto a long backboard. Similar techniques should be used for moving people onto stretchers and basket litters.

Immobilizing a victim who is suspected of having a spinal injury on a long backboard requires four rescuers. One rescuer is needed to maintain in-line stabilization throughout the process, and three rescuers are needed to actually move the victim to the board. It is critical that the victim with a suspected spinal injury be moved in such a way to avoid any unnecessary jolting or twisting of the spinal column. For this reason, the rescuer who applies and maintains in-line stabilization directs the other rescuers in their actions to ensure that the victim's head and body are moved as a unit. When dangers at the scene are life-threatening to the victim and rescuers or the victim is not suspected of having a cervical spine injury and is just being relocated, this process may be performed with only two rescuers — one to maintain in-line stabilization and one to move the victim.

Extremities Lift/Carry

The extremities lift/carry is used on either a conscious or an unconscious victim. This technique requires two rescuers.

Chair Lift/Carry

The chair lift/carry is used for either a conscious or an unconscious person. Be sure that the chair used is sturdy; do not attempt this carry using a folding chair (**Figure 15.13**).

Figure 15.13 Two fire brigade members demonstrating the chair lift/carry.

Incline Drag

The incline drag is used by one rescuer to move a victim down a stairway or incline and is very useful for moving an unconscious victim. The rescuer stands behind the victim, grasps the victim's wrists, then rises and drags the victim to safety.

Webbing Drag

One rescuer can use a section of webbing to perform a drag (**Figure 15.14, p. 470**). The loop of webbing is passed under and around the victim's torso to assist the rescuer in moving the victim.

Fire Brigade Member Drag Rescue Device (DRD)

Downed fire brigade members may be dragged using the drag rescue device (DRD) located in modern structural fire fighting coats. The rescuer can pull the DRD by hand or by putting a tool through the DRD and one or more rescuers pull on the tool.

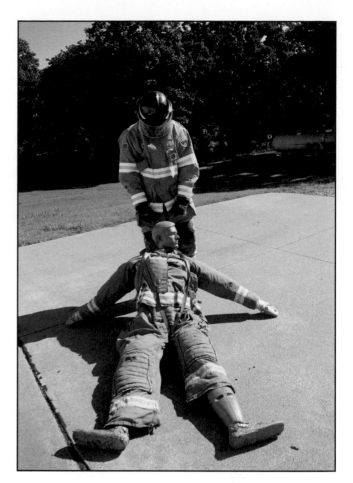

Figure 15.14 A fire brigade member demonstrating the webbing drag.

Rescue Scene Emergency Power and Lighting Equipment

While a variety of tools and equipment may be used in performing search, rescue, and extrication operations, the items most commonly used by fire brigades are emergency power and lighting equipment. Many incidents occur in poor lighting conditions such as during the hours of darkness and in windowless buildings. These conditions create the need to artificially light the scene, which provides a safer, more efficient atmosphere in which to work. Fire brigade members must be knowledgeable of when and how to properly and safely operate the emergency power and lighting equipment.

Power Plants

Generators are the most common power source used for emergency services; they can be portable or vehicle-mounted **(Figure 15.15)**. Portable generators by definition are light enough to be carried by one or two people. These generators generally supply 110-and/or 220-volt capacities and are powered by small gasoline or diesel engines. They are extremely useful when electrical power is needed in an area that is not accessible to the vehicle-mounted system or when less power is needed.

Figure 15.15 Generators may be classified as portable or vehicle-mounted.

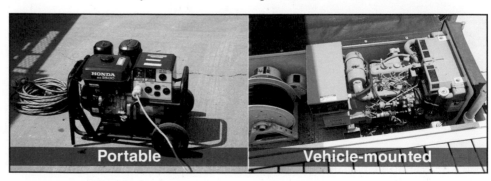

Portable   Vehicle-mounted

Vehicle-mounted generators usually have a larger power-generating capacity than portable units. In addition to providing power for portable equipment, vehicle-mounted generators provide power for the floodlighting system on the vehicle. Vehicle-mounted generators can be powered by gasoline, diesel, or propane gas engines or by hydraulic or power take-off systems. Fixed floodlights are usually wired directly to the unit through a switch, and outlets are also provided for other equipment. Outlets on these power plants generally deliver 110 and 220 volts, and may include capacities greater than 50 kilowatts. Mounted generators with a separate engine are noisy, making communication difficult near them.

Lighting Equipment

Lighting equipment can be divided into two categories: portable and fixed **(Figure 15.16)**. Portable lights are used in areas where fixed lights are not able to illuminate because of opaque obstructions or when additional lighting is necessary. Portable lights generally range from 300 to 1,000 watts. Power may be supplied by a cord from either a portable power unit or a vehicle-mounted power plant. The lights usually have handles for ease of carrying and large bases for stability. Some portable lights are mounted on telescoping stands, which allow them to be directed more effectively.

Figure 15.16 Lighting equipment may also be classified as portable or vehicle-mounted.

Fixed lights are mounted to an apparatus, and their main function is to provide overall lighting of the emergency scene. Fixed lights are usually mounted so that they can be raised, lowered, or turned to provide the best possible lighting. Often, these lights are mounted on telescoping poles that allow both vertical and rotational movement. More elaborate designs include hydraulically operated booms with a bank of lights. These banks of lights generally have a capacity of 500 to 1,500 watts per light. The amount of lighting should be carefully matched with the amount of power available from the power plant. Overtaxing the power plant gives poor lighting, may damage the power generating unit or the lights, and restricts the operation of other electrical tools using the same power supply.

 Intrinsically Safe Equipment

Electrical appliances such as temporary lighting, electrical tools should be rated and in good condition for the hazardous electrical classification of the area where they might be used. If the flash fire or explosion risk exists, selected appliances must be intrinsically safe. Fire brigade members should consult NFPA 70, *National Electrical Code*, to ensure the equipment to be purchased meets the appropriate class or classes of hazard.

Auxiliary Electrical Equipment

A variety of other equipment may be used in conjunction with power plants and lighting equipment. Electrical cables or extension cords are necessary to conduct electric power to portable equipment. Cords may be stored in coils, on portable cord reels, or on fixed automatic rewind reels. Twist-lock receptacles provide secure, safe connections. Electrical cable should be waterproof, explosion-proof, and have adequate insulation with no exposed wires. Junction boxes may be used when multiple connections are needed. The junction box has several outlets and is supplied through one inlet from the power plant. All outlets should be equipped with ground-fault circuit interrupters and conform to NFPA 70, *National Electrical Code*, and OSHA 1910 Subpart S.

In situations where fire brigades frequently work together with other organizations and have either different sizes or different types of receptacles (for example, one has two prongs, the other has three), adapters should be carried so that equipment can be interchanged. Adapters should also be carried to allow rescuers to plug their equipment into standard electrical outlets.

Special Rescue Situations and Extrication

NFPA 1081 (2018): 5.2.4, 6.2.8

Fire brigade members may encounter many different scenarios involving rescue and extrication. Extrication involves removing and treating victims who have become trapped by some type of man-made machinery or equipment. Extricating a victim or victims from a motor vehicle would be a common example of extrication. Specialized rescues can include rescue from collapsed structures, confined spaces, trench cave-ins, electrical contact, water and ice, facility machinery, and elevators. These rescue operations require advanced training and equipment.

Fire brigade managers need to be aware of and plan for potential rescue and extrication situations. Because of the level of risk and technical expertise involved, many fire brigades establish contracts or have mutual aid agreement with local fire departments or private companies to perform rescue and extrication operations. For those fire brigades that elect to perform such operations themselves, the specific procedures for these types of rescue and extrication situations may be found in other IFSTA manuals.

Fire brigade members should be educated on special rescue situations so that they can identify the need for a special rescue team. Fire brigade members may also be used to assist rescue personnel and retrieve necessary tools and equipment. Fire brigade members should be familiar with their organization's capabilities for handling special rescue situations.

Rapid Intervention Crew Operations (RIC)

NFPA 1081 (2018): 5.2.9, 6.2.10

Rapid intervention crews are tasked with locating and assisting fire brigade members who have become trapped, lost, or incapacitated during interior structural fire fighting. Rapid intervention crews may be two or more fire brigade personnel who are equipped, trained, and assigned the task once they arrive on scene. In some brigades, personnel may be designated and permanently assigned as the RIC.

Either departmental SOPs or the IC will establish the exact number of RICs needed at the scene. Crews are added as necessary if the incident escalates or the number of operations increases, which allows flexibility in RIC composition based on the type of incident and number of personnel on scene.

Each RIC consists of two or more personnel wearing complete PPE and respiratory protection. The team should be equipped with a radio, flashlight, TI, any special rescue tools needed, RIC pack, and other equipment necessary to perform a rescue of other emergency personnel **(Figure 15.17)**. Although individual RIC members may be assigned other minor emergency scene duties, they must be prepared to stop whatever they are doing and deploy immediately if needed.

Figure 15.17 Examples of some of the equipment that RIC personnel may use at an incident.

The RIC should report to the IC and may perform such tasks as:

- Staging equipment
- Selecting proper PPE/SCBA and ensuring its readiness
- Sizing up the building for possible paths of egress
- Monitoring for signs of potential building collapse
- Completing a 360-degree survey if possible
- Developing a rescue plan for the incident
- Removing barriers to egress
- Conducting air monitoring tasks
- Monitoring radio traffic for distress calls
- Clearing windows
- Placing ladders
- Establishing a second means of egress (set additional ladders)
- Opening exits
- Illuminating the building

CAUTION: When working as a RIC member, be careful that other assigned duties will not interfere with your primary rescue capacity.

Chapter Review

1. What safety precautions should be followed when searching a burning facility?

2. When following a hoseline through a structure, how can you tell the direction of the nozzle and the direction of the water supply?

3. What is the difference between a primary and secondary search?

4. What techniques can be used to search exterior process units?

5. List three methods of carrying victims to safety.

6. What are the two categories of lighting equipment?

7. What is the minimum number of members that should be assigned to a RIC?

Discussion Questions

1. What areas in your facilities may require special search methods?

2. What special rescue situations may arise at your facilities?

Key Terms

Freelance — To operate independently of the incident commander's command and control.

MAYDAY — Internationally recognized distress signal.

Primary Search — Rapid but thorough search to determine the location of victims; performed either before or during fire suppression operations. May be conducted with or without a charged hoseline, depending on local policy.

Rapid Intervention Crew (RIC) — Two or more firefighters designated to perform firefighter rescue; they are stationed outside the hazard and must be standing by throughout the incident.

Rekindle — To reignite because of latent heat, sparks, or smoldering embers; rekindling can be prevented by proper overhaul.

Secondary Search — Slow, thorough search to ensure that no occupants were overlooked during the primary search; conducted after the fire is under control by personnel who did not conduct the primary search.

Skill Sheet List

The following skill sheets should be used to evaluate the skills described in this chapter:

NOTE: Students should wear the PPE appropriate to the NFPA 1081 level (Incipient, Advanced Exterior, Interior Structural, etc...) being evaluated.

Common Advanced Exterior and Interior Structural Facility Fire Brigade Member Training Requirements

Chapter Contents

This chapter provides information that addresses the following job performance requirements of NFPA 1081, *Standard for Facility Fire Brigade Member Professional Qualifications (2018).*

5.1.2.1	5.2.6	5.3.1	5.3.5	5.3.9	6.2.1	6.2.6	6.3.3	6.3.6
5.2.3	5.2.7	5.3.3	5.3.6	6.1.2.3	6.2.4	6.2.9	6.3.4	6.3.10
5.2.5	5.2.8	5.3.4	5.3.8	6.1.2.4	6.2.5	6.3.2	6.3.5	6.3.11

Learning Objectives

1. Review the protocols for maintaining fire scene safety. [5.2.8, 6.2.5]
2. Review the elements of conducting fire safety surveys. [5.3.1, 6.3.10]
3. Describe the hazards posed by different utilities. [5.1.2.1, 5.2.3, 5.3.5, 5.3.6, 5.3.9, 6.1.2.3, 6.2.1, 6.3.5, 6.3.6, 6.3.11]
4. Review concepts of water supply. [5.1.2.1, 5.2.7, 6.1.2.3, 6.2.6]
5. Explain the different methods of fire suppression. [5.2.3, 6.2.1]
6. Describe the different spill/leak/release control operations. [5.3.5, 6.3.5]
7. Review fire control operations. [5.2.3, 5.2.8, 5.3.3, 5.3.9, 6.2.1, 6.2.5, 6.3.3, 6.3.11]
8. Review hose and handlines operations. [5.2.3, 5.2.6, 6.2.1, 6.2.4]
9. Review the principles of fire streams. [5.2.3, 6.2.1]
10. Review the use of standpipe and hose systems. [5.1.2.1, 5.2.5, 6.1.2.3, 6.2.9]
11. Review the use of master stream appliances. [5.3.3, 6.3.3]
12. Describe the methods of suppressing fires in stacked and piled materials. [5.2.3]
13. Review the basics of fire protection systems. [5.1.2.1, 5.2.5, 5.3.8, 6.1.2.3, 6.2.9, 6.3.2]
14. Explain the principles of foam generation and expansion. [5.3.4, 6.3.4]
15. Describe the different types of foam concentrates. [5.3.4, 6.3.4]
16. Describe the challenges and principles of creating and using foam. [5.3.4, 6.3.4]
17. Describe the different foam application techniques. [5.3.4, 6.3.4]
18. Review the types of special extinguishing agents. [5.1.2.1, 5.3.6, 5.3.8, 5.3.9, 6.1.2.3, 6.3.2, 6.3.6, 6.3.11]
19. Review the types of special agent-based extinguishing systems. [5.1.2.1, 5.2.5, 5.3.8, 6.1.2.3, 6.2.9, 6.3.2]
20. Describe the fire suppression methods using different special extinguishing agents. [5.3.6, 6.3.6]
21. Review the methods of property conservation. [5.2.5, 6.2.9]
22. Describe the concepts and procedures of overhaul. [5.2.3, 5.2.6, 6.2.1, 6.2.4]
23. Explain the procedures of gross decontamination. [6.1.2.4]

Chapter 16
Hazard Control and Fire Suppression Operations

Advanced exterior and interior structural fire brigade personnel may face similar fire fighting operations in their facilities. This chapter will address those situations, operations, and procedures that are common to both levels. Section C, Chapter 17, will then address those situations and procedures unique to advanced exterior level fire brigade personnel while Section D, Chapters 18 and 19, will address those unique to the interior structural level.

This chapter will describe:

- Fire suppression methods
- Spill/leak/release control operations
- Suppressing fires in stacked and piled materials
- Extinguishing fires with fire fighting foams
- Suppressing fires with special extinguishing agents
- Overhaul

Review Section: Fire Scene Safety

NFPA 1081 (2018): 5.2.8, 6.2.5

Fire brigade members should follow common safety protocols during fire scene operations. These protocols include:

- **Using the brigade's personnel accountability system** — Such as the tag (passport), SCBA tag, or computer-based electronic accountability systems.
- **Using local communications procedures** — Know the local routine and emergency communications procedures and follow incident management communications processes.
- **Following emergency evacuation procedures** — Know when evacuation is necessary, what signals are used to call for an evacuation, how to locate emergency exit location, and how to maintain team integrity during an evacuation.
- **Utilizing safe havens** — Know when sheltering-in-place is necessary, what constitutes a safe haven, where safe havens are located on the facility, and how to access them.
- **Identifying and mitigating incident hazards** — Know what hazards are located at the facility, what additional hazards are created by fire fighting, rescue, and overhaul operations, and how to report and mitigate such hazards.
- **Following emergency air supply operational procedures** — Know the procedures to follow in the event of failure of breathing apparatus during an emergency.

Review Section: Fire Safety Surveys

NFPA 1081 (2018): 5.3.1, 6.3.10

Fire safety surveys gather data and recommendations that can help personnel have a safe physical work environment and prevent fires from occurring. These surveys also help the fire brigade members become familiar with the structures and operations at their facility.

Fire brigade personnel should follow their organization's procedures for conducting fire safety surveys. The fire brigade leader should contact the facility manager to schedule the survey for a suitable day and time. Coordinating with the facility manager will ensure the survey coincides with the availability of necessary building personnel.

While conducting a fire safety survey, the following guidelines may apply:

- Report to the department supervisor and state the purpose of the visit.

- Have a fire brigade member working in the area help with the survey/inspection because of his or her familiarity with the area, the processes, and personnel.

- Maintain a courteous attitude at all times.

- Compliment employees when favorable conditions are found.

- Make constructive comments regarding the elimination of hazardous conditions.

- Survey the entire building or facility both inside and outside **(Figure 16.1)**.

- Thank the supervisor(s) and employees for their time and assistance in the survey.

After conducting the survey, the fire brigade member should conduct an exit interview to describe the conditions found to the unit supervisor or facility manager. The exit interview informs management of the hazards and deficiencies found and the appropriate means to correct them.

The findings of the fire safety survey should be reported to facility management in accordance with company policy. This report should identify any hazards found, recommended corrections, and the time limits for making such corrections. A reinspection is conducted to ensure that corrections have been made. Fire safety survey reports and records should be written and maintained in accordance with company policy.

Figure 16.1 Fire brigade personnel conducting a fire safety survey.

Review Section: Fire Hazards

A fire hazard is a condition that encourages a fire to start or increases the extent or severity of a fire. Basic fire chemistry suggests fire cannot survive without a fuel supply, sufficient heat source, oxygen supply, and a self-sustained chemical reaction (fire tetrahedron). Therefore, eliminating as many of these elements as possible can prevent hazardous fire conditions. For more information on fire dynamics and behavior, refer to Chapter 3 of this manual or to IFSTA's **Essentials of Fire Fighting**.

Common hazards include:

- Poor housekeeping and improper storage of materials:
  - Improper storage of small quantities of flammable or combustible liquids
  - Improper storage of flammable or combustible materials in electrical or mechanical rooms
  - Improper storage of materials in exit ways or stair wells
  - Improper disposal or storage of oil/chemical soaked rags
  - Improper use, storage, and disposal of floor cleaning compounds
- Defective or improperly used heating, lighting, or power equipment
- Improper electrical wiring or temporary electrical wiring used in place of permanent power sources
- Misuse of fumigation substances and flammable or combustible liquids
- Buildups of combustible dusts
- Improper smoking and disposal of smoking materials

Factors that can contribute to the spread or severity of a fire include:

- Blocking fire doors open
- Existence of party walls, common attics, cocklofts, and other open voids
- The quantity and types of fuel(s) (fuel loading)

Target hazard locations include:

- Lumber mills and yards
- Paper manufacturing plants
- Consumer goods manufacturing facilities
- Electrical power generation plants
- Chemical manufacturing facilities
- Oil refineries and bulk storage facilities
- Fabrication and machining facilities
- Paint facilities

Special fire hazards arise as a result of the processes or operations that are characteristic of the individual occupancy. Commercial, manufacturing, refinery, and other facilities have particular hazards.

Review Section: System Readiness Documentation

When conducting fire surveys, the readiness of fire detection and suppression systems must be documented for the record and systematically stored. Records should be kept for every inspection performed on fire detection and suppression systems. Most often the fire alarm or suppression system contractor and/or the facility manager maintain these records. All documents and records pertaining to a facility's fire detection and suppression systems should be kept within the company's document management system.

These documents and reports include the following:

- Inspection reports, forms, and letters
- Fire reports
- Investigation reports

These records provide a historical perspective of fire protection activities within that facility. Record-keeping must be accurate since these records could be subpoenaed for legal actions.

Hazards Posed by Utilities

NFPA 1081 (2018): 5.1.2.1, 5.2.3, 5.3.5, 5.3.6, 5.3.9, 6.1.2.3, 6.2.1, 6.3.5, 6.3.6, 6.3.11

Controlling building utilities (electric, natural gas, and water supplies) may help control the fire and limit damage. The locations and means of control will vary among types of structures, although some general concepts can be applied and will be introduced in the appropriate section below.

The Incident Commander (IC) or your supervisor will determine which utilities must be controlled and will ensure that facility SOPs are followed. The IC will notify the appropriate facility personnel which facility utilities need to be shut off and which personnel will accomplish these tasks, and when.

Only the utility provider or plant facilities personnel are responsible for turning utilities back on and should attempt to do so. The utility provider or plant facilities personnel will have to determine if the building and the building's utility distribution system are safe before the service can be reestablished. Turning the electricity or natural gas back on could reignite the fire due to damaged wiring, pipes, or appliances.

Situational Awareness: Building Utilities

When assigned a task, it is essential to communicate all observations (using all senses - sight, sound, touch, and smell), identifying and reporting anything unusual for safety. In addition to those observations, the following conditions specific to building utilities should be noted and communicated:

- Location of utility services: electric, gas, and water meters
- Status of power to or within the structure (on or off)
- Damage to utilities: broken pipes, downed power lines, unauthorized modifications to utilities
- Presence and condition of fire department connections and/or fire suppression systems
- Presence and condition of standpipes
- Location of alternative utility sources (solar panels, LPG powered generators)

Electricity

Electricity usually comes from a commercial power company or an alternative source such as solar panels, wind generators, or fuel-powered generators. Electric service must be disconnected when there is a structure fire to eliminate electricity as a source of heat energy and a potential electrocution hazard to emergency responders. In some cases, structures are total electric, meaning that electricity is the sole power source for light, heat, and cooking. In other cases, electricity only provides lighting while a form of gas provides hot water, heating, and cooking. Fire brigade personnel must be able to control the flow of electricity into structures.

Commercial Power Supply

Commercial power companies provide electricity to a variety of facilities. Electric lines connect structures to the main power grid. Electrical power lines enter facilities from above or below ground and connect to transformer or motor control center (MCC). Energy isolation locations and devices should be identified in the fire brigade prefire plans. The safest way to cut commercial power to a structure is at the main disconnects or line interrupters **(Figure 16.2)**.

> **WARNING:** The operation of energy isolation devices should only be handled by qualified facility personnel.

Electrical power to the entire building should not be shut off until ordered because it is necessary to operate elevators, air-handling equipment, process units, and other essential systems in all types of occupancies. Shutting off or *securing* the electrical power in commercial/industrial occupancies can

Figure 16.2 Facility prefire plans should identify where electrical power enters a structure.

stop essential chemical processes or safety systems and create an unsafe situation. The decision to shut off the power is based on knowledge gained through preincident surveys.

Both high-voltage and low-voltage systems may be found in a building, each supplying some of the power needed to operate the building services. If power is shut off to the entire building or any device in it, the main energy isolation device should be locked out and tagged out to prevent it from being turned back on before it is safe. If lockout/tagout devices are not available, assign a fire brigade member with a portable radio to stand at the switch.

In many structure fires, it helps for electrical power to remain on to provide power for lighting, ventilation equipment, fire pumps, and other essential systems. The IC will make this decision in consultation with the **Incident Safety Officer (ISO)**. When a fire involves only one area of a structure, it would be counterproductive to shut off power to the entire building. When the building becomes damaged to the point that service is interrupted or an electrical hazard is created, a qualified personnel should turn off the main panel. As always, fire brigade personnel must follow their brigade's SOPs.

Alternative Energy Sources

Fire brigade personnel should be alert for installations with alternative emergency power capabilities such as solar panel arrays, wind turbines, battery banks, or liquid/gas-fueled generators. Where these sources are present, removing the meter or turning off the master switch may not turn off the power.

One solar panel can generate enough electricity to kill a person; therefore, solar panels and photovoltaic panels (PV panels) are marked with red warning labels. Most solar panel arrays have two shutoff switches, one on each side of the power inverter. There is also a shutoff switch on the electric meter. Closing any of these switches will shut off power inside the structure. But, it will not turn off the solar panel array. As long as there is any amount of natural or artificial light, the panel is always on and generating power. When performing tactical vertical ventilation on a roof with solar panels, completely avoid these panels.

WARNING: Solar panels generate current whenever there is a light source (sunlight, moonlight, artificial lighting) and are always energized.

Fires involving solar panels have increased hazard as the electrical current that the panel produces cannot be effectively controlled. This current may travel back down the water stream and cause electrical shock to the hose team (Backstrom and Dini 2011). Once the flames are extinguished, note that the damaged panel may still produce electricity. Pooling water can increase the potential for electrical shock. Damaged panels should only be removed by a trained electrician.

 Safe Distance from Solar Panels

According to UL research, when dealing with fires in solar panels crews should use the reach of the stream and apply water from a minimum of 15 feet (5 meters) away when using an automatic nozzle on straight stream and 20 feet (6 meters) away when using a smooth bore (Backstrom and Dini 2011).

A structure may have wind turbines providing alternative power in addition to or in place of the power company. Wind turbines will continue to generate energy as long as the blades continue to rotate. The power at the building/facility can be secured at the meter box through the main power shutoff, however the power line from the wind turbine to the meter will remain energized. Some wind generating systems also employ backup battery bank systems.

WARNING: Wind turbines will continue to generate energy as long as the blades rotate.

Another type of alternative power system is a backup battery bank or uninterruptible power supply (UPS). These are used to maintain critical components that handle safety shutdown processes and do not require high voltage.

Fuel-powered generators are primarily used to replace the power company's service when service is interrupted **(Figure 16.3)**. In some locations, the generator may be the sole source of power for a structure. Shutting off the generator should control these systems. If the system supplements the power company's service, shut off the supply at the meter box.

NOTE: When shutting off building utilities, always assume there is an alternative source of energy present. Always use caution and refer to local policy for further guidance.

Figure 16.3 An example of an electrical generator found at an industrial facility.

Figure 16.4 Fire brigade members should be trained on gas utility shut-off locations.

Gas Utilities

To control gas utilities, fire brigade members must have a working knowledge of the hazards and correct procedures for handling incidents involving gas and liquefied petroleum gas (LPG). Many commercial and industrial facilities use natural gas or LPG for cooking, heating, or industrial processes **(Figure 16.4)**.

Natural Gas

Natural gas in its pure form is methane, which has a flammability range of 5 percent to 15 percent. Natural gas is lighter than air, so it tends to rise and diffuse in the open. Both methane and natural gas are nontoxic. Natural gas and methane are are classified as asphyxiants because they may displace air in a confined space and lead to suffocation. Natural gas has no odor of its own, so the utility companies add mercaptan, which causes a distinctive sulphur-like odor, like rotten eggs to help personnel detect the presence of the gas.

When ordered, the natural gas supply to a structure must be shut off at the meter. The meter is usually located outside the structure near the foundation or on the easement near the property line. However, it may be inside the structure in a basement or mechanical space. In some industrial and institutional occupancies, critical equipment and processes depend upon an uninterrupted supply of natural gas; for example, natural gas fuels emergency generators in some hospitals or other facilities.

The shutoff is an inline valve located on the owner supply side of the meter between the distribution system and the meter. When the valve is open, the *tang* (a rectangular bar) is in line with the pipe. To close the valve, use a spanner wrench, pipe wrench, or similar tool to turn the tang until it is 90 degrees to the pipe. If shutting off the inline valve does not stop the gas supply to the structure, take no further action and contact qualified personnel. They will provide:

- An emergency response crew equipped with nonsparking tools
- Distribution system maps
- Training and experience needed to help control the flow of gas

Underground leaks may produce visible signs such as bubbling, dying vegetation, darkening of the soil, and hissing sounds. The local utility company or qualified personnel should be contacted if the gas must be shut off or when any emergency involving natural gas occurs in its service area. Only utility company or qualified personnel are responsible for turning gas utilities back on after they have been shut off.

CAUTION: Natural gas that leaks underground in wet soil can lose its odorant and become difficult to detect without instruments.

Liquefied Petroleum Gas (LPG)

Also known as *bottled gas*, liquefied petroleum gas (LPG) refers to fuel gases stored in a liquid state under pressure. While there are two main gases in this category — butane and propane — propane is the most widely used. Propane is used primarily as a fuel gas in:

- Agricultural applications

- Commercial, institutional, and industrial facilities

- Motor vehicles **(Figure 16.5)**

Figure 16.5 The lift truck on the left runs on LPG while the pickup truck on the right uses compressed natural gas (CNG).

Lift Truck   **Pickup Truck**

Propane gas has no natural odor, but added mercaptan gives it a distinctive smell. The gas is nontoxic, but it is classified as an asphyxiant because it may displace normal breathing air in a confined space and lead to suffocation.

LPG is about 1 1/2 times as heavy as air, so it will sink to the lowest point possible. The gas is explosive in concentrations between 2 percent and 9.5 percent. LPG is shipped from its distribution point to its point of usage in cylinders and in tanks on cargo trucks. It is stored in cylinders and tanks near its point of use. Steel piping and copper tubing connect the tank or cylinder to gas powered appliances. Shutting the tank valve can stop the supply of gas going into a structure. An LPG leak will produce a visible cloud of vapor that hugs the ground. A fog stream of at least 100 gpm (400 L/min) can be used to dissipate this cloud of unburned gas.

Steel piping and copper tubing connect the tank or cylinder to gas powered appliances. Shutting the valve to the fuel container may stop the supply of gas going into a structure. A shutoff valve should be located at the point where the supply line from the LPG tank enters the structure. This valve may be similar to the type used for natural gas or water supply lines. There will also be a control valve located on the LPG tank. Turning the gas back on is the responsibility of the owner and the LPG supplier.

Water

When pipes are broken or damaged during an incident, it will be necessary to shut off the water supply to prevent water damage. Water shutoff valves are located underground with the water meter. Their location will depend on the location of water distribution lines in the jurisdiction. Residential water shutoff keys or pipe wrenches are used to turn the tang 90 degrees to the pipe. The valve may be located inside the structure. Use caution when touching water pipes because the electrical ground wire may be connected to the water pipe in residential structures.

Commercial structures and large institutional and industrial facilities have larger diameter supply lines than residential single-family structures. Above ground shutoff valves may be of the OS&Y-type while underground valves are usually equipped with a square-shaped tang. This will require a special water shut-off key that the fire brigade may assign to certain units or the water department may have to provide **(Figure 16.6)**. Restoring the water supply will be the responsibility of the water department or the owner.

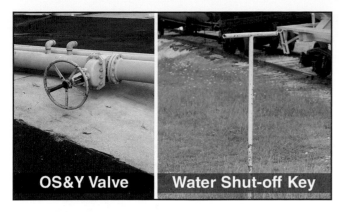

Figure 16.6 Two means of shutting off water to a facility, an OS&Y valve on the left and a water shut-off key on the right.

OS&Y Valve

Water Shut-off Key

Review Section: Water Supply

NFPA 1081 (2018): 5.1.2.1, 5.2.7, 6.1.2.3, 6.2.6

Facility water supplies should be identified on preincident plans. There are two basic types of water supply systems in North America: public and private. Public water supply distribution systems are generally a function of local government. A private water supply system may provide water under contract to a municipality, region, or single property.

Water is supplied from natural freshwater sources, such as wells, springs, rivers, lakes, and ponds. To ensure constant pressure, water distribution systems may incorporate elevated storage tanks throughout the system to create pressure through gravity. Elevated gravity storage tanks are usually constructed of steel or concrete.

Three methods for moving water through the system are:

- Gravity systems
- Direct Pumping systems
- Combination systems

Review Section: Hydraulic Principles

The water distribution system consists of a network of piping and isolation and control valves that carry the water under pressure to the points of use. In fire service hydraulics, pressure is the force that moves water through a conduit, whether a pipe or a hose. Fire brigade members need to understand the following terms:

- Static pressure
- Residual pressure
- Flow (velocity) pressure

Review Section: Water Supply Operability

Fire hydrants can provide a consistent volume of water under constant pressure. On the other hand, fire hydrants and water supply systems can fail, with failures or reduction in water supply (volume) or pressure resulting from:

- Damaged hydrant valves and connections
- Broken water mains
- Greater demand than the system can provide
- Hydrants located on dead-end water mains
- Closed isolation valves
- Restricted mains caused by sediment and mineral deposits
- Frozen pipes or hydrants

When a hydrant is taken out-of-service, the water or fire department, or facility AHJ should take the following actions:

- Place "Out-of-Service" tags or devices on the hydrant.
- Notify personnel within the hydrant's coverage district that it is out-of-service and approximately when it will return to service .
- Notify hydrant repair personnel.

    Reasons for a hydrant to be out-of-service may include:

- Damage to the hydrant, water system piping, or pump that support that location
- Repairs or upgrades being performed on the water system
- Obstructions placed within the hydrant
- A frozen hydrant during cold temperatures

Review Section: Water Supply Component Operations

Fire hydrants are located along all portions of a water distribution system. Regionally, hydrant manifolds, or simply called manifolds, are used in place of hydrants and serve the same function. Factors that affect hydrant location and spacing include:

- Types of building construction
- Types of occupancies
- Building densities (number of structures within the facility/site)
- Sizes of water mains
- Required fire flows for occupancies within a given area

    Common fire hydrants used in North America are:

- Dry-barrel hydrants
- Wet-barrel hydrants
- Dry hydrants
- Underground hydrants

    Firefighters use a variety of tools when making fire hydrant connections or accessing and controlling water supplies to include:

- Hose clamps
- Spanner wrenches
- Hydrant wrenches
- Rubber mallets
- Gate valves
- Hydrant valves

Fire Suppression Methods

NFPA 1081 (2018): 5.2.3, 6.2.1

Knowledge of fire extinguishment is necessary to understand fire control. This section describes methods fire brigade members use to interrupt the fire tetrahedron and extinguish a fire. These methods include:

- Temperature reduction
- Fuel removal

- Oxygen exclusion
- Chemical flame inhibition

Temperature Reduction

One of the most common methods of fire control and extinguishment is cooling with water. To extinguish a fire by reducing its temperature, enough water must be applied to absorb the heat being generated and stop the gas-phase chemical reaction **(Figure 16.7)**.

Figure 16.7 Fire brigade personnel practicing water application techniques.

Cooling reduces the temperature of a fuel to a point where it does not produce sufficient vapors to burn. The use of water for cooling is the most effective method available for the extinguishment of smoldering fires.

Water can be used to control burning gases and reduce the temperature of hot products of combustion in the upper gas layer. Cooling burning gases:

- Limits or stops flaming combustion in the upper layer
- Slows the pyrolysis process of combustible materials
- Reduces radiant heat flux from the upper layer
- Reduces the potential for flashover

A coordinated combination of cooling hot fire gases from the exterior using a straight stream paired with tactical ventilation lowers the risk that a ventilation-limited fire will reignite and re-enter the growth stage when it receives more oxygen. This tactic may lead to full fire extinguishment or may make the interior tenable for fire attack or search and rescue. Research and testing have shown that this tactic can make the environment tenable for victims and could save their lives.

As water absorbs heat from the environment, its temperature increases, converting liquid into steam. When water is converted to steam, it absorbs five times more energy compared to warming the liquid to the boiling point. The vaporizing water also rapidly expands approximately 1,700 times. Excess steam production can increase the chances for steam burns, reduce visibility, and disrupt the thermal layer. Because of this expansion rate, fire brigade members should avoid creating steam.

Control steam production as follows:

- Use proper nozzle technique.
- Apply the appropriate amount of water.
- Apply water using the most effective discharge pattern (fog, straight, or solid stream based upon scene conditions).

If the right amount of water is used with proper nozzle technique as described in this chapter, the hot gases within the fire compartment will contract. The contraction of the hot gases may offset the expansion of the steam. If the cooling process is effective, steam production will be kept to a minimum.

Fuel Removal

Removing the fuel source effectively extinguishes any fire. Removing fuel at a structure fire is rarely an option as an extinguishment method. Removing fuel is a more common tactic at:

- Flammable/combustible liquid fires
- Flammable gas fires
- Exterior stacked material fires
- Wildland fires

Closing a flammable gas pipeline valve will cut off the flow of gas to a fire **(Figure 16.8)**. The flame may then be controlled, extinguished, or allowed to burn out safely. Allowing a fire to burn until all available fuel is consumed while fire brigade members protect exposures is another example of fuel removal. For instance, flammable liquid spills may create greater environmental harm if they are extinguished with water, creating substantial runoff and contaminating soil or bodies of water. The best solution may be to allow the fire to burn, maximizing thermal damage but minimizing groundwater pollution.

A fuel source may be removed as follows:

- Stopping the flow of a liquid fuel
- Closing valves to stop the emission of gaseous fuels
- Moving solid fuels out of the path of the fire

Figure 16.8 A fire brigade member practicing fuel removal by closing a flammable gas valve.

Oxygen Exclusion

Reducing the oxygen available to the combustion process reduces a fire's growth and may result in extinguishment over time. In its simplest form, this method is used to extinguish stove-top fires when a cover is placed on a pan of burning grease. Flooding a compartment with an inert gas such as carbon dioxide displaces the oxygen and disrupts the combustion process; it also reduces the chance for occupant survivability. Blanketing some fuels with **foam** can displace the oxygen from the product vapor **(Figure 16.9)**. None of these methods work on fuels that are self-oxidizing such as ammonium nitrate found in fertilizer.

Figure 16.9 Fire brigade personnel using fire fighting foam to extinguish a training fire. *Courtesy of Marathon Petroleum Corporation.*

Limiting the fire's air supply can be a highly effective fire control action. The simplest example of this is when a building occupant closes the door to the fire room before leaving the building. This limits the air supply to the fire and can prevent flashover. Control of doors and windows into and within the structure can aid in controlling the flow path of oxygen to heated, fuel rich products of combustion.

Figure 16.10 Dry-chemical agents inhibit or interrupt the combustion reaction.

Chemical Flame Inhibition

Extinguishing agents such as some dry chemicals, halogenated agents (Halons), certain micelle encapsulators, and Halon-replacement **clean agents**, inhibit or interrupt the combustion reaction and stop flame production **(Figure 16.10)**. This method of extinguishment is effective on flaming (gas-phase) fires. These agents do not easily extinguish non-flaming (condensed phase) fires because there is no effective means to cool the fuel and stop the chemical chain reaction. The high agent concentrations and extended periods necessary to extinguish smoldering fires make these agents impractical in these cases.

Spill/Leak/Release Control Operations

NFPA 1081 (2018): 5.3.5, 6.3.5

Spills, leaks, and releases of flammable or combustible liquids or flammable gases occur frequently at industrial and other sites. The following section will cover topics that will assist the industrial fire brigade member in dealing with these types of emergencies.

Vapor Suppression

Vapor suppression is the action taken to reduce the emission of vapors at a flammable or combustible liquid spill. Fire fighting foams are effective on spills of flammable and combustible liquids if the foam concentrate is compatible with the material. Water-miscible (capable of being mixed) materials such as alcohols, esters, and ketones destroy regular fire fighting foams and require an alcohol-resistant foam agent. In general, the required application rate for applying foam to control an unignited liquid spill is substantially less than that required to extinguish a spill fire.

Fire brigade members must be trained in the techniques of vapor suppression. Training for extinguishment of flammable liquid fires does not necessarily qualify a fire brigade member to mitigate vapors produced by flammable liquid spills.

Other Spill Control Tactics

Rather than attempting to confine the dispersion, defensive spill control tactics such as ventilation and vapor dispersion are aimed at reducing the amount of harm caused by the material. This is done by diluting the concentration or changing its physical and/or chemical properties.

Ventilation

Ventilation involves controlling the movement of air by natural or mechanical means. Ventilation is used to remove and/or disperse harmful airborne particles, vapors, or gases when spills occur inside structures. The same ventilation techniques used for smoke removal can be used for hazmat incidents. When conducting negative-pressure ventilation, fans and other ventilators must be compatible with the atmosphere where they are being operated. Equipment to be used in a flammable atmosphere must be intrinsically safe to reduce the danger of ignition. When choosing the type of ventilation to use, remember that positive-pressure ventilation is usually more effective than negative-pressure ventilation when it comes to removing atmospheric contaminants. Some experts consider ventilation to be a type of vapor dispersion.

Vapor Dispersion

Vapor dispersion is the action taken to direct or influence the course of airborne hazardous materials. Pressurized streams of water from hoselines or unattended master streams may be used to help disperse vapors. These streams create turbulence, which increases the rate of mixing with air and reduces the concentration of the hazardous material. After using hoselines for vapor dispersion, it is necessary for fire brigade members to confine and analyze runoff water for possible contamination.

Release Control

Gases have a wide range of use in commercial and industrial settings. Gases are found universally in storage cylinders, large tanks, and distribution systems. In addition to the fire and explosion hazards posed by released flammable gases, any gas under pressure presents dangers to fire brigade members. These dangers include the possible violent failure of the container due to over pressurization and release of the material. Additionally, gases can be corrosive and toxic, and some are oxidizers.

Gas Container Types

All compressed gases must be confined in special containers designed to withstand pressure. Generally, containers that hold compressed gases are referred to as **pressure vessels**. The pressure in these vessels may range anywhere from approximately 40 to 4,000 psi (280 kPa to 28 000 kPa) {2.76 bar to 276 bar}.

There are many sizes and shapes of pressure vessels such as one-ton chlorine containers, breathing air cylinders on self-contained breathing apparatus (SCBA), acetylene bottles used on welding carts, portable fire extinguishers, and cylinders used in cascade systems.

Three basic types of containers used to handle compressed gases are pressure cylinders, pressure tanks, and pipelines **(Figure 16.11)**. The difference between pressure cylinders and pressure tanks is minimal. The designation of either tank or cylinder depends on which design criteria and regulations the container was built to meet. Previously, containers that were small, portable, and contained high pressures were termed cylinders. Large containers designed to be used in a fixed installation and typically containing low to moderate pressures were referred to as *tanks*. Because of regulatory changes, these distinctions no longer apply. The following sections describe basic types of containers.

Pressure Cylinders

Pressure cylinders are manufactured in accordance with the requirements established by the Department of Transportation (DOT) and the Canadian Transport Commission (CTC), whose requirements are the same. A wide variety of gases are transported in cylinders, and these

Figure 16.11 Examples of pressure cylinders (top), a pressure tank (middle), and a pipeline that contain pressurized gases (bottom).

cylinders are considered dependable performers within the industry. Pressure cylinders have the following characteristics:

- Range in size from the small, handheld types to those with a maximum capacity of 1,000 pounds (454 kg)

- Usually transported in an upright position

- Made of steel, aluminum, or composite construction (aluminum and fiberglass or aluminum and carbon fiber)

- Must have some type of pressure-relieving device (exceptions include disposable cylinders and some containers for poison gases such as methyl bromide and hydrogen cyanide)

Pressure Tanks

These tanks are constructed to comply with requirements set forth by the American Petroleum Institute (API) or the American Society of Mechanical Engineers (ASME). Tanks are most commonly found in fixed facilities but may also be found on motor vehicles and railcars. Tanks used in transportation are subject to additional criteria beyond API and ASME requirements. Pressure tanks have the following characteristics:

- Made of steel, aluminum, or composite construction (aluminum and fiberglass or aluminum and carbon fiber)

- Must have some type of pressure-relieving device (exceptions include some containers for poison gases, such as methyl bromide and hydrogen cyanide)

Pipelines

Pipelines carry compressed gases and are found in many forms. Petroleum and natural gas products are often transported through pipeline systems. Other industrial gases such as oxygen, anhydrous ammonia, and hydrogen may be piped within or between facilities.

Gas Emergencies

Immediately upon arrival at incidents involving gases, fire brigade members must pursue answers to the following questions:

- What is the wind direction?

- What gas is involved?

- What type and size of container is involved?

- Is there mechanical damage to a container?

- Is there a leak?

- Is there fire?

- Is there flame impingement on a container?

- What is the availability of water?

- Are there air inlets for structures and equipment?

- Can the fuel supply valve be turned off safely?

- What is the vapor density of the material involved?

- What are the possible/potential ignition sources?

Flammable gas containers and pipelines can be identified by placards, labels, or other signage. Fire brigade members should be trained to recognize these identifiers and use them to locate information about the appropriate gas or gases in the **Emergency Response Guidebook (ERG)**.

Emergencies involving flammable gases can be categorized based on whether, or not, fire is present. In the following sections, scenarios explain the immediate concern and primary objective that need to be taken for each. In most cases, the indicated general procedures below should be followed in any gas emergency:

Figure 16.12 The Emergency Response Guidebook (ERG) can provide important information during a gas emergency.

- Rely on the ERG or equivalent response guides for suggestions on evacuation distances **(Figure 16.12)**.
- Determine wind direction and initiate evacuation downwind.
- Eliminate ignition sources to prevent ignition or reignition, particularly when dealing with flammable gases.
- Do not allow anyone in or near the area until the arrival of specialists who have both the necessary technical knowledge and resources to handle the emergency.
- Set up unattended portable master stream nozzles to cool tanks and exposures (if there is a fire) and then have personnel withdraw to a safe distance.
- Execute any feasible rescues.

Flammable Gas Leaks (No Fire)

The first concern at incidents involving flammable gas leaks without fire is to prevent ignition. The primary objective is to turn off the flow of gas and then eliminate all ignition sources. If the gas is a liquefied petroleum gas (LPG) type, consider downwind ignition sources up to ½ mile (805 m) away because the vapors are heavier than air and can flash back significant distances. Isolate the area until the incident is completely stabilized.

Locate the valves to see if the leak can be controlled. If valves, valve stems, pressure-relief valves, fusible plugs or the structural integrity of the vessel have been compromised, isolate the area, move all personnel out of the area, and eliminate all ignition sources. **Table 16.1** provides some basic actions that can be taken by fire brigade members when dealing with flammable gas leaks in which there is no fire.

Table 16.1 First Responder Actions at Flammable Gas Leak (No Fire) Incidents	
Strategic Goal	**Actions (Tactics)**
Isolation	Isolate and evacuate the area according to *ERG* guidelines.
Fire Control	Eliminate all ignition sources.
Protection	Stay out of low areas. (Many gases are heavier than air and will collect in low-lying areas or confined spaces.)
Spill Control: Vapor Suppression and Confinement	Use water spray to reduce vapors or divert vapor cloud drift, and confine runoff water as appropriate.
Spill Control: Confinement	Prevent vapors and/or runoff water from entering waterways, sewers, basements, or confined areas.
Leak Control	Stop leak by closing remote valve if it is safe to do so.
Fire Control	Ground all equipment used to handle the product/containers, use nonsparking tools, explosion-proof ventilation fans, etc.
Actions to Avoid	
Do not direct water at the source of the leak or safety devices because icing may occur.	

Flammable Gas Leaks Involving Fire or Flame Impingement

The immediate concern at a flammable gas leak incident involving fire or flame impingement is to protect exposures (particularly any tanks) by cooling. The primary objective is to turn off the flow of gas. Fire situations involving flammable gases are extremely serious. Ideally, the next objective is to direct large quantities of water onto all sides of the tank (or tanks) as quickly as possible. Water is used at a pressurized container fire for cooling the tank and reducing the internal vapor pressure — not for fire extinguishment.

Lessons learned from historical review of LPG catastrophes include:

- Large-capacity containers may fail violently within 10 to 20 minutes of direct-flame impingement. Fire brigade members must factor both the response time and the possible setup time for equipment when determining a course of action.

- Boiling liquid expanding vapor explosions (BLEVEs) of large-capacity containers typically create nonsurvivable fire conditions within 500 feet (152 m) and create severe tank shell fragmentation from 2,500 to 4,000 feet (762 m to 1 219 m).

- Unless cooling water is adequate and uninterrupted quantities can be applied on the exposed tank or container, rescue and evacuation activities need to be performed quickly followed by a total withdrawal from the area.

A flame impinging directly onto a tank shell quickly weakens the metal. Water must be directed onto the area of flame impingement, especially if flame impingement is in the tank's vapor space. A minimum of 500 gpm (2 000 L/min) must be played on each large highway tanker or rail tank car at each point of flame impingement (**Figure 16.13**). An obvious sheen of water needs to be seen rolling down the tank shell to ensure that the water is not being converted to steam before it cools the tank. Streams must be directed from each side to maximize total coverage of the tank shell. Fire brigade members need to concentrate on the upper vapor space and allow water to flow down the sides. **Table 16.2** provides some basic actions that can be taken by fire brigade members when dealing with flammable gas leaks threatened by or involved in fire.

Figure 16.13 Illustrating how water should be applied to points of impingement during fires involving flammable gas tanks.

There are no absolute clues as to when a tank rupture might occur. However, some warning signals that indicate a situation is becoming worse include:

- The pressure-relief device operates, indicating that pressure is building in the tank. Actions must be taken to reduce pressure.

- The pitch of the sound from the pressure-relief valve increases (becomes sharper) as the gas exits at a greater velocity, indicating a continuing increase in pressure.

- The size of the torch, and the volume and pitch of sound from the pressure-relief valve, continue to increase because of a greater volume of gas rushing out, indicating an increase in internal boiling and vapor production. If the fire or torch coming from the pressure in the tank is also increasing, on-scene cooling techniques are obviously inadequate.

- A pinging, popping, or snapping sound occurs, indicating that the metal has been softened by high heat and is stretching.

Table 16.2
First Responder Actions at Flammable Gas Leak
(Involving Fire) Incidents

Strategic Goal	Actions (Tactics)
Isolation	Isolate and evacuate area according to *ERG* guidelines.
Fire Control Withdraw	**STAY AWAY from tanks engulfed in fire.**
Fire Control Extinguishment	**Do not extinguish a leaking gas fire unless the leak can be stopped.**
Protection	Move undamaged containers from the fire area if it is safe to do so. (Damaged containers should be moved only by specialists or technicians).
Fire Control: Exposure Protection	Cool containers with flooding quantities of water until well after fire is extinguished.
Fire Control: Withdraw	Withdraw immediately in case of rising sound from venting safety devices or discoloration of tanks.
Fire Control: Extinguishment	Fight tank fires from maximum distance or use unattended hose streams.
Fire Control: Extinguishment/ Withdrawal	Use unattended hose streams for massive fires. If this action is not possible, withdraw from the area and let the fire burn.
Fire Control: Exposure Protection	Protect exposures.

Actions to Avoid

Do not direct water at the source of the leak or safety devices because icing may occur.

- Dry spots or visible steam appear on the tank surface, indicating insufficient cooling. If this situation occurs when water is applied, the tank shell is over 212°F (100°C) and more water is needed.

- An impinging flame, usually in an isolated location, causes discoloration of the shell, indicating a weakening of the metal. The color of the tank turns from gray to an off-white, and small pieces of paint and metal flake off.

- A bulge or bubble appears on the tank shell, indicating a serious localized heating of the shell in the vapor space. The metal is softening and beginning to deform because of inadequate cooling of the shell.

Review Section: Fire Control Operations

NFPA 1081 (2018): 5.2.3, 5.2.8, 5.3.3, 5.3.9, 6.2.1, 6.2.5, 6.3.3, 6.3.11

Fire brigade members use the following methods to interrupt the fire tetrahedron and extinguish a fire:

- Temperature reduction
- Fuel removal
- Oxygen exclusion
- Chemical flame inhibition

Fire brigade members can control steam production in the following ways:

- Use good nozzle technique.
- Apply the appropriate amount of water.
- Apply water using the most effective form (fog, straight, or solid stream based upon existing conditions).

Removing fuel is a more common tactic at fires involving materials such as:

- Exterior stacked materials
- Flammable liquids/gases
- Vehicles

Limiting the fire's air supply by control of doors and windows into and within the structure can aid in controlling the flow path of oxygen to heated, fuel-rich products of combustion. On a larger scale, flooding a compartment with an inert gas such as carbon dioxide displaces the oxygen and disrupts the combustion process. Blanketing some fuels with foam can displace the oxygen. Removing or limiting a fire's access to ambient oxygen will not work on fuels that are self-oxidizing, such as ammonium nitrate found in fertilizer.

Extinguishing agents, such as some dry chemicals, halogenated agents (Halons), and Halon-replacement "clean" agents, inhibit or interrupt the chemical chain reaction and stop flame production. This method of extinguishment is effective on flaming (gas-phase) fires. These agents do not easily extinguish non-flaming (condensed phase) fires because there is no effective means to cool the fuel and stop the chemical chain reaction.

Personnel commonly apply fire streams using the following methods:

- Direct attack

- Indirect attack

- Combination attack

The three main uses for a master stream are as follows:

- For direct fire attack

- As exposure protection and/or cooling

- To supplement hoselines that are operating in the area

Fixed master stream devices should be used as specified in the facility's emergency plan or SOPs. A fire brigade member should be stationed at the master stream device while water is flowing. This position allows the fire brigade member to change the direction or pattern of the stream when required, or shut down the master stream device as the situation changes.

Fire brigade members should be taught to continuously evaluate the hazards at a fire and recognize when a fire has grown beyond their capabilities. They should be familiar with the fire brigade's methods of communicating an evacuation or exit from a hazardous area, and of possible evacuation routes within the site or facility. Once outside the hazardous area, the fire brigade or team leader should account for all team members.

To suppress an incipient stage Class A fire, fire brigade members should choose the appropriate extinguisher(s) or handline(s) available at their facility and operate in accordance with brigade's SOPs. Test the extinguisher or handline prior to approaching the fire to ensure it is operational. Approach the fire with caution while maintaining an escape route should the fire grow beyond the incipient stage. If possible, personnel should direct the agent at the base of the fire and sweep from side-to-side. If direct application is not possible, then an indirect attack should be attempted. As flaming combustion subsides and the fire darkens down, the fire brigade members may move closer and adjust the fire stream pattern. In stacked or piled materials, the fire brigade member should break apart the materials using a pike pole to allow agent to reach the seat of the fire. Once the fire is extinguished, overhaul the fire scene and ensure the fire is fully extinguished.

Fire brigade members must exercise caution when attacking fires involving flammable and combustible liquids. The first precaution is to avoid standing in pools of fuel or water runoff containing fuel. Protective clothing can absorb fuel in a wicking action. When protective clothing is saturated, points of contact with skin may develop chemical burns or absorb toxic materials, and materials can catch fire if an ignition source is present. Even if the wicking action does not occur, the pool of liquid itself may ignite and present extreme danger.

Unburned vapors are usually heavier than air and form pools or pockets of vapors in low spots where they may ignite. Fire brigade personnel should not enter a flammable liquid vapor cloud because their personal protective equipment (PPE) will not protect them if ignition occurs. Fire brigade members must control all ignition sources in a leak area.

Vehicles, smoking materials, electrical fixtures, and sparks from steel tools can provide an ignition source sufficient to ignite leaking flammable vapors. An increase in the intensity of sound or fire issuing from a relief valve may indicate that rupture of the vessel is imminent. Fire brigade members should not assume that relief valves are sufficient to safely relieve excess pressures under severe fire conditions. Large and small flammable liquid vessels have killed fire brigade members, firefighters, and bystanders after rupturing when exposed to flames.

Class B foam is the recommended agent for controlling flammable liquid fires involving polar solvents, such as alcohols and lacquers, that mix with liquids. Alternately, water can be used to control Class B fires involving hydrocarbon liquids, such as gasoline, kerosene, and other petroleum products, that do not mix with water. Accidents involving vehicles transporting flammable fuels and gas utilities also require Class B fire control techniques.

The hazards of fighting Class C fires include potential electrical burns or electrocution if using Class A extinguishing on energized equipment. Energized Class C fires should be fought using non-conductive extinguishing agents to prevent such injuries. Procedures for fighting Class C fires should include ensuring that appropriate power breakers are opened to disconnect power flow into structures. Once the power has been turned off, fires in electrical equipment may self-extinguish or the type of fire will change from Class C to another fire class based on its fuel if it continues. Clean extinguishing agents, such as carbon dioxide, Halon, or FM-200 can be used to prevent further damage to equipment. Multipurpose dry chemical agents may require significant clean-up after use in addition to being chemically active with some electrical components.

Combustible metals (Class D fuels) present the dual hazards of burning at high temperatures and being reactive to water. Water is only effective at suppressing these fires when it can be applied in large enough quantities to cool the metal below its ignition temperature. The usual method of control is to protect exposures and permit the metal to burn itself out. Fire brigade members may shovel or spray special extinguishing agents from special extinguishers in quantities large enough to cover the burning metal.

Some commercial cooking facilities and other industrial facilities have onsite kitchens that use high-efficiency cooking equipment (which is highly insulated and slow to cool) to heat cooking media such as vegetable or animal oil and fats (Class K fuels). Fire brigade members should be familiar with the operation of the wet chemical fire extinguishers and suppression systems intended to suppress Class K fires at their facility. If equipped, the fire suppression system should be activated before using a Class K extinguisher. Extreme care should be taken when suppressing Class K fires to avoid directing the extinguishing agent into the cooking media at too close a range or too steep of an angle.

Review Section: Hose and Handline Operations

NFPA 1081 (2018): 5.2.3, 5.2.6, 6.2.1, 6.2.4

Attack and supply hose are commonly manufactured in 50 or 100 foot (15 or 30 m) lengths or sections. High-strength, lightweight synthetic materials have the same relative weight of traditional sections of hose. Synthetic nitrile rubber hoses are more chemical resistant than traditional fire hose, dry faster, and can be decontaminated and cleaned more easily.

Lightweight hose is ideal for use in Class II standpipe systems or fire hose reels. This type of hose uses a lower working pressure than fire attack hose. Booster hose has a stiff outer membrane to maintain the shape of the hose and is coiled around a reel for storage. This type of hose is typically used for small fires (such as trash, wildland, or car fires).

Suction hose (also called *intake hose*), is used to connect the pumper to a hydrant or other water source. It will not collapse under the vacuum conditions needed during drafting and intake. Some hard-suction hose is constructed of a rubberized, reinforced material; other hoses are made of heavy-duty corrugated plastic.

Large soft sleeve hose is used to connect the pumper intake to a pressurized water source. Referred to as soft suction hose, it is not rigid and cannot be used for drafting because it will collapse under vacuum.

Review Section: Preconnected Hose Loads for Attack Lines

Preconnected hoselines, simply called *preconnects*, are primarily used for fire attack. These hoselines are connected to a discharge valve and placed in an area other than the main hose bed. Preconnected hoselines generally range from 50 to 250 feet (15 m to 75 m) in length. Preconnected attack lines can be carried in the following places:

- Longitudinal beds
- Raised trays
- Transverse beds (sometimes called *cross lays* or *Mattydale hose beds*)
- Tailboard compartments
- Side compartments or bins
- Front bumper wells (sometimes called *jump lines*)
- Reels

  Some common loads for preconnects include the:
- Preconnected flat load
- Triple layer load
- Minuteman load

Review Section: Booster Hose Reels

Booster hoselines are rubber-covered hose of varying lengths and diameters that are usually carried preconnected and coiled on reels, making it ideal for quick first-attack on small exterior fires. These hoses retain their internal capacity while on the reel and do not have to be fully unreeled before use. Direct connection provides instant water flow no matter what length of hose is needed. These booster hose reels may be mounted in any of several places on apparatus or within facilities.

Review Section: Standpipe/High-Rise Hose Packs

Standpipe/high-rise hose packs are preassembled hose rolls, bundles, or packs that are carried on an apparatus or stored in a hose house or hose box. These packs are ready to carry aloft (or into a building) and connect to the building's standpipe system. These hose bundles are easily carried on the shoulder or in specially designed hose packs complete with nozzles, fittings, and tools.

Review Section: Other Hoselines

Some 2½-inch (65 mm) or larger attack hoselines may be preconnected or use supply hose as attack line. Wye appliances are used in connection with a reverse lay because the wye connection is fastened to the 2½- or 3-inch (65 mm or 77 mm) supply hose. Attack lines in hose bundles can be connected to the wye and advanced to the fire.

Review Section: Hose Team Duties

Fire brigade members may operate larger hoselines in teams of two or three responders. The nozzle operator is responsible for controlling the nozzle, selecting the appropriate discharge pattern, appropriately applying the agent, and directing the agent to where it will be most effective. The second member on the line helps maintain control of the hoseline, maneuver the hoseline, and guide it around obstacles. If it becomes necessary to retreat, the second member can help by pulling or moving the hose along the exit path. Larger attack hoselines may require a third fire brigade member be assigned to help maintain control of the line and with maneuvering it at the scene.

Hoselines can be deployed more easily before they are charged because water adds weight, rigidity, and pressure that makes the hose difficult to maneuver. Because of the size of many industrial and commercial facilities, fire brigade members may need to enter the involved structure with uncharged or charged hoselines and connect to the water supply once near the fire's location. Other hoseline techniques that fire brigade members should be familiar with include:

- Working line drag
- Extending a section of hose
- Retrieving a loose hoseline
- Replacing burst sections

Review Section: Operating Small Attack Lines

One or two fire brigade members can operate small hoselines, such as booster lines and 1½-, 1¾-, and 2-inch (38 mm, 45 mm, and 50 mm) hoselines **(Figure 16.14)**. Small hoselines can require additional fire brigade members when the hose is charged and obstructions must be negotiated.

Figure 16.14 These photos demonstrate how one (left) or two fire brigade members (right) can operate small attack lines.

One-Fire Brigade Member Method. One fire brigade member can operate an attack hoseline during exterior fire suppression or overhaul operations. The nozzle operator holds the nozzle with one hand and holds the hose just behind the nozzle with the other hand. The hoseline is then rested against the waist and across the hip. Pistol grip nozzles are held with the pistol grip in one hand while holding the operating bale in the other.

Two-Fire Brigade Members Method. Two fire brigade members should handle each attack line during interior structural fire fighting operations. The nozzle operator holds and operates the nozzle. The backup fire brigade member takes a position on the same side of the hose about 3 feet (1 m) or approximately an arm's length behind the nozzle operator. The second fire brigade member holds the hose with both hands and rests it against the waist and across the hip or braces it with the leg. The backup fire brigade member is responsible for keeping the hose straight behind the nozzle operator and at a level comfortable for the nozzle operator.

Three-Fire Brigade Members Method. Three fire brigade members can easily maneuver a small handline. All personnel may be located on the same side of the hose or the backup personnel may be positioned opposite each while serving as anchors.

Review Section: Operating Large Attack Lines

Fire brigade members must also be able to deploy, advance, and place large attack hoselines of 2½-and 3-inch (65 mm and 77 mm) or larger hose into operation. The following sections discuss methods that can be used with these large attack hoselines.

One-Fire Brigade Member Method. One fire brigade member may be assigned to operate a large hoseline during exposure protection or overhaul operations. A large loop is formed that crosses over the hoseline about 2 feet (0.6 m) behind the nozzle. The fire brigade member sits on the intersection where the hose crosses over itself and directs the fire stream to the point of application.

Two-Fire Brigade Members Method. Two fire brigade members assigned to handle a large hoseline may need a means to anchor the hoseline to offset nozzle reaction. Hose straps or rope hose tools may be used to assist in anchoring the hose by looping a hose strap or rope hose tool around the hose a short distance from the nozzle, placing the large loop across the back and over the outside shoulder. The operator then holds the nozzle with one hand and the hose just behind the nozzle with the other hand. Leaning slightly forward helps control the nozzle reaction. A backup person can serve as an anchor about 3 feet (1 m) back and use a hose strap or rope hose tool around the hose to absorb some of the nozzle reaction.

Three-Fire Brigade Members Method. When using large-size hoselines, the three-fire brigade member method can assist with mobility of the hoseline. The nozzle operator is positioned in the same way as described for the two-fire brigade member method. Some fire brigades prefer the first backup fire brigade member to stand directly behind the brigade member at the nozzle, with the third fire brigade member kneeling on the hose behind the second brigade member. Another method is for both fire brigade members to serve as anchors by kneeling on opposite sides of the hoseline. Or all brigade members can use hose straps and remain in a standing position, which is the most mobile method.

Review Section: Fire Streams

NFPA 1081 (2018): 5.2.3, 6.2.1

A *fire stream* is a stream of water or other extinguishing agent after it leaves a fire hose nozzle until it reaches the desired target.

Fire streams are used for the following:

- Apply water or foam directly onto burning material to reduce its temperature and access to oxygen.
- Apply water or foam into open flames to reduce the temperature so that firefighters can advance handlines.
- Reduce the temperature of the upper gas layers.
- Disperse hot smoke and fire gases from a heated area.
- Create a water curtain to protect firefighters and property from heat.
- Create a barrier between a fuel and a fire by covering the fuel with a foam blanket.

Fire streams can be best described in the following terms:

- The fire stream patterns they form
- The nozzles that create those patterns
- The types of control valves that permit the flow of water through the nozzle
- The factors that limit a fire stream

The size of the nozzle opening or orifice, and nozzle pressure determines the quantity of water flowing from the nozzle. The size of the opening also influences the reach or distance of the fire stream. Finally, the type of nozzle determines the shape of the fire stream.

While steam production is necessary for effective and efficient use of water as an extinguishing agent, care must be taken to apply the appropriate amount of water in the correct place to achieve the desired effect. If applied incorrectly, a heat inversion can cause the heated layer to expand downward, endangering occupants and firefighters inside the room.

Pressure loss and gain from friction loss and elevation differences can influence fire stream effectiveness. In general, the smaller the hose diameter and the longer the hose lay, the higher the friction loss at a given pressure and flow rate. In a fire fighting operation, elevation refers to the position of the nozzle in relation to the pumping apparatus, which is at ground level. When a nozzle is *above* the fire pump, there is a *pressure loss*. When the nozzle is *below* the pump, there is a *pressure gain*.

Fire streams are classified in three sizes: low-volume streams, handline streams, and master streams. The major types of fire stream patterns are solid, fog, straight, and broken.

There are five limiting factors that affect the reach of a fire stream:

- Gravity
- Water velocity
- Fire stream pattern
- Water droplet friction with air
- Wind

When operating a smooth-bore nozzle, the operator should control the nozzle as follows:

- Cradle the hoseline under one arm while holding the nozzle or nozzle pistol grip in one hand.
- Pull back slowly on the bale with the other hand to open the nozzle.
- As the pressure increases, lean forward with legs apart, one foot forward, weight evenly distributed on both feet.

The reaction from a fog nozzle will vary depending on the setting of the fog nozzle. When the fog nozzle is set on straight stream or narrow stream pattern, the reaction is similar to that of a smooth bore nozzle. As the fog pattern widens, the reaction decreases, making the nozzle easier to handle.

Fire brigade members need to monitor the effectiveness of fire streams. If the streams are not reaching the fire or are overshooting the fire, then the streams need to be adjusted to reach the seat of the fire. As the fire banks down, the fire brigade members can adjust their position or the fire stream pattern to continue extinguishment.

Review Section: Standpipe and Hose Systems
NFPA 1081 (2018): 5.1.2.1, 5.2.5, 6.1.2.3, 6.2.9

Standpipe and hose systems are designed to provide a means for rapidly deploying fire hoses and operating fire streams at locations that are remote from the fire apparatus. Horizontal standpipes reduce the time and effort needed to manually advance a hoseline several hundred feet (meters) to reach the seat of the fire. During overhaul, horizontal standpipes can also reduce the amount of hose needed to reach areas that sprinklers already control. A standpipe may be the primary means for manual extinguishment and overhaul of a fire, and an essential element in a building's design. The facilities primary water source may service the standpipe system or fire brigade personnel may provide the water supply or augment the existing supply using a fire department connection (FDC).

Standpipe systems are activated manually. Fire brigade members should be trained to operate the standpipe systems and ensure that pressure regulating valves are used and functioning properly. Once handlines are attached and deployed, then the appropriate valves should be opened. All standpipe discharges should be equipped with a pressure regulating device. The fire brigade should flush the standpipe prior to connecting any hose lines.

In most cases, little is required of fire brigade members in supporting operating standpipe systems. Fire brigade members should make sure that the control valve is open so that the system can function as designed, and ensure that it remains open until water flow is no longer required. Fire brigade members can communicate with incoming fire and emergency service units to direct them to the appropriate FDC.

Review Section: Master Stream Appliance

NFPA 1081 (2018): 5.3.3, 6.3.3

The four main uses for a master stream are:

- Direct fire attack

- Indirect fire attack

- Supplement handlines already attacking the fire from the exterior

- Protect exposures

Master streams should only be operated in unoccupied structures as the high pressure flow can injure personnel inside the structure or interfere with search and rescue operations. High volumes of water added to a structure may cause structural collapse. Master stream devices must be properly positioned to apply an effective stream on a fire. Master stream nozzles can be adjusted up and down and right and left, but must be shut down before it can be relocated. Fire brigade members should aim the master stream so that it enters the structure at an upward angle, causing it to deflect off the ceiling or other overhead objects, diffusing it into smaller droplets, and providing maximum extinguishing effectiveness. The introduction of master streams into a structure may interfere with ventilation operations at the scene. Master stream operations should be carefully coordinated with ventilation operations to prevent this.

There are two approaches for providing fire exposure protection. The first and most effective approach is to direct the stream at the structure's exposed surface. The stream should strike the surface and run down it. If the surface is wide, multiple devices can be used or one unit can sweep the face and keep it wetted. Position the master stream device so that the stream covers the most surface area possible. The second approach is to create a water curtain between the fire and the exposure **(Figure 16.15)**. This approach can be effective if the exposure has multiple surfaces, such as densely placed trees.

Figure 16.15 To provide exposure protection, master streams can be applied directly to a structure's surface (left) or sprayed between a structure and a fire as a water curtain (right).

Deploying a master stream device and the necessary water supply hoselines usually requires a minimum of two fire brigade members, although more personnel can accomplish it faster. Once a device is in place, one fire brigade member can operate it. When water is flowing, at least one fire brigade member should be stationed at the master stream device at all times. If the situation is too dangerous to have fire brigade members stationed at the device, it can be securely anchored in position and activated, then fire brigade members can withdraw to a safe distance.

The use of master streams can introduce large quantities of water into outside facilities as well as inside structures. This water can add weight to an already weakened structure and contribute to further secondary damage to the structure and its contents.

Suppressing Fires in Stacked and Piled Materials

NFPA 1081 (2018): 5.2.3, 6.2.1

Stacked and piled combustible materials can be found around all types of facilities. Conditions include:

- Raw materials such as those found at sawmills, lumberyards, and manufacturing facilities
- Coal and biomass outside a refinery or quarry/mine
- Bales of used cardboard or pallets near large retail stores and distribution centers
- Bales or large rolls of hay or cotton at an agricultural center or mill
- Loose combustible materials, such as building materials, fertilizers, office supplies at manufacturing or warehouse facilities
- Materials with different hazard classes and storage requirements stored outdoors, potentially without shelter

In addition to the expected combustible loads, some facilities may need to track atypical loads. Transient combustibles are materials that are brought into a facility on a temporary basis and may impact the facility's fire load and risk. This is a particular concern during an outage, turnaround maintenance periods, or major facility renovations. Facilities should have a program to monitor transient combustibles brought into facilities as part of a combustible loading program.

The value of transient materials will vary widely, but the possibility that any portion can be salvaged once a fire starts is small. The greatest danger is to exposures, primarily nearby structures and ground cover. There is also the potential, especially in modern construction, for fire to spread to the interior of an exposed structure.

When responding to a fire in transient materials, the goal is to confine the fire to the pile or point of origin. Depending on the material and how involved the fire is, fire streams should be directed at the extreme edge of the fire, controlling the spread. Use a straight stream from a distance and then shift to a fog pattern when advancing towards the fire.

As the quantity of fire is reduced, move the nozzle closer to the stacked material using the fog pattern for protection. Other personnel can use pike poles and hay hooks to break up or pull apart the stacked or piled material so that the stream can reach all the burning material. For larger stacks and piles of materials, backhoes and front-end loaders may be used to break up the materials. Fires, and response to fires, in stacked and piled materials may cause the materials to collapse. For example, large rolls of paper become heavier as they absorb water during fire fighting operations, lose vertical strength, and then collapse. As fire damages the materials low in the stack or pile or as the upper materials are become saturated with water, the stack or pile may collapse or fall over. Flying embers may also spread the fire requiring additional units to perform spark patrol downwind of the fire.

Review Section: Fire Protection Systems

NFPA 1081 (2018): 5.1.2.1, 5.2.5, 5.3.8, 6.1.2.3, 6.2.9, 6.3.2

There are two general types of sprinkler coverage: full and partial sprinkler coverage. A full coverage sprinkler system protects the entire building. A partial sprinkler system protects only certain areas, such as high-hazard areas, exit routes, or designated locations.

A sprinkler system starts with a water main and continues into the system's control valve. The riser is the vertical piping to which the sprinkler valve, one-way check valve, FDC, alarm valve, main drain, and other components get attached. The feed main is the pipe connecting the riser to the cross mains. Cross mains service branch lines on which the sprinklers are installed. Cross mains extend past the last branch lines and are capped to facilitate flushing. System piping decreases in size from the riser outward.

Sprinklers are fixed-spray nozzles that are opened individually. When a heat-responsive element such as a fusible link activates, the cap or plug in the sprinkler opens, allowing water to discharge. Deluge systems use open sprinklers which lack the heat-responsive element. Deluge systems do not operate individually, but the entire system operates at once. Early-suppression fast-response (ESFR) sprinklers react five to ten times faster than traditional sprinklers. Sprinklers are commonly rated according to the temperature at which they are designed to operate.

Every sprinkler system is equipped with a main water control valve that is used to interrupt the water supply to the system in order to replace sprinklers, perform maintenance, or interrupt operations. Most main water control valves are of the indicating type and manually operated.

Types of indicating control valves include the following:

- Outside stem and yoke (OS&Y) valve
- Post indicator valve (PIV)
- Wall post indicator valve (WPIV)
- Post indicator valve assembly (PIVA)

The system's water supply should be capable of delivering the required volume of water to the highest sprinkler at a residual pressure of at least 15 psi (105 kPa). A connection to a public water system with adequate volume, pressure, and reliability is a good source of water for automatic sprinklers. Some facilities use private water sources to supply sprinkler systems. Fire pumps are typically incorporated into the sprinkler system to supplement water flow. A pumping apparatus can be connected to the sprinkler FDC to provide additional water and pressure.

There are basically four types of sprinkler systems used in facilities:

- Wet-pipe sprinkler systems
- Dry-pipe sprinkler systems
- Preaction sprinkler systems
- Deluge sprinkler systems

Sprinkler systems are activated in the following ways:

- Automatically by either a detector or a combination of detectors
- Manually by someone operating a manual station and putting the system through its complete cycle of operation, including the predischarge alarm

Where required, sprinkler systems should be equipped with warning devices to alert employees to immediately evacuate the area. Run-off water from sprinkler system operations in industrial plants or other facilities may be contaminated with oils or other hazardous materials and should be retained for cleanup.

The fire brigade should inspect sprinkler systems regularly. Fire brigade members should be trained to activate the system, if necessary. They are also responsible for assisting in the evacuation of affected personnel, accounting for everyone displaced by the evacuation, and preventing unauthorized entry into the affected area. Personnel should be prepared to help supplement the water supply to a sprinkler system. Fire brigade members should be prepared to shut down sprinkler systems or close off individual sprinklers to reduce water damage. Exercise caution in shutting down sprinkler systems prior to reaching extinguishment as this response may result in additional fire damage to the facility.

Extinguishing Fires with Fire Fighting Foams

NFPA 1081 (2018): 5.3.4, 6.3.4

Fire fighting foam works by forming a blanket of foam on the surface of burning fuels — both liquid and solid. Fire fighting foam extinguishes and/or prevents ignition in several ways **(Figure 16.16):**

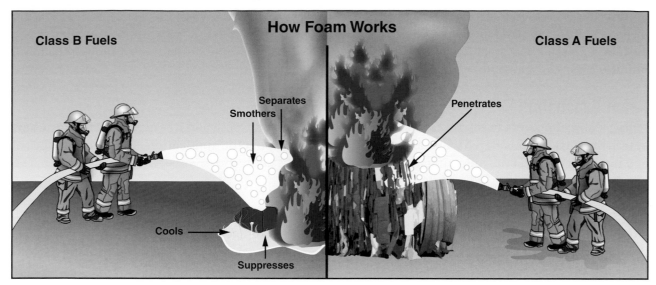

Figure 16.16 Illustrating how Class B and Class A fire fighting foams work.

- **Separating** — Creates a barrier between fuel gases and possible ignition sources
- **Cooling** — Lowers the temperature of the fuel and adjacent surfaces
- **Smothering** — Prevents air from reaching the fuel and mixing with the vapors and prevents the release of flammable vapors
- **Penetrating** — Lowers the surface tension of water and allows it to penetrate fires in Class A materials

Most fire fighting foams are **Class A foams** intended for use on ordinary combustibles (Class A fuels) or Class B foams intended for use on flammable liquids. On solid fuels, Class A foam blankets and cools the fuel and stops the burning process. Additionally, Class A foam lowers the surface tension of water, allowing the foam/water to penetrate deeper into fuels to extinguish the fire. The penetration works best on porous fuels.

After controlling the flames, the water in the foam is slowly released into the fuel as the foam collapses and returns to a liquid. This action provides a cooling effect on the fuel. With liquid fuels, the Class B foam blanket also prevents or reduces the release of flammable vapors from the surface of the fuel. Class B foam is especially effective on the two basic categories of flammable liquids: hydrocarbon fuels and polar solvents.

Foam Generation

A **foam proportioner** mixes foam concentrate and water to produce a foam solution. Air is then added to the solution through mechanical agitation, or aeration, to produce the finished foam **(Figure 16.17)**. The foam concentrate, water, and air must be blended in the correct ratio; removing any element results in no foam production or poor-quality foam.

Figure 16.17 Common components of a foam handline.

Aeration is needed to produce enough bubbles to form an effective foam blanket. Proper aeration produces uniform-sized bubbles that provide a longer-lasting blanket. A foam blanket is required to maintain an effective cover for the period of time required for extinguishment. Even though the foam bubbles dissipate, a residual foam layer is still present.

Foam Expansion

Foam expansion refers to the increase in volume of a foam solution when it is aerated. This key characteristic must be considered when a foam concentrate for a specific application is chosen. Degrees of expansion depend on the following factors:

- Type of foam concentrate used
- Accurate proportioning (mixing) of the foam concentrate in the solution
- Quality of the foam concentrate being added (shelf-life or storage conditions)
- Method of aeration and sizing of bubbles

    NOTE: Table 16.3 shows common foam expansion descriptions, ratios, and uses.

Table 16.3 Foam Expansion		
Classifications	**Ratios**	**Uses**
Low-expansion	20:1	Effective for controlling and extinguishing most Class B fires.
Medium-expansion	20:1 to 200:1	Used to suppress vapors from hazardous materials spills when applied at expansion ratios of 30:1 and 55:1.
High-expansion	200:1 to 1,000:1	Typically used in confined spaces such as shipboard compartments, basements, mines, and enclosed aircraft hangars.

Foam Concentrates

To be effective, foam concentrates must be chosen to match the fuel to which they are applied. **Appendix D** highlights the common types of foam concentrates.

> **CAUTION:** Failing to match the foam type and concentrate to the burning fuel will result in an unsuccessful extinguishing attempt and could endanger fire brigade members.

Both Class A and Class B foams may be used with fog nozzles, air-aspirating foam nozzles, medium- and high-expansion devices, and apparatus-mounted systems such as **compressed air foam systems (CAFS)**. Not all CAFS are rated for both types of foam. Review the manufacturer's ratings for a system when adding concentrate to CAFS. Foam concentrates have solvent characteristics and are mildly corrosive. Thoroughly flush equipment after use.

> **CAUTION:** Mixing different types of foam can result in substandard quality foam and can foul pumps and other equipment.

Class A Foam

Foams specifically designed for use on Class A fuels (ordinary combustibles) are increasingly used in wildland and structural fire fighting. Class A foam is a special formulation of hydrocarbon-based surfactants. These surfactants reduce the surface tension of water in the foam solution, allowing better water penetration into the fuel, thereby increasing its effectiveness. Aerated Class A foam coats and insulates fuels, preventing pyrolysis and ignition from an adjacent fire.

Class B Foam

Class B foam is used to prevent the ignition of or to extinguish fires involving flammable and combustible liquids. Class B finished foam also suppresses vapors from unignited spills. The types of liquid fuels that Class B foam is effective on are:

- **Hydrocarbon fuels** — Petroleum-based combustible or flammable liquids that float on water such as gasoline.

- **Polar solvents** — Flammable liquids that mix readily with water such as ethanol.

As a general rule, Class B foams designed solely for hydrocarbon fires will not extinguish polar solvent fires, regardless of the concentration at which they are used. Many types of foam that are intended for polar solvents may be used on hydrocarbon fires, but this should not be attempted without confirmation from the manufacturer that this is an intended application.

A small number of foam concentrate products on the market can be used for both hydrocarbon and polar solvents. Some of these products suggest a 3 percent mixture for hydrocarbons and a 6 percent mixture for polar solvents. Some can be used at 3 percent mixture for either type. As always, check the manufacturer's instructions, which are often included on the bucket label.

Two common Class B Foams, aqueous film forming foam (AFFF) and film forming fluoroprotein foam (FFFP), may be applied with either fog nozzles or foam nozzles. The minimum amount of foam solution that must be applied, referred to as the rate of application, for Class B foam varies depending on several variables:

- Type of foam concentrate used

- Whether the fuel is on fire

- Type of fuel (hydrocarbon/polar solvent) involved

- Whether the fuel is spilled or contained in a tank

- Whether the foam is applied via either a fixed system or portable equipment

   NOTE: If the fuel is in a tank, the type of tank will have a bearing on the application rate.

Unignited spills create vapor hazards that may ignite. A foam blanket can be applied to suppress the vapors, separating fuel from oxygen. The depth of the foam blanket and application techniques will depend on the type of foam and manufacturer's recommendations.

Foam concentrate supplies should be available on the fireground at the proportioning location before application starts. Once application has started, it should continue uninterrupted until extinguishment is complete. Stopping and restarting may allow the fire to consume whatever foam blanket has been established.

Because polar solvent fuels have differing affinities for water, it is important to know application rates for each type of solvent. Underwriters' Laboratories (UL) lists proper foam application rates according to manufacturer's instructions. For more complete information on application rates, consult NFPA 11, *Standard for Low-, Medium-, and High-Expansion Foam*, and the foam concentrate and delivery system manufacturers' recommendations.

Foam for Specific Applications

Numerous types of foams and water additives are available for specific applications according to their properties and performance. Each jurisdiction should train fire brigade members on the various water-additives used on apparatus. Follow the jurisdiction's SOPs and the manufacturer's instructions for using these additives.

Foam Hazards

Foam concentrates, either at full strength or diluted, pose minimal health risks to fire brigade members. In both forms, foam concentrates may be mildly irritating to the skin and eyes; affected areas should be flushed with water. Some concentrates and their vapors may be harmful if ingested or inhaled. Concentrates can also degrade PPE if allowed to remain on the clothing for a long period of time. As a result, field decontamination is important at incidents where foam has been used. Gear should also be washed after every use to prevent degradation and to ensure the PPE functions properly. Consult the manufacturer's safety data sheets (SDS) for information on any specific foam concentrate.

Most Class A and Class B foam concentrates are mildly corrosive, even though they are used in small percentages and in diluted solutions. Follow proper flushing procedures to prevent damage to equipment. Pumps, eductors, hoselines, and nozzles must be thoroughly flushed and washed to remove concentrate residue.

The effect of the finished foam after it has been applied to a liquid fuel fire or spill is a primary environmental concern. The rate at which environmental bacteria causes it to decompose is used to rate a foam's biodegradability. This decomposition process results in the consumption of oxygen. In a river, stream, pond, or lake, the reduction in oxygen can kill fish and other animals. Therefore, fire brigade members should take care to prevent foam from directly entering bodies of water. The less oxygen required to degrade a particular foam, the better or the more environmentally friendly the foam is when it enters a body of water.

The chemical properties of Class A and Class B foams and their environmental effects vary depending on the type of concentrate and the manufacturer. Consult the manufacturers' safety data sheets for environmental impact information. Many jurisdictions require that the use of foam above certain quantities must be reported to the local or state environmental protection office. The specific amounts vary depending upon the jurisdiction.

Foam Proportioning

Proportioning describes the mixing of water with foam concentrate to form a foam solution. For maximum effectiveness, foam concentrates must be proportioned at the specific percentage for which they are designed. This percentage rate varies with the intended fuel and is written on the outside of every foam container. Failure to follow correct procedure, such as trying to use 6 percent foam at a 3 percent concentration, will result in poor-quality foam that may not perform as desired.

Most fire fighting foam concentrates are intended to be mixed with 94 to 99 percent water. When using 1 percent foam concentrates, 99 parts water are mixed with 1 part foam for a 100 percent foam solution. When using 3 percent foam concentrate, 97 parts water are mixed with 3 parts foam concentrate to create 100 parts foam solution. For 6 percent foam concentrate, 94 parts water mixed with 6 parts foam concentrate equals 100 percent foam solution **(Figure 16.18)**.

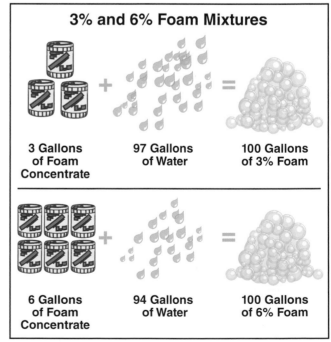

3% and 6% Foam Mixtures

| 3 Gallons of Foam Concentrate | 97 Gallons of Water | 100 Gallons of 3% Foam |

| 6 Gallons of Foam Concentrate | 94 Gallons of Water | 100 Gallons of 6% Foam |

Figure 16.18 Illustrating the correct mixtures of 3% and 6% foam concentrates with water.

The proportioning percentage for Class A foams can be adjusted, within limits recommended by the manufacturer, to achieve specific objectives. To produce a dry, thick foam suitable for exposure protection and creating fire breaks in wildland fires, the foam concentrate can be adjusted to a higher percentage. To produce wet (thin) foam that rapidly penetrates a fuel's surface, the foam concentrate can be adjusted to a lower percentage. Most Class A foams are mixed in proportions of 1 percent or less.

Class B foams are mixed in proportions from 1 percent to 6 percent. Some multipurpose Class B foams designed for use on both hydrocarbon and polar solvent fuels can be used at different concentrations, depending on which of the two fuels is burning. Always follow the manufacturer's recommendations for proportioning.

Some types of proportioning equipment are designed for mobile apparatus and others are designed for fixed fire protection systems. The selection of a proportioner depends on the following:

- Foam solution flow requirements
- Available or correct water pressure
- Intended type of equipment used to generate the foam (truck, fixed, or portable)
- Foam agent to be used

Proportioners and delivery devices work together. Using a foam proportioner that is not compatible with the delivery device, even if the same manufacturer makes them, can result in unsatisfactory foam or no foam at all.

There are three basic methods by which foam may be proportioned:

- Eduction
- Injection
- Premixing

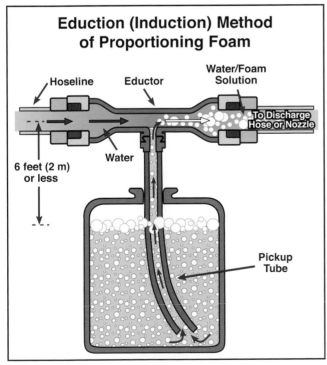

Eduction (Induction) Method of Proportioning Foam

Hoseline   Eductor   Water/Foam Solution

To Discharge Hose or Nozzle

6 feet (2 m) or less   Water

Pickup Tube

Figure 16.19 Illustrating the eduction (induction) method of proportioning foam.

Eduction

The eduction (induction) method of proportioning foam uses the pressure energy in the stream of water to induct (draft) foam concentrate into the fire stream. This is achieved by passing the stream of water through an **eductor**, a device that uses the **Venturi Effect** to draw the foam through a hose connected to the foam concentrate container and into the water stream **(Figure 16.19)**. In-line eductors and foam nozzle eductors are examples of foam proportioners that use this method.

NOTE: For foam educators to work properly, their gallons/liters per minute (GPM/LPM) rates must match the nozzle.

Injection

The injection method of proportioning foam uses an external pump or head pressure to force foam concentrate into the fire stream at the correct ratio for the water flow **(Figure 16.20)**. These systems are commonly employed in apparatus-mounted or fixed fire protection system applications.

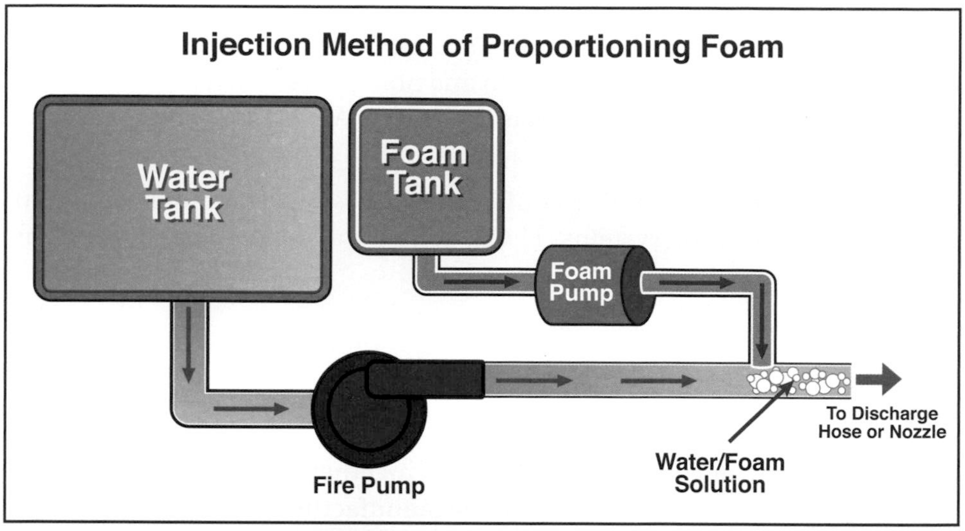

Figure 16.20 Illustrating the injection method of proportioning foam.

Injection Method of Proportioning Foam

Water Tank

Foam Tank

Foam Pump

Fire Pump

Water/Foam Solution

To Discharge Hose or Nozzle

Figure 16.21 The premix method is commonly used with portable fire extinguishers, wheeled extinguishers, and twin-agent systems.

Fire Extinguisher | Wheeled Extinguisher | Skid-mounted Twin-agent Unit

Premixing

Premixing is one of the more commonly used methods of proportioning. Premeasured portions of water and foam concentrate are mixed in a container. Typically, the premix method is used with **(Figure 16.21)**:

- Portable extinguishers
- Skid-mounted twin-agent units
- Wheeled extinguishers
- Vehicle-mounted tank systems

Premixed solutions are discharged from a pressure-rated tank using a compressed inert gas or air. An alternative method of discharge uses a pump and a non-pressure-rated atmospheric storage tank. The pump discharges the foam solution through piping or hose to the delivery devices. Premix systems are limited to a one-time application. When used, the tank must be emptied and refilled before it can be used again. Since most Class A foam solutions are biodegradable, mixing the solution and storing it for long periods can result in decreased foaming ability.

Foam Proportioners

Two other pieces of equipment, in addition to a pump and length of fire hose, are needed to produce a foam fire stream: a foam proportioner and a foam delivery device (nozzle or generating system). The proportioner and delivery device/system must be compatible to produce usable foam. Foam proportioning simply introduces the appropriate amount of foam concentrate into the water to form a foam solution. A foam-generating system/nozzle adds the air into foam solutions to produce finished foam. Proportioning systems include portable in-line and nozzle foam eductors, apparatus-mounted, or compressed air foam systems (CAFS).

In-line Foam Eductors

The in-line eductor is the most common type of foam proportioner used in the fire service. This style of eductor is designed to be directly attached to the pump panel discharge outlet or connected at some point in the hose lay **(Figure 16.22)**. When using an in-line eductor, it is important to follow the manufacturer's instructions about inlet pressure and the maximum hose lay between the eductor and the appropriate discharge nozzle.

The eductor pickup tube is connected to the eductor at this low-pressure point. A pickup tube submerged in the foam concentrate draws the concentrate into the water stream, creating a foam/water solution.

Figure 16.22 An in-line eductor, pickup tube, and foam pail.

Foam Nozzle Eductors

A foam nozzle eductor operates on the same basic principle as an in-line eductor; however, this eductor is built into the nozzle rather than into the hoseline. As a result, its use requires the foam concentrate to be available where the nozzle is operated. If the foam nozzle is moved, the foam concentrate container must also be moved. The size and number of concentrate containers required magnify the logistical problems of relocation. Use of a foam nozzle eductor can also compromise fire brigade member safety. Fire brigade members cannot always move quickly, and they may have to leave their concentrate supplies behind if they are required to retreat. Many facilities use these types of nozzles on master stream devices.

Apparatus-Mounted Proportioners

Three of the various apparatus-mounted foam proportioning systems are installed in-line eductors, around-the-pump proportioners, and balanced-pressure proportioners. These proportioners can be mounted on any type of fire apparatus including fire boats.

Compressed Air Foam Systems (CAFS)

Compressed air foam systems (CAFS) are mounted on many types of fire fighting apparatus. A standard centrifugal pump supplies the water. A direct-injection foam-proportioning system mixes foam solution with the water on the discharge side of the pump. An onboard air compressor adds air to the mix before it is discharged from the apparatus.

Fog Nozzles Vs. Foam Nozzles

Foam can be delivered through fog nozzles or foam nozzles. There are advantages and disadvantages to either type of nozzle. Fog nozzles may be used to apply foam solution or finished foam. Foam nozzles aspirate air into foam solution as it passes through the nozzle. Dual agent nozzles discharge foam and another agent, usually dry chemical agent **(Figure 16.23, p. 512)**. Each jurisdiction should train fire brigade members on the types of nozzles and devices used in the local jurisdiction. The sections that follow provide broad definitions of fog and foam nozzles and some of the advantages and disadvantages of each.

Fog Nozzles

Fog nozzles can be used with foam solutions to produce a low-expansion, short-lasting foam. These nozzles break the foam solution into tiny droplets and use the agitation of water droplets moving through air to achieve foaming action. Some nozzle manufacturers have foam aeration attachments to increase aeration of the foam solution.

Advantages include:

- Widely available on most apparatus
- May allow for variable flow and pattern of application
- Allows for adjustable gallonage of water for different applications
- Faster application when using a preconnected hoseline
- Fog nozzle may allow a margin of safety if the foam supply is lost
- Greater reach than foam nozzles

Disadvantages include:

- Operator error is more likely to produce low-quality foam.
- Requires additional equipment and setup time, such as the need to add an aerator to create a foam nozzle.
- May not create the same quality of foam as specialized equipment; less air, wetter foam.
- May create the appearance of better flow than is actually being produced.
- Needs maintenance more frequently if consistently used for foam.
- Necessary to match flow of water with all equipment and adjust all equipment to make changes.
- Fog nozzles generally do not provide optimal foam expansion, and as a result, they do not make the best use of the foam supply.

Figure 16.23 Foam being discharged through a fog nozzle (top), a foam nozzle (middle), and a dual agent nozzle (bottom).

Foam Nozzles

A foam nozzle is the most effective appliance for the generation of low, medium, or high-expansion foam. It inducts air into the foam solution using the Venturi Principle. This nozzle is designed to provide the aeration required to make the highest quality foam possible. These nozzles provide the best expansion of the agent. The reach of the stream is less than that of a standard fog nozzle.

Advantages include:

- Typically produces higher quality foam than fog nozzles
- Useful in blanketing operations

Disadvantages include:

- Not at versatile as a fog nozzle

- Limited reach compared to other nozzles

Dual Agent Nozzles

Dual agent nozzles combine the reach of a water foam stream with the application of dry chemical agents. This type of nozzle is particularly useful for pressure fires with an associated ground fire.

Assembling a Foam Fire Stream System

To provide a foam fire stream, a fire brigade member or apparatus driver/operator must be able to correctly assemble the components of the system in addition to locating problem areas and making adjustments. The most common reasons for failure to generate foam or for generating poor-quality foam include:

- Eductor and nozzle flow ratings do not match, preventing foam concentrate from inducting into the fire stream.

- Air leaks at the proportioning device cause suction loss.

- Improper cleaning of proportioning equipment causes clogged foam passages.

- Nozzle is not fully open, restricting water flow.

- Hose lay on the discharge side of the eductor is too long, creating excess back pressure and causing reduced foam pickup at the eductor.

- Hose is kinked and restricts or stops flow.

- Nozzle is too far above the eductor, which causes excessive elevation pressure.

- Mixing different types of foam concentrate in the same tank results in a mixture too viscous to pass through the eductor.

- Improper pressure at the pump for the rated device.

Foam Application Techniques

Use the correct techniques when applying foam from handline or master stream nozzles. If incorrect techniques are used, such as plunging the foam into a liquid fuel, the effectiveness of the foam is reduced. The techniques for applying Class B foam to a liquid fuel fire or spill include the *roll-on method*, *bank-down method*, and *rain-down method* (**Figure 16.24**).

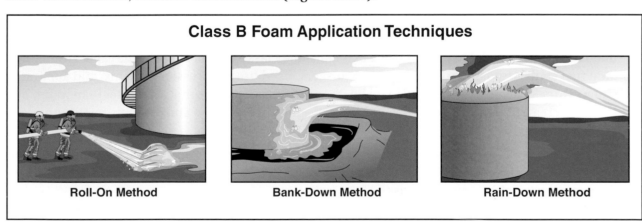

Class B Foam Application Techniques

Roll-On Method   Bank-Down Method   Rain-Down Method

Figure 16.24 Illustrating the roll-on, bank-down, and rain-down methods of Class B foam application.

Roll-On Method

The roll-on method directs the foam stream on the ground near the front edge of a burning liquid spill. The foam then rolls across the surface of the fuel. Fire brigade members continue to apply foam until it spreads across the entire surface of the fuel and the fire is extinguished. It may be necessary to move the stream to different positions along the edge of a liquid spill to cover the entire pool. This method is used only on a pool of ignited or unignited liquid fuel on open ground.

Bank-Down Method

The bank-down method may be employed when an elevated object is near or within the area of a burning pool of liquid or an unignited liquid spill. The object may be a wall, tank shell, or similar vertical structure. The foam stream is directed onto the object, allowing the foam to run down and onto the surface of the fuel. As with the roll-on method, it may be necessary to direct the stream onto various points around the fuel area to achieve total coverage and extinguishment of the fuel. This method is used primarily on fires contained in diked pools around storage tanks and fires involving spills around damaged or overturned transport vehicles.

Rain-Down Method

The rain-down method is used when the other two methods are not feasible because of the size of the ignited or unignited spill area or the lack of an object from which to bank the foam. This method directs the stream into the air above the fire or spill and allows the foam to float gently down onto the surface of the fuel. The nozzle operator can sweep the stream back and forth over the entire surface of the fuel until it is completely covered and the fire is extinguished. It may be more effective for the fire brigade member in some situations to direct the stream at one location to allow the foam to collect there and then float out from that point.

NOTE: With the rain-down method, a percentage of the firefighting agent may never reach the seat of the fire, particularly during high wind conditions.

Review Section: Special Extinguishing Agents

NFPA 1081 (2018): 5.1.2.1, 5.3.6, 5.3.8, 5.3.9, 6.1.2.3, 6.3.2, 6.3.6, 6.3.11

Fire brigade members may use a variety of special extinguishing agents during fire control operations. These special extinguishing agents include:

- **Deionized water mist** — Deionized water makes Class A extinguishers safe to use on energized electrical equipment (Class C). The fine spray also enhances the water's cooling and soaking characteristics and reduces scattering of the burning materials.

- **Aqueous film forming foam (AFFF)** — For extinguishing Class B fires or suppressing vapors from small liquid fuel spills. Used in portable fire extinguishers, fixed fire suppression systems, and apparatus extinguishing systems. The finished foam floats on the surface of fuels that are lighter than water. The vapor seal created by the film of finished foam extinguishes the flame and prevents reignition.

- **Clean agents** — Halon replacements that are effective on Class A, B, and C fires. Clean agents are discharged as rapidly evaporating liquids that leaves no residue. These agents effectively cool and smother fires in Class A and Class B fuels, and the agents are nonconductive so they can be used on energized electrical equipment (Class C) fires.

- **Carbon dioxide (CO_2)** — Discharged from portable fire extinguishers and fixed fire suppression systems, CO_2 is a gaseous agent used on Class B and C fires. When released, the carbon dioxide gas displaces available oxygen and smothers the fire. Even though CO_2 discharges at subzero temperatures, it has little if any cooling effect on fires. Carbon dioxide produces no vapor-suppressing film on the surface of the fuel; therefore, reignition is always a danger.

- **Dry chemicals** — Discharged from portable fire extinguishers, fixed suppression systems, and some vehicle-mounted systems, dry chemicals are used on Class A-B-C fires and/or Class B-C fires. Dry chemicals smother fire or inhibit the chemical chain reaction.

- **Dry powders** — Usually discharged from portable fire extinguishers, dry powders are used to control and extinguish Class D combustible metal fires. When applied to a burning metal, the dry powder creates a smothering blanket.

- **Wet chemicals** — Used on Class K fires, wet chemicals extinguish fires involving cooking fats, greases, and vegetable and animal oils. Wet chemicals are usually discharged from portable fire extinguishers or installed fire suppression systems.

Review Section: Special Agent-based Extinguishing Systems

NFPA 1081 (2018): 5.1.2.1, 5.2.5, 5.3.8, 6.1.2.3, 6.2.9, 6.3.2

Special extinguishing systems typically use an extinguishing agent other than water or in addition to water. Special extinguishing systems are activated in the following ways:

- Automatically by either a detector or a combination of detectors

- Manually by someone operating a manual station and putting the system through its complete cycle of operation

  Types of special extinguishing systems include the following:

- **Water-mist** — These systems are designed to extinguishing Class A and Class B fires by discharging a fine mist of water. The mist absorbs larger quantities of heat than water-spray or automatic sprinkler systems.

- **Carbon dioxide** — Three types of carbon dioxide (CO_2) systems — total flooding systems, local application systems, and hoselines — are used to protect different types of hazards in industrial settings. Both total flooding and local application systems can be designed using either high-pressure or low-pressure CO_2 containers. The reduction of oxygen in a confined space is the most serious problem involving carbon dioxide systems. Any level of oxygen that will not support combustion will also not support human life.

- **Dry chemical** — There are two main types of dry chemical systems: total flooding systems and local application systems that may be used in storage areas for flammable and combustible liquids, flammable solids, chemicals, or ammunition. The chemicals used as extinguishing agents are not toxic but can irritate the eyes and respiratory tract. If a dry chemical system has discharged into a confined space, no one should enter the space without SCBA until the space is thoroughly ventilated.

- **Foam** — Foam extinguishing systems are best suited for use on fires involving flammable or combustible liquids, and most of these systems are found in manufacturing and industrial areas where these hazards are present. Brigade members should stay away from large fires involving flammable liquids, and they should avoid walking through or otherwise disturbing a foam blanket. Disturbing the foam blanket can allow flammable vapors to escape and reignite. Common foam concentrate types include:
  - Regular Protein Foam
  - Film Forming Fluoroprotein Foam
  - Alcohol-Resistant AFFF (AR-AFFF)
  - High-Expansion Foam
  - Fluoroprotein Foam
  - Aqueous Film Forming Foam (AFFF)
  - Vapor-Mitigating Foam
  - Emulsifiers

- **Wet chemical** — These systems are best suited for Class K applications in commercial fryers, grills, range hoods, plenums, and ducts that use animal fats or vegetable oils. Wet chemical agents can extinguish grease or oil fires in four ways: fuel removal, cooling, smothering, and flame inhibition. Wet chemical agents can cause floors to become slippery. A wet chemical agent is typically a solution of water and/or potassium carbonate or potassium acetate sprayed onto the fire. These agents are not recommended for electrical fires because they are conductive.

- **Clean-agent** — Clean agents are gaseous or volatile fire extinguishing chemicals that do not conduct electricity and do not leave a residue when they evaporate. Common approved Halon replacement agents include Halotron™, Inergen™, FE-200™, and FE-13™. Entry should be denied to anyone not wearing SCBA or supplied air respirator (SAR) until personnel have sampled and determined that the atmosphere in any space where the agent has been discharged is within safe limits.

Suppressing Fires Using Special Extinguishing Agents

NFPA 1081 (2018): 5.3.6, 6.3.6

Fire brigade members may also use special extinguishing agents such as dry chemicals, dry powders, clean agents, and wet chemical agents to extinguish fires involving Class B, C, D, and K fires. While these agents were discussed in Chapter 4, Portable Fire Extinguishers, for use on small fires, this chapter will address larger scale fire fighting operations using these agents.

Wheeled Dry Chemical and Clean Agent Extinguisher Operations

Fire brigade members should remember to position wheeled extinguishers upwind of a fire and remove all of the extinguisher's hose from its storage position before charging the unit. They should also remember to test the extinguisher prior to attacking the fire and be prepared for a strong nozzle reaction.

While some dry chemical agents are effective on Class A fires, most dry chemical agents are most effective on Class B fires. When discharging the agent, fire brigade members should direct the discharge at the base of the fire and sweep the agent stream back and forth **(Figure 16.25)**. Because dry chemicals can obscure vision, it may be necessary to stop discharging momentarily to determine effectiveness. If necessary, reposition and apply the agent from another angle. Dry chemical agents may be used inside a structure but can irritate the lungs. Fire brigade members using a wheeled dry chemical extinguisher inside a facility should wear SCBA for respiratory protection. After extinguishing the fire, the facility should be ventilated to remove heat, smoke, other products of combustion, and dry chemicals still suspended in the air.

> **CAUTION:** Remember that dry chemical is corrosive and can damage sensitive equipment!

NOTE: If using dry chemical agents on Class C fires, confirm that equipment is de-energized.

Clean agents are effective on Class B and C fires. The agent should be directed at the base of the fire and swept from side to side. Following extinguishment, the facility should be ventilated to remove heat, smoke, other products of combustion, and clean agent still suspended in the air.

Figure 16.25 Dry chemical agents should be directed at the base of a fire.

Suppressing Class D Fires

Fires involving Class D, combustible metals, require different fire fighting tactics than the other classes of fires. Water will not extinguish Class D fires and can cause the burning metal to spall and spread the burning material. Dry chemicals, CO_2, and clean agents have no effect on the burning metal.

To suppress Class D fires, fire brigade personnel should use dry powders such as Met-L-X, Lith-X, Na-X, or other similar agents that match the materials that are burning. These agents may be discharged from an extinguisher or may be shoveled onto the burning metal from a bulk container. These agents melt, flow, and encapsulate the burning metal, isolating it from the surrounding environment.

Fire brigade personnel should wear PPE and SCBA when using these agents, particularly in enclosed spaces. Personnel should not come in contact with the burning material. They must cover the burning material with the appropriate dry powder agent. This may require multiple applications until such time as the material is totally covered and isolated. Enclosed spaces should be ventilated. Ensure that the Class D materials have had time to cool prior to beginning overhaul. A thermal imager (TI) can be used to assist with this.

Suppressing Class K Fires

Class K fires involve cooking fats, greases, and vegetable and animal oils in commercial kitchens. These fires are most often suppressed using installed Class K wet chemical systems or portable fire extinguishers. Fire brigade members should be aware of potential Class K hazards within their facility, as well as how to operate installed Class K systems and extinguishers. The agent should be applied across the surface of the burning materials. When applied properly, the agent will combine with the oils and create a soapy foam on the surface of the material.

If there is a hood system installed, it should be activated prior to using the portable extinguisher. Activating the hood system should isolate the fuel, turn on ventilation, and discharge agent onto the surface fire as well as plenum spaces.

Water Additives

Water additives are used for the control and suppression of fires by reducing water's surface tension and increasing its penetrating and spreading abilities. They may also provide enhanced cooling, emulsification, and mitigation of flammable vapors. Water additives can be used for one or more of the following categories of fire hazards:

- Deep-seated fires (agricultural products, coal, wood-based products, tire storage, hay/straw, etc.)
- Two and three-dimensional fires (transformers, hydraulic/lubricating oils, flammable liquid rack storage, etc.)
- Wildland fires

Micelle Encapsulating Agents

Micelle encapsulating agents (also called micelle encapsulators) interrupt the free radical chain reaction, encapsulate the fuel, and reduce the temperature. The free radicals are unburned gases produced during the combustion process that turn into smoke and soot. A micelle or "chemical cocoon" is a droplet of the fuel surrounded by water and an emulsifying agent, rendering the fuel non-flammable.

Review Section: Property Conservation

NFPA 1081 (2018): 5.2.5, 6.2.9

Property conservation operations (also called salvage or loss control operations) are the activities that personnel perform before, during, and after a fire has been extinguished to minimize losses to property.

During property conservation operations, fire brigade members attempt to save property and reduce further damage from water, smoke, heat, and exposure during or immediately after a fire. Proper salvage operations involve preincident planning, knowledge of salvage procedures, and the tools and equipment necessary to perform the job. Improvisation is often necessary when personnel are presented with unique situations and limited equipment. The protection of damaged property from weather and trespassers is also critical.

Two types of damage result from a fire: primary damage from heat and smoke and secondary damage from fire suppression activities. A structure's vulnerability to weather and vandalism following fire suppression is also considered a form of secondary damage.

Review Section: Loss Control

Specialized tools and equipment used in loss control operations may include:

- Salvage covers, vinyl or plastic tarps, or rolls of plastic sheets
- Absorbent materials
- Water vacuums, sprinkler chocks or tongs, squeegees, mops, and buckets
- Automatic sprinkler kit
- Carryalls
- Floor runners

In commercial and industrial occupancies, the value of a building's contents may exceed the replacement cost of the structural materials. The data, documents, and information stored in or on computers, filing cabinets filled with records, and computer backup drives are critical to the operation of a business.

Review Section: Water Removal

Plans must also address the removal of water used during and after fire, spill, leak, and release control operations. This water will be contaminated, and the fire brigade should have a plan in place for its removal, retention, and ultimate disposition.

Salvage procedures include:

- Moving contents to a safe location in the structure
- Removing contents from the structure
- Protecting the contents in place with salvage covers

Removing contents from the structure will help protect them from further primary and potential secondary damage. This method may interfere with fire suppression and ventilation crews that are using the same doors to enter the structure and may also interfere with the flow path of air to the fire. Contents should be stacked on surfaces that are dry, such as a parking lot or driveway, and not near areas where fire brigade members may be collecting debris for disposal. Contents stored outside require protection from theft or vandalism. The method most often used to protect contents is to leave them in the room in which they are found. Fire brigade members gather contents into compact piles that they can cover with a minimum of salvage covers. Grouping contents in this manner allows more items to be protected than if they were covered in their original position. Be cautious of high-piled stock, such as boxed materials or rolled paper that is wetted at its base. The moisture often causes the material to expand and push out interior or exterior walls. Wetness also reduces the material's strength and may cause the piles to collapse.

After fire brigade members have protected the building's contents, their next salvage consideration is normally to remove excess water. Water accumulates or is absorbed in areas that may lack adequate drainage. Accumulations of water place additional weight on structural members and can contribute to their collapse. Water weighs 8.33 pounds per gallon (1 kg per liter); therefore 1,000 gallons (4 000 liters) of water equates to 8,330 pounds (4 000 kg) of additional weight to a structure. Such accumulations can damage machinery, utilities, and stored merchandise. Elevator and heating, ventilation, and air conditioning (HVAC) equipment can be adversely affected, as well. Due to environmental concerns, fire suppression runoff water may need to be retained and treated.

Water traps made of plastic sheeting can be constructed in various ways. Using plastic sheeting is appropriate for collecting small amounts of water. Fire brigade members can use salvage covers, plastic sheeting, duct tape, and a stapler to construct troughs to divert water. Lightweight and flexible plastic sheeting can be shaped or wrapped around almost anything to create a trough. With plastic sheeting, personnel can divert water through a door or window or into a nearby drain. Dikes made of salvage covers or plastic can also be positioned across doorways or stairways to limit water spread.

Facility fire brigade members may be able to stop water from flowing or prevent it from spreading into undamaged areas. One way to limit water damage is to stop the flow of water from sprinklers after a fire is extinguished. Sprinklers can be plugged with wedges or sprinkler tongs. Sprinkler control valves can be isolated or closed to control the flow of water to the system, but they should never be closed unless the fire is extinguished and the IC authorizes the valve closing. Floor or unit valves should be used to terminate the water flow to specific parts of the system whenever possible so that the rest of the system remains in service.

Immediately after the correct valve has been closed, personnel should open the drains (main or auxiliary) to relieve system pressure. This action allows water remaining in the system to flow to the building's exterior rather than into the building through open sprinklers. The facility fire brigade member assigned to close the control valve must remain at the valve so that it may be quickly reopened if necessary. The industrial fire brigade or fire and emergency services organization must explain the limitations of the sprinkler system before returning it to service.

The primary objective of industrial fire brigade members when removing water is to remove it quickly and safely without damaging unaffected areas of the building. Several of the following means are used to route water:

- Sewer drains or soil-pipe openings
- Stairways
- Water chutes
- Catchalls
- Scuppers
- Hoselines

Review Section: Weather Damage Prevention

Following an incident, doors, windows, and ventilation openings should be covered with plywood, heavy plastic, or some similar materials to keep out weather. Openings in roofs should be covered with plywood, roofing paper, heavy plastic sheeting, or tar paper. Use appropriate roofing nails if roofing paper, tar paper, or plastic is used. Place strips of lath along the edges of the material and nail them in place.

Overhaul

NFPA 1081 (2018): 5.2.3, 5.2.6, 6.2.1, 6.2.4

Overhaul refers to all operations conducted after the main body of the fire has been extinguished and includes the following activities:

- Searching for and extinguishing hidden or remaining fire
- Placing the facility and its contents in a safe condition
- Determining the cause of the fire
- Recognizing and preserving evidence area of origin or of potential arson

Advanced exterior and interior structural fire brigades use the same tools, equipment, and basic procedures for conducting overhaul operations. The difference lies in the location where the overhaul is conducted: outside or inside.

The IC and the lead fire investigator should authorize when overhaul should begin. Once the order is given, fire brigade members should try to make the building, its contents, and the fire area in as safe and habitable condition as possible. Overhaul shouldn't tear up things unnecessarily, while making sure the fire is completely out.

Salvage operations performed during fire fighting will directly affect any overhaul work that may be needed later. Many of the tools and equipment used for overhaul are also those used for forcible entry, ventilation, and salvage operations. Tools and equipment used for overhaul may include the following:

- **Pike poles and plaster hooks** — Open ceilings to inspect for fire extension.
- **Axes** — Open walls and floors.
- **Prying tools** — Remove door frames, window frames, and baseboards.
- **Power saws, drills, and screwdrivers** — Install temporary doors and window coverings.
- **Carryalls, buckets, and tubs** — Carry debris or provide a basin for immersing smoldering material.
- **Shovels, bale hooks, and pitchforks** — Move baled or loose materials.
- **Thermal imagers (TIs)** — Check void spaces and look for hot spots.

An officer not directly engaged in overhaul should direct overhaul operations. If a fire investigator is on the scene, he or she should be involved in planning and supervising overhaul activities to avoid disturbing potential evidence needed to determine fire cause.

Overhaul Safety

The first consideration before beginning overhaul operations is safety. After a fire has been controlled, there is time to plan and organize overhaul activities. The overhaul plan should provide the highest possible degree of safety to fire brigade members and others who might be allowed on the scene. The steps to establish safe conditions include:

- Inspecting the premises and identifying hazards
- Developing an operational plan
- Providing needed tools and equipment
- Eliminating or mitigating hazards (including shutting off any remaining utilities, as directed)
- Monitoring the atmosphere for carbon monoxide (CO) and hydrogen cyanide (HCN) levels before removing SCBA

Toxic gases that continue to be produced from a smoldering fire are a significant threat to fire brigade members during overhaul operations. Even if the air in a structure appears free of smoke, toxic products of combustion can exist in dangerous concentrations. Carbon monoxide (CO) and hydrogen cyanide

In outside storage areas, advanced exterior fire brigade personnel should move boxes/crates or stacks of product or pull them apart to locate hidden fire. Moving these materials should be done with caution to prevent the materials from tipping over or collapsing onto emergency responders. As fire is found, it should be extinguished with water or other appropriate extinguishing agent(s).

If the fire has expanded to other areas in the structure, fire brigade members must determine the path that it traveled (concealed wall spaces, unsealed pipe chases, and others). If floor beams have burned ends where they enter a party wall, flush the voids in the wall with water. Also, inspect the other side of the wall to determine whether the fire or water has come through. Thoroughly check insulation materials because they can retain hidden fires for prolonged periods. It is usually necessary to remove insulation material to extinguish fire in it. Do not make random openings in walls or ceilings.

Understanding the basic concepts of building construction will help when searching for hidden fires. If the fire has burned around windows or doors, pull open these areas to expose the inner parts of the frame or casing and visually verify full extinguishment. When fire has burned around a combustible roof or cornice, open the cornice and inspect for hidden fires. In structures using balloon construction, check the attic and basement for fire extension.

Figure 16.26 A fire brigade member practicing removing wall coverings to locate and extinguish a hidden fire.

Search for hidden fires in concealed spaces below floors, above ceilings, or within walls and partitions. First, move the furnishings of the room to locations where they will not be damaged. If it is not possible to move the contents, protect them with salvage covers. Remove only enough wall, ceiling, or floor covering to verify complete extinguishment **(Figure 16.26)**. Weight-bearing members should not be disturbed. To locate possible fire extension into the wall cavity, inspect openings such as:

- Electrical receptacle
- Electrical switches
- Return air ducts
- Heating vents
- Telephone connections
- Cable connections

The walls and ceilings in kitchens, bathrooms, and utility rooms contain ventilation fans and pipes, ducts, and other passages that permit fire to extend. If these rooms show evidence of fire spread, the walls and ceiling should be inspected.

When opening concealed spaces, consider whether the space contains electrical wiring, gas piping, or plumbing. Electrical outlets, gas connections, and water faucets all indicate the presence of utilities. Consideration should be given to the future repair of the structure. While openings must often be made to check for extension and allow extinguishment, they should be made in a neat and planned manner. This reduces the work necessary for future restoration and shows a fire brigade member's professionalism.

Ceilings may be opened from below using a pike pole or other appropriate overhaul tool. To open lath and plaster ceilings, break the plaster and then pull off the lath. Some plaster ceilings have wire mesh imbedded in the plaster. When these ceilings start to come down, they may fall in one large piece. Some newer plaster ceilings are backed with gypsum wallboard instead of wooden lath. Metal or composition ceilings may be pulled from the joists in a similar manner.

When pulling any ceiling, do not stand directly under the area to be opened. Position yourself between the area being pulled and a doorway to keep the exit route from being blocked with falling debris. Always wear full PPE including respiratory protection when pulling ceilings **(Figure 16.27)**.

| **CAUTION:** | When pulling any ceiling, stand clear of any falling debris. |

Small burning objects are frequently uncovered during overhaul. Because of their size and condition, it is often more effective to submerge the object in water than to drench it with hose streams. Bathtubs, sinks, lavatories, and wash tubs work for this purpose. Large smoldering items such as bales of cardboard, padded office furniture, and packing materials should be taken outside the structure to be extinguished in coordination with

Figure 16.27 Fire brigade members should not stand directly under the part of a ceiling being pulled down.

the fire investigator's instructions. Investigators may want pictures of the furniture in place before it is moved for extinguishment. Scorched or partially burned articles may help an investigator in preparing an inventory or determining the cause of the fire. Fire brigade members need to work in close coordination with the fire investigator to ensure potential evidence is not disturbed.

Wetting agents such as Class A foam used at low percentages should be used to extinguish hidden fires. The penetrating qualities of wetting agents facilitate extinguishment in cotton, upholstery, and baled goods. The only way to ensure that fires in bales of items such as rags, cotton, and hay are extinguished is to break them apart.

Once the fire is thought to be extinguished and overhauled, put a fire watch in place to monitor the fire area. Facility management may have specific fire watch procedures that must be followed.

Gross Decontamination Following Overhaul
NFPA 1081 (2018): 6.1.2.4

Wearing contaminated PPE can lead to absorption of carcinogens or radiological materials through the skin. Over time, these contaminants may result in various cancers or other medical problems for fire brigade personnel.

Figure 16.28 Gross decontamination should be performed following a fire to remove contaminates that increase the risk of cancer.

The fire brigade should have written policies and procedures regarding the reduction of carcinogens or radiological particulates from personnel and PPE following a fire. If not removed at the scene, these products of combustion may be transported to the fire brigade's station where they contaminate that facility, as well as fire brigade personnel.

Following some basic, **gross decontamination** procedures of all PPE and equipment to remove soot and particulate matter is a best practice for reducing the risk of cancer later in life. Gross decon should follow fire brigade procedures and manufacturer's specifications.

Recommended procedures which can be performed before leaving the scene include **(Figure 16.28)**:

- Using a soft bristle brush and damp towel to remove large debris from PPE
- Removing all turnout gear, if possible
- Using wet wipes/baby wipes or wet towel to remove soot from the top down (head, face, jaw, neck, underarms, hands and lower legs)
- Using a hoseline to rinse off all PPE and equipment
- Bagging contaminated equipment for travel back to the station or fire brigade equipment locker or room
- Showering immediately upon returning to the station
- Cleaning of PPE, tools, equipment, and apparatus interiors

Chapter Review

1. What protocols should be followed when maintaining fire scene safety?
2. What guidelines should be followed during a fire safety survey?
3. Where is liquefied petroleum gas primarily used?
4. What conditions can cause a water supply to fail?
5. What type of agents inhibit or interrupt the combustion reaction and stop flame production?
6. What questions should be answered when arriving on the scene of a gas emergency?

7. What methods can be used to extinguish combustible metals?

8. How long are typical preconnected attack hoselines?

9. What are the five factors that limit the reach of fire streams?

10. What are the benefits of standpipes?

11. What are the four main uses for master streams?

12. What conditions can result in stacked and piled combustible materials?

13. List the four types of sprinkler systems used in facilities.

14. Name the four ways that fire fighting foam extinguishes and/or prevents ignition.

15. What factors affect the expansion of foam?

16. What are the two types of liquid fuels for which Class B foam is effective?

17. What hazards are associated with Class A and Class B foams?

18. Name and describe the three basic methods by which foam may be proportioned.

19. Name and describe two types of foam proportioners.

20. What are the disadvantages to using fog nozzles with foam solution?

21. What are the most common reasons for failure to generate foam or for generating poor-quality foam?

22. Name and describe the three foam application techniques.

23. List four types of special extinguishing agents.

24. Name and describe three special extinguishing systems.

25. What dry powders are used to suppress Class D fires?

26. What methods could be used to remove water as part of property conservation?

27. What are the indicators of possible loss of structural integrity?

28. What recommended gross decontamination procedures should be performed before leaving the scene?

Chapter 16 End Notes

Backstrom, Robert, David A. Dini. 2011. "Firefighter Safety and Photovoltaic Installations Research Project." Underwriters' Laboratories. Accessed Online.

Key Terms

Class A Foam — Foam specially designed for use on Class A combustibles. Class A foams are becoming increasingly popular for use in wildland and structural fire fighting.

Clean Agent — Fire suppression material that leaves little or no residue when used.

Compressed Air Foam System (CAFS) — Generic term used to describe a high-energy foam-generation system consisting of an air compressor (or other air source), a water pump, and foam solution that injects air into the foam solution before it enters a hoseline.

Eductor — Portable proportioning device that injects a liquid, such as foam concentrate, into the water flowing through a hoseline or pipe.

Emergency Response Guidebook (ERG) — Manual that aids emergency response and inspection personnel in identifying hazardous materials placards and labels; also gives guidelines for initial actions to be taken at hazardous materials incidents. Developed jointly by Transport Canada (TC), U.S. Department of Transportation (DOT), the Secretariat of Transport and Communications of Mexico (SCT), and with the collaboration of CIQUIME (Centro de Información Química para Emergencias).

Foam — Extinguishing agent formed by mixing a foam concentrate with water and aerating the solution for expansion; for use on Class A and Class B fires. Foam may be protein, fluoroprotein, film forming fluoroprotein, synthetic, aqueous film forming, high expansion, alcohol type, or alcohol-resistant type.

Foam Proportioner — Device that injects the correct amount of foam concentrate into the water stream to make the foam solution.

Gross Decontamination — Quickly removing the worst surface contamination, usually by rinsing with water from handheld hoselines, emergency showers, or other water sources.

Incident Safety Officer (ISO) — Member of the command staff responsible for monitoring and assessing safety hazards and unsafe conditions during an incident, and developing measures for ensuring personnel safety. The ISO enforces all applicable safety laws and regulations and departmental safety-related SOPs. During small incidents, the incident commander may act as the ISO.

Overhaul — Operations conducted once the main body of fire has been extinguished; consists of searching for and extinguishing hidden or remaining fire, placing the building and its contents in a safe condition, determining the cause of the fire, and recognizing and preserving evidence of arson.

Pressure Vessels — Fixed-facility storage tanks with operating pressures above 15 psi (130 kPa){1.03 bar}.

Proportioning — Mixing of water with an appropriate amount of foam concentrate in order to form a foam solution.

Vapor Suppression — Action taken to reduce the emission of vapors at a hazardous materials spill.

Venturi Effect — Physical law stating that when a fluid, such as water or air, is forced under pressure through a restricted orifice, there is an increase in the velocity of the fluid passing through the orifice and a corresponding decrease in the pressure exerted against the sides of the constriction. Because the surrounding fluid is under greater pressure (atmospheric), it is forced into the area of lower pressure.

Wetting Agent — Chemical solution or additive that reduces the surface tension of water (producing wet water), causing it to spread and penetrate more effectively; may also produce foam through mechanical means. Detergent is a mild form of wetting agent.

Skill Sheet List

The following skill sheets should be used to evaluate the skills described in this chapter:

NOTE: Students should wear the PPE appropriate to the NFPA 1081 level (Incipient, Advanced Exterior, Interior Structural, etc...) being evaluated.

The following skill sheets may be used as a review to evaluate the skills described in previous chapters:

NOTE: Students should wear the PPE appropriate to the NFPA 1081 level (Incipient, Advanced Exterior, Interior Structural, etc...) being evaluated.

Advanced Exterior Facility Fire Brigade Member Only

Chapter Contents

JPRs addressed in this chapter

This chapter provides information that addresses the following job performance requirements of NFPA 1081, *Standard for Facility Fire Brigade Member Professional Qualifications (2018)*.

5.2.3   5.3.6   5.3.13

5.3.5   5.3.12

1. Describe the proper procedures for responding to an incident in an apparatus. [5.3.12]

2. Explain the methods for extinguishing exterior Class A fires. [5.2.3]

3. Describe the information for fire control operations and identification for storage tanks. [5.3.5, 5.3.6]

4. Describe the types of bulk-capacity fixed-facility containers. [5.3.5]

5. Explain the types of tank fire suppression systems and equipment. [5.3.5]

6. Describe the fire suppression methods for extinguishing tank fires. [5.3.5]

7. Explain the method for developing basic strategies for handling tank fires. [5.3.5]

8. Describe the water supply needed to combat fires at industrial sites. [5.3.5]

9. Explain the methods for fire brigade members to perform foam calculations. [5.3.5]

10. Describe the methods for performing fire suppression operations on process units. [5.3.5]

11. Explain methods for extinguishing vehicle fires. [5.3.13]

Chapter 17
Fire Suppression Operations

Mount

Dismount

Figure 17.1 Fire brigade members should maintain three points of contact while mounting and dismounting apparatus.

Chapter 17 will address fire suppression operations at the advanced exterior level. Fire brigade personnel at this level may respond to emergencies while driving or riding on apparatus. Types of fires they may fight include:

- Exterior Class A fires such as those in:
  — Small unattached structures
  — Large trash containers
- Exterior Class B fires such as those in tank farms or processing units
- Vehicle fires

Apparatus Response

NFPA 1081 (2018): 5.3.12

Some fire brigades have fire apparatus; at these locations, fire brigade members may respond to emergencies riding on such apparatus. Your response to an emergency begins the moment you are notified of the emergency. If you are in the fire station or work location, then you must safely reach your apparatus, don the appropriate PPE, mount the apparatus, and fasten your seatbelt before your apparatus can respond.

Mounting and Dismounting Apparatus

You should mount the apparatus using the available handholds and steps built for that purpose, maintaining three points of contact while mounting or dismounting. Face the apparatus, grip the handholds firmly with both hands then step up into the apparatus. When dismounting, back out of the cab using the handholds and steps. Do not exit an apparatus face first as this presents a serious trip or fall hazard **(Figure 17.1)**.

Exiting your vehicle can be particularly hazardous, so always use extreme caution. Whenever possible, drivers and passengers should mount and dismount on the side of the vehicle opposite from oncoming traffic. If you must dismount on the exposed side, watch for oncoming vehicles before opening your door, and wait for a break in traffic before exiting.

Response Hazards for Passengers

There are numerous hazards to fire brigade members while riding in an apparatus. These may include but are not limited to:

- Excessive noise levels that may damage hearing
- Loose equipment that might strike the fire brigade members
- Danger of falls inside the apparatus if not seated and belted in
- Danger of injury during vehicle accidents

> **CAUTION:** Never stand on or in a moving apparatus or ride outside of the cab.

Safe Practices When Riding Apparatus

Follow your organization's SOPs for riding in an apparatus. NFPA 1500™ prohibits the wearing of fire fighting helmets inside the cab of fire apparatus. Helmets should be secured inside the cab during movement. Personnel should not stand or ride on apparatus tailboards, sidesteps, or running boards. Additional guidelines for safely riding in an apparatus include **(Figure 17.2)**:

- Always be seated and securely belted in before the apparatus moves.
- Always wear hearing protection or radio headsets.
- Secure all loose tools and equipment.
- Close cab doors securely.
- On unenclosed apparatus, close safety gates or bars securely.

Figure 17.2 Fire brigade members should wear seat belts and some type of hearing protection while riding inside an apparatus.

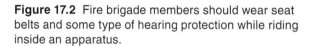

Alternate Means of Emergency Response

Many fire brigades respond to an emergency on foot, some in fire apparatus, and others respond on other types of vehicles such as bicycles, scooters, and utility vehicles. The facility fire brigade organizational statement and SOPs should identify the means of response and the site specific safety protocols to be followed.

Exterior Class A Fires

NFPA 1081 (2018): 5.2.3

Exterior fires may occur in stacked and piled materials, small unattached structures, and trash containers. These fires can create a hazard to nearby structures, flammable/combustible storage tanks, parked vehicles, and vegetation. How you extinguish these fires will depend on the type of material involved, weather conditions, and the type and quantity of extinguishing agent you use.

Situational Awareness: Exterior Class A Fires

The following conditions specific to Class A exterior fires should be observed and communicated:

- Changes to the configuration of the materials
- Changes to fire brigade member locations based upon changes in fire spread or other factors
- Indicators of imminent collapse
- Spread of fire to exposures
- Wind direction and speed
- Effectiveness of fire attack

Small Unattached Structures

Small unattached structures (storage buildings, sheds) can be found in many facilities. Their age, construction type and material, and value will cover a wide spectrum. NFPA does not define what constitutes a small structure, only that such a fire should be attacked from the exterior. Unless there is some compelling reason to try to save the structure, the primary mission is to prevent fire spread to exposures and then extinguish the fire. **Class A foam concentrate** and fog streams are effective for exposure protection, advancing close to the fire, and extinguishment.

Because small structures are used for storage, you can assume hazardous materials may be inside the building. The volume of smoke and fire, as well as the color of the smoke, can provide an indication of the primary materials that are on fire. Apply a straight stream from the exterior to extinguish most fires. If there is any question of the hazard, protect exposures, prevent fire spread, and allow the structure to self-extinguish.

Trash Container Fires

Trash containers may be as small as a garbage can or as large as a heavy trash container. Toxic products of combustion will be present in trash container fires of all types, so full PPE and SCBA should be worn when attacking any trash container fire **(Figure 17.3)**. The refuse may include:

- Hazardous materials or plastics that emit highly toxic smoke and gases
- Aerosol cans and batteries that may explode when exposed to heat
- Biological waste in marked or unmarked containers

Figure 17.3 PPE and SCBA should be worn while attacking fires in large trash containers.

It may help to attack the fire using Class A foam. In some fire brigades, it is SOP to use a master stream to flood the container with water to drown any hidden fire. However, this technique can present containment problems if the water used to fill the container becomes contaminated. Once the fire has been controlled, it may be possible to use standard overhaul techniques to complete the extinguishment.

Baghouses or dust collection systems may be commonly found in an industrial environment to separate dusts and small particles from an atmosphere. **Combustible dust** within enclosures such as a baghouse or dust collector poses fire, flash fire, and explosion hazards. Although most baghouses and dust collectors are located exterior to the building, some may be located inside. Fire brigade members need to be familiar with the hazards associated with baghouses and dust collection systems including protecting themselves and others from flash fires and explosions.

Exterior Class B Fires

NFPA 1081 (2018): 5.3.5, 5.3.6

Fire brigade members must be prepared to control Class B hydrocarbon hazards such as storage tank fires, petrochemical processing units, spills, leaks, and releases should they occur on company property **(Figure 17.4)**. The following sections provide information about operations and tactics, identification of materials and storage types, and product hazards.

Figure 17.4 An example of a Class B hydrocarbon fire. *Courtesy of Williams Fire & Hazard Control Inc. / Brent Gaspard.*

Storage Tank Fire Control Operations

As production needs rise in today's society and industrial age, there is an increase in the need for storing and moving of liquid and gas products to areas that require their use. Systems that move liquids and gases use a network of pipes, valves, and tanks. The storage and transportation of these products in large quantities create the potential for a large-scale hazardous event to occur. The methods used to mitigate such emergencies have been practiced at industrial sites around the world for many years.

When dealing with bulk storage tanks, industrial fire brigade members should be familiar with the following standards: American Petroleum Institute's (API) Recommended Practice 2021, *Management of Atmospheric Storage Tank Fires*, and NFPA 30, *Flammable and Combustible Liquids Code*. These codes provide valuable information that can assist the industrial fire brigade with bulk storage tank issues. Additional information on product identification can be found in IFSTA's Hazardous Materials for First Responders manual.

NOTE: Special agents, such as dry chemicals, clean agents, and CO_2, may be effective on small Class B fires, however, facilities may lack the quantities of these agents needed for larger fires.

Storage Tank Identification

The presence of certain storage vessels, tanks, containers, packages, or vehicles is a certain indication of the presence of hazardous materials. These containers can provide useful information about the materials inside, so it is important for first responders to recognize the shapes of the different types of packaging and containers in which hazardous materials are stored and transported.

Types of containers can be categorized in different ways:

- Bulk versus nonbulk (referring to capacity as defined by the U.S. Department of Transportation [DOT] and Transport Canada [TC])
- Pressure versus nonpressure (referring to the design of the container based on the pressure within)
- Bulk-capacity fixed-facility containment systems versus transportation packaging (referring to the facility or mode)

Bulk-Capacity Fixed-Facility Containers

Fixed-facility bulk-capacity containers include buildings, aboveground storage tanks, machinery, underground storage tanks, pipelines, reactors, open piles or bins, vats, storage cabinets, and other fixed on-site containers. This section focuses on storage tanks holding bulk quantities of hazardous materials.

Storage tanks may be atmospheric or pressurized, and they are discussed in the same sections as atmospheric tanks and pressure tanks, respectively **(Figure 17.5)**. The following sections highlight the features of these tanks.

Atmospheric **Pressure**

Figure 17.5 Examples of an atmospheric tank and a pressure tank found at some facilities.

Atmospheric/Nonpressure Storage Tanks

Atmospheric/nonpressure (also called atmospheric) storage tanks are designed to hold contents under little pressure. The maximum pressure under which an atmospheric/nonpressure tank is capable of holding its contents is 0.5 psi (3.45 kPa) {0.03 bar}. Common types of atmospheric/nonpressure tanks are horizontal tanks, ordinary cone roof tanks, floating roof tanks, lifter roof tanks, and vapor dome roof tanks. **Table 17.1, p. 536-537** provides pictures and examples of various atmospheric storage tanks and also describes underground storage caverns.

Table 17.1
Atmospheric/Nonpressure Storage Tanks

Tank Type

Horizontal Tank

Cone Roof Tank

Open Top Floating Roof Tank

Floating Deck

Covered Top Floating Roof Tank

Vents around rim provide differentiation from Cone Roof Tanks

Covered Top Floating Roof Tank with Geodesic Dome

Descriptions

Horizontal tanks: Cylindrical tanks sitting on legs, blocks, cement pads, or something similar; typically constructed of steel with flat ends. Horizontal tanks are commonly used for bulk storage in conjunction with fuel-dispensing operations. Old tanks (pre-1950s) have bolted seams, whereas new tanks are generally welded. A horizontal tank supported by unprotected steel supports or stilts (prohibited by most current fire codes) may fail quickly during fire conditions.

Contents: Flammable and combustible liquids, corrosives, poisons, etc.

Cone roof tanks: Have cone-shaped, pointed roofs. When it is partially full, the remaining portion of the tank contains a potentially dangerous vapor space.

Contents: Flammable, combustible, and corrosive liquids

Open top floating roof tanks (sometimes just called *floating roof tanks*): Large-capacity, aboveground holding tanks. They are usually much wider than they are tall. As with all floating roof tanks, the roof actually floats on the surface of the liquid and moves up and down depending on the liquid's level. This roof eliminates the potentially dangerous vapor space found in cone roof tanks. A fabric or rubber seal around the circumference of the roof provides a weather-tight seal.

Contents: Flammable and combustible liquids

Internal floating roof tanks (sometimes called *covered [or covered top] floating roof tanks):* Have fixed cone roofs with either a pan or deck-type float inside that rides directly on the product surface. This tank is a combination of the open top floating roof tank and the ordinary cone roof tank.

Contents: Flammable and combustible liquids

NOTE: Floating roof tanks covered by geodesic domes are used to store flammable liquids.

Continued

Table 17.1 (continued)
Atmospheric/Nonpressure Storage Tanks

Tank Type	Descriptions
Lifter Roof Tank 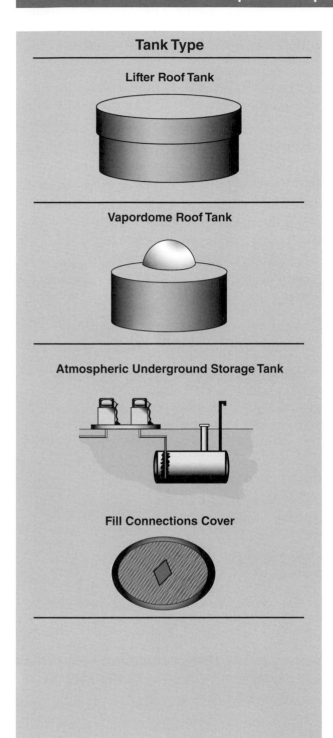	**Lifter roof tanks:** Have roofs that float within a series of vertical guides that allow only a few feet (meters) of travel. The roof is designed so that when the vapor pressure exceeds a designated limit, the roof lifts slightly and relieves the excess pressure. **Contents:** Flammable and combustible liquids
Vapordome Roof Tank	**Vapordome roof tanks:** Vertical storage tanks that have lightweight aluminum geodesic domes on their tops. Attached to the underside of the dome is a flexible diaphragm that moves in conjunction with changes in vapor pressure. **Contents:** Combustible liquids of medium volatility and other nonhazardous materials
Atmospheric Underground Storage Tank **Fill Connections Cover**	**Atmospheric underground storage tanks:** Constructed of steel, fiberglass, or steel with a fiberglass coating. Underground tanks will have more than 10 percent of their surface areas underground. They can be buried under a building or driveway or adjacent to the occupancy. This tank has fill and vent connections located near the tank. Vents, fill points, and occupancy type (gas/service stations, private garages, and fleet maintenance stations) provide visual clues. Many commercial and private tanks have been abandoned, some with product still in them. These tanks are presenting major problems to many communities. **Contents:** Petroleum products
	Underground storage caverns: Rare and technically are not "tanks." First responders should be aware that some natural and manmade caverns are used to store natural gas. The locations of such caverns should be noted in local emergency response plans.

According to the U.S. Environmental Protection Agency (EPA), catastrophic failures of aboveground atmospheric/nonpressure storage tanks can occur when flammable vapors in a tank explode and break either the side or shell-to-bottom seam. These failures have caused tanks to rip open and (in rare cases) hurtle through the air. A properly designed and maintained storage tank will break when over pressured along the shell-to-top seam, which is more likely to limit the fire to the damaged tank and prevent the contents from spilling.

The following examples of catastrophic shell-to-bottom seam failures illustrate the potential dangers:

- In 1995, the combustible vapor inside two large, 30-foot diameter by 30-foot high (9 m by 9 m) storage tanks exploded during a welding operation on the outside of one tank. The explosion propelled both tanks upward — one landing more than 50 feet (15 m) away. The flammable liquid inside was instantly released and ignited, resulting in a massive fire that caused five deaths and several serious injuries.

- In 1992, while workers were welding the outside of an empty liquid storage tank, residual vapor in the tank exploded and propelled it upward and into an adjacent river. Three workers were killed and one was injured.

Shell-to-bottom seam failures are more common among old storage tanks. Steel storage tanks built before 1950 generally do not conform to current industry standards for explosion and fire venting situations. Atmospheric/nonpressure tanks used for storage of flammable and combustible liquids should be designed to fail along the shell-to-roof seam when an explosion occurs in the tank. This feature prevents the tank from propelling upward or splitting along the side. Several organizations have developed standards and specifications for storage tank design.

Many other safety issues arise once atmospheric/nonpressure tanks become involved in or are exposed to fire. Emergency response planning is essential to prevent injuries or deaths caused by the special problems presented by tank fires and emergencies.

Storage Tank Terminology

NFPA categorizes fixed-facility storage tanks as *pressure* and *nonpressure*. NFPA also singles out **cryogenic liquid storage tanks** for special recognition. Descriptions are as follows:

- **Nonpressure tanks (also called atmospheric tanks)** — If these tanks are storing any product, they will normally have a small amount of pressure (up to 0.5 psi [3.45 kPa] {0.03 bar}) inside, which makes the term nonpressure something of a misnomer under most circumstances. Responders should be aware that even non-pressure tanks probably have some internal pressure.

- **Pressure tanks** — These tanks are divided into the following two categories:
  - Low-pressure storage tanks that have pressures between 0.5 psi to 15 psi (3.45 kPa to 103 kPa) {0.03 bar to 1.03 bar}.
  - Pressure vessels that have pressures above 15 psi (103 kPa) {1.03 bar}.

- **Cryogenic liquid tanks** — These tanks have varying pressures, but some can be very high (over 300 psi [2 068 kPa] {20.7 bar}). They are usually heavily insulated with a vacuum in the space between the outer and inner shells.

Pressure Storage Tanks

Pressure storage tanks are designed to hold contents under pressure. NFPA uses the term to cover both low-pressure storage tanks and pressure vessels (with higher pressures). **Table 17.2, p. 539-540** provides pictures and examples of various pressure tanks.

Tank Fire Suppression Systems and Equipment

When fires occur in outdoor storage tanks, industrial fire brigades can utilize a number of different suppression methods depending on the situation they face and the resources they possess. This section addresses outdoor storage tank protection systems as well as types of storage type roofs and the appropriate foam application equipment and methods for each.

Table 17.2
Low-Pressure Storage Tanks and Pressure Vessels

Tank/Vessel Type	Descriptions

Dome Roof Tank

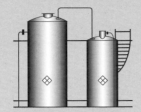

Dome roof tanks: Generally classified as low-pressure tanks with operating pressures as high as 15 psi (103 kPa). They have domes on their tops.

Contents: Flammable liquids, combustible liquids, fertilizers, solvents, etc.

Spheroid Tank

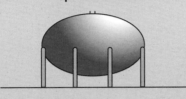

Spheroid tanks: Low-pressure storage tanks. They can store 3,000,000 gallons (11 356 200 L) or more of liquid.

Contents: Liquefied petroleum gas (LPG), methane, propane, and some flammable liquids such as gasoline and crude oil

Noded Spheroid Tank

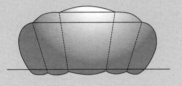

Noded spheroid tanks: Low-pressure storage tanks. They are similar in use to spheroid tanks, but they can be substantially larger and flatter in shape. These tanks are held together by a series of internal ties and supports that reduce stresses on the external shells.

Contents: LPG, methane, propane, and some flammable liquids such as gasoline and crude oil

Horizontal Pressure Vessel*

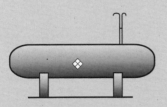

Horizontal pressure vessels:* Have high pressures and capacities from 500 to over 40,000 gallons (1 893 L to over 151 416 L). They have rounded ends and are not usually insulated. They usually are painted white or some other highly reflective color.

Contents: LPG, anhydrous ammonia, vinyl chloride, butane, ethane, liquefied natural gas (LNG), compressed natural gas (CNG), chlorine, hydrogen chloride, and other similar products

Spherical Pressure Vessel

Spherical pressure vessels: Have high pressures and capacities up to 600,000 gallons (2 271 240 L). They are often supported off the ground by a series of concrete or steel legs. They usually are painted white or some other highly reflective color.

Contents: Liquefied petroleum gases and vinyl chloride

Continued

Table 17.2 (continued)
Low-Pressure Storage Tanks and Pressure Vessels

Tank/Vessel Type	Descriptions
Cryogenic-Liquid Storage Tank	**Cryogenic-liquid storage tanks:** Insulated, vacuum-jacketed tanks with safety-relief valves and rupture disks. Capacities can range from 300 to 400,000 gallons (1 136 L to 1 514 160 L). Pressures vary according to the materials stored and their uses. **Contents:** Liquid carbon dioxide, liquid oxygen, liquid nitrogen, etc.

* It is becoming more common for horizontal propane tanks to be buried underground. Underground residential tanks usually have capacities of 500 or 1,000 gallons (1 893 L or 3 785 L). Once buried, the tank may be noticeable only because of a small access dome protruding a few inches (millimeters) above the ground.

Outdoor Storage Tank Protection Systems

Outdoor petroleum storage tanks can be protected with foam systems. Because the design of petroleum storage tanks differs widely, each requires foam systems tailored to its particular characteristics. Fire brigade members may encounter fixed cone roof tanks, external floating roof tanks, and internal floating roof tanks each utilizing unique foam systems.

In the fire and emergency services, the following three accepted delivery methods for applying finished foam are available **(Figure 17.6)**:

- **Type I discharge outlet** — Fixed system device that conducts and delivers finished foam onto the burning surface of a liquid without submerging it or agitating the surface. No longer manufactured and considered obsolete, it may still be used in some isolated facilities and areas.

- **Type II discharge outlet** — Fixed system device that delivers foam gently onto the liquid surface by spraying the foam against the inside of the tank shell and letting it slide down onto the fuel. It is designed to lessen submergence of the foam and agitation of the surface.

- **Type III delivery method** — Includes master streams and handlines that deliver finished foam in a manner that causes it to fall directly onto the surface of the burning liquid and does so in a way that causes general agitation.

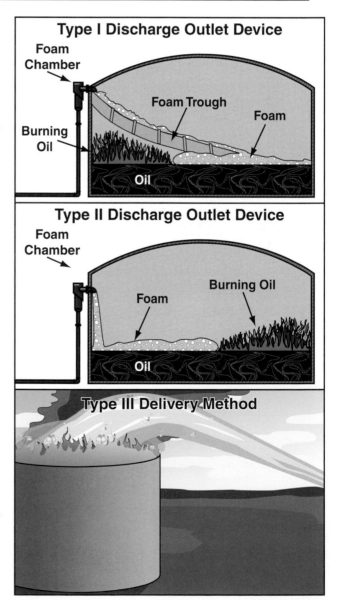

Figure 17.6 Examples of Type I, II, and III foam discharge devices and methods.

Figure 17.7 An example of a foam chamber through which finished foam is discharged into a tank.

Table 17.3
Number of Fixed Foam Discharge Outlets for Fixed-Roof Tanks Containing Hydrocarbons or Flammable and Combustible Liquids Requiring Alcohol-Resistant Foams

Tank Diameter (or Equivalent Area)		Minimum Number of Discharge Outlets
Feet	Meters	
Up to 80	Up to 24	1
Over 80 to 120	Over 24 to 36	2
Over 120 to 140	Over 36 to 42	3
Over 140 to 160	Over 42 to 48	4
Over 160 to 180	Over 48 to 54	5
Over 180 to 200	Over 54 to 60	6
* Plus 1 outlet for each additional 5,000 ft² (465m²)		

Reprinted with permission from NFPA 11-2016, *Standard for Low-, Medium-, and High-Expansion Foam*, Copyright © 2015, National Fire Protection Association, Quincy, MA. This reprinted material is not the complete and official position of the NFPA on the referenced subject, which is represented only by the standard in its entirety which may be obtained through the NFPA website at www.nfpa.org.

Fixed Cone Roof Tanks

A cone roof tank stores flammable, combustible, and corrosive liquids. It has a cone-shaped, pointed roof. Tanks over 50 feet (15 m) in diameter are designed with a weak roof-to-shell seam that breaks when/if the container becomes over pressurized. A disadvantage of this type of tank is that when it is partially full, the remaining portion of the tank contains a potentially dangerous vapor space that can be explosive if the area is exposed to an ignition source.

Surface Application. Fixed foam discharge outlets (commonly referred to as foam chambers) apply the finished foam to the surface of the burning fuel. The finished foam is applied by one or more foam chambers installed on the shell of the tank just below the roof joint **(Figure 17.7)**. If two or more foam chambers are used on one tank, they must be equally spaced around the perimeter of the tank. **Table 17.3** shows the minimum number of foam chambers required for a tank based on its size. A foam solution pipe is extended from the proportioning source outside the dike wall to the foam chambers. A deflector is located inside the tank shell to deflect the discharge against the shell.

The foam chamber contains an orifice plate (sized for the required flow and inlet pressure), air inlets, an expansion area, and a discharge deflector to direct the gentle application of the expanded foam down the inside of the tank. This device also contains a vapor seal that prevents the entrance of vapors into the foam chamber and the supply pipe. Foam chambers are typically supplied by a fixed or semifixed system arrangement. The piping to the foam chambers is supplied by a fixed **fire pump** and foam proportioning system or mobile apparatus. The minimum fixed system application rate of foam for hydrocarbon fires (as specified by NFPA 11, *Standard for Low-, Medium-, and High-Expansion Foam*) is 0.10 gpm/foot² (4.1 L/min/m²). The duration of application varies from 20 to 55 minutes, depending on the exact type of discharge devices and the flash point of the fuel. The 20-minute time period relates to seal fires while 55-minute time period relates to full circumference fires. The application rate and discharge time for tanks containing polar solvent fuels vary widely. Consult the manufacturer of the foam concentrate used in the system for the requirements for each specific case.

Surface applications using foam chambers have several advantages. First, each system is engineered specifically for a particular application. Second, less foam concentrate is lost or wasted when compared to extinguishing the fire using monitors or nozzles. Surface application may be used on both hydrocarbon and polar solvent fuels and with a variety of foam concentrates. The primary disadvantage with these systems is that they can be damaged by an initial explosion or fire. This situation requires manual fire fighting techniques to control the incident. A disadvantage of a fixed system is that it may be damaged in an explosion when a fire starts.

Subsurface Injection. **Subsurface injection (SSI)** has benefits over other system types. SSI systems inject finished foam at the base of the tank allowing it to float to the top of the fuel where it forms a blanket over the surface of the liquid **(Figure 17.8)**. Finished foam that is subsurface injected expands less than finished foam applied through surface application or manual application equipment. A 4:1 expansion ratio is common for subsurface injection.

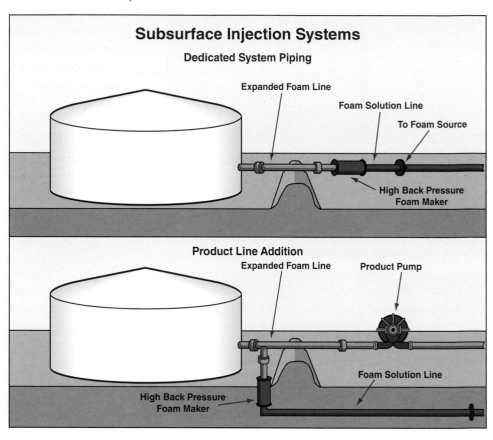

Figure 17.8 There are two types of subsurface injection systems. (a) Dedicated system piping in which foam is injected through a dry pipe that is dedicated to the foam system. (b) Product line addition in which foam is injected into the tank product line.

The finished foam is discharged into the tank using independent foam delivery lines. These foam lines must be spaced equally around the edge of the tank. **Table 17.4** shows the number of discharges required based on the size of the tank and amount of fuel in the tank. Tanks often collect a layer of water at the base, as a result of condensation and leaks. Finished foam must discharge above the layer of water commonly found resting in the bottom of the tank. Attempting to pump finished foam through the layer of water results in the foam's destruction.

Most subsurface injection systems are semi-fixed systems. The piping that supplies the discharge(s) runs from the discharge(s) to an intake manifold outside the dike area. An independent fire pump (usually a pumping apparatus) connected to either a fire hydrant or static water supply source pumps the foam solution into the system. Some subsurface injection systems are completely fixed systems supplied by a dedicated fire pump and foam concentrate supply.

Table 17.4
Minimum Number of Subsurface Foam Discharge Outlets for Fixed-Roof Tanks Containing Hydrocarbons

Tank Diameter		Minimum Number of Discharge Outlets	
Feet	Meters	Flash Point Below 100°F (37.8°C)	Flash Point 100°F (37.8°C) or Higher
Up to 80	Up to 24	1	1
Over 80 to 120	Over 24 to 36	2	1
Over 120 to 140	Over 36 to 42	3	2
Over 140 to 160	Over 42 to 48	4	2
Over 160 to 180	Over 48 to 54	5	2
Over 180 to 200	Over 54 to 60	6	3
Over 200	Over 60	6	3
		plus 1 outlet for each additional 5,000 ft² (465 m²)	plus 1 outlet for each additional 7,000 ft² (697 m²)

Notes:

(1) For Class IA liquids, see 5.2.6.1.1. (NFPA 11-2016 5.2.6.1.1: Subsurface injection systems shall not be used for protection of Class IA hydrocarbon liquids or for the protection of alcohols, esters, ketones, aldehydes, anhydrides, or other products requiring the use of alcohol-resistant foams.

(2) Table 5.2.6.2.8 of NFPA 11 is based on extrapolation of fire test data on 25 ft (7.5 m), 93 ft (27.9 m), and 115 ft. (34.5 m) diameter tanks containing gasoline, crude oil, and hexane, respectively.

(3) The most viscous fuel that has been extinguished by subsurface injection where stored at ambient conditions [60°F (15.6°C)] had a viscosity of 2,000 SSU (440 centistokes) and a pour point of 15°F (-9.4°C). Subsurface injection of foam generally is not recommended for fuels that have a viscosity greater than 2,000 SSU (440 centistokes) at their minimum anticipated storage temperature.

(4) In addition to the control provided by the smothering effect of the foam and the cooling effect of the water in the foam that reaches the surface, fire control and extinguishment can be enhanced further by the rolling of cool product to the surface.

Two primary advantages of subsurface injection systems are as follows:

- Finished foam is efficiently delivered to the surface of the fuel without being affected by wind or thermal updrafts.

- The chance of subsurface foam equipment being damaged by the initial explosion or fire is substantially less than that of fixed, surface-application equipment.

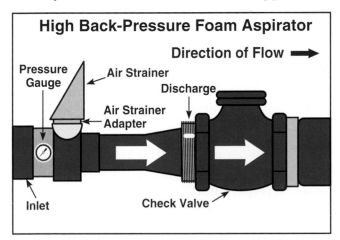

High Back-Pressure Foam Aspirator

Direction of Flow ➡

Pressure Gauge
Air Strainer
Discharge
Air Strainer Adapter
Inlet
Check Valve

Figure 17.9 High back-pressure foam aspirators may be installed in the subsurface foam injection line because of the high pressure created by the product in the storage tank. Air pressure is added to the foam to help it overcome the resistance of the product.

Because of the amount of piping involved in these systems and the back pressure of the fuel in the storage tank, a foam maker that supplies finished foam under pressure is required. The high back-pressure foam maker (or forcing foam maker) is an in-line aspirator **(Figure 17.9)**. High back-pressure aspirators supply air directly to the foam solution through a Venturi action. This action typically produces low-air content but homogeneous and stable finished foam.

For both the subsurface injection system and the fixed system surface application method, NFPA 11 recommends the application rate of 0.10 gpm/foot² (4.1 L/min/m²) for hydrocarbon fires. The duration of application varies from 30 to 55 minutes, depending on the flash point of the fuel. Fluoroprotein, AFFF, AR-AFFF, and FFFP concentrates are most commonly used for subsurface injection.

Subsurface injection systems cannot protect tanks containing polar solvent fuels. The fuel would destroy the finished foam before it ever reached the surface. Regular protein foam concentrates cannot be used for subsurface injection. Protein finished foam becomes saturated with the flammable liquid and burns after rising to the surface.

NOTE: Subsurface foam systems cannot be used with hydrocarbon products (such as Bunker C oil and asphalt) that have viscosities above 2,000 SSU/SUS (440 centistokes) at 60°F (15°C) or with any fuels heated above 200°F (93°C). SSU/SUS (Saybolt Universal Seconds) and centistokes are measurements of viscosity used in the petroleum industry and defined by the American Society for Testing and Materials (ASTM) standards.

External Floating Roof Tanks

The external floating roof tank (sometimes referred to as the open-top floating roof tank) is similar to the cone roof tank except that it has no fixed roof. A pontoon-type roof or double-deck roof floats directly on the flammable liquid surface. These tanks are excellent for the storage of flammable fuels such as gasoline that release large quantities of vapors. By having the roof float on the surface of the liquid, ignition potential is greatly reduced.

The only place where the surface of the flammable liquid may be exposed is at the seal where the shell and roof come together. Fixed foam protection systems are usually designed to extinguish a fire in the seal area. Full-surface fires are only possible if the entire floating roof sinks or tilts. If this situation occurs, unless the fixed system was designed for a full circumference fire, it is necessary to launch a full-scale fire fighting attack using monitors and/or mobile foam apparatus.

The space between the roof and the tank shell is equipped with a mechanical shoe seal or tube seal **(Figure 17.10)**. The mechanical shoe seal (also called the pantograph seal) consists of a fabric seal that is anchored to the top of the roof and rides on the inside of the tank wall. The actual mechanical shoe (or pantograph) is attached below the fabric seal to keep the roof properly aligned within the tank. The tube seal is constructed of urethane foam that is contained within an envelope. The seal is connected to the edge of the roof around the entire circumference of the tank. A secondary weather shield is usually installed above the main seal.

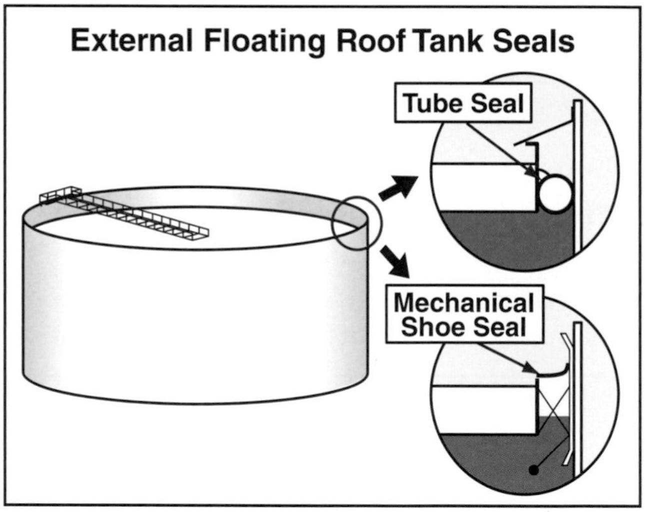

Figure 17.10 An illustration showing the mechanical shoe and tube seals found on external floating roof tanks.

Two basic types of fixed foam systems are used to protect the seal area of external floating roof tanks: foam chambers on the tank shell and foam discharges on the floating roof.

Tank Shell Foam Chambers. This system involves the discharge of finished foam into the seal area from foam chambers mounted on steel plates above the top rim of the tank shell. A finished foam dam is required to retain the foam over the seal or weather shield **(Figure 17.11)**. This dam is normally 12 or 24 inches (300 or 600 mm) in height. The dam must be located at least 1 foot (0.3 m) but no more than 2 feet (0.6 m) from the wall of the tank. When a secondary seal is installed, the finished foam dam should extend at least 2 inches (50 mm) above the top of the secondary seal.

NFPA 11 contains the requirements for foam application rate, duration of discharge, and spacing of the foam chambers. For top-of-seal foam discharge, an application rate of 0.3 gpm/foot² (12.2 L/ min/ m²) and discharge duration of 20 minutes are specified for all tanks, regardless of whether they contain hydrocarbon or polar solvent fuels. The foam chambers must be a maximum of 40 feet (12.2 m) apart

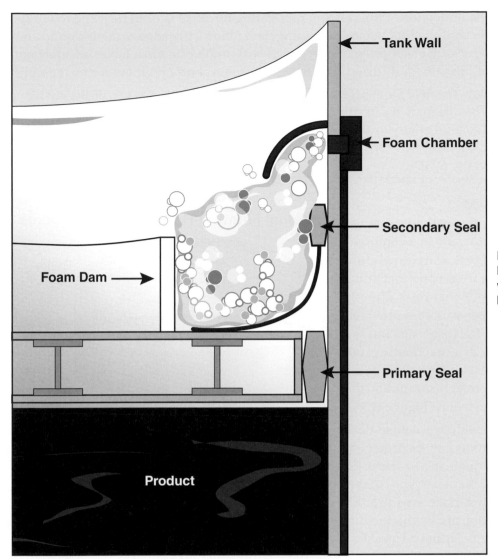

Figure 17.11 A foam dam keeps foam in the seal area where a fire can most likely be contained.

Tank Wall

Foam Chamber

Secondary Seal

Foam Dam

Primary Seal

Product

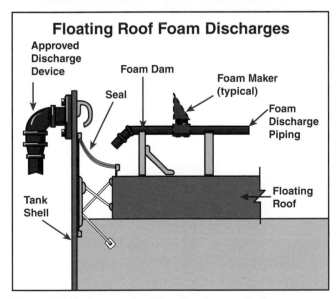

Floating Roof Foam Discharges

Approved Discharge Device

Foam Dam

Foam Maker (typical)

Seal

Foam Discharge Piping

Tank Shell

Floating Roof

Figure 17.12 At some facilities, fixed foam discharges are positioned directly on the tank's floating roof.

on tanks with 12-inch (300 mm) dams and 80 feet (24.4 m) apart on tanks with 24-inch (600 mm) dams. Fluoroprotein, AFFF, AR-AFFF, and FFFP concentrates or their alcohol-resistant counterparts may be used in these systems.

Floating Roof Foam Discharges. Another method for protecting external floating roofs is to have the foam discharges located on the roof itself. These systems fall into one of two categories: those that provide finished foam to the top of the seal and those that supply foam beneath the seal.

Systems that provide top-of-seal protection are basically the same as foam chambers located on the tank shell described previously. The only real difference is that the foam discharges and the piping that supply them are located on the roof **(Figure 17.12)**. A feed line may either run up the side of the tank and down the stairway, or through the inside of the tank to the underside of the floating roof. A flexible hose is used near the top of the system to allow for movement of the roof. A circle of piping then follows the edge of the tank and connects to the foam makers. Tanks that are protected by top-of-seal protection must have finished foam dams of the same specifications previously listed for systems with foam chambers mounted on the walls.

Systems that provide below-the-seal protection have basically the same design as top-of-seal systems. The primary difference is that the foam discharge orifices in below-the-seal systems actually penetrate the seal to apply finished foam directly to the surface of the fuel. Additionally, the application rate changes to 0.5 gpm/foot² (20.4 L/min/m²) with a discharge duration of 10 minutes. These systems may be of the fixed or semifixed variety.

Internal Floating Roof Tanks

The internal floating roof tank (sometimes referred to as a *covered floating roof tank*) is a combination of the fixed cone roof tank and the external floating roof tank. It has a fixed cone roof and a pan or deck-type float inside that rides directly on the product surface. Open vents are provided around the shell between the fixed roof and the floating roof. Increasingly, external floating roof tanks are being retrofitted with a geodesic dome or steel roof outer cover to protect the tank and the product from the weather elements **(Figure 17.13)**.

NFPA 11 states that tanks with steel double-deck roofs or pontoon floating roofs may be protected

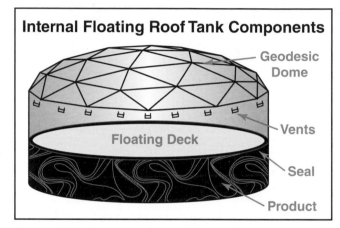

Internal Floating Roof Tank Components

Geodesic Dome

Floating Deck

Vents

Seal

Product

Figure 17.13 Components of an internal floating roof tank.

by a system designed to extinguish a seal fire. Any of the systems described in the external floating roof tanks section may be used on these types of tanks. All other types of internal floating roof tanks must be protected against a full surface area fire. Any of the surface application systems described in the Fixed Cone Roof Tank section of this chapter may be used. According to NFPA 11, subsurface and semi-subsurface injection systems cannot be used for protecting internal floating roof tanks. The application rates and discharge duration times described for external floating roof tanks and fixed cone roof tanks apply for internal floating roof tanks, depending on which type of system is used.

Tank Fire Suppression Methods

The fire suppression method or methods used to control and extinguish tank fires depend upon the type of fire and conditions found at the scene. This section addresses ground spill fires, fire suppression methods for vent fires, rim seal fires in tanks with external floating roof and internal floating roofs, full surface liquid fires, and obstructed surface fires with wholly or partially sunken roofs.

Ground Spill Fires

Fire brigade members should focus on stopping the fires from spreading to or impinging upon storage tanks that are not involved. This prevents the stored materials from being heated, releasing vapors, or triggering chemical reactions.

Unless the endangered materials are heat sensitive, the cooling of impinging fires should take top priority. Heat-sensitive materials should be identified during preincident planning.

Vent Fires

Many vent fires ignite via lightning or static electricity. By properly applying dry chemical and or foam in the area of the vent, the vapor which is exiting the tank can be extinguished. This type of fire control method must be coordinated as soon as possible since the longer the vents burn the more susceptible the roof is to collapsing or failing. The hotter the metal area around the vent becomes, the harder it is to extinguish. By cooling the tank, the vapor pressure inside the tank may be reduced and the vent may then close, extinguishing the fire.

Figure 17.14 An illustration of a rim seal fire on an external floating roof tank.

Rim Seal Fires (External Floating Roof Tanks)

Rim seal fires are the most prominent fire involving external floating roofs. These fires are commonly caused by lightning or static electricity **(Figure 17.14)**. The industry method of choice for extinguishment is the extension of foam handline(s) up the roof access stair way to the gauger's platform. When necessary, multiple hand portable fire extinguishers may be effective. Specialized devices can be used to extinguish the seal area directly under the platform. Many companies have installed seal fire nozzles and hose stations, and piped the access to the roadway next to the tank so that foam may be injected over the edge of the tank into the seal area.

> **CAUTION:** Fire control methods must avoid sinking or flipping the roof from the weight of suppressant, therefore master streams should not be used for rim seal fire extinguishment.

Rim Seal Fires (Internal Floating Roof Tanks)

If there is a fixed system on the tank, that system should be used to extinguish a rim seal fire on an internal floating roof tank. If no fixed system is available, foam should be applied into the tank through the vents in sufficient quantity to extinguish the fire. Generally, the area inside the tank is too "rich" (above the flammable range) and burning only occurs when the vapor exits the tank at the vent. This fire must then be extinguished at the vent.

Figure 17.15 An over-the-top attack on a full surface liquid fire. *Courtesy of Williams Fire & Hazard Control Inc. / Brent Gaspard.*

Full Surface Liquid Fires

Full surface liquid fires require a coordinated over-the-top attack (Type III delivery method) with foam and large flow devices **(Figure 17.15)**. During preincident planning, a plan of attack is developed for this type of fire that calculates proportioning/delivery systems, and the amount of water and foam concentrate required to deliver foam over a 65-minute period. Full surface liquid tank fires may take up to 12,000 gpm of foam applied for up to 65 minutes to extinguish. Experts in this type of fire should be contacted as soon as possible to consult on tactics.

Obstructed Surface Fires with Wholly or Partially Sunken Roof

Over-the-top foam application is the most appropriate method to control and extinguish obstructed surface fires with a wholly or partially sunken roof. Foam must be applied rapidly to extinguish the fire and prevent reignition. This type of fire has all of the issues of a full surface liquid tank fire and the additional difficulty of potentially difficult access to apply foam to the tank.

Developing a Fire Suppression Strategy

There are three basic strategies for handling tank fires: passive, defensive, and offensive. Depending on the conditions found at each particular incident, the IC will decide on the best strategic approach for the particular incident.

Strategies

Each of the three basic strategies may be employed under certain situations. The following section addresses when a given strategy may be employed and identifies the basic procedures to be used with that strategy.

Passive Strategy

Used when:

- Sufficient resources are not available to attempt a safe and thorough extinguishment
- Immediate evacuation is necessary because of the imminent risk of a boilover, tank failure, or other threat to life

Procedures:

- Evacuate the area and deny entry
- Allow the fire to burn out
- No fire fighting activities are involved in a passive approach

Defensive Strategy

- Used when the condition of the tank or resources will not support an offensive strategy.
- Procedures focus on using master streams to stop the spread of the fire to uninvolved materials or other adjacent exposed tanks.

Offensive Strategy

Used when:

- Necessary to perform rescue operations
- The spread of the fire to uninvolved materials or other tanks would pose a significant hazard increase
- Sufficient resources are readily available to achieve extinguishment and restore normal conditions
- Procedures focus on aggressive fire attack in order to extinguish the fire

Suppression Agents

When choosing an appropriate strategy to combat a tank fire, the Incident Commander must determine if adequate resources, particularly the appropriate proportioning/delivery systems and necessary quantities of extinguishing agent, are available. Foam agents are recommended when dealing with flammable or combustible liquids.

The foam type and expansion rate must match the hazards posed by the particular flammable or combustible liquid. Selecting and applying the appropriate foam agent for the material is the only way to create an adequate barrier to separate oxygen from the fuel.

In some cases, mixed or twin agent applications may be the best approach to extinguishing a fire. The use of mixed or twin agents provides greater extinguishing capability than the application of a single agent. Fire brigade members should follow manufacturers' recommendations when twin agents are used.

Water Supply and Delivery

Because tank fires at industrial sites require mass application of foam and water, industrial sites must have adequate water supplies that can be operated at the pressures needed to combat these fires. Most industrial sites have high-volume pumps that are able to provide the necessary fire flow at the proper pressure. These pumps may be of the fixed, portable, or industrial pumper type (**Figure 17.16**).

Where large quantities of water must be transported by hose with little loss or no loss in pressure due to friction loss, large diameter hose is used. Large diameter hose comes in a variety of sizes, to include 5-, 6-, 7-, 10-, and 12-inch diameters (**Figure 17.17**). Industrial fire brigade members must be thoroughly familiar with the water supply and pump systems found at their site. They must also be equally familiar with the types and usage of large diameter hose their brigade uses.

Figure 17.16 Three types of pumps found at an industrial facility: a fixed pump (top), a portable pump (middle), and an apparatus-mounted pump (bottom).

Figure 17.17 Two examples of large diameter hose (LDH): 5-inch LDH (left) and 10-inch LDH (right).

Foam Calculations

To successfully extinguish tank fires, fire brigade members must:

- Select and have ready the required amounts of the appropriate type of foam concentrate based upon local requirements and manufacturer's recommendations.

- Ensure that foam concentrate and water are properly proportioned, and sufficient finished foam application can be sustained for at least 65 minutes when Type III is used.

- Ensure that the expansion ratio of the foam matches the foam delivery system being used.

- Ensure that foam solution with the correct application rate has been properly calculated for fire extinguishment per manufacturer's recommendations.

Process Unit Fire Suppression Operations

Process unit fire suppression requires the fire brigade to enter an area of a facility where pressurized pipes or equipment containing potentially flammable liquids and hazardous materials are present. This entry must be approached with great caution as equipment seals or piping can fail at any time during an emergency situation.

When process unit fire suppression operations are considered, large volumes of water must be delivered to the fire area via master streams. The purpose of the master stream is to cool adjacent process equipment and/or help to dilute vapors that may be escaping from vessels or piping. In some process units, fixed monitors or deluge systems are available to deliver water streams almost immediately. At some facilities this water delivery must be done by manually setting up portable monitors which will require more time. The advantage of setting up these master streams is water can be delivered to begin cooling the structures in the area, and to control and contain the fire while members of the fire brigade are gathering and organizing to begin a planned attack on the nearest isolation point to block in the fuel sources which will eventually extinguish the fire.

If the source of the fuel cannot be isolated or "blocked in" at a location that is remote from the fire, then the brigade should assemble and begin to attack the area in order to close valves and isolate the fuel. This attack should happen using at least two hose lines connected to separate water supplies. At least two members of the fire brigade should operate the hose line, three is preferable especially if the hose team must pull hoses up to elevation via stairs to reach the valves.

Usually when dealing with process unit flammable liquid fires, a power cone pattern is used to push the fire back from the hoseline team and control the flame front at the source. The fog pattern is used as a protective pattern for the hose team, especially if a retreat is required. Water is used as cooling and protection for the structures and personnel making the entry. Before a team may advance to elevation, any spill fires underneath the area where they will be entering should be controlled through the use of foam, foam blankets and possibly some Class B portable extinguishers. Personnel should be located on hoselines to maintain the foam blanket while the hose teams travel to, and work at elevation.

When the hose line teams have reached the valves, one or both teams will set up a water pattern over the isolation valve to provide protection of the personnel, cool the equipment and to control the flame front. To make the valve closure, one of the backup members on the hose team will come to the front of the hoselines and close the isolation valve making sure they do not break through the water pattern **(Figure 17.18)**. While this is happening the nozzle personnel must ensure that water patterns remain stable and do not move unnecessarily. Once the valve is shut, and the fuel "depressurizes," the fire should go out.

The hose teams should cool the valve area and the surrounding metal areas making sure nothing in the area reignites. Other equipment and seals may have been damaged during the fire and begin to leak if all fuel sources within the area of concern have not been blocked in by this time. Peripheral activities may also take place during the fire attack such as search and rescue, unit stabilization, runoff containment, etc.

Figure 17.18 A fire brigade member reaching through two fog streams to close a flammable gas valve.

Vehicle Fires

NFPA 1081 (2018): 5.3.13

The fire brigade may respond to motorized vehicle fires. These fires may result from a collision, a malfunction of the vehicle's propulsion system, or an intentional act. Wear full PPE including SCBA when combating vehicle fires. Vehicle fires generate a wide variety of toxic and nontoxic smoke and vapors **(Figure 17.19)**. Treat the incident the same as a structure fire, until the atmosphere is tested and determined safe.

Figure 17.19 The fire on this vehicle is giving off large amounts of toxic and nontoxic smoke and vapors.

Vehicles and Mobile Equipment

A variety of vehicles and mobile equipment may be found at facilities. These may include:

- Passenger vehicles and pickups
- Forklifts
- Telehandlers
- Tractor trailer rigs
- Front-end loaders
- Light equipment utility vehicles

Fire protection at vehicle fires can range from someone using a portable fire extinguisher to a crew of fire brigade members with fully charged hoselines. Personnel must always follow local protocols. When using hoselines, at least two fire brigade members equipped with full PPE, including SCBA, should have at least one 1½-inch (38 mm) charged and ready for use.

Modern vehicles use a variety of power sources, sometimes in combination:

- Gasoline
- Electricity
- Biofuels
- Compressed or liquefied natural gas (CNG or LNG)
- Diesel
- Hybrids (fuel and electricity)
- Hydrogen

Vehicle Scene Safety

Upon arrival at a vehicle fire or incident, determine if the incident scene will necessitate traffic being diverted and request assistance, as needed. Follow the U.S. Department of Transportation (DOT) or provincial/territorial Traffic Incident Management System (TIMS) guidelines for protecting the scene from vehicular traffic in order to establish a safe working zone around the incident. Identify any potential hazardous materials that may be involved in the fire or incident. Once scene safety is established, focus on saving the vehicle occupants and extinguishing the fire. Determine if there are victims in the vehicle and if they require extrication. Determine if the vehicle is on fire or leaking fuel. Confirm the type of fuel and select the appropriate extinguishing agent.

Before attacking the fire or commencing with extrication, isolate the vehicle from any ignition sources or eliminate the ignition source. Next, stabilize the vehicle (if safely possible), secure the area around any downed power lines, and address any additional hazards.

Avoiding Common Injuries at Vehicle Scenes

When approaching the vehicle, avoid components that are under constant pressure such as bumpers and sometimes hoods and trunk lids. These components incorporate hydraulic or pneumatic struts. If the fire heats these struts, they can explode and the bumper may be forcefully ejected. Likewise, the struts used to support the engine hood and trunk lid can also be launched from the vehicle with tremendous force. Anyone standing in the travel path could be injured or killed **(Figure 17.20)**.

> **WARNING:** Avoid pressurized components to prevent injury from failing struts.

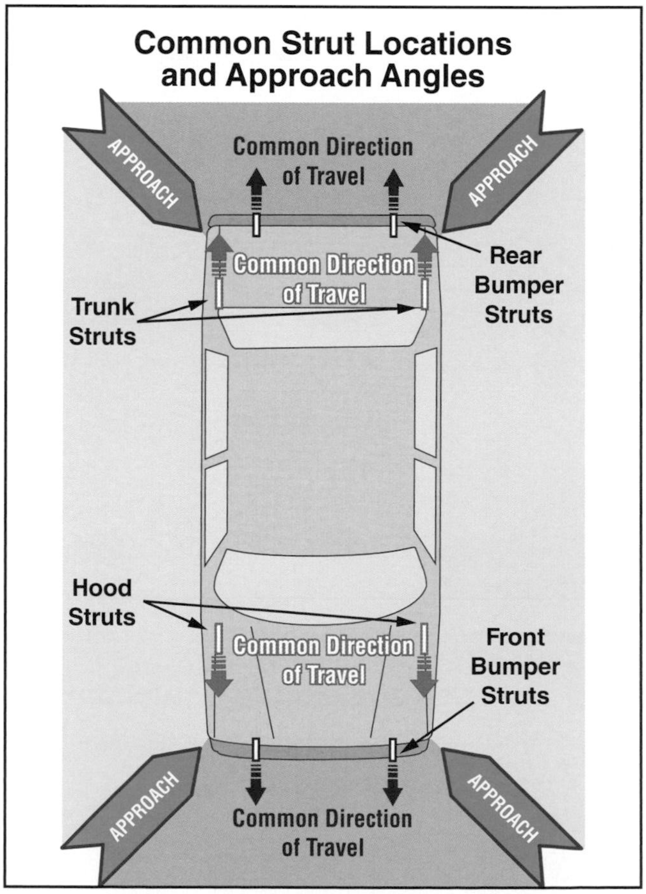

Common Strut Locations and Approach Angles

APPROACH — Common Direction of Travel — APPROACH — Rear Bumper Struts — Trunk Struts — Common Direction of Travel — Hood Struts — Front Bumper Struts — Common Direction of Travel — APPROACH — Common Direction of Travel — APPROACH

Figure 17.20 During vehicle fire suppression operations, fire brigade members should approach the vehicle from a 45-degree angle to avoid potential exploding hydraulic or pneumatic struts.

Controlling Fuel Leaks

Fuel may be found leaking from a tank or fuel lines. This fuel can add to the risk of fire or intensify a burning fire. Controlling fuel leaks can be accomplished in various ways.

- Broken fuel line may be:
  - Crimped with pliers
  - Plugged with rubber, plastic, or wooden plugs
- Broken or punctured fuel tanks may be:
  - Plugged with rubber, plastic, or wooden plugs
  - Sealed with a fuel resistant sealing compound

Selecting Hose Streams for Vehicle Fires and Flash Fire Protection

In most vehicle incidents, one or two 1½- or 1¾-inch (38 mm to 45 mm) handlines can extinguish a vehicle fire or provide flash fire protection if a fire has not yet occurred. As soon as possible, a second line should be deployed as a life safety backup. For large vehicles, such as tractor trailers, larger handlines (2½- or 3-inch [65 mm or 77 mm]) may be necessary. It may be necessary to use defensive fire fighting techniques such as deploying unstaffed master stream devices and isolating and denying entry to the area.

Vehicle Fire Attack

The basic procedures for attacking a fire in a vehicle are as follows:

- Use one or more hose streams between the burning vehicle and any exposures for exposure protection.
- Position for attack uphill and upwind of the fire to avoid standing in the path of leaking fuels running downhill.
- Attack the fire a 45-degree angle from the side of the vehicle to avoid the potential for injuries from exploding hydraulic or pneumatic struts.
- Be prepared for nozzle reaction during agent application.
- Use an appropriate nozzle pattern when applying agent and adjust the pattern as needed.
- Extinguish any fire near the vehicle occupants first.
- Extinguish any ground fire around or under the vehicle.
- Extinguish any fire remaining in or around the vehicle.
- Chock the vehicle to prevent horizontal movement.
- Isolate fuel or power source

A backup hoseline should be deployed as quickly as possible. Portable fire extinguishers can extinguish some fires in the vehicle's engine compartment or electrical system and some alternative fuel types.

Apply water to cool combustible metal components that are exposed to fire. If combustible metal components become involved, apply large amounts of water to protect adjacent combustibles while applying Class D extinguishing agent to the burning metal.

Some vehicles may contain extraordinary vehicle hazards requiring you to isolate the area and take special precautions. Extraordinary vehicle hazards may include:

- Large-capacity saddle fuel tanks
- Pressurized natural gas tanks
- Alternative fuel tanks and power sources

Once the fire has been controlled, conduct overhaul as quickly as possible to check for extension and hidden fires. Other overhaul considerations include disconnecting the battery, securing air bags, and cooling fuel tanks and any intact, sealed components. Be aware that air bags can deploy from numerous locations within the vehicle's cab.

Fires that originate in certain compartments of a vehicle require special tactics or skills. The sections that follow highlight some of these special fire attack situations.

Engine or Trunk Compartment Fires

If a fire is isolated to the trunk or engine compartment, you will need to gain access in order to extinguish the fire. To gain access to the engine compartment or trunk, first try conventional methods such as the release lever or button near the driver's seat. If these methods do not work, then use forcible entry methods similar to those listed in Chapter 14, Forcible Entry.

Before attempting forcible entry, cool the front and rear bumper struts to prevent accidental activation from heat exposure. Forcing entry into the engine compartment or trunk can be accomplished with manual or power tools. Once the trunk is open, direct the hose stream into the space until the fire is extinguished. Use one of a variety of methods to access the hood or trunk, such as:

- Pry the hood or trunk free with a Halligan or crowbar and prop it open.
- Remove the metal around the key or latch.
- Attack from the side with an axe and lever the hood or trunk open.
- Direct hose streams under the car.
- Use a piercing nozzle to pierce the hood or trunk.

In many engine compartment fires, the fire can be controlled before the hood can be opened using one of these methods:

- Direct a hose stream through the grill or air scoop.
- Drive a piercing nozzle through the hood, fenders, or wheel wells. This is not a safe tactic for hybrid or electric vehicles.
- Make or cut an opening large enough for a hose stream to be introduced.
- Use a pry tool to create an opening between the hood and the fender, and then direct a straight stream or narrow fog nozzle in the opening.

> **WARNING:** Piercing the hood of hybrid or electric vehicles could result in electrocution.

Passenger Compartment Fires

When attacking a fire in the passenger compartment, use the appropriate nozzle and pattern for the situation. Attempt to open the door. If it is locked, the driver may have the key. If normal entry is not possible, break a window then attack the fire with a medium fog pattern.

Undercarriage Fires

The following three methods can be used for fires in the undercarriage **(Figure 17.21)**:

- If there is a hazard in getting close to the vehicle, use a straight stream from a distance to reach under the vehicle.
- If the vehicle is on a hard surface such as concrete or asphalt, direct the stream downward and allow the water to deflect up toward the underside of the vehicle.
- Open the hood and direct the stream through the engine compartment.

Tire Fires

At times, brakes or tires will overheat and cause a truck to catch fire. The use of a dry chemical fire extinguisher generally only knocks the fire down for a short period of time. Apply water or foam to fully cool and extinguish the fire. Use caution and only approach large truck tires on fire from a 45-degree angle. People have been injured and killed by truck tires exploding and or coming off the rim. A tire fire can spread to the vehicle itself or its contents.

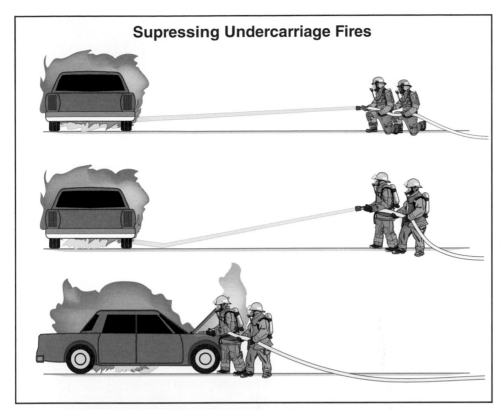

Supressing Undercarriage Fires

Figure 17.21 Three methods for attacking vehicle undercarriage fires.

WARNING: A truck tire exploding or forcibly separating from the rim can kill a person.

Alternative Fuel Vehicles

Alternative fuels create different risks to emergency responders. **Table 17.5, p. 556** shows the flammability and other hazards associated with alternative fuels. The information in the table is drawn from various manufacturers' Safety Data Sheets (SDS).

Visual indicators on vehicles, such as vehicle or fuel logos, may indicate the presence of alternative fuels. Most car manufacturers provide Emergency Response Guides for their vehicles that include emergency response procedures, notices, cautions, warnings, and dangers. These guides can provide information that will enhance safety at the scene. Alternative fuels currently include:

- Natural gas (CNG and LNG)
- Liquefied Petroleum Gas (LPG)
- Electric or hybrid electric
- Ethanol/methanol
- Hydrogen

CAUTION: There may be no visual indicators that a vehicle uses an alternative fuel source.

NOTE: For additional training and guidance regarding fire suppression operations on alternative fuel vehicles consult NFPA's *Alternative Fuel Vehicles Safety Training Program*.

Table 17.5
Flammability and Other Hazards of Alternative Fuels

Alternative Fuel	Flammability			Other Hazards
	Flash Point	Auto-Ign. Temp.	LFL/UFL	
Natural Gas **CNG** **LNG**	Flammable Gas < -306° F (< -188° C)	900-1,170° F (482-632° C) 999° F (537° C)	Flammable Gas < -306° F (< -188° C)	• Pressurized gas or liquid • Can displace oxygen and cause suffocation • Contact may cause burns or frostbite • Anesthetic effects in high concentrations
Liquefied Petroleum Gas (LPG)	61.88° F (16.6° C)	685.4° F (363° C)	3.3% to 19%	• Pressurized gas or liquid • Can cause narcotic effects in high concentrations • May cause severe eye, respiratory tract, or skin irritation
Ethanol	< -5.8° F (< -21° C)	Approximately 480° F (250° C)	1.3% to 7.3%	• May be fatal if swallowed or enters airways • May cause eye irritation • Can be absorbed through the skin • May cause drowsiness or dizziness • Extreme exposure may cause unconsciousness, asphyxiation, and death
Methanol	51.8° F (11° C)	725° F (385° C)	6% to 36%	• Burns with a clear flame • Inhalation may irritate mucous membranes and cause headache, nausea, and loss of consciousness • Ingestion may cause blindness or death • Repeated exposure may cause systemic poisoning, brain disorders, and blindness
Biodiesel	51.8° F (11° C)	725° F (385° C)	6% to 36%	• Burns with a clear flame • Inhalation may irritate mucous membranes and cause headache, nausea, and loss of consciousness • Ingestion may cause blindness or death • Repeated exposure may cause systemic poisoning, brain disorders, and blindness
Hydrogen	Flammable Gas	932-1,1059.8° F (500-571° C)	4% to 76%	• Pressurized gas • Burns with an invisible flame • Can displace oxygen and cause suffocation • Contact may cause burns or frostbite
Electric/Hybrid Electric (Prismatic Nickel Metal Hydride Batteries)	Not Applicable	Not Applicable	Not Applicable	• Short-circuiting may cause thermal injuries • Sparks due to short-circuit may ignite a fire • Danger of contact with high voltage

Natural Gas Vehicle Fuel (CNG and LNG)

Natural gas is used in vehicles in the form of compressed natural gas (CNG) and liquefied natural gas (LNG). A CNG or LNG diamond logo may be affixed to the front and rear of the vehicle. Fuel tanks are usually located in the trunk area, under side panels, in the open bed of pickup trucks, or on the back deck of forklifts. CNG and LNG tanks can rupture if exposed to fire resulting in an explosion. A pressure-relief device and vent and a fuel shutoff valve may be located in the wheel well with a placard nearby.

CNG is stored under high pressure. Tactics for fires or leaks involving CNG vehicles include:

- If no fire is visible:
  - Use a gas detector to locate leaks, shutoff valves, and eliminate any ignition sources.
  - Stay clear of any detected vapor clouds.
- If fire is visible:
  - Allow fuel to burn itself out.
  - Use water or foam to extinguish if necessary.
  - Cool the container from a safe distance.
  - Use fog stream to disperse vapor clouds.
  - Avoid contact with high velocity jet of escaping gas.

LNG is stored in a liquid state by cooling to –260°F (–162°C) in double-walled, vacuum-insulated pressure tanks. It is lighter than water and has a vapor cloud that is heavier than air. Frost on the fuel tank exterior indicates tank failure. If there is no fire or leak:

- Stabilize the vehicle.
- Set the emergency brake or chock the tires.
- Turn off the ignition.
- Shut off the gas cylinder valve handle.

Tactics and guidelines for fires or leaks involving LNG include the following:

- Avoid contact with LNG.
- Stay clear of vapor clouds identified.
- Shut off the ignition to stop the fuel flow to a leak or fire.
- Use Purple K dry-chemical agent or high-expansion foam on the surface of LNG fire.
- Use sand or dirt to prevent LNG from entering storm drains.

LPG Vehicle Fuel

Liquefied petroleum gas (LPG), also known as propane, is the third most common vehicle fuel type after gasoline and diesel, and is safer than gasoline. An LPG vehicle may be marked with a logo. The following tactics should be used at incidents involving LPG vehicles:

- Use gas detectors to determine leaks and isolate leaks from ignition sources.
- Allow the fire (if present) to self-extinguish.
- Use foam or water when necessary for extinguishment.
- Direct fire streams at the top of the LPG tank to provide adequate cooling.
- Stay clear of any identified vapor clouds.

Electric or Hybrid Electric

Electric or hybrid electric vehicles should have certain visible indicators such as the vehicle name, logo, charging port on a side or the front of vehicle, and a distinctive profile.

Batteries may be located in the engine compartment, trunk area, or under the vehicle. When the engine is running, there may not be any noise. Most electric and hybrid electric vehicles also contain a 12-volt battery system with separate battery and wiring harness.

If no fire is visible, secure the vehicle, chock wheels, turn off the ignition, and remove the key. If smoke is visible, wear full PPE and SCBA because the fumes are toxic until air monitoring indicates that the atmosphere is clear. Do not approach the vehicle if it is on fire or there is arcing under the hood. Establish scene security and protect exposures. Avoid contact with all fluids because they may include battery acid that can cause injuries.

Electric vehicles run solely on electricity stored in batteries that must be recharged periodically. There are many types, designs, and locations of vehicle battery packs. When trying to extinguish fires involving electric vehicles, fire brigade members should:

- Use inertia switches and pilot circuits to shut off a high-voltage system. It will take approximately five minutes for energy in the system to dissipate.
- Avoid orange high-voltage cables because electrocution is possible. Blue and yellow color-coded cables also present an electrocution hazard although they do not carry high voltage.
- Wear full PPE.
- Use insulated tools when opening compartments or cutting wires.
- Use water or foam to extinguish the vehicle fire, and specific recommended extinguishing agent for battery pack fires.

WARNING: Do not cut orange, blue, or yellow electrical cables.

Hybrid vehicles combine battery powered electrical systems with gasoline, diesel, bio-diesel, and natural gas to run the engine. Some hybrid vehicles use a roof-mounted photovoltaic solar panel as a power source. Shut off power with the ignition or power switch and remove the ignition key. For vehicles with keyless, push-button startup, locate keyring remote and move it 20 ft (6 m) or more away from the vehicle to make sure that the vehicle doesn't turn on. Water is the recommended extinguishing agent, although specific agents or tactics may be required for specific fuels or battery types.

Ethanol/Methanol

Ethanol and methanol are gasoline blends. They are water-soluble, electrically-conductive, clear liquids that have a slight gasoline odor. Ethanol and methanol use the same fuel tanks as conventional gasoline engines. The vehicle may not have a visible logo.

If no fire is visible or leak is detected, secure the vehicle, chock the tires, and turn off the ignition. If a fuel leak is suspected, use caution and approach in full PPE and SCBA, with hoselines deployed and charged. If the vehicle is leaking or on fire, establish a control zone and request a hazardous materials response team.

Hydrogen

Hydrogen-fueled vehicles are in use in some areas of North America, though most are still in the concept stage. Hydrogen is colorless, odorless, non-toxic, and energy efficient. According to NFPA 325, *Guide to Fire Hazard Properties of Flammable Liquids, Gases, and Volatile Solids*, it has an ignition temperature of 932°F (500°C) with a flammability range between 4 percent and 75 percent. Because the flame is invisible during the day, you should use a TI to see the flame. Vehicles are marked with a manufacturer's logo, and the vented fuel cell is in the trunk. Tactics for a leak and a fire include shutting off the ignition, isolating the fuel from ignition sources, and chocking the wheels. Do not extinguish the fire. Instead, protect the exposures and allow the fuel to burn off. If extrication is required, do not cut C-posts which contain the vents.

Chapter Review

1. What safety guidelines should fire brigade members when riding apparatus?

2. What methods can be used to extinguish an exterior Class A trash container fires?

3. In what ways can types of storage tank be categorized?

4. What are some examples of catastrophic failures of atmospheric/nonpressure storage tanks?

5. Describe the three types of accepted delivery methods for applying finished foam to outdoor storage tanks.

6. What are the extinguish methods for rim seal fires in external floating roof tanks?

7. Name and describe the three basic strategies for fire suppression of tank fires.

8. What may be required to deliver a large water supply to an industrial fire?

9. What must fire brigade members do to ensure foam will successfully extinguish tank fires?

10. What fire suppression methods can be used on process unit fires?

11. What methods can be used to access hood or trunk fires?

Key Terms

Class A Foam Concentrate — Foam specially designed for use on Class A combustibles. Class A foams, hydrocarbon-based surfactants are essentially wetting agents that reduce the surface tension of water and allow it to soak into combustible materials more easily than plain water. Class A foams are becoming increasingly popular for use in wildland and structural fire fighting.

Combustible Dust — Combustible particulate solids that, when suspended in air, create a flash fire or explosion hazard.

Cryogenic Liquid Storage Tank — Heavily insulated, vacuum-jacketed tanks used to store cryogenic liquids; equipped with safety-relief valves and rupture disks.

Fire Pump — (1) Water pump used in private fire protection to provide water supply to installed fire protection systems. (2) Water pump on a piece of fire apparatus.

Pressure Storage Tank — Class of fixed facility storage tanks divided into two categories: low-pressure storage tanks and pressure vessels.

Process Unit — Part of a facility in which raw materials undergo one or more stages of chemical conversion to become a finished product. Reactors within the unit may use liquids, gases, and or solids (or combinations of them) to enable the chemical conversion. Support functions within the unit may be physical or mechanical in nature.

Subsurface Injection — Application method where foam is pumped into the bottom of a burning fuel storage tank and allowed to float to the top to form a foam blanket on the surface of the fuel.

Surface Application — Application method where finished foam is applied directly onto the surface of the burning fuel or unignited fuel spill.

Skill Sheet List

The following skill sheets should be used to evaluate the skills described in this chapter:

NOTE: Students should wear the PPE appropriate to the NFPA 1081 level (Incipient, Advanced Exterior, Interior Structural, etc...) being evaluated.

Interior Structural Facility Fire Brigade Member Only

Chapter Contents

JPRs addressed in this chapter

This chapter provides information that addresses the following job performance requirements of NFPA 1081, *Standard for Facility Fire Brigade Member Professional Qualifications (2018)*.

6.2.1   6.2.9

6.2.6

1. Describe the fire brigade tactics for interior fire suppression operations. [6.2.1, 6.2.9]

2. Explain the specific conditions that should be observed and communicated while maintaining situational awareness during structural fire attack. [6.2.1]

3. Identify the considerations for making entry for an interior fire attack. [6.2.1]

4. Explain the process of gas cooling. [6.2.1]

5. Describe the direct, indirect, combination, and transitional attack methods. [6.2.1]

6. Explain the considerations for attacking interior fires in the upper levels of structures. [6.2.1, 6.2.6]

7. Explain the considerations for attacking interior fires below structures. [6.2.1]

8. Describe the methods for performing exposure protection. [6.2.1]

9. Recognize the importance of special tactics when dealing with high temperature duty equipment fires. [6.2.1]

10. Describe the considerations for advancing hoseline into a structure. [6.2.1]

11. Explain the considerations for advancing hoseline vertically. [6.2.1]

12. Describe the considerations for advancing hoseline up a ladder. [6.2.1]

Chapter 18
Fire Suppression Operations

Previous sections of this manual presented the basic knowledge and skills necessary to control and extinguish fires. To apply that knowledge and skills to interior fire suppression, it is necessary to learn about:

- Fire brigade tactics for interior fire suppression operations
- Building utility
- Interior structural fire attack
- High temperature duty equipment fires
- Advancing hoselines into and within structures

The scope of interior fire attack is determined by each fire brigade management and needs to be clearly outlined in the fire brigade's organizational statement, SOPs, and training programs. Some fire brigades may conduct interior fire attack from an exterior opening. Others conduct interior fire suppression operations deeper within their structures. The more intensive interior operations become, the more intensive the training the fire brigade members must receive to prepare them for these operations **(Figure 18.1)**. Some fire brigades use interior fire suppression operations only for the purpose of supporting imminent rescue of missing or entrapped personnel during a fire.

Figure 18.1 Interior structural fire brigade members attacking a fire inside a structure.

Fire Brigade Tactics for Interior Fire Suppression Operations

NFPA 1081 (2018): 6.2.1, 6.2.9

Saving lives in danger is always the first consideration. However, at times, the best way to save those victims is to simultaneously suppress the fire. Then, fire brigade members should make all possible efforts to minimize damage to property. This can be accomplished through proper fire control tactics and good loss control techniques.

The rescue, exposure protection, ventilation, confinement, and extinguishment functions at a structural fire must be performed in a coordinated manner for the operation to be successful. The following information highlights a typical response to a fire in a structure and details the responsibilities of the personnel involved.

Initial Fire Brigade Response

The first fire brigade member to arrive at the scene usually initiates Incident Command and conducts a size-up to determine the fire's location and other pertinent information. This size-up should identify the present state of the fire and known on-scene hazards. Depending on the conditions found, this team may also need to perform search and rescue functions or exposure protection. The fire brigade leader makes a report on conditions regarding the exact location, exposures, conditions found at the incident, and, if necessary, additional resources needed **(Figure 18.2)**. Because of the two-in/two-out rule, the initial team may be limited to conducting rescue and protecting exposures.

Once the location of the fire is known, the team will position the initial attack hoseline to cover the following priorities:

- Intervene between trapped occupants and the fire, or protect rescuers

- Protect primary means of egress

- Protect **interior exposures** (other rooms or areas)

- Protect safety critical process equipment

- Protect **exterior exposures** (other buildings, piping, and cable trays)

- Operate master streams

Figure 18.2 The fire brigade leader establishes command and reports on conditions found at the incident scene.

Rapid Intervention Crew (RIC)

Fire brigade members and the incident commander continually evaluate the incident scene to determine any possible safety concerns that may develop. It is not always possible to predict when an emergency situation (trapped fire brigade members) or equipment malfunction (SCBA failure) will occur. When these situations arise, the incident commander must be prepared to immediately deploy rescue personnel or a rapid intervention crews (RIC) to assist other fire brigade members **(Figure 18.3)**. Providing personnel to rescue fire brigade members is addressed in NFPA 1500™, *Standard on Fire Department Occupational Safety and Health Program.*

Figure 18.3 Rapid intervention crews must be prepared to deploy to assist trapped or disoriented fire brigade members.

The exact number of rapid intervention crews are determined by the number of entry points into fire areas during the initial phases of the incident. Then crews are added as the incident escalates or the number of operations increases. This allows flexibility in RIC composition based on the type of incident and numbers of personnel on scene. The rapid intervention crew consists of at least two members wearing appropriate personal protective clothing, equipment, and any special rescue tools and equipment that may be necessary to effect rescue of emergency personnel.

Fire Brigade Team Leader/Incident Commander

Upon arriving at the scene, the fire brigade team leader may assume command after a formal transfer of command. If the team leader takes command, he or she coordinates the overall activities at the scene. The situation must be constantly evaluated to ensure that the resources on the scene allocated properly. The need for additional resources should be constantly considered. If additional companies are called for, the fire brigade team leader should assign them according to the action plan as they arrive. The team leader may also have to coordinate between other entities such as mutual aid units, EMS personnel, and utility crews.

Fires at Properties Protected by Fixed Fire Extinguishing Systems

Fire brigade personnel should be familiar with the fixed fire extinguishing systems in buildings protected by their fire brigade. Fire brigade operating guidelines at these occupancies must consider and prioritize the necessity of supporting these systems. These systems include the following:

- Sprinkler systems
- Standpipe systems
- Dry chemical hood systems
- Carbon dioxide systems
- Halogenated/clean agent systems
- Foam systems

Some dangers involved when dealing with fires in a fixed fire extinguishing system occupancy include:

- Oxygen depletion during activation of specialized fire protection systems
- Poor visibility
- Energized electrical equipment
- Toxic environmental exposures

Standard operating procedures used at these occupancies are most likely to be incorporated as a part of the preincident plan. This plan includes a detailed account of the construction features, contents, protection systems, and surrounding properties. The preincident plan also outlines the procedures to be used by each fire brigade team according to the conditions they find. A building map showing water supplies, protection system connections, and the placement of fire brigade teams should be an integral part of the plan and must be updated to reflect changes affecting fire brigade operations. One such SOP might address when to stop the flow of water from an activated sprinkler to prevent additional water damage and conserve property.

Structural Fire Attack

NFPA 1081 (2018): 6.2.1, 6.2.6

Extinguishing a structure fire may take a few minutes or several hours, depending on the size and scope of the structure, the fire, its location, and available resources. Your duties and assigned tasks will depend on:

- Fire brigade SOPs
- Assigned duties
- Amount of fire involvement
- Type of structure involved

This section will focus on the strategy and tactics used to suppress structure fires including:

- Making entry
- Direct, indirect, and combination fire attacks
- Fires in upper levels of structures
- Exposure protection
- Gas cooling
- Transitional attack
- Belowground structure fires

 Fireground Considerations

During fireground operations, fire brigade members should:

- Always wear appropriate PPE, including SCBA, when on the fireground.
- Maintain situational awareness.
- Maintain communication throughout the operation.
- Observe fire conditions throughout the operation.
- Utilize enough personnel to advance the line to the intended location.
- When possible and safe to do so, leave one fire brigade member at each 90-degree turn to assist in advancing hose.
- Always coordinate attack with ventilation.

Situational Awareness: Structural Fire Attack

The following conditions specific to structural fire attack should be observed and communicated:

- Location and extent of the fire
- Changes in fire behavior
- Hazards encountered including process equipment and the presence of combustible dust (flash fire or explosion)
- Locations of safe havens and alternate exits

- Changes to structural stability
- Location of any victims or occupants
- Wind direction and strength
- Fire threat to exposures

Making Entry

The IC or supervisor will decide where and from what direction to make entry for an interior fire attack. Generally, attack hoselines are placed to protect fire brigade personnel, occupants, and property.

Every member of the crew should conduct a quick entry check before entering a burning building, and maintain a high level of situational awareness while inside the structure **(Figure 18.4)**. Entry check begins well before reaching the entry point and may include visual observations and the use of a thermal imager (TI). The following are also pre-entry considerations critical to fire brigade personnel safety and effectiveness:

- Reading fire behavior indicators
- Understanding the crew's tactical assignment
- Identifying potential emergency escape routes (other doors, windows)
- Evaluating forcible entry requirements
- Identifying ground hazards (slip, trip, and fall)
- Identifying overhead hazards (wires, overhangs, and structural stability)
- Verifying that radios are receiving and transmitting on the correct channel
- Ensuring that self-contained breathing apparatus (SCBA) is on, cylinder is full, and operating properly
- Ensuring that all personal alert safety system (PASS) devices are on and operating properly
- Doing a buddy check to ensure other team members are prepared to enter the structure

Figure 18.4 Fire brigade members should check each one another's PPE and SCBA prior to entering a structure.

Interior fire attack crews advancing hoselines must carry the tools and equipment needed to open interior doors, check concealed spaces for fire extension, or to make an emergency exit. This equipment could include such tools as:

- Portable radio
- Pike pole
- Forcible entry tools
- Hand light
- Thermal imager (TI)

Before entering the building or the fire area, the fire brigade member assigned to the nozzle should **(Figure 18.5)**:

- Bleed the air from the hoseline
- Check the pattern setting
- Open the nozzle fully to ensure adequate flow
- Ensure hose is kink free

Figure 18.5 The nozzle operator should test the handline prior to entering a building.

Opening the bale slightly while waiting for water to arrive hastens this process. Without rapidly opening and closing the nozzle, fire brigade members should either test the range of stream patterns of the nozzle or set the proper nozzle pattern for the attack to verify that the nozzle is working properly.

When an interior attack is planned on a structure fire, fire brigade personnel should position themselves in a safe area near the building entrance. From this location, look for fires near the entrance. Make sure fires in the following areas are extinguished before moving forward so there are no fires in your exit route if you have to retreat:

- Fascia or soffits, boxed cornices
- Open windows and doors
- Exterior overhangs
- Entry or exit points

When the attack crew moves to the building entrance, they should stay low and out of the doorway while the door is forced open. Use a TI or apply a small amount of water spray to the surface of the door in order to check the door for heat. If the door is very hot, the water will evaporate and convert to steam. Excessive heat may be observable from the smoke, air flow, and other fire behavior indicators. Even if there are no signs of heat, you should still anticipate heat and fire beyond the door. The door should remain closed until the hoseline is charged and the crew is ready to enter.

If the fire is ventilation-controlled and the door is opened, a significant increase in heat release rate can quickly occur. Unburned fuel in the form of smoke will escape at the top of the doorway, while fresh air will enter at the bottom, providing oxygen for fire development. In this situation, cooling the hot gases overhead can reduce the risk of ignition and provide a safer operating environment.

Figure 18.6 Prior to making entry, a straight stream of water should be discharged into the heated overhead in a side-to-side motion.

You must observe the smoke movement and air flow when the door is opened: fast air movement in at the bottom and smoke moving out at the top indicates an active fire in the structure. With the hoseline in place, open the door and observe conditions. Apply water to the ceiling using a straight stream in a side-to-side motion to improve conditions in the entry **(Figure 18.6)**. When conditions improve, advance to the seat of the fire cooling the overhead as you advance.

If preflashover conditions are observed upon opening the door (high volume of turbulent smoke and a low neutral plane), apply water to the hot gas layer but do not enter the structure. If necessary, close the door, retreat, and use different tactics to improve interior conditions before attempting reentry.

Wind and open doorways create flow paths within the structure that increase fire growth and spread, and can cause fire brigade member casualties. Because wind can cause unpredictable changes to the fire, you should attack with the wind to your back. To determine the best entry point based upon wind direction, the IC should complete a thorough size-up and do a 360-degree survey, whenever possible, before deploying attack hoselines. Doors throughout the structure between the entrance and the fire should be controlled to limit air flow along the flow path. A fire brigade member may be stationed at each door to help move hose and control the door.

Fire brigade members must control the door as it is opened. Place a rope hose tool or utility strap over the doorknob or use a forcible entry to "capture" the door so it can be quickly pulled closed if needed. Once entry is made, the door should be closed enough to limit airflow into the structure without pinching or constricting the hoseline.

CAUTION: Always maintain door control to control the flow path.

A conventional guideline in the fire service for many years has been to "attack the fire from the unburned side." Major fire departments and NIST/UL have performed fire analysis and laboratory tests that largely disprove this traditional guideline (Kerber 2012 "Analysis of Changing ..." and Kerber 2012 "Analysis of One ..."). The research changed the fire service's understanding of structure-fire behavior factors including:

- Greater heat release rates of modern building construction materials and modern furnishings
- Increased effect of wind on fire expansion and development

Findings from NIST and UL Research

In research published from NIST and UL, data showed that modern furnishings and modern building construction materials present new challenges for emergency responders (Kerber 2012 "Analysis of Changing ..." and Kerber 2012 "Analysis of One ..."). Traditional tactics (mainly those tactics that predate the rise of lightweight, engineered construction) such as using ventilation alone to create tenable, interior conditions are shown in the research to be ineffective or detrimental to fire suppression.

These studies collectively came to one conclusion: The most efficient and safe way to suppress fires in modern construction and furnishings is to apply water to a fire as quickly as possible and coordinate this water application with ventilation. These studies support this conclusion with the following findings, among others:

- Lightweight construction may be in danger of structural collapse shortly after fire brigade personnel arrive.

- Modern furnishings create large volumes of fuel rich smoke very quickly.

- Fires in modern construction become ventilation-limited before reaching flashover.

- Fire brigade personnel are likely to find preflashover or prebackdraft conditions on-scene when they arrive.

- No amount of additional ventilation will bring a fire under control.

- Ventilating and applying water as close to fire as possible produced the best results in the tests in terms of emergency responder safety, suppression effectiveness, and improvements to interior conditions.

Fire suppression, as shown in these and other experiments, should be a primary consideration alongside controlling the fire's access to new oxygen. Applying water to the fire as soon as safely possible – from the interior or exterior – is the best way, often the only way, to improve conditions.

Gas Cooling

Gas cooling is a way of reducing heat release from the hot gas layer. This technique is effective when faced with a **shielded fire**; that is, a fire that cannot be seen from a doorway because it is located in a remote part of the structure or objects are shielding the fire. In these situations, water cannot be directly applied onto the burning material without entering the room and working under the hot gas layer.

The hot gas layer accumulating in the upper levels of the compartment can present problems for the members of the hoseline crew. Remember that *smoke is fuel*, and it may transition to rollover, flashover, or a smoke explosion at any time. In addition, hot smoke radiates heat to furniture and other combustibles in the compartment. This increases pyrolysis which adds more flammable fuel to the gas layer. Cooling the hot gas layer slows the transfer of heat to other combustibles and reduces the chances of the overhead gases igniting.

To cool the hot gas layer, direct short bursts or pulses of water into it. Direct the stream upward toward the gas layer and quickly and smoothly open and close the nozzle while avoiding water hammer. The length of the pulse will depend on the size of the space, varying from less than a second to much longer. The nozzle pattern may need to be adjusted based on the fire conditions in the compartment and its configuration and size. In narrow hallways, the nozzle pattern may need to be restricted. In large-volume compartments or when the upper layer temperature is extremely high, the duration of the pulses may need to be increased.

WARNING: Water directed into the hot gas layer can evaporate into steam that can cause serious burns.

Figure 18.7 Two fire brigade members making a direct attack on an interior structural fire.

The reach of the stream is also important for cooling the gas layer. If water droplets fall out of the overhead smoke layer, it means that the gases have been cooled and spraying water into the smoke is no longer necessary. If the fire burns unchecked, the gas layer will regain its heat, and the gas-cooling technique may have to be repeated. The gas-cooling technique should be repeated as necessary, while the hose team advances under the gas layer toward the fire.

Direct Attack

Depending on the nature and size of the fire, fire brigade members may use a direct, indirect, or combination method of attacking the fire. Hoseline selection and stream selection are made when the fire attack is conducted.

A direct attack on the fire using a solid or straight stream uses water most efficiently on free-burning fires (**Figure 18.7**). The water is applied directly onto the burning fuels until the fire is extinguished. Another effective technique is to direct the stream onto the ceiling and walls, which can slow or stop the pyrolysis process on these hot surfaces. Water should not be applied long enough to upset the thermal layering (sometimes called *thermal balance*) in the compartment; the steam produced will begin to condense, causing the smoke and heat to drop rapidly to the floor and move sluggishly thereafter.

 Fires in Overhead Spaces

Whenever a fire is suspected of being in the overhead space, coordinate the opening of the space with the IC. Charged hoselines should be in place to apply water to the fire in the overhead space immediately upon ventilating the space. Apply the following tactics (NIOSH 2005):

- When responding to any report of a structure fire, always check the roof before entering the building.
- When advancing into the building, check the ceiling at intervals. If there is a haze of smoke, the first fire brigade member in the door checks this area. Use a pike pole to lift ceiling tiles or remove ceiling materials.
- When entering another portion of the building, repeat the process.
- Use extreme caution because opening concealed spaces can result in backdraft conditions.
- If smoke or fire is found above the ceiling, remove all ceiling tiles or material until the source is located.
- Position personnel between the nearest exit and the concealed space to be opened.
- Be aware of the location of other fire brigade members in the area.
- Do not allow the fire to extend overhead or to block the exit path.
- When ceilings are higher than can be reached with a pike pole, use an A-frame ladder or attic ladder to gain access.

Indirect Attack

The indirect attack can be made from inside or outside a structure. The attack is made by directing the stream toward the ceiling to cool the room or by banking the stream off of the walls **(Figure 18.8)**. This method usually produces more steam than a direct attack and must be coordinated with ventilation. While an indirect attack cools the fire environment, it results in a fairly uniform temperature from floor to ceiling and fills the compartment with a mixture of smoke and steam. However, this may be the only method of attack possible until temperatures are reduced.

To make an indirect attack on the fire from the exterior, a solid or straight stream is introduced through an opening (in a doorway or window) and directed at the ceiling where the temperature is the highest. Discharge water until the desired effect (room cooling, fire control) is reached. Once the temperatures of the heated overhead and the room have been reduced, hoselines can be advanced inside and fire brigade members can make a direct attack on the body of the fire.

To make an indirect attack from an interior position, the fire brigade members advance near to the seat of the fire and use the ceiling and walls to deflect or bank the stream onto the fire. This will break up the stream(s) resulting in conversion

Figure 18.8 These fire brigade members are using an indirect attack, bouncing the stream off of the ceiling and onto the fire.

of water to steam. Because the indirect attack will create a large volume of steam, fire brigade members should be aware that this will potentially affect the thermal balance and cause the temperature to rise in the compartment. The room may need to be ventilated to allow steam to escape before it is safe to enter.

Combination Attack

A combination attack combines cooling the hot gas layer at the ceiling level using an indirect attack with a direct attack on the fuels burning near the floor level. To combine both attacks, move the nozzle from the area overhead to the floor in a Z, T, or rotational manner **(Figure 18.9)**. Excessive application of water may cause unnecessary water damage and disturbance of the thermal layering.

Transitional Attack

Transitional attack uses an exterior fire attack through a ventilation opening to help a fire transition from ventilation-limited conditions to fuel-limited conditions. Transitional attack reduces the potential for flashover and creates a more survivable interior environment. Following this transitional attack, an interior attack crew can more easily make entry and reach the seat of the fire to complete fire suppression. Transitional attack is not a new tactic. Fire research shows it to be very effective at combatting fires in buildings with modern, synthetic furnishings and structures built with lightweight construction (Kerber "Analysis of Changing ..." 2012). Through water application to the heated gases within the structure, transitional attack also reduces temperatures within the structure to increase occupant and fire brigade member survivability.

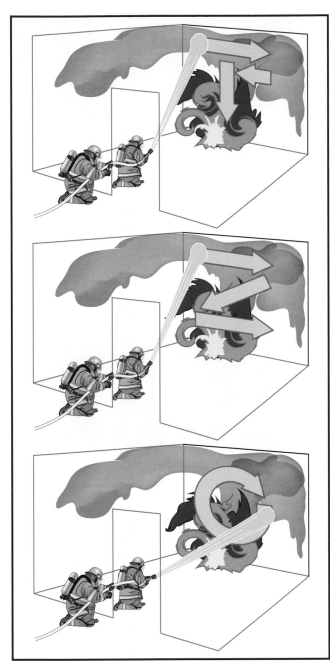

Figure 18.9 Illustrating combination attack methods.

Short applications (approximately 30 seconds) of a solid or straight stream applied in a side-to-side motion into the super-heated products of combustion overhead can inhibit flashover conditions. A straight stream may be the best nozzle pattern to use in well-involved, unventilated interior fires. Compared to a fog stream, a straight stream will not upset the thermal layering as much, will generate less steam, and will have better reach to knock down the main body of a fire.

Once the fire's location is determined and fire attack hoselines have been deployed, proceed with transitional attack if instructed to do so. A door or window should be opened near the fire and water applied into the heated gases in the structure. The transitional attack can continue to flow water until the desired change in the fire has been achieved.

After the transitional attack, the temperatures within the structure will have been reduced, increasing survivability for victims and fire brigade members. Fire brigade members will then have a safer path to the fire. If an interior crew is not ready to enter following transitional attack, conduct transitional attack again if temperatures rise in the structure or the fire grows before their entry.

If transitional attack is performed correctly, then it may be possible for interior crews to enter the structure while water is being applied from the exterior. However, if performed incorrectly, interior fire crews could be put at risk. This requires close coordination and communication. When in doubt, do not enter the structure until exterior water application ends.

Fires in Upper Levels of Structures

Multistory structures may contain standpipe systems. Depending on the local building code, age of the structure, and occupancy classification, a standpipe may be required in structures three stories or higher. In structures that lack standpipes, fire attack may include entering the building at a stairwell nearest to the fire and moving up the closest stairway to the fire location. Always check for fire extension below the fire floor before advancing up the stairs. More personnel will be required to advance the fire hose and ensure that there are no kinks or bends in the hose.

In structures equipped with standpipe systems, the location of the standpipe connection determines the fire attack method. Standpipe connections in older structures may be located in corridors or near open stairwells. Most modern structures have the standpipes located in protected stairways. If standpipe connections are located in unprotected locations, the attack hoseline is connected on the floor below the fire floor and advanced up the nearest stairwell.

If the standpipe connection is located in a protected stairway, hoselines may be connected on the fire floor. Extra sections of the attack hoseline may be flaked up the stairway to the first landing above the fire floor so it will feed more easily into the fire floor as the line is advanced. In addition to attacking the fire directly, crews should be checking floors above the fire floor for fire extension and any victims.

Fires in upper levels of structures, especially high-rise buildings, can require large numbers of personnel to conduct large-scale evacuations, carry tools and equipment to upper levels, and maintain a sustained fire attack. In many cases, fire brigade members must carry additional tools and equipment up many flights of stairs **(Figure 18.10)**. Elevators must not be used to transport fire crews to the fire floor. The fire may damage the elevator or its controls and strand the fire brigade members in the elevator car or deposit them directly onto the fire floor. Some fire brigades allow elevators to be used to transport personnel, fire fighting tools, and equipment to a staging area normally located two floors below the fire floor. This should only be accomplished if the fire brigade can control the elevator. Always follow the fire brigade SOPs when using elevators in fire buildings.

Figure 18.10 Fire brigade members may need to carry hose, tools, and other equipment up stairwells to reach fires on upper floors.

Personnel must exercise caution in the streets around the outside perimeter of tall structures that are on fire. Glass and other debris falling from far above the street can severely damage equipment, cut hoselines, and injure or kill fire brigade members. To minimize the danger, cordon off safe paths into the building. Conditions dictate the size and shape of the cordoned area.

Belowground Structure Fires

Fires originating in basements or sub-basements (also called subfloors in some locations) are some of the most difficult and dangerous structure fires. The IC must make a thorough and accurate risk/benefit analysis before committing personnel into a structure subject to a basement fire.

Basements, subfloors, and tunnels in commercial structures may have construction features similar to those in residential structures, though they may be more robust if there is a significant fuel load on the main floor. In older Type III construction, the first floor joists may be exposed wood joists or even heavy timbers. In more modern structures, the floors may be exposed or unexposed concrete panels or metal C-joists. These floors are designed to support the weight of machinery, products, and upper stories. Some structures may have multiple subfloors used for mechanical spaces or parking garages.

Exposure to fire may weaken metal floor supports. Heavy objects on the floor above the fire can increase the chances of floor collapse because the added weight accelerates the failure of supporting members. Unprotected steel girders and other supports elongate when exposed to temperatures of 1,000° F (538° C) or more and have been known to topple walls during a fire. The longer duration that steel supports are subjected to fire, the more likely they are to fail.

In some commercial structures, standpipe connections are located in stairwells leading to the subfloors. Attacking a fire in these lower levels follows the same process used for upper floors.

A risk/benefit analysis of a commercial basement is performed in the same way as one for a residential basement. Preincident surveys and inspections help determine the type of basement ceiling construction and the amount of fire it can withstand before a collapse. The location of standpipe connections, potential ventilation air flow paths, and the amount of breathing air needed to access a basement fire will influence the tactics used.

Exposure Protection

Preventing a fire from spreading to unaffected areas is a critical tactic. Unaffected areas are referred to as *exposures* and may exist inside or outside of a structure. **Exposure protection** can take a number of forms depending on the location and type of exposure and the resources available to the fire brigade.

Interior exposure protection generally involves closing doors or other openings between the fire area and the unaffected area and the proper use of tactical ventilation to ensure limited smoke movement. Controlling ventilation with positive pressure in adjoined, uninvolved areas of a structures can also pressurize those areas and isolate the fire to one area of an overall structure. Passive forms of exposure protection, such as fire-rated walls and doors, are also used to prohibit fire and smoke movement.

In order to determine which doors and openings must be kept closed and where to locate ventilation fans, take note of the following:

- Arrangement of the building
- Location of the fire
- Potential flow path(s) of fresh air to the fire
- Planned or ongoing tactical ventilation

To protect exterior exposures, either remove the endangered persons, property, or items or apply a protective spray of water or foam extinguishing agent between the fire and the exposure. Removing exposures is especially useful at fast-moving fires, ground cover fires, and flammable liquid fires. The following are actions consistent with removing the exposure:

- Evacuating persons who are in the path of the fire
- Relocating parked vehicles or railroad cars
- Using forklifts or other heavy equipment to move piled storage
- Relocating fire apparatus in the path of fast-moving fires

The most likely approach to exterior exposure protection is using water spray or foam extinguishing agents to place a protective cover on the exposure, especially if the exposure is an adjacent structure. This spray keeps the exposed surface cool, limiting the effect of radiated heat on the exposure.

High Temperature Duty Equipment Fires

Most industries have types of equipment that generate large quantities of heat as they operate. Generally, these types of equipment are categorized as either low temperature duty or high temperature duty equipment. Low temperature duty equipment operates at 500° F (260° C) or less. High temperature duty equipment operates at temperatures greater than 500° F (260° C). Examples of high temperature duty equipment include heat exchangers, heaters, reactors, industrial dryers, and other types of equipment that generate high temperatures during operation.

Industrial fire brigades must develop special tactics for dealing with fires involving these types of equipment. Discharging cold water onto cast iron devices such as heat exchangers, heaters, reactors, or such can cause metal failure, an explosive reaction, or cause the equipment shells to warp. Heaters, tanks, and steam lines may fall over or rupture when sprayed with cold water. In situations where internal fires occur in equipment designed to generate heat, such as a heater, the best course of action may be to shut off the fuel supply to the unit, prevent the fire from spreading to other materials and equipment, and allow the internal fire to burn itself out. An alternate method of fire suppression in such a system is to inject steam into the unit.

Advancing Hoselines Into and Within Structures

NFPA 1081 (2018): 6.2.1

Once hoselines have been laid out, they must be advanced into position for applying water onto the fire. Many of these procedures have already been described in Chapter 5 of this manual. Deploying hose over flat surfaces with no obstacles is very simple using most deployment methods. Advancing hoselines becomes considerably more difficult when hoses must be deployed up or down stairways, from standpipes, up ladders, and/or deep into buildings. Hoselines can be deployed more easily before charging because water adds weight and pressure that makes the hose difficult to maneuver. However, it is often unsafe to enter burning buildings with uncharged hoselines; therefore, a fire brigade member must know how to handle uncharged and charged lines **(Figure 18.11)**. You must also know how to add more hose to extend a hoseline.

Figure 18.11 One facility fire brigade member can advance an uncharged hoseline up a stairway, but it may take two or more personnel to advance a charged hoseline.

Advancing Hose into a Structure

The working line drag is one of the quickest and easiest ways to advance a charged hoseline at ground level. Before advancing hose into a structure, you must be alert for potential dangers such as backdraft, flashover, and structural collapse. The uncharged attack hoseline is advanced to the designated point of entry. A fire brigade member may need to remain at each corner or doorway to help guide the hoseline into the structure. Observe the following general safety guidelines when advancing a hoseline into a burning structure:

- Check for and remove kinks and bends from the hoseline as it is advanced.
- Open the nozzle fully, which bleeds air from the hose, and check for adequate water flow.
- Select the desired pattern.
- Position the nozzle operator and all hose team members on the same side of the hoseline.
- Check for heat using a TI. If you don't have a TI, you can spray a small amount of water at the top of the door and see if steam is produced.

   NOTE: It is a good safety practice to assume that there is heat behind any door.

- Stay low and avoid being in the path of ventilation openings such as doorways or windows.
- Keep doors closed until ready to enter.
- Control openings to limit flow path effects.
- Chock self-closing doors to prevent the door from closing and pinching the hoseline.

Advancing Hose Vertically

Advancing hose up and down stairways can be very difficult. When conditions allow, the hoseline should be advanced uncharged. The shoulder carry works well for stairway advancement because the hose is carried instead of dragged and is deployed as needed. The minuteman load and carry is also excellent for use on stairways.

Figure 18.12 Fire hose should be laid against the outside wall while advancing it up a stairway.

Advancing Hose Up and Down Stairways

When advancing hose up a stairway, lay the uncharged hose against the outside wall to keep the stairs as clear as possible and avoid sharp bends and kinks in the hose **(Figure 18.12)**. Advancing an uncharged hoseline down a flight of stairs is much easier than advancing a charged hose down the stairs. However, advancing an uncharged line down stairs is recommended only when the fire is very minor or not present.

> **WARNING:** While deploying an uncharged line is easier, an uncharged line offers no protection if fire conditions worsen.

When advancing a charged hoseline up a stairway, excess hose should be deployed on the stairs toward the floor above the fire floor. The weight of the water and gravity will make extending the excess hoseline onto the fire floor easier. If possible, position a fire brigade member at every turn or point of resistance to aid in deployment of the charged hoseline and at doorways to control ventilation flow paths.

Advancing a charged hoseline down a stairway can be almost as difficult as advancing one up stairs. Because deploying excess hose down the stairway would obstruct the stairs, excess hose should be stretched outside the stairway, such as in a hallway or room adjacent to the stairway, and fire brigade members positioned on the stairs to feed the hose down to the nozzle team. Fire brigade members must also be positioned at corners and pinch points. You must also have enough hose to reach the fire including the distance in the stairs, around corners, and onto the fire floor.

Standpipe Operations

While preconnected hoselines may be able to access fires on lower floors, fires beyond the reach of these lines require that hose be carried to the standpipe outlet closest to the fire. One approach is to have preassembled hose rolls, bundles, or packs on the apparatus ready to carry upstairs and connect to the

Figure 18.13 A fire brigade member preparing to connect a high-rise pack to a standpipe.

building's standpipe system. How these high-rise packs are constructed is a matter of local preference, but the most common are hose bundles that are easily carried on the shoulder or in specially designed hose packs complete with nozzles, fittings, and tools **(Figure 18.13)**.

NOTE: Fire brigade personnel should be aware of the class or classes of standpipes within their facility or facilities. Refer to Chapter 6, Fire Protection, Detection, and Suppression Systems, for further information.

Hose must be carried to the fire floor over an aerial ladder or up an interior stairway. Regardless of how the hose is brought up, fire crews normally stop one floor below the fire floor and connect the attack hoselines to the standpipe. If the standpipe connection is in an enclosed **smoke tower** (also known as smokeproof enclosure or smokeproof stairway), it is acceptable to connect on the fire floor. The standpipe connection is usually in or near the stairway. You can get a general idea of the fire floor layout when you observe the floor below.

Be alert for pressure-regulating devices and follow your SOPs for removal or connection. If 1½-, 1¾-, or 2-inch (38, 45, or 50 mm) hose is used, placing a gated wye on the standpipe outlet will permit the attachment of a second attack hose if needed. A 2½-inch (65 mm) attack line may be used depending on the size and nature of the fire. Ensure the standpipe is flushed out and operating correctly prior to connecting hose lines. While the standpipe connection is being completed, any extra hose should be deployed up the stairs toward the floor above the fire. When two lines are advanced from the same standpipe connection, deploy one down the lower set of stairs and the other up the stairway to lessen the chances of the two hoselines becoming entangled. When fire extinguishment is complete, the water in the hoselines should be drained down a floor drain, out a window, or down a stairway to prevent unnecessary water damage.

When standpipes are not available but stairways are accessible, one of the safest ways to get hose to an upper story is to carry it up the stairs in a bundle and lower the female end over a balcony railing or out a window to connect to a water source. Another method is to hoist the hose and attached nozzle up to a window or landing using a rope.

Improvising a Standpipe

Most building codes mandate the installation of standpipes in structures three stories and higher. However, older buildings and those less than three stories may not have standpipes, or standpipe connections may be obstructed or out of service as a result of:

- Construction
- Sabotage

- Demolition
- Natural disasters like earthquakes

One way to supply water to a building without a standpipe system is to create an improvised standpipe. There are two methods for improvising standpipes: the interior stairway stretch and the outside stretch.

CAUTION: When fire brigade members must improvise a standpipe system, there will be a delay in applying water to the fire. This delay must be considered in planning the overall fire fighting strategy.

The interior stairway stretch is a labor-intensive task used in stairways that have an open shaft or stairwell in the center. Fire brigade members must be able to determine if a pressurized hose will fit within the space between the handrail openings. To improvise the standpipe, an uncharged hoseline is suspended in the middle of the stairs rather than laying it on the stairs and around each corner. Hose rolls or bundles can be carried up the stairs, secured to a hand rail and the end lowered to the point where another section is attached to it. Secure the hose to the hand rails for support at appropriate intervals to reduce the tendency of water weight to pull the hose back down once the hose is charged **(Figure 18.14)**.

An outside stretch can be used for lower floors of high-rise buildings. Supply hose can be hoisted up the exterior of the building to the desired floor using a rope. Because the weight of the water in the charged line can cause the hose to fall back down the building, some of the hoseline can be extended into windows and secured to available anchor points inside the building at an interval of approximately every three stories **(Figure 18.15)**.

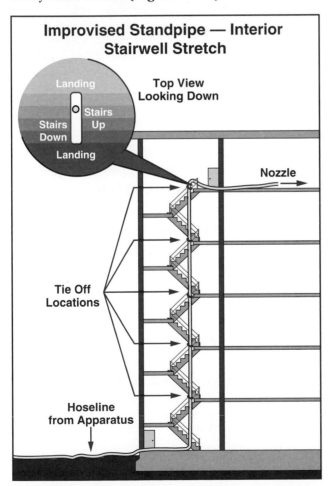

Figure 18.14 Illustrating how to improvise a standpipe by stretching a hoseline up the center of an interior stairwell.

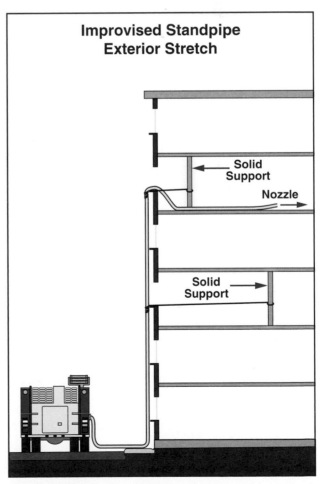

Figure 18.15 Illustrating how to improvise a standpipe by stretching a hoseline up the side of a building.

Advancing Hose Up a Ladder

If standpipes are not available, stairways are not accessible, or there is no other viable option, it may be necessary to advance the hose up a fire service ground ladder or aerial device. Advancing fire hose up a ladder is easier and safer with an uncharged line. In most cases, the fire brigade member heeling the ground ladder can help feed the hose to those on the ladder **(Figure 18.16)**. If the hose is already charged with water, it may help to drain the hose before advancing it up the ladder.

To avoid overloading the ladder, only one person is permitted on each section of the ladder. Rope hose tools or utility straps can be used for this advancement. The hose can be charged once it has reached the point from which the fire attack will be made.

> **WARNING:** Do not exceed the rated weight capacity of the ladder. If the hose cannot be passed up the ladder without exceeding the load limit, it should be hoisted up.

Sometimes, fire brigade members must operate a hoseline from a ground ladder or supported aerial ladder (the tip of the aerial ladder must be in contact with the windowsill). When doing so, the fire brigade member should use a leglock or ladder belt to prevent a fall.

Figure 18.16 The fire brigade member footing the ladder can assist the personnel on the ladder by feeding hose up towards them.

Aerial platforms can be used as portable standpipes for advancing a hoseline onto a floor. A high-rise pack is placed on the platform along with the attack line crew. When the platform arrives at the desired floor and the window is opened, the hose is attached to the discharge outlet on the platform. The crew advances the hoseline onto the floor and the hose is charged.

NOTE: The use of an aerial platform as a portable standpipe limits the movement or use of the aerial platform for other purposes such as emergency rescue.

Chapter Review

1. What are the priorities that the initial fire brigade response team should cover?

2. What conditions should be observed while maintaining situational awareness during structural fire attack?

3. What pre-entry considerations are critical to fire brigade personnel safety and effectiveness?

4. When is gas cooling effective?

5. Name each method for attacking fire and describe the conditions under which each of these are most useful.

6. What conditions may determine how a fire is attacked in the upper levels of structures?

7. What construction features may present hazards in belowground structure fires?

8. What factors determine which doors and openings must be kept closed to protect interior exposures?

9. What are some special considerations when extinguishing high temperature duty equipment fires?

10. What are safety guidelines for advancing a hoseline into a burning structure?

Discussion Questions

1. What measures can be taken to protect or remove exposures in your facilities?

2. Is there high temperature duty equipment in your facility? If so, what special considerations should be taken if there is a fire?

Chapter 18 End Notes

Kerber, Stephen. 2012. "Analysis of Changing Residential Fire Dynamics and Its Implications on Firefighter Operational Timeframes," Underwrtiers' Laboratories. Accessed Online.

Kerber, Stephen. 2012. "Analysis of One and Two-Story Single Family Home Fire Dynamics and the Impact of Firefighter Horizontal Ventilation," Underwriters' Laboratories. Accessed Online.

Kerber, Stephen, Daniel Madrzykowski, James Dalton, and Bob Backstrom. 2012. "Improving Fire Safety by Understanding the Fire Performance of Engineered Floor Systems and Providing the Fire Service with Information for Tactical Decision Making," Underwriters' Laboratories. Accessed Online.

National Institute for Occupational Safety and Health (NIOSH). 2005. *"Preventing Injuries and Deaths of Fire Fighters Due to Truss System Failures,"* NIOSH Publication No. 2005-132. Accessed Online.

Key Terms

Exposure Protection — Covering any object in the immediate vicinity of the fire with water or foam.

Exterior Exposure — Building or other combustible object located close to the fire building that is in danger of becoming involved due to heat transfer from the fire building.

Gas Cooling — Directing water into the hot gas layer to reduce the heat release rate in a compartment.

Interior Exposure — Areas of a fire building that are not involved in fire but that are connected to the fire area in such a manner that may facilitate fire spread through any available openings.

Shielded Fire — Fire that is located in a remote part of the structure or hidden from view by objects in the compartment.

Smoke Tower — Fully enclosed escape stairway that exits directly onto a public way; these enclosures are either mechanically pressurized or they require the user to exit the building onto an outside balcony before entering the stairway. *Also known as* Smokeproof Enclosure *or* Smokeproof Stairway.

Transitional Attack — Fire attack from the exterior through a ventilation opening. The attack cools the fire compartment and helps transition the fire from ventilation-limited conditions to fuel-limited conditions.

Skill Sheet List

The following skill sheets should be used to evaluate the skills described in this chapter:

NOTE: Students should wear the PPE appropriate to the NFPA 1081 level (Incipient, Advanced Exterior, Interior Structural, etc...) being evaluated.

Interior Structural Facility Fire Brigade Member Only

Chapter Contents

JPRs addressed in this chapter

This chapter provides information that addresses the following job performance requirements of NFPA 1081, *Standard for Facility Fire Brigade Member Professional Qualifications (2018)*.

6.2.3

Learning Objectives

1. Review the concepts of fire dynamics. [6.2.3]

2. Explain the different reasons for tactical ventilation. [6.2.3]

3. Describe the safety considerations that should be followed when ventilating. [6.2.3]

4. Identify the different types of ventilation tools and equipment. [6.2.3]

5. Describe the different methods of horizontal ventilation. [6.2.3]

6. Describe the processes of vertical ventilation. [6.2.3]

7. Describe the methods for ventilating specific compartments and structures. [6.2.3]

8. Explain the effects of building ventilation systems can have in fire situations. [6.2.3]

Chapter 19
Tactical Ventilation

While the term *ventilation* is traditionally used in the fire service, the activity is more accurately referred to as tactical ventilation. Tactical ventilation is the planned and systematic removal of heated air, smoke, gases, or other airborne contaminants from a structure, replacing them with cooler and/or fresher air to meet the incident priorities of life safety, incident stabilization, and property conservation. Ventilation must be coordinated with fire suppression operations to prevent unwanted consequences for crews or victims.

Many of the specific ventilation techniques discussed in this chapter are used to control and move air and products of combustion in residential and small- to mid-size structures. While the basic principles of flow path control during fire attack still apply to larger structures, site-specific ventilation strategies must be developed for specialized buildings commonly protected by facility fire brigades.

In some facility areas, pre-engineered systems exist to maintain control of air quality, air flow, and temperature. These systems are designed specifically to control hazards within buildings and process areas, and they may or may not continue to operate during an incident. Techniques to control hazards during an incident should be identified in preincident planning, and must be specifically designed based on engineering studies that address expected air flow and thermodynamic requirements.

Ventilation may occur before, during, or after fire suppression operations start. Some examples of unplanned ventilation include failure of windows, doors, and structural members as a result of heat/fire exposure. Unplanned ventilation can significantly influence fire behavior in ventilation-limited fires.

Correctly implemented, tactical ventilation improves conditions during an incident. However, if ventilation is improperly applied, the results can harm occupants, fire brigade members, and the structure.

The concepts presented in this chapter are based on and expanded from the information found in Chapter 3, Fire Dynamics, including fire behavior in compartments, stages of fire development, and the reaction of building construction to fire.

Review Section: Fire Dynamics
NFPA 1081 (2018): 6.2.3

Interior structural fire brigade members need to have a scientific understanding of fire dynamics. The fire triangle and fire tetrahedron models are used to explain the elements of fire and how fires can be extinguished. The fire triangle consists of three elements necessary for combustion to occur: fuel, oxygen, and heat. The fire tetrahedron model includes the chemical chain reaction to explain flaming or gas-phase combustion. Remove any one of these elements and the fire will be extinguished.

As a fuel burns, its chemical composition changes, creating new substances called the products of combustion. Common products of combustion include heat, smoke, ash, water vapor, carbon monoxide (CO), carbon dioxide (CO_2), and hydrogen cyanide (HCN).

For a fire to start and continue to burn, heat must be transferred from one point or object to another. Heat transfers from warmer objects to cooler objects. Heat transfers occurs by three mechanisms: conduction, convection, and radiation. Conduction is the transfer of heat through and between solids. Convection is the transfer of thermal energy by the circulation or movement of a fluid (liquid or gas). Radiation is the transmission of energy as electromagnetic waves, such as light waves, radio waves, or X-rays, without an intervening medium.

Oxygen in the air is the primary oxidizing agent in most fires. Normally, air consists of about 21 percent oxygen. At normal ambient temperatures (68°F [20°C]), materials can ignite and burn in oxygen concentrations as low as 15 percent. When oxygen concentration is limited, the flaming combustion will diminish, causing combustion to continue in the nonflaming mode. Nonflaming or smoldering combustion can continue in extremely low oxygen concentrations when the surrounding environment's temperature is relatively low. However, at high ambient temperatures, flaming combustion may continue in considerably lower oxygen concentrations.

When the oxygen concentration is higher than normal, materials exhibit different burning characteristics. Materials that burn in normal oxygen levels will burn more intensely and may ignite more readily in oxygen-enriched atmospheres. Some petroleum-based materials will autoignite in oxygen-enriched atmospheres.

Oxygen is also important to life. As the oxygen in a structure is consumed by fire, the amount of oxygen available to support life diminishes. Between 15 percent to 19 percent concentrations, coordination is impaired. Between 10 percent to 12 percent concentrations, an exposed human experiences dizziness, headache, and fatigue. Around 8 percent to 10 percent concentrations, mental failure, nausea, vomiting, and unconsciousness occur. Exposures below 8 percent can result in death in as soon as 8 minutes.

The four stages of fire development can be generally defined as follows:

- **Incipient stage** — When the three elements of the fire triangle come together and the combustion process begins.

- **Growth stage** — More of the initial fuel package becomes involved and the production of heat and smoke increases. If there are other fuels close to the initial fuel package, radiant heat from the fire may begin to pyrolize nearby fuels which could spread the fire to new fuel packages.

- **Fully Developed stage** — Occurs when all combustible materials in the compartment are burning at their peak heat release rate based on the available oxygen.

- **Decay stage** — As the fire consumes the available fuel or oxygen and the heat release rate begins to decline, the fire enters the decay stage.

Thermal layering is the tendency of gases to form into layers according to temperature, gas density, and pressure. Provided that there is no mechanical mixing from a fan or a hose stream, the hottest gases will form the highest layer, while the cooler gases will form the lower layers. Changes in ventilation and flow path can significantly alter thermal layering. The flow path is defined as the space between the air intake and the exhaust outlet. Multiple openings (intakes and exhausts) create multiple flow paths.

As the mass and energy of the hot gas layer increases, so does the pressure. Higher pressure causes the hot gas layer to spread downward within the compartment and laterally through any openings such as doors or windows. If there are no openings for lateral movement, the higher pressure gases have no lateral path to follow to an area of lower pressure. As a result, the hot gases will begin to fill the compartment starting at the ceiling and filling down.

The interface between the hot gas layers and cooler layer of air is commonly referred to as the neutral plane because the net pressure is zero, or neutral, where the layers meet. The neutral plane exists at openings where hot gases exit and cooler air enters the compartment. At these openings, hot gases at higher than ambient pressure exit through the top of the opening above the neutral plane. Lower pressure air from outside the compartment entrains into the opening below the neutral plane.

Backdraft occurs in a space containing a high concentration of heated flammable gases that lack sufficient oxygen for flaming combustion. When potential backdraft conditions exist in a compartment, the introduction of a new source of oxygen will return the fire to a fully involved state rapidly (often explosively). A backdraft can occur with the creation of a horizontal or vertical opening. Backdraft indicators include:

- **Building indicators** — Interior configuration, fuel load, thermal properties, amount of trapped fuel gases, and a lack of ventilation
- **Smoke indicators** — Pulsing smoke movement around small openings in the building; smoke-stained windows
- **Air flow indicators** — High velocity air intake
- **Heat indicators** — High heat, crackling or breaking sounds
- **Flame indicators** — Little or no visible flame

Reasons for Tactical Ventilation

NFPA 1081 (2018): 6.2.3

Tactical ventilation during fire attack is a tool to help fire brigade members control a fire. Tactical ventilation is also used during overhaul and loss control to evacuate smoke from structures after the fire has been extinguished.

Tactical ventilation activities, whether creating openings in the structure or closing/covering openings, should be coordinated with an emphasis on controlling oxygen availability to a fire. As described in Chapter 3, Fire Dynamics, whenever a fire has sufficient access to oxygen and fuel, it will grow and spread.

Ventilation also allows fire brigade members to control where hot gases and smoke exhaust from a structure **(Figure 19.1)**. Controlling exhaust openings may improve visibility inside the structure so that interior crews can work more effectively. Exhaust openings can also be used during overhaul to facilitate removal of smoke or toxic gases after fire extinguishment.

Figure 19.1 Smoke and heat are removed from a structure through roof ventilation.

Controlling Oxygen Availability

Fires contained within a compartment (room) or structure consume available fuel and oxygen as they burn. As the fuel and the oxygen burn, they undergo a chemical reaction that produces heated toxic gases, unburned hydrocarbons, and carbon particles (soot). As the oxygen inside the room or structure gets consumed, the fire burns less efficiently, and the amount of unburned fuel in the combustion products increases. If the compartment or structure does not ventilate before consuming most of the available oxygen, the fire enters a state of ventilation-limited decay. These conditions indicate a compartment fire that is waiting for more oxygen to re-enter the growth stage, and may lead to rapid fire development. Any ventilation of such an environment will add the oxygen that the fire needs. Without following ventilation immediately with exterior or interior fire attack to cool the gases and surfaces in the fire room, the added oxygen will allow the fire to grow. The greater the length of time between ventilation and the application of water, the greater the fire's growth.

Flow Path Control

Controlling available flow paths can be as simple as keeping an exterior door closed until a charged line is in place or as complex as performing vertical ventilation. However, even with coordinated tactical ventilation, there will be an increase in the combustion rate when oxygen is made available to a ventilation-limited fire, until water is applied to cool the fire gases. To control the flow path, fire brigade members assigned to ventilation operations can be positioned at doors that the fire fighting crew passes through along their entry path. Normally, this is the entry door in building fires. The person or personnel assigned to control doors would be tasked to close any doors as much as the hoselines in use will allow. Additionally, these personnel can help pull additional hoseline deeper into the structure or shift it around, if necessary **(Figure 19.2)**.

Figure 19.2 A fire brigade member stationed at a door can control the flow path into the structure and assist with hose management.

Ventilation and fire fighting operations must be coordinated to maximize effectiveness. Personnel should receive and follow specific instructions of when and where to ventilate. Creating additional unplanned openings disrupts the ventilation strategy, which risks losing control of the fire. As heat and smoke get exhausted, the fire fighting crew can move closer to the seat of the fire for extinguishment.

> **CAUTION:** Creating additional unplanned openings or freelancing disrupts the ventilation strategy, which in turn loses control of the fire.

An effective way of controlling ventilation is to cover openings rather than creating more openings. Before interior attack, closing exterior doors and windows or using smoke control devices and/or wind control devices to cover ventilated windows will reduce the oxygen available to the fire. *Closing* any openings hinders fire growth until an attack can be planned and established. In general, closing openings helps control the fire unless closing those openings goes against an established incident strategy.

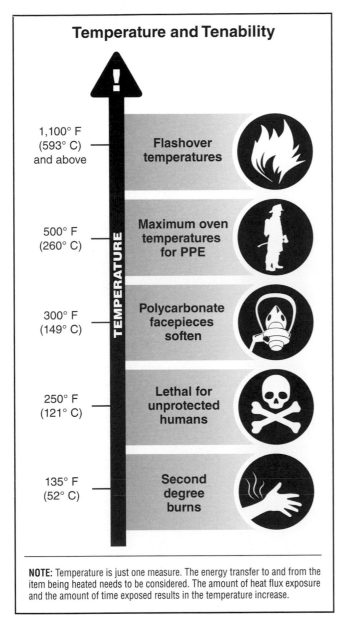

Temperature and Tenability

TEMPERATURE

1,100° F (593° C) and above — **Flashover temperatures**

500° F (260° C) — **Maximum oven temperatures for PPE**

300° F (149° C) — **Polycarbonate facepieces soften**

250° F (121° C) — **Lethal for unprotected humans**

135° F (52° C) — **Second degree burns**

NOTE: Temperature is just one measure. The energy transfer to and from the item being heated needs to be considered. The amount of heat flux exposure and the amount of time exposed results in the temperature increase.

Figure 19.3 As the temperature in a structure on fire increases, the tenability for victims and fire brigade members within the structure decreases.

Rapid Fire Development Potential

A growing fire can generate temperatures in excess of structural PPE limits in a few minutes. If the existing ventilation can support fire growth, flashover may occur less than five minutes after ignition. These environments are untenable for occupants and fire brigade members in full PPE **(Figure 19.3)**.

When fresh air (oxygen) from ventilation is introduced into the room, the heated gases can quickly reignite, causing rapid fire development. Fire brigade members and occupants cannot survive rapid fire development conditions. To prevent rapid fire development from occurring, use the appropriate water stream application techniques to cool the heated gases, and know how and when to properly release those gases with appropriate ventilation methods and procedures.

Ventilation without coordination could lead to rapid fire development. No amount of additional ventilation at this stage will cause the fire to become fuel-limited or prevent rapid fire development. The longer the structure or compartment is allowed to ventilate without water being applied, the sooner rapid fire development occurs.

Even if ventilation initially appears to be effectively cooling the interior and removing smoke and toxic gases, the period of effectiveness is likely to be short-lived. The additional oxygen from ventilation — whether the opening is the first or one of several — allows the fire to grow toward flashover. To prevent flashover, ventilation needs to be coordinated with fire attack almost immediately, at the very least within the short amount of time when ventilation alone improves conditions. Proper ventilation alone decreases the rate of fire spread and increases visibility for a very short period. Ventilation and water application are both necessary to bring a fire under control.

Once water has been applied, ventilation can improve the conditions fire brigade members need for successful interior operations. The air entrained through ventilation openings should improve conditions, rather than contribute to fire growth, allowing fire brigade members to enter the structure to perform search and rescue and fire suppression operations. The potential for flashover while fire brigade

Figure 19.4 A fire attack team preparing to enter a structure after receiving the go-ahead from the ventilation team.

Figure 19.5 Smoke and heated gases rising through a ventilation hole in the roof of this structure.

members operate inside is also reduced, which makes them safer. If ventilation is intended to allow fire brigade members to enter for interior fire attack, then the attack team must be ready to enter with charged handlines in place before tactical ventilation begins **(Figure 19.4)**.

Removing Hot Gases and Smoke

Ventilation takes advantage of the buoyancy of fire gases, allowing them to escape from the structure. During ventilation operations, gases flow from the interior to the exterior because the interior gases, heated by the fire, have become less dense **(Figure 19.5)**. Gases less dense than air are buoyant, tend to rise, and move toward areas of lower pressure. As the less dense, higher pressure, hot gases escape, they create a lower pressure that draws in cooler ambient air from down low.

The primary mode of heat transfer from one compartment to another in a structure fire is convection **(Figure 19.6)**. Convection occurs because the natural buoyancy of smoke moves toxic gases and heat from one room to another. If not coordinated, the same ventilation operation

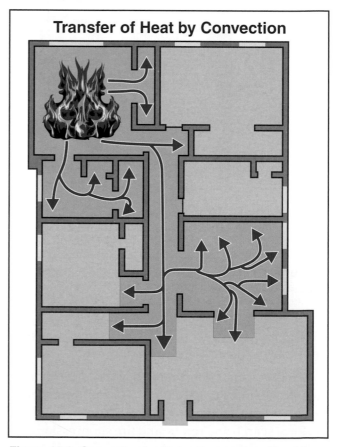

Figure 19.6 Convection facilitates the transfer of heat from one compartment to another.

that changes the flow path within the structure can move additional heat and smoke to areas not originally involved in the fire.

Because fires inside structures are almost always ventilation-limited, tactical ventilation may provide the fire with the necessary oxygen to grow, rather than creating a more tenable environment for fire brigade members. Tactical ventilation can be an effective strategy only if coordinated with an immediate fire attack.

Studies have shown that ventilation openings remove less heat and smoke than previously thought and alter the flow path within the structure. This alteration of the flow path introduces more air into the structure (Zevotek and Kerber 2016). This air carries sufficient oxygen to alter the fire's natural development and intensify its growth.

Even though ventilation openings introduce air, they are necessary in many incidents to allow smoke, heat, and toxic gases to escape. Controlling the process is key and requires water application in addition to ventilation. Water application to the hot gas layers combined with tactical ventilation can minimize the effect of the new air on fire growth. Water application to the fire compartment begins to shift fire development from ventilation-limited to fuel-limited conditions. Ventilation alone will not achieve this transition.

Tactical ventilation implemented during or after suppression can create an interior environment or egress path with the following, more tenable conditions:

- Increased oxygen concentration
- Reduced concentration of toxic products of combustion
- Reduced temperature levels
- Increased visibility to aid in fire fighting operations and primary search operations

CAUTION: Once a structure fire has become ventilation-limited, additional ventilation will cause fire growth and spread.

Applications for Life Safety

As the highest incident priority, life safety applies to occupants who may be trapped in the structure and the fire brigade members who must enter it to rescue them. Tactical, coordinated ventilation can be used to alter the fire flow path away from trapped occupants. Although this tactic allows oxygen into the structure, it may be necessary to create tenable egress areas for fire brigade members to rescue victims or trapped occupants **(Figure 19.7)**.

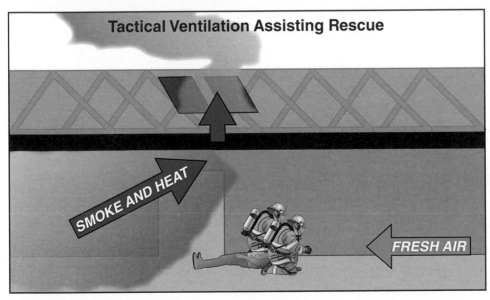

Tactical Ventilation Assisting Rescue

SMOKE AND HEAT

FRESH AIR

Figure 19.7 Tactical ventilation can create tenable egress areas to assist rescue operations.

Applications for Interior Operations: Interior Fire Attack and Search and Rescue

The removal of smoke and gases should create areas where fire brigade members can move and work inside a structure. As heat and smoke are exhausted, the fire fighting crew can then move closer to the seat of the fire for extinguishment. In addition, the ventilation should be organized to prevent the fire from spreading toward searching fire brigade members. As a tactic for search and rescue, tactical ventilation should be delayed until lines are charged and crews are ready. Keep the fire ventilation-limited as long as possible to prevent fire spread.

In terms of search and rescue, all rescue teams (entry team, exterior attack teams if needed, ventilation teams, door control monitors) should be ready to go before initiating ventilation. Ensuring that everyone's actions are coordinated helps to control the amount of oxygen allowed into the structure. Search crews should communicate their observations to the IC and exterior crews who are coordinating ventilation so that exterior fire brigade members can adjust activities as needed. The goal is to complete a rescue without increasing the hazard to trapped victims, harming entry fire brigade members, spreading the fire to new compartments, or allowing the fire to enter rapid fire development.

Clearing Smoke During Overhaul

Once the fire is suppressed, ventilation can be established to accelerate the clearing of smoke and hot gases within the structure. Clearing the structure of smoke should make the environment more tenable for victims and make it easier to find any survivors.

Ventilation can be performed as part of overhaul and property conservation. Removing smoke from buildings after fire extinguishment minimizes smoke damage to the structure **(Figure 19.8)**. Response to a fire should minimize property damage to the greatest extent possible.

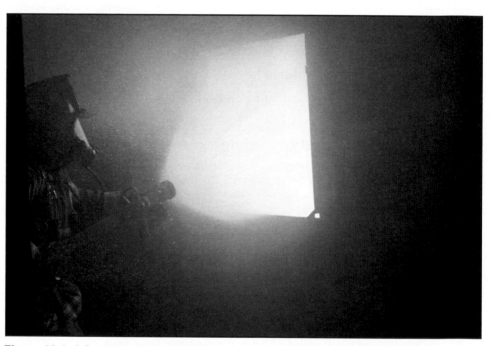

Figure 19.8 A fire brigade member using hydraulic ventilation to clear a room of smoke.

Safety Considerations When Ventilating

NFPA 1081 (2018): 6.2.3

Successful tactical ventilation conducted in conjunction with fire attack depends on:

- Careful planning
- Communication of scene observations to the IC
- Systematic application of procedures for removing the contaminants
- Coordination with other fireground activities

- Recognition that all openings (doors, windows, other openings) are capable of providing ventilation
- Recognition of the advantages and disadvantages of environmental conditions (wind, temperature) at the scene.

Situational Awareness: Tactical Ventilation

The IC should have access to and be using (if available) pre-fire plans to help aid in their ventilation plan. Communicating situational observations when assigned a tactical ventilation task is essential for personnel safety. Also, the following conditions specific to tactical ventilation should be communicated to crew members and/or a supervisor:

- Location and extent of the fire
- Changes to fire behavior, spread, and growth, including signs of rapid fire development
- Effect that ventilation at a location will have on the fire and/or exposures
- Effectiveness of planned ventilation: desired flow and exhaust efficiency
- Locations where smoke is escaping the structure (under eaves, vented windows, around doors)
- Type of building construction
- Building's structural integrity
- Condition of the building contents
- Indications of potential structural collapse, especially roofs and floors
- Locations of overhead power lines, solar panels, and guide wires
- Locations of two escape locations for roof crews
- Changes to the roof or floor's structural integrity
- Coordination of fireground operations with ventilation
- Wind direction and strength

Wind Conditions

Any opening in a building, whether part of the building design or created by the fire, allows the surrounding atmosphere to affect what is happening inside the building. Whenever possible, fire brigade members should use the wind to their advantage (work with the wind) during ventilation. Winds as slow as 10 mph (15 kph) can affect structure fires, potentially making them wind-driven. If winds are at these speeds or faster, fire brigade members are safest working with the wind at their backs. See Chapter 3, Fire Dynamics, for more information about the effects of wind and wind-driven fires.

Exposures

When beginning tactical ventilation operations, fire brigade members must consider internal and external **exposures**. Internal exposures include the building occupants, contents, and any uninvolved rooms or portions of the building. In some industrial settings, internal exposures may include areas of safety related concerns such as an operator's routes to safety shut down a process or safety critical equipment. When ventilation does not release heat and smoke directly above the fire, some routing of the smoke becomes necessary. The routes the smoke and heated fire gases would naturally travel to exit may be the same routes needed for evacuation and response.

When ventilation exhaust points are located below the highest point of the building, products of combustion may ignite portions of the building above the exhaust point. For example, heat and fire gases may be drawn into open windows or attic vents, and they may also ignite the eaves of the building or adjacent structures.

Evaluate the surroundings of a potential ventilation opening. Radiation and/or direct flame contact can affect external exposures, including structures located adjacent to the fire building. Window-mounted air conditioning units or heating, ventilation, and air conditioning (HVAC) intake vents may draw smoke into adjacent buildings. Nearby structures and vegetation can be ignited if convection carries hot fire brands or embers aloft. Fire may be drawn into exterior windows or openings of the adjacent exposures **(Figure 19.9)**.

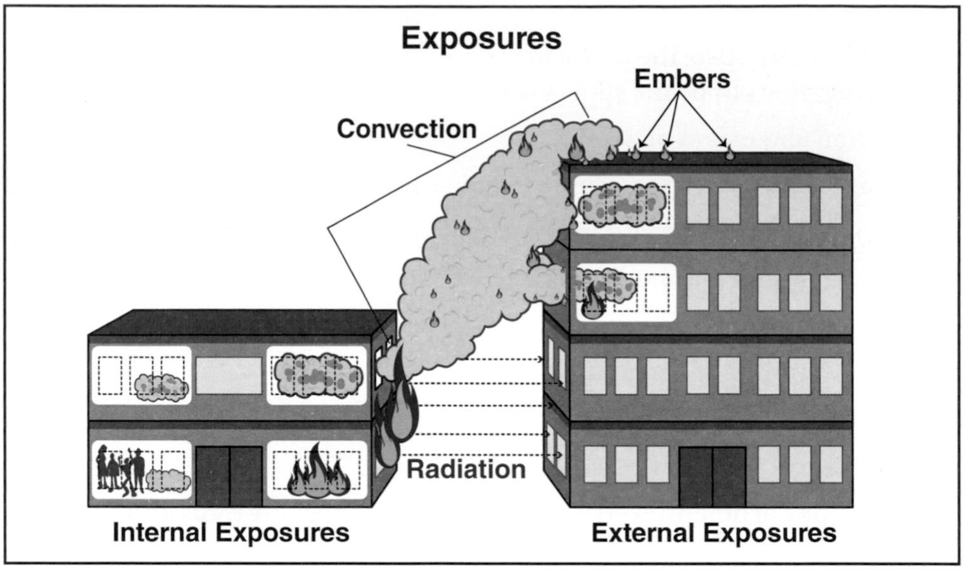

Figure 19.9 Radiation, convection, and direct contact with embers can transfer heat from the structure on the left to the one on the right.

Ventilation Location

Before selecting a place to ventilate, fire brigade members should gather as much information as possible about the fire, the building, and the occupancy. As a fire brigade member, you will be told where to ventilate. Conditions can change between the time that orders are given and actions are taken. It is each fire brigade member's responsibility to communicate observations and concerns while performing ventilation.

Structural Integrity

Prior knowledge of the roof's construction and the building's layout can help fire brigade members gauge roof integrity. This knowledge, gained through preincident planning, can identify structural elements that may contribute to roof failure during a fire. Examples of such structural elements can include:

- Lightweight roof trusses
- Open floor plans under wide expanses with limited truss supports
- Prior structural damage to the roof

NOTE: Some model building codes require placarding or signage on structures to indicate the presence of lightweight construction, most notably floor and roof systems.

If the roof is suspected or known to be unstable, the IC should not place personnel on or under it. If roof ventilation is ordered, the ventilation team should check the roof before stepping onto it and continue to check the roof ahead of their progress as they cross it. If fire has vented through the roof or has been burning under the roof prior to fire brigade arrival, roof ventilation should not be considered until after the fire has been suppressed and the roof structure can be evaluated. Indications of possible roof collapse include **(Figure 19.10)**:

- Melting asphalt
- Smoke coming from the roof
- Fire coming from the roof

Figure 19.10 The fire and smoke venting from this roof are strong indicators of possible roof collapse. *Courtesy of Ron Jeffers, Union City, NJ.*

- Building systems such as HVAC units sagging or leaning
- Spongy roof (a normally solid roof that yields and then springs back when walked upon)
- Burn time, if known

The ventilation team should maintain communication with other crews at the scene to receive updates on the progress of the fire and observed conditions. If the roof begins to lose integrity during roof ventilation operations, personnel should evacuate the roof and notify command.

Ventilation Tools and Equipment

NFPA 1081 (2018): 6.2.3

Fire brigade members use a variety of tools and equipment to perform ventilation and/or gain access to ventilation locations. Other tools are used to create the openings where fire gases and smoke will exit the structure. Additional tools and equipment assist in moving fire gases and smoke from a structure more efficiently.

Ground and roof ladders help fire brigade members access locations to be used for ventilation. The use of ground and roof ladders was covered in Chapter 13, Ground Ladders. Thermal imagers serve as useful tools for monitoring the impact of ventilation or identifying possible ventilation locations. See Chapter 15, Search and Rescue and Rapid Intervention Crew (RIC) Operations for more on thermal imager use. The following sections address:

- Tools for creating openings
- Air movement equipment
- Inspection and maintenance of ventilation equipment

Tools for Creating Openings

Common tools for creating ventilation openings include, but may not be limited to **(Figure 19.11, p. 596)**:

- **Axes** — Breaking windows and chopping holes through roof decking
- **Power or chain saws** — Cutting holes through roof decking or other obstacles
- **Pike poles** — Pulling or opening ceilings

Figure 19.11 Ventilation can be accomplished using axes, power saws, chain saws, and pike poles.

Air Movement Equipment

Common equipment used to move air through a structure or out ventilation openings include, but may not be limited to **(Figure 19.12)**:

- **Air Movement Devices** — Include blowers, fans, and smoke ejectors that generate air flow

- **Hoselines and Nozzles** — Used for hydraulic ventilation operations and resetting the fire

- **Flexible Ducts** — Used to control the flow of fire gases and smoke during ventilation operations

- **Stacking and Hanging Devices** — Used to position air movement devices in doors and windows

- **Generators and Electrical Power Cords** — Used to provide power for electrically powered air movement devices

- **Wind Control Device (WCD)** — Heavy curtain or similar device used to cover exterior window and door openings to limit ventilation and/or prevent wind from adversely affecting ventilation conditions

- **Smoke Control Device** — Heavy curtain or similar device used to block interior or exterior window and door openings to limit ventilation

Inspection and Maintenance of Ventilation Equipment

Like other fire fighting tools and equipment, ventilation tools and equipment should receive routine inspection and maintenance. Because maintenance of powered equipment varies, fire brigade

Figure 19.12 Examples of air movement equipment commonly used in tactical ventilation operations.

members must become familiar with the manufacturer's maintenance instructions and follow them. As with other equipment, inspections of ventilation equipment should be well documented. Equipment that fails inspection should be marked out of service. The AHJ should establish SOPs that, at a minimum, outline the following items:

- Common items to be inspected
- Inspection and maintenance schedule
- Level of maintenance that fire brigade members provide
- When to outsource maintenance
- Procedures for documenting inspection and maintenance

NOTE: The inspection and maintenance of hand tools used during ventilation are described in Chapter 9, Post Incident Operations.

Horizontal Ventilation

NFPA 1081 (2018): 6.2.3

Natural, **mechanical**, and **hydraulic ventilation** are all varieties of horizontal ventilation. Natural horizontal ventilation entails opening doors and windows to allow air currents and pressure differences to remove smoke and heat from the building. Mechanical ventilation involves the use of fans and ejectors to create pressure differences. Hydraulic ventilation uses water streams to ventilate compartments and create pressure differences.

Natural Horizontal Ventilation

When conditions are appropriate, natural horizontal ventilation operations should work with atmospheric conditions, taking advantage of natural air flow. Natural ventilation requires no additional personnel or equipment to set up and maintain.

Wind Assisted Ventilation

When the IC gives the order, windows and doors on the **downwind side** of the structure (low pressure side) should be opened first to create an exhaust point. Openings on the **upwind side** of the structure (high pressure side) are then opened to permit fresh air to enter forcing the smoke toward the **exhaust openings (Figure 19.13)**.

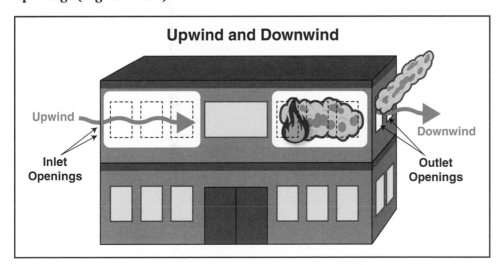

Figure 19.13 Windows should be opened on the downwind side before opening ones on the upwind side to ventilate heated fire gases and smoke from a structure.

Natural Ventilation Before or During Fire Suppression

Once the fire has been located, the IC will make decisions about how best to reach the seat of the fire and extinguish the fire. If only a single opening is made, such as opening a door, this vent will serve as the intake for air and exhaust for smoke. Opening windows or doors may allow fire brigade members to apply water with a straight stream from the exterior, making the fire compartment tenable for a follow-up, interior attack.

Door control is another strategy in natural ventilation. Doors can be coordinated in open and closed positions to change the available flow path within a structure.

Fire brigade members should control natural ventilation as much as possible at a scene. Ventilating the structure and then abandoning control of the opening will allow the fire to grow. Natural ventilation only provides a small amount of time, maybe less than a minute, before conditions deteriorate.

Natural Ventilation After Fire Suppression

Once the fire is extinguished, multiple natural ventilation openings can speed the process of removing smoke. Use caution when using natural ventilation for this purpose because it can result in additional property damage. Mechanical solutions can assist with clearing the smoke quickly.

Mechanical Horizontal Ventilation

Mechanical ventilation may be necessary when the natural flow of air currents and the currents that the fire creates are insufficient to remove smoke, heat, and fire gases from the structure. Mechanical ventilation is accomplished using fans, blowers, and smoke ejectors to create negative or positive pressure. **Negative pressure** means artificially *lowering* the pressure inside the structure so fresh air from outside moves in more quickly. In contrast, **positive pressure** means artificially *raising* the pressure inside the structure so that smoke and fuel gases move toward lower-pressure openings more quickly.

Do not upset the effects of horizontal ventilation. For instance, opening a door or window on the upwind side of a burning building before creating a ventilation exhaust opening on the downwind side may pressurize the building, intensify the fire, and cause the fire to spread to uninvolved areas. Take advantage of air currents created by horizontal ventilation. If an obstruction blocks the established currents in the entry opening, the positive effects of horizontal ventilation may be reduced or eliminated.

Although mechanical methods can be applied to both horizontal and vertical ventilation, it is most often used for horizontal. Mechanical ventilation actions may involve pulling the smoke and fire gases out through an opening or pushing fresh air into the structure and displacing the gases. Any equipment used to facilitate ventilation should be placed and awaiting coordination of other tactics. The equipment should be activated in a coordinated fashion with other activities. Air movement equipment is designed to augment the effects of natural ventilation, meaning that air will be introduced to the fire more quickly. All activities must be coordinated to ensure that using air movement equipment does not worsen fire conditions.

Mechanical Horizontal Ventilation Before and During Fire Suppression

Mechanical horizontal ventilation accelerates the exchange of fresh air into a structure filled with smoke and hot gases. If the fire is not under control, this accelerated exchange of gases can do more harm than good. Mechanical horizontal ventilation will add air to the structure more quickly than natural ventilation. If this tactic is used to create visibility and a flow path for interior operations, then all equipment must be in place; all crews must be coordinated and ready before opening intake and exhaust locations and starting the air movement devices.

Requirements of mechanical ventilation include:

- Access to a power source
- Special equipment
- More dedicated resources and personnel than natural ventilation

WARNING: Never direct a fog stream into a horizontal exhaust opening when interior attack crews are inside the structure because it will force smoke, heat, and steam toward them.

Mechanical Horizontal Ventilation Uses After Fire Suppression

Even in the absence of fire, contaminated atmospheres must be cleared quickly and thoroughly from a building or other confined space. For example, buildings filled with a flammable or toxic gas must be ventilated quickly but safely. Confined spaces containing low oxygen levels can benefit from the introduction of fresh air as the products of combustion are removed. Clearing contaminated structures of smoke reduces smoke damage and improves relations with home or business owners. In these and many other situations, mechanical ventilation is the most effective technique to use.

Exhaust from gas-powered fans can add carbon monoxide (CO) to a structure during overhaul. Fire brigade members should continue to wear SCBA and monitor the environment until there is confirmation that the atmosphere is safe **(Figure 19.14)**. Ventilation after fire suppression should lower carbon monoxide levels. If it does not, gas-powered fans may be the reason.

Figure 19.14 Personnel conducting overhaul operations should wear SCBA. *Courtesy of Ron Moore, McKinney (TX) Fire Department.*

> **CAUTION:** Gas-powered fans may add CO to the structure during ventilation operations. Wear SCBA until atmospheric monitoring confirms that the environment is safe.

Some of the advantages of using mechanical ventilation to clear contaminated atmospheres include:

- Supplements and enhances natural ventilation
- Ensures more control of air flow
- Speeds the removal of contaminants
- Reduces smoke damage

Negative-Pressure Ventilation

Negative-pressure ventilation (NPV) is the oldest type of mechanical ventilation. Air movement equipment is used to develop artificial air flow to pull smoke from the structure or to enhance natural ventilation. The negative pressure created draws smoke and hot fuel gases out of the structure and draws fresh air into the structure. Fans can be placed in windows, doors, or roof vent openings to exhaust the smoke, heat, and gases from inside the building to the exterior **(Figure 19.15)**. NPV

Figure 19.15 A smoke ejector is positioned in a doorway to draw smoke and heated gases from a structure.

requires electricity, generally supplied by a cord run from a generator to the fan. NPV also requires that the opening around the fan be sealed to prevent outside air from being drawn in around the fan. NPV is not as effective as other ventilation options for removing smoke.

Safety guidelines for using smoke ejectors are as follows:

- Keep the intake side of the ejector free from obstructions, such as debris, curtains, or drapes.
- Turn off smoke ejectors when moving them.
- Carry smoke ejectors using the handles provided for that purpose.
- Ensure that people, clothing, curtains, or draperies are not near to or could be drawn into the blades before starting a smoke ejector.
- Avoid standing in the outlet area of the smoke ejector; the discharged air may contain flying debris.

Positive-Pressure Attack

Positive-pressure fans work best on fires confined to a compartment. The intent is to use high volume fans set up at **intake** openings to create a slightly higher pressure in adjacent compartments and force the products of combustion (smoke) to the exterior of the structure through exhaust opening(s) that either exist or have been created. This becomes a challenge because a growing fire creates pressure. For the tactic to be effective, the fan must create enough pressure to force smoke and heat to the desired exhaust openings. Smoke will exhaust toward the **positive-pressure attack (PPA)** intake if the pressure is not sufficient. Controlling the flow within the structure this way during the initial stages of the fire, before suppression, is known as positive-pressure attack. When done correctly PPA reduces the thermal effect on fire brigade members as they perform an interior operation. If PPA is not applied correctly, the potential for rapid fire development and spread surges.

The opening where the fan is set up and air flow is introduced is known as the intake. The location where the intended products of combustion will be exhausted from the structure is known as the **exhaust (Figure 19.16)**. The sizes, types, and uses of fans will vary greatly from one fire brigade to the next. Therefore, fire brigade members should be familiar with their fire brigade's fans and related resources. Follow the manufacturer's recommendations along with the standard operating procedures of your department for the location of the fan.

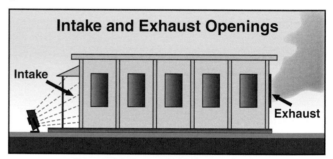

Figure 19.16 Examples of intake and exhaust opening locations used in a tactical ventilation operation.

The two main considerations for PPA are fire location and exhaust-to-intake-size ratio. The ratio compares the surface area of all exhaust openings with the surface area of all compartment intake openings. PPA is only an effective tactic if the location of the fire is known and the appropriate exhaust-to-intake-ratio (greater than 1 to 1) can be achieved **(Figure 19.17)**.

When creating new exhaust openings, consider the pressure needed to force products of combustion out of the structure. Fans will work best with exhaust openings located in the fire compartment. Exhaust openings located at some distance from the fire compartment can interfere with the established flow path, weakening a fan's ability to force smoke and heat toward the fire compartment exhaust openings. This can raise the pressure in the fire compartment higher than the pressure in the rest of the structure. The high pressure area pushes flow toward a low pressure area, drawing the heat, smoke, and fire toward the new exhaust point **(Figure 19.18)**.

Creating the necessary pressure in the adjacent compartments becomes difficult because the fan is just one system component creating pressure. The fire also creates pressure as it grows, which, when combined with the pressure from the fan, will result in flow in unexpected directions. Reducing the fire-generated pressure is not possible, so fire brigade members must control the fan-created pressure or apply water to cool the fire. Creating a large enough exhaust opening to ensure that the fire room pressure remains lower than the remainder of the structure will allow fire brigade members to control the flow path and the fire. The size of that exhaust must exceed the intake to the fire compartment.

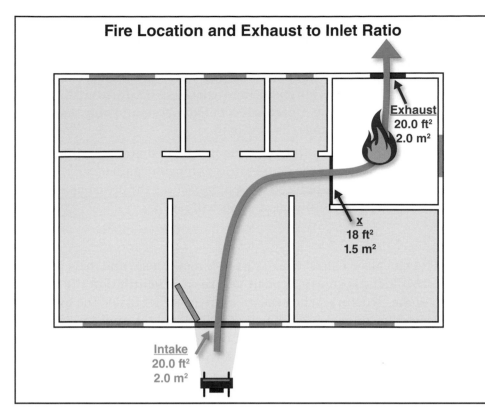

Figure 19.17 Illustrating the concepts of fire location and exhaust-to-intake size ratio.

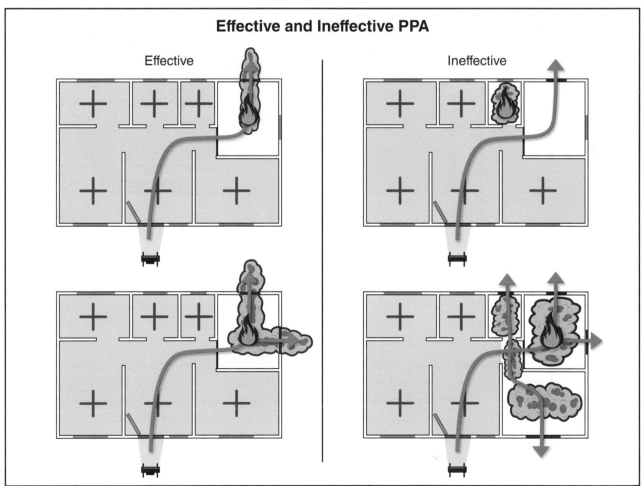

Figure 19.18 Illustrating effective and ineffective positive-pressure attack.

Positive-Pressure Attack Coordination

Like all ventilation tactics, PPA requires coordination between crews. When changes are made to the flow path, fire may rapidly develop. Crews operating inside the structure can be cut off from their escape route, trapping them in the structure. Search and rescue operations have a high potential to change the flow if crews open and close doors during PPA. Crews must enter and exit the structure from the intake area only, taking care not to block the intake opening. Once inside, personnel should only search the open compartments; opening interior doors will change the flow path.

The application of water to the fire compartment will reduce the fire-related pressure differences immediately, making PPA more effective. The decreased temperatures along the path of approach allows this to happen faster. Although temperatures are reduced while approaching the fire compartment, crews should apply water to the fire compartment as soon as streams will reach.

Positive-Pressure Ventilation

The high-volume fans utilized in PPA can also be used to exhaust the smoke, heat, and toxic gases to the exterior after fire suppression. This tactic is known as **positive-pressure ventilation (PPV)**. PPV accelerates the natural ventilation of the structure. When the pressure is higher inside the building, the smoke inside moves toward selected, lower-pressure exhausts. Unlike PPA, PPV application places less emphasis on the exhaust-to-intake ratio. When PPV is applied, the goal is to increase the pressure to a level higher than the exterior of the structure, not higher than the fire can produce **(Figure 19.19)**. This allows for more exhaust openings to create more flow. The more air the fan can move through the structure, the faster the interior environment will approach ambient conditions.

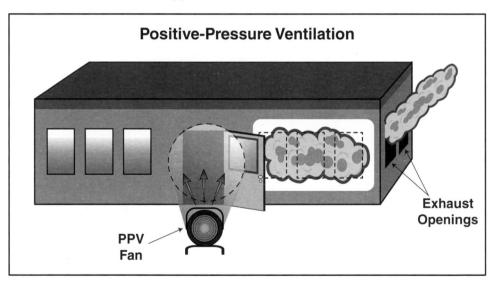

Figure 19.19 Positive-pressure ventilation accelerates the natural ventilation of a structure.

When using PPV to remove smoke after fire suppression, ventilation will be most effective when started soonest. The increased ventilation effectiveness from the fan will decrease temperatures, decrease toxic gas concentration, and increase visibility. All of these lead to safer and more effective interior operations, such as search and rescue, overhaul and salvage.

Although PPV can expedite the ventilation of the structure, it may also hide fire extension while fans are running. Smoldering fires can be intensified with the additional airflow. When using PPV, it is important to identify and control fire extension. Once interior conditions improve, shutting off the fan or closing the intake briefly allows interior crews to evaluate smoke conditions and identify possible extensions before they become larger hazards.

To ensure an effective PPV operation, take the following actions:

- Ensure the exhaust surface area exceeds the intake area.
- Monitor PPV fan operation.

- Maintain communications between the IC, the interior attack crews, and PPV operator.
- Take advantage of wind conditions.

  The advantages of PPV compared with NPV include:

- Fire brigade members can set up PPV blowers without entering a smoke-filled environment.
- PPV is equally effective with horizontal ventilation or vertical ventilation because it supplements natural air currents.
- Removal of smoke and heat from a structure is more efficient.
- Exposed buildings or adjacent compartments can be pressurized to reduce fire spread into them.

  The disadvantages of PPV are as follows:

- The structure must have some remaining compartmentation.
- Exhaust from gas-powered fans can add carbon monoxide to a structure.
- Hidden fires may be accelerated and spread throughout the building.

Positive-Pressure Ventilation in Commercial and Multistory Buildings

When using PPV to ventilate a multistory building, it is best to apply positive pressure at the lowest point at ground level. By opening and closing doors, it is possible to direct the positive pressure throughout the building until the building is free of smoke. If a single fan cannot provide sufficient pressure and air flow, PPV fans can be set up on upper floors and at the entry point to increase the air flow **(Figure 19.20)**. Exit points can then be opened to remove the smoke one floor at a time, starting with the floor most heavily charged with smoke. Either cross-ventilating floors or directing smoke up a stairwell and out the stairwell rooftop opening are methods for removing smoke one floor at a time. Blowers larger than those typically carried on an engine or ladder truck may be available for use in multistory and large volume buildings.

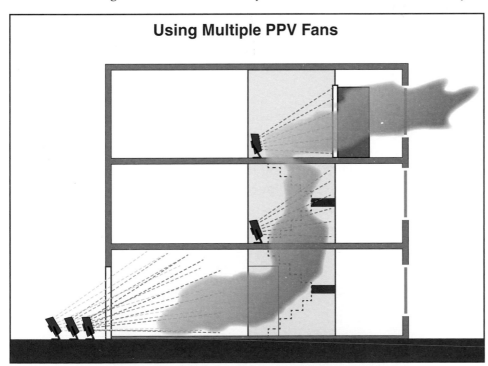

Using Multiple PPV Fans

Figure 19.20 Multiple PPV fans can be used to assist positive-pressure ventilation in multistory buildings.

The main problem in using PPV in aboveground operations is coordinating the opening and closing of the doors in the stairwell used to ventilate the building. To control openings or pressure leaks, one person is placed in charge of the pressurizing process. It helps to use portable radios and have fire brigade members patrol stairwells and hallways.

Hydraulic Ventilation

Hydraulic ventilation:

- Can be used to clear a room or building of smoke, heat, steam, and gases after a fire has been controlled.
- Uses a spray stream from a fog nozzle to entrain smoke and gases and carry them out of the structure through a door or window.
- Requires fire brigade members to operate the nozzle within the contaminated atmosphere.

To perform hydraulic ventilation, set a fog nozzle on a pattern wide enough to cover the exhaust opening through which the smoke will be drawn or pulled **(Figure 19.21)**. The farther from an exhaust opening, the more air entrains into the fog pattern. The more air entrained, the more heated gases get ventilated from the room. The larger the opening, the faster ventilation will occur.

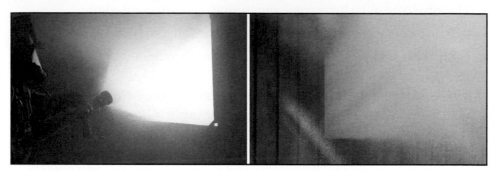

Figure 19.21 Hydraulic ventilation as seen from the interior (left) and the exterior (right).

Hydraulic ventilation has disadvantages including:

- If done incorrectly, water damage may increase within the structure.
- More ice will form on the ground surrounding the building when temperatures are below freezing.
- The fire brigade members operating the nozzle must remain in the heated, hazardous atmosphere throughout the operation.

Vertical Ventilation

NFPA 1081 (2018): 6.2.3

Vertical ventilation involves creating openings in a roof or using existing openings to channel smoke, hot gases, and products of combustion out of the structure. Cutting a hole in the roof above the fire or opening existing roof access doors, scuttles, or skylights are all examples of vertical ventilation. For vertical ventilation to be effective, a horizontal inlet opening at or below the level of the fire is needed to provide a flow path for fresh air to enter the structure **(Figure 19.22)**.

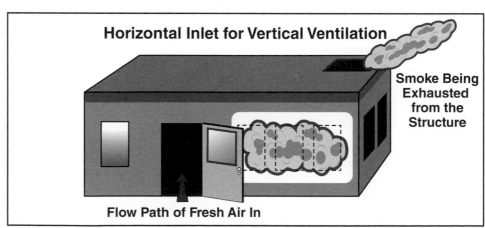

Figure 19.22 A ventilation opening above the fire exhausts hot fire gases and smoke. A horizontal opening at or below level of the fire provides a fresh air flow path.

Requirements for Successful Vertical Ventilation

Vertical ventilation presents the following increased risks:

- Placing personnel above ground level
- Working on both peaked and flat surfaces
- Working above the fire
- Working on roofs that may have been weakened because of age or fire damage

Trained fire brigade members who conduct a well-coordinated attack can avoid ventilation problems. Some common factors that can reduce the effectiveness of vertical ventilation are:

- Improper use of mechanical ventilation
- Uncoordinated ventilation
- Fog streams directed into ventilation openings
- Burn-through of the roof, floor, or walls
- Additional openings between the attack team and the upper opening
- Improper location of the vertical ventilation opening

Vertical ventilation is often impractical or impossible. In these cases, other strategies, such as the use of strictly horizontal ventilation, must be employed. Some of the safety precautions that should be observed include:

- Work with the wind at your back or side when cutting a roof opening to protect yourself from heat, smoke, and embers.
- Ensure that main structural supports do not get cut when creating a ventilation opening.
- Guard the ventilation opening to prevent personnel from falling into it.
- Evacuate the roof promptly when ventilation work is complete or when ordered to leave.
- Use lifelines, roof ladders, or other means to prevent personnel from sliding and falling off the roof.
- Make sure that a roof ladder (if used) is firmly secured over the peak of the roof before working from it.
- Exercise caution when working around electric wires, solar panels, and guide wires.
- Ensure that all personnel on the roof are wearing full PPE, including SCBA, and that they are wearing their masks and breathing SCBA air.
- Stay out of range of those who are swinging axes and operating power saws.
- Remain aware of overhead obstructions within the range of your swing.
- Start power tools on the ground to ensure operation but make sure they are shut off before hoisting or carrying them to the roof.
- When using a power saw, make sure that the angle of the cut is away from the body.
- Extend ground ladders at least three rungs above the edge of the roof or top of the parapet wall, and secure the ladder to the wall, roof, or railing **(Figure 19.23, p. 606)**.
- When operating from aerial ladder platforms, the floor of the platform should be even with or slightly above roof level.
- Check the roof for structural integrity before stepping onto it, and use all available methods to continue to monitor the roof's structural integrity throughout the operation.
- Before and after ventilating, walk along load-bearing walls and the strongest points of the roof structure whenever possible.
- When the roof has been opened, penetrate the ceiling below to enhance ventilation.

Figure 19.23 A fire brigade member securing a ground ladder to a railing on a building's roof.

| **CAUTION:** Limit the number of personnel on the roof to only those needed to accomplish the task assigned.

| **WARNING:** Roof ladders do not increase fire brigade member safety on fire-weakened roofs.

| **WARNING:** Never direct a fog stream into a vertical exhaust opening when interior attack crews are inside the structure. It will force smoke, heat, and steam down on them.

Before stepping off a ladder, parapet wall, or other place of safety onto the roof of a burning building — especially if smoke or darkness obscures the roof — fire brigade members should strike the roof surface with the blunt end of a pike pole, rubbish hook, or axe **(Figure 19.24)**. When a tool strikes a roof, roofs with intact sheathing will feel solid, and the tool will tend to bounce off the surface. Striking the roof will only determine if its sheathing is intact.

Figure 19.24 Fire brigade members should sound the roof before stepping onto it.

Sounding provides no information about the structural members beneath the sheathing. Buildings with lightweight construction may have roof trusses that fail under fire before the roof sheathing. When this occurs, the sheathing may sound solid but will fail under your weight.

> **WARNING:** Sounding the roof does not provide enough information to ensure the roof's structural integrity. It should not be the only means used to determine the stability of the roof.

Remember, however, that roofs with several layers of composite shingles or other roof coverings may not respond to sounding. They may sound solid when struck with a tool even though the fire may have severely damaged the roof supports. Also, roofs covered with tile or slate cannot be sounded; the tiles/slates must be removed to reveal the underlying structure.

Spongy roofs will sag when pushed or walked on and spring back into shape. Spongy roofs generally indicate that the roof decking is failing.

NOTE: Some roofs are spongy with no fire involvement. Know the roof types in your response area.

Spongy Roof

Spongy roofs are usually associated with flat roofs, but the condition can apply to pitched roofs. Where lightweight construction materials are used, roofs may feel solid even though the structural members supporting the decking have burned or weakened. The roof will not feel spongy. Whether or not the roof springs back is an important piece of information about its structural integrity, but it is not the only indicator to check.

Use preincident planning information to identify buildings that have lightweight, bowstring, or engineered truss supported roofs. These roofs may fail early in a fire and are extremely dangerous to work on or under.

Be aware of the following warning signs of an unsafe roof condition:

- Melting asphalt
- Smoke or fire coming from the roof
- Building systems such as HVAC units sagging or leaning

Rotary saws, carbide-tipped chain saws, and chain saws with adapted features are excellent for roof-cutting operations **(Figure 19.25)**. They are faster and less damaging than axes and other manual cutting tools. The saw operator must have good footing and maintain control of the saw at all times. Working on a pitched roof from a roof ladder, an axe, a rubbish hook, or Halligan can be used to provide a secure foothold for the saw operator. In most cases, it is safest to turn off the saw when it is being transported to or from the point of operation — especially when climbing or descending a ladder.

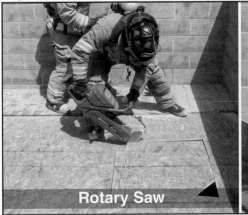

Figure 19.25 Ventilation openings being cut with a rotary saw and a chain saw.

The roof ventilation team should be in constant communication with their supervisor or the IC. The teams should maintain situational awareness and report changes they see to the supervisor based upon the information in the situational awareness section above. Responsibilities of the roof ventilation team leader include:

- Ensuring the roof is safe to stand/walk on (sounding, visual observation)
- Ensuring that only the required openings are made
- Directing efforts to minimize secondary damage (damage from fire fighting operations)
- Coordinating the team's efforts with those of fire brigade members inside the building
- Ensuring the safety of all personnel who are assisting with ventilation operations
- Ensuring there are two means of egress from the roof
- Ensuring an adequate exhaust opening size
- Ensuring the team leaves the roof as soon as their assignment is completed

> **CAUTION:** Work in groups of at least two, but with no more personnel than absolutely necessary to perform the assigned task.

Before cutting any type of ventilation hole, you should cut an inspection hole in the roof. Inspection holes help to determine the location of a fire, the presence of fire below the roof, and construction features of the roof. Comparing observations from multiple inspection holes can provide information about fire spread. Inspection holes are used in offensive and defensive ventilation operations. There are two primary types of inspections holes: the **kerf cut** and the triangle cut.

The kerf cut is the easiest and fastest inspection hole to cut. Make a single cut in the roof surface using a rotary saw, chain saw, or axe **(Figure 19.26)**. The resulting hole should be the width of the saw or axe blade. The only information a kerf cut provides is whether or not smoke or flame is escaping from the cut. It is usually not wide enough to see through, so it does not allow for visual inspection. Presence of smoke will provide some indication of conditions below the roof. If flames come through the kerf cut, leave the area, and do not proceed with the ventilation cuts.

The triangle cut may provide a better view of conditions beneath the roof. Using a power saw, the cut can be created from a single kerf cut if conditions indicate a need for it. The triangle cut consists of three overlapping cuts that form a triangle **(Figure 19.27)**. Remember that heated smoke, gases, and sometimes fire will exit the inspection hole.

Figure 19.26 An example of a kerf cut.

Figure 19.27 A large triangular cut can provide a view of conditions below the roof deck.

Existing Roof Openings

Existing roof openings, such as scuttle hatches, skylights, monitors, ventilating shafts, and stairway doors, may be found on the various types of roofs. Almost every roof opening will be locked or secured in some manner. Scuttle hatches are normally square, and large enough to permit a person to climb onto the roof. A scuttle hatch may be metal or wood, and generally does not provide an adequate opening for ventilation purposes. If skylights contain ordinary shatter-type glass, they may be opened easily. If they contain wired glass, Plexiglas, acrylic plastic, or Lexan plastic, they are very difficult to shatter and are more easily opened by removing the frame. The sides of a monitor may contain glass (which is easily removed) or louvers made of wood or metal. The sides, which are hinged, are easily forced at the top. If the top of the monitor is not removable, at least two sides should be opened to create the required draft. Stairway doors may be forced open in the same manner as other doors of the same type.

 Translucent Corrugated Roofing Panels Safety Advisory

The National Institute for Occupational Safety and Health (NIOSH) Fire Fighter Fatality Investigation and Prevention Program has issued an advisory regarding firefighter safety when operating on roofs containing translucent corrugated panels. Fire fighting personnel and facility workers have been seriously injured and killed from falls through these panels. These panels may not be readily apparent during operations. These panels should be identified during pre-fire planning, and brigade members should immediately inform the incident commander if they are identified on a roof where members may be working. This report can be found through the NIOSH website.

Existing openings should be used for vertical ventilation purposes whenever possible. Typically, it is quicker to open one of these existing openings than it is to cut a hole in the roof. However, fire brigade members must realize that these openings are rarely in the best location or large enough for adequate ventilation. Most often they will simply supplement holes that have to be cut.

Roofs

Fire brigades should formulate plans for dealing with types of roof construction specific to their jurisdiction. The best way for fire brigades to determine the material from which roofs are constructed is through inspection and preincident planning surveys. When cutting through a roof, the fire brigade member should make the opening rectangular or square to facilitate repairs to the roof. One large opening, at least 4 × 4 feet (1.2 m by 1.2 m), is much better than several small ones.

Power equipment for opening roofs is most useful and often provides a means by which ventilation procedures may be accelerated. Rotary rescue saws, carbide-tipped chain saws, or ventilation saws are excellent for roof-cutting operations. Care should always be taken to ensure that the saw operator has good footing and does not operate the saw in a manner that might allow it to accidentally come in contact with any parts of the body. Always turn off the saw when it is being transported to or from the point of operation.

Flat Roofs

Flat roofs are most commonly found on commercial, industrial, and hospital buildings. This type of roof may or may not have a slight slope to facilitate water drainage. The flat roof is frequently pierced by chimneys, vent pipes, shafts, scuttles, and skylights **(Figure 19.28, p. 610)**. The roof may be surrounded and/or divided by parapets, and it may support water tanks, air conditioning equipment, antennas, and other obstructions that may interfere with ventilation operations.

The structural part of a flat roof is generally similar to the construction of a floor that consists of wooden, concrete, or metal joists covered with sheathing. The sheathing is covered with a layer of waterproofing material and an insulating material. Other flat roofs are constructed with poured reinforced concrete or lightweight concrete, precast gypsum, or concrete slabs set within metal joists. The materials used in flat-roof construction determine what equipment will be necessary to open holes in it.

Figure 19.28 This flat roof has numerous locations where vent pipes, duct work, and other objects penetrate the roof decking.

Pitched Roofs

The pitched roof is elevated in the center and forms an angled plane to the edges. Pitched-roof construction involves rafters or trusses that run from the ridge to a wall plate on top of the outer wall at the eaves level. The rafters or trusses that carry the sloping roof can be made of various materials. Over these rafters, the sheathing material is applied either squarely or diagonally. Sheathing is sometimes applied solidly over the entire roof. Pitched roofs sometimes have a covering of roofing paper applied before shingles are laid. Shingles may be wood, metal, composition, asbestos, slate, or tile.

Pitched roofs on industrial buildings may have rolled felt material applied over the sheathing. This is then usually mopped with asphalt roofing tar. Instead of wood sheathing, gypsum slabs, approximately 2 inches (50 mm) thick, may be laid between the metal trusses of a pitched roof. Fire brigade personnel may only know of these conditions based on inspection surveys.

Pitched roofs have a more pronounced slope than flat roofs. This incline may be gradual or steep **(Figure 19.29)**. The procedures for opening pitched roofs are quite similar to those for flat roofs except that additional precautions must be taken to prevent slipping.

Other types of pitched roofs may require different opening techniques. For example, some slate and tile roofs may require no cutting. Slate and tile roofs can be opened by using a large sledgehammer to smash the slate or tile and the thin lath strips or the 1 × 4 inch (25 × 100 mm) boards that support the tile or slate. Tin roofs can be sliced open and peeled back with tin snips or a large device similar to a can opener.

Figure 19.29 The roof on the left has a gradual pitch while the one on the right has a steeper pitch.

Gradual   Steep

Arched Roofs

Arched roofs have many desirable qualities for certain types of buildings (**Figure 19.30**). One form of arched roof is constructed using the bowstring truss for supporting members. The lower chord of the truss may be covered with a ceiling to form an enclosed cockloft or roof space. Such concealed, unvented spaces create dangerous ventilation problems and contribute to the spread of fire and early failure of the roof. cutting holes in the walls in the gable ends of the building may be the safest option for ventilating this type of construction.

Figure 19.30 An example of an arched roof.

WARNING: Some fire service personnel have been injured and others killed when bowstring trussed roofs failed. When a significant amount of fire exists in the truss area of a roof structure, fire brigade members should not be on or under a truss roof.

Trussless arched roofs are made up of relatively short timbers of uniform length. These timbers are beveled and bored at the ends where they are bolted together at an angle to form a network of structural timbers. This network forms an arch of mutually braced and stiffened timbers. Being an arch rather than a truss, the roof exerts a horizontal reaction in addition to the vertical reaction on supporting structural components. A hole of considerable size may be cut or burned through the network sheathing and roofing anyplace without causing collapse of the roof structure. The loads are distributed to less damaged timbers around the opening.

Cutting procedures for opening arched roofs are the same as for flat or pitched roofs except that a roof ladder cannot always be used on an arched roof. Regardless of the method used to support the fire brigade member, the procedure is difficult and dangerous because of the curvature of the roof. Because of the potential for sudden collapse of this type of roof under fire conditions, fire brigade members should work only from an aerial ladder or platform extended to the roof.

Concrete Roofs

The use of precast concrete is very popular with certain types of construction. Precast roof slabs are available in many shapes, sizes, and designs. These precast slabs are hauled to the construction site, ready for use. Other builders form and pour the concrete on the job. Roofs of either precast or reinforced concrete are extremely difficult to break through, and opening them should be avoided whenever possible. Natural roof openings and horizontal openings should be used on buildings with heavy concrete roofs.

A popular lightweight material made of gypsum plaster and portland cement mixed with aggregates, such as perlite, vermiculite, or sand, provides a lightweight floor and roof assembly. This material is sometimes referred to as lightweight concrete. Lightweight precast planks are manufactured from this material, and the slabs are reinforced with steel mesh or rods. Lightweight concrete roofs are usually finished with roofing felt and a mopping of hot tar to make them watertight.

Lightweight concrete roof decks are also poured in place over permanent form boards, steel roof decking, paper-backed mesh, or metal rib lath **(Figure 19.31)**. These lightweight concrete slabs are relatively easy to penetrate. Some types of lightweight concrete can be penetrated with a hammer-head pick, power saw with concrete blade, jackhammer, or any other penetrating tool.

Metal Roofs

Metal roof coverings are made from several different kinds of metal and are constructed in many styles. Light-gauge steel roof decks can either be supported on steel frameworks or they can span wider spaces. Other types of corrugated roofing sheets are made from light-gauge cold-formed steel, galvanized sheet metal, and aluminum. The light-gauge cold-formed steel sheets are used primarily for the roofs of industrial buildings. Corrugated galvanized sheet metal and aluminum are seldom covered with a roof material, and the sheets can usually be pried from their supports.

Figure 19.31 A concrete roof was poured over this steel decking.

Metal cutting tools or power saws with metal cutting blades must be employed to open metal roofs. Metal roofs on industrial buildings are usually provided with adequate roof openings, skylights, or hatches. Older buildings may have roofs that are made of large, fairly thin sheets of tin laid over lath strips. These can be opened by cutting with a power saw, axe, or a large sheet-metal cutter similar to a can opener.

 Rain Roofs

Sometimes buildings will develop a roofing issue and the decision is made to add an additional roof over the original. These can be called a "rain roof" or "a roof-over." This creates two separate roofs and creates large void spaces. The facility's prefire plans should clearly identify these types of situations.

Vertical Ventilation Methods

Vertical ventilation involves making an opening that allows a vertical exhaust opening for heated gases and smoke. The type of exhaust opening and the method for making it will depend on the type of roof in which the opening is being made. When making the actual cuts for an exhaust opening in any type of roof, ventilation openings must be large enough to match the fire.

Ventilating Flat Roofs

Square or rectangular openings are the most common types made in a flat roof. These openings can be made between the roof trusses or with the truss in the middle of the opening. When the truss is in the middle of the opening, a **louver cut** is used **(Figure 19.32)**.

Ventilating Shingle-Covered Pitched Roofs

On shingle-covered pitched roofs, cut a few inches (mm) below the peak on the downwind side. Always cut exhaust openings at or very near the highest point on the roof when possible. Work from a roof ladder with the hooks attached to the ridge line **(Figure 19.33)**. On extremely steep roofs, it may be necessary to work from an aerial apparatus.

Ventilating Slate or Tile-Covered Pitched Roofs

Slate and tile roof coverings may be attached to solid sheathing or to *battens* (strips of wood attached to rafters) that have spaces between them. Removing the individual roofing tiles or using a large sledgehammer to smash them are both methods for opening a slate or tile roof. If the sub roof is solid, then a ventilation hole is cut in the standard manner for pitched roofs. A hole may not need to be cut in the battens if there is enough space between them for ventilation to take place.

Figure 19.32 A fire brigade member practicing ventilating a flat roof.

Figure 19.33 A fire brigade member practicing ventilating a pitched roof that is covered with shingles.

Ventilating Metal Roofs

Thin metal roofs can be sliced open with an axe, carbide tip chain saw, or rotary saw and peeled back. Metal cutting tools or power saws with metal cutting blades can be used to open thick metal roofs. On industrial buildings with thick metal roofs, it may be easier and faster to open skylights, monitors, or scuttle hatches. Older buildings may have roofs that are made of large pieces of sheet metal laid over skip sheathing. Use power saws, axes, or large sheet metal cutters to open sheet metal roofs.

Metal roofs sometimes have skylight panels that may not support the weight of a fire brigade member. There may also be designated walking areas on these roofs which indicate the safe areas.

> **CAUTION:** When in doubt, assume that skylights will not support your weight.

Creating Trench Cuts

The purpose of a **trench cut** (also referred to as trench or strip ventilation) is to create a defensible line ahead of the fire's spread **(Figure 19.34)**. Fire brigade members can attack this defensible area with hose streams when the fire ventilates at the trench cut. A trench cut is usually ordered when the IC has determined that the main body of the fire is too large to extinguish. With the burning portion of the building abandoned as a loss, the IC will give the order for a trench cut.

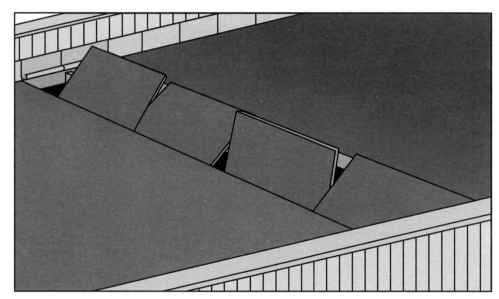

Figure 19.34 Trench cuts are used to create firebreaks.

Trench cuts are created ahead of the advancing fire: how far ahead is based upon the fire's rate of growth. Generally, the distance is far enough to ensure that the fire will not reach the personnel creating the cut before they have finished their work. Multiple fire brigade members (often six to ten personnel) should be assigned to create the cut quickly enough to be effective. These fire brigade members should have charged hoselines present in case they cannot complete the cut in time and need to attack the fire while retreating.

A trench cut should be created only in coordination with other vertical ventilation openings. Exhaust openings closer to the fire allow some of the heat and smoke to escape, which gives the trench cut crew time to complete the trench. Without this coordination, the fire will quickly be drawn to, and burn past, the unfinished trench and spread throughout the building while endangering fire brigade members on the roof.

A trench is created in two steps. First, make two parallel cuts that extend from one exterior wall to the opposite exterior wall. Next, remove the roof material between the cuts and push down the ceiling material below. The distance between the cuts should be large enough to prevent fire from burning past the opening and small enough not to compromise roof integrity. A trench cut should be 4 or more feet (1.2 or more meters) wide and extend the width of the building.

The advantages of a trench cut include:

- Can be used to establish a defensive position in the attic space for fire attack among structures with a common attic **(Figure 19.35)**.

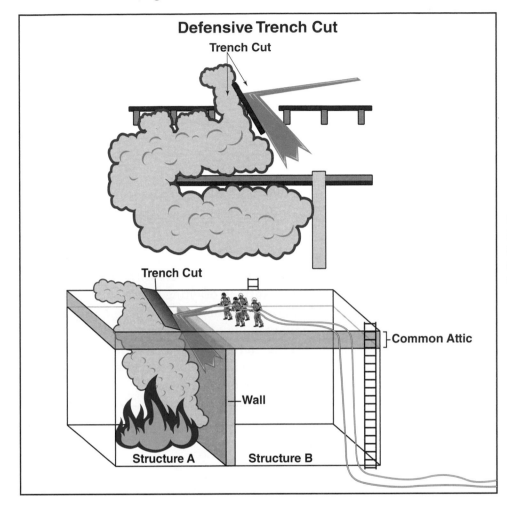

Defensive Trench Cut

Trench Cut

Trench Cut

Common Attic

Wall

Structure A   Structure B

Figure 19.35 A fire stream deflected into a common attic through a trench cut can be used to establish a defensive position.

- Works well in large buildings.

Disadvantages of trench cutting include:

- Can be time-consuming or physically taxing on personnel.
- Can place fire brigade members in the dangerous position of working ahead of the fire.
- Can cause the fire to spread more rapidly and potentially destroy the structure, if it is created improperly or at the wrong time.

Ventilation of Specific Compartments and Structures

NFPA 1081 (2018): 6.2.3

Some compartments and structures will pose significant challenges to fire brigade members as they attempt to employ tactical ventilation. Among the most challenging structural fires are:

- Basement fires
- Fires in windowless buildings
- High-rise fires

Basement/Sub-basement Fires

Basement and sub-basement fires can be among the most challenging situations fire brigade members face. In a basement fire, the fire's stage must be known before starting ventilation. Unless the basement has vents installed, heat and smoke will quickly spread upward into the building. Without effective ventilation systems, access to the basement is difficult because fire brigade members would have to descend through the intense rising heat and smoke to get to the seat of the fire. Ventilating basement fires must be coordinated with fire attack.

Basements may be difficult to access and ventilate. Access to the basement may be through interior or exterior stairs, cellar doors, exterior windows, or hoistways. Iron gratings, steel shutters, wooden doors, or combinations of these may block many outside entrances to basements.

Methods for Ventilating Basements/Sub-basements

Basement ventilation can be accomplished in several ways. If the basement has ground level windows or even below ground level windows in wells, horizontal ventilation can be employed effectively. Piercing and cellar nozzles can be used before ventilation to reduce the risks associated with ventilating a windowless basement.

Natural paths from the basement, such as stairwells and hoistway shafts, can be used to evacuate heat and smoke if there is a way to expel the heat and smoke to the atmosphere without placing other portions of the building in danger **(Figure 19.36)**. As a last resort, an opening may be cut in the floor near a ground level door or window, and the heat and smoke can be forced from the opening through the exterior opening using fans. If other methods are not available or not effective, interior vertical ventilation may be required. This tactic may require working on fire weakened floors above the fire. Only use this tactic when you are sure the floor will support the weight of necessary personnel. Sound the floor to assess the stability of the floor sheathing before proceeding with cuts.

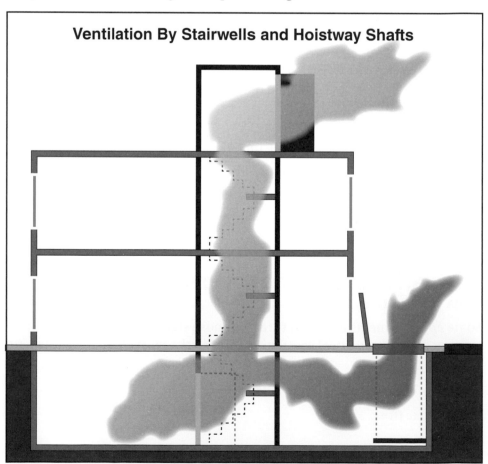

Figure 19.36 Heated fire gases and smoke can be vented from a basement using stairwells and hoistway shafts.

Ventilation By Stairwells and Hoistway Shafts

Breaching Floors

Breaching a floor assembly may be necessary to ventilate an area, apply water to a fire, or rescue trapped occupants. The breaching tools and methods used will depend on the type of floor construction.

Subfloor construction is typically wood, concrete, or concrete over corrugated steel decking. These supports may be finished with a variety of covering materials. Concrete slab floors are common in residential, commercial, and industrial occupancies. Even upper floors of buildings may be finished with lightweight concrete. The upper floors of multistory buildings may be wooden subfloors over wooden joists or I-beams.

The feasibility of opening a floor during a fire fighting operation depends upon the materials used in the floor's construction. A wood floor may not be penetrated easily, particularly if it is installed over a concrete slab. The type of floor construction should be determined during preincident planning surveys.

Fires in Windowless Buildings

Windowless buildings complicate fire fighting and ventilation operations. Creating the openings needed to ventilate a windowless building may delay the operation for a considerable amount of time.

Ventilating this type of building can be difficult, and the problems involved vary depending on the size, occupancy, configuration, and type of construction materials used. Windowless buildings usually require mechanical ventilation for the removal of smoke. Most buildings of this type are automatically cooled and heated through ducts. HVAC equipment can sometimes effectively clear an area of smoke. However, unless specifically designed for this purpose, these systems are more likely to cause the spread of heat and fire. In windowless and high-rise structures these systems need to be brought under fire brigade control as soon as possible. If building environmental systems are designed to contain products of combustion and operating properly, they should be allowed to work. If not, the IC should be notified and steps should be taken to control the system manually.

High-Rise Fires

High-rise buildings (also called high-rise structures) may house process equipment, hospitals, hotels, apartments, or offices. Because there are more occupants in high-rise structures than in other structures, life safety considerations are an even higher priority. Tactical ventilation in a high-rise building must be carefully coordinated to ensure the safest and most effective use of personnel, equipment, and extinguishing agents. Far more personnel are required for search and rescue and firefighting operations in high-rise buildings.

NOTE: High-rise buildings are designed around their passive and active fire protection systems. It is important to ensure these systems remain in place, work properly, and are regularly maintained.

Fire, smoke, and toxic gases can spread rapidly through pipe chases (shafts), stairways, elevator shafts, unprotected ducts, and other vertical and horizontal openings in high-rises. These openings contribute to a **stack effect**, creating an upward draft and interfering with evacuation and ventilation **(Figure 19.37, p. 618)**.

Heated smoke and fire gases travel upward until they reach the top of the building or they are cooled to the temperature of the surrounding air. When this equalization of temperature occurs, the smoke and fire gases stop rising, spread horizontally, and stratify (form layers). In some cases, such as high-rise buildings, these layers of smoke and fire gases will collect on floors (levels) below the top floor of the high-rise. This point is known as the neutral pressure plane. Additional heat and smoke will eventually force these layers to expand and move upward to the top floor of the building. Horizontal smoke spread and hot gas layer development can also occur when an exhaust opening does not match the fire size.

Tactics involving horizontal or vertical ventilation using mechanical means must be developed to address the ventilation and life hazard problems inherent in stratified smoke. In many instances, ventilation must be accomplished horizontally with the use of mechanical ventilation devices and the building's HVAC systems.

Tactical vertical ventilation in high-rise buildings must be considered during preincident planning. In many buildings, only one stairwell penetrates the roof. This stairwell can be used like a chimney to ventilate smoke, heat, and fire gases from various floors, while another stairwell is used as the escape route for occupants. However, during a fire, the doors on uninvolved floors must be controlled so occupants do not accidentally enter a ventilation stairwell as they are evacuating. Doors to stairwells should be controlled, and fire brigade members should be assigned to monitor the doors. Remember that when ventilating the top of a stairwell, you will be drawing the smoke and heat to you or anyone else in the stairwell between the fire floor and the roof. When an enclosed secondary stairwell is used for evacuating occupants, PPV fans should be located at the bottom floor to pressurize the stairwell and keep smoke from entering it.

In some high-rise structures, ventilation fans are built into the top of the stairwell to assist in ventilation. When activated, these fans draw smoke from the fire floor into the stairwell and out the top. This may make it difficult for the fire suppression team to make entry onto the fire floor from this stairwell. The safest and most effective technique may be to pressurize the stairwells with PPV fans to confine the smoke on the floors. Fire brigade members can advance to the fire floor in a safe atmosphere.

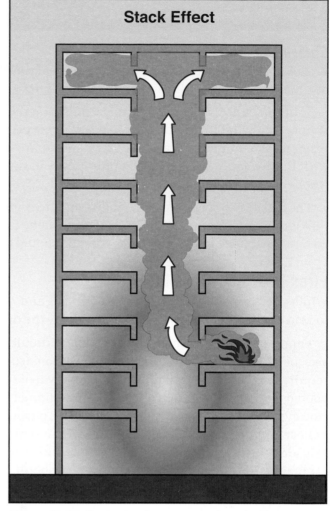

Figure 19.37 Illustrating the concept of stack effect.

NOTE: Under some conditions, elevator shafts that penetrate the roof may be used for ventilation.

WARNING: Do not use stairwells or elevator shafts simultaneously for evacuation and exhaust path. The exhaust path will carry heat and byproducts of combustion through the shaft making it untenable to occupants and fire brigade members.

The Effects of Building Ventilation Systems in Fire Situations

NFPA 1081 (2018): 6.2.3

Most modern buildings have HVAC systems. Fire brigade members should be aware that these systems can significantly contribute to the spread of smoke and fire throughout a structure. Preincident planning should include information on the design capabilities of HVAC systems. Diagrams of the duct system and information on fire protection systems (sprinkler, smoke, or heat detection) within the ductwork should also be included. Fire personnel should be familiar with the location and operation of controls that will manually shut down the system when so desired.

Because the system may draw heat and smoke into the duct before it is shut down, fire brigade members should always check around the ductwork for fire extension during overhaul operations. Also, personnel should be familiar with the best ways to rid the system of smoke before reactivating it.

Smoke control systems are used in buildings involving either a large number of people or a large quantity of combustibles such as high rises, shopping malls, and buildings with open atriums (**Figure 19.38**). These systems involve not only the mechanical systems, but the doors, partitions, windows, shafts, ducts, fan dampers, wire controls, and pipes. Smoke control systems should be identified during preincident planning sessions. Because of the variety and complexity of these systems, fire brigade members should not attempt to operate them under fire conditions. Building engineers should be called to the scene to operate the system under the fire brigade's direction.

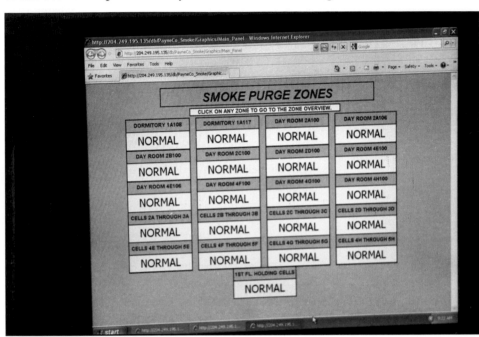

Figure 19.38 Some smoke control systems can be controlled by computer programs such as this one.

Chapter Review

1. What are the four stages of fire development?

2. How can ventilation be used to control flow paths?

3. What are indications of a possible roof collapse?

4. Name and describe four types of air movement equipment.

5. How is wind-assisted ventilation carried out?

6. What is the difference between positive and negative pressure?

7. What are the disadvantages of hydraulic ventilation?

8. What common factors can reduce the effectiveness of vertical ventilation?

9. What are some challenges for ventilating a basement or sub-basement?

10. What effects can building ventilation systems have in a fire situation?

Chapter 19 End Notes

NIOSH Safety Advisory: "Translucent Corrugated Roof Panels," 2016 Accessed online.

Zevotek, Robin, Stephen Kerber. 2016. "Study of the Effectiveness of Fire Service Positive Pressure Ventilation During Fire Attack in Single Family Houses Incorporating Modern Construction Practices," Underwriters Laboratories. Accessed online.

Key Terms

Downwind Side — Side of a building away from the wind, the low pressure side.

Exhaust — In terms of ventilation, the location where hot gases and the products of combustion leave a structure.

Exhaust Opening — Intended and controlled exhaust locations created or improved at or near the fire to allow products of combustion to escape the building.

Exposures — Structures or separate parts of the fireground to which a fire could spread.

High-Rise Building — Building that requires fire fighting on levels above the reach of the department's equipment. The *Uniform Building Code (UBC)* defines a high-rise building as one greater than 75 feet (23 m) in height, but other fire and building codes may define the term differently. *Also known as* High-Rise.

Hydraulic Ventilation — Ventilation accomplished by using a spray stream to draw the smoke from a compartment through an exterior opening.

Intake — In terms of ventilation, the location where air is being entrained toward a fire.

Kerf Cut — Single cut the width of the saw

Louver Cut — Rectangular exhaust opening cut in a roof, allowing a section of roof deck (still nailed to a center rafter) to be tilted, thus creating an opening similar to a louver.

Mechanical Ventilation — Any means other than natural ventilation; may involve the use of fans, blowers, smoke ejectors, and fire streams.

Natural Ventilation — Techniques that use the wind, convection currents, and other natural phenomena to ventilate a structure without the use of fans, blowers, smoke ejectors, or other mechanical devices.

Negative Pressure — Artificially lowering the pressure inside a structure so the fresh air from outside moves in more quickly.

Negative-Pressure Ventilation (NPV) — Technique using smoke ejectors to develop artificial air flow and to pull smoke out of a structure. Smoke ejectors are placed in windows, doors, or roof vent holes to pull the smoke, heat, and gases from inside the building and eject them to the exterior.

Positive Pressure — Artificially raising the pressure inside a structure so that smoke and fuel gases move toward lower-pressure openings more quickly.

Positive-Pressure Attack (PPA) — The use and application of high volume ventilation fans before fire suppression that are intended to force heat and smoke toward desired exhaust openings.

Positive-Pressure Ventilation (PPV) — Method of ventilating a room or structure by mechanically blowing fresh air through an inlet opening into the space in sufficient volume to create a slight positive pressure within and thereby forcing the contaminated atmosphere out the exit opening.

Stack Effect — Phenomenon of a strong air draft moving from ground level to the roof level of a building. The air movement is affected by building height, configuration, and temperature differences between inside and outside air.

Tactical Ventilation — Planned, systematic, and coordinated removal of heated air, smoke, gases or other airborne contaminants from a structure, replacing them with cooler and/or fresher air to meet the incident priorities of life safety, incident stabilization, and property conservation.

Trench Cut — Defensive tactic that involves cutting an exit opening in the roof of a burning building, extending from one outside wall to the other, to create an opening at which a spreading fire may be cut off.

Upwind Side — Side of a building against which the wind is blowing, the high pressure side.

Vertical Ventilation — Ventilating at a point above the fire through existing or created openings and channeling the contaminated atmosphere vertically within the structure and out the top; done with openings in the roof, skylights, roof vents, or roof doors.

Skill Sheet List

The following skill sheets should be used to evaluate the skills described in this chapter:

NOTE: Students should wear the PPE appropriate to the NFPA 1081 level (Incipient, Advanced Exterior, Interior Structural, etc...) being evaluated.

Facility Fire Brigade Leader

Chapter Contents

JPRs addressed in this chapter

This chapter provides information that addresses the following job performance requirements of NFPA 1081, *Standard for Facility Fire Brigade Member Professional Qualifications (2018)*.

7.1.3

1. Explain the importance of fire brigade leadership.

2. Review the facility fire brigade organizational structure. [7.1.3]

3. Describe the different organizational principles that have been integrated into the IMS. [7.1.3]

4. Describe the key elements of leadership. [7.1.3]

5. Identify the key elements necessary for meeting supervisory responsibilities. [7.1.3]

6. Identify considerations for establishing priorities for the unit. [7.1.3]

7. Describe the methods for anticipating and resolving problems. [7.1.3]

8. Describe the methods for establishing and communicating goals and objectives. [7.1.3]

9. Identify the methods for building an effective team. [7.1.3]

10. Describe the best methods to motivate and support personnel. [7.1.3]

11. Identify the methods for applying management principles. [7.1.3]

12. Describe the methods for information management and record keeping. [7.1.3]

Chapter 20
Fire Brigade Leader Basics

Responding to an emergency as a fire brigade member and taking directions is very different from providing the directions as the Incident Commander (IC). The fire brigade leader must ensure the safety of the personnel under their direction, and also ensure stabilization of an emergency incident. Stepping between the roles of follower and leader may be difficult.

This chapter covers the fire brigade organization and information management and record keeping. It also provides an overview of leadership, ethics, and their application. It describes supervision and the skills required to execute the job of fire brigade leader effectively. Finally, it addresses management principles that the successful fire brigade leader as a supervisor must understand and apply.

Introduction to Fire Brigade Leadership

There are many names that facilities may call their fire brigade leader such as site incident commander (SIC), fire brigade captain, fire team leader (FTL), emergency response coordinator (ERC), or emergency team leader (ETL). These terms may be considered synonymous and are used within this text as fire brigade leader or incident commander. The National Incident Management System – Incident Command System (NIMS-ICS) includes terms such as team leader, division supervisor, or task force leader that should be reflected in the site emergency plan. Serving as a facilities fire brigade leader is most often a collateral (secondary) duty to your primary job function at your place of work.

OSHA 1910.156(c)(1) and NFPA 1081 Competencies

Both OSHA and the NFPA address the competencies expected of fire brigade members and leadership.

OSHA 1910.156(c)(1)

The employer shall provide training and education for all fire brigade members commensurate with those duties and functions that fire brigade members are expected to perform. Such training and education shall be provided to fire brigade members before they perform fire brigade emergency activities. Fire brigade leaders and training instructors shall be provided with training and education which is more comprehensive than that provided to the general membership of the fire brigade.

NFPA 1081

1.2.2

The intent of this standard shall be to ensure that personnel serving an incipient facility fire brigade member, advanced exterior facility fire brigade member, interior structural fire brigade member, facility fire brigade leader, facility fire brigade coordinator, and support member are qualified.

Chapters 20 and 21 provide additional information for the fire brigade leader. However, it is a best practice to continue to attend training regularly that is related to your task as an IC. It is also import to regularly serve in the capacity as an IC or a Safety Officer, whether during drills or actual responses, to be proficient with this important skill set.

Leadership is critical in emergency situations where personal risks are high and hazardous conditions can change rapidly. Motivating personnel is essential to limiting injuries, assuring accountability, and attaining operational goals. In nonemergency operations and during daily work activities, leadership is essential for using resources efficiently and ensuring a safe and healthy environment.

There are many different opinions regarding leadership. Leadership has been called a trait, a behavior, a skill, a talent, a characteristic, a science, and an art. Fire brigade leaders should read and take classes that reinforce their leadership skills as part of their professional development. Some fire brigades have mentoring programs that assist personnel as they undergo personal development. This can be particularly helpful as personnel move into leadership positions. They should understand the fundamentals of leadership, supervisory methods, and management principles and apply them daily. Along with leadership, a fire brigade leader must learn two additional skills — supervision and management. These two skills are different, but are interconnected.

Review Section: Facility Fire Brigade Organizational Structure
NFPA 1081 (2018): 7.1.3

Fire brigade leaders must be familiar with all organizational levels and responsibilities within their fire brigade. At a minimum, this includes being familiar with:

- Appropriate OSHA and NFPA standards
- Appropriate local regulatory requirements such as in the United Kingdom, European Union, or United States
- Brigade's organizational statement
- Level(s) of operational capability
- Standard operating procedures (SOPs)
- Mutual and automatic aid agreements
- IMS used by the brigade
- Brigade communication procedures

- Emergency reporting procedures
- Interaction with facility management
- Information management and record keeping
- Leadership and supervision
- How to issue clear and concise assignments

Occupational Safety and Health Administration (OSHA), National Fire Protection Association (NFPA) 600, *Standard on Facility Fire Brigades* (2015); and NFPA 1081, *Standard for Facility Fire Brigade Member Professional Qualifications* (2018) outline the duties and training requirements for facility fire brigade members.

The basic types of facility fire brigades include:

- **Incipient** — Members must be able to safely combat the fire without entering the IDLH environment. Members are not required to wear self-contained breathing apparatus (SCBA) or thermal protective clothing. They must be able to fight the fire effectively using only portable fire extinguishers or small handlines, which flow up to 125 gallons per minute (gpm) (473 L/min).

- **Advanced exterior only** — Members may take offensive fire fighting action within the incident hot zone only from the exterior of a structure. Appropriate SCBA and thermal protective clothing must be provided to fire brigade members, and the personnel must be trained how to use them. Advanced exterior only fire brigade members must be able to use handlines that flow up to 300 gpm (1 140 L/min), master streams, or similar devices to manually apply specialized agents.

- **Interior structural only** — Members may take offensive fire fighting action from only within the incident hot zone of the interior of a structure. Appropriate types of SCBA and thermal protective clothing must be provided to fire brigade members, and the personnel trained in how to use them. The interior structural only fire brigade members must be able to use handlines that flow up to 300 gpm (1 140 L/min), master streams, or similar devices to manually apply specialized agents.

- **Advanced exterior and interior structural** — Members of this type of fire brigade may take offensive fire fighting action within the incident hot zone from the exterior of a structure or from within the structure itself. Personnel must be trained how to use appropriate types of SCBA and thermal protective clothing. The advanced exterior/interior structural fire brigade members must be able to use handlines that flow up to 300 gpm (1 140 L/min), master streams, or similar devices to manually apply specialized agents.

Common duty positions within fire brigades include:

- Senior facility manager
- Fire brigade leader
- Fire brigade training coordinator
- Fire brigade management official
- Fire brigade member
- Fire brigade support member

Organizational Principles
NFPA 1081 (2018): 7.1.3

Fire brigades follow certain basic principles of organizational structure based on organizational theory, research, and practice in both public and private organizations. These principles, which have been integrated into the IMS, include:

- Scalar structure
- Unity of command
- Division of labor
- Decision-making authority
- Span of control

Incident Command System Principles

ICS principles include:

- **Establish & Maintain Command** — A single integrated organization to manage the emergency response must be clearly established from the beginning of an incident, and maintained throughout the lifecycle of the incident. ICS requires that one individual/person maintain authority and responsibility over all emergency response activities – the Command Function. In certain circumstances, the Command responsibilities may be carried-out through single, coordinated, or unified command structure.

- **Organization by Function** — ICS requires that functional responsibilities (i.e. Command, Operations, Planning, Logistics, Safety, etc.) be clearly identified in the structure of the emergency response organization, which allows all responders to operate more efficiently; and also facilitates organizational growth, as needed.

- **Chain of Command and Unity of Command** — Chain of command refers to the orderly line of authority within the organization. Unity of command means that each responder takes direction from only one designated leader within the organization.

- **Modular Organization** — A modular approach allows the response organization to be appropriately scalable for the size and complexity of the emergency response incident. The organization can expand as the size and/or complexity of the incident increases; and organizational elements (Sections, Branches, Divisions, Groups, Units, etc.) can be added to the structure, as needed.

- **Objectives-Driven Response** — An effective and successful response requires a clear set of objectives, consistent with incident/organization's priorities. Incident objectives are established by Command and, depending on the size of the emergency response organization, cascaded down through the organization.

- **Incident Action Planning (IAP)** — Each emergency response incident under ICS requires an incident action plan that provides a coherent means of describing the operational and support activities. Under a simplified Operational Planning Process, the resulting emergency response activities are recording in the Incident Briefing form, with additional ICS forms attached, as needed, tactical pre-incident plans or verbal communications initially.

- **Common and Consistent Terminology** — ICS uses a common set of terms to define organizational functions, incident facilities, resource descriptions, and position titles; as well as other emergency response incident management terms.

- **Span of Control** — Span of control refers to the number of individuals or resources that can be effectively managed by a supervisor during an incident. ICS recommends a leader's span of control should range from three to seven individuals, with five representing the optimal level.

- **Coordination and Management of Resources** — Incident Resources are defined as personnel, teams, equipment, supplies, and facilities in support of emergency response incident management activities. Centralized resource coordination helps to maintain an accurate and up-to date picture of the resources in use, available, or potentially available for assignment.

- **Integrated Communications** — Incident communications are facilitated through the development and use of a common communications plan that adequately supports the operations structure and appropriately links operations with support personnel.

- **Accountability** — After Command has been established, personnel and equipment should only respond to the incident when requested by Command or designee. All responding resources should be "checked-in;" and all arriving personnel be appropriately briefed and outfitted prior to assignment.

- **Information and Intelligence Management** — ICS has an established process for gathering, analyzing, sharing, and managing incident-related information and intelligence. Common Operating Picture or "COP" can be designed to ensure all data collected on scene is properly analyzed, vetted and shared in a variety of ways to suit the needs of the various organizational functions.

Figure 20.1 An example of a scalar organizational structure showing where fire brigades personnel fit within the organization.

The pyramid diagram, titled **Scalar Organizational Structure**, shows from top to bottom:
- Senior Facility Manager
- Fire Brigade Management Official
- Fire Brigade Leader(s)
- Assistant Fire Brigade Leaders
- Driver/Operators (if applicable)
- Fire Brigade Members
- Support Memebers (if applicable)

Scalar Structure

The common organizational structure used in the fire and emergency services is scalar, which is defined as having an uninterrupted series of steps or a chain of command. Decisions and information are directed from the top of the organizational structure down through intermediate levels to the base of the structure **(Figure 20.1)**. Feedback and information, in turn, are transmitted up through the structure to the top positions.

Direct communication at lower organizational levels allows for quicker actions and reactions. Within this scalar structure, certain decision-making authority is delegated to lower levels, and communication is enhanced. Information is generally centralized for decision-making.

Decision-Making Authority

Authority refers to the legal ability of an individual to make and implement decisions for which the individual is held accountable. The fire brigade leader has changing decision-making roles throughout an incident. There are two types of decision-making models: centralized authority and decentralized authority. Authority may also be delegated in either system.

Centralized Authority

In a centralized authority model, decisions are made by one person at the top of the structure. This model works well in very small organizations such as an individual fire company. In large organizations, the leader's span of control may be exceeded unless decision-making authority is delegated.

Accountability for decisions is almost always centralized. The fire brigade leader delegates to officers the authority to make decisions and implement plans, but the fire brigade leader is still accountable to the authority having jurisdiction (AHJ) and the public for any decisions made.

Decentralized Authority

In a decentralized authority model, decisions are made at a lower level (basically delegation of authority), with the effects of the decisions reported through the structure. To work effectively, the fire brigade leader must ensure that all members understand the direction, values, and goals of the organization. Decision-making authority should be delegated to the lowest level possible.

In a decentralized model, decision-making authority is limited to only those tasks over which personnel have been given authority. For example, the fire brigade leader might give assistant brigade leader the authority to make policy changes while granting a shift captain (or chief) authority over servicing equipment at the shift level. The shift captain/chief would have full, decision-making authority where equipment service was concerned but would not be able to set policy for the organization, even if the policy applied to equipment.

The fire brigade leader may also decentralize the authority to make certain decisions only in specific areas. For example, a fire brigade leader may dictate what tasks are to be performed but delegate to the fire brigade officer the authority to decide when and in what order the tasks are performed.

Decentralization of authority allows for the expeditious handling of most matters. With decisions made at lower levels in an organization, upper management personnel are freed to concentrate on other areas of responsibility. The details resulting from a decision do not have to be reported, but the effects of the decision do. For example, depending upon an organization's size and structure, a fire brigade leader may not need to know what type of maintenance is being performed on an apparatus, merely that the apparatus will be out of service for maintenance.

With decentralization of authority, duplication of effort may occur. To avoid this, policies must define what decisions can be made and under what conditions. A review system should be established to ensure accountability and study the effects of decentralized decisions.

Delegation of Authority

Delegation is the process of providing subordinates with the authority, direction, and resources needed to complete an assignment. The decision to delegate authority to finish a task is often difficult. The fire brigade leader may worry that the delegated task will not be completed in a manner that meets the organization's standards. Feelings like these are natural and show that the officer wants to do a good job. Concerns about delegating tasks can be alleviated through good communication and a training program that builds knowledge, skills, abilities, and trust.

When delegating a task, a fire brigade leader must ensure that the assigned employee is capable of doing the job. While picking the right person for the right job, officers should look for opportunities to challenge subordinates with tasks to build their knowledge, skills set, and confidence.

Authority and responsibility go hand-in-hand. Delegation of an assignment must be accompanied with appropriate authority and trust that the individual will achieve the desired results using proper methods (responsibility). When assigning a task, the fire brigade leader should:

- Describe the task and its relationship to the overall goal or objective.

- Identify available resources.

- Identify time and safety constraints that apply to the assignment.

Unity of Command

Unity of command states that each subordinate must have only one supervisor during an emergency incident. In contrast, during non-emergency situations, most fire brigade members have their line organization supervision and their fire brigade organization supervision which must co-exist.

During an emergency, the employee and the supervisors may face a number of problems if an employee is required to report to more than one supervisor, including:

- The employee is interrupted in the performance of a task and ordered to do something different. The supervisor ordering the first task thinks that it has been completed, which may not be true.

- The employee executes tasks poorly while trying to do two (perhaps conflicting) tasks at once.

- The employee plays the supervisors against each other so that neither supervisor knows exactly what the employee is doing, and the employee may do little or no work.

- The employee becomes frustrated while attempting to follow the conflicting orders of different supervisors and gives up both tasks.

Violations of unity of command lead to confusion and frustration by both subordinates and supervisors. Organizations that employ unity of command provide adequate direction and accountability, allowing all workers to be more productive and efficient. Unity of command depends on the use of the chain of command and functional supervision.

Chain of Command

Chain of command is the path of responsibility from the top of the organization to the bottom and vice versa. Although each member reports to a supervisor directly, every member is still responsible to the fire brigade's leadership indirectly through the chain of command.

With unity of command, supervisors divide the work into specific job assignments without losing control. The fire brigade's leadership can issue general orders that filter through the chain of command and translate into specific work assignments at various levels within the organization.

When a subordinate sidesteps the immediate supervisor and takes a problem to a higher officer, the unity of command is broken. The superior officer should instruct the subordinate to follow the chain of command and take the problem to the immediate supervisor.

Sidestepping can be destructive to organizational unity and cohesiveness and exclude the person best able to solve the problem — the immediate supervisor. There are times when it may be acceptable to bypass a level in the chain of command. Personnel should always consult local policy prior to taking such actions. For example, if the immediate supervisor is viewed as part of the problem or does not resolve the problem, the subordinate may be justified in bypassing the chain of command using skip level notification.

All officers should instruct their subordinates in the proper method of handling problems through the chain of command. They must be willing, prepared, and able to handle their subordinates' problems. To reduce sidestepping the chain of command, officers should:

- Be available to listen to their subordinates' problems.
- Listen to problems sincerely, give them full consideration, and address their perception.
- Take action and notify the employee of your actions.
- Take a problem to the next level in the chain of command when it cannot be solved at the officer's level of authority.

Functional Supervision

Functional supervision is an organizational principle that allows workers to report to more than one supervisor. Functional supervision deviates from unity of command when personnel are assigned by their supervisor or a senior officer to perform duties that fall under the authority of another supervisor. The subordinates report to the second supervisor on matters relating to that function. For this arrangement to work, both supervisors must communicate with each other and closely coordinate their activities.

Functional supervision is often useful when the distinction between line and staff functions becomes blurred. A shift captain may report to the fire brigade leader or other line supervisor during emergency activities and routine nonemergency activities. The shift captain/chief may report to a facility's fire marshal when the shift is engaged in some specialized activity such as code enforcement or dealing with a fire protection system. For all other activities, they report to their regular supervisor. For this arrangement to work, both supervisors must communicate with each other and closely coordinate their activities.

Span of Control

Span of control refers to the number of subordinates and/or number of functions that one individual can effectively supervise. This principle applies equally to supervising the fire brigade or the officers of several companies under the direction of an IC. There is no absolute rule for determining how many subordinates or functions that one person can supervise effectively. The number varies with the situation but is usually considered to be somewhere between three and seven **(Figure 20.2, p. 632)**.

While a wider span of control can have advantages in nonemergency operations, it is not recommended for the majority of emergency operations. The NIMS-ICS model is based on a span-of-control ratio of one supervisor to three to seven subordinates or functions. NIMS-ICS suggests an optimum of five. The variables that affect span of control in any given situation include the:

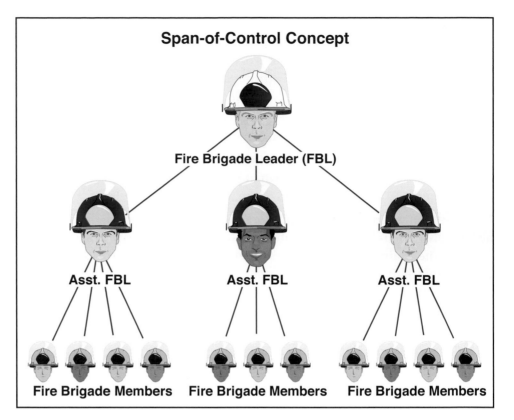

Figure 20.2 Illustrating the concept of span of control used to effectively supervise personnel or functions.

- Ability and experience of the supervisor
- Ability and experience of subordinates
- Nature of the task:
  — Urgency
  — Conditions under which it must be performed
  — Complexity
  — Rate at which it must be performed
  — Similarity/dissimilarity to tasks being performed by others
- Proximity of subordinates to the supervisor and each other
- Ease/reliability of communications medium
- Consequences of a mistake

Effective supervision is easier when the tasks are relatively simple and repetitive, all workers are well-trained, and workers are performing the same or similar tasks. Little supervision may be required when subordinates are working near the supervisor or other coworkers so that they can ask questions or get help easily.

Effective supervision is extremely difficult when:

- Tasks being performed are very complex
- Workers' level of training is minimal
- Workers are performing dissimilar tasks
- Workers are widely separated from the supervisor and each other

These variables may be manageable in some cases. However, when a worker's mistake could result in fatalities or injuries during training or an incident, the effective span of control may need to be reduced to a safe operational level. Examples of proper span of control include when:

- A shift captain/chief supervises the members of that shift (three to seven subordinates)
- A fire brigade leader supervises the shift captains/chiefs

If an IC fails to delegate authority properly at a major incident, the span of control may be exceeded. As a result, the IC may attempt to directly control the entire incident, making all decisions at all levels. Making every decision in the absence of good delegation can be quickly overwhelming and can cause:

- Chaos at the incident scene
- Breakdowns in communication and coordination
- Confused, inefficient operations at best and perhaps losses of life and property

Division of Labor

Division-of-labor consists of dividing large jobs into smaller tasks to be assigned to specific individuals. In the fire brigade, division of labor is important for the following reasons:

- Assigning responsibility
- Preventing duplication of effort
- Making specific, clear-cut assignments
- Demands of other work tasks

All positions within the organization must be clearly defined for the division-of-labor principle to be effective. Analyzing each position is the key to identifying all the skills and knowledge necessary for that job. Job analyses and job descriptions are critical to assist personnel in performing their many tasks. All personnel must know what their responsibilities are and understand what is expected of them.

Cross-training should be provided so that company personnel are able to perform a variety tasks with proficiency. Cross-training enables different companies to work together well because each company officer understands the capabilities, requirements, and needs of the other.

Leadership

NFPA 1081 (2018): 7.1.3

Fire brigade leaders serve their respective units and must understand key elements of leadership. To be effective, they should understand:

- Leadership traits
- Leadership skills development
- Leadership skills
- Crew resource management
- Command presence
- Ethics

Leadership Traits

It is important to understand that no single leadership trait is appropriate for every circumstance. Traits are used in combinations that best serve the goals of the organization and incident command. Leadership traits that fire brigade leaders should cultivate include:

- **Supervisory ability** — Planning, organizing, directing, and controlling in order to coordinate the efforts of the unit to accomplish objectives
- **Decisiveness** — Making decisions quickly and effectively
- **Intelligence** — Using logic and reason in making decisions

- **Self-assurance** — Demonstrating self-confidence when making decisions
- **Initiative** — Accomplishing goals and objectives with a minimum of supervision
- **Desire for professional success** — Gaining additional responsibility and influence within the organization
- **Integrity** — Applying consistently a set of morals or values to the decision-making process
- **Personal security** — Being secure in the leadership position
- **Sense of priority** — Determining an effective order of action to achieve a desired outcome
- **Vision** — Having a dream or concept of the way things can or should be
- **Industriousness** — Working hard to fulfill duties
- **Interpersonal skills** — Successfully working with others to accomplish tasks
- **Empowerment** — Providing support for others to succeed in accomplishing organizational and personal goals
- **Innovation and creativity** — Seeking continuously new and imaginative methods for accomplishing the mission of the organization
- **Consistency** — Applying procedures, policies, rewards, and discipline evenly and fairly over time
- **Preparedness** — Being ready for potential situations
- **Proactiveness** — Anticipating, embracing, and meeting change
- **Strong communicator** — Being able to provide clear direction

Leadership Skills Development

The first step in developing leadership skills is to study successful leaders and curate your own list of leadership traits. This list becomes the personal criteria or benchmark standard that the leader uses to assess him or herself. The fire brigade leader also uses the standard as a checklist of personal leadership traits. Individual differences, perceptions, and personal bias can influence the checklist.

Another method involves an anonymous survey of the fire brigade leader's subordinates, peers, and superiors in a feedback evaluation that includes objective responses to questions about the officer's leadership traits. This method, too, can be very subjective.

It is common to use a combination of these methods. A neutral party may compile the results. Once a fire brigade leader has determined the characteristics that are present and those that are lacking, it is time to develop a strategy for improving the weaker skills. No leader is outstanding in all situations.

Depending on the area that appears to need attention, an officer may choose to follow any number of paths to improvement such as:

- Courses
- Seminars/workshops
- Books or other literature on the leadership topics
- Counselors/mentors

Leadership Skills

Leadership traits may be summarized according to a variety of actions that most good leaders take:

- **Seeing opportunities** — Having the ability to view situations from all angles while still understanding that tradition can provide direction.
- **Identifying challenges** — Recognizing potentially problematic situations ranging from personality conflicts to political intrigue that may confront the workgroup, brigade, or unit. Recognition requires monitoring both the internal and the external climate of the organization.

- **Communicating** — Being able to express ideas clearly and being able to listen to and interpret feedback from others who are either internal or external to the organization.

- **Planning for success** — Generating plans, implementing them, and evaluating their effectiveness. Effective planning saves energy, time, resources, lives, and frustration.

- **Building trust** — Creating an environment of mutual trust within the organization, community, service area, and profession.

- **Understanding the system** — Determining first what needs to be improved.

- **Inspiring a shared vision** — Sharing the vision for your brigade's success with subordinates and ensuring it is in line with the organization's mission.

- **Enabling others to act** — Giving subordinates the tools and methods to solve the problem or make the change.

- **Modeling desired behavior** — Providing a good personal example, especially when work becomes more difficult.

- **Encouraging subordinates** — Sharing the glory with your subordinates, while keeping the troubles to yourself (and superiors as appropriate).

- **Establishing priorities:**
  - The top priority is the emergency response.
  - The second priority is pre-emergency readiness through training, planning, and maintenance.
  - The third priority is administration, including facility maintenance, documentation, etc.

Crew Resource Management

Originally created by the airline industry and referred to as "Cockpit Resource Management," Crew Resource Management (CRM) is a method to improve situational awareness, communication, leadership practices, and decision making. As it originated, CRM was designed to reduce the authoritarian culture within the cockpit while still maintaining the command hierarchy. The concept is credited to NASA psychologist John Lauber who studied the culture and communication processes within the cockpit in the late 1970s. CRM is designed to create a culture where authority can be respectfully questioned. It is important for a subordinate to follow a five-step process when questioning authority:

1. Gain the attention of the supervisor (e.g. "Hey Chief" or "Lieutenant Smith")

2. Concisely state the concern or hazard (e.g. "I am concerned this fire is getting away from us" or "That tank is concerning to me")

3. Communicate the problem (e.g. "We are about to run out of water" or "It sounds like that tank is venting through the emergency relief valve and may BLEVE soon")

4. Identify a potential solution (e.g. "We should secure that hydrant as a water supply quickly" or "We should consider increasing the evacuation zone")

5. Gain agreement (e.g. "Does that sound like the appropriate solution to you, sir?")

CRM has been identified as a mechanism to improve situational awareness, decision making, and communication within the fire service. While the action steps and implementation may take a cultural shift within the organization or profession, the benefits have been proven to avoid catastrophes and improve the level of safety within organizations that have implemented the CRM philosophy.

Command Presence

Command presence is the ability to identify the components of a situation, assess the need for action, determine the nature of the necessary intervention, initiate action, and to be perceived as having the ability to take the action. Command presence inspires confidence from subordinates, the administration, and the public **(Figure 20.3)**.

Effective fire and emergency services leaders can have command presence in all of their assigned emergency and nonemergency duties. To achieve command presence, it may be helpful to have or develop the following attributes:

- Self-confidence
- Trustworthiness
- Consistency
- Responsibility
- Acceptance
- Expertise

Figure 20.3 A fire brigade leader, such as the one in the center of this photo, should demonstrate command presence during both emergency and nonemergency situations.

Along with these personality characteristics, leaders can take the following eight steps to create command presence:

Step 1: Determine what the situation is.

Step 2: Know what resources are available to apply to the situation.

Step 3: Develop the strategy and tactics required to resolve the situation.

Step 4: Listen to all points of view, when appropriate.

Step 5: Make the decision.

Step 6: Implement the decision.

Step 7: Evaluate the decision and modify as necessary.

Step 8: Take responsibility for the decision.

Ethics

Fire brigade leaders must understand the importance of ethical conduct and how to adhere to it. This conduct may involve relationships with others, the decision-making process, or simply choosing between right and wrong. Not all decisions are clear and may involve many choices that fall into the gray range between the two extremes.

Ethics: Three-Step Check

Step 1: *Is it legal?* — *Will I be violating civil law, professional standards, or company policy?*

Step 2: *Is it fair to all concerned?* — *Have I based my decision on all the facts as I know them? Will my decision support the mission of the organization?*

Step 3: *How will it make me feel about myself?* — *Will it make me proud? Would I feel good if my decision was published in the newspaper? Would I feel good if my family knew about it?*

To ensure the organization maintains an ethical culture, the ethics program needs to include a written code of ethics or ethics policy. This code is a brief, one- or two-page statement of the organization's values and the expected behavior both of the management and the membership.

An essential part of the ethics program is the written code of ethics that is specific to the organization that creates it. Numerous organizations including the International Association of Fire Chiefs (IAFC) have established codes of ethical conduct which are posted on their website. Expressing the organization's code of ethics in written form provides management and employees with a visible standard to follow. A code of ethics provides fire brigade leaders with an idea of what is expected of them, their subordinates, and their organizations.

The responsibility for the development of an ethical culture within the organization belongs to everyone in the organization. The administration and all employees must support, communicate, and personally adhere to the adopted code of ethics. Formal training for all personnel should be provided beginning with entry-level employee training and extending to fire officer training courses.

Fire brigade leaders must use ethical decision-making to manage issues as they arise, and provide a positive example of how to apply ethics to all decisions and actions. The organization's culture depends in large part on the ethical behavior of officers and others in positions of leadership and authority. Officers must be honest in their presentation of their decisions, both in communicating the decision and results of the decision. Honesty generates acceptance for the decision and builds trust in the officer who made that decision.

Supervision

NFPA 1081 (2018): 7.1.3

The definitions of the terms **supervision** and **management** are similar and often used interchangeably. This manual uses the terms to describe two distinctly different but associated fire officer responsibilities:

- **Supervision** — Includes the processes of directing, overseeing, and controlling the activities of other individuals.

- **Management** — Refers to the administration and control of projects, programs, situations, or organizations.

Training in supervision and management techniques is readily available at institutions of higher education and business seminars. Most fire brigade leaders are responsible for supervising fire brigade personnel or small groups. The experience gained at this level creates the foundation for supervising larger and more complex groups as the officer advances.

A fire brigade leader has the following basic functions that are common to most supervisory positions:

- Meeting supervisory responsibilities
- Establishing priorities for the unit
- Solving problems
- Establishing and communicating goals and objectives
- Building an effective team
- Motivating and supporting personnel
- Applying management principles

Meeting Supervisory Responsibilities

All supervisors have specific major responsibilities to an organization regardless of its type. No activity, project, or incident is finished until all assigned tasks have been completed. By accomplishing each of these responsibilities, the fire brigade leader can ensure an efficient and cohesive unit.

As part of all their responsibilities, fire brigade leaders must exhibit strong, positive leadership qualities at all times. A fire brigade leader must adhere to a standard of ethical, moral, and legal behavior that motivates subordinates to do the same. Key elements of a successful fire brigade leader's supervisory style include:

- Encouraging employee participation in the decision-making process.
- Delegating or involving members of the unit in planning.
- Respecting the judgment of employees.
- Teaching, enforcing, and following health and safety rules.
- Being a coach and mentor to employees.
- Showing consideration for diversity within the unit.
- Acknowledging accomplishments.
- Treating each member of the unit fairly and equitably.
- Referring a member to the organization's employee assistance program (EAP) is usually the most effective method for assisting employees on how to resolve personal problems.
- Keeping accurate records.
- Keeping lines of communication open at all times.
- Not contributing to or allowing situations that make other people feel uncomfortable or impose upon their personal dignity.
- Providing positive motivation for subordinates.

A supervisor must be consistent in meeting these responsibilities. Lack of consistency undermines a fire brigade leader's authority and ability to lead. Inconsistency can create relationships within the unit that distract attention from the primary goals of the organization and take energy, time, effort, and attention to repair.

Establishing Priorities for the Unit

A fire brigade leader's priorities are based primarily on the services provided and the mission of the organization. Having priorities helps the fire brigade leader:

- Maintain focus on the important activities.
- Manage time more effectively and direct energy toward the goals and objectives that provide the greatest good for the unit and community.
- Minimize competing priorities to reduce stress and frustration.
- Identify the unit's goals and objectives.

The first line supervisor should categorize activities into three levels of priority: emergency response, preparation for emergency response, and organizational duties. To meet these priorities, the fire brigade leader considers the following preparation activities:

- **Indirect preparation for emergency response** — Fire brigade leaders must be technically and tactically proficient and should ensure unit members are physically and mentally prepared to respond to emergency situations during their work shift.

- **Direct preparation for emergency response** — These activities include training and drilling as a team; ensuring the readiness of the personal protective equipment (PPE), apparatus, and tools; and developing preincident plans for occupancies and hazards within the response area.
- **Application of efficient organizational skills** — This category includes the completion of reports and records, facility maintenance, and other administrative duties assigned to the officer.

Fire brigade leaders who establish priorities for personnel and relate those priorities to their job functions are more likely to frame their expectations clearly. Fire brigade leaders who adhere to these priorities set strong examples for members of their units.

Solving Problems

As supervisors, fire brigade leaders should anticipate problems that may occur to prepare themselves for finding effective solutions. Such preparation can aid fire brigade leaders in brainstorming applicable solutions that can be applied to resolve a problem.

Anticipating Problems

A supervisor must recognize a potential problem, then develop and implement an effective and fair solution. For example, monitoring interaction among unit members is one way to anticipate personnel problems. Fire brigade leaders should counsel employees when necessary and listen to their concerns and solutions in order to mitigate tension between unit members. The supervisor must be familiar with and follow the organization's policies when handling employee problems. They may need to refer the employee to the organization's EAP or human resources department.

A supervisor should recognize developing situations and attempt to defuse them. A strong command presence can help the supervisor defuse the situation quickly and efficiently. Angry or emotional individuals will not hear rational solutions to problems. Once the individual or involved parties are calm, counseling can determine the root cause of the incident and find a solution. A complete record of the incident and counseling session should be kept to protect all parties involved and the supervisor from unsubstantiated accusations at a later date. This record should be kept confidential in accordance with the organization's policies and procedures.

Brainstorming

Understanding the brainstorming process of problem solving ensures that the team does not limit member participation. If a suggestion is valid and valuable, publicly acknowledge the contribution. If it is not, explain privately to the individual why it will not work or cannot be implemented. When using brainstorming, fire brigade leaders should:

- Encourage team members to be open and honest in their comments to foster an atmosphere of trust and respect within the group.
- Allow the team to have input in establishing measurements for success. The supervisor will then have fair and equitable guidelines on which to base awards or discipline.
- Take advantage of the existing diversity of team members. Capitalize on the strength of each member based on background, education, and experience. Diversity of membership assists in obtaining balanced team decisions. Team diversity is the best tool for combating **groupthink**.
- Understand that team members have outside influences that could impact their on-duty performance such as family, health, finances, and nonwork-related situations. The fire brigade leader must be prepared to give the employee guidance regarding organizational priorities.

Establishing and Communicating Goals and Objectives

A fire brigade leader must be able to establish certain short-range objectives, based on established priorities, to meet the long-range goals assigned to the unit. These objectives and the goals of the organization must be communicated to unit members. The acronym SMART can be used to establish objectives that are:

- Specific
- Measurable
- Attainable
- Relevant
- Time-bound

 SMART Objectives

SMART (Specific, Measurable, Attainable, Realistic, Timely) objectives are an important aspect of a fire brigade leader's duty to manage and lead their crew. An example is:

Using the fire brigade's approved assessment tool, the fire brigade leader will conduct an annual assessment of each crewmember at the end of June.

This objective is:

Specific – Conduct an annual assessment.

Measurable – Can be measured at the end of June.

Attainable – Reasonable time has been provided to complete this task.

Realistic – Task should be a regular duty of a brigade office.

Timely – Based on when all assessments must be completed and submitted.

Fire brigade leaders must communicate instructions clearly and concisely at emergency incidents, because there may be little or no time for subordinates to ask questions. Subordinates must be able to understand the commander's intent based on the directions that are given.

Groups work more efficiently and effectively toward a common goal when officers communicate goals and objectives clearly and provide periodic progress reports (feedback) to the unit. Employees who are involved in the process of establishing objectives will have more incentives to fulfill the objectives.

Employees should be involved in establishing goals and objectives using one of three methods:

- **Require the employee to accomplish a specific task** —The supervisor knows the best practice to perform the task, and has all the information necessary to make the decision, and the employee is thoroughly trained in performing the task as required.

- **Delegate tasks** — Allows employees to select the specific method for accomplishing the task. Involves giving the employee the authority to accomplish the task. The fire brigade leader must have confidence in the ability of the employees to accomplish the task.

- **Use democratic leadership principles** — Gives members of the fire brigade an opportunity to establish goals and objectives during the planning stage.

Democratic Leadership Approach

While fire brigade leaders seek employee involvement, they retain the responsibility for the task being completed regardless of which approach they use. In the democratic leadership approach, for example, a fire brigade leader may be involved in the decision-making process for purchasing a new fire apparatus. The fire brigade leader gathers information from unit members, coordinates efforts with all shifts, and provides input from the standpoint of apparatus users.

The fire brigade leader serves as a unit member, facilitator, and coach guiding the unit toward developing the apparatus specifications. Unit members may also assist in developing operational policies and procedures to include the apparatus' use, care, maintenance and logistical support.

Building an Effective Team

Fire brigade leaders usually supervise the smallest subdivision of a department. The unit typically consists of personnel, facilities, apparatus, and equipment appropriate to carry out their assigned duties. An effective unit exhibits teamwork, i.e. working together toward a desired objective.

To help create an effective team, a fire brigade leader should:

- Inform each person how they fit into the team, what is expected of them, what to expect of the leader, what the team's objectives are, and how accomplishing the objectives affects them.

- Have frequent planning meetings with the team to determine progress, explain deviations from the plan, resolve problems, and celebrate accomplishments.

- Work with individual team members to establish personal goals and objectives. Make certain they understand what responsibilities and authority they have, and they can be comfortable asking for assistance when necessary.

- Encourage team members to make suggestions or provide solutions for problems.

A fire brigade leader guides the individuals in the group and focuses their efforts on becoming a cohesive team. This journey usually follows a four-stage development model that includes *forming, storming, norming, and performing:*

- **Forming** — Employees are initially uncertain of their roles in the group. They are not certain that they can trust or work with the other members. As relationships grow within the group, trust and respect develop, and the members begin to see themselves as part of the group. Group members become enthusiastic about the challenges of a new project or task. This phase is critical within the team-development process and one in which a fire brigade leader can have a significant effect.

- **Storming** — Conflict may result at this stage as members jockey for informal leadership or attempt to exert their own influence over the group. Conflict may occur when a new officer joins an existing unit that contains older, more experienced fire brigade members. The leader is supportive in this stage and actively listens to members and provides explanations for decisions. The most critical aspect of successful team development is to reduce the amount of time the group spends in the storming phase.

- **Norming** — The group establishes and adheres to its own set of norms and values. Members become closer and more cohesive. The fire brigade leader must be aware of team norms and values as much as possible to make sure that those norms don't violate the sense of decency. The leader transitions into the role of team member, allowing other team members to share leadership responsibilities.

- **Performing** — The supervisor works to maintain team spirit as the group accomplishes its objectives. The group is a true team with leadership shared by all members.

Motivating and Supporting Personnel

The best way to support and motivate personnel is to create a working environment where personnel can be invested in their work and excel in their positions. The fire brigade leader can create this work environment using a number of methods including:

- Empowering employees
- Providing rewards and incentives
- Coaching, counseling, and mentoring members of the unit
- Celebrating accomplishments

Empowering Employees

Empowering employees requires the supervisor to relinquish some authority and have confidence in employees' skills, judgment, and abilities. The supervisor is helping to increase their self-image and productivity through employee empowerment. Empowering employees is a form of delegation that:

- Allows subordinates to take responsibility for their actions and decisions.
- Helps build self-esteem and motivation within the employee.
- Is based on giving decision-making power to employees instead of the supervisor retaining it.
- Gives employees a vested interest in a project and the organization.
- Allows employees to use special, non-job related skills such as photography, calligraphy, computer skills, or other hobbies to assist with projects.

The fire brigade leader should begin with small attainable projects if unit members have not experienced the empowerment process previously. The following steps can be used:

Step 1: Identify the problem. The solution must be attainable.

Step 2: State that all solutions will be considered but the best one will be adopted. Tell the unit that they must prioritize the suggested solutions and include a contingency in the event the best choice cannot be used.

Step 3: Explain the reality that outside forces may prevent the adoption of some results.

Rewarding Employees

Fire brigade leaders usually do not have authority to grant raises or provide monetary rewards for employees. That does not mean that they cannot provide rewards and incentives for good work within the unit.

Rewards are critical as motivational techniques in departments/organizations. Some rewards and incentives fire brigade leaders may provide include:

- Writing a letter for their file
- A simple pat on the back
- Challenge coins
- Holding group gatherings or parties to create cohesiveness and spirit
- Making positive statements on the skills and abilities of members of the unit to improve self-esteem and team pride
- Making appropriate comments on an employee's job performance evaluations
- Acknowledging a unit's or an individual's accomplishments to the organization's administration

The incentive's size or value is not the critical part of providing incentives for accomplishments; it is that the fire brigade leader made an effort to acknowledge an individual's contribution. Reward and award programs are critical to the volunteer staffing component and improve morale in combination and career departments/organizations.

Most organizations have award programs that the fire brigade leader should use. Rewards and awards must be earned in order to validate the incentive. When a person is presented with an unearned reward or award, disrespect is shown to that individual and to those who truly deserved the recognition.

Rewards should be given as soon as possible following the accomplishment. Delaying the award or reward lessens the value of the recognition. Consistency must be applied in the types of rewards given, situations that result in rewards, and justifications for giving them.

Coaching Employees

Coaching is a process of giving motivational direction, positive reinforcement, and constructive feedback to employees in order to maintain and improve their performance. Effective feedback needs to be positive, immediate, direct, and frequent. As a coach, the fire brigade leader teaches and directs the subordinate through encouragement and advice **(Figure 20.4)**.

Figure 20.4 A fire brigade leader coaching his personnel during a break at a structural fire fighting exercise.

An effective coach helps a subordinate establish a goal, determine how to reach it, and provides suggestions when they are requested. Telling subordinates what to do and how to do it is not as effective because the subordinates will not feel responsibility for the process.

Counseling Employees

Counseling is a formal process which assists participants in identifying and resolving personal, behavioral, or career problems that are adversely affecting performance. Sessions may be scheduled on a periodic basis such as annually, before promotional examinations, or when the subordinate exhibits unacceptable behavior.

Counseling should occur in private, and a record should be kept of the session. The fire brigade leader must adhere to the organization's counseling policies and procedures. The fire brigade leader must also be familiar with any labor/management agreement regarding the right to union representation during counseling sessions and the grievance procedures established by the agreement.

The following four-step method of counseling can be used:

Step 1: Describe the current performance — Describe levels in a positive manner. Specifically state the required behavior and expectations. Explain how and why current behavior is not acceptable. Use specific examples to identify how behaviors can improve.

Step 2: Describe the desired performance — State in detail exactly what action is expected or required, in order to provide clear direction for the employee.

Step 3: Gain a commitment for change — Ask the employee to agree to the new level of performance. The agreement may be considered a contract and become part of the employee's formal personnel record.

Step 4: Follow up the commitment — Observe the employee following the counseling session to determine whether performance improves, or schedule a follow-up meeting to discuss progress. If change does not occur, subsequent counseling sessions may be required. If unacceptable behavior continues after subsequent counseling, follow organization policy on disciplinary action.

Mentoring Employees

Mentoring is used to better prepare individuals for their roles and responsibilities within the organization under the direction of a positive role model **(Figure 20.5)**. Mentoring programs enhance individual skills and improve productivity. Mentoring includes:

- Providing guidance in career choices.
- Assisting in gaining specialized training.
- Providing outside resources.
- Making challenging work assignments.
- Monitoring the achievements of subordinates.
- Encouraging diversity training.

Figure 20.5 Mentoring personnel is an important job for fire brigade leaders.

Both mentors and mentees should participate voluntarily and enthusiastically in the program. Mentoring, when approached as a mandatory activity, may make the individuals involved resentful and may limit their participation.

Some business texts suggest a mentor should not be a direct supervisor to the subordinate. In the U.S. Air Force mentoring model, the immediate supervisor serves as the primary mentor for each subordinate in a unit. Mentoring should not restrict the subordinate's ability to seek additional counseling and professional development advice from other sources or mentors.

Supervisors must make themselves available to subordinates who seek career guidance and counsel. The accomplishments of both the mentor and subordinate should be acknowledged throughout the process.

Acknowledging Accomplishments

Acknowledge the accomplishment of objectives as soon as possible. This acknowledgment signals the completion of a project and shows members of the fire brigade that their contributions are important. Announce the completion of the project to the rest of the organization and congratulate participants on the results. Keep celebrations and acknowledgements appropriate so that they continue to having meaning for fire brigade members and must be earned.

Applying Management Principles

A fire brigade leader may be required to manage incidents or projects and should be familiar with basic management principles. As supervisors, fire brigade leaders must be able to apply proven management principles. These principles are based on management theories that have been developed, applied, and validated over the past century.

Managing is the process of controlling or directing available resources for the purpose of achieving a goal or objective through the use of authority or persuasion. An effective fire brigade leader must:

- Be aware of relevant management functions.

- Develop and refine the skills necessary to carry out those functions.

All organizational personnel bear some responsibility for the achievement of that organization's goals and objectives. As supervisors, fire brigade leaders are directly responsible for the effective and efficient use of resources under their command. The primary resources are generally considered to be:

- Fire brigade members

- Facilities

- Apparatus (vehicles)

- Tools and equipment

- Corporate or organizational authority

This section provides the fire brigade leader with a basic knowledge of the management functions, the skills required to be an effective manager, and the planning function. The fire brigade leader must realize that management, like leadership and supervision, is a broad topic and cannot be completely presented in a single reference.

Management Functions

For the scope of this manual, the management process will be limited to four functions:

- *Planning* — Encompasses the broadest view of the organization (creation of the mission statement and setting goals and objectives) and the narrowest (development of tactical plans for accomplishing a specific objective).

- *Organizing* — Coordinating tasks and resources to accomplish the unit's goals and objectives as follows:

  — Establishing the internal structure of the fire brigade

  — Creating divisions of labor

  — Coordinating the allocation of resources

  — Taking responsibility for tasks and flow of information within the fire brigade

  — Filling of positions with qualified people

- *Directing* — Guiding, influencing, inspiring, and motivating employees to achieve the goals and objectives within a group. Directing is a proactive approach to managing, as the fire brigade leader applies the concepts of leading and supervising.

- *Controlling* — Establishing and implementing the mechanisms to ensure that objectives are attained; includes setting performance standards, measuring and reporting the actual performance, comparing the performance standard with the actual performance, and taking preventive or corrective action to close the gap between the two levels of performance.

These four functions are essential to the management of fire brigades. Fire brigade leaders must develop the skills necessary to apply relevant functions to the duties assigned to them during both emergency or nonemergency operations and duties.

Management Skills

Proper application of the management functions requires the fire brigade leader to possess certain management skills. While most fire brigade leaders or officer candidates may have the knowledge to perform the technical tasks of the fire brigade, they may need to continually develop the interpersonal and management skills to be an effective fire brigade leader.

The following management skills are necessary for an effective fire brigade leader:

- **Administrative Skills** — Methods and techniques required to perform certain tasks as a manager such as computer skills; knowledge of laws, codes, ordinances, and labor/management agreements; report writing skills; data analysis skills for problem solving and risk identification, and other skills that will be used to prepare budgets, create reports, or develop specifications. These are in addition to the skills required of the officer as an emergency responder, such as the ability to manage an incident, apply strategic and tactical concepts to situations, and the knowledge of specialized emergency response skills.

- **Human and Communication Skills** — Interpersonal skills that include the ability to work with other people and supervise subordinates; success or failure often hinges on one's ability to communicate effectively.

- **Conceptual and Decision-making Skills** — Skills that include the ability to understand abstract ideas and solve problems; also the ability to understand the organization as a whole and recognize how the various parts are interrelated.

Planning Function

Planning determines in advance what an organization, a group, or an individual should do and how it will get done. It is the foundation of the management process. While facility fire brigade managers and administrative staff develop formal organizational plans, it is the fire brigade leaders who must plan how to implement them.

Planning should be documented in a timely manner. Documentation provides evidence of the decisions that were made and serves as a guide for future planning. Should the results of the planning fail to meet the required goal, the documentation will assist in determining why the plan needs to be altered and how to do it. Fire brigade leaders must know the organization's plans, how the planning process works, how to apply it at the brigade or team, and the process for altering existing plans.

Plans are generally classified based on the frequency with which they are used. Two broad categories are established: standing plans and single-use plans. Plans may also be categorized as strategic, tactical, operational/administrative, and contingency. Plan descriptions:

- **Standing** — Policies, procedures, and rules that are used frequently to manage the day-to-day emergency and nonemergency unit activities. These help ensure the consistent and equal application of authority while defining responsibility within the organization.

- **Single-Use** — Accomplish a specific objective such as the development of a program, project, or budget. These plans are usually intended to reach an objective within a short period of time.

- **Strategic** — Chart the course of the organization over an indefinite future that is divided into definite time components. The plan attempts to take into account the external factors that will affect the organization such as changes in the economy, demographics, service requirements, hazards, and technology.

- **Operational/Administrative** — Focus on how objectives will be accomplished. They deal with those factors that are within the control of the organization, objective, and fact-based while strategic plans are subjective.

- **Contingency** — Create alternative plans that can be implemented in the event of unforeseen events that make original plans unsuitable.

Task Management

The fire brigade leader is responsible for completing or ensuring delegated tasks have been completed. Planning, organizing, controlling, and evaluating skills are required to complete a task. Some steps in this process include:

- Establishing and communicating the plan for task completion to employees. The plan contains the sequence of steps, the time schedule for step completion, and the assignment of duties, responsibility, and authority.

- Ensuring that the schedule is realistic with attainable objectives. Attainable objectives should be based on the application of available resources to include personnel, funding, time, and materials.

- Organizing employees to work as a team with an objective or a goal in focus. Leadership and the creation of team spirit are essential to the success of the unit.

- Delegating the appropriate amount of responsibility and authority to employees to give them a sense of ownership in the project. However, final responsibility and authority always remains with the fire brigade leader.

- Evaluating the quality and completion of the task. Monitor progress to determine whether the plan is being followed or a change must be made to resolve unforeseen difficulties. For more complex tasks, the use of such tools as flow charts or **program (or project) evaluation and review technique (PERT) charts** to track task progress may be advisable.

Information Management and Record Keeping

NFPA 1081 (2018): 7.1.3

Each fire brigade should have an established information management and record keeping program in place. Provisions must be made in the organizational statement and in the brigade's SOPs that identify what documentation is necessary, who must prepare it, and how this information is to be maintained. The fire brigade leader must be familiar with the organization's system and how to use it effectively.

Records management programs need to allow personnel to input and extract information effectively. Supervisors must understand the records management process of an organization. An organization's records management system may perform the following actions:

- Operate efficiently and effectively.
- Prepare short-, medium-, and long-range plans.
- Meet legal and AHJ obligations and requirements.
- Meet the expectations of internal and external customers and stakeholders.
- Identify and safeguard historically important records.
- Assign tasks and identify responsible individuals.

  Systematic management of records assists the organization in performing the following actions:
- Know what records the organization has and how to locate them easily.
- Save administrative costs, both in staff time and storage capacity.
- Support decision-making processes.
- Be accountable.
- Monitor the accomplishment of strategic goals and objectives.
- Provide administrative continuity in the event of a disaster.
- Protect the interests of internal and external customers and stakeholders.

Fire brigade leaders generate raw data and create reports that become part of the system. They may also be responsible for analyzing information for the purpose of assisting in decision-making, establishing, or monitoring trends. They must follow their organization's record management system and strive for accuracy in the collection of data used in records and reports.

Record Types

Fire brigades primarily maintain divisional budget, inventory, maintenance (preventive and corrective), activity, and personnel records. Records categories may include such topics as:

- Training
- Performance
- Attendance
- Fire safety surveys
- Training sessions
- Drills
- Actual responses (incident reports)
- Critiques of incident responses
- Lessons learned
- Near misses
- Inspections of personal protective equipment
- Inspection dates and inventory of brigade equipment, including who performed it
- Maintenance records for all equipment
- Specifications for all equipment purchased
- Fit testing for any respirator equipment or self-contained breathing apparatus
- Medical
- Exposures (or suspected exposures) to hazardous materials

Divisional Budget

Fire brigade or divisional budget records may include all information used to create them, budget status reports, past budgets, and budget requests that were not funded. Purchasing records, contracts, surplus sales, and other similar records should also be retained with this information.

Fire brigade leaders should maintain the data they used to create their budget requests, justifications for requests, and processes used to generate requests. They should also maintain all records relating to purchases or purchase requests that they make and what has been spent on each item.

Inventory

The fire brigade generally maintains inventory and fixed-assets records. These records should be accurate and include information on all materials, equipment, facilities, land, and apparatus in the possession of the organization.

A copy of all inventory records for the unit's apparatus, personnel, equipment, and facilities should be maintained. Fire brigade leaders may be responsible for performing periodic inventories of their areas of responsibility. Any changes in inventory must be noted, reported, and, in some cases, justified.

Fire brigade leaders may need to establish and maintain an inventory of necessary supplies at each station. The facility may be stocked with disaster preparedness supplies in the event of a natural disaster or other uncontrollable circumstances. Each brigade office or station should be prepared to operate for a number of hours without the ability to procure certain items.

Fire brigade leaders can often order supplies through an online program arranged through the organization or they may work with local vendors and companies to maintain the supplies in the station. The organization may already have certain vendors of choice that fire brigade leaders can utilize. Supplies can be obtained with a purchase order or with an organizational credit card.

Maintenance

Fire brigades keep maintenance records on stations, other facilities, vehicles, tools, and equipment. These records are usually kept in two distinct categories: preventive and corrective. Both sets of maintenance records hold significant legal value when an organization has to go to court over an incident involving a piece of its equipment. The fire brigade leader, fire marshal, or facility fire protection engineer usually maintains and analyzes records.

Preventive maintenance is performed to prevent damage, reduce wear, and extend the useful life of an item, vehicle, or facility. Records that are compiled during the preventive maintenance of apparatus, facilities, or pieces of equipment can provide the information necessary to predict a trend or justify a replacement so it is usually performed according to a predetermined schedule. Past experience, industry standards, and manufacturers' recommendations combine to form the basis for a schedule of periodic inspection and maintenance. Frequent inspection and cleaning often reveal incipient problems that are relatively easy and inexpensive to correct. Examples of preventive maintenance include, but are not limited to:

- Periodic inspection, cleaning, and maintenance of fire station floor coverings, heating and air-conditioning systems, fire extinguishers, and appliances.
- Apparatus engine oil changes and chassis lubrication.
- Annual fire pump tests.
- Periodic tests and calibrations of electronic meters (pump panel gauges, monitoring devices, and air-quality testing instruments).
- Fire hose inspections and annual testing.
- Annual and after-each use inspections of ground ladders, respiratory breathing equipment, and personal protective equipment (PPE).

Corrective maintenance (repairs) is may be necessary due to an unforeseen event. Damage may occur because of an accident, overuse, operator error, or abuse. When an item is damaged or ceases to function, it must be repaired or replaced as soon as possible.

Deciding to repair or replace an item is often based on its maintenance record and life expectancy. The corrective maintenance record is a critically important part of the decision-making process in the following ways:

- Showing that an item is relatively new would probably indicate that the item should be repaired
- Showing that an item is old and has a history of increasingly frequent failures or breakdowns may indicate the need to replace the item with something newer and more reliable

Activity (Incident Reports)

Activity records are the basis for planning and justifying budget requests. These records provide historical documentation of all events, incidents, and projects that members of the organization participated in during a specific time period. Activity records are contained in the company/station logbook and on forms provided for each type of activity. Records include information about:

- Emergency and nonemergency responses
- Investigations
- Communications
- Inspections
- Training

Personnel

Personnel records include training, performance, attendance, hazardous materials or biological/medical exposures, and medical. Personnel information must be kept current as it may be needed in an emergency or a line-of-duty death (LODD).

Personnel records are confidential with the exception of attendance records (daily personnel roster) and similar documents. Fire brigade leader must be careful to protect confidentiality and keep all personnel records secure. Personnel records may be maintained in the facility's fire brigade, administrative, human resources, or occupational health (medical) offices.

Training records are essential components of a successful training program. Accurate records give an organization long-term inventories of its training activities. The fire brigade leader must document company level training and should include:

- Topic of training session
- Date of training
- Participants

- Time designated for training
- Location
- Outcomes

Performance is documented and measured through personal job performance evaluations. These are part of an individual's personnel file which are maintained by the organization for each employee. The supervisor may also retain a copy for future job performance evaluations. These records (like medical records) are confidential. Performance evaluations are an important part of an officer's ability to help steer a subordinate's career in a successful direction. Evaluations can help individuals:

- Spot trends and habits in personal performance and behavior
- Reinforce good skills and discipline
- Correct unfavorable behaviors
- Improve their knowledge, skills, and abilities
- Set future goals and objectives

Attendance records that support training requirements are also maintained. These records document that an individual or unit has completed a specified number of hours of training in a specific topic. Attendance records can also establish a trend for nonparticipation that may result in changing training or activity schedules or termination from the brigade if applicable.

The facility's occupational health office maintains hazardous materials or biological/medical exposure records that document significant individual exposures to hazardous materials such as chemical, and biological, radiological, and nuclear materials are part of an individual's medical record. Because of the delayed effects of some of these hazards and the compounding effect of others and OSHA regulations, the organization must retain accurate records for 30 years following the end of an individual's employment. Attendance records may also be used to support exposure records when a facility is determined to contain a toxic atmosphere such as a carbon monoxide leak from a gas-powered water heater.

Medical records are kept on all employees for the duration of their employment plus 30 years or longer. This record includes the individual's pre-employment medical examination, periodic medical evaluations and examinations, post-medical-leave examination, exposure reports, and the postemployment or termination medical examination. Fire brigade leaders must record:

- All job-related injuries or illnesses that affect personnel assigned to them
- Non job-related illnesses when they result in the use of sick or injury leave
- Trends that might indicate the abuse of sick leave

Hard Copy and Electronic Data Storage/Retrieval Formats

Records and reports may be in written (hard copy), digital, or both formats, depending upon the facility. The methods for cataloging and storing the files vary. Much of how this procedure is done depends on the size of the facility fire brigade and the number of facilities it is responsible for protecting. Hard copy files may be kept in secure filing cabinets or vaults onsite or off site. Digital files are generally kept onsite with backup copies stored in secure offsite locations.

Many organizations maintain all types of records using some form of electronic data collection, analysis, organization, distribution, and storage/retrieval system. They are also using computer-based word processors for writing reports and completing forms. Fire brigade leaders must learn to use the computer-based system in their organizations if they are to stay current and function at maximum efficiency **(Figure 20.6)**.

Figure 20.6 Fire brigade leaders should be familiar with the computer systems and programs used at their facility.

The variety of hardware and software available for electronic records management is ever expanding. In terms of hardware, fire brigade leaders must learn to operate the components that are required to make any computer function. In terms of software, they must learn to use programs designed for their organization's particular operating system. Countless software programs are available for these systems, and many of them able to function on different operating systems. Fire brigade leaders must understand company policies and procedures regarding the proper use of computer systems, access to the Internet, and various issues that are specific to the use of computers.

 Computer-Use Concerns

Fire brigade personnel must be aware of certain situations that can result from using computers the company owns. They must also communicate these concerns to their subordinates to prevent any potential problems. The following list gives computer-specific concerns that brigade personnel must be aware of when using the organization's computer system:

- **Copyright** — Material found on the Internet may be copyright-protected. If a member wishes to use the material for training purposes or providing information in reports, it is important to gain permission from the original author or the agency that owns the web site or content.

- **Password Protection** — Members may be assigned a password that allows access to either a computer or the Internet/intranet. Passwords are created to prevent the unauthorized use of a computer or access to records that are not public. Members must not provide their passwords to anyone else.
- **Viruses** — Computer systems are the target of viruses (infection/disruption programs) and spyware (private information access programs). Viruses and spyware disrupt computer systems or access information that is not normally available to the public. Fire brigade leaders must ensure that the organization's computer security and protection programs (firewalls and antivirus and antispyware programs) are not compromised and must report any evidence that a virus or spyware is present on a computer.
- **Unauthorized Use** — Fire brigade leaders must adhere to all policies that define the appropriate use of an organization's computers and limit access to the Internet. Generally, only software that is licensed to an organization can be installed on its computers. There may be restrictions placed on the use of organization-provided equipment for personal use.

Chapter Review

1. Why is leadership important in emergency situations?
2. What are the basic types of facility fire brigades?
3. What is the difference between centralized and decentralized authority?
4. What variables affect the span of control in any given situation?
5. Name and describe five leadership traits that fire brigade leaders should cultivate.
6. What are the key elements of a successful fire brigade leader's supervisory style?
7. What preparation activities should be taken into consideration when establishing unit priorities?
8. What should be considered when brainstorming to solve problems?
9. Name and describe the three possible methods for involving employees in establishing goals and objective.
10. Name and describe the four-stage development model for creating an effective team.
11. What is the four-step method for counseling an employee?
12. What managements skills are necessary for an effective fire brigade leader?
13. Why are corrective maintenance records critically important to the decision-making process?

Discussion Questions

1. What may be some effective activities to help build teamwork and trust in your fire brigade?
2. What type of records will you likely be responsible for at your facility?

Key Terms

Groupthink — A pattern of thinking that includes self-deception, peer pressure, and conformity to group ethics and values.

Management — Process of accomplishing organizational objectives through effective and efficient handling of resources; official, sanctioned leadership.

Program (or Project) Evaluation and Review Technique (PERT) Chart — A statistical tool used in project management that is designed to analyze and represent the tasks involved in completing given project.

Supervision — The act or function of overseeing something or somebody.

Facility Fire Brigade Leader

Chapter Contents

JPRs addressed in this chapter

This chapter provides information that addresses the following job performance requirements of NFPA 1081, *Standard for Facility Fire Brigade Member Professional Qualifications (2018)*.

7.1.3	7.2.2	7.2.4	7.2.6
7.2.1	7.2.3	7.2.5	

1. Review the aspects of fire dynamics. [7.2.2]

2. Review the aspects of incident management systems. [7.1.3, 7.2.1]

3. Describe how the Incident Commander uses NIMS-ICS to manage an incident. [7.2.2, 7.2.3]

4. Review rapid intervention crew operations (RIC). [7.2.3]

5. Describe the methods for managing incident scene priorities. [7.2.2, 7.2.4]

6. Describe the methods of developing and implementing Incident Action Plan (IAP). [7.2.2, 7.2.4]

7. Explain the considerations for the allocation and coordination of resources. [7.2.2, 7.2.4]

8. List incident support scene operations. [7.2.5]

9. List the actions for terminating the incident. [7.2.5]

10. Explain the challenges of maintaining safety during a training evolution. [7.2.3, 7.2.6]

11. Describe the methods of using the ICS model to supervise training. [7.2.3, 7.2.6]

12. Describe the methods for evaluating a training evolution. [7.2.3, 7.2.6]

13. Identify potential environmental issues that may occur at training evolutions. [7.2.3, 7.2.6]

14. Explain the process of an accident investigation of a training evolution. [7.2.3, 7.2.6]

Chapter 21
Incident Management and Training Responsibilities

During emergencies, facility fire brigade leaders must prioritize their response efforts and implement their organization's incident management system, most often the National Incident Management System — Incident Command System (NIMS-ICS). This chapter addresses three incident prioritization models:

- **Incident Priorities:** Life safety, incident stabilization, and property/environmental conservation
- **RECEO-VS:** Rescue, Exposures, Confinement, Extinguishment, Overhaul, Ventilation, and Salvage
- **SLICE-RS:** Size-up, Locate, Identify, Cool, Extinguish, Rescue, and Salvage

Fire brigade leaders use a variety of different incident plans to coordinate their emergency response efforts. This chapter describes the following types of incident plans:

- Preincident plan
- Operational plans
- Incident Action Plans (IAP)
- Incident Safety Plan

This chapter also explains NIMS-ICS terminology and the following working components:

- Working with Unified Command
- Using communications
- Implementing NIMS-ICS
- Transferring command
- Tracking resources
- Documenting incidents
- Terminating the incident
- Interacting with outside agencies

The final part of this chapter addresses the fire brigade leader's role in supervising training evolutions.

Review Section: Fire Dynamics

NFPA 1081 (2018): 7.2.2

Advanced exterior and interior structural fire brigade members need to have a scientific understanding of fire dynamics. The fire triangle and fire tetrahedron models are used to explain the elements of fire and how fires can be extinguished. The fire triangle consists of three elements necessary for combustion to occur: fuel, oxygen, and heat. The fire tetrahedron model includes the chemical chain reaction to explain flaming or gas-phase combustion. Remove any one of these elements and the fire will be extinguished.

As a fuel burns, its chemical composition changes, creating new substances called the products of combustion. Common products of combustion include heat, smoke, ash, water vapor, carbon monoxide (CO), carbon dioxide (CO_2), and hydrogen cyanide (HCN).

For a fire to start and continue to burn, heat must be transferred from one point or object to another. Heat transfers from warmer objects to cooler objects. Heat transfers occurs by three mechanisms: conduction, convection, and radiation. Conduction is the transfer of heat through and between solids. Convection is the transfer of thermal energy by the circulation or movement of a fluid (liquid or gas). Radiation is the transmission of energy as electromagnetic waves, such as light waves, radio waves, or X-rays, without an intervening medium.

Oxygen in the air is the primary oxidizing agent in most fires. Normally, air consists of about 21 percent oxygen. At normal ambient temperatures (68°F [20°C]), materials can ignite and burn in oxygen concentrations as low as 15 percent. When oxygen concentration is limited, the flaming combustion will diminish, causing combustion to continue in the nonflaming mode. Nonflaming or smoldering combustion can continue in extremely low oxygen concentrations when the surrounding environment's temperature is relatively low. However, at high ambient temperatures, flaming combustion may continue in considerably lower oxygen concentrations.

When the oxygen concentration is higher than normal, materials exhibit different burning characteristics. Materials that burn in normal oxygen levels will burn more intensely and may ignite more readily in oxygen-enriched atmospheres. Some petroleum-based materials will autoignite in oxygen-enriched atmospheres.

Oxygen is also important to life. As the oxygen in a structure is consumed by fire, the amount of oxygen available to support life diminishes. Between 15 percent to 19 percent concentrations, coordination is impaired. Between 10 percent to 12 percent concentrations, an exposed human experiences dizziness, headache, and fatigue. Around 8 percent to 10 percent concentrations, mental failure, nausea, vomiting, and unconsciousness occur. Exposures below 8 percent can result in death in as soon as 8 minutes.

The four stages of fire development can be generally defined as follows:

- **Incipient stage** — When the three elements of the fire triangle come together and the combustion process begins.

- **Growth stage** — More of the initial fuel package becomes involved and the production of heat and smoke increases. If there are other fuels close to the initial fuel package, radiant heat from the fire may begin to pyrolize nearby fuels which could spread the fire to new fuel packages.

- **Fully Developed stage** — Occurs when all combustible materials in the compartment are burning at their peak heat release rate based on the available oxygen.

- **Decay stage** — As the fire consumes the available fuel or oxygen and the heat release rate begins to decline, the fire enters the decay stage.

Thermal layering is the tendency of gases to form into layers according to temperature, gas density, and pressure. Provided that there is no mechanical mixing from a fan or a hose stream, the hottest gases will form the highest layer, while the cooler gases will form the lower layers. Changes in ventilation and flow path can significantly alter thermal layering. The flow path is defined as the space between the air intake and the exhaust outlet. Multiple openings (intakes and exhausts) create multiple flow paths.

As the mass and energy of the hot gas layer increases, so does the pressure. Higher pressure causes the hot gas layer to spread downward within the compartment and laterally through any openings such as doors or windows. If there are no openings for lateral movement, the higher pressure gases have no lateral path to follow to an area of lower pressure. As a result, the hot gases will begin to fill the compartment starting at the ceiling and filling down.

The interface between the hot gas layers and cooler layer of air is commonly referred to as the neutral plane because the net pressure is zero, or neutral, where the layers meet. The neutral plane exists at openings where hot gases exit and cooler air enters the compartment. At these openings, hot gases at higher than ambient pressure exit through the top of the opening above the neutral plane. Lower pressure air from outside the compartment entrains into the opening below the neutral plane.

Backdraft occurs in a space containing a high concentration of heated flammable gases that lack sufficient oxygen for flaming combustion. When potential backdraft conditions exist in a compartment, the introduction of a new source of oxygen will return the fire to a fully involved state rapidly (often explosively). A backdraft can occur with the creation of a horizontal or vertical opening. Backdraft indicators include:

- **Building indicators** — Interior configuration, fuel load, thermal properties, amount of trapped fuel gases, and a lack of ventilation

- **Smoke indicators** — Pulsing smoke movement around small openings in the building; smoke-stained windows

- **Air flow indicators** — High velocity air intake

- **Heat indicators** — High heat, crackling or breaking sounds

- **Flame indicators** — Little or no visible flame

Review Section: Incident Management System

NFPA 1081 (2018): 7.1.3 , 7.2.1

The Incident Command System (ICS), a component of NIMS, is the basis for safe and efficient incident scene management. As a result of Homeland Security Presidential Directive 5, the National Incident Management System (NIMS) is required to be used.

NIMS-ICS is designed to be applicable to both small, single-unit incidents that may last a few minutes to complex, large-scale incidents involving several agencies and many mutual aid units that possibly last for days or weeks. NIMS-ICS combines command strategy with organizational procedures to provide a functional, systematic organizational structure. The ICS organizational structure clearly shows the lines of communication and chain of command.

NIMS-ICS involves five major organizational functions:

- **Command** — The Incident Commander (IC) is the person in overall command of an incident. The IC develops and implements a strategic plan that sets long-term goals and objectives for an incident. The IC has the authority to call resources to the incident and release them from it. Other positions within the Command staff may include:
  — Incident Safety Officer (ISO)
  — Intelligence Officer (IO)
  — Liaison Officer (LO)
  — Public Information Officer (PIO)

- **Operations** — The Operations Section Chief reports to the IC and is responsible for the management of all operations that affect the primary mission. The Operations Section Chief directs tactical operations to meet the IC's strategic goals. Operations may be subdivided into multiple Branches.

- **Planning** — The Planning Section is responsible for the development of the incident concerning its collection, evaluation, dissemination, and use of information. Planning also maintains the status of all resources assigned to the incident. Command uses this to develop strategic goals and contingency plans. Units under the Planning Section include the following:

- Resource Unit

- Situation Status Unit

- Demobilization Unit

- Technical specialists whose services are required

- **Logistics** — The Logistics Section provides services to support the incident. The following Branches are within Logistics:

  - Support Branch — delivers supplies, facilities, and ground support (vehicle services)

  - Service Branch — provides medical, communications, and food services

- **Finance/Administration** — The Finance/Administration Section tracks and documents all costs and financial aspects of the incident. Generally, this section is activated only on large-scale, long-term incidents.

Unified Command

Unified Command is established when more than one agency has incident jurisdiction or when incidents cross political jurisdictions. These agencies work together through the designated members of the Unified Command to establish a common set of objectives and strategies and a single **incident action plan (IAP)**. Personnel who may be included in Unified Command during incidents in fixed facilities may include:

- Facility IC

- Local fire department IC

- State environmental control

- Local or state emergency management agency

- Police agencies and federal agencies

Communications

Emergency incident communications take a variety of forms. Face-to-face, verbal communication is the most efficient form of communication, but an operation may necessitate using telephone and radio communication as well. Mobile and portable radios are usually the primary communications media.

When making assignments face-to-face, the IC should:

- Remain calm and speak clearly (command presence).

- Call incident personnel by the NIMS-ICS position he or she occupies. For example, the Incident Commander is always called "IC." The incident name may be included ("Warehouse IC") if more than one incident is in progress.

- Issue assignments clearly and concisely, addressing safety considerations and desired outcomes.

- Recipients should repeat assignments to ensure the message has been accurately received.

Personnel should exercise proper radio discipline as well as the following protocols:

- Transmit all radio communications in plain English ("clear text").

- Confine transmissions to essential information and keep them as brief as possible.

- Emergency transmissions always have priority over other traffic.

- Avoid transmitting whenever anyone declares that he or she has emergency traffic.

- Remain calm and speak clearly.

- Call incident personnel by the NIMS-ICS position he or she occupies.

- Issue assignments clearly and concisely, addressing safety considerations and desired outcomes.

- Recipients should repeat assignments to ensure the message has been accurately received.

Implementing the System

The first person arriving on the scene of an emergency should initiate NIMS-ICS. This person may need to sound an alarm to notify the other facility personnel of the emergency. This individual should then begin to size up the situation to answers the following questions:

- What has occurred?
- What is the current status of the emergency?
- Is anyone injured or trapped?
- What is likely to happen in the foreseeable future?
- Can the emergency be handled with the resources on scene or en route?
- Is there a preplan for this emergency?
- Does the emergency fall within the scope of the training received?

This individual is temporarily in command of the incident. If the emergency is beyond the scope of this individual's training, command should be transferred to someone more qualified at the earliest opportunity. Meanwhile, the individual should do whatever he or she is qualified to do, such as notifying plant safety personnel of the situation, assisting with evacuations, and initiating the IMS by naming the incident and announcing the location of the **Incident Command Post** (**ICP** or sometimes just CP for Command Post).

The IC should begin to formulate an incident action plan using any existing preplan information. The plan should reflect the following priorities:

- Ensure personnel safety and survival.
- Rescue or evacuate endangered occupants.
- Eliminate the hazard.
- Confine the emergency to its initial area when responders arrived.
- Protect exposures.
- Extinguish the fire/eliminating the hazard.
- Perform loss control (overhaul and salvage).
- Clean up and protect the environment.
- Conduct incident termination (return situation to as near normal as possible).
- Document the incident response.

There should be only *ONE* Incident Commander, even when Unified Command is used. To avoid the confusion that conflicting orders cause, the IC should issue all orders through the chain of command. The IC will gather and organize enough resources to handle the incident. The Incident Commander can appoint a Command staff to help gather, process, and disseminate information, if needed.

All incident personnel must function according to the incident action plan. Fire brigade leaders should follow SOPs, and they should direct every action toward achieving the goals and objectives specified in the plan.

Transfer of Command

When the nature and the scope of an incident are beyond the IC's capabilities, this individual must be prepared to transfer command to the next arriving person with a higher level of expertise or authority. Transfer of command should be done face to face; however, if this interaction is not feasible, it can be done over the radio. Command can only be transferred to someone who is on the scene. The person relinquishing command must provide the person assuming command with a situation status report which should include the following information:

- What happened
- Whether anyone was injured or trapped
- What has been done so far
- What is currently underway
- Whether the problem has stabilized or is getting worse
- What resources are on scene or en route and their assignments
- Whether it appears that current resources are adequate for the situation or that more resources need to be called in

The person assuming on-scene command should acknowledge receipt of the status report by repeating it back to the other person. If the reiteration is accurate, the person assuming on-scene command is ready to accept control of and responsibility for the management of the incident. The former on-scene IC can then be reassigned to an operating unit or retained at the ICP as an aide or as a member of the Command staff. Once command is transferred, the former on-scene IC should announce the change to avoid any possible confusion.

Command and control of the incident does not transfer automatically when the information has been exchanged. If the problem does not exceed the level of training of the first on-scene IC and the senior member is satisfied with the manner in which the first on-scene IC is handling the situation, he or she may choose to leave the first on-scene IC in command. If the senior member is unsatisfied with how the situation is being handled, he or she assumes on-scene command and control of the incident.

Tracking Resources

NIMS-ICS provides a means of tracking incident personnel and equipment. The incident action plan must contain a tracking and accountability system with the following elements:

- A procedure for checking in at the scene
- A way of identifying the location of each unit and all personnel on scene
- A procedure for releasing units no longer needed

Incident Documentation

Assign a team member to document the actions taken at an incident. This documentation should include the following:

- What was done
- Who was on the scene
- Resources requested
- Timeline of events

Terminating the Incident

Once the incident is under control, those resources no longer needed should be released from the incident, especially mutual aid units. NIMS-ICS will assist with demobilizing. A formal demobilization plan helps to recover loaned equipment, such as portable radios, and in identifying and documenting any damaged or lost equipment.

Incident Management

NFPA 1081 (2018): 7.2.2 , 7.2.3

Figure 21.1 A fire brigade leader issuing orders to members of his response team.

The incident commander is responsible for incident management. The IC may be the plant operations superintendent or other designated plant personnel depending upon the type, size, and organization of a given facility. The fire brigade leader on the scene would be responsible for operations within one part of the incident command system **(Figure 21.1)**.

Mitigation of any emergency incident requires fire brigade personnel to gain control of the scene as quickly as possible and maintain that control throughout the incident. Unfortunately, emergency incidents are rarely the same and a variety of problems may exist that will challenge the management of them.

Incident scene management applies to all types of emergency responses and all levels of resource commitment from single-resource situations to multijurisdictional and multiagency disasters requiring many resources. By learning and applying incident scene management at single-resource situations, fire brigade leaders will perfect the skills that can be applied to more complex situations later.

The fire brigade leader must be prepared to take command of an incident and utilize fire brigade resources to mitigate the incident. To accomplish this, the fire brigade leader needs to operate within an incident management system, such as NIMS-ICS.

Operating Within NIMS-ICS

NIMS-ICS establishes an organizational structure for all types of emergency incidents. Fire brigade leaders must use NIMS-ICS on all incidents that are beyond the incipient stage and during training evolutions.

The first-arriving fire brigade member establishes the NIMS-ICS, makes decisions, and takes actions that will influence the rest of the operation. The initial decisions must be based on the organization's incident scene management procedures. Essential to all emergency incident scene management is the management of emergency response resources:

- Personnel
- Equipment
- Apparatus (if available)
- Materials

All members of the organization, especially fire brigade leaders, must be familiar with the system and trained in its application. All agencies with mutual or automatic aid agreements must know and use the same system. This system may require extensive cross-training at all organizational levels among units of the participating agencies. These levels may include: independent EMS providers, law enforcement agencies, and public works.

NFPA 1081 requires the fire brigade leader to be able to develop an initial action plan or plan of operation. According to NFPA 1561, *Standard on Emergency Services Incident Management System and Command Safety*, an incident action plan establishes the overall strategic decisions and assigned tactical objectives for an incident.

Initial Action Plan

The fire brigade leader will need to develop an initial action plan consisting of appropriate actions, such as fire suppression, rescue, water supply, and ventilation, that can be implemented during the initial phase of the incident. The number of resources initially at the scene will determine the exact implementation. Fire brigades may use a tactical worksheet for the fire brigade leader to document the initial actions being taken. This worksheet may serve as the initial action plan. This sheet also serves as a checklist of tasks the fire brigade leader should address. The fire brigade leader will need to prioritize these actions based on available resources. The fire brigade leader should not hesitate to call for additional resources if the judgment is made that the resources on-scene or dispatched are inadequate to deal appropriately with the incident.

Transfer of Command

Organizational policies will determine the transfer of command process. For example, when the fire brigade leader transfers command to a higher ranking officer, the receiving IC should review the initial action plan to determine the actions already taken (**Figure 21.2**).

Long duration events that are greater than one operational period or shift will require a formal written IAP. In addition, the ICS will likely expand to include functions of the Planning Section to assist with the development of the IAP. Fire brigade leaders, based on their training and experience, may be asked to serve in this role or reassigned to other operational aspects of the incident.

Manageable Span of Control

Span of control is the number of direct subordinates that one supervisor can effectively manage. An effective span of control ranges from three to seven subordinates per supervisor, with five considered the optimum number. Variables such as proximity, similarity of function, and subordinate capability affect the span of control. Supervisors can more easily keep track of their subordinates and monitor their safety if an effective span of control is maintained.

The number of subordinates can be higher in the following situations:

Figure 21.2 The initial fire brigade leader (right) briefing the new fire brigade leader (left) during a transfer of command.

- Subordinates are within sight of the supervisor and are able to communicate with each other.

- Subordinates are performing the same or similar functions.

- Subordinates are skilled in performing the assigned task.

Personnel Accountability

An essential element of the NIMS-ICS is personnel accountability. Fire brigade leaders are responsible for knowing where their subordinates are at all times and what tasks they have been assigned. The initial IC should implement the organization's accountability system soon after arrival on the scene **(Figure 21.3)**.

Figure 21.3 A fire brigade member (left) handing his accountability tag to the accountability officer (right).

Recognizing Incident Priorities

Incident scene management should reflect the overall incident priorities — life safety, incident stabilization, and property conservation. While the terms may be slightly different in various types of emergencies, the actual priorities remain the same. These priorities are always considered in the following order:

1. **Life safety.** The first and highest priority is *always* life safety. However, rescue may not be the first *action* taken by the first-in responders. In some cases, it is necessary to control the hazard before attempting a rescue, and the benefits of taking action must be balanced with the risk involved.

2. **Incident stabilization.** The second priority is to isolate and/or mitigate the hazard. If a fire can be controlled or a hazardous materials release contained, then the situation can be stabilized.

3. **Property conservation.** Conserving property (which includes protecting the environment) — can be addressed. Once the hazard is stabilized and contained, it is no longer a threat to adjacent properties.

To accomplish the incident priorities, the first-arriving IC must know the type of emergency incident and then gather as much information as possible to make command decisions. Size-up is the ongoing process of evaluating an emergency situation to determine:

- What has happened (nature and scope of the incident)
- What is happening
- What is likely to happen
- What resources are available with the initial response
- What actions are necessary to effect control
- What additional resources will be needed to mitigate the incident

The fire brigade leader begins to actively size up the emergency when the alarm sounds and emergency notification is received. The fire brigade leader combines information from the appropriate **preincident plan** with information regarding the current emergency. This information may include the description of the incident, weather conditions, and units assigned to the incident. The fire brigade leader takes into account the brigade's resources, such as the number of personnel available and their knowledge, skills, and abilities, plus the equipment and materials, that may be needed to control the emergency.

Upon arrival, the fire brigade leader as the initial IC will normally:

- Establish command and communicate who is in command (using NIMS-ICS).

- Perform a 360-degree check or delegate another trained or qualified person to perform the 360-degree as part of the size-up **(Figure 21.4)**.

Figure 21.4 A fire brigade leader and a fire brigade member conducting a 360-degree check of burn building during a structural fire training exercise.

NOTE: For large structures, a 360-degree might not be possible. In these situations, the IC should try to see at least 2 sides as a minimum.

- Determine offensive or defensive mode.

- Assign tasks.

- Begin completing the fire brigades' tactical worksheet(s) giving a short report and identifying special hazards.

The fire brigade leader determines whether additional resources are needed as well as the number and types of resources. In some fire brigades, operational guidelines define when to request additional resources. A factor in this determination is the lead/reflex time (amount of time to request and obtain additional resources). Once on the scene, the fire brigade leader must also determine how the incident is developing and how rapidly it is expanding. When additional resources are operational at the scene, the fire brigade leader must determine where the incident will be in both intensity and location.

A fire brigade leader can use any number of size-up processes or models. In his book, *Fire Fighting Tactics*, Lloyd Layman described the following considerations needed for analyzing any emergency situation:

- **Facts** — Things that are true.

- **Probabilities** — Things that are likely to happen.

- **Own situation** — Officer's own knowledge about the situation.

- **Decision** — Initial use of resources followed by supplemental resource needs.

- **Plan of operation** — Information compiled into incident action plan.

Facts

Facts are what the officer knows and is actually observing. Based on the report of the emergency, the telecommunications center may provide the majority of this information. Some of these items include:

- Time (month, day, hour)
- Location
- Nature of the emergency (fire, hazardous materials release, structural collapse)
- Life hazard (occupants and responders)
- Exposures (adjacent uninvolved property)
- Weather (wind, temperature extremes, humidity)
- Number of potential trapped or injured victims
- Personnel and equipment responding (number and type of resources that will be available to control the incident)

The fire brigade leader combines all of the previous information with the knowledge gained from building surveys, preincident plans, and training in fire or hazard behavior. If the information available indicates additional or specialized resources are needed, a request should be made as soon as possible.

Probabilities

Probabilities are things that are not known for certain, but based on the facts, are likely to happen. Actual observation can transform a probability into a fact. The following questions must be answered regarding the probabilities of a fire emergency situation:

- In which direction is the fire likely to spread?
- Are exposures, such as safety related systems, critical equipment, or pressure vessels, likely to become involved?
- Are explosions likely and is a secondary explosion possible? Is a secondary collapse likely?
- Is there a potential for an evacuation of people? Are there people with special needs that cannot self-evacuate?
- Are additional resources likely to be needed? If so, what types and how many?

When sizing up a fire incident, many of the decisions in the probabilities phase can be made easier and with greater accuracy if the fire brigade leader has some knowledge of:

- Fire behavior and smoke indicators (from past experience, training, and education)
- The building or topography involved (from preincident planning)

Own Situation

The fire brigade leader's own situation is one set of facts that is known about the overall incident situation. The following facts are among those to consider:

- Number and types of resources responding to or already at the scene
- Additional resources available immediately, with some delay, and with considerable delay
- Capabilities and limitations of resources
- The fire brigade leader's ability to deal with the situation based on training and experience
- Abilities of fire brigade members

Decision

Lloyd Layman identified two or more decisions that must be made in the ongoing size-up process — an initial decision and one or more supplemental decisions based on the three incident priorities. The initial decision may be seen as having three segments:

1. Whether resources at the scene and those en route are adequate for the situation

2. How to deploy the resources already at the scene in the most effective manner

3. What to do with the resources that arrive (immediate deployment or staging)

As the incident progresses and the situation changes, additional decisions have to be made. For instance, the IC must decide if the initial deployment of resources is producing the desired results or if the units need to be redeployed. On large incidents (those lasting more than an operational period), consideration must be given to relief personnel and additional supplies. More supplemental decisions will be required and more functional positions of NIMS-ICS may need to be activated if an incident continues for an extended period of time.

Plan of Operation

Information gathered in the size-up process serves as a basis for making decisions about how to manage the incident. Depending upon the nature and scope of the incident, the plan of operation or IAP may be simple or complex. The plan does not need to be in writing on relatively small, routine incidents involving only the initial response team, but there must be a plan. Large, complex incidents require a written IAP, often with numerous annexes. An IAP normally covers a single operational period.

Scene Control

Scene control begins with the IC establishing command and controlling the environment. Scene control is essential to ensuring the life safety of responders, victims, and bystanders. Controlling the movements of nonemergency personnel near a high-hazard area contributes to life safety on the scene.

Controlling the perimeter facilitates the use of a personnel accountability system. It also helps in accounting for victims. Establishing three operating **control zones** (commonly labeled hot, warm, and cold) is the most common and effective way to control the perimeter of an incident scene. Facility security personnel or fire brigade support members should cordon off the zones with rope or fireline and tape to:

- Signs
- Utility poles
- Fence posts
- Other objects

There is no universal distance or area that should be cordoned off for each zone or from the incident scene. Zone boundaries should be established by considering the:

- Amount of area needed by fire brigade personnel to work
- Degree of hazard presented by elements involved in the incident
- Wind and weather conditions
- General topography of the area.

The three control zones can be described as follows **(Figure 21.5)**:

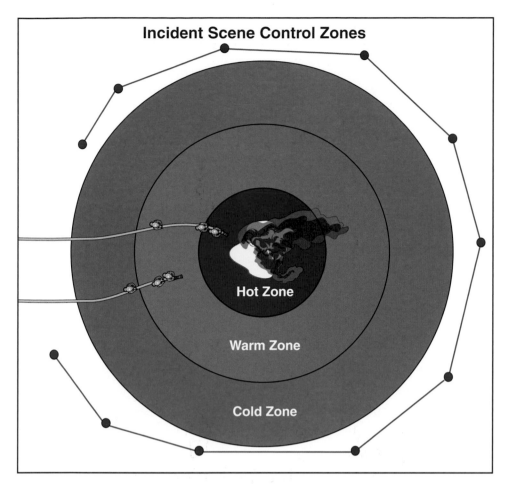

Incident Scene Control Zones

Hot Zone

Warm Zone

Cold Zone

Figure 21.5 Illustrating the concept of incident scene control zones at a fire.

- **Hot zone** — Area where resolving the problem takes place. Only personnel who are directly involved in disposing of the problem are allowed, which limits crowds and confusion at the most critical area of the scene. The size of the zone may vary greatly, depending upon the nature and extent of the problem. Personnel requirements:

  — Trained appropriately to manage the situation

  — Dressed in complete personal protective equipment (PPE) designed for the specific hazard

  — Participated in the incident's personnel accountability system

- **Warm zone** — Area immediately outside the hot zone for personnel who are directly supporting the work being performed by those in the hot zone. For example, personnel who are operating hydraulic tool power plants and providing emergency lighting and fire protection in support of the operation in the hot zone. These personnel are in full PPE and ready to enter the hot zone. In hazardous materials incidents, a decontamination station is normally assembled in this zone.

- **Cold zone** — Area immediately surrounding the hot and warm zones — may include the ICP with a rapid intervention crew (RIC) nearby, rehabilitation area, and staging areas for personnel and portable equipment. The outer boundary of this area would be the control line for other facility personnel.

Fire brigade leaders need to communicate effectively with facility security personnel about traffic safety needs at the incident scene. Coordination with the facility security personnel will help alleviate problems with closing traffic lanes, controlling gates, and providing directions for incoming fire apparatus.

Review Section: Rapid Intervention Crew Operations (RIC)

NFPA 1081 (2018): 7.2.3

Rapid intervention crews (RICs) are tasked with locating and assisting fire brigade members who have become trapped, lost, or incapacitated during interior structural fire fighting. Rapid intervention crews may be two or more fire brigade personnel who are equipped, trained, and assigned the task once they arrive on scene. In some brigades, personnel may be designated and permanently assigned as the RIC.

Either departmental SOPs or the IC will establish the exact number of RICs needed at the scene. Crews are added as necessary if the incident escalates or the number of operations increases. This allows flexibility in RIC composition based on the type of incident and number of personnel on scene.

Each RIC consists of two or more personnel wearing complete PPE and respiratory protection. The team should be equipped with the following:

- Radio
- Flashlight
- Thermal imager (TI)
- RIC pack
- Special rescue tools or other equipment necessary to perform a rescue of other emergency personnel

NOTE: Although individual RIC members may be assigned other minor emergency scene duties, they must be prepared to stop whatever they are doing and deploy immediately if needed.

The RIC should report to the IC and may perform such tasks as:

- Staging equipment
- Sizing up the building for possible paths of egress
- Completing a 360-degree survey if possible
- Removing barriers to egress
- Monitoring radio traffic for distress calls
- Clearing windows
- Placing ladders
- Establishing a second means of egress (set additional ladders)
- Opening exits
- Illuminating the building

Incident Scene Operations

NFPA 1081 (2018): 7.2.2, 7.2.4

Fire brigade leaders must be able to make sound decisions under extreme pressure. Even small incidents can generate a great deal of stress for fire brigade leaders when they establish the NIMS-ICS. Deploying resources and determining the appropriate strategy and tactics to control the incident can also be stressful. A fire brigade leader must employ the following to accomplish incident priorities:

- Proven leadership styles
- Proper resource management
- Supervisory skills
- Knowledge of fire behavior, rescue operations, and operational tactics

The organization should impress upon its personnel a risk-management philosophy. The IFSTA Principles of Risk Management are as follows:

- Activities that present a significant risk to the safety of members shall be limited to situations when there is a potential to save endangered lives.

- Activities that are routinely employed to protect property shall be recognized as inherent risks to the safety of members, and actions shall be taken to avoid these risks.

- No risk to the safety of members shall be acceptable when there is no possibility to save lives or property.

When applying these principles, keep in mind the following three key points:

1. Emphasize team integrity because it is vital to safety

2. Remember, no property is worth the life of a fire brigade member.

3. Do not commit fire brigade members to interior offensive fire fighting operations in unoccupied abandoned or derelict buildings.

Three basic decision-making processes can be used in coordination with one another. Incident Priorities embraces the three broad incident priorities explained earlier in this chapter. Lloyd Layman's RECEO-VS represents a historic perspective focusing on key strategies and tactics needed to resolve an incident, primarily fire-related incidents. SLICE-RS is the newest decision-making process that fire brigade members may find useful. These three processes provide a set of criteria that officers may follow to resolve an incident.

Incident Priorities Approach

In the Incident Priorities approach to decision making, the fire brigade leader must address the questions posed under each tactical priority:

- Life safety

- Incident mitigation

- Property conservation

Life Safety

The first-arriving fire brigade leader must consider life safety as the first priority:

- If lives are in danger, what is their survivability profile? Human life is obviously the first priority, but also consider livestock for sheltering in place, evacuation, or rescue.

  — If rescue is contemplated, the first consideration is to provide safe ingress and egress for both occupants and firefighters.

  — Rescue of livestock, while desirable, does not meet the criteria for taking great risks.

- How many personnel are in need of being sheltered in place, evacuated, or rescue?

- What resources (personnel, equipment, time, etc...) will be needed to accomplish these actions?

Incident Mitigation (Stabilization)

To mitigate an incident, the fire brigade leader must ask:

- What type of incident (structural fire, ground cover fire, hazardous materials release, or natural disaster) must be mitigated?

- What hazards will responders face?

- What resources are needed and what are available to mitigate the incident?

- What strategies and tactics are available based on the information gathered during size-up?

Property Conservation

To conserve property, the fire brigade leader must ask:

- What property (structures, vehicles, environment) is endangered?
- What property can be saved?
- What secondary property can be affected (waterways, sewers, wetlands)?

RECEO-VS

In his book, *Fire Fighting Tactics*, Lloyd Layman identified the major priorities in emergency situations. Even though his list of priorities is couched in fire control terms, he also acknowledged that the same priorities could be applied to any type of emergency. These priorities are represented by the acronym RECEO (ree-cee-oh). Layman also included two other functions that are almost exclusively related to structure fires — *ventilation* and *salvage*. Layman intended RECEO to be both a list of priorities *and* a sequence of operations. He did not include ventilation and salvage in the list because they are not needed in every fire. Also, they are not always performed at the same point in the fires where they are used.

Rescue

Rescue identifies the life safety aspect of emergency scene priorities. In most facility fire brigades, the term is taken to include humans and valuable livestock in the affected unit or facility. However, the term is not limited to facility employees; it also includes the fire brigade members. It can be argued that the fire brigade member's life safety is the most important. The basis for this idea is that if a fire brigade member is disabled by an injury, the fire brigade member cannot rescue the facility occupants. Whether this position is valid or not, clearly the fire brigade members' life safety is at least as important as the employee's. Therefore, fire brigade leaders should neither expect nor allow their fire brigade members to sacrifice themselves by taking unnecessary risks on the incident scene.

Addressing the rescue or life safety priority can place the IC in one of the most stressful situations in any emergency. Life safety, being the first and highest priority, takes precedence over any and all other considerations. This means that in order to facilitate a rescue, a building, facility, or unit may be allowed to burn to the ground, if necessary, in order to facilitate a rescue. As well, emergency responders should not be ordered into emergency situations to recover a body or into areas that are already lost. Most areas and their contents are insured and even if they are not, they can usually be replaced. Of course, there are irreplaceable items, but no object is worth a human life.

Only defensive operations will be conducted if the danger to fire brigade members is not acceptable. At no time will operations exceed the scope of the fire brigade as defined in its organizational statement and SOPs.

Exposures

Layman uses the term *exposures* to describe the need to limit the fire or other emergency to the area of origin **(Figure 21.6)**. Similar to the idea of sacrificing an area to facilitate a rescue, limiting the event to the area of origin means, *if necessary*, allowing the area of origin to burn in order to save adjacent areas that are uninvolved or only slightly involved. If the first-arriving emergency responders have only enough resources to begin to resolve the problem or to keep it from spreading — but not both — then they should focus their efforts on keeping the problem from spreading to uninvolved areas. Attacking the source of the problem may be the best way to protect the exposures. If not, attacking the source of the problem becomes a lower priority than protecting the adjacent but uninvolved areas. Prevent the spread of fire to adjacent areas by applying fixed monitors. Another example would be damming or diking a hazardous materials spill to prevent the spread of the material.

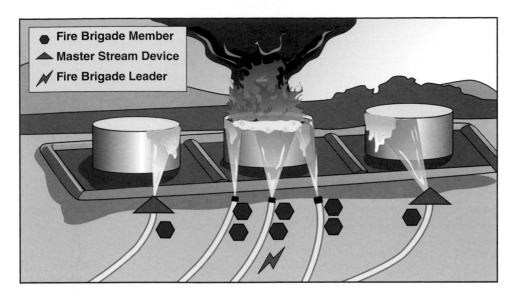

Figure 21.6 Illustrating how exposure protection operations can prevent a fire from spreading from one tank to another.

Confinement

Confinement is used to describe the need to confine the fire or other problem to the smallest possible area within the property of origin. In the case of a structure fire, the priority is to confine the fire to the area or room of origin, if possible. If it is not possible to confine the fire to the *area or room of origin*, it should be limited to the *floor of origin*. If this is not possible, it should be confined to the *building or structure of origin*. This principle can be applied to other types of emergencies as well — limiting a hazardous materials spill to the smallest area of the property in which it originated, for example. One can think of it as building a box around the area of the emergency.

Extinguishment

Even though Layman used the fire-specific term *extinguishment*, the idea is to mitigate the problem. Mitigation can mean extinguishing a fire, stopping the flow of a hazardous material, or mitigating a building collapse. If the size-up was accurate and the incident plan was sound, the incident can usually be resolved successfully and in a timely manner.

Overhaul

Layman also included restoring the scene to as near normal as possible. After a fire has been knocked down, any and all hidden fire must be found and extinguished. After a hazardous materials release has been stopped, liquids must be cleaned up and packaged for proper disposal and any residues neutralized. Following a vehicle accident, the roadway must be cleared, any spilled liquids picked up or neutralized, and traffic flow restored. This phase of the operation can be made much easier if the proper resources were called to the scene based on an accurate initial or supplemental size-up.

Ventilation

Ventilation is the systematic removal of heated air, smoke, gases, or other airborne contaminants from a structure and replaced with cooler and/or fresher air to reduce damage and to facilitate fire control operations. Fire progression determines when ventilation is needed; therefore, it is said to *float*, meaning it can be used.

The following ventilation techniques are effective:

- During the implementation of the *RECEO* model.

- During rescue or extinguishment phases to allow personnel to enter the structure and work in a less hazardous environment.

- When determining the correct type and location in conjunction with the rescue or extinguishment phase because improper ventilation can increase the possibility of fire spread.

Salvage

Salvage is attempting to save property and reduce further damage from water, smoke, heat, and exposure during or immediately after a fire by removing property from a fire area, by covering it, or other means. Take action to protect buildings and contents from preventable damage. Remove property from a hazardous environment or protect it in place.

Assigning personnel to perform salvage is a judgment decision based on the resources available, completion of the other RECEO-model tasks, and the value or importance of the property.

SLICE-RS and Incident Priorities

A newer acronym, SLICE-RS, summarizes structural fire fighting tactical goals. SLICE-RS is not meant to replace RECEO-VS. It is recommended that the first-arriving fire brigade member or members use SLICE-RS to initiate command and control of an incident. The SLICE-RS method incorporates the latest research about:

- Ventilation control
- Flow paths
- Modern fire behavior into tactical priorities

While the research into some of these topics is critical to improving fire brigade member safety, it has been difficult to incorporate some of the findings into common fireground tactics. SLICE-RS is composed of five sequential actions and two actions of opportunity. The five sequential actions include:

1. **S**ize-up
2. **L**ocate the fire
3. **I**dentify and control the flow path
4. **C**ool the space from the safest distance
5. **E**xtinguish the fire

   The two actions of opportunity include:

- **R**escue
- **S**alvage

Using one or more of the three decision-making processes, the IC can begin to develop and implement the initial action plan. The following sections describe this process.

Developing and Implementing an IAP

In order for the resources assigned to an incident to work together effectively and in a coordinated effort, they must all work from the same plan. Each resource, whether an individual fire brigade team or an entire fire brigade, must know what the strategic goals and tactical objectives are for the incident and what their individual roles are in achieving those objectives. This level of coordination requires a clearly defined plan for all to follow. NFPA 1081 indicates that facility fire brigade leaders should be able to develop an "initial action plan" and produce "operational plans" to include appropriate actions to be implemented during the initial phase of the incident. As the incident develops further, a more formal, written incident action plan or IAP is developed. This IAP identifies strategic goals, tactical objectives, and support requirements for the incident.

During an incident, the IAP is based on the first-in fire brigade leader's information gathered in the initial size-up and on preincident planning. The size-up attempts to determine:

- What has happened
- What is happening
- What is likely to happen
- What resources are needed to safely and effectively handle the situation

Preincident Plan

Facility fire brigades should survey and preplan their entire facility. The survey should include the following:

- Life risk
- Property and equipment in the facilities or areas to gather information about the buildings and their contents
- Any extraordinarily hazardous materials or processes
- Any impediments to access/egress
- Any built-in fire protection devices or systems
- Anything that would affect fire behavior or fire suppression and/or rescue efforts in the area

The data gathered is then analyzed and translated into operational plans for the areas surveyed. Plans should include sketches, diagrams, maps, or photographs of key features of the occupancy.

Operational Plans

Operational plans are used to identify the following:

- Resources needed to mitigate a hazard
- Resource assignments
- Safety factors relating to incident control

In most fire brigades and emergency operations centers (EOC), operational plans (also called *prefire plans*, *preincident plans*, or *strategic plans*) identify the specific resources needed to successfully deal with a variety of hypothetical incidents at a particular location or occupancy. The incident scenarios analyzed are considered to be the most likely to occur at the location in question. Operational plans often include the following provisions for a number of possible contingencies.

- A facility that uses or stores large quantities of toxic or highly flammable materials. Personnel create and analyze:
  - Response plans involving flammable materials.
  - Areas of safe refuge for employees
  - Safe areas of entire facility.
- Resource deployments. Scenarios based on increasingly larger and more complex hypothetical incidents help planners to identify the resources that may be needed and to identify how they can by deployed to the best advantage.
- Unusually severe weather conditions. These conditions could greatly increase the potential for the spread of fires to exposures or the spread of hazardous materials by air movement. The operational plans for occupancies that store large quantities of flammable liquids might specify that a bulk foam transport be a part of the initial alarm assignment so that large quantities of foam are immediately available if needed.

In essence, the data gathered at any particular target hazard is used to project the strategic and tactical possibilities and probabilities at that location. Based on these scenarios, the resources needed are compared to the resources available to the fire brigade. If required resources are more than or different from what the facility has available, planners can then recommend the purchase of the needed resources or the development of mutual aid or automatic aid agreements with nearby facilities or departments that do have the needed resources.

Incident Action Plans (IAP)

The IC can devise a plan for the safe and efficient mitigation of an incident by using the information obtained in the initial size-up and any other information available in an operational plan **(Figure 21.7)**. As previously mentioned, there must be a plan for relatively small, routine incidents. The plan does not need to be in writing, but it must be communicated throughout the on-scene organization.

On larger, more complex incidents, the plan should be in writing. The plan must be distributed to the leaders of all units assigned to the incident and the information communicated to all incident personnel. This plan should be practiced, evaluated, and updated, as necessary. It is also important to have a written record of what was done during the incident because subsequent litigation is a possibility with every incident. Every incident requires its own action plan, and all IAPs have certain common elements. Every IAP is unique because the factors that they address vary in importance from one incident to the next. The incident action plan specifies the strategic goals and tactical objectives for the next operational period, usually 12 hours.

Figure 21.7 A fire brigade leader using an incident action plan to brief his personnel.

Incident Safety Plan

The Incident Commander (IC) or the Incident Safety Officer (ISO) must develop an incident safety plan based upon the IC's strategies and tactics outlined in the incident action plan **(Figure 21.8)**. The incident safety plan varies according to the type of incident. It is based on the risk management model and takes into consideration the potential hazards and the risks involved.

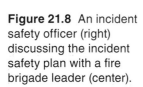

Figure 21.8 An incident safety officer (right) discussing the incident safety plan with a fire brigade leader (center).

Operational Implementation

Following the initial size-up, the first-in fire brigade leader implements the following operational decisions:

- Establishes goals and objectives.
- Assigns appropriate resources.
- Considers the need for additional resources.

The strategic goals of an incident are the overall desired outcomes, and the tactical objectives are the activities used to reach those outcomes. Both are included in the IAP and must be communicated to all incident personnel.

Strategic Goals

The overall plan for controlling the incident is to implement the strategic goals, which are broad, general statements of the overall outcomes to be achieved. Before an incident occurs, strategic goals should be translated into fire brigade SOPs. Three of the overall priorities — life safety, incident stabilization, and property conservation — dictate these goals.

These priorities should always guide the development of the incident action plan. Deciding how to meet them dictates the tactical objectives for the incident. Strategic goals and tactical objectives must be constantly evaluated and reevaluated. The continual process of size-up ensures that these goals and objectives are being accomplished. As goals and objectives are met, the situation changes. As the situation changes, so do the priorities. Fire brigade leaders must be flexible enough to cope successfully with a rapidly changing situation.

Tactical Objectives

Achieving tactical objectives leads to the completion of goals. Tactical objective statements are more specific than strategic goal statements. Tactical objectives are statements of measurable outcomes. How these objectives are achieved is determined by how the plan is implemented. The following are examples of some common tactical objectives:

- Provide for the safety of fire brigade members, occupants, and others.
- Contain the incident to a specified geographic area.
- Mitigate the problem.
- Restore the scene.

Strategic goals and tactical objectives must be constantly evaluated to ensure that they are being accomplished. As goals and objectives are met and situations change, so do the priorities.

Command Options

According to Book I of Fire Protection Publications' **Incident Command System (ICS) Model Procedures Guide**, a variety of Command options are available to the fire brigade leader at an incident. The first-arriving fire brigade leader or member has several Command options from which to choose when arriving at the incident, depending on the situation. The establishment of a command post may be a top priority if a fire brigade leader without fire brigade personnel readily available initiates Command. The following Command options define the fire brigade leader's direct involvement in tactical activities.

Investigation Option

Upon arrival, an incident may not have visible indicators of a significant event. These situations generally require that the first-arriving fire brigade member investigates, while other fire brigade members are responding. The fire brigade leader should assume Command and begin to investigate the situation, using a portable radio to command the incident.

Fast-Attack Option

Situations that require immediate action to stabilize the incident mandate the fire brigade leader's assistance to carry out the critical operation. In these situations, the fire brigade leader accompanies the crew to provide the appropriate level of supervision. Examples of these situations include:

- Offensive fire attacks (especially in marginal situations)

- Critical life-safety situations (such as rescues) that must be achieved in a compressed time

- Any incident where the safety and welfare of responders are of major concern

- Working incidents that require the fire brigade leader to further investigate

Where fast intervention is critical, the fire brigade leader uses a portable radio to keep his or her involvement in the attack without neglecting Command responsibilities. The Fast Attack option should not last more than a few minutes within the Immediately Dangerous to Life and Health (IDLH) atmosphere and will end with one of the following:

- The situation is stabilized.

- The situation is not stabilized or transfer of Command has not taken place. The fire brigade leader should withdraw to the exterior outside of an IDLH atmosphere, and establish a command post. At some time, the fire brigade leader must decide whether to withdraw the remainder of the team/crew — based on the team/crew's capabilities and experience, safety issues, and the ability to communicate with the team/crew. A team/crew should not enter or remain in a hazardous area without radio communications capabilities. Interior teams/crews should consist of a minimum of two personnel with two personnel on the exterior to meet the two-in/two-out rule.

- Command is transferred to another fire brigade member.

 Two-in/Two-out Rule

CFR 1910.134(g)(4) describes the Two-in/Two-out Rule for entering IDLH environments. It states:

Procedures for interior structural firefighting. In addition to the requirements set forth under paragraph (g)(3), in interior structural fires, the employer shall ensure that:

1910.134(g)(4)(i)

At least two employees enter the IDLH atmosphere and remain in visual or voice contact with one another at all times;

1910.134(g)(4)(ii)

At least two employees are located outside the IDLH atmosphere; and

1910.134(g)(4)(iii)

All employees engaged in interior structural firefighting use SCBAs.

Note 1 to paragraph (g): One of the two individuals located outside the IDLH atmosphere may be assigned to an additional role, such as **Incident C**ommander in charge of the emergency or safety officer, so long as this individual is able to perform assistance or rescue activities without jeopardizing the safety or health of any firefighter working at the incident.

Note 2 to paragraph (g): Nothing in this section is meant to preclude firefighters from performing emergency rescue activities before an entire team has assembled.

Other regulatory groups and organizations such as NFPA have also adopted this standard. While this section describes interior fire fighting, it would also apply any time an IDLH environment could or does exist and entry is required. At an exterior fire, such as vehicle fire, woods fires, or outside trash/rubbish fires, the Two-in/Two-out Rule would not apply.

Command Post Option

Large, complex, or rapidly evolving incidents require immediate strong, direct, overall Command. In such cases, the fire brigade leader will initially assume an exterior, safe, and effective Command position and maintain that position until he or she is relieved by a higher-ranking person. The Command position should initiate a tactical worksheet and use it to manage this type of incident.

If the fire brigade leader selects the Command option, he or she can assign the following options to the remaining crew members:

- Place the team/crew into action with the remaining members. One of the team/crew members will serve as the *acting* fire brigade leader and will be provided a portable radio. The collective and individual capabilities and experience of the crew will regulate this approach. Interior team/crews must consist of a minimum of two persons.

- Assign the team/crew members to work under the supervision of another fire brigade leader. The fire brigade leader assuming Command must communicate with those personnel regarding the assignment.

- Assign the crew members to perform staff functions to assist Command. Every effort should be made to maintain team/crew integrity.

A fire brigade leader assuming Command continues to be fully responsible for the Command functions. The officer has a choice of offensive or defensive modes and degrees of personal involvement in the tactical activities. The initiative and judgment of the officer are of great importance. The operational modes identified in the next section are guidelines to assist the officer in planning appropriate actions.

Operational Modes

One of the first decisions the initial IC needs to make is based on a risk/benefit evaluation. The IC must assess the current conditions and determine whether the potential benefits are worth having firefighters take unnecessary risks. Fire brigade members' lives may be jeopardized attempting to put out a fire in a facility where there is danger of collapse or where damage is so extensive there is nothing worth saving. Other fire brigade members are asked to risk their safety to rescue victims with little or no chance of survival.

Should the IC decide the risk is worth the benefits, the next thing that must be determined is how long fire brigade members can be expected to sustain an interior attack. The IC may not know how long the fire has been burning prior to their arrival or the fire's intensity. The length of time fire brigade members can be expected to sustain an interior attack may therefore be limited. The available resources and needed fire flow should be a part of the IC's considerations. Not enough resources or available water may mean that the risk outweighs the benefits.

NOTE: Upon request, some facility control rooms provide a 10-minute time check via radio to assist with personnel accountability in hazardous environments.

Although it may be the hardest decision an IC can make, there are times when attempting to make a rescue or an interior attack may be too great a risk to the safety of the fire brigade members. Failure to do a risk/benefit evaluation is the ultimate example of not being responsible for the safety of their personnel.

Offensive Mode. In an offensive mode, the IC shall assess the risk to fire brigade members and take actions to reduce these risks. Should the IC choose the offensive mode, it means that an aggressive interior attack is worth the risk and that sufficient resources are available to meet the incident demands.

Defensive Mode. In a defensive mode, the risk versus gain to fire brigade members is too significant to make an interior fire attack. The probability of saving lives is highly unlikely and the risk to fire brigade members in attempting to save property outweighs the gain. Therefore, a defensive mode is the most appropriate choice in these situations. Protecting the exposed buildings from further loss and confining the fire to the structure(s) involved is considered a defensive mode. When operating in the defensive mode, the IC needs to maintain accountability of personnel.

Indicators for a defensive operation include:

- Danger of imminent collapse
- Building is lost
- Conditions indicate survival is unlikely of any victims trapped inside
- Not enough resources are available to effectively deal with the problems

NOTE: Anytime the decision is made to switch from one operational mode to another (also referred to as a *transitional attack*), particular attention should be given to make sure the switch is communicated to all personnel at the incident and that confirmation of the change is received.

Additional Resource Allocation

The IC should anticipate the need for calling additional resources if it appears that the incident has the potential to be a long-term operation. These additional resources may be held in reserve, used to relieve first-arriving units, or assigned tactical objectives on the incident. One or more staging areas may have to be established.

Coordinating Multiple Resources

Facility fire brigades may be required to interact with outside agencies at various times. This interaction may be the result of formal mutual aid pacts with other local emergency response organizations. The following agencies are typically those with which brigades may interact **(Figure 21.9)**:

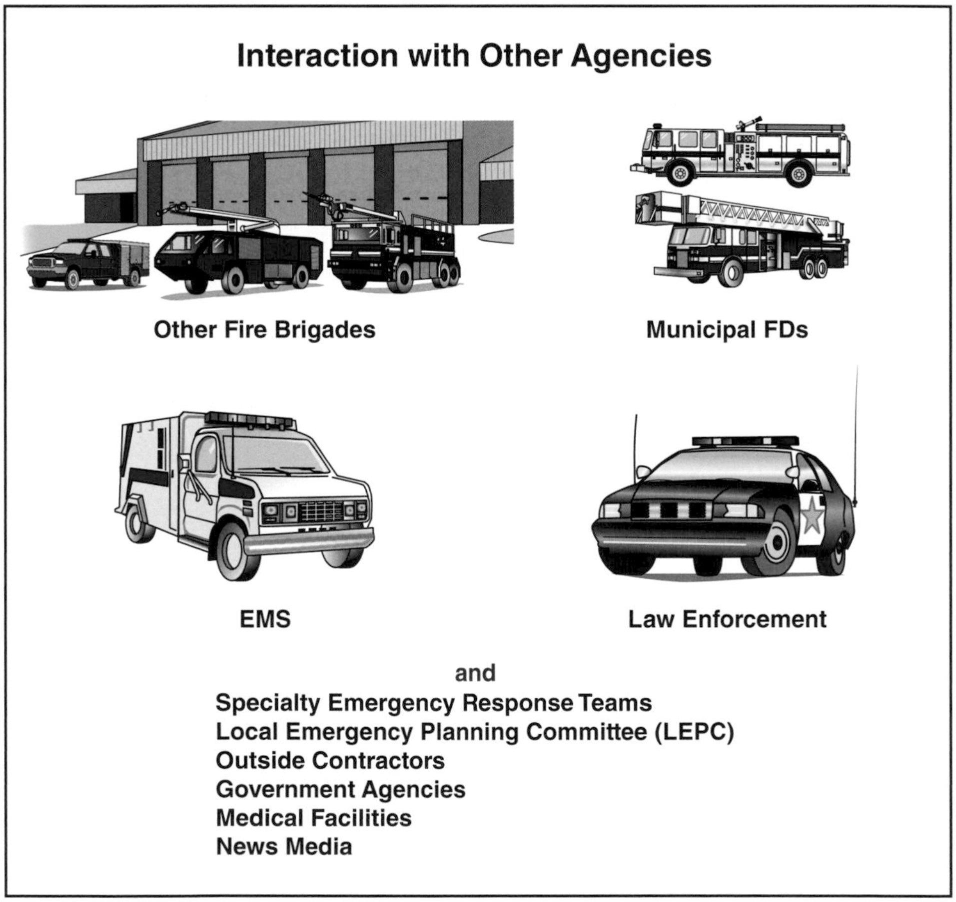

Interaction with Other Agencies

Other Fire Brigades

Municipal FDs

EMS

Law Enforcement

and
Specialty Emergency Response Teams
Local Emergency Planning Committee (LEPC)
Outside Contractors
Government Agencies
Medical Facilities
News Media

Figure 21.9 During an emergency, fire brigades may interact with a variety of other agencies.

- Facility fire brigades from other facilities or sites to include those that provide mutual or automatic aid
- Municipal fire departments
- Specialty emergency response teams (hazardous materials, confined space, and technical rescue)

- Emergency medical services (EMS)
- Local law enforcement agencies
- Outside contractors
- Local Emergency Planning Committee (LEPC)
- Government agencies
- News media
- Medical facilities

An effective working relationship with outside agencies must be developed well before any actual incident occurs. All parties must agree upon the roles and responsibilities of each party involved in the plan in order to have cooperation during an emergency. All parties must know exactly what is expected of them before they need to act at an incident. Mutual aid agreements must be regularly reviewed and maintained to ensure an adequate response to the facility when needed.

Outside agencies can schedule an on-site visit to begin the development of this relationship. The visit should include a full review of potential hazards. Local fire and EMS officials, with the assistance of the facility fire brigade, can develop a preincident plan for the facility. Law enforcement agencies can develop a contingency plan to handle wide-area evacuations. Preincident planning should include all external agencies that may be involved during an actual incident. In summary, cooperation and planning must be required for agencies to work together effectively in an emergency.

Regardless of how carefully considered and how well written the operational plan may be, it must be tested in one or more joint training exercises. Several full-scale exercises may be needed before all personnel can feel comfortable that the plan will function as intended. After each exercise, leaders should conduct a comprehensive, nonthreatening critique of the exercise. All aspects of the plan should be subjected to objective review, and any deficiencies that emerge should be corrected. When the plan has been found to be fully functional, it should then be tested at least annually to:

- Be updated as necessary
- Allow current personnel an opportunity to refresh themselves on their roles and responsibilities
- Indoctrinate replacement personnel in the plan's requirements

A mutual aid agreement provides reciprocal assistance from one fire agency to another during an emergency. This agreement is based upon a prearrangement between the agencies involved and generally made upon the request of the receiving agency. Automatic aid agreements are often established between two or more agencies to automatically dispatch predetermined resources to any fire or other emergency reported in the geographic area covered by the agreement. These areas are generally where the boundaries between jurisdictions meet or where jurisdictional "islands" exist.

Mutual and automatic aid agreements between facility fire brigades, other facilities, and local municipal fire departments can prove highly beneficial to all parties. These agreements can provide the facility with the advantage of having additional resources, such as fire fighting apparatus, extinguishing agents, and personnel, available in the event of a catastrophic incident. Mutual and automatic aid agreements can benefit the municipal fire department by making available specialized extinguishing agents, equipment, and personnel trained to use them in the event the municipality experiences an emergency involving materials related to a particular industry.

Mutual and automatic aid agreements contain the following:

- Establishes the roles and responsibilities in written documents of all agencies identified.
- Identifies who will be in charge of an incident and identifies who will provide what types of services or support so that no confusion arises during an emergency
- Addresses the procedures to be followed and the following:

- Structure of the organization

- On-site standard operating procedures

- Incident Management System

- Communication protocols

- Integration of operational personnel into teams under a Unified Command Structure

Once a mutual or automatic aid agreement is reached, joint training sessions and drills should be scheduled and conducted for the facility fire brigade and fire department personnel. The fire department members should receive familiarization training on the industrial site to include:

- Access to the site and facilities

- Available water sources

- Site layout and hazards

- Site apparatus, personal protective equipment, and tools and equipment

- Site standard operating procedures

- Specialized extinguishing agents available on site **(Figure 21.10)**

Figure 21.10 This supply of fire fighting foam is an example of one type of specialized extinguishing agent that might be found at a facility.

- Specialized fire fighting tools and equipment available on site

- On-site communications equipment and procedures

Joint training sessions and drills between facility fire brigades and local municipal fire departments develop more than just their fire fighting and emergency response skills. They also develop a cooperative attitude that lays the foundation for successful joint emergency operations.

Implementing Incident Support Operations
NFPA 1081 (2018): 7.2.5

During the course of an incident, it may become necessary to implement various incident support operations. Trained personnel familiar with fire brigade procedures should carry out each of these operations. Incident support operations may include:

- Scene lighting
- Traffic control
- Rehabilitation
- Escort duty

Terminating the Incident

NFPA 1081 (2018): 7.2.5

The **termination** phase of an emergency operation involves a wide variety of activities. If appropriate, these activities may include but are not limited to:

- Conducting medical evaluations of incident personnel
- Retrieving equipment used in the operation
- Releasing appropriate units and returning them to service
- Determining the cause of the incident
- Releasing the scene to those responsible for the property
- Setting a fire or reflash watch in place
- Conducting a hot wash or debrief of the incident

When the incident has been brought under control, release the resources that are no longer needed. This release is especially important when mutual aid units have been called in. Having NIMS-ICS in place will assist in demobilizing in a methodical and efficient manner. Adhering to a formal demobilization plan helps to recover loaned equipment, such as portable radios, and to identify and document any damaged or lost equipment.

Direct Personnel During a Training Evolution

NFPA 1081 (2018): 7.2.3, 7.2.6

Fire brigade leaders supervise **training evolutions** as part of their job. Fire brigade leaders need to know how to conduct training evolutions in a safe manner. This section addresses:

- The Safety Challenge
- Using ICS to supervise training
- Training evolution evaluation
- Environmental issues at training evolutions
- Accident investigation

The Safety Challenge

The challenge for the fire brigade leader is to provide realistic training situations that are similar to actual emergencies while still providing the maximum level of safety. The sections that follow describe various aspects of the challenge of providing safe training evolutions for students and fire brigade leaders.

Organizational and Administrative Support

In addition to fire brigade leaders incorporating safety into the training curriculum, changes in organizational policy can reduce the number of training accidents. Some of the recommendations provided by the United States Fire Administration (USFA) include the following:

- Follow established guidelines and currently accepted organizational procedures as well as training and safety standards.

- Conduct live-burn evolutions in a variety of training props or structure types to provide realistic fire fighting experiences **(Figure 21.11)**.
- Train fire brigade members and emergency responders to recognize the visual and physical clues to impending danger (such as changes in smoke conditions) and anticipate fire behavior in a variety of building types.

Figure 21.11 Fire brigade leaders may conduct live-fire training involving flammable liquids or structural fires.

To reduce the potential risks to personnel, all fire and emergency services organizations regulated by legally adopted NFPA standards are required to have a risk-management plan. After implementing the plan, fire brigade leaders must monitor its effectiveness. Risk-management plans are designed to accomplish the following objectives:

- Identify risks.
- Evaluate the potential for injury or damage, based on the frequency and severity of risk.
- Establish appropriate controls to minimize or eliminate the risk.

The **risk-management plan** includes all job-related activities in which fire and emergency services personnel normally participate, including emergency, nonemergency, training, and support activities. NFPA 1500™, *Standard on Fire Department Occupational Safety and Health Program*, provides detailed guidelines for developing a risk-management plan. IFSTA's **Occupational Safety, Health, and Wellness** manual is also an excellent resource for establishing safety and health programs.

The organization's administration plays a role in supporting and enforcing safety, fitness, health, and wellness programs in all aspects of the organization's operations. It is the administration's responsibility to perform the following actions:

- Provide adequate personal protective equipment (PPE).
- Make certain that all proper equipment is provided.
- Ensure that all apparatus and equipment are maintained.
- Confirm that all safety equipment is properly installed and operating.
- Provide policies and procedures for the safe use of the apparatus and equipment.
- Address the fitness, health, and wellness of personnel by providing the following:
  — Employee assistance programs
  — Job-related physical fitness testing
  — Annual medical evaluations and periodic examinations
  — Health and wellness related information and training

Review: NFPA 1403, Standard on Live Fire Training Evolutions

An essential element for planning live-fire training is NFPA 1403. Fire brigade leaders must be familiar with the requirements of this standard for all live-fire training in purpose-built burn buildings and burn props. The fire brigade leader-in-charge of any training evolution, the designated safety officer, and the organization's administration must enforce safety requirements.

Unsafe Behavior

Injuries and fatalities during training are usually the result of unsafe acts by persons who are unaware or uninformed of potential hazards, who are ignorant of the safety policies, or who fail to follow safety procedures. Casualties may also be caused by conditions in the physical environment that were not examined or considered as potential hazards. Almost all accidents are predictable and preventable.

Normalization of deviation is a way that safety can become compromised over time. When deviating from SOPs becomes the normal behavior rather than an exception, the value of the SOPs becomes marginalized. When those procedures deal with safety, it is likely that the frequency of change means that safe practices are not being followed or constantly being added and removed from procedures. Constant change is as ineffective as a complete lack of change.

Human factors generally lead to unsafe behavior in fire and emergency services training. Before allowing participation in a training scenario, the fire brigade leader should determine whether any of the following factors apply to an individual student and take the appropriate action:

- **Improper attitude** — Address unsafe attitudes or behaviors so that the individual does not create or become involved in an accident. Fire brigade leaders should monitor their classes for signs of high-risk behavior, such as students who are:
  - Irresponsible or reckless
  - Inconsiderate or uncooperative
  - Fearful of, or phobic about, the situation
  - Egotistical or jealous
  - Intolerant or impatient
  - Excitable or oversensitive
  - Obsessive or absentminded

- **Complacency** — Students may perceive some safety procedures as unnecessary, perhaps because they have been so well-practiced. Fire brigade leaders should ensure that students are not avoiding or overlooking safety steps during any training evolution.

- **Lack of knowledge or skill** — If students are unprepared for an evolution, fire brigade leaders must address the situation by providing additional training, including supervised practice time. Fire brigade leaders must be sure that students are:
  - Sufficiently informed about the training
  - Capable of interpreting the training and convinced of its need
  - Experienced in requisite knowledge and skills and capable of decisive actions
  - Properly trained and able to recognize potential hazards/risks

- **Physical limitations** — Fire brigade leaders should be aware of any physical limitations that could lead to training injuries or fatalities. These limitations could include any of the following:
  - Inability to see or hear well enough for the situation
  - Physical characteristics that reduce a student's ability to perform safely
  - Limited strength or aerobic capacity
  - Effects of a medical condition, allergy, illness, or mental condition
  - Reduced reaction times due to substance abuse or legally prescribed medications

Hazard and Risk Analysis

A hazard and risk analysis data identifies potential problem areas and is the foundation for any risk-management plan. For example, a planned driver/operator training evolution may require novice or inexperienced personnel to drive apparatus on public streets or highways. This situation creates a potential risk to both personnel and the public. The fire brigade leader should search for a more suitable location and use cones to simulate traffic. After personnel have gained experience in this setting, subsequent evolutions can be held on public streets.

When fire brigade leaders create a **lesson plan** for skills training, they perform a task analysis to determine the necessary tasks and the order in which they should be performed. The fire brigade leader should examine these tasks and ensure that they can be safely performed on the available training ground. For example, if the roof at an acquired structure looks unlikely to support the weight of multiple fire brigade members, then roof ventilation training cannot occur without reinforcing the roof or acquiring a different structure.

Fire brigade leaders should follow all aspects of the organizational risk-management plans. Before teaching lessons, fire brigade members should also heed any potential risks outlined in prepared lesson plans and assess potential risks in the training environment. Fire brigade leaders must eliminate hazardous environments near training areas. If hazards cannot be eliminated or sufficiently minimized, fire brigade leaders must move the training to another location.

Training evolutions should have an appropriate instructor to student ratio. This ratio depends on the level of risk and hazards. For performance training evolutions, the ideal ratio is one instructor for every five students. For classroom training, the ratio may be one to twenty.

NOTE: Even with policies in place and instructions from which to work, skills training can be unpredictable.

When investigators review injury records, they should prioritize potential hazards that have led to injuries in the past while considering the following two factors:

1. Frequency of the hazardous activity and how this relates to the frequency of accidents or injuries

2. Relative severity of the potential loss

NOTE: Ideally, all hazards are addressed as high priorities, but prioritizing hazards is often a necessity imposed by limited resources.

 Hazards and Risks

In everyday conversation, the terms *hazard* and *risk* are often used interchangeably; technically, they describe two different things. *Hazard* refers to a condition, substance, or device that can directly cause an injury or loss. *Risk*, on the other hand, is the likelihood of suffering harm from a hazard. Risk can also be thought of as the potential for failure or loss. In other words, risk is the exposure to a hazard, and a hazard is the source of a risk.

Using ICS to Supervise Training

The ICS model adopted by many jurisdictions in North America is based on NFPA 1561, *Standard on Emergency Services Incident Management System and Command Safety*. It provides guidance and direction for the management and control of all types of emergency incidents, ranging from single company responses to multiple agency and jurisdiction incidents. These guidelines can also be applied to large-scale skills-training exercises and operational training evolutions. Using ICS also increases the safety and accountability of students.

The ICS model should be used at all types of training evolutions, whether they involve live fire or not. Students and fire brigade leaders will then become familiar with ICS roles and procedures. The sections that follow describe topics related to implementing an ICS during large-scale skills exercises and operational training evolutions.

Incident Command System Duties and Functions

Fire brigade leaders should have a working knowledge of Incident Command Systems, and they should implement the ICS that their agency has adopted. ICS is adaptable to a wide variety of situations and is therefore a useful tool for organizing training evolutions.

The fire brigade leader should staff the ICS positions that are necessary to effectively manage the training evolution. Examples of ICS positions include the following:

- Incident Commander (IC) or Lead Instructor
- Logistics Officer
- Division or Group Supervisor
- Ignition Officer
- Public Information Officer (PIO)
- Safety Officer
- Staging Officer
- Communications Officer
- Water Supply Officer

Training Plan or IAP

Every lesson requires a lesson plan, and operational training evolutions can be described as large-scale lessons. The lesson plan for these evolutions must be based on either the plans used at actual incidents, an agency approved training plan, or an IAP. Fire brigade leaders can adapt the various IAP forms in the NIMS-ICS system to create the training evolution IAP. Similar to operational IAPs, training plans usually contain the following elements:

- **Objectives** — Clearly stated and measurable objectives to be achieved in a specific time interval
- **Organization** — ICS-defined units and agencies that are involved and the roles they will play in the command structure
- **Assignments** — Specific unit tactical assignments for students and fire brigade leaders; usually divided by branch, division, and group
- **Support materials** — Includes site plans, access or traffic plans, and locations of support activities such as staging, rehabilitation, and logistics
- **Safety message** — Information concerning personnel safety at the training incident, including a site-safety plan

At the end of the training evolution, the training plan is used as part of the **postincident analysis** and critique. It is an instrument for evaluating both the students' learning achievements and the overall effectiveness of the training.

Figure 21.12 A fire brigade leader conducting an informal postincident critique following a training evolution.

Training Evolution Evaluation

At the termination of the practical training evolution, a **postincident critique** or analysis should be held **(Figure 21.12)**. The postincident critique fulfills the following purposes:

- Evaluates student skills and learning
- Evaluates the practical training evolution

- Determines safety problems that need to be corrected
- Trains students in the postincident critique process
- Evaluates the fire brigade leader's supervisory and teaching skills

If the evaluators determine that students have not attained the learning objectives for the evolution, provide further training and restage the evolution. If it is identified that the evolution did not provide the level of training necessary to meet the learning objectives, redesign the evolution to provide that level.

If safety problems are discovered, correct them immediately before the evolution is used again. If the fire brigade leader did not provide adequate supervision or instruction, recommend that he or she pursue additional professional development.

Along with the IAP, the postincident critique should be used to generate a report on the training evolution. This report should contain the recommendations for changes to the evolution and be sent to the organization's leadership. All reports should be maintained in the organization's record system.

Environmental Issues at Training Evolutions

In the United States, the Environmental Protection Agency (EPA) regulates activities that affect the nation's water, atmosphere, and soil. In addition, in each of the individual states, similar agencies enforce their own rules and regulations that may affect training evolutions. Fire brigade leaders and management must be familiar with federal, state, and local environmental regulations. By doing so, they can apply for the necessary permits before conducting any training that may release harmful agents into the environment.

NOTE: Canada also has laws that protect the environment. Fire brigade leaders conducting training in Canada should become familiar with Canadian law and take the appropriate measures to train safely and legally.

Water

Runoff water from training evolutions can contaminate rivers, streams, lakes, ponds, and other bodies of water. Training facilities should have systems that trap, contain, and clean contaminated liquids from training props, especially when using flammable liquids. Some municipal fire and emergency services organizations may also have storm drains that are equipped with filtration systems. However, the vast majority of training divisions do not have the ability to clean contaminated materials from runoff water before it reaches streams, rivers, or lakes.

Fire brigade leaders and management should contact the local environmental AHJ or environmental protection office to determine the specific regulations they will have to follow. Sometimes an evolution will release such a diluted level of contaminant that it may not cause any environmental damage. But even in such cases, permits may be required.

Atmosphere

Live fire exercises will involve the release of hydrocarbons into the atmosphere, which may be controlled or prohibited by local open-burning ordinances. These ordinances may require acquiring a permit and displaying it at the training site. Fire brigade leaders should take the following steps to ensure that training does not pose a threat to the environment:

Step 1. Adhere to all environmental rules and regulations imposed by all levels of government.

Step 2. Meet environmental protection guidelines for the use of Class B (flammable/combustible) liquids.

Step 3. Ensure that weather conditions do not spread contaminants into populated areas.

Step 4. Provide spark and cinder control for adjacent areas.

Soil

Water runoff that contains byproducts of combustion, fuels, and nonbiodegradable extinguishing agents can contaminate soil. Large quantities of these materials are considered hazardous waste, even small quantities must be removed after training, along with any contaminated soil. Training agencies must take steps to avoid soil contamination because this can be costly and could result in litigation. Fire brigade leaders and management should consult either the EPA or their local environmental agency about the relevant rules and regulations.

Perform training on a nonporous, concrete surface that can be cleaned with inert materials if it is not possible to meet the containing water runoff requirements. Training agencies should also consider using training-type foam extinguishing agents that are nontoxic and biodegradable.

NOTE: Available specialized training foams can reduce the contamination runoff in both water and soil. These foams would replace the standard foams that personnel would use at an incident.

NOTE: Additional information on Class B fuels can be found in IFSTA's **Aircraft Rescue and Fire Fighting** manual.

Accident Investigation

Fire brigade leaders or members who are involved in or witness an accident are often afraid to provide information, thinking that they may get someone in trouble. But an investigation cannot be resolved and future accidents cannot be prevented when personnel withhold valuable information. After any injury or fatality, investigators must determine the sequence of events and their cause. Their job is about fact-finding, not fault-finding; they try to determine only what caused the accident, not who to blame for it. After any training accident, the fire brigade leader should do the following:

- Report the accident according to its organizational policies.
- Answer any questions asked by investigators about the accident.
- Complete any appropriate forms.
- Decide whether or not the training evolution can continue after the accident has occurred.
- Obtain statements immediately after the accident from persons involved and potential witnesses.
- Hold/secure any PPE or equipment used by the individual(s) injured for inspection.

Chapter Review

1. Name and describe the four stages of fire development.

2. What are the five major organizational functions of NIMS-ICS?

3. Name and describe the three main incident priorities.

4. What tasks should the RIC perform?

5. What are the five sequential actions of SLICE-RS?

6. What is the difference between strategic goals and tactical objectives?

7. What subjects should be covered when fire brigade members are receiving familiarization training on a mutual or automatic aid agreements?

8. What activities take place during the termination phase of an emergency operation?

9. Name and describe the factors of unsafe behavior that should be identified and addressed before any student is allowed to participate in a training scenario.

10. What elements should be included in a training plan?

11. What is the purpose of a postincident critique on a training evolution?

12. What steps should fire brigade leaders take to ensure training does not pose a threat to the atmosphere?

13. What actions should a fire brigade leader take after any training accident?

Discussion Question

1. With what agencies does your facility have mutual or automatic aid agreements? What is the level of familiarity that they have with your facility? What level of familiarity does your fire brigade have with their facilities?

Key Terms

Control Zones — System of barriers surrounding designated areas at emergency scenes intended to limit the number of persons exposed to the hazard, and to facilitate its mitigation. At a major incident there will be three zones — restricted (hot), limited access (warm), and support (cold).

Incident Action Plan (IAP) — Written or unwritten plan for the disposition of an incident; contains the overall strategic goals, tactical objectives, and support requirements for a given operational period during an incident. All incidents require an action plan. On relatively small incidents, the IAP is usually not in writing; on larger, more complex incidents, a written IAP is created for each operational period and disseminated to All units assigned to the incident. When written, the plan may have a number of forms as attachments.

Incident Command Post (ICP) — Location at which the incident commander and command staff direct, order, and control resources at an incident; may be co-located with the incident base. Also called Command Post (CP).

Lesson Plan — Teaching outline or plan for teaching that is a step-by-step guide (or general guidelines) for presenting a lesson or presentation. It contains information and instructions on what will be taught and the teaching procedures to be followed. It covers lessons that may vary in length from a few minutes to several hours.

Normalization of Deviation — State of a safety culture in which acting against SOPs becomes normal behavior rather than an exception.

Postincident Analysis — Overview and critique of an incident by members of all responding agencies, including dispatchers. Typically takes place within two weeks of the incident. In the training environment it may be used to evaluate student and instructor performance during a training evolution.

Postincident Critique — Meeting to discuss strategy and tactics, problems, SOP changes, or training changes derived from a postincident analysis report; usually led by a chief officer some time after a major incident.

Preincident Plan — Document, developed during preincident planning that contains the operational plan or set procedures for the safe and efficient handling of emergency situations at a given location, such as a specific building or occupancy. *Also known as* Preplan.

Risk-Management Plan — Written plan that identifies and analyzes the exposure to hazards, selects appropriate risk management techniques to handle exposures, implements those techniques, and monitors the results.

Termination — The phase of an incident in which emergency operations are completed and the scene is turned over to the property owner or other party for recovery operations.

Training Evolution — Operation of fire and emergency services training covering one or several aspects of fire fighting.

Skill Sheet List

The following skill sheets should be used to evaluate the skills described in this chapter:

NOTE: Students should wear the PPE appropriate to the NFPA 1081 level (Incipient, Advanced Exterior, Interior Structural, etc...) being evaluated.

Facility Fire Brigade Training Coordinator

Chapter Contents

JPRs addressed in this chapter

This chapter provides information that addresses the following job performance requirements of NFPA 1081, *Standard for Facility Fire Brigade Member Professional Qualifications (2018)*.

8.2.1   8.2.4

8.2.3

1. Explain the considerations for scheduling training sessions. [8.2.1]

2. Describe the methods for verifying instructor qualifications. [8.2.1]

3. Explain the characteristics of verbal communication that apply to an instructor in a classroom. [8.2.1]

4. Describe the methods for planning and organizing content for training classes. [8.2.1]

5. Describe the different teaching methodologies that a training coordinator should be familiar with. [8.2.1]

6. Describe the different psychomotor skill instruction methodologies that a training coordinator should be familiar with. [8.2.1]

7. Explain the different types of increased hazard exposure training. [8.2.1]

8. Describe the guidelines for administering written and performance tests. [8.2.3]

9. Identify the importance of a training coordinator's familiarity with fire brigades fire control and emergency operation procedures. [8.2.3]

10. Explain the importance of emphasizing safety and health policies and procedures during training. [8.2.3]

11. Describe the methods for planning for safe training. [8.2.3]

12. Identify the types of education and training records and reports. [8.2.4]

13. Describe the basic processes for writing training reports. [8.2.4]

Chapter 22
Training Coordinator Duties

NFPA 1081 tasks the fire brigade training coordinator with two primary functions:

- Handling training-related functions
- Operating at the safety officer level in the Incident Management System

The standard outlines the job performance requirements for both functions. This chapter will address the training function duties and responsibilities performed by the training coordinator. Chapter 23 will address the training coordinator's safety officer duties and responsibilities.

The training coordinator is responsible for the education and training of the facility fire brigade. This training may include entry-level training for new hires as well as recurring proficiency training for members of the fire brigade.

The training coordinator should be trained and qualified to levels of the facility fire brigade. Additionally, the training coordinator should be trained to the appropriate level (or levels) of NFPA 1041, *Standard for Fire Service Instructor Professional Qualifications*, as determined by fire brigade management. Training in accordance with NFPA 1041 can provide the training coordinator with the background for conducting training as well as leading other instructors in a training program. Additional instructor training programs may be available through local technical or community colleges and some corporate training programs.

The primary training duties of the fire brigade training coordinator include:

- Scheduling training sessions
- Verifying the qualifications of instructors
- Leading or ensuring training classes are conducted
- Verifying the skills and knowledge of facility fire brigade members
- Maintaining education, training, and drill **records**

Scheduling Training Sessions

NFPA 1081 (2018): 8.2.1

The fire brigade training coordinator schedules education and training sessions for the organization. Typically, the fire brigade training instructor knows the training needs of the fire brigade members and of the available resources that can be used to facilitate training. Considerations for scheduling training sessions include the following:

- **Sufficient planning period** — Schedule long enough in advance to ensure the session is well planned with a timeline for delivery.
- **Student availability** — Schedule training sessions at a time when as many students as possible are available.

- **Mandated staffing levels** — Work within fire brigade requirements for keeping minimum personnel levels available for emergency response. It may be necessary to schedule the training session more than once in order to accommodate all trainees and still meet staffing levels.

- **Facilities availability** — Ensure whatever training environment is needed for the session is available. This could include arranging for use of a structure or apparatus on a certain date or scheduling the use of a local training facility. Scheduling a facility could require planning a number of months in advance.

- **Facility policies and procedures** — If another facility is selected as a training location, the training coordinator should learn the policies and procedures for the facility and follow them during training. Part of this discovery may be determining if there are adjunct instructors at the facility who can assist with training.

- **Equipment availability** — Ensure that any equipment needed is available at the time of training. This might include arranging for the use of an apparatus, or it could include the requisition of certain equipment from the fire brigade.

The training coordinator should familiarize the other fire brigade instructors with the fire brigade's policies and procedures for scheduling and delivering training **(Figure 22.1)**. Scheduling policies may include any of the following:

- Which personnel are authorized to schedule training

- Which areas of training are authorized and/or needed

- Which instructors are responsible for which training

- Who approves training expenses

Figure 22.1 A fire brigade training coordinator (seated) discussing a training schedule with an instructor.

Procedures may include timelines for completion of certain training or mandated training at certain times of the year. Each fire brigade has its own way of announcing training to personnel, and training coordinators must know these procedures. Instructors should contact the training coordinator to request any training resources that may be needed.

Verifying Instructor Qualifications

NFPA 1081 (2018): 8.2.1

One of the facility fire brigade training coordinator's responsibilities is to ensure that the instructors are trained and qualified to teach in the classroom and conduct live fire exercises in those areas. The training coordinator is also responsible for evaluating instructor performance to ensure the quality of the training program is maintained.

Selecting Qualified Instructors

The fire brigade training coordinator must look for the following factors when selecting qualified instructors for the fire brigades training program:

- Trained and qualified in the subject matter topic(s) to be taught
- Trained and qualified at the same level as the fire brigade and as an instructor (preferably to NFPA 1041)
- Physically capable of safely performing all required tasks to be taught
- Professional in appearance and demeanor
- Ability to communicate clearly and concisely — verbally and in written form.
- Effectively use visual and other training aids

The fire brigade training coordinator should also look for the following personal characteristics shared by effective instructors:

- Desire to teach
- Leadership abilities
- Ingenuity, creativity, and flexibility
- Conflict-resolution skills
- Personal integrity
- Sincerity

- Motivation
- Preparation and organizational skills
- Empathy
- Fairness
- Honesty

The training coordinator may gather some of this information by examining the candidates' training records **(Figure 22.2)**. Other information may be gathered by observing the candidate's duty performance and behavior and by interviewing each candidate. Instructor candidates should prepare for the interview by:

Figure 22.2 A training coordinator and a fire brigade leader reviewing the training records of potential instructors.

- Being honest with themselves and the fire brigade training coordinator about their ability levels and knowledge
- Recognizing their strengths and weaknesses
- Relying upon their strengths as much as possible. Candidates should find courses or training materials to help them improve in areas where they are weak.

NOTE: If qualified instructors cannot be found for a training class or program, training cannot continue until instructors have completed the necessary skills training needed to be qualified.

Evaluating Instructors

The facility fire brigade training coordinator conducts routine **evaluations** of the instructors to maintain a staff of qualified instructors. Instructor evaluations are based on observations of each instructor made by the training coordinator, fire brigade leaders, and students. These evaluations also help to inform the training coordinator's formal evaluation of an instructor, which addresses classroom and training ground conduct and teaching ability.

A systematic personnel evaluation program that establishes guidelines and requirements for all evaluations should be included in the fire brigade's training section. The training coordinator should know the fire brigade's evaluation policies, including its requirements for privacy, documentation, and the monitoring of the results of the evaluation. The training coordinator should conduct formal evaluations as well as provide ongoing, informal feedback on each instructor's performance.

It is important to praise effective instructors in front of students and peers. But if instructors are performing below expectations, comments and suggestions for improvement should be offered in private.

 Observation as Evaluation

Consider evaluation an ongoing process. The training coordinator can gather multiple types of data, most of which is based on observing instructors as they teach. With feedback received from the training coordinator's observations, instructors can change or modify instructional methods in response to supervisor feedback. Observations may also indicate changes that need to be made to a course or course materials.

Informal evaluations may occur often. This evaluation is based on the observation of the instructors in their work environments. Informal evaluations have the advantage of immediacy. For example, the training coordinator may wish to review course outcomes and student evaluations with instructors after a training class. This debriefing allows the training coordinator to immediately address performance weaknesses and to identify potential problems with course materials. The training coordinator should document informal evaluations for future reference.

The formal evaluation may occur on a regular schedule (such as annually) or as needed. It uses the results of the informal observations as well as students' instructor evaluations to generate comments and suggestions. Formal evaluations are always held in private.

An evaluation form should address criteria for the skills and behaviors an instructor should possess and may include the following points:

- Preparation of training materials and props
- Classroom management considerations
- Effective interaction with students
- Proper use of verbal and nonverbal communication techniques
- Proper use of audiovisual training aids or other equipment

- Communication of all learning objectives to students enrolled in the course

- Appropriate use of questions

- Use of appropriate instructional methods

The training coordinator should first give positive feedback during a formal or informal critique before addressing areas in which the evaluated instructor should improve. The training coordinator should give constructive suggestions that show the instructors how to improve specific aspects of their teaching performance. Comments should refer to observed or credibly reported behaviors.

After the formal evaluation, the training coordinator must hold the instructor accountable for making any necessary improvements. Without accountability, the instructor has no motivation to change. The training coordinator should conduct further observations to determine whether the instructor has adequately addressed specific deficiencies identified during the evaluation. If not, the training coordinator must hold additional formal meetings with the instructor to determine whether supplementary training would be beneficial. If this step does not raise the instructor's performance to the required level, the instructor may have to be removed from teaching duties.

Inexperienced or underperforming instructors may benefit from observing or working with a more experienced instructor, who acts as a mentor and models appropriate teaching methods. Working with other instructors gives inexperienced instructors opportunities to observe models of the desired instructional methods and teaching behaviors. Mentors must be carefully selected to ensure that they model appropriate methods to their inexperienced colleagues.

Leading Training Classes

NFPA 1081 (2018): 8.2.1

The fire brigade training coordinator may also lead or conduct training classes in the classroom and on the training ground. The following sections provide an overview of the key skills the training coordinator must master to lead training classes.

Verbal Communications

The first step toward becoming an effective public speaker is to identify the characteristics displayed by effective speakers. Characteristics that apply to the training coordinator as an instructor in the classroom include the following:

- **Audience-centered** — The speaker knows the audience and adapts his or her topic, speech organization, presentation style, and personal appearance to this audience. The instructor understands the facility's processes, services, operational hazards, products, and terminology. This involves matching the instructor's presentation style to the students' learning styles.

- **Good development of ideas** — Effective speakers create interesting, appealing, and memorable ways of presenting their information. This may include the following:

  — Using relevant examples

  — Telling stories to which the audience can relate

  — Using effective metaphors

- **Good organization of ideas** — Effective speakers organize their material so that their audience is never lost during the presentation.

- **Best choice of words** — It is important not to speak above the intellectual level of the audience by using words they might not understand. It is just as important not to talk below the level of the audience members, insulting their intelligence by being too basic.

- **Good delivery skills** — Effective speakers use the following communication techniques to enhance the words that they have chosen:

  — Keep appropriate eye contact with the audience members **(Figure 22.3)**.

  — Speak to the entire audience and not to just one section or one side of the room.

  — Use appropriate gestures to illustrate mental pictures or emphasize key points.

  — Pause periodically so that students can think about what they have heard and ask questions. A good instructor should never feel pressured by silence.

  — Refrain from adding too many "war stories" to presentations.

- **Good vocal characteristics** — Major elements are as follows:

  — Pronunciation: pronouncing each word correctly, stressing the right words or syllables, and pausing where appropriate.

  — Good grammar: correct tense, possession, pronoun agreement, etc.

Figure 22.3 A training coordinator conducting a classroom lecture to fire brigade personnel.

  — Inflection: varying the tone (pitch) of words, syllables, or phrases to emphasize important points.

  — Variety: changes in loudness, tone, and rate of speech.

  — Enunciation: clearly emphasizing each syllable, accent, and pause. The opposite of enunciating is slurring.

  — Projection: speaking loudly and clearly enough to be heard in the back of the room or auditorium.

  — Rate of speech: speed at which words are spoken. Effective instructors will speak more slowly when presenting new information or emphasizing important points, or when students need to take notes. As students become more familiar with the material, instructors can speak more quickly.

- **Conversational tone** — A relaxed tone makes listeners feel at ease and ready to receive information.

- **Positive attitude** — Effective speakers display a positive attitude about the subject matter they are presenting.

- **Appropriate use of humor** — Appropriate humor can create a relaxed atmosphere and get the attention of the audience. However, instructors should avoid inappropriate humor that may offend members of the audience.

- **Personal style** — Effective speakers use a personal style, capitalizing on their own unique experiences and abilities.

Presentation Planning

Instructors can plan for presentations in the following ways:

- Understand the facility's products, services, processes, hazards, and terminology.

- Practice the delivery of a presentation. Attempt to put into practice the characteristics of effective public speakers described in the previous section of this chapter.

- Make a video recording of the presentation and review it for distracting actions and speech patterns. Making a recording also enables instructors to experiment with different ways to present materials, which can increase instructional effectiveness.

- Check the presentation materials to ensure that they are complete, in order, and correct for the topic.

- Analyze the presentation to ensure that it is logical in its sequence.

- Get plenty of rest the night before a presentation.

- Relax before a training session.

- Select comfortable clothing in which to deliver a presentation, and always dress appropriately.

- Anticipate potential problems and prepare to resolve them should they occur. Have a backup plan for unanticipated technology failures, including hard copies of presentation.

Organization Format

This format follows the basic concept of telling the listener or student the topic of the presentation, detailing the topic, and then restating the main points. The information can be presented in a variety of logical sequences. Descriptions of the three parts are as follows:

- **Opening or introduction** — Use the opening of the presentation to get the attention of students. Introduce students to the topic and purpose of the presentation, and tell them how it relates to them or their jobs. Also present a brief summary or outline of the main points to help students remain focused.

- **Body** — Present the information by using a logical sequencing approach along with supporting facts and information. Separate the body of a long presentation into smaller, easily understood segments. Ensure that each segment conveys a single point or idea and has its own opening, body, and summary. Link segments by using transition phrases in their summaries.

- **Summary or conclusion** — Review the objective of the presentation and how it is relevant to the overall goal of the course. Emphasize the main points and introduce the next lesson or the demonstration that is associated with the presentation.

Methods of Sequencing

Experts in the fields of teaching methodology and speech communication have established ways of effectively sequencing information in a presentation. The sequence depends on the topic and the organization of the lesson plan. Generally accepted sequences for instructional delivery include the following:

- **Known-to-unknown** — Begin with information that students are familiar with or already know before leading them into unfamiliar or unknown material. This method is effective because it gives students an opportunity to base their learning experience on something they already recognize.

- **Simple-to-complex** — Start by teaching the basic knowledge or skill, and then introduce more difficult or complex knowledge as the lesson progresses. Basic knowledge and skills are necessary foundations for mastering more complex knowledge and skills.

- **Whole-part-whole** — Begin this sequence with an overview of the entire topic or a demonstration of the complete skill in real time. Next, divide the topic or skill into subsections or steps, and describe or demonstrate each of them. Close by providing a summary of the entire topic or a demonstration of the complete skill.

- **Step-by-step** — Teach each individual step in the correct order and then have students practice them in the same order. A variation on this sequence is called *progressive-part*, in which steps 1 and 2 are learned before progressing to step 3. After mastering 1, 2, and 3, the student learns step 4, and so on. Finally, the student must perform all steps sequentially in a single skill.

Transitions

Instructors use transitions for continuity and consistency to move students from one portion of the lesson to the next without losing their attention. Transitions preview what will happen next or relate an upcoming concept or skill to a previous one. Effective transitions can create interest, keep attention, and make logical connections between portions of the lesson. The lesson plan should contain the location of the necessary transitions for the benefit of both experienced and inexperienced instructors.

Knowing when to use transitions is a question of timing. Transitions can be used effectively at the following times:

- Ending one topic and beginning another
- Ending a complete lesson within a series or course
- Starting a new lesson within a series or course
- Moving from one teaching method into another
- Providing rest breaks for students and instructors

Verbal and nonverbal are the two types of transitions for use in oral communication. These types may be used separately or together. With practice, the instructor can learn how to use them effectively and with variety.

Verbal Transitions

Verbal transitions provide a summary and/or preview within a single sentence or two. Types and examples of verbal transitions include the following:

- **Summary statement and preview** — Example: *Now that you understand how to operate the components of the SCBA, our next step is to learn how to assemble them into a working system.*

- **Review of the lesson or course agenda** — Example: *Today we saw a demonstration and received some practical training over how to use Class B foam to extinguish a flammable liquid fire.*

- **Change of media** — Example: *In order to illustrate what we have been discussing in the slide presentation, we will now view a video clip that shows how rapidly a fire can develop in a controlled environment.*

Nonverbal Transitions

Nonverbal transitions help an instructor to emphasize a point within a topic. They may consist of a change of facial expression, a pause, a change in vocal pitch or rate of speaking, a gesture, or physically moving from one point to another.

Nonverbal transitions may also be used to move from one teaching method into another. This kind of transition may create some disturbance to student concentration because it involves an obvious change. Altering the light level, turning on audiovisual equipment, or assembling a model takes time and cannot be accomplished effectively while the instructor is lecturing. To make these transitions less noticeable, the instructor may plan on having an aide assemble equipment while the instructor lectures or call for a break when new equipment needs to be set up for the next portion of the lesson.

Teaching Methodologies

The fire brigade training coordinator and instructors should be familiar with a variety of teaching methodologies. These methodologies include the:

- Four-step method of instruction
- Demonstrations
- Effective questioning
- Illustrated lectures
- Class discussions

Four-Step Method of Instruction

Taken as a whole, the four-step method is a widely accepted structure for teaching a lesson. The four-step method of instruction consists of the following four parts:

- **Preparation.** Refers to preparing students to learn and involves an instructor establishing how the lesson is relevant to the students' needs. The instructor can accomplish this by performing the following actions:
  - Introduce the topic
  - Gain the students' attention
  - State the learning objectives
  - Explain how the information or skill in the lesson is directly relevant to the students' jobs
  - Motivate the student to learn the information
  - State the lesson's key points so that students are prepared to listen for them

- **Presentation.** The instructor presents the lesson content in an orderly, sequential outline. The following items are listed with each key point on the outline:
  - Teaching methods
  - Learning activities
  - Demonstrations and practices
  - Listing of instructional support materials needed for the lesson such as audiovisuals, worksheets, and handouts to present the information to students

- **Application.** The instructor provides opportunities for students to learn through the following:
  - Activities
  - Exercises
  - Discussions
  - Work groups
  - Skill practices **(Figure 22.4)**
  - Practical training evolutions
  - Similar learning activities

Figure 22.4 An instructor monitoring trainees as they practice hose operations.

- Most learning takes place during the application step, making this step critically important. Application can be combined with presentation so that students apply the lesson content during activities that require them to think, manipulate tools, or demonstrate skills. Typically, application is related to performing the operations or steps of a task. Students may also demonstrate skills during an exercise that are not directly related to the steps involved to complete a given task, such as how to do any of the following:
  — Give a presentation
  — Lead a group discussion or brainstorming session
  — Apply research methods
  — Demonstrate outlining and writing techniques
- **Evaluation.** Students demonstrate how much they have learned through a written, oral, or practical examination. Written tests are typically used to evaluate whether students have learned cognitive information. Practical tests are used to evaluate skill ability. The purpose of evaluation is to determine whether students achieved the lesson objectives or course outcomes.

Illustrated Lectures

In the illustrated lecture format, the instructor explains a topic through spoken words and the use of audiovisual aids, such as:

- Computer-generated slide presentations such as PowerPoint® or Keynote®. Computer-generated slide presentations are the most widely accepted visual aid that instructors use to accompany their lectures. These presentations are tools to help illustrate key points or generate discussion. They should rarely constitute an entire lesson or be the foundation on which the lesson is built.
- Illustrations on dry-erase boards or chalkboards
- Drawings and photographs
- Recorded video on DVD or computer

The illustrated lecture format is an effective method for providing:

- Facts
- Rules and regulations
- Clarifications
- Examples
- Definitions

It allows a speaker to reach an audience of any size — from a single student to a full auditorium. Many students can be taught at the same time while the instructor only prepares one presentation. Another advantage is that students are familiar with this format. They are aware of what to expect and what is expected of them.

When giving an illustrated lecture, consider the following:

- Incorporate time for asking questions into lesson plans. Pose questions to students throughout the lecture, and allow them to ask questions either during the lecture or at the end of the session.
- Be prepared to ask questions extemporaneously when it becomes clear that the students may be losing interest. Direct questions to students who are paying less attention than others.
- Use effective listening skills to pay attention to student feedback.
- Avoid presenting too much information at once; students need time to process new material, especially if they are also taking notes.

- Provide supplemental information using handouts and reference lists.

- Break lectures into smaller segments of about 12-18 minutes. Intersperse these lecture segments with discussion groups or skill practice time.

- Provide a note-taking guide to allow students to take notes on the verbal portion of the lecture without having to also write information from the slide presentation.

- At the end of each segment, have students work in pairs or small groups to compare notes, ask each other questions, and discuss the lecture material.

- Give students three minutes at the end of the class to write down everything they remember from the lesson.

- Provide a clear preview of the information that will be contained in the lecture.

- Include only essential and relevant information in the lecture.

- Review frequently after each lecture segment and at the end of the lesson.

Demonstrations

Demonstrations are an effective way to teach manipulative skills, physical principles, and mechanical functions **(Figure 22.5)**. In the cognitive domain, demonstrations are used to illustrate theoretical or scientific concepts that students are not expected to perform. In the psychomotor domain, they are used to model a task or skill that students must learn to perform; this is the most common use of demonstrations for training in the fire and emergency services.

Figure 22.5 An instructor demonstrating how to operate a vehicle-mounted air cylinder reservicing system.

Emphasize Safety and Health

Because of the hazardous nature of fire brigade work, instructors must emphasize the importance of safety and health while demonstrating every step of a skill or task. Instructors should identify hazards at each skills station as a way to help mitigate these known hazards. Students may want to be able to perform a skill quickly when they first learn it, but skill and speed come only with practice. Trying to perform a skill without having carefully learned the steps or developed coordination can be a safety and health hazard. Instructors should always stress the importance of safety and health when demonstrating a procedure, during practice time, and in final student evaluations.

The instructor demonstrates a task while explaining how and why it is performed. The students absorb this information through sight and hearing. One preferred method for demonstrating a psychomotor skill, whole-part-whole, is as follows:

Step 1: Perform the skill at normal speed so that students can see an overview of the skill.

Step 2: Perform the skill at a slower speed, emphasizing each part individually, so that students can see the details of the skill.

Step 3: Perform the skill a third time, at normal speed, with explanation during performance.

When students practice the skill, they use psychomotor skills and add the sense of touch to their learning experiences. The following positive advantages can easily outweigh any disadvantages when using demonstrations in both the cognitive and psychomotor domains:

- Students can receive immediate feedback.
- Instructors can readily observe behavioral changes.
- Students have a high level of interest when participating.
- Instructors can easily determine whether students have achieved the learning objectives.
- Learning skills correctly, in a safe environment and under careful supervision, gives students the confidence to perform the same skills on the job.

Potential drawbacks of the demonstration method include the following:

- Instructors must plan for extensive preparation and cleanup times, especially when using such items as power tools, hose, and breathing apparatus.
- Careful lesson planning is important because assembly and practice can use much of the class time.
- Large groups of students require extra equipment for practice and additional instructors for supervising, coaching, and enforcing safety regulations. Students who are practicing potentially dangerous skills for the first time require careful monitoring.
- Skills that must be performed or practiced outside depend on the weather conditions. Instructors must have a contingency plan available in the event of inclement weather conditions.

Class Discussions

The discussion method allows for interaction between instructors and students. The instructor talks *with* the group rather than *to* the group. Group members talk to the instructor and to each other, either in small groups or as one large group.

Lesson plans may include instructions for structured discussion sessions in either large or small groups. These instructions usually provide topics for discussion. As instructors become more experienced, discussions may result spontaneously as a response to student questions. Instructors should remember that discussions are less predictable than lectures in terms of the amount of class time they require.

During a discussion, instructors and students can interact in the following ways:

- Exchange views and ideas
- Provide examples based on experiences
- Form a consensus
- Ask questions and receive answers
- Arrive at conclusions

For this method to be effective, students must have a basic knowledge of the subject before the discussion begins. The discussion method is not an appropriate format for introducing new material to inexperienced students.

A variety of techniques may be used to direct the outcome of a discussion. These techniques apply to both large and small group discussions and include the following:

- **Brainstorming** — Students try to generate as many ideas as they possibly can, operating under the principle that there are no bad ideas. The group then evaluates the ideas and decides which ones have the most merit. Brainstorming requires students to use creative thinking to propose a solution to a problem based on their knowledge and experience.

- **Nominal group process** — In this format, the discussion closely imitates an organizational decision-making process that students will encounter in their jobs. This technique is more structured than brainstorming and requires that ideas be more realistic.

- **Agenda-based process** — The instructor provides an agenda of topics or key points, which students then research and prepare **reports** to give to the group. In the discussion, students may ask questions or express opinions on the reports.

Effective Questioning

Instructors use questions for a variety of reasons, both to receive feedback on how instruction is progressing and also to stimulate student interest and critical thinking. Questions may also be used to achieve the following objectives:

- Promote discussion and critical thinking.

- Stimulate interest and arouse curiosity.

- Motivate students to acquire knowledge on their own.

- Assess students' level of understanding.

- Control the behavior of disruptive or nonparticipating students.

- Provide an opportunity for students to openly express their ideas and opinions.

- Provoke interest that generates related questions.

- Review and summarize information.

- Assess whether students have achieved the lesson's learning objectives.

Students' responses to questions can also help instructors recognize the need to alter a lesson plan or adjust their teaching style. For example, instructors may realize that they need to incorporate techniques more appropriate to their students' learning styles.

Some curriculum developers include prepared questions in their lesson plans. Instructors should also know how to create their own effective questions. Being able to create a good question allows the instructor to evaluate prepared questions so that the questions can be improved, if needed. Guidelines for developing and asking questions include the following:

- Plan and/or review questions in advance.

- Write and arrange questions in a logical order.

- Phrase questions clearly.

- Ask only one question at a time.

- Be sure that the wording of the question doesn't make the answer obvious.

- Allow a wait time.

- After waiting, call on a student directly.

- Distribute questions evenly amongst the students.

- Ask questions at a variety of levels and of a variety of types.

- Adapt questions to students' ability level.

- Ask appropriately challenging questions.

- Avoid asking questions too soon.

- Follow up on student answers.

NOTE: Never use questions to intimidate, embarrass, or humiliate students.

When considering which kind of question to ask, instructors should consider what they want to accomplish at that particular point in the lesson. Instructors can use the following types of questions to start discussions, stimulate thinking, provide feedback on how training is being received, and enable students to assess their learning and manage their own learning gaps:

- Rhetorical
- Open
- Overhead
- Redirected
- Closed
- Direct
- Relay

Instructors should prepare for student responses to questions they pose and understand the proper way of responding to those answers or new questions. Some basic guidelines for instructors are as follows:

- Use positive reinforcement.

- When a student answer is only partially correct, positively reinforce the correct portion, then redirect the question back to the student or ask another student to complete the answer.

- Always provide correct answers if the students do not. Providing correct answers benefits the entire class.

Answering students' questions is one of the most difficult things for instructors to do. Some students may pose questions that on the surface appear to be logical but are really complex, illogical, or off the topic. An instructor can respond to these types of questions in the following ways:

- Provide the answer to a question when you know the answer or are the best person to have the answer. When neither of these is the case, defer the question to a more knowledgeable source such as a senior instructor or administrator. Be aware that the question could be controversial or distract the class.

- Direct a question to another participant when there is a high probability that another participant will respond correctly. This approach can be used to generate group discussion.

- Defer questions that are beyond the scope of the course, or tell students that they will learn the answer later in the course.

- Defer questions that require time to research the correct answer. Never bluff students by providing false or misleading information. Doing so can destroy an instructor's credibility.

Psychomotor Skills Instruction

The development of psychomotor skills typically occurs in the following three phases:

- **Cognitive phase** — The student is a beginner and is developing the basic procedure of the skill through verbal and visual stimulus. The student is using trial and error to strengthen his or her understanding of the skill, which involves a great deal of effort. The instructor has a great deal of influence with his or her students. It is critical that the instructor has as much patience as possible as to not discourage the student and be a positive influence. A step-by-step skill sheet is helpful in this phase and will keep the student on track.

- **Associative phase** — The student gets more comfortable with performance of the skill. Initial errors are realized and overcome, and connections between the steps are developed and strengthened. There is an increase in fluidity of performance, but the student typically still needs to think about the steps that need to be completed. In this phase, the instructor is more of an evaluator and a coach than a teacher. The student understands what needs to be done and is refining those actions in his or her own mind. The student has associated the cognitive knowledge with the skill and muscular movements needed to complete the skill.

- **Autonomous phase** — This phase is associated with the appearance of effortless approach to the task and the ability to adapt the task to varying environments. As the student progresses and the actions become smoother, the actions will become quicker. The student is moving toward the point where

Figure 22.6 A fire brigade instructor coaching a fire fighting team during the autonomous phase of psychomotor skills development.

he or she no longer needs to think about the action. The instructor has now become the coach and is there to help the students refine their efforts **(Figure 22.6)**.

As an instructor, it is important to use a systematic and structured approach to psychomotor skill instruction. A sequential approach to psychomotor instruction is:

- **Preparation** — The instructor is ready to teach the skill and is familiar with the skill level of the student.

- **Conceptualization** — The student is given the cognitive elements of the skill. The student learns what to do in a big picture context including possible problems and common errors.

- **Visualization** — The instructor demonstrates the skill in its entirety, giving a basis of how the student is expected to perform.

- **Verbalization** — The instructor verbalizes the skill to the student, breaking down the task into subtasks in the correct order. The student should be able to verbalize the steps, which will assist in placing the steps in the correct order.

- **Practice** — A deliberate and conscious effort to refine the skill performance. Critical for ultimate success and eventual mastery.

- **Feedback** — Critical for correction of errors. It is important for students to feel that they are succeeding. However, it is equally critical for the students to understand where they are not meeting the instructor's expectations and to correct observed problems.

- **Mastery** — Perform the skill routinely without error.

  NOTE: This will not occur in initial training but should be strived for over the course of a career.

- **Autonomy** —The ability to adapt the skill in real-life situations without error.

Psychomotor Skills Demonstrations

Before the instructor starts a skills demonstration, he or she should provide the following information:

- Explain the skill.

- Describe its importance.

- Explain how it relates to other skills.

- Give the requirements for the number of people who are required to perform it.

- Explain when the skill should be performed.

After this general overview, the instructor should perform the skill at normal speed, then perform it again slowly while explaining each step. Next, the instructor should encourage students to ask questions. The instructor should repeat the slow-speed demonstration until students are able to verbalize the steps of the skill. At this point, students are ready to practice the skill themselves. The slow-speed demonstration is the transition between the presentation step and the application step.

The instructor guides and coaches the students as they practice. As the students practice in small groups, instructors have the students critique and coach each other. Once or twice during a practice session, instructors may need to demonstrate the entire skill. Instructors must show the skill steps correctly and in sequence. The end of the session is a particularly good time to do this. Instructors should encourage students to practice skills during rest breaks, free time, and at the beginning of the next training session. Students are ready for evaluation when they have perfected the skill.

Planning, preparation, and practice are essential to a successful skills demonstration. The instructor who does not appear proficient at a skill will lose credibility with students and waste valuable training time by having to repeat or correct skill steps.

Evolution Control

Both simple and complex practical training evolutions must be controlled. Controlling an evolution involves the following elements:

- **Supervising** — Instructors directly supervise students to make sure they practice skills safely and correctly.

- **Monitoring** — Instructors observe the progress of the evolution to make sure students accomplish the learning objectives.

- **Teaching** — Instructors present new or related information during the evolution, when appropriate.

- **Managing** — Instructors apply the elements of the NIMS-ICS to control and coordinate the evolution as though it was an actual emergency situation.

To effectively control a training evolution, there must be a sufficient number of instructors to supervise all the students. A ratio of three to seven students to one instructor is an optimal student to instructor ratio. In high hazard training evolutions this ratio is reduced. For example, NFPA 1403 mandates a maximum student to instructor ratio of five to one.

Simple Training Evolutions

Simple training evolutions share some training techniques in common with psychomotor skills training. The main difference is the number of students involved and the training location. Simple training evolutions involve small numbers of students performing a single skill that requires only a few tasks. Examples include the following **(Figure 22.7)**:

- Donning and doffing PPE

- Using a portable fire extinguisher

- Forcing entry through a door

- Deploying and advancing an attack hoseline

Figure 22.7 Three examples of simple training evolutions.

These training evolutions may involve from one to five active students and require only one or two instructors for supervision. Students repeat the evolution until they are able to perform it without error. When more than one student is involved, they rotate positions so that each student has the opportunity to experience and practice each part of the skill.

The instructor begins an evolution by performing the following actions:

- Explains the purpose of the evolution as it relates to the learning objectives or outcomes.
- Demonstrates the evolution. When the evolution involves more than one person, it may require an experienced group of responders to perform the evolution.
- Relates the evolution to the classroom lecture.
- Emphasizes the safety requirements for the evolution.

When the students begin practicing, the instructor monitors the students' performance. If students perform poorly, make an error, or violate safety protocols, the instructor should stop them immediately and correct their behavior. Immediate correction forces students to recognize the problem and adjust their behavior.

NOTE: Do not forget to use positive reinforcement when applicable.

Instructors need to perform simple training evolutions as though students were involved in a real emergency incident, including typical staffing levels and the use of appropriate PPE. During training, instructors must follow all applicable policies and procedures, including using the NIMS-ICS, that would affect personnel at a real incident.

Increased Hazard Exposure Training

Examples of increased hazard exposure training scenarios include:

- Live fire exercises
- Hazardous materials
- Hazardous processes
- Evolutions that require the use of power tools

Increased hazard exposure training is dangerous even under very controlled conditions. NFPA 1041 therefore requires that a Level II Instructor supervise both students and Level I Instructors during this type of training.

Only a prepared and qualified instructor can lead increased hazard exposure training evolutions. The instructor should learn the qualifications that his or her state/province and municipality requires for these types of training evolutions. The instructor must meet these qualifications before continuing with the training. The training should be postponed if the instructor has any doubts at all about his or her qualifications or experience. Schedule the training when the instructor has gained the proper qualifications and becomes more knowledgeable about the standards and regulations that apply.

Live-Fire Training

Live-fire training is an important part of both entry-level and experienced fire brigade member training. Entry-level personnel learn new skills and experienced personnel develop their existing skills. Live-fire training evolutions may be the only experience some personnel receive and may involve the following categories **(Figure 22.8, p. 710)**:

Figure 22.8 Fire brigade personnel performing fire suppression activities during live-fire training evolutions inside a structure and outside.

- Scenarios at **purpose-built structures** at training facilities built for interior live-fire training
- Scenarios involving exterior fires, including transportation fires, facility specific fires, and flammable/combustible liquid fires at a remote site or a training facility
- Mobile burn units and flashover training units

> ### NFPA 1403, Standard on Live Fire Training Evolutions
> To ensure the highest level of safety, all live-fire training evolutions must meet the requirements of the appropriate sections of the most current edition of NFPA 1403. While this standard is not legally mandated in all jurisdictions, noncompliance with the standard has resulted in injuries and fatalities for which instructors were held criminally and civilly responsible. Any instructor leading live-fire training should make every effort to prepare and instruct based upon this standard.

Exterior Fires

Exterior fire-suppression training may include evolutions that simulate low fire load fires, transportation fires, flammable/combustible liquids fires, and wildland fires. This training can be conducted at a permanent training facility or a remote site, with one or more companies or training agencies. Depending upon the location of the training and the type of fuel used (such as Class B fuels), there may be environmental requirements that should be met. Instructors should check with the AHJ that enforces the federal, state, and local environmental regulations. In addition, many exterior fires such as those with exterior props or Class B materials may be governed by requirements in NFPA 1403.

Small Prop Fires. These fires train entry-level fire brigade members how to use portable handheld extinguishers to control all classes of fires. Training evolutions usually take place outside, in an area where the spread of fire is limited or nonexistent. They involve small quantities of fuel, which typically consists of Class A materials (in the form of shipping pallets) or Class B materials contained in small burn pans. Similar LPG- or natural gas-supplied burn pans are also available.

Instructors demonstrate the appropriate procedure based on the type of fuel and extinguisher. Students then repeat the procedure, practicing it until they are proficient. In all cases, a backup extinguishing system must be present, usually in the form of an experienced crew with a charged attack hoseline.

Figure 22.9 A variety of live-fire training props that fire brigade personnel may use.

Medium to Large Prop Fires. These training fires use permanent training props that are contained in burn pits. They are typically fueled by Class B materials such as LPG, natural gas, or other flammable/combustible liquids. The valves located outside the pit are used to turn off fuel supplies. A fuel-control officer supervises this process. An ignition officer is designated to start the fire using an approved ignition device. Medium to large props include the following **(Figure 22.9)**:

- Vehicle props
- Shipboard props
- Railcars
- Mobile props specifically designed to simulate flammable liquid and gas fires using propane

- Large trash container props
- Aircraft fire simulators
- Propane tanks

Flammable/Combustible Liquid Fires. Simulating fires in flammable/combustible liquid, LPG, and natural gas storage, production, and pipeline facilities is usually restricted to purpose-built props in permanent training facilities. They require piped fuel supplies, control valves, product- and water-containment diking, high-capacity water supplies, and water-decontamination capabilities. Evolutions generally involve multiple-company training.

Wildland Fires. Training fire personnel to control wildland and/or wildland/urban interface (areas where structures mix with wildland fuels) fires. Training evolutions will vary, depending on the skills required to meet the local dangers that wildland fires create. The nature of wildland fires makes them unpredictable and highly hazardous. A controlled burn can be affected by weather, wind direction, and other factors beyond the instructor's control. Therefore, training students on safety is even more of a concern during this type of training. The National Wildland Coordinating Group (NWCG) provides national standards for wildland training.

Verifying Fire Brigade Members Knowledge and Skills

NFPA 1081 (2018): 8.2.3

The fire brigade training coordinator must be able to verify the knowledge and skills of the fire brigade members and trainees. This task involves administering tests and observing and evaluating individual and group performances.

Whether a test is given online, face-to-face, on a testing platform, or using a **learning management system (LMS)**, test administration begins before the test is given. Instructors should inform students of the following:

- The type of test they will be given
- What content will be covered
- The test environment
- Which materials to bring (paper, pencil, pen, notes, books, PPE, etc.). The instructor should consider the test location's physical environment, making sure that students have the following **(Figure 22.10)**:
  — Appropriate lighting
  — Comfortable seating
  — Quiet surroundings
  — Regulated temperature

Figure 22.10 Instructors should check the testing location's physical environment.

SOPs

The fire brigade should have written SOPs for the evaluation of personnel's knowledge and skills. These SOPs should be followed during any evaluation period. The training coordinator and instructors should review these SOPs at least annually and modify them as necessary to ensure that the quality and efficiency of the evaluation processes are maintained.

Administering Written Tests

Instructors should adhere to the following guidelines when administering written tests:

- Before the test:
  — Ask the testing organization or agency to determine whether there are any specific instructions or protocols for administering the test.
  — Report to the testing location an appropriate amount of time before testing begins.
  — Maintain security of tests at all times.
  — Rearrange classroom seating when necessary so that it is conducive for taking written tests.
  — Eliminate loud talking or noises outside the testing room.
  — Eliminate all potential distractions within the room.
  — Have students place all backpacks, purses, books, and other unnecessary items out of the way or in an assigned area.

— Ensure that all electronic devices are turned off and secured.

— Inform students of expectations, including misconduct rules.

— Make sure that students do not bring written or electronic notes into the testing room, unless these are specifically approved by the examination guidelines.

Remind students to follow instructions on the answer sheet correctly.

- During the test:

  — Watch for signs of **academic misconduct**, such as:

    - Students whose eyes "wander" around the room.

    - Answers written on clothing, skin, or shoes, or on papers lying on the floor near students' desks.

    - Students talking to each other during the test.

  — Ensure that the environment remains quiet and safe for students.

  — If students are allowed to leave the testing area to use the restroom, refreshment area, or other rehabilitation facilities, make sure they do not take the test instrument or paper with them (verify with AHJ prior to test for policy).

  — Supply extra paper, writing implements, and answer sheets.

  — If possible, have testing aides on hand to assist with difficult students or situations, or to perform tasks such as handing out or collecting tests and evaluation forms.

- After the test:

  — Do not allow students to change their answers once answer sheets have been submitted.

  — Review the test (at an appropriate time) with students to clarify any objectives they may not have understood. This may occur at the following class in the case of formative tests but may not be possible with summative tests.

  — Maintain the security of tests and answer sheets, especially when scoring tests and recording grades in accordance with AHJ guidelines.

  — Return test materials to the proper authority if another instructor will be scoring and grading them.

  — Identify answer sheets with identical incorrect answers or sequences of answers on multiple test sheets. These could be indications of academic misconduct.

Administering Performance Tests

Specific guidelines for administering performance tests are as follows:

- Before the test:

  — Ensure that the subject matter of the test matches the subject matter that is being tested.

  — Provide students with adequate practice time during class time leading up to the test date.

  — Provide rehabilitation facilities such as restrooms or refreshment areas.

  — Ensure that tests are not biased through wording, timing, or unattainable criteria.

  — Include all test administration rules in the test instructions.

  — Read the instructions aloud to the students exactly as they are written. Do not paraphrase because this may alter the test results.

  — Provide students with the time limits for each test and clearly state the times for emphasis.

  — Explain the purpose of each test.

  — Encourage students to ask questions if they do not understand something.

- During the test:
  - Give the test to each student in exactly the same manner.
  - Follow task appropriate skills evaluation checklists **(Figure 22.11)**.
  - Record students' scores on performance checklists as each one takes the test. Do not wait until the end of the testing period to record scores.
- After the test — Keep all test scores confidential.

Fire Control and Emergency Operation Procedures

The fire brigade training coordinator should know the fire brigade's fire control and emergency operation procedures. This allows the training coordinator to adapt training to meet the fire brigade's training needs for entry-level and recurring proficiency training. The training coordinator should conduct a routine review of the fire brigade's operational procedures to determine any changes. Any modifications to those procedures should be reviewed and modifications made to the brigade's training program to ensure the changes have been delivered to all personnel.

Figure 22.11 The instructor in the background is using a skills evaluation checklist to evaluate the performance of the two students.

Safety and Health Policies and Procedures

The training coordinator also needs to know the fire brigade's safety and health policies and guidelines for each emergency services training course. In addition, the fire brigade should conduct emergency operations using NIMS-ICS. The training coordinator should be familiar with the locally adopted ICS and accountability model procedures and then integrate them into training exercises.

When safety is continually emphasized during training, students are more likely to use safe practices during emergency response operations. The training coordinator and instructors are the primary role models for safety and health and must take that role seriously. Instructors cannot just mention safety guidelines and expect students to follow them. Instructors must demonstrate and reinforce these guidelines. Because instructors constantly interact with personnel in planning and presenting courses, they set the stage and serve as role models for following safety requirements. Following safety guidelines or plans that the organization develops or adopts has a significant effect on reducing injuries and fatalities in training and at emergency incidents.

Instructors must devote appropriate time in every training session to discuss all aspects of safety. Safety should be planned well before the activity starts and reflected during the training session through awareness and practice. Instructors can increase awareness and help prevent accidents during training in the following ways:

- Describe applicable safety requirements or procedures to students by doing the following:
  - Provide rules and guidelines in writing.
  - Read aloud the written rules and guidelines as the students read them silently.

— Have students sign a statement saying that they have read and understood all safety rules and regulations. In some fire brigades and organizations, this signature is mandatory.

- Create a training and safety plan for any high-hazard drill or application, and brief all instructors and students on the plan before training begins.

- Describe the proper safeguards and equipment used for preventing accidents.

- Describe possible hazards and explain the necessary precautions.

- Brief students on relevant techniques, procedures, tools, facility characteristics, and appropriate safety rules before starting the evolution.

- Plan carefully for training scenarios.

- Ensure that appropriately trained personnel assist in supervising scenarios.

- Review emergency procedures, emergency evacuation plans, and verbal or alarm alerts with students before the evolution.

- Inspect and repair tools, equipment, props, and apparatus before starting training sessions.

- Assign a safety officer to each training scenario based upon a prepared training and safety plan.

- Assign additional (more than the minimum) personnel for safety positions depending upon the scale of the training evolution and the severity of danger.

- Model and reinforce safety policies and procedures by personally adhering to them.

- Be aware of human factors among students that can contribute to unsafe conditions such as improper attitude, complacency, lack of knowledge or skill, and physical limitations.

Training personnel must identify and eliminate potential hazards when planning practical training evolutions. They must also plan to address the necessary precautions to prevent injury while training, train students to recognize job hazards, and teach them how to control or eliminate these hazards. These steps help minimize the level of risk and prevent injuries.

When dealing with high-hazard training evolutions, the instructor cannot function as both instructor in charge of training and safety officer. An instructor should appoint another qualified individual as the safety officer for the training evolution. The safety officer must be familiar with the evolution in which they are working. The safety officer cannot be just somebody present. He or she needs to know what the training is about and what may happen at any given time.

NOTE: Establish and use training and safety plans during all types of emergency incidents and high-hazard training evolutions. Also include use of a personnel accountability system.

Planning for Safe Training

Training ground instruction requires thorough planning. Instructors need to be familiar with the skills they are teaching. This experience provides a firm foundation for teaching practical training evolutions. Before leading instruction on the training ground, experienced instructors should practice so that they can safely and correctly perform the skills they will demonstrate. The following sections explain important actions regarding planning safe training.

Inspecting and Repairing Facilities and Props

It is important to inspect training facilities, props, tools, and equipment before beginning a course or scenario **(Figure 22.12, p. 716)**. Inspections ensure that they are in working condition and that the training environment will be safe. If inspections show that equipment is unsafe or badly damaged, the training coordinator should report this to the AHJ. The training coordinator should either reschedule training, train without the faulty equipment, or conduct the training at a facility with functional equipment.

Figure 22.12 The training coordinator and another fire brigade member inspecting a training facility and props.

Some inspection, maintenance, and repair can be assigned to class members as a training activity. But maintaining some items, such as breathing equipment, requires certified or authorized personnel. The AHJ should establish an inspection time schedule based on industry practice, manufacturer's recommendations, and local needs.

The training coordinator should keep thorough records of all maintenance, repairs, inspections, and replacements. The records provide a basis for developing an accurate operating budget, justifying repairs or replacements, and assessing equipment's overall value. In all cases, maintenance and repairs that are beyond the capabilities of students or instructors should be delegated to certified or authorized repair personnel.

Identifying Training Hazards

Training coordinators and instructors should be knowledgeable with prepared lesson plans, the training facility, any training prop, and the evolution to be conducted to identify the hazards associated with training. Students should be informed during the training briefing of hazards they will face as part of training. If the appropriate hazards are not addressed in a lesson plan, training personnel need to modify the lesson plan to include appropriate safety instructions or postpone the training.

Common Causes of Injury During Fire Brigade Activities

The fire brigade training coordinator must know the common causes of injuries that occur during fire brigade activities. The training coordinator can then identify the potential hazards that may exist during fire brigade training and take correct actions to prevent accidents and injuries. Some of the common causes of injury during fire brigade activities include:

- Overexertion and strains
- Falls, trips, and slips
- Object strikes individual
- Coming into contact with an object
- Exposure to fire products
- Thermal exposure, causing burns to exposed skin resulting from improperly wearing of thermal protective clothing

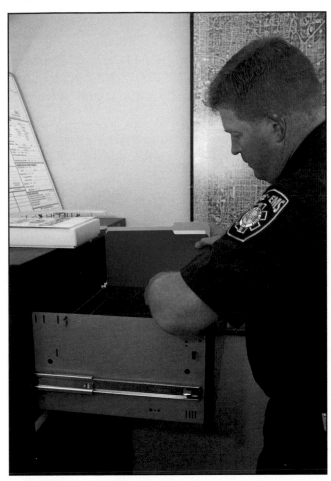

Figure 22.13 Training records should be stored in a secure location.

Maintaining Education, Training, and Drill Records

NFPA 1081 (2018): 8.2.4

Training records are permanent accounts of past events or of actions taken by an individual or the fire brigade. Training records consist of the following:

- Types and hours of training provided
- Names of personnel in attendance
- Learning outcomes achieved
- Training resources expended

NOTE: From these records, raw data can be used to develop reports or demonstrate the effectiveness of the division or agency's training program.

Training reports are official, factual accounts of a training event, presented either verbally or in writing. Following a training event, a written report is compiled, detailing all pertinent activities related to the training event. Training reports keep administrators informed of the accomplishments, problems, and daily training activities of the fire brigade and its members. These reports can also provide data that enable an organization to make informed decisions about operations and strategic planning.

Records may consist of standardized forms, narratives, or a simple list of names. They may be handwritten, typed, or computer-generated. Reports are generally in essay format and either typed or computer-generated. Both reports and records must be stored in a secure location but be easily accessible to appropriate personnel **(Figure 22.13)**.

Types of Education and Training Records and Reports

Documentation of training is a critical part of the day-to-day activities of the training coordinator and instructors. This documentation may be used in many ways for the benefit of the students, instructors, the fire brigade, and the training section. This information can be divided into two main categories: training records and training reports.

Education and Training Records

Training coordinators and instructors must be able to accurately complete many types of record forms and do so according to organizational policies and procedures. This may be as simple as keeping a daily attendance sheet during a course. The following are types of training records that may need to be completed as a part of the instructor's duties:

- **Attendance records** — Evidence that individuals have completed a specified number of hours of training in a specific topic such as respiratory protection or hazardous materials incident response.

- **Applications for certification** — Forms that students submit after a certification course; students may require an instructor's assistance and/or signature to complete these forms.

- **Incident/injury records** — Documentation of student injuries during training. These records may be completed by the instructor or by an investigative team. These records may be requested for public view after they have been completed but should be kept private internally and not shared without proper authorization or cause.

- **Test records** — Documentation of scores on individual tests given during coursework; test results must remain secure after becoming part of a trainee's personal training records and/or personnel files.

- **Scheduling records** — Documentation about what training has been approved by the organization. Usually completed as part of the training scheduling process and may be kept as a history of training offered by the organization.

- **Resource request** — Documentation of what resources an instructor needs to teach a certain lesson. The AHJ may have a particular form that the instructor needs to complete in order to obtain the needed resources. Instructors should follow the policies and procedures in their organizations for requesting the resources that they need for training.

All training records should be considered private. Test scores and medical information are especially sensitive. Only the instructor and student should have access to test scores. Instructors should not post records publicly or report test results over e-mail. Test scores should be communicated directly to the student in writing. The same rules apply to certification records.

Training Reports

Training coordinators and instructors must be able to accurately complete many types of reports, and do so according to organizational policies and procedures. The following are types of training reports that may need to be completed as a part of the instructor's duties:

- **Attendance Reports** — Used as a transcript of students who attended a single class or an individual's transcript for all of the training the person attended within the organization.

- **Certification/Qualification/License** — Identifies the members who have specific certifications/ qualifications or license for the purpose to maintain recertification or licensure. Can include the date of issue and, if required, the date for recertification.

- **Test Report** — Generated from all test scores for a particular class.

- **Instructional/Contact hours** — Generated for all classes taught or supported (external training) by the organization. Contact hours is the exact number of hours the student had in the class. Instructional hours are generated by taking the contact hours multiplied by the total number of students in the class.

- **Competency Reports** — Provided on individuals from the setup of the initial course. Examples in using these reports could be for specific tasks or JPR's addressed in the fire brigade organizational statement, but could be applicable to any requirement.

Records and reports can also be considered legal documents that track the training career of a student. Fire brigade training coordinators are not responsible for managing their facility's entire record system but should be familiar with the fire brigade's filing system.

Drill Records

Drills are held on a recurring basis at each facility depending on the facility's function and the type of drill being conducted. The training coordinator should ensure that all fire brigade personnel who participate during these activities are included in the drill's documentation.

Report Writing

Training coordinators and instructors must be able to write clear, concise, and accurate reports based upon witnessed events and the records that are available to them. They must also ensure that all written reports are accurately completed, properly filed, delivered in a timely fashion, and securely stored.

The most difficult portion of most reports is the report narrative. A report narrative should answer the five questions important to the report: who, what, when, where, and why. To keep report narratives simple and concise, organize them based upon the following parts:

- **Heading** — Contains basic information similar to the heading of a memo or electronic mail (e-mail) communication. It includes the date, name of the recipient(s), name of the sender or author, and subject of the report. Some organizations have a formal template or format that provides a space for all of this information.

- **Introduction** — Provides a brief overview of the report in a single paragraph. Includes the purpose of the report, time period covered by the report, and name or names of the people involved in writing the report.

- **Body** — Contains all information relating to the report, including the following:

  — Reason for the report

  — Specific and concrete facts based on accurate figures and data; may include visually effective graphs and tables

  — Problems that were discovered

  — Proposed solutions

- **Conclusion/summary** — A final paragraph (or two) that summarizes main points and recommends changes or other actions.

Chapter Review

1. What information may scheduling policies include?

2. What criteria should be included in a formal instructor evaluation?

3. Name and describe four characteristics of verbal communication.

4. List five ways an instructor can plan for presentations.

5. Name and describe the three parts of an organizational format.

6. What are the four generally accepted sequences for instructional delivery?

7. At what times can transitions be used effectively?

8. What techniques can be used to direct the outcome of class discussions?

9. Name and describe the three phases of the development of psychomotor skills.

10. What props may be used in exterior fire training?

11. List three actions that should be taken after administering a written test.

12. List three actions that should be taken before administering a performance test.

13. What is the benefit of the training coordinator knowing the fire brigade's fire control and emergency operation procedures?

14. List four ways instructors can increase awareness and help prevent accidents during training.

15. What are common causes of injury during fire brigade training activities?

16. Name and describe three types of training records.

17. What are the three main parts that should be used in a report narrative?

Discussion Questions

1. What teaching methodologies have you used? Did you find them effective?

2. What methodologies have you used during psychomotor skill instruction? Did you find them effective?

3. What challenges have you faced when administering or taking a written test?

Key Terms

Academic Misconduct — Any unethical behavior in which students present another student's work as their own, or gain an unfair advantage on a test by bringing answers into the testing area, copying another student's answers, or acquiring test questions in advance.

Associative Phase — Stage of motor learning in which the learner develops and strengthens the connections between steps in a skill, increasing fluidity of the overall skill through practice and performance.

Autonomous Phase — Final stage of motor learning in which the learner has demonstrated a mostly automatic progression through the steps of a skill, without having to rely on heavy cognitive application.

Cognitive Phase — Primary stage of motor learning in which the learner acquires the general understanding of the skill to be performed.

Evaluation — Systematic and thoughtful collection of information for decision-making; consists of criteria, evidence, and judgment.

Learning Management System (LMS) — Software application used for the administration and delivery of educational curricula, training resources, and evaluative tools.

Purpose-Built Structure — Building specially designed for live-fire training; fires can be ignited inside the building multiple times without major structural damage.

Records — Permanent accounts of past events or of actions taken by an individual, unit, or organization.

Reports — Official accounts of an incident, response, or training event, either verbally or in writing.

Skill Sheet List

The following skill sheets should be used to evaluate the skills described in this chapter:

NOTE: Students should wear the PPE appropriate to the NFPA 1081 level (Incipient, Advanced Exterior, Interior Structural, etc...) being evaluated.

Facility Fire Brigade Training Coordinator

JPRs addressed in this chapter

This chapter provides information that addresses the following job performance requirements of NFPA 1081, *Standard for Facility Fire Brigade Member Professional Qualifications (2018).*

8.2.2

1. Describe the risk/benefit analysis considerations of size-up. [8.2.2]

2. Identify the processes of creating and maintaining emergency SOPs. [8.2.2]

3. Review the aspects of fire dynamics. [8.2.2]

4. Identify the processes of creating and maintaining live-fire training procedures. [8.2.2]

5. Identify the processes of creating and maintaining medical emergency procedures. [8.2.2]

6. Describe the processes for creating reporting and investigation procedures for incidents and injuries. [8.2.2]

7. Identify the processes for selecting an infection control officer and creating infection control procedures. [8.2.2]

8. Describe the different types of hazards to consider in emergency scene assessment. [8.2.2]

9. Describe the different types of utility hazards. [8.2.2]

10. Identify the importance of identifying areas of wildland urban interface (WUI). [8.2.2]

11. Describe the different types of hazards at vehicle incidents. [8.2.2]

12. Explain the different types of hazards when placing apparatus. [8.2.2]

13. Describe the tasks of establishing rapid intervention crews (RICs). [8.2.2]

14. Describe the tasks of establishing and monitoring rehabilitation areas. [8.2.2]

15. Explain the importance and basic principles of a personnel accountability system. [8.2.2]

Chapter 23
Incident Safety Officer Duties

In the United States, OSHA requires the assignment of an Incident Safety Officer (ISO) at each emergency. NFPA 1081 tasks the fire brigade training coordinator with the role of serving as a safety officer during training evolutions and potentially during emergency incidents. Fire brigade training coordinators should be trained to meet NFPA 1521, *Standard for Fire Department Safety Officer Professional Qualifications*, which specifies the job performance requirements for incident safety officers. The materials in this chapter provides an overview of the duties and responsibilities of an incident safety officer. Throughout this chapter we will use training coordinator and incident safety officer interchangeably or occasionally "training coordinator/ISO."

Size-up
NFPA 1081 (2018): 8.2.2

The fire brigade training coordinator, acting as the ISO, must conduct a size-up of each emergency from a perspective of risk management. A risk management assessment essentially covers every aspect of incident operations. The training coordinator/ISO must have the experience and training to quickly identify and stop any safety-related issue. The ISO must maintain the big picture of the incident while monitoring each division or group operating on the scene **(Figure 23.1)**. Personnel safety is the first priority when considering which strategies and tactics to employ at an incident. The ISO should utilize a recognized risk management framework during an incident assessment. The sections that follow describe a number of risk assessment methods that have been developed to help individuals make informed strategic decisions at incidents.

Figure 23.1 An incident safety officer checking on a fire brigade member during a training evolution.

Risk Management Framework

Fire brigade members are expected to take calculated risks to provide for life safety, incident stabilization, and property conservation. Calculated risks mean that they should not blindly go into a situation, but rather gather information through size-up and determine what level of risk is acceptable for the given situation.

The following sections provide safety and risk/benefit analysis considerations. The ISO should be familiar with all of them and apply the concept that best fits the situation. The ISO may find that a single approach fits the need of the situation, but at other times a multifaceted approach may be needed.

10 Rules of Engagement for Structural Fire Fighting

In 2001, the International Association of Fire Chiefs (IAFC) developed a model policy called *The 10 Rules of Engagement for Structural Fire Fighting*. The policy was developed to help ensure that all firefighters return home safely. The *10 Rules* are as follows:

- **Acceptability of Risk**

1. No building or property is worth the life of a firefighter.

2. All interior fire fighting involves an inherent risk.

3. Some risk is acceptable, in a measured and controlled manner.

4. No level of risk is acceptable where there is no potential to save lives or savable property.

5. Firefighters shall not be committed to interior offensive fire fighting operations in abandoned or derelict buildings.

- **Risk Assessment**

6. All feasible measures shall be taken to limit or avoid risks through risk assessment by a qualified officer.

7. It is the responsibility of the Incident Commander to evaluate the level of risk in every situation.

8. Risk assessment is a continuous process for the entire duration of each incident.

9. If conditions change and risk increases, change strategy and tactics.

10. No building or property is worth the life of a fire fighter.

Phoenix (AZ) Fire Department Model

The risk management concept is clearly stated in the decision-making model developed by the Phoenix (AZ) Fire Department (PFD). The model is a departmental SOP that is used to help PFD officers in making sound emergency response decisions. The essence of the model is as follows:

- Each emergency response is begun with the assumption that *they can protect lives and property.*

- They will *risk their lives a lot, if necessary, to save savable lives.*

- They will *risk their lives a little, and in a calculated manner, to save savable property.*

- They will *NOT risk their lives at all to save lives and property that have already been lost.*

Phoenix Model Simplified
- Risk a lot to save a lot.
- Risk a little to save a little.
- Risk nothing to save nothing.

Risk Management Criteria

Each fire brigade should define risk management criteria for those members either making command decisions or assessing decisions such as the ISO. When an incident occurs, the IC and the ISO must ensure that strategic and tactical decisions focus on safety and reducing. Risk management criteria should be in conjunction with the above stated risk/benefit analysis and include consideration of the following:

- Incident hazards
- Laws, codes, regulations, and standards
- Building construction
- Hazardous energy sources
- Limited personnel

- Imminent hazards
- Facility operations
- Fire dynamics and smoke characteristics
- Traffic hazards
- Competency levels of on-scene personnel

Emergency SOPs

NFPA 1081 (2018): 8.2.2

Figure 23.2 A fire brigade training coordinator/incident safety officer reviewing his organization's written policies.

Written policies and procedures are essential for the effective and efficient operation of any fire brigade **(Figure 23.2)**. Procedures identify benchmarks for behavior and performance that remain static in a dynamic workplace or response environment. The procedures place into writing the fire brigade's expectations based on the organizational model and the strategic and operational plans. Procedures may need to be created for the following reasons:

- A safety issue is identified that requires new procedures.

- Changes have occurred in industry standards, accepted best practices, or laws, codes, and regulations.

- A safe work behavior is identified that the organization wants to formalize through the procedure development process, such as wearing seatbelts on apparatus at all times.

The steps for determining the need for a new policy or procedure are summarized below:

- **Identify the problem or requirement for a policy or procedure** — Determine whether a policy or procedure is necessary to address the problem. Some problems may be best addressed on an individual basis and do not require a formal policy or procedure.

- **Collect data to evaluate the need** — Use quantitative or qualitative data that may come from personnel interviews, product literature, or activity reports. Data collection may also involve reviewing best practices, prior incident reports, industry standards, and regulations.

- **Select the best response to the need** — Determine the best policy or procedure to solve the problem. Remember that this selection may include no policy or procedure at all.

- **Select alternative responses** — Select a second best choice if a contingency is indicated. External influences may make it necessary to select a policy or procedure other than the first choice. Personnel safety should be the priority when selecting alternatives.

- **Recommend the policy or procedure that best meets the need** — The ISO will make recommendations on policy and procedure approval based on the operational need.

- **Establish a revision process or schedule** — Create a revision process as part of the policy or procedure. This process may be general for all policies and procedures or may be one that is specific to the policy that has been selected.

- **Consider the need for legal adoption of policy and procedure** — Because policies and procedures may have the effect of law, the jurisdiction may need to formally adopt them. Formal approval requires that the policy or procedure be supported by documentation.

NOTE: FEMA's *Developing Effective Standard Operating Procedures for Fire and EMS Departments* is a resource that can assist the ISO with developing SOPs as a part of the fire brigade.

Effectiveness Assessment and Criteria

The SOP manual is a collection of documents that should address the administrative and operational needs of the fire brigade. The individual documents in the manual should be reviewed regularly for appropriateness and effectiveness. Each fire brigade needs to determine the frequency schedule for reviewing the SOP manual. At a minimum, this review needs to occur at least every two to three years based on OSHA requirements. Unscheduled reviews may occur when specific SOPs are identified in a postincident analysis or as a part of an investigation. An SOP review should include those operations that were successful as well as those that were unsuccessful. The SOPs should be assessed within the scope of the incident in which they apply. This assessment may include everyday fire brigade operations in addition to emergency or nonemergency incidents and training evolutions.

> **CAUTION:** When SOPs change too frequently, they lose their effectiveness. Change SOPs only as necessary or during scheduled review.

Each incident or training exercise is unique. SOPs must provide the guidance necessary to address an all-hazards, multi-discipline approach, but with enough flexibility to be useful in a myriad of situations. When determining the criteria for assessing the effectiveness of SOPs, the ISO should concentrate on the safety and health aspects. The criteria may be answered by asking the following questions:

- Did the incident or exercise come to a successful conclusion? Why or why not?

- Did the SOPs provide enough guidance for a coordinated team effort?

- Were the SOPs applicable and relevant to current practices?

- Did the SOPs provide enough flexibility for fire brigade members to adapt to the situation?

- Did any injuries, fatalities, illnesses, or exposures occur?

- Did the incident risk analysis lead to a positive incident strategy and subsequent tactics?

- Did a deviation of SOPs occur? Was the deviation appropriate or inappropriate?

- Did any SOPs or actions of fire brigade members violate any laws, codes, regulations, or standards?

When answering these questions, the ISO should remember that the goal is to improve the performance of fire brigade members while ensuring that their continuing safety and health are considered part of the goal. These questions will guide the process of determining if the organization's SOPs are adequate and effective. The ISO should ensure the effective management of the policy and procedure review process.

Fire Brigade Operational SOPs

Fire brigade operational SOPs should be standardized to provide consistent expectations of performance during incidents. The SOPs should not be so detailed as to limit the ability of members in carrying out their tasks. They should provide direction or guidance regarding goals to accomplish. When assessing the effectiveness of SOPs for fire brigade operations, the review team (including the training coordinator/ISO) should evaluate the overall performance on an operation in relation to the guidance of the SOP. The team should determine whether the SOP is effective and provides the needed guidance for the responders to bring the incident to a successful conclusion.

The ISO's role on the team is to assess the SOP and the incident to determine if the safety and health aspects were addressed **(Figure 23.3)**. The ISO will play a more significant role if any injury, fatality, illness, or exposure occurred during an operation. Should any of these situations occur, the ISO will investigate, identify causes, and recommend corrective actions to reduce the likelihood of a reoccurrence. The ISO should also determine any mutual aid or automatic aid operational or equipment differences that may affect responder safety and health.

Figure 23.3 An ISO working with a team to review their organization's SOPs.

Training Practices

When evaluating training practices, the ISO serves mainly in the proactive phase prior to training being conducted. The ISO ensures procedures are in place, so training evolutions can provide and replicate the realistic response environment in a safe and prudent manner. This replication is beneficial in assessing training practices and allows for testing the adequacy and effectiveness of SOPs in a controlled environment. The ISO will also assist in evaluating SOPs after training evolutions are conducted. This process can be viewed as a cyclical sequence of reviews. The same scrutiny can be used to assess the training environment.

Safety Subjects to Include

The ISO's role is specific to the safety and health concerns of fire brigade members. In this role, the ISO will focus on topics that improve safety in the workplace. The ISO should consider the following list of safety subjects when assessing the effectiveness of SOPs as they relate to the safety and health of members in all fire brigade operations:

- Use of ICS and accountability of all members
- Use of incident safety officers and technical advisors

- An incident action plan that includes a risk analysis of the incident
- Recurring or frequent injuries based on fire brigade records, such as sprains and strains
- Include the importance of member physical fitness
- Training, inspection, and use of proper protective clothing and equipment
- Use of rapid intervention crews
- Use of backup teams
- Rehabilitation of members
- Compliance with safety and health laws, codes, regulations, and standards
- Training on newly implemented practices and any new apparatus or equipment that will be put into service
- Emergency vehicle operations

Compliance with Laws, Codes, Regulations, and Standards

Litigation is a legitimate consideration in the development and revision of SOPs. SOPs document operational practices on paper, so all members have the same expectations. The ISO will serve on a team or committee of fire brigade members that addresses compliance with SOPs. The ISO's role is to ensure the department's SOPs are in compliance with the following safety and health requirements:

- State, provincial, and/or federal regulations
- State, provincial, and/or local traffic and vehicle operation laws
- Apparatus, equipment, and protective clothing specifications standards
- NFPA consensus standards, codes, and guides
- NIMS and ICS compliance
- Environmental protection regulations that may influence SOP development/revision

SOP Creation

During an assessment of current fire brigade SOPs, the ISO should identify any new SOPs to be created to ensure firefighter safety and health. The need for new procedures may also result from research such as new equipment specifications or the review of prior emergency incidents at the local or other facilities. The ISO should use the facility's standard format that matches the facility's safety and health manual. He or she should also consider transcribing material from other sources that inform the creation of the procedure into the SOP.

SOP Format and Distribution

Generally, the procedures manual contains:

- A statement of purpose
- A statement of scope
- A contents page
- The procedures or policies organized according to specific topic or function
- Appendices that contain copies of forms that are referred to in the body of the text

Each page should contain basic information (such as Subject, Procedure Number, Supersedes, and others) at the top that assists the reader in navigating the document. Because the policy and procedures manual must be revised periodically, the number and location of each copy must be available to the administration. Archived copies should be retained for future reference. The ISO should follow all facility or company requirements for including new and revised procedures to the current and archived policies and procedures manual.

New SOPs may be distributed in a variety of formats to fire brigade members, including paper documents or email distribution lists. Using a networked server system to upload SOPs to a central database ensures that all members can access the most current revision at any time and be alerted to updates. ISOs should use the method approved for their company or facility. The ISO's responsibilities may assure the fire brigade members are trained on new or revised health and safety procedures.

Material Added from Other Sources

SOPs are written from a broad spectrum of information from other sources. When using the following sources as information in SOPs ensure that the information is properly cited or acknowledged:

- Laws, codes, regulations, and standards
- Other jurisdictions' SOPs
- Reports from research and investigative agencies
- Manufacturer recommendations
- Federal, state, or local emergency management plans
- Postincident analyses
- Manuals

SOP Revision

An effectiveness assessment may also indicate existing SOPs that require revision. Revising SOPs should be done only when there is a need. The ISO should learn to recognize when there are deviations from existing, well-written procedures and when the procedures themselves are poorly-written, no longer current, or no longer effective. For newly created and revised SOPs, the ISO should monitor the implementation of the new procedures and verify that they are being followed as intended.

Verification of Procedures

SOPs are written to provide guidance and expectations for job performance. SOPs are living documents that are written, followed, reviewed, and updated or removed. This cyclical pattern includes verification that SOPs are used appropriately. The ISO will verify SOP use during the postincident analysis process. In addition, verification of SOP use will occur during any accident/incident investigation involving an injury, fatality, illness, or exposure. The ISO will also determine if any deviation in SOP occurred. If any deviation occurred, the ISO will document the facts and outcome of the incident. The ISO should not police the operational setting. Instead, the ISO can rely on fire brigade leaders to supervise operations within the fire brigade's chain of command. This process places the enforcement of policy within the command structure at a supervisory level, and maintains the unity of command concept.

SOP Revision Process

A process for revising policies and procedures should be established to ensure that they are flexible enough to adapt to changing operational and organizational requirements. The revision process is included in the policy or procedures manual and is based on answers to the following questions:

- When does the policy or procedure need to be revised? Is there a specific timetable?
- What conditions or circumstances would cause the policy or procedure to need revision?
- To what degree should the policy or procedure be revised: completely, partially, or not at all?

The answers to some of these questions will be up to the company or facility to determine. Indications that a policy or procedure needs to be revised may include:

- Increase in policy infractions.
- Injuries or property loss due to a failure of the procedure.
- Change in the resources used to accomplish the task.
- Change in the problem that the policy or procedure was intended to solve.

The policies and procedures of the organization must be continually monitored for effectiveness. Policies and procedures are most effective when they are dynamic documents that are subject to constant scrutiny, review, and revision. The steps for revising policies and procedures are generally the same as those used to create a new policy or procedure.

Review Section: Fire Dynamics

NFPA 1081 (2018): 8.2.2

Advanced exterior and interior structural fire brigade members need to have a scientific understanding of fire dynamics. The fire triangle and fire tetrahedron models are used to explain the elements of fire and how fires can be extinguished. The fire triangle consists of three elements necessary for combustion to occur: fuel, oxygen, and heat. The fire tetrahedron model includes the chemical chain reaction to explain flaming or gas-phase combustion. Remove any one of these elements and the fire will be extinguished.

As a fuel burns, its chemical composition changes, creating new substances called the products of combustion. Common products of combustion include heat, smoke, ash, water vapor, carbon monoxide (CO), carbon dioxide (CO_2), and hydrogen cyanide (HCN).

For a fire to start and continue to burn, heat must be transferred from one point or object to another. Heat transfers from warmer objects to cooler objects. Heat transfers occurs by three mechanisms: conduction, convection, and radiation. Conduction is the transfer of heat through and between solids. Convection is the transfer of thermal energy by the circulation or movement of a fluid (liquid or gas). Radiation is the transmission of energy as electromagnetic waves, such as light waves, radio waves, or X-rays, without an intervening medium.

Oxygen in the air is the primary oxidizing agent in most fires. Normally, air consists of about 21 percent oxygen. At normal ambient temperatures (68°F [20°C]), materials can ignite and burn in oxygen concentrations as low as 15 percent. When oxygen concentration is limited, the flaming combustion will diminish, causing combustion to continue in the nonflaming mode. Nonflaming or smoldering combustion can continue in extremely low oxygen concentrations when the surrounding environment's temperature is relatively low. However, at high ambient temperatures, flaming combustion may continue in considerably lower oxygen concentrations.

When the oxygen concentration is higher than normal, materials exhibit different burning characteristics. Materials that burn in normal oxygen levels will burn more intensely and may ignite more readily in oxygen-enriched atmospheres. Some petroleum-based materials will autoignite in oxygen-enriched atmospheres.

Oxygen is also important to life. As the oxygen in a structure is consumed by fire, the amount of oxygen available to support life diminishes. Between 15 percent to 19 percent concentrations, coordination is impaired. Between 10 percent to 12 percent concentrations, an exposed human experiences dizziness, headache, and fatigue. Around 8 percent to 10 percent concentrations, mental failure, nausea, vomiting, and unconsciousness occur. Exposures below 8 percent can result in death in as soon as 8 minutes.

The four stages of fire development can be generally defined as follows:

- **Incipient stage** — When the three elements of the fire triangle come together and the combustion process begins.

- **Growth stage** — More of the initial fuel package becomes involved and the production of heat and smoke increases. If there are other fuels close to the initial fuel package, radiant heat from the fire may begin to pyrolize nearby fuels which could spread the fire to new fuel packages.

- **Fully Developed stage** — Occurs when all combustible materials in the compartment are burning at their peak heat release rate based on the available oxygen.

- **Decay stage** — As the fire consumes the available fuel or oxygen and the heat release rate begins to decline, the fire enters the decay stage.

Thermal layering is the tendency of gases to form into layers according to temperature, gas density, and pressure. Provided that there is no mechanical mixing from a fan or a hose stream, the hottest gases will form the highest layer, while the cooler gases will form the lower layers. Changes in ventilation and flow path can significantly alter thermal layering. The flow path is defined as the space between the air intake and the exhaust outlet. Multiple openings (intakes and exhausts) create multiple flow paths.

As the mass and energy of the hot gas layer increases, so does the pressure. Higher pressure causes the hot gas layer to spread downward within the compartment and laterally through any openings such as doors or windows. If there are no openings for lateral movement, the higher pressure gases have no lateral path to follow to an area of lower pressure. As a result, the hot gases will begin to fill the compartment starting at the ceiling and filling down.

The interface between the hot gas layers and cooler layer of air is commonly referred to as the neutral plane because the net pressure is zero, or neutral, where the layers meet. The neutral plane exists at openings where hot gases exit and cooler air enters the compartment. At these openings, hot gases at higher than ambient pressure exit through the top of the opening above the neutral plane. Lower pressure air from outside the compartment entrains into the opening below the neutral plane.

Backdraft occurs in a space containing a high concentration of heated flammable gases that lack sufficient oxygen for flaming combustion. When potential backdraft conditions exist in a compartment, the introduction of a new source of oxygen will return the fire to a fully involved state rapidly (often explosively). A backdraft can occur with the creation of a horizontal or vertical opening. Backdraft indicators include:

- **Building indicators** — Interior configuration, fuel load, thermal properties, amount of trapped fuel gases, and a lack of ventilation
- **Smoke indicators** — Pulsing smoke movement around small openings in the building; smoke-stained windows
- **Air flow indicators** — High velocity air intake
- **Heat indicators** — High heat, crackling or breaking sounds
- **Flame indicators** — Little or no visible flame

Live-Fire Training Procedures

NFPA 1081 (2018): 8.2.2

All live-fire training procedures must follow applicable laws, codes, regulations, and standards. Live-fire training evolutions must be treated as though they were real world incidents. The common saying "train like you respond," puts this into context. In order to conduct live-fire training evolutions, the ISO is responsible for ensuring SOPs are in place and for monitoring the safety and health of all participating members. Live-fire training procedures must anticipate all types of live-fire exercises the fire brigade conducts. Firefighter/fire brigade member injuries and fatalities during live-fire training in fixed facility should be reviewed for lessons learned and recommendations. These reports provide valuable information that the ISO should review and determine if a revision to SOPs is needed.

The training coordinator/ISO should ensure full compliance with legal mandates. NFPA 1403, *Standard on Live Fire Training Evolutions*, is the guiding document for conducting live-fire training; in addition, federal, state/provincial, and local regulations, such as acquiring burn permits, will influence the fire brigade's SOPs.

All live-fire training evolutions share some common safety and health requirements. The ISO's main responsibility is to ensure procedures are in place that address the safety and health concerns for members during all live-fire training evolutions. To that end, safety officer training must include specific knowledge of the type of fire/class hazards found within the facility, structural types and integrity, chemical exposures, and fire dynamics.

The ISO should consider the following topics, and their repercussions, in live-fire training SOPs:

- Class A, B, C, D, and K fires
- Interior versus exterior setting requirements
- Facility equipment hazards
- Fuel loading and location of fire
- Weather
- Safety officer(s) present
- Rapid intervention crew
- Rehabilitation and emergency medical procedures
- Preburn inspection procedure
- Prohibition on live victims during training
- Reassessment of the structure/facility after each live-fire evolution

In addition, procedures should address the following requirements of live-fire training:

- Protective clothing and equipment inspections
- Water supply needs
- Emergency plans
- Communications plans
- Resource allocation considerations
- Accountability
- Air management

NFPA 1403 lists specific requirements for fixed facilities for live-fire training. While fixed facilities can provide a more controlled environment, age and technological features of each facility will vary. The ISO is responsible for ensuring procedures are in place for the inspection of the facility. This review includes a preburn inspection, an annual or more frequent structural inspection, and a 5-year structural inspection performed by a licensed engineer **(Figure 23.4)**. These inspections must include an evaluation

Figure 23.4 An ISO and fire brigade members inspecting a live-fire training building.

that all openings and safety devices are operational and functioning as designed. Destructive or non-destructive testing may need to be performed if structural damage is found. The facility owner shall evaluate the structural integrity annually, per NFPA 1403. NFPA 1403 further states that this inspection shall include core sampling of the concrete to determine if **delamination** has occurred.

Medical Emergency Procedures

NFPA 1081 (2018): 8.2.2

Fire brigades should have SOPs addressing accidents or incidents where a member is injured or becomes ill. Having these guidelines in place before an injury or illness can ease some of the stress in making the right decisions.

Developing an SOP on medical emergency procedures should address the following key areas:

- Recognizing the signs and symptoms of injuries and illnesses
- Providing rehabilitation at emergency scenes and training evolutions
- Ensuring there are qualified emergency medical personnel with equipment on-scene
- Evaluating the seriousness of the injury/illness
- Treating the injured/ill member or members
- Notifying the immediate supervisor of the injured/ill member or members
- Obtaining the right medical transportation resource for the member or members
- Having the member or members transported to the appropriate medical facility

To help organize the information in a standard format, the ISO can use ICS Form 206, *Medical Plan*, from the Incident Management System (IMS). This form can be distributed and kept with the tactical worksheets and other Incident Commander/FBL documents.

In addition to the above guidelines, the fire brigade leader will have additional responsibilities that may include:

- Notifying fire brigade and facility management through the chain of command
- Notifying other fire brigade members (this may be limited to life-threatening injuries/illnesses)
- Notifying the family (when the injured/ill member or members are unable to do so)
- Ensuring the proper paperwork is completed and forwarded through the chain of command

Procedures should outline *who* is responsible for *what* in order to prevent duplicate or missed responsibilities. The procedures should be specific enough so those individuals filling a position understand their responsibilities, and general enough so all participants understand the reasons for those responsibilities. As with other SOPs, the ISO must follow up during accident investigations and postincident analysis to ensure that the medical emergency procedures are being followed.

The SOP should provide enough guidance to be flexible to the situation and promote good decision-making options. In addition, local EMS protocol should be followed in regards to the treatment and transport of any injured or ill member.

> **WARNING:** Ill or injured fire brigade members should never be allowed to transport themselves to a medical facility for treatment, regardless of the apparent mildness of their condition.

Incident and Injury Reporting Procedures

NFPA 1081 (2018): 8.2.2

The ISO will investigate incidents that result in hazardous conditions, injuries, illnesses, exposures, and fatalities involving organization members. Property damage and near-miss occurrences shall be investigated with the goal of preventing future events. Included with this are incidents involving apparatus, vehicles, facilities, and equipment owned and operated by the organization. Review the procedures in use at the time of the incident and develop corrective procedures as necessary. Some aspects of investigation SOPs are as follows:

- **Immediate responsibility** — Ensure that transportation and medical treatment are provided for any injured personnel. Develop and implement procedures that ensure this care is provided at the most appropriate health-care facility (may include establishing appropriate contracts with health-care facilities and private ambulance services).

- **Agency cooperation** — If the public is involved, work closely with law enforcement agencies to ensure complete and accurate reporting in the event of litigation or liability. Include this information as part of the postincident analysis.

- **Deviations or drift from policy** — Evaluate and document any deviation or drift in policy.

- **Incident review** — Include recommendations to the organization's chief/manager or AHJ for corrective action to prevent future injuries, fatalities, or property-loss incidents.

- **Investigating and reporting** — Develop and review the investigation and review procedures periodically; ensure compliance with federal, state/territorial/provincial, and local requirements.

Reporting Procedures

The ISO should ensure that SOPs address the reporting requirements for all fire brigade members. The ISO uses this documentation to record the incident for analysis and look for trends, control measures, or corrective actions that may prevent a recurrence. In addition, worker's compensation claims and disability claims require thorough documentation.

Typically, the reporting process will involve affected members notifying their fire brigade leader, or instructor if in a class or training, of the situation. The fire brigade leader then makes the appropriate notifications, following the chain of command.

Federal and state/provincial regulations require reporting of certain injuries, fatalities, illnesses, or exposure events that occurs with a fire brigade member. For example, in the United States, OSHA 29 CFR 1904 requires reporting of any of the following occurrences:

- Death
- Days away from work, restricted work, or transfer to another job
- Medical treatment beyond first aid
- Loss of consciousness
- A significant injury or illness diagnosed by a physician or other licensed health care professional

NOTE: The ISO should work with the person in the company or facility to make sure injuries are properly reported to required reporting agencies.

The ISO should always follow their company's policy for reporting any workplace injury or illness. Many companies task their health and safety staff or occupational health services to handle any workers' compensation claims. An SOP should provide a flowchart of decision points and notifications for incidents and injuries. This standardized process will ensure an important element is not missed. ISOs should be versed in their local jurisdictional requirements, as OSHA requirements are the minimum standard.

Investigation Procedures

The ISO should maintain familiarity with company or facility requirements for investigation processes. The company or facility procedure should address the individual responsibilities in the investigation, the documentation process of the investigation, and the final written report. The procedure should define incidents, and establish both the authority for investigating each type of incident and a procedure for incident investigation. Initial incident investigation responsibilities will be dependent on the company or facility procedures.

When an incident occurs, an investigation is conducted to determine the root cause or the most basic reason for the incident and its source or origin. Incident investigations should be objective, impartial, and directed toward fact-finding, not fault-finding. Investigations should never be intended as punishment for those involved. When a workplace incident investigation is conducted, all participants and witnesses should be interviewed and all relevant factors documented. Investigations should result in recommendations for SOP review and/or revision and how to prevent future incidents, injuries, and losses. Several reasons to investigate workplace incidents are to identify and document the following conditions:

- Root cause of an incident
- Previously unrecognized hazards
- Apparatus/equipment obsolescence, defects, or design flaws
- Additional training needs
- Improvements needed in safety policies and procedures
- Facts that could have a legal impact on an incident case
- Prevent future incidents from occurring
- Historical trends

NOTE: According to NFPA 1500™, investigations are not limited to accidents, but include job-related and illnesses, fatalities, exposures to infectious diseases and hazardous materials or atmospheres, and near-miss incidents.

Infection Control Procedures

NFPA 1081 (2018): 8.2.2

The fire brigade is responsible for ensuring an infection control officer is appointed if the brigade is responsible for EMS or if the facility deals with pathogens. This person may be the ISO. In some departments, the infection control officer may be assigned to the EMS Division or another organizational department, such as Human Resources or Occupational Health Services. If the positions are assigned separately, the ISO and the infection control officer will work closely to ensure compliance with all applicable legal mandates. The ISO is responsible for assessing the infection control program and ensuring SOPs are in place to protect the workforce. The ISO must be knowledgeable of and ensure SOPs comply with the following:

- NFPA 1500™, *Standard on Fire Department Occupational Safety and Health Program*
- NFPA 1581, *Standard on Fire Department Infection Control Program*
- NFPA 1582, *Standard on Comprehensive Occupational Medical Program for Fire Departments*
- 29 CFR 1910.132 *Personal Protective Equipment*
- 29 CFR 1910.134 *Respiratory Protection*
- 29 CFR 1910.1020 *Access to Employee Exposure and Medical Records*
- 29 CFR 1910.1030 *Bloodborne Pathogens*
- Ryan White HIV/AIDS Treatment Extension Act of 2009, Part G – Notification of Possible Exposure to Infectious Diseases

An infectious agent exposure can occur in a fire brigade facility, on a fire brigade apparatus, at an emergency or nonemergency event, or while cleaning or disinfecting equipment and/or apparatus. Infectious diseases are not detectable by the senses — they are invisible. The ISO must help the brigade to recognize the potential of exposure and proper steps for protection and preventing transmission of the disease. The training coordinator/ISO is responsible for ensuring SOPs are established and provide guidance on preventing infectious disease exposure and transmission. The following list provides some highlighted topics from NFPA 1581 that should be addressed in SOPs:

- Annual training and education as required by law.

- How fire brigade facilities must be cleaned and disinfected.

- How apparatus and equipment must be cleaned and disinfected.

- How protective clothing and equipment must be laundered, disinfected, or properly discarded.

- Process for fire brigade members to receive immunizations and infectious disease screening.

- Placement of warning labels on containers and the proper disposal of contaminated items.

SOPs must address the before, during, and after phases of a potential exposure. By ensuring all three phases are addressed in SOPs, exposure and disease transmission can be minimized. First, the prevention phase ("before") procedures should include the awareness of the potential for exposure, the allocation of protective clothing and equipment, vaccinations and immunizations, and training. Second, during any potential situation where an infectious agent exposure exists, members must have the knowledge to recognize the potential, the protective clothing and equipment to protect themselves, and the training to properly the situation. Third, the post-exposure phase ("after") will include documentation of the exposure, any needed follow-up evaluations and procedures, counseling, and required notifications.

Emergency Scene Hazard Assessment
NFPA 1081 (2018): 8.2.2

Fire brigade operations are inherently hazardous and can impose high physical demands from fire brigade members. Exterior and interior fire brigade members carry out their tactical objectives in toxic environments with limited workspace while wearing heavy protective clothing and equipment. When physiological and environmental hazards are factored in, the physical demands on fire brigade members are intensified. The weather, extreme heat and cold temperatures, cardiac strain, and noise place additional stress on the human body. Fire brigade leaders and the training coordinator/ISO must monitor personnel to ensure they are functioning within their physical capabilities.

Weather Conditions
Weather conditions can have an adverse effect on all types of operations, and can affect the health and stamina of fire brigade members. The ISO must be able to monitor changes in weather conditions and notify the IC of potential hazards. Adverse weather conditions include storms, high humidity and temperatures, freezing rain, snow, extreme cold temperatures, and high wind.

The ISO should monitor daily weather forecasts and be alert to inclement weather statements. Personnel should pair the forecasts with actual real-time conditions and understand how it may affect emergency operations. During operations, the ISO can contact the local weather service office for updated weather conditions or use cellular or wireless devices, if they are available at the scene. Adverse weather can also reduce the operational capacity of equipment and apparatus. During emergency operations, the ISO should monitor the following weather-related conditions:

- **Ice** — Ice increases the difficulty of advancing attack or supply hoselines, performing vertical ventilation, and doing forcible entry. Surfaces, hoses, ladders, and apparatus can become ice-covered, causing slipping hazards. Ice and snow accumulation on a structure can cause ground ladders to slip or move, and accumulation on power lines can cause them to sag or fail. Ice, sleet, and snow can also melt or move causing unstable surfaces for ladder placement, stabilizers, and vehicles. Ice may not be visible, increasing the slipping hazard.

- **Snow** — Snow creates some of the same difficulties as ice. It can obscure tripping hazards, obstacles, and unstable structural features, such as skylights on a roof.

- **Rain** — Rain and fog can reduce your ability to see the entire scene. It can make metal surfaces slippery and it can freeze on equipment and apparatus as the temperature drops.

- **Humidity** — High humidity can cause smoke to remain close to the ground, obscuring visibility of the structure. It can also affect personnel, causing them to tire quickly, raising body core temperature, and dehydrating through perspiration loss.

- **Wind** — High winds can create dangerous fire behavior changes in all types of fire suppression operations. Winds as slow as 10 mph (15 kph) can be deadly if personnel are not alert to the rapidly changing conditions. The ISO must continuously monitor wind velocity and direction to ensure personnel and hose streams are not placed in a downwind position. Generally, wind speeds greater than 20 mph (30 kph) will reduce aerial ladder load capacity. The ISO should ensure the aerial ladder operations are within the manufacturer's guidelines.

- **Storms and Other Conditions** — Lightning is a significant concern for all fire brigade members operating at emergency events. Ladder operations should be curtailed and personnel should take all possible precautions to ensure their safety. Storms can cause downed power lines and trees that can block access to an area, especially during hurricane or severe thunderstorms. Hail can injure personnel and damage equipment and apparatus. Flash flooding or rapidly flowing water can flood low-lying areas and underground spaces. Visibility reducing situations (dust storms, fog, and blizzards) can create scene operation hazards.

Heat and Cold Stress

Both hot and cold environments can fatigue personnel. The ISO is responsible for monitoring resource and personnel availability and making recommendations to the IC when needed.

In extremely hot climates, personnel may rapidly succumb to heat stress and require rehabilitation earlier and more frequently than normal. They may also become dehydrated, requiring additional fluids and medical care. Extreme cold temperatures can cause skin and clothing to stick to metal tools and equipment, cause frostbite injuries, and reduce stamina. Hoselines, pumps, and water supplies can freeze, causing a loss in water supply or pressure. Hose, tools, and equipment can be damaged or become inoperable. Conditions relating to extreme weather conditions may include:

- **Hot or Humid Conditions** — Personnel operating at a scene with high intensity activity must be provided proper work/rest periods and follow the recommendations in NFPA 1584, *Standard on the Rehabilitation Process for Members During Emergency Operations and Training Exercises*, or the U.S. Department of Health and Human Services (HHS) Publication Number 2016-106, *Criteria for a Recommended Standard Occupational Exposure to Heat and Hot Environments*. Personnel must also be monitored when operating at traffic scenes or other activities where radiated heat from road and concrete surfaces significantly increases heat-related illness potential.

- **Cold Conditions** — Cold weather can freeze fire hoses and couplings and create icy conditions in areas where water is being applied during fire suppression activities. The ISO must monitor for the development of hazardous conditions and communicate them to the IC. The ISO must monitor personnel for signs of hypothermia and/or frostbite and ensure rehabilitation provides relief from the elements.

Cardiac-related Events

Cardiac-related events at emergency incidents are a leading cause of firefighter/fire brigade member illness and death. Annually, the NFPA publishes a firefighter fatality report in which cardiac and cardiac-related issues continue to be leading causes of firefighter fatalities. Research is beginning to show these fatalities can occur at the scene or after personnel have returned to service. The physical demands required in many operational and training settings are extremely intense. Not all personnel are prepared to meet this physical demand. Some fire brigade members may have hidden, undiagnosed cardiac disease that may precipitate into sudden cardiac arrest. It is critical that medical surveillance monitoring and proper rehabilitation is established at emergency and planned events as stated in the department's SOPs. The importance of rehabilitation services at the scene cannot be overemphasized. All fire brigade personnel should be cleared from the medical evaluation and rehabilitation area prior to being reassigned or returned to available status. Early detection of a possible cardiac event is critical to saving lives.

Noise

Emergency incidents have several sources of noise that can adversely affect personnel. Facility equipment, generators, equipment, radio communications, and even apparatus can add to the noise level. Repeated exposure to high levels of noise is known to cause permanent hearing loss. The fire brigade's safety and health program should address awareness of high noise situations and preventive hearing protection options. The ISO should evaluate noise levels and the hearing protection provided for their personnel. Recommendations should be made to the IC if unsafe noise conditions exist so modifications and corrections can be made. High noise levels can also lead to a condition called *tunnel hearing*. Tunnel hearing can cause people to concentrate so closely on one task that they lose their sense of situational awareness. The IC, other fire brigade leaders, and the ISO must maintain acute situational awareness during any incident by listening to other personnel, asking questions about the operation, and monitoring any incident changes. The IC and other personnel should be alerted if there is any indication that personnel safety is or will become compromised.

Changes to Building Loads and Forces

During fire suppression activities, water is a significant added load that can cause early collapse of roof structures. A large defensive fire will have multiple master streams in place, which only compounds the added weight load from water to the structure. Additionally, a heavy master stream concentrated in a single area may produce enough force to topple walls or parapets.

The ISO must assess the application of water based upon the use of master streams and the overall volume of water being added to the structure. All added water and added force from fire streams affects structural stability. Appropriate collapse zones should be established to forecast potential structural collapse.

Fire Suppression Systems

During the incident size-up, fire brigade members should assess the operation of fire suppression systems at a location. Fire suppression systems utilize liquid or gaseous-based agents. Fire brigade members must assess the type of system in operation and the location where it is operating. This information can indicate the seat of the fire and target initial operations in the right location. Standpipe systems should be charged as soon as possible to supplement the main water system and/or provide a delivery point of water for hoselines.

> **WARNING:** If fire brigade members are unsure if a gaseous fire protection system has activated and need to enter the protected space, SCBA should be used.

Structural Collapse Indicators

Knowledge of building construction is important to help the ISO recognize the potential for structural collapse. Unprotected structural members that have been exposed to high temperatures from fire and the increased weight from fire suppression activities can collapse with little or no warning. Knowing the construction material and how fire affects the materials will assist in the risk benefit analysis. This information is gathered as part of the preincident survey and on-scene size-up for building construction.

The stage of the fire can easily indicate the quantity of heat that the structure has been exposed to and the potential for structural collapse. Fires in the incipient stage will not have generated sufficient heat or flame to cause unprotected steel or wood frame construction to collapse. However, collapse potential increases in the growth stage as heat increases in the upper levels of the space and flame spreads to and consumes the combustible structural members. In the decay stage and during post-suppression activities, collapse becomes likely due to the weakened state of structural members and the buildup of water.

Building contents such as stored materials, furniture, and machinery also contribute to structural collapse. Like knowledge of the construction type, knowledge of the contents is gained through preincident surveys and inspections. The contents within a structure or stored in attics or on roofs may contribute to collapse in the following three ways:

- Adding to the fuel load in the building, and generating higher temperatures and rapid combustion that will weaken the structure

- Adding weight to the weakened structural members, causing them to collapse more rapidly

- Retaining water, which increases their weight and applies more stress on structural members

The existing materials within a building plus the added water load during suppression can have a direct effect on structural stability. Every gallon (4 liters) of water that is used to suppress the fire adds approximately 8 pounds (4 kilograms) of weight to floors that may already be weakened. The added weight may cause floors to pancake down or push walls out, resulting in a complete failure of the structure. As an estimate, 300 gpm (1 140 L/min) over 10 minutes can add approximately 10 tons (9 T) to the structure.

Besides the factors listed above, indicators of potential or imminent collapse include:

- Roof sagging, pulling away from parapet walls, or feeling spongy (soft) under foot

- Floors sagging or feeling spongy (soft) under foot

- Chunks of ceiling tiles or plaster falling from above

- Movement in the roof, walls, and floors

- Noises caused by structural movement

- Little or no water runoff from the interior of the structure

- Cracks appearing in exterior walls with smoke or water appearing through the cracks

- Evidence of existing structural instability, such as the presence of tie rods and stars that hold walls together

- Loose bricks, blocks, and stones falling from buildings

- Deteriorated mortar between the masonry **(Figure 23.5, p. 742)**

- Walls that appear to be leaning

- Structural members that appear to be distorted

- Fires beneath floors that support heavy machinery or other extreme weight loads

- Prolonged fire exposure to the structural members, especially trusses

- Structural members pulling away from walls

- Excessive weight of building contents

Figure 23.5 The crumbling mortar and loose bricks in this wall may weaken its structural stability.

> **WARNING:** Structural collapse can occur with little warning. If indicators start to appear, collapse is imminent and personnel must be withdrawn from the structure and the collapse zone.

Heat release rates in industrial or manufacturing facilities may be high enough to cause steel joists, wooden trusses, or gratings to fail in a short amount of time. However, time is only one indicator of structural collapse and often not the most reliable. Collapse of structures using lightweight construction can occur earlier in the incident and may not provide you with the warning indicators listed above. A thorough preincident survey and size-up of the incident scene will provide you with some indication of the presence of lightweight construction.

If a collapse is possible, the structure and surrounding area should be evacuated. The hazard should be communicated and the fire brigade leader should conduct a personnel accountability report (PAR) to determine if all personnel are accounted for.

NOTE: The area outside the structure should be evacuated to distance of at least 1½ times the height of structure in all directions.

Utility Hazards
NFPA 1081 (2018): 8.2.2

Assessing utility hazards at an incident is not a complex task, but does require attentiveness. Utilities include all electrical, gas, and water services to a location. These services can be located above or below ground. Main service disconnects are usually identifiable but not always easily found. Preincident planning can make this process simple if disconnects are indicated on a site map. Additionally, any supplemental utility services, such as generator or fuel cell power sources, should also be identified during preincident planning.

Building Utility Component Assemblies

Building utilities will typically have similar components at the main shutoff point and throughout the building. Manufacturing, industrial, commercial, and other facility/site locations may have different sized utility services entering the buildings. Not all locations will have municipal utility service, so each location must be assessed for actual utility service presence. The main utility components addressed in this chapter are electrical, natural gas, and water services.

Electricity Component Assemblies

Electrical service can be above or below ground from the main feeder line. The electrical service will enter through a main service point where the main shutoff is located. When necessary, the main shutoff should be used to isolate the power to the location and not the individual circuit breakers. Lockout/tagout devices should be utilized when operations require it.

In addition to the main power source, all locations should be assessed for alternate sources of power. These alternate sources include generators, solar power, and/or wind power, and they may automatically turn on when the main power is turned off. Personnel should ensure that all sources of power are isolated at the main disconnect as soon as possible.

> **WARNING:** Only properly trained personnel should de-energize electrical power sources.

Natural Gas Component Assemblies

Natural gas is not available in all locations, but should be identified when present. Main gas service valves should only be operated by trained personnel. Personnel should also ensure a secondary source of gas, such as propane, is not located on the property.

Water Systems Component Assemblies

Water can be supplied by a water company, a well system, an elevated storage tank system, or a combination of these. Personnel should determine if the water system needs to be isolated. During fire suppression activities, the water system should remain on to ensure water is available for the fire suppression system. After the fire has been extinguished, the water service may be turned off, especially if a water line break exists. In most cases, the water system is left on.

Common Utility Gases

Utility gas comes in two forms, natural gas and propane. Both forms are considered safe under normal conditions; however, when leaks or a transportation accident occurs, fire and emergency services personnel must work with the utility company to stabilize the incident. The ISO should be knowledgeable of the properties of these gases and the hazards associated with them. The ISO must monitor the scene for changing conditions or situations in which crews begin to operate in an unsafe location.

Natural Gas (Methane-Based)

Natural gas can be used in heating and cooling systems, for cooking, and in vehicles. It is transported via underground gas lines, railcar, or tanker trucks. Natural gas is used in industry, commercial, and residential properties. Natural gas is an odorless gas that is lighter than air. In order to detect the presence of natural gas, gas utilities use an additive called mercaptan to give it its distinctive rotten egg odor. Natural gas is a safe energy source when maintained within its storage system. When released, natural gas is flammable, and can be explosive under the right conditions. Any fire brigade response to a suspected natural gas leak should include assistance from the gas utility. Gas utility employees have the necessary training, equipment, and resources to detect, isolate, and repair any natural gas leak. If natural gas is leaking from a gas line, fire brigade personnel may use a fog stream to disperse the concentration of gas at the site and reduce the chance of an explosion.

> **CAUTION:** Soil may "scrub" the mercaptan odor from natural gas as it travels through the ground. As a result, odor alone is not always an accurate detector of gas leaks.

Propane

Liquid petroleum gas (LPG), commonly called propane, is stored in pressurized tanks on property where natural gas is unavailable. Propane, an odorless gas that is heavier than air, is transported by railcar and tanker truck. In order to detect the presence of propane, the propane industry uses an additive called ethyl mercaptan to give the gas a distinct odor. Like natural gas, propane is a safe energy source when maintained within its storage system. When released, propane is flammable, and can be explosive under the right conditions. Any fire brigade response to a reported propane leak should include notification of the responsible propane company that services the specific location. Propane company employees have the necessary training, equipment, and resources to detect, isolate, and repair any leaks.

Propane tanks exposed to direct flame contact pose an extreme risk to fire and emergency services personnel. When sufficiently heated, propane tanks will explode, sending shrapnel long distances. This occurrence is commonly referred to as a boiling liquid expanding vapor explosion (BLEVE). Fire suppression crews may set up water monitors that do not require constant attendance.

Pressurized Vessels

Pressurized vessels holding gases and liquids in industrial operations are common and include many different products **(Figure 23.6)**. In the utility realm, pressurized vessels are used to produce steam and heat in the form of boiler units. OSHA defines a pressurized vessel as a container designed to operate above 15 pounds per square inch gauge (psig) (approximately 200 kPa).

Figure 23.6 Examples of pressurized vessels that may be found at some facilities.

Emergencies involving pressure vessels require special care. Responders should not attempt to isolate operations of the pressure vessel system without specific training on proper procedures. Responders should obtain assistance from facility maintenance personnel to ensure unintended consequences do not result.

Common Electrical Grid Arrangements

Electrical service to a facility can be from more than one service or direction. The electrical grid is established similarly to a municipal water system. A single point in the system can be fed from two or more feeder lines. Fire brigade members should rely on the electrical utility company to provide technical information about the specific power grid supply when necessary. Fire brigade members should never come in contact with any down power lines, with or without power. Electrical utility personnel should move all lines.

Assistance from Utility Companies or Agencies

Fire and emergency services organizations should establish and maintain positive working relationships with all local utility companies. The dispatch SOPs should outline utility company notification for any incident that may require a utility service to be secured. The ISO should ensure an escort is provided to the utility company technician to ensure accountability and communications are maintained. The escort can then report directly to the IC when the utility service has been secured.

Wildland Fire Development

NFPA 1081 (2018): 8.2.2

The boundary between wildland areas and facility/industrial site growth has become known as a wildland urban interface (WUI). This interface has continued to expand over the years until it has impinged on communities and industrial/manufacturing or other facilities and sites. While many facility fire brigades may not encounter wildland fires, others may be within a WUI. In such cases, the fire brigade management must assess their facility's level of wildland fire risk.

The risk management plan should identify the WUI areas within the facility/site, the fire brigade's response, and resources needed to mitigate a fire event. The risk management plan should also identify potential wildland spread, starting from nearby wildland areas and affecting the local community. Wildland fire behavior is a specialized field of study. For more detailed information on wildland training, refer to the National Wildland Coordinating Group.

Vehicle Incident and Apparatus Placement Hazards

NFPA 1081 (2018): 8.2.2

Some facilities or sites may be quite large and have a series of roads and railways to allow personnel to perform their duties and to allow transport vehicles (forklifts, trucks, and trains) to bring in raw materials and carry away finished products. These vehicle movements increase the possibility of a vehicle incident at the facility/site. Emergency responders have been injured and killed during emergency operations on or near roadways. At such facilities, the fire brigade should establish SOP guidelines on how to properly protect a scene and the personnel operating at the scene. NFPA 1500™ provides criteria for traffic incidents. This standard can be adapted for any incident on or near a roadway for proper scene protection.

Vehicle Incident Hazards

All vehicle incident events require a scene assessment to determine which hazards exist, and any changing conditions that may affect the safety of responders or occupants. The use of protective clothing and equipment must be considered depending on the type and complexity of the incident and comply with minimum best practice standards. The following sections provide details of common vehicle incident hazards.

Traffic

The response to traffic-related incidents requires planning. SOPs should outline proper scene control with signage, rope or barrier tape, retroreflective cones, or (if the brigade has apparatus) apparatus placement. Additionally, it is crucial to have a traffic incident preplan with law enforcement. If local law enforcement assistance is required, operations between law enforcement and the fire brigade must be coordinated in advance to help avoid disagreements in scene safety. NFPA 1500™ and the Manual of Uniform Traffic Control Devices (MUTCD) and Traffic Incident Management System are excellent tools for coordinating a traffic incident preplan. The ISO should incorporate traffic and scene control procedures into the fire brigade's training program and SOPs. During vehicle incident operations, the ISO should conduct a risk assessment and monitor operations to ensure the fire brigade personnel follow appropriate safety and operational procedures.

Flammable and Combustible Liquids

Any fluid leaking from a vehicle creates a hazard. Fluids create potential slip hazards and environmental hazards. Depending on the type of vehicle and its cargo, inhalation and skin burns are also hazards that should be considered. Vehicles designed to transport cargo may leak hundreds of gallons of hazardous liquids.

All leaking fluids should be isolated and protected to prevent a fire and/or injury. A vapor suppressant can be applied to spilled gasoline or diesel to reduce the risk of fire. An absorbent material can be applied to any leaking liquid to reduce the risk of slips, but also to isolate the spill area. Any extrication operation should have at least one protective precharged hoseline readily available in the event of a fire.

Combustible Metals

Class D metals such as magnesium, titanium, and lithium, used in or being carried by vehicles, are difficult to extinguish when on fire. Direct water application to a burning exotic metal can create a spectacular reaction, at times with explosive results. It can also endanger personnel operating nearby.

Combustible metals are categorized differently from other combustibles and have differing extinguishment recommendations. If the correct extinguishing agent is unavailable for a specific combustible metal, the best course of action is to let it burn itself out.

Electrical Systems

Hybrid vehicles have a variety of battery systems with different voltage and current capacities. The ISO should ensure that the hybrid vehicle high-voltage system is isolated according to manufacturer recommendations. Supplemental restraint systems may have stored energy capacity for various periods of time after the battery system has been isolated. Fire brigades can obtain computer software or other printed material outlining the presence of and general location of battery components and wiring. Specifically, the location of the main batteries and any color-coded wiring should be identified. Orange wiring was universally used in hybrid vehicles to identify high voltage; however, newer models will have multiple color-coding in the wiring system. Hybrid or electric vehicles are virtually silent. Firefighters should ensure these vehicles are placed in park and turned off, even if they cannot hear the vehicle running.

Alternative Fuels

Alternative fuel vehicles are gaining popularity but are not common in the U.S. Alternative fuel powered vehicles use hydrogen, liquid natural gas (LNG), or liquid petroleum gas (LPG). These fuels are stored as compressed gases in tanks that may be visible to responders. Other possible but rarely found fuels are alcohol-based racing fuel and vegetable oil. During the incident size-up, personnel should determine the type of fuel used in a vehicle. Fire brigade members should be aware of these fuels when extrication or fire suppression activities are required.

Apparatus Placement Hazards

If the fire brigade has emergency response apparatus, the ISO must be able to identify potential apparatus placement hazards and recommend corrective actions. Apparatus placement at emergency incidents is dictated by the specific circumstances of the incident and the surrounding environment. Fire brigade leaders and apparatus driver/operators must be trained in the general guidelines for safe and effective apparatus placement. These guidelines may be in the department's SOPs manual or in the incident management plan. The ISO must participate in the development of these policies and plans to ensure a safe working environment. Examples of common apparatus placement hazards include:

- **Proximity to Exposures** — If the fire has the potential to threaten exposures, the apparatus should be positioned so the fire streams can be deployed to protect those exposures. In some cases, the apparatus itself can be an exposure. Avoid positioning the apparatus in a location that subjects it to high levels of radiant heat, falling embers, or other products of combustion.

- **Backing Procedures** — Backing fire apparatus can be a hazardous action because of the vehicle's size and mirrors that do not provide a full view around the apparatus. Backing incidents generally account for a significant percentage of all damage repair costs. Although most injuries sustained in these collisions are minor, fatalities have occurred during backing incidents. Proper backing techniques can eliminate these accidents. All fire brigades should develop a policy for backing apparatus. Always follow SOPs and company procedures for backing procedures.

> **CAUTION:** The driver/operator must not rely solely on backup cameras to provide a full and accurate view of the scene. Spotters are still required.

- **Wind Direction** — Attempt to position the apparatus upwind of an incident whenever possible. This positioning may negate the need for the driver/operator to wear SCBA while operating the vehicle and reduce the possibility of the apparatus becoming an exposure if fire conditions worsen.

- **Terrain** — Apparatus should be parked on hard surfaces whenever practical. When operating at an incident involving hazardous or flammable liquids, an uphill position eliminates the chance of a hazardous liquid flowing underneath the apparatus. Similarly, at vehicle fires, an uphill position will protect the apparatus from burning fuel that may leak from the vehicle. One exception to the uphill rule involves wildland fires. Apparatus and personnel should be downhill of the main body of fire as wildland fires move uphill faster than on flat terrain or downhill.

- **Placement to Divert Traffic at Nonvehicular Incidents** — Proper positioning of an apparatus can provide a safety barrier that protects the scene, victims, and emergency personnel. Proper positioning also provides a protected work area. When positioning apparatus, driver/operators must allow for adequate parking of additional fire brigade apparatus. Driver/operators must allow enough distance to prevent a moving vehicle from striking and forcing fire apparatus into the work area. Where possible, driver/operators should position apparatus at a 45-degree angle into the curb. This practice helps to direct motorists around the scene. During pump operation, the pump panel should be positioned at curbside if that position protects the pump panel operator from oncoming traffic. If it does not, the apparatus should be positioned so that the pump panel operator is in a downstream position with the apparatus protecting him or her from traffic.

- **Control Zone Hazards** — The driver/operator must not position the apparatus under overhead obstructions, too close to a potential structural collapse/fire spread, or in the access or egress path of other apparatus. The ISO should establish a policy that requires the driver/operator to chock the apparatus wheels when the vehicle is parked at the incident scene. Driver/operator training must also address weight limitations of roadbeds, bridges, or parking structures and incident traffic in and around the facility/site. Equipment carried in the cab area must be secured as well. Most importantly, the driver/operator must ensure that all persons on the apparatus are seated and belted.

Establishing Rapid Intervention Crews (RICs)

NFPA 1081 (2018): 8.2.2

A rapid intervention crew (RIC) is required for any incident or training exercise where a crew enters an immediately dangerous to life or health (IDLH) atmosphere as defined in NFPA 1500™. NFPA 1500™ defines two incident phases with regards to RICs. First, during the early stages of the incident the assignment of an *initial rapid intervention crew* (IRIC) of two members from the initial attack crew must be staged outside and remain in contact with the interior crew. This complement of two member's interior and two member's exterior of the IDLH also complies with OSHA 29 CFR 1910.134, *Respiratory Protection* regulation (two-in/two-out rule). Second, after the initial stages of work by the first-arriving team, a dedicated RIC shall be assigned with four members. RIC personnel should also be assigned during live fire training exercises.

Both the IRIC and RIC must be fully equipped with personal protective clothing and equipment that is consistent with that of the interior crew(s) **(Figure 23.7)**. SOPs should outline the requirement of IRIC/RIC, training of members who can potentially be assigned to this function, and the performance standards for IRIC/RIC responsibilities. Fire and emergency service organizations should evaluate the following standards for specific RIC deployment and training criteria:

- NFPA 1407, *Standard for Training Fire Service Rapid Intervention Crews*
- NFPA 1500™, *Standard on Fire Department Occupational Safety and Health Program*
- NFPA 1561, *Standard on Emergency Services Incident Management System and Command Safety*
- NFPA 1710, *Standard for the Organization and Deployment of Fire Suppression Operations, Emergency Medical Operations, and Special Operations to the Public by Career Fire Departments*
- NFPA 1720, *Standard for the Organization and Deployment of Fire Suppression Operations, Emergency Medical Operations, and Special Operations to the Public by Volunteer Fire Departments*

Figure 23.7 RIC personnel standing by in case they are needed to locate and rescue disoriented or trapped personnel.

Assigning RICs

The IC is responsible for ensuring an IRIC or RIC is assigned to any incident where crews enter an IDLH atmosphere. In the ICS structure, IRIC/RIC report to the IC or, if assigned, the operations section chief. NFPA 1500™ states that additional consideration should be given to complex incidents in which RIC becomes a tactical-level management component of the ICS structure.

According to NFPA 1500™, an IRIC can have one member staged ready for rescue deployment while the second member performs other duties — as long as they are noncritical to the overall safety of the operation and personnel. IRIC/RIC typically stage at the point of entry of the interior crew with all needed equipment ready to deploy in the event of missing, lost, or trapped firefighter(s). The IRIC/RIC should monitor the movement, location, actions, and radio communications of those personnel within the IDLH in the event an interior member/crew declares a MAYDAY emergency.

NFPA 1500™ includes a provision for the IC to assign multiple RICs when the size and/complexity of the incident dictate this need. This situation will typically arise in commercial or industrial settings where multiple points of entry are separated by some distance. NFPA 1500™ recommends the IC consider assigning a RIC at each point of entry when deployment from one location will not be sufficient in performing a rescue. Further consideration for assigning RICs can be made at each tactical-level management component in a geographical area of the incident. The ISO should independently evaluate the incident and the assignment of RIC(s), and make recommendations to the IC if a deficiency is noted.

Increasing RIC Capabilities

RIC members should have specific training in performing a downed fire brigade member rescue that is outlined in NFPA 1407. At a minimum, a RIC should have full personal protective clothing and equipment to operate in an IDLH atmosphere that is consistent with that being used by the interior crew. Some common equipment that may be used by RICs include, but may not limited to:

- Universal air connection for SCBAs
- Spare facepiece
- Spare SCBA cylinder
- Portable radio with a dedicated channel or talk group
- Rope
- Charged hoseline
- Forcible entry tools
- Flashlights
- Thermal imager
- Harness

The capabilities of RIC should be evaluated to ensure an adequate number of personnel are available with the proper training and equipment to support the RIC function. Most incidents can be handled with the first alarm assignment resources; however, ICs and ISOs should not get complacent in managing the incident with this initial allotment of resources. Requesting additional resources, or the upgrading an assignment, should be supported within the organizational SOPs. A RIC activation must be planned for in the incident action plan (IAP) and in the decision-making process of the IC. The number of personnel needed to perform a rescue of a downed fire brigade member can include several crew rotations. Research has shown that rescuing a downed fire brigade member(s) is difficult and may occur in stages. Just locating a downed fire brigade member may take crews more than one attempt. During a rescue, the IC must ensure a constant assignment of RIC outside the IDLH. This requirement may include having multiple rotations of crews prepared to fulfill the RIC function until the rescue operation is complete or the incident is stabilized.

The ISO should evaluate the potential need for multiple RICs and recommend resource needs to the IC. Mutual and/or automatic aid assistance may be needed to fulfill this resource need. Interoperability of radio communications and SCBA components should be preplanned before an incident occurs in which this assistance is requested.

Communicating Hazards to RICs

The RIC should quickly assess the incident for potential hazards. The IC or the ISO should brief the RIC(s) on the assessment of the incident and those hazards identified in the preincident plan. Alternate points of access and egress should be identified and communicated to the RIC. Additionally, a RIC should monitor radio traffic during the incident for any specific hazard communication from the interior crews, the ISO, and/or the IC.

Establishing Rehabilitation Areas

NFPA 1081 (2018): 8.2.2

Rehabilitation areas should be established in accordance with the recommendations of NFPA 1584, *Standard on the Rehabilitation Process for Members During Emergency Operations and Training Exercises.* Fire brigade personnel can be exposed to significant stress and exertion during incident response and training. Providing a process of rest, rehydration, nourishment, and body temperature regulation can improve the overall health and wellbeing of fire brigade members **(Figure 23.8)**. Providing rehabilitation services to members should be a standardized process that ensures work/rest cycles and medical evaluation. This process should include recommendations for when members can continue working at an incident, be released to finish their assigned duty shift, or receive further medical care. It is the fire brigade's responsibility to support rehab operations with SOPs, training, and funding.

Figure 23.8 Rehab should be set up during emergency operations and training evolutions.

Identifying the Rehabilitation Needs

Rehabilitation of some type should always be mandatory. The level of rehabilitation should be consistent with the size and scope of the incident, and the needs of fire brigade members operating at the incident. The fire brigade's SOPs should provide general guidelines for identifying rehabilitation needs at incidents or training exercises. Further consideration should be given to but not limited to:

- Level of exertion
- Likelihood of fatigue
- Duration of the incident or training exercise
- Environmental factors and heat/cold stress potential
- Work/rest cycle needs
- Psychological needs

While on the scene, the rehabilitation area is the best opportunity for the ISO or other assigned personnel to assess fire brigade members for stress indicators. Over time, normal levels of stress can cause detrimental health effects, such as sleep deprivation, fatigue, depression, and illness.

Fire brigade members not only deal with the day-to-day stresses of life and work; they also transition quickly from routine work assignments to emergency operations. These rapid transitions add to normal levels of stress as do the fire suppression activities that follow. Long-term stress can also be a contributing factor to cardiovascular disease. Incident-related stress combined with cumulative stress can be contributing factors when a firefighter suffers sudden cardiac arrest while on a scene. Fire brigade members who are sleep deprived, overstressed, or otherwise exhausted should not be allowed back into operational duty without sufficient rest.

ISOs should ensure that the rehabilitation manager checks fire brigade members in and out of the rehab area and that they are medically cleared to leave the scene when the incident is terminated. The physical and psychological effects of the incident (increased body temperature, exertion or overexertion, mental and physical fatigue, and dehydration) continue to affect fire brigade members after incidents are terminated. Sudden cardiac arrest can also occur after a responder has returned to the routine duties or has returned home. The effects of stress do not miraculously disappear simply because the incident is terminated. Any fire brigade members showing signs of distress should remain in rehab until the symptoms subside, receive medical treatment before leaving the scene, or be sent to a medical treatment facility for additional care.

Identifying Rehabilitation Locations

Locating the rehab function within close proximity to on-scene medical support is a logical approach. Trained medical personnel, along with medical supplies, and transportation are then located in one area. Medical personnel can monitor personnel in rehab for core body temperature, hydration, blood pressure, heart rate, and other vital signs. They can provide immediate assistance and transportation if a fire brigade member shows symptoms of heat stress, cardiovascular problems, or other ailments. If the emergency incident is too far from a medical facility by ground transport, an emergency helipad may be established at or near the incident area.

Setting Up Rehab Areas

Rehabilitation should be set up close to the incident scene but far enough away to permit personnel to remove all personal protective clothing and equipment. For this reason, the rehab area needs to be in the cold zone and provide relief from the environment. The IC is responsible for establishing rehab and assigning the rehab manager responsibilities at protracted or large-scale incidents. The ISO should ensure the rehab areas are properly located and operated.

NFPA 1584 recommends the following considerations of a rehab area:

- Be clear of any vehicle exhaust
- Be clear of any personal protective clothing and equipment
- Have limited noise interference
- Shelter from hot/cold environments
- Have active and passive cooling measures available
- Have fluid replenishment
- Have nourishment available as needed
- Medical surveillance
- Personnel accountability and documentation

Medical surveillance needs to be incorporated into the rehab area. On some incidents, such as hazardous materials response, fire brigade members should receive a premedical screening before entering warm and hot zones. Premedical surveillance should include evaluating baseline vitals and hydrating personnel prior to conducting hot zone activities and postmedical surveillance after operations are terminated.

Personnel entering postmedical surveillance and rehab should be given time to remove their protective clothing and equipment, rehydrate, and use the restroom before being medically evaluated — unless a medical emergency exists. Medical personnel should be readily available to evaluate all members that report to rehab. Medical personnel should be given the authority to keep personnel in rehab or recommend ambulance transport to a medical facility when needed. Postmedical surveillance should include vital sign assessment, body temperature, and the evaluation of symptoms of dehydration, heat/cold stress, cardiovascular illness, stroke, or other ailment.

Rehab Officer Responsibilities

The Responder Rehabilitation Manager reports to the IC, ISO, or Logistics depending on the facility incident command system structure. The person given this assignment is responsible for:

- Locating the rehab area
- Securing medical personnel to monitor fire brigade members
- Obtaining the needed resources for rehydration and replenishment
- Maintaining documentation on all personnel that report to rehab

The Rehab Manager will make any need requests through the proper chain of command established for a particular incident. Fire brigade SOPs should outline what documentation is gathered and retained regarding medical surveillance of personnel.

Ensuring the Use of Rehab

Ensuring the use of rehab begins with the fire brigade management. Support from the fire brigade's leadership is critical to having an effective rehab operation. This support should filter down the chain of command to all fire brigade members and reinforce a positive safety culture. The fire brigade should promote a process of communicating rehab needs as personnel monitor their own health and that of fellow crewmembers. Finally, the training coordinator/ISO should assess the use of rehab at incidents and training exercises and provide recommendations if deficiencies exist. The ISO should also include an assessment of rehab in the postincident analysis so future rehab use is improved.

Personnel Accountability

NFPA 1081 (2018): 8.2.2

Each fire brigade must adopt an existing personnel accountability system or develop its own system of accountability that identifies and tracks all personnel working at an incident. The fire brigade should standardize the system so that it is used at every incident. All members must be trained on the system and participate in it when operating at an emergency incident. Each fire brigade should communicate its accountability system with mutual and automatic aid partners so that all crews have working knowledge of the system. The system must also account for those individuals who respond to the scene in vehicles other than emergency response apparatus.

Due to constant change at an emergency incident, personnel accountability is vital. The IC must know who is at the incident, where each person is located, and under which specific tactical function they are working. For example, SCBAs can malfunction or run out of air; and fire brigade members can get lost in structures. Without having an accountability system, it is impossible to determine who and how many members may be trapped inside a structure or injured. Firefighters and fire brigade members have died because they were not discovered missing until it was too late.

> **WARNING:** Personnel accountability systems ensure that all fire brigade members can be found at an incident.

Fire brigade leaders are responsible for keeping track of the members of their team. When operating in the hot zone, the team members should remain within sight of each other. When the atmosphere is obscured, they should stay in contact using other means (voice or touch). When broadcasting a personnel accountability report to the IC, the fire brigade leader must clearly state who they are accounting for in the report. Fire brigade SOPs must define how and when this communication is to occur.

The system should indicate:

- Individuals assigned to each team or staff position
- Names of people responding individually
- Time of arrival
- Assigned duty or team
- Time of release from the scene

The ISO is responsible for ensuring the system is in place and that all members are in compliance. The ISO must have the authority to enforce the use of the system and correct any violations. Working through the IC, the ISO may enforce the accountability system and advise the IC of any deficiencies.

Chapter Review

1. What are *The 10 Rules of Engagement for Structural Fire Fighting?*
2. Name and describe the steps for determining the need for a new policy or procedure.
3. What are common indicators of potential backdraft?
4. What topics should an ISO consider in live-fire training SOPs?
5. What responsibilities may a fire brigade leader have during medical emergencies?
6. What conditions should be identified and documented during a workplace incident investigation?
7. What topics from NFPA 1581 should be addressed in infection control SOPs?
8. What hazards can ice create at emergency scenes?
9. What steps can be taken to reduce the likelihood of a cardiac-related event?
10. How can the contents of a building contribute to a structural collapse?
11. What hazards are associated with liquid petroleum gas (LPG)?
12. What should a wildland fire risk management plans include?
13. What are some considerations for dealing with traffic hazards at vehicle incidents?
14. Name and describe three common apparatus placement hazards.
15. What common equipment may be used by RICs?
16. What are some factors that should be considered when identifying rehabilitation needs at incidents or training exercises?
17. What information should personnel accountability system reports include?

Key Terms

Delamination — Occurs after fresh concrete is poured and compacted. The solids (cement and aggregate) settle causing the excess mix water and entrapped air to be displaced and migrate toward the surface.

Skill Sheet List

The following skill sheets should be used to evaluate the skills described in this chapter:

NOTE: Students should wear the PPE appropriate to the NFPA 1081 level (Incipient, Advanced Exterior, Interior Structural, etc...) being evaluated.

Support Member

Chapter Contents

JPRs addressed in this chapter

This chapter provides information that addresses the following job performance requirements of NFPA 1081, *Standard for Facility Fire Brigade Member Professional Qualifications (2018)*.

9.1.7	9.2.1	9.2.3	9.2.5	9.2.7	9.2.9
9.1.8	9.2.2	9.2.4	9.2.6	9.2.8	9.2.10

Learning Objectives

1. Describe the basic duties of fire brigade support members. [9.1.7, 9.1.8]

2. Describe the different possible site-specific fire brigade support member duties. [9.2.1, 9.2.2, 9.2.3, 9.2.4, 9.2.5, 9.2.6, 9.2.7, 9.2.8, 9.2.9, 9.2.10]

Chapter 24
Support Member Duties

Some fire brigades utilize support members to perform specialized response duties during a fire or other emergency. NFPA 600 and NFPA 1081 describe the basic roles, responsibilities, and job performance requirements for fire brigade support members. According to these standards, fire brigade support members are not expected to perform fire fighting or other related operations. Instead they will perform only those specialized tasks which the fire brigade has determined to be part of their function. It is the responsibility of each fire brigade management team to identify the specific duties required of support members at their specific facility or site. This manual shall address the NFPA 1081 job performance requirements for basic support member duties as well as a number of site specific duties.

Fire brigade support members may be facility workers with general knowledge and experience who are trained to operate in a support function during an emergency. Or they may be workers with specialized knowledge and experience who can apply their specialties to support the fire brigade during an emergency. Specialists may include:

- Electricians
- Plumbers
- Heating, ventilation, and air conditioning personnel
- Process control operators
- Site security personnel

NOTE: The skills to be performed by support members are so site specific, that specific training and testing should be developed at each facility.

Fire brigade support members must meet the medical requirements for the position as described in NFPA 600 and meet the appropriate JPRs outlined in NFPA 1081. After initial training they should receive additional training and education and participate in a fire brigade drill at least annually. To learn to perform their duties safely during fire suppression operations, realistic training and drills should include supporting live fire training evolutions under controlled conditions.

Fire brigade support members are not allowed to operate in the warm or hot zones of an incident. Because they will not operate in the warm or hot zones, they do not need to wear thermal personal protective equipment (PPE) or self-contained breathing apparatus (SCBA).

Basic Support Member Duties

NFPA 1081 (2018): 9.1.7, 9.1.8

To support fire brigade operations, fire brigade support members need training commensurate to their job duties. At a minimum, support members need to train annually on the following subjects and attend a drill as directed by fire brigade management **(Figure 24.1)**:

Figure 24.1 Fire brigade members and support personnel receiving a safety briefing before an annual drill. *Courtesy of Marathon Petroleum Corporation.*

- Operating within an incident management system (see Chapter 1)
- Operating within the site's emergency response operations plan (see Chapter 1)
- SOPs and safety procedures (see Chapter 1)
- Facility/**site-specific hazards** (see Chapter 2 and local documentation)
- Facility/site-specific duties (see local documentation)

Basic duties assigned to support members may include initiating a response and responding to an emergency with appropriate equipment. Both of these duties require the support member to have a thorough understanding of the fire brigade's SOPs, the facility layout, emergency procedures, and the communications and emergency equipment used at the facility.

Initiate an Emergency Response

Fire brigade support members must be trained to receive a report of an emergency, gather the appropriate information regarding the emergency, and relay the information to the other members of the fire brigade. To accomplish this task, they must be proficient in using the facility's telephone, radio, intercom, and installed alarm systems.

If the report is from an installed alarm system, the support member may only be able to identify the type and location of the emergency. If the report comes from facility personnel, the support member should gather the following information:

- Location of the emergency
- Type of emergency
- Number of personnel involved, including those injured or missing
- Determine if evacuation has been initiated

The support member uses the appropriate communications system to alert the other brigade members and relay the information to them **(Figure 24.2)**. The support member then responds to the emergency as outlined in their duties.

Figure 24.2 A fire brigade support member relaying information to other fire brigade members.

Respond to an Emergency

Fire brigade support members must be thoroughly trained in the facility's layout, special hazards, and the emergency response procedures to be followed at that location. Personnel must be:

- Provided the equipment appropriate to the fire brigade level at the facility.
- Trained to use each piece of equipment safely and effectively.
- Trained to recognize response hazards.
- Able to respond to an emergency so that all team members arrive safely.

The fire brigade's SOPs should identify the procedures support members are to follow in the event of an emergency. These procedures should include:

- Where to report
- What tools to bring
- To whom to report
- Additional duties needed

Site-Specific Support Member Duties

Fire brigade managers must determine the duties and responsibilities for support members at each facility based on site-specific requirements. Some support member duties that may be included in such a site-specific list are:

- Building evacuation
- Electrical power control
- Process control
- Salvage operations
- Escort duties
- Sprinkler system control
- Facility utility control
- Fire pump/fire water system operations
- Traffic control and site security
- General support services

Communications between support members and the IC are critical during emergency operations. The IC must be able to give directions to support members and receive reports from them. The IC must be able to tell support members which control mechanisms to operate, what actions to take (open or close valves, shut down processes), and when to perform these tasks in coordination with emergency operational procedures. When conducting system or process control operations, the support member should remain at the controls until new orders are received or the individual has been replaced by another support member.

Building Evacuation
NFPA 1081 (2018): 9.2.1

Fire brigade support members may be tasked with conducting building evacuations. In this role, they may be called "facility fire brigade wardens" or other similar titles. To conduct building evacuations, support members should be familiar with the facility and fire brigade SOPs for building evacuation.

The support member should know how to announce an evacuation. Evacuation notifications can be accomplished:

- Vocally in smaller structures or locations with few occupants.

- Using a local or facility alarm system such as a fire alarm.

- Using a local public alert/announcing (PA) system.

- Using a pager or telephone alerting system.

The support member may also be responsible for checking to ensure that personnel have evacuated the facility or area. One approach is for support members to physically check the offices, rooms, or process areas involved. They must be able to accomplish this without placing themselves in danger. Another approach is for the support member to go to the assembly area or areas and conduct a roll-call or head count **(Figure 24.3)**. The IC should be informed if personnel are missing or unaccounted for and where the person or persons were last seen or thought to be located.

Figure 24.3 A fire brigade warden conducting roll-call in an assembly area.

Sprinkler System Control
NFPA 1081 (2018): 9.2.2

During a fire, automatic sprinkler systems can be an invaluable asset to a facility and the facility fire brigade personnel. These systems can extinguish some fires before they become too large or slow the spread of fire until fire brigade personnel can begin manual fire suppression operations.

The key to sprinkler system operations is to ensure they remain in operation and are not shut down until it is necessary. If they are shut down too early, a fire can grow beyond the system's ability to control it.

Fire brigade support members, sometimes called "fire brigade sprinkler valve operators" or other titles, have proven useful in maintaining control of sprinkler systems during emergencies. To maintain control of a facility's automatic sprinkler system, the support members should be trained on the sprinkler system or systems found at the facility. They should know which valves control the water flow to the system, how to operate those valves, and how to determine if the sprinkler system is operating properly. The support member should remain at the control valve until relieved or given a new assignment by the IC. The support member should be equipped with a portable radio or other communication device.

Electrical Power Control
NFPA 1081 (2018): 9.2.3

Fires and other emergencies at a facility may require the electrical power into the facility, or part of the facility, be controlled. Fire brigade support members, sometimes known as fire brigade electricians, must be properly qualified to control the facility's electrical power system. They must know which control panels, buttons, or levers control power to specific locations within the facility and they must know how to operate those control devices. During an emergency, these support members can be stationed at critical power control points within or around the facility to operate the power controls **(Figure 24.4)**. The support member should be equipped with a portable radio or other communication device in order to remain in contact with the IC. Lockout/tagout devices should be used when power is to be shut off to ensure it remains off until it is time to restore power.

Figure 24.4 A facility electrician assisting the fire brigade by controlling the electrical power during an incident.

Facility Utility Control
NFPA 1081 (2018): 9.2.4

Fire brigade support members can also assist during emergency operations by providing control of facility utilities such as HVAC, steam, water, and gas systems **(Figure 24.5)**. These members, who may also be called "fire brigade utility control technicians" or other titles, may be personnel who handle these systems for the facility as part of their regular jobs. All personnel shall be qualified on the system before manipulating any equipment.

Qualified fire brigade support members must understand the hazards associated with the gases used at their facilities in order to operate gas system controls safely. Support members should only operate gas system controls if the location is away from the emergency, because they do not wear PPE or SCBA.

Process Control
NFPA 1081 (2018): 9.2.5

Facilities may contain a variety of production/manufacturing processes depending on the type of facility. These processes may include:

Figure 24.5 A fire brigade utility control technician standing by to operate HVAC controls.

- Petrochemical and refinery
- Power generation
- Computer systems

Some processes can be shut down quickly and safely and require limited restart time and effort. Others, however, cannot be shut down quickly, may involve hazardous shut down procedures, or take a significant amount of time and effort to restart. Still others cannot be shut down at all during an emergency. The local shutdown policies and procedures should be documented and followed during each emergency.

It is common for each process or series of processes at a facility to have a control room or rooms. These control rooms may be simple or complex depending on the process or processes being operated. Some control rooms are constructed as safe havens to ensure that process operations can continue during an emergency. Walls, floors, and ceiling are constructed of nonflammable materials with penetrations fire stopped to prevent fire, smoke, and other products of combustion from entering. These control rooms are often equipped with air, power, and communications systems that are independent of the rest of the facility.

Due to the highly technical aspects of process controls, the fire brigade support members may be assigned from the process unit or units involved. This helps ensure that the support member is familiar with the process, the controls, and control room systems.

Fire Pump/Fire Water System Operations
NFPA 1081 (2018): 9.2.6

Some facilities are equipped with fire pumps or entire fire water systems designed to support fire suppression activities at the facility. Fire brigade support members, called "fire brigade fire pump operators" at some facilities, can support fire suppression operations by operating the facilities fire pumps and fire water system operations. These personnel should be qualified to operate fire pump motors, controls, and valves. In the event of pump or system failure, the support member shall notify the IC of the failure. If qualified to troubleshoot and resolve the problem, the support member should take the appropriate actions.

Salvage Operations
NFPA 1081 (2018): 9.2.7

Fire brigade support members, also called "fire brigade salvage personnel," are tasked with performing salvage or property conservation operations in the cold zone. Because they are not authorized to wear PPE or SCBA, they should not operate in the warm or hot zones.

Salvage operations may include:

- Removing products, cargo, or facility equipment from areas adjacent to the warm zone to protect them from damage associated with fire spread or fire suppression activities **(Figure 24.6)**

- Covering products or equipment with salvage covers or plastic sheets

- Closing doors, windows, vents, and scuppers to prevent the introduction of smoke, products of combustion, and water

- Capturing, channeling, or removing water runoff

Figure 24.6 A support member practicing salvage operations by moving stacks of pallets during a facility training evolution.

Fire brigade salvage personnel should be trained to use salvage covers or plastic sheets to cover materials and equipment as well as to construct water catchalls and chutes. Additional training may include the use of lift dollies or trucks to move heavier objects to safety.

Traffic Control and Site Security
NFPA 1081 (2018): 9.2.8

As mentioned previously, some facilities/sites are quite large and may have a system of roads or railroad tracks to move raw materials and finished products from place to place. Warehouse sites may have multiple buildings with roadways between them. Other locations, such as hospitals have emergency room and delivery docks where ambulances and delivery vehicles come and go on a regular basis.

Facility security personnel may act as fire brigade support members in providing traffic control during such emergencies. These personnel should be trained in setting up **traffic control devices** such as traffic cones, barricades, or other scene isolation materials. They should also be knowledgeable of the facility/site and trained in directing traffic around the accident scene. While performing these operations, the fire brigade support member should watch traffic conditions carefully to prevent being struck by moving vehicles. They should wear a reflective vest to help alert drivers to their presence. During nighttime operations, they may help set up portable lights, warning flashers, and use flashlights to help direct traffic.

Another concern at many facilities is the matter of security. Facilities/sites are often surrounded by tall **security fences** to keep nonemployees off the premises, or in the case of penal facilities, to keep inmates from fleeing. Access to such facilities is often through monitored and controlled vehicle and personnel gates **(Figure 24.7)**. The facility/site may also require a roving patrol to ensure the security of buildings and hazardous locations.

Figure 24.7 A facility security officer opening a gate and giving directions to a responding fire crew.

Escort Duties
NFPA 1081 (2018): 9.2.9

Because facilities/sites are often entry controlled locations, visitors must often be escorted while on the premises. This is particularly true during emergency situations where mutual or automatic aid personnel and apparatus and technical experts may respond to the scene. **Escort duty** is another task that can be assigned to fire brigade support members. Key elements for support members who will serve as facility escort include:

- Being familiar with the facility/site itself
- Knowing the facility's/site's SOPs for escort duty
- Having a good sense of direction
- Having the ability to interact with personnel in a professional manner

As escorts, the support members deliver their charges to specified locations in a timely manner. They should monitor the personnel under their charge to ensure they do not try to enter off-limits areas.

General Support Services

NFPA 1081 (2018): 9.2.10

Other duties that fire brigade support members may perform would be considered general support services. Depending on the facility/site, this could be a simple list of a few additional duties or a complex list of many. The fire brigade's SOPs should identify those specific tasks that support members can conduct in the cold zone to support fire brigade operations. The fire brigade support members must be trained to perform the tasks safely and efficiently. Some examples of general support services include:

- Cleaning and maintenance of tools and equipment **(Figure 24.8)**
- Carrying tools and equipment from storage locations to a tool cache near the emergency scene
- Helping set up the rehabilitation site
- Fill and stage air cylinders
- Returning tools and equipment to service after an emergency

Figure 24.8 Some support members may assist the fire brigade by cleaning and maintaining the brigade's tools and equipment. *Courtesy of Marathon Petroleum Corporation.*

Chapter Review

1. What information should a support member gather when a report of an emergency comes from facility personnel?

2. How can support members give evacuation notifications?

3. List three examples of general support services that support members may perform.

Discussion Question

1. What site-specific duties at your facility might fire brigade support members perform?

Key Terms

Escort Duty — An assignment in which one or more facility personnel are responsible for accompanying or guiding a person, group of people, or vehicle(s) while they are on-site.

Security Fence — A fence designed to prevent illegal entrance to a facility or site.

Site-Specific Hazard — Hazard that sometimes or always exists at the facility for which the fire brigade is responsible, but does not exist in most other occupancies.

Traffic Control Device — Signs, signals, markings, and other devices used to regulate, warn, or guide traffic. These devices are positioned on, over, or adjacent to a street, highway, pedestrian facility, or bikeway by an AHJ to direct traffic.

Skill Sheet List

The following skill sheets should be used to evaluate the skills described in this chapter:

NOTE: Students should wear the PPE appropriate to the NFPA 1081 level (Incipient, Advanced Exterior, Interior Structural, etc...) being evaluated.

Contents

Emergency Phone Call

Step 1: Answer the telephone. Identify the department, station or facility, unit, and yourself.

Step 2: Record information about the emergency **(Figure 1.1)**.

    a. Type of emergency

    b. Location of the emergency

    c. Number and location of people involved

    d. Caller's name, location, and phone number

Step 3: Provide life safety directions if the caller is at immediate risk.

Step 4: Transfer information to the dispatch center, responding units, or personnel as required by local SOPs **(Figure 1.2)**.

    a. Incident information

    b. Information from the preincident plan developed for the specific address or facility

Step 5: Confirm that units are notified and on assignment.

Step 6: End the phone call.

Step 7: If required, respond to the incident.

    a. Maintain situational awareness.

    b. Use response equipment safely.

Figure 1.1

Nonemergency Phone Call

Step 1: Answer the telephone. Identify the department, station or facility, unit, and yourself.

Step 2: Record the caller's information and message.

    a. Date and time

    b. Caller's name and phone number

    c. Message

    d. Your name

Step 3: Provide the caller with information, if necessary.

Step 4: Post the message or transfer the call to the recipient or other department as necessary.

Step 5: End the phone call.

Figure 1.2

Step 1: Gather notes and other information on the incident.
    a. Times
    b. Location
    c. Occupant information
    d. Unit(s) and personnel involved
    e. Actions taken
    f. Outcome of incident (fire loss, cause, injuries, etc.)

Step 2: Record information on incident report form (written or electronic version) **(Figure 2.1)**.

Step 3: Review incident to ensure that all information fields are completed and the information is accurate. Make corrections or revisions as necessary.

Step 4: Finalize and process the report **(Figure 2.2)**.
    a. Sign the report.
    b. Save the electronic report.
    c. File or forward the report as appropriate.

Figure 2.1

Figure 2.2

Step 1: Recognize the need for evacuation.

Step 2: Initiate emergency evacuation methods **(Figure 3.1)**.

Step 3: Identify hazards.

Step 4: Proceed toward a safe haven using facility evacuation routes.

Step 5: Ensure all team members are accounted for and the team remains intact **(Figure 3.2)**.

Figure 3.1

Figure 3.2

Routine Traffic

Step 1: Rotate the selector knob to the assigned frequency **(Figure 4.1)**.

Step 2: Monitor radio traffic until air is clear **(Figure 4.2)**.

Step 3: Hold the microphone in transmit position 1 to 2 inches (25 mm to 50 mm) from your mouth.

Step 4: Depress the transmit button, holding down until finished with the transmission.

Step 5: Transmit a routine traffic message using department codes and local SOPs **(Figure 4.3)**.

Emergency Traffic

Step 1: Depress the transmit button, holding down until finished with the transmission **(Figure 4.4)**.

Step 2: Announce "emergency traffic" (or facility's standard emergency traffic break-in message), interrupting air traffic as necessary.

Step 3: Wait for Incident Commander (IC) or dispatch to acknowledge.

Step 4: Transmit emergency traffic message following local SOPs **(Figure 4.5)**.

Step 5: Repeat message until Command verifies given information.

Figure 4.1

Figure 4.2

Figure 4.3

Figure 4.5

Figure 4.4

Step 1: Communicate emergency using communication device.

Step 2: Announce emergency over your communication device per local SOPs. Pause. Repeat as often as necessary **(Figure 5.1)**.

Step 3: Provide Command your situational information per local SOPs.

Step 4: Activate PASS device, if available.

Step 5: Isolate yourself or escape the environment, if possible **(Figure 5.2)**.

Step 6: Activate a flashlight to increase visibility. Use a tool or other object to make noise **(Figure 5.3)**.

Figure 5.2

Figure 5.1

Figure 5.3

Step 1: Contact the area supervisor or manager to notify them about the survey **(Figure 6.1)**.

Step 2: Survey and record concerns related to the exterior of the facility/process areas for the following, if applicable:

    a. Roof

    b. Chimneys and spark arrestors

    c. Yards

    d. Fuel storage areas

    e. Outside waste burners

    f. Garages, sheds, barns, and other outbuildings

    g. Flammable liquids and gases

    h. Lightning protection

    i. Security devices

    j. Foam delivery monitors

    k. Fixed fire protection equipment

    l. Facility access

Step 3: Survey and record concerns related to the interior of the facility/process areas for the following, if applicable:

    a. Combustible materials

    b. Mechanical devices **(Figure 6.2)**

    c. Electrical wiring and equipment

    d. Portable heating units

    e. General housekeeping practices

    f. Fire detection and suppression systems

    g. Electrical distribution panels

    h. Gas appliances

    i. Oil-burning installations

    j. Furnaces, hot water heaters, and vent pipes

    k. Accumulated waste

    l. Flammable and combustible liquids and other hazardous materials

    m. Emergency markings, postings, and equipment inspections

Step 4: Discuss the results of the survey with the appropriate officials or area supervisors/managers **(Figure 6.3)**.

    a. Comment on the conditions found and make mitigation recommendations.

    b. Answer any questions.

Figure 6.1

Figure 6.2

Figure 6.3

Operate a stored-pressure water extinguisher

Step 1: Size up fire, ensuring that it is safe to fight with an extinguisher.

Step 2: Identify the class of fire.

Step 3: Select the appropriate extinguisher.

Step 4: Check that the extinguisher is properly charged.

Step 5: Pull pin at top of extinguisher to break the inspection band **(Figure 7.1)**.

Step 6: Test to ensure proper operation **(Figure 7.2)**.
   a. Point nozzle in safe direction.
   b. Discharge very short test burst.

Step 7: Carry extinguisher to within reach of fire.
   a. Escape route identified
   b. Held upright
   c. Positioned upwind of fire

Step 8: Aim nozzle toward base of fire.

Step 9: Discharge extinguishing agent **(Figure 7.3)**.
   a. Squeeze handle.
   b. Sweep slowly back and forth across entire width of fire.

Step 10: Cover entire area with water until fire is completely extinguished **(Figure 7.4)**.

Step 11: Back away from the fire area **(Figure 7.5)**.

Step 12: Tag extinguisher for recharge and inspection.

Operate a dry chemical (ABC) extinguisher

Step 1: Size up fire, ensuring that it is safe to fight with an extinguisher.

Step 2: Identify the class of the fire.

Step 3: Select the appropriate extinguisher.

Step 4: Check that the extinguisher is properly charged.

Step 5: Pull pin at top of extinguisher to break the inspection band **(Figure 7.6)**.

Step 6: Test to ensure proper operation **(Figure 7.7)**.
   a. Point nozzle horn in safe direction.
   b. Discharge very short test burst.

Step 7: Carry extinguisher to within stream reach of fire.
   a. Escape route identified
   b. Hold upright
   c. Position upwind of fire

Step 8: Aim nozzle toward base of fire.

Step 9: Discharge extinguishing agent **(Figure 7.8)**.
   a. Squeeze handle.
   b. Sweep slowly back and forth across entire width of fire.
   c. Avoid splashing liquid fuels.

Step 10: Cover entire area with dry chemical until fire is completely extinguished.

Step 11: Back away from the fire area **(Figure 7.9, p. 780)**.

Step 12: Tag extinguisher for recharge and inspection.

Operate a carbon dioxide (CO$_2$) extinguisher

Step 1: Size up fire, ensuring that it is safe to fight with an extinguisher.

Step 2: Identify the class of the fire.

Step 3: Select the appropriate extinguisher.

Step 4: Check that the extinguisher is properly charged.

Step 5: Pull pin at top of extinguisher to break the inspection band **(Figure 7.10, p. 780)**.

Step 6: Hold the horn by the handle in order to avoid a shock.

Step 7: Test to ensure proper operation **(Figure 7.11, p. 780)**.
   a. Point horn in safe direction.
   b. Discharge very short test burst.

Step 8: Carry extinguisher to within stream reach of fire.
   a. Identify escape route.
   b. Hold upright.
   c. Position upwind of fire.

Step 9: Aim horn toward base of fire.

Step 10: Discharge extinguishing agent **(Figure 7.12, p. 780)**.
   a. Squeeze handle.
   b. Sweep slowly back and forth across entire width of fire.

Step 11: Cover entire area with gas cloud until fire is completely extinguished.

Step 12: Back away from the fire area **(Figure 7.13, p. 780)**.

Step 13: Tag extinguisher for recharge and inspection.

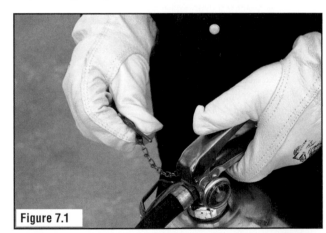

Figure 7.1

Figure 7.2

Figure 7.3

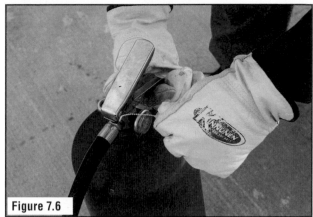

Figure 7.6

Figure 7.4

Figure 7.7

Figure 7.5

Figure 7.8

Figure 7.9

Figure 7.10

Figure 7.11

Figure 7.12

Figure 7.13

NOTE: If using two-way couplings (Storz or quarter-turn), the steps should be modified for that type of hose. References to male or female ends can be replaced with action at either end of the hose.

Couple – Foot-Tilt Method

Step 1: Stand facing the two couplings so that one foot is near the male end.

Step 2: Place a foot on the hose behind the male coupling.

Step 3: Apply pressure to tilt the coupling upward.

Step 4: Grasp the female end **(Figure 8.1)**.

    a. Place one hand behind the coupling.

    b. Place the other hand on the coupling swivel.

Step 5: Make the connection.

    a. Bring the two couplings together.

    b. Align the Higbee cut.

    c. Turn the swivel clockwise with thumb **(Figure 8.2)**.

Couple – Two-Fire Brigade Member Method

Step 1: Fire brigade member #1: Grasp the male coupling with both hands.

Step 2: Fire brigade member #1: Bend the hose behind the coupling.

Step 3: Fire brigade member #1: Hold the coupling and hose tightly against the upper thigh or midsection with the male threads pointed outward **(Figure 8.3, p. 782)**.

Step 4: Fire brigade member #2: Grasp the female coupling with both hands.

Step 5: Fire brigade member #2: Bring the two couplings together and align their positions.

Step 6: Fire brigade member #2: Turn the female coupling counterclockwise until the threads line up or are seated **(Figure 8.4, p. 782)**.

NOTE: A click may be heard when the couplings are properly aligned.

Step 7: Fire brigade member #2: Turn the female swivel clockwise to complete the connection **(Figure 8.5, p. 782)**.

Uncouple – Knee-Press Method

Step 1: Grasp the hose behind the female coupling.

Step 2: Stand the male coupling on end, with feet set well apart for balance.

Step 3: Place one knee on the hose and shank of the female coupling **(Figure 8.6, p. 782)**.

Step 4: Loosen the connection.

    a. Apply body weight.

    b. Snap the swivel quickly in a counterclockwise direction **(Figure 8.7, p. 782)**.

Uncouple – Two-Fire Brigade Member Method

Step 1: Both fire brigade members: Compress the gasket in the coupling.

    a. Grip respective couplings firmly with both hands.

    b. Press the coupling toward the other student **(Figure 8.8, p. 783)**.

Step 2: Both fire brigade members: Loosen the connection.

    a. Keep arms stiff.

    b. Use weight of both bodies to turn each coupling counterclockwise **(Figure 8.9, p. 783)**.

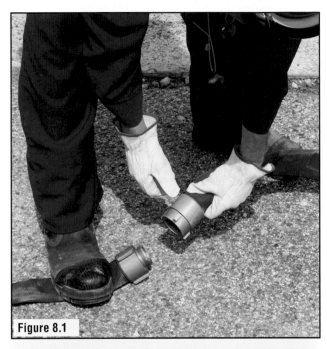

Figure 8.1

Figure 8.2

Figure 8.3

Figure 8.6

Figure 8.4

Figure 8.7

Figure 8.5

Figure 8.8

Figure 8.9

CAUTION: Always stand clear of closed caps. Do not lean over the top of the hydrant.

Step 1: Remove the hydrant cap **(Figure 9.1)**. Use a hydrant wrench if the cap is too tight.

Step 2: Inspect the hydrant for exterior damage and check for debris or damage in inside outlet.

Step 3: Place the hydrant wrench on the valve stem operating nut and hand tighten.

Step 4: While standing clear of any line of fire hazards, flush the hydrant to ensure that it is free of debris **(Figure 9.2)**.

Step 5: Connect the intake hose to the pump intake **(Figure 9.3)**. Hand tighten the connection.

Step 6: Make the hydrant connection to the steamer outlet (use with adapter as needed) **(Figure 9.4)**. Hand tighten the connection.

Step 7: Open the hydrant slowly until the hose is full **(Figure 9.5)**.

Step 8: Tighten any leaking connections using a rubber mallet or spanner wrench.

Figure 9.2

Figure 9.1

Figure 9.3

Figure 9.4

Figure 9.5

Step 1: Check the hard-suction couplings **(Figure 10.1)**.

    a. Remove any dirt or debris.

    b. Replace worn gaskets.

Step 2: Connect the sections of hard-suction hose (if necessary).

    a. Align sections.

    b. Hand tighten the connection.

    c. Use rubber mallet to make an airtight connection, if necessary.

    d. Keep the hose off of the ground.

Step 3: Check dry hydrant for damage or obstructions.

Step 4: Connect to the dry hydrant **(Figure 10.2)**.

    a. Hand tighten the connection.

    b. Use rubber mallet to make an airtight connection, if necessary.

Step 5: Prepare the pump intake for coupling by removing the cap and keystone intake valve, if applicable.

Step 6: Connect the hard-suction hose to the pump intake **(Figure 10.3)**.

    a. Align the sections.

    b. Hand tighten the connection.

    c. Use rubber mallet to make an airtight connection, if necessary.

Step 7: Dismantle drafting equipment and return to proper storage per local SOPs.

Figure 10.2

Figure 10.1

Figure 10.3

NOTE: Fire brigade members should be positioned on the same side of the hose.

Step 1: Deploy hoseline.

Step 2: Remove the standpipe outlet cap **(Figure 11.1)**.

    a. Check the condition of the outlet threads.

    b. Check for any obstructions in the outlet.

    c. Flush standpipe to ensure proper operation.

    d. Ensure the gasket is in place in the hoseline coupling.

Step 3: Connect the female coupling to the standpipe outlet **(Figure 11.2)**. Hand tighten the connection.

Step 4: Advance the nozzle end of the hoseline to the fire **(Figure 11.3)**.

Step 5: Open the standpipe outlet valve **(Figure 11.4)**.

Figure 11.3

Figure 11.1

Figure 11.4

Figure 11.2

Step 1: Pull necessary length of supply hose to reach from supply to FDC.

Step 2: Remove the cover from the FDC fitting **(Figure 12.1)**.

Step 3: Make sure FDC inlet is not blocked with debris **(Figure 12.2)**.

Step 4: Align the supply line coupling with the FDC coupling **(Figure 12.3)**.

Step 5: Connect supply line to FDC **(Figure 12.4)**.

Figure 12.1

Figure 12.3

Figure 12.2

Figure 12.4

NOTE: If using two-way couplings (Storz or quarter-turn), the steps should be modified for that type of hose. References to male or female ends can be replaced with action at either end of the hose.

Step 1: Lay the hose straight and flat on a clean surface.

Step 2: Roll the male coupling over onto the hose, forming a coil that is open enough to allow the fingers to be inserted, but not so loose that the roll will fall apart when carried **(Figure 13.1)**.

Step 3: Continue rolling the coupling over onto the hose, keeping the edges of the roll aligned on the remaining hose to make a uniform roll **(Figure 13.2)**.

Step 4: Lay the completed roll on the ground.

Step 5: Tamp any protruding coils down into the roll with a foot **(Figure 13.3)**.

Figure 13.1

Figure 13.2

Figure 13.3

NOTE: If using two-way couplings (Storz or quarter-turn), the steps should be modified for that type of hose. References to male or female ends can be replaced with action at either end of the hose.

Method One

Step 1: Lay the hose straight and flat on a clean surface.

Step 2: Start the roll from a point 5 or 6 feet (1.5 or 1.8 m) off center toward the male coupling **(Figure 14.1)**.

Step 3: Roll the hose toward the female end, leaving sufficient space at the center loop to insert a hand for carrying **(Figure 14.2)**.

Step 4: Extend the short length of hose at the female end over the male threads to protect them **(Figure 14.3)**.

Figure 14.1

Method Two

Step 1: Lay the hose straight and flat on a clean surface.

Step 2: Grasp either coupling end and carry it to the opposite end. The looped section should lie flat, straight, and without twists **(Figure 14.4)**.

Step 3: Stand at the looped section, facing the coupling ends.

Step 4: Start the roll on the male coupling side about 2½ feet (750 mm) from the bend (1½ feet [450 mm] for 1½-inch [38 mm] hose) **(Figure 14.5)**.

Step 5: Roll the hose toward the male coupling **(Figure 14.6)**.

NOTE: If the hose behind the roll becomes tight during the roll, pull the female side back a short distance to relieve the tension.

Step 6: Lay the roll flat on the ground as the roll approaches the male coupling.

Step 7: Draw the female coupling end around the male coupling to complete the roll **(Figure 14.7)**.

Figure 14.2

Twin Donut Roll Method

Step 1: Lay the hose straight and flat on a clean surface and form two parallel lines from the loop end to the couplings, with couplings next to each other.

Step 2: Start the roll by folding the loop end over and upon the two hose lengths **(Figure 14.8, p. 792)**.

Step 3: Roll both lengths simultaneously toward the coupling ends to form a twin roll **(Figure 14.9, p. 792)**.

Step 4: Insert a strap through the center of the roll for carrying purposes **(Figure 14.10, p. 792)**.

Figure 14.3

Figure 14.4

Figure 14.6

Figure 14.5

Figure 14.7

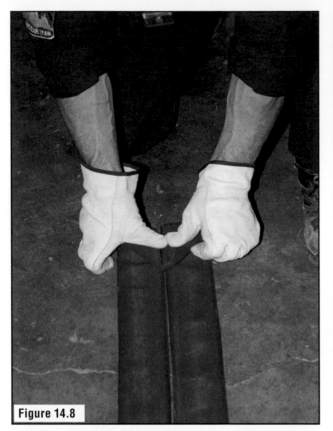

Figure 14.8

Figure 14.10

Figure 14.9

NOTE: Load the hose in a manner that allows it to deploy without the need to flip the couplings so that the hose does not catch in the hose bed.

Step 1: Place first coupling at a front corner of the hose bed.

Step 2: Lay the hose flat in the hose bed from front to back **(Figure 15.1)**.

Step 3: Fold the hose back on itself (make a loop) and lay the hose in the opposite direction **(Figure 15.2)**.

Step 4: Repeat until hose covers the bottom of the hose bed.

Step 5: Start the second layer repeating Steps 2 and 3.

Step 6: Continue layering until all hose is loaded **(Figure 15.3)**.

Step 7: Finish hose load as required by local SOPs **(Figure 15.4)**.

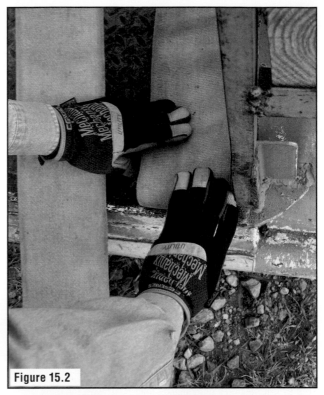

Figure 15.2

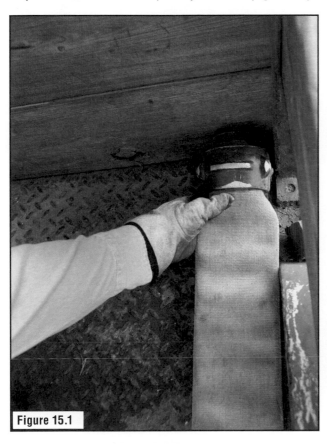

Figure 15.1

Figure 15.3

Figure 15.4

NOTE: Load the hose in a manner that allows it to deploy without the need to flip the couplings so that the hose does not catch in the hose bed.

Step 1: Lay the first length of hose in the bed on edge against the side of the bed with the male coupling at the front of the bed and the length of the hose going to the rear **(Figure 16.1)**.

Step 2: Fold the hose at the rear of the hose bed so that the bend is even with the rear edge of the bed. **(Figure 16.2)**.

Step 3: Lay the hose back to the front of the hose bed.

Step 4: Continue laying the hose in parallel folds across the hose bed to complete the first tier.

    a. Stagger the folds at the rear edge of the bed so that every other bend is approximately 2 inches (50 mm) shorter than the edge of the bed **(Figure 16.3)**.

    b. This stagger may also be done at the front.

Step 5: Finish the first tier **(Figure 16.4)**.

Step 6: If a second tier is needed, angle the hose upward to start the second tier.

Step 7: Make the first fold of the second tier directly over the last fold of the first tier at the rear of the bed.

Step 8: Continue with the second and succeeding tiers in the same manner as the first, progressively laying the hose in folds across the hose bed.

Step 9: If making a combination load, start with the male couple to the rear and reverse the above steps.

Step 10: After completing the load in one bed, move to the opposite hose bed and load the hose in the same manner as the first side.

Step 11: When the load is complete, connect the last coupling on top with the female coupling from the first side.

Step 12: Lay the connected couplings on top of the hose load.

Step 13: Pull out the slack so that the crossover loop lies tightly against the hose load.

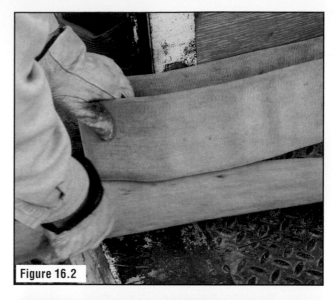

Figure 16.2

Figure 16.3

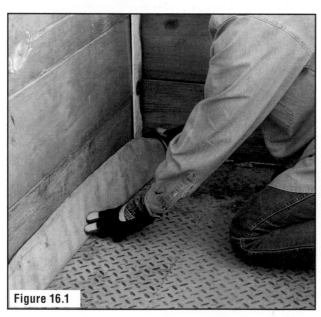

Figure 16.1

Figure 16.4

NOTE: Load the hose in a manner that allows it to deploy without the need to flip the couplings so that the hose does not catch in the hose bed.

Step 1: Attach the female coupling to the discharge outlet **(Figure 17.1)**.

Step 2: Lay the first length of hose flat in the bed against the side wall.

Step 3: Angle the hose to lay the next fold adjacent to the first fold and continue building the first tier **(Figure 17.2)**.

Step 4: Make a fold that extends approximately 8 inches (200 mm) beyond the load at a point that is approximately one-third the total length of the load **(Figure 17.3)**.

NOTE: This loop will later serve as a pull handle.

Step 5: Continue laying the hose in the same manner, building each tier with folds laid progressively across the bed.

Step 6: Make a fold that extends approximately 14 inches (350 mm) beyond the load at a point that is approximately two-thirds the total length of the load.

NOTE: This loop will also serve as a pull handle.

Step 7: Complete the hose load.

Step 8: Attach the nozzle and place it on top of the load **(Figure 17.4)**.

Figure 17.3

Figure 17.1

Figure 17.2

Figure 17.4

NOTE:	Start the load with the sections of hose connected and the nozzle attached.
Step 1:	Connect the female coupling to the discharge outlet.
Step 2:	Extend the hose in a straight line on the ground pointing straight away from the hose bed (either directly behind the hydrant or other water source or to the side) **(Figure 18.1)**.
Step 3:	Pick up the hose at a point two-thirds the distance the nozzle, creating a fold.
Step 4:	Carry this fold back to the hydrant or other water source and place it on the ground, creating an "S" shape in the hose.
Step 5:	Adjust the hose so that the nozzle is a short distance back from the fold (1 foot [300 mm]).
Step 6:	Using several fire brigade members, pick up the entire length of the three layers, one at a time starting with the piece attached to the discharge outlet.
Step 7:	Begin laying the hose into the bed by folding over the three layers into the hose bed **(Figure 18.2)**.
Step 8:	Fold the layers over at the front of the bed **(Figure 18.3)**.
Step 9:	Lay them back to the rear on top of the previously laid hose.
	a. If the hose compartment is wider than one hose width, alternate folds on each side of the bed.
	b. Make all folds at the rear even with the edge of the hose bed.
Step 10:	Continue to lay the hose into the bed in an S-shaped configuration until the entire length is loaded **(Figure 18.4)**.
Step 11:	Optional: Secure the nozzle to the first set of loops using a rope or strap.

Figure 18.2

Figure 18.1

Figure 18.3

Figure 18.4

NOTE: Load the hose in a manner that allows it to deploy without the need to flip the couplings so that the hose does not catch in the hose bed.

Step 1: Connect the first section of hose to the discharge outlet. Do not connect it to the other lengths of hose.

Step 2: Lay one layer of the connected hose flat in the bed with the remaining hose hanging out of the bed for connecting and loading later **(Figure 19.1)**.

NOTE: If the discharge outlet is at the front of the hose bed, lay the hose to the rear of the bed and then back to the front before it is set aside. This provides slack hose for pulling the load clear of the bed.

Step 3: Couple the remaining hose sections together.

Step 4: Attach a nozzle to the male end **(Figure 19.2)**.

Step 5: Place the nozzle on top of the first length at the rear.

Step 6: Angle the hose to the opposite side of the bed and make a fold.

Step 7: Lay the hose back to the rear.

Step 8: Make a fold at the rear of the hose bed.

Step 9: Angle the hose back to the other side and make a fold at the front.

NOTE: The first fold or two may be longer than the others to facilitate the pulling of the hose from the bed.

Step 10: Continue loading the hose to alternating sides of the bed in the same manner until the complete length is loaded.

Step 11: Connect the male coupling of the first section to the female coupling of the last section **(Figure 19.3)**.

Step 12: Lay the remainder of the first section in the bed in the same manner **(Figure 19.4)**.

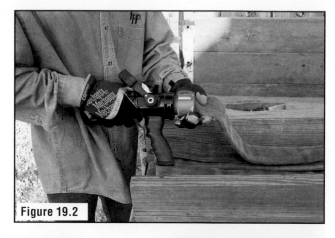

Figure 19.2

Figure 19.3

Figure 19.1

Figure 19.4

Flat Hose Method

Step 1: Put one arm through the longer pull loop.

Step 2: Grasp the shorter pull loop with the same hand.

Step 3: Grasp the nozzle with the opposite hand **(Figure 20.1)**.

Step 4: Pull the load from the bed using the pull loops **(Figure 20.2)**.

Step 5: Advance toward the fire until the hose is fully extended, checking to be sure that the hose is free of kinks **(Figure 20.3)**.

Minuteman Hose Method

Step 1: Grasp the nozzle and pull loops, if provided.

Step 2: Pull the load approximately one-third to one-half of the way out of the hose bed.

Step 3: Face the direction of travel.

Step 4: Place the hose load on the shoulder with the nozzle against your stomach **(Figure 20.4, p. 800)**.

Step 5: Walk away from the hydrant or other water source, pulling the hose out of the bed by the pull loop **(Figure 20.5, p. 800)**.

Step 6: Advance toward the fire until the hose is fully extended, allowing the load to play out from the top of the pile. Check to be sure the hose is free of kinks **(Figure 20.6, p. 800)**.

Triple Layer Method

Step 1: Place the nozzle and fold of the first tier over the shoulder.

Step 2: Face the direction of travel **(Figure 20.7, p. 801)**.

Step 3: Walk away from the hydrant or other water source **(Figure 20.8, p. 801)**.

Step 4: Pull the hose completely out of the bed.

Step 5: Drop the folded end from the shoulder when the hose bed has been cleared **(Figure 20.9, p. 801)**.

Step 6: Advance toward the fire until the hose is fully extended, checking to be sure that the hose is free of kinks **(Figure 20.10)**.

Figure 20.2

Figure 20.1

Figure 20.3

Figure 20.4

Figure 20.6

Figure 20.5

Figure 20.7

Figure 20.9

Figure 20.8

Figure 20.10

NOTE: Fire brigade members should be positioned on the same side of the hose.

Step 1: Position alongside the hoseline as directed, facing the direction of travel.

Step 2: Place the hose over the shoulder with a coupling in front, resting on the chest **(Figure 21.1)**.

NOTE: The coupling may be the nozzle coupling or a connection along the hoseline.

Step 3: Hold the coupling in place and pull with the shoulder.

Step 4: Advance toward the fire until the hose is fully extended **(Figure 21.2)**.

Figure 21.1

Figure 21.2

NOTE: Fire brigade members should be positioned on same side of hose with one fire brigade member controlling the nozzle and one on backup.

Step 1: Hold the hose with one hand behind the nozzle and the opposite hand on the nozzle shutoff valve.

Step 2: Adjust the nozzle to the desired stream.

Step 3: Aim the nozzle at the target and wait for the backup fire brigade member to communicate readiness.

Step 4: Open the nozzle fully **(Figure 22.1)**.

Step 5: Hold the stream on the target **(Figure 22.2)**.

Step 6: Close the nozzle slowly to avoid water hammer **(Figure 22.3)**.

Figure 22.1

Figure 22.2

Figure 22.3

Step 1: Position the hose so that it extends straight back for at least 10 feet (3 m).

Step 2: Stand facing the objective with feet spread at least shoulder width apart.

Step 3: Hold the hose with one hand behind the nozzle and the opposite hand on the nozzle shutoff valve **(Figure 23.1)**.

Step 4: Prepare to absorb the reaction force of the nozzle using one of the following methods:

  a. Anchor the hose by placing a foot on it. Make an "S" so that the hose at the top of the "S" rests against the hip or waist area. Place the back foot on the bottom of the "S."

  b. Attach a hose strap or webbing to the hose and then place it over the shoulder **(Figure 23.2)**.

Step5: Operate the nozzle **(Figure 23.3)**.

Figure 23.2

Figure 23.1

Figure 23.3

Step 1: Nozzle fire brigade member: Hold the hose with one hand behind the nozzle and the opposite hand on the nozzle shutoff valve.

Step 2: Backup fire brigade member: Grasp the hose with both hands **(Figure 24.1)**.

Step 3: Nozzle fire brigade member: Operate the nozzle.

Step 4: Backup fire brigade member: Absorb the reaction force of the nozzle and assist the nozzle fire brigade member in controlling the elevation of the stream **(Figure 24.2)**.

NOTE: Hose straps can be used to better control the hose, if necessary. If used, attach straps and loops so that each person shares the backward force from the nozzle.

Figure 24.1

Figure 24.2

Step 1: Form a loop immediately behind the nozzle using approximately 25 feet (7.5 m) of the hose.

Step 2: Pass the nozzle beneath the loop so that the loop rests on the end of the hose approximately 2 feet (600 mm) behind the nozzle **(Figure 25.1)**.

Step 3: Secure loop by tying the hose at the crossover point with a hose strap **(Figure 25.2)**.

Step 4: Kneel or sit on the hose at the crossover point.

Step 5: Hold the hose with one hand behind the nozzle and the opposite hand on the nozzle shutoff valve.

Step 6: Operate the nozzle **(Figure 25.3)**.

Figure 25.3

Figure 25.1

Figure 25.2

NOTE: Fire brigade members should be positioned on the same side of the hose.

Step 1: Nozzle fire brigade member: Hold the hose with one hand behind the nozzle and the opposite hand on the nozzle shutoff valve **(Figure 26.1)**.

Step 2: Backup fire brigade member: Grasp the hose with both hands **(Figure 26.2)**.

Step 3: Nozzle fire brigade member: Operate the nozzle **(Figure 26.3)**.

Step 4: Backup fire brigade member: Absorb the reaction force of the nozzle and assist the student in controlling the elevation of the stream.

NOTE: Hose straps can be used to better control the hose, if necessary. If used, attach straps and loops so that each person shares the backward force from the nozzle.

Figure 26.1

Figure 26.2

Figure 26.3

Step 1: Confirm order with IC to deploy master stream device.

Step 2: With assistance, retrieve monitor.

Step 3: Carry the monitor unit to the set-up area **(Figure 27.1)**.

Step 4: Position the monitor on a solid, level surface.

Step 5: Secure monitor **(Figure 27.2)**.

NOTE: Make sure any hoses connected to a portable ground monitor are straight behind, in-line, for 6-8 feet (2-3 m) to help stabilize the monitor.

Step 6: Adjust the nozzle to the proper elevation.

Step 7: Secure the anchor lock, if applicable.

Step 8: Extend hoseline to the monitor.

Step 9: Connect the hoselines to the monitor unit.

Step 10: Hand tighten the swivel couplings.

Step 11: Check the tip size, ensuring proper tip for situation, or select desired fog pattern stream **(Figure 27.3)**.

Step 12: Signal to charge the line.

Step 13: Steady the monitor.

Step 14: Adjust the direction of water flow as necessary.

Step 15: Operate master stream device by aiming the stream in correct direction and hitting the designated target **(Figure 27.4)**.

Step 16: Continue to evaluate and forecast a fire's growth and development.

Figure 27.3

Figure 27.4

Figure 27.1

Figure 27.2

Step 1: Bring additional sections of hose to the nozzle end of the hoseline **(Figure 28.1)**.

Step 2: Open the nozzle slightly.

Step 3: Restrict the flow of water.

    a. Apply a hose clamp approximately 5 feet (1.5 m) behind the nozzle or **(Figure 28.2)**,

    b. Call for the hoseline to be shut down at the pump panel or,

    c. Use break-away feature on the nozzle, if equipped.

Step 4: Remove the nozzle **(Figure 28.3)**.

Step 5: Add the new section(s) of hose **(Figure 28.4, p. 810)**.

Step 6: Reattach the nozzle **(Figure 28.5, p. 810)**.

Step 7: Recharge the hoseline by slowly releasing the hose clamp or calling for the line to be charged **(Figure 28.6, p. 810)**.

Step 8: Check the nozzle pattern and bleed the air from the hoseline.

Figure 28.2

Figure 28.1

Figure 28.3

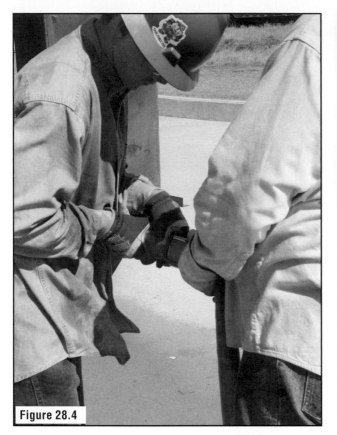

Figure 28.4

Figure 28.6

Figure 28.5

Step 1: Call for hoseline to be shut down or use a hose clamp to stop the flow.

Step 2: Retrieve two sections of replacement hose **(Figure 29.1)**.

Step 3: Remove burst section of hose **(Figure 29.2)**.

Step 4: Couple replacement sections of hose into the hoseline **(Figure 29.3)**.

Step 5: Recharge the hoseline by slowly releasing the hose clamp or calling for the line to be charged **(Figure 29.4)**.

Step 6: Communicate that the hoseline is again in operation.

Figure 29.4

Figure 29.1

Figure 29.2

Figure 29.3

NOTE: Any damage or impairment to a control valve must be reported so that repair or replacement of the valve can be accomplished. During an emergency, water for extinguishment must come from another source, such as a pumper supplying water through a fire department connection.

OS&Y

Step 1: Unlock and remove the chain, if necessary.

Step 2: Confirm with Command prior to turning the OS&Y valve **(Figure 30.1)**.

Step 3: Turn the OS&Y valve clockwise until the valve is fully closed and the stem is flush with the wheel.

Step 4: Confirm with Command prior to opening the OS&Y valve.

Step 5: Open the OS&Y valve by turning it counterclockwise until fully opened **(Figure 30.2)**.

Step 6: Back off the OS&Y valve one-quarter turn clockwise.

PIV

Step 1: Unlock the PIV wrench from the PIV body.

Step 2: Position the PIV wrench on stem nut **(Figure 30.3)**.

Step 3: Confirm with Command prior to closing the PIV valve.

Step 4: Turn it clockwise slowly until the target window indicates CLOSED or SHUT **(Figure 30.4)**.

Step 5: Confirm with Command prior to opening the PIV valve.

Step 6: Turn it counterclockwise until it is fully open and the target window indicates OPEN.

Step 7: Back off the PIV valve, turning it clockwise one-quarter turn ensuring that the target window remains OPEN.

Step 8: Replace and lock the wrench onto the PIV body.

Figure 30.2

Figure 30.3

Figure 30.1

Figure 30.4

Step 1: Access the activation panel/valve **(Figure 31.1)**.

Step 2: Notify personnel that system is about to be activated **(Figure 31.2)**.

Step 3: Following local/manufacturer procedures, activate the fixed suppression system using the necessary electrical or mechanical methods **(Figure 31.3)**.

Step 4: When applicable, follow appropriate local/manufacturer shutdown procedures.

Figure 31.1

Figure 31.2

Figure 31.3

NOTE: Two students must make initial folds to reduce the width of the cover. Steps 1 through 8 are performed simultaneously by both students on opposite sides of the cover. Steps 9 through 12 may be performed by both students who are stationed at the same end of the roll.

Step 1: Grasp the cover with the outside hand midway between the center and the edge to be folded.

Step 2: Place the other hand on the cover as a pivot midway between the outside hand and the center **(Figure 32.1)**.

Step 3: Bring the fold over to the center of the cover, creating an inside fold (center) and an outside fold **(Figure 32.2)**.

Step 4: Grasp the corner with the outside hand.

Step 5: Place the other hand as a pivot on the cover over the outside fold.

Step 6: Bring this outside edge over to the center, and place it on top of and in line with the previously placed first fold.

Step 7: Fold the other half of the cover in the same manner.

Step 8: Straighten the folds **(Figure 32.3)**.

Step 9: Fold over about 12 inches (300 mm) at each end of the cover to make clean, even ends for the completed roll.

Step 10: Start by rolling and compressing one end into a tight compact roll. Roll toward the opposite end **(Figure 32.4)**.

Step 11: Tuck in any wrinkles that form ahead of the roll as the roll progresses **(Figure 32.5)**.

Step 12: Secure the completed roll with inner tube bands or Velcro® straps or tie with cords.

Figure 32.3

Figure 32.4

Figure 32.1

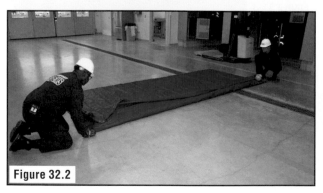

Figure 32.2

Figure 32.5

33

Spread a rolled salvage cover using the one-fire brigade member method.
[NFPA 1081, 4.2.2, 5.2.5, 6.2.9]

Step 1: Position at one end of the object(s) to be covered.

Step 2: Unroll a sufficient amount and cover the end of the object(s) **(Figure 33.1)**.

Step 3: Unroll toward the opposite end of the object and let the rest of the roll fall into place at the end **(Figure 33.2)**.

Step 4: Stand at one end of the cover.

Step 5: Grasp the open edges where convenient, with one edge in each hand **(Figure 33.3)**.

Step 6: Open the sides of the cover over the object by snapping both hands up and out.

Step 7: Open the other end of the cover over the object in the same manner.

Step 8: Tuck in all loose edges at the bottom **(Figures 33.4 and 33.5)**.

Figure 33.3

Figure 33.1

Figure 33.4

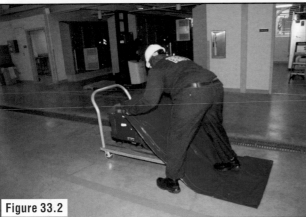
Figure 33.2

Figure 33.5

34

NOTE: Two students must make initial folds to reduce the width of the cover. Steps 1 through 7 are performed simultaneously by both students on opposite sides of the cover. Steps 8 through 12 may be performed by both students who are stationed at the same end of the fold.

Step 1: Grasp the cover with the outside hand midway between the center and the edge to be folded.

Step 2: Place the other hand on the cover as a pivot midway between the outside hand and the center.

Step 3: Bring the fold over to the center of the cover. This will create an inside fold (center) and an outside fold **(Figure 34.1)**.

Step 4: Grasp the corner of the cover with the outside hand.

Step 5: Place the other hand as a pivot on the cover over the outside fold.

Step 6: Bring this outside edge over to the center and place it on top of and in line with the previously placed first fold.

Step 7: Fold the other half of the cover in the same manner **(Figure 34.2)**.

Step 8: Straighten the folds **(Figure 34.3)**.

Step 9: Grasp the same end of the cover and bring this end to a point just short of the center.

Step 10: Use one hand as a pivot and bring the folded end over and place on top of the first fold **(Figure 34.4)**.

Step 11: Fold the other end of the cover toward the center, leaving about 4 inches (100 mm) between the two folds **(Figure 34.5)**.

Step 12: Place one fold on top of the other for the completed fold; the space between the folds now serves as a hinge **(Figure 34.6)**.

Figure 34.3

Figure 34.4

Figure 34.5

Figure 34.1

Figure 34.2

Figure 34.6

Step 1: Lay the folded cover on top of and near the center of the object to be covered.

Step 2: Separate the cover at the first fold **(Figure 35.1)**.

Step 3: Separate the next fold and unfold it toward one end of the object to be covered.

Step 4: Grasp the end of the cover near the center with both hands to prevent the corners from falling outward.

Step 5: Bring the end of the cover into position over the end of the object being covered **(Figure 35.2)**.

Step 6: Unfold the other end of the cover in the same manner over the object **(Figure 35.3)**.

Step 7: Stand at one end.

Step 8: Grasp the open edges where convenient, with one edge in each hand.

Step 9: Open the sides of the cover over the object by snapping both hands up and out **(Figure 35.4)**.

Step 10: Open the other end of the cover over the object in the same manner **(Figure 35.5)**.

Step 11: Tuck in all loose edges at the bottom **(Figure 35.6)**.

Figure 35.3

Figure 35.4

Figure 35.1

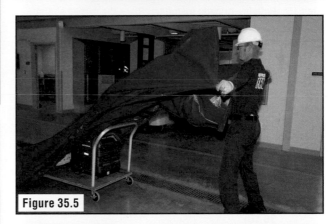

Figure 35.5

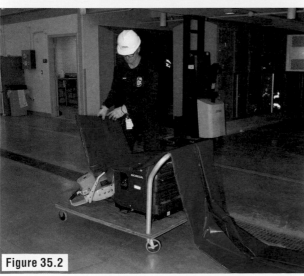

Figure 35.2

Figure 35.6

NOTE: Two students must make initial folds to reduce the width of the cover. Steps 1 through 11 are performed simultaneously by both students. Steps 12 through 18 are performed by the respective students. Steps 19 through 21 are performed simultaneously by both students.

Step 1: With the cover stretched lengthwise, grasp opposite ends of the cover at the center grommet.

Step 2: Pull the cover tightly between each fire brigade member.

Step 3: Raise the center fold high above the ground.

Step 4: Shake out the wrinkles to form the first half-fold **(Figure 36.1)**.

Step 5: Spread the half-fold on the ground **(Figure 36.2)**.

Step 6: Smooth the half-fold flat to remove the wrinkles **(Figure 36.3)**.

Step 7: Stand at each end of the half-fold and face the cover.

Step 8: Grasp the open-edge corners.

Step 9: Place a foot at the center of the half-fold, making a pivot for the next fold.

Step 10: Stretch the part of the cover being folded tightly between each student.

Step 11: Make the quarter-fold by folding the open edges over the folded edge **(Figure 36.4)**.

Step 12: Fire brigade member #1: Stand on one end of the quarter-fold.

Step 13: Fire brigade member #2: Grasp the opposite end and shake out all the wrinkles **(Figure 36.5)**.

Step 14: Fire brigade member #2: Carry this end to the opposite end, maintaining alignment of outside edges **(Figure 36.6)**.

Step 15: Both fire brigade members: Place the carried end on the opposite end, aligning all edges.

Step 16: Both fire brigade members: Place the folded cover on the ground and position at opposite ends.

Step 17: Fire brigade member #2: Stand on the folded end of the cover.

Step 18: Fire brigade member #1: Shake out all wrinkles and alight all of the edges **(Figure 36.7)**.

Step 19: Grasp the open ends and use the inside foot as a pivot for the next fold **(Figure 36.8)**.

Step 20: Bring the open ends over and place them just short of the center fold **(Figure 36.9)**.

Step 21: Fold the opposite side in the same manner **(Figure 36.10)**.

Figure 36.1

Figure 36.2

Figure 36.3

Figure 36.4

Figure 36.5

Figure 36.9

Figure 36.6

Figure 36.10

Figure 36.7

Figure 36.8

NOTE: These steps are done with both fire brigade members performing the steps simultaneously.

Step 1: Stretch the cover along one side of the object to be covered **(Figure 37.1)**.

Step 2: Separate the last half-fold by grasping each side of the cover near the ends.

Step 3: Lay the edge of the cover near the object to be covered **(Figure 37.2)**.

Step 4: Make several accordion folds in the inside hand.

Step 5: Place the outside hand about midway down the end hem.

Step 6: Place inside foot on the corner of the cover to hold it in place **(Figure 37.3)**.

Step 7: Pull the cover tightly between each student.

Step 8: Swing the folded part down, up, and out in one sweeping movement in order to pocket as much air as possible.

Step 9: Pitch or carry the accordion folds across the object when the cover is as high as each student can reach, causing the cover to float over the object **(Figure 37.4)**.

Step 10: Guide the cover into position as it floats over the object.

Step 11: Straighten the sides for better water runoff **(Figure 37.5)**.

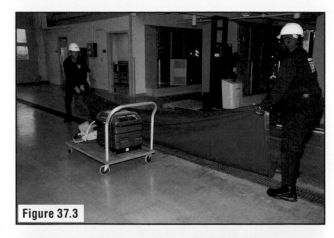

Figure 37.3

Figure 37.4

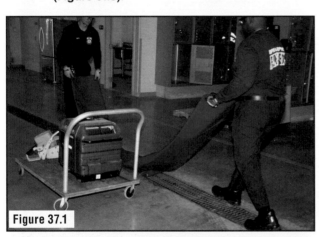

Figure 37.1

Figure 37.5

Figure 37.2

NOTE: These steps are done with both students performing the steps simultaneously.

Without Pike Poles

Step 1: Open the salvage cover.

Step 2: Lay the cover flat at the desired location.

Step 3: Roll the opposite edges of the salvage cover toward the center of the cover until there is 1 to 3 feet (0.3 m to 1 m) between the rolls **(Figures 38.1 and 38.2)**.

Step 4: Turn the cover over, keeping the rolls in place **(Figure 38.3)**.

Step 5: Adjust the chute to collect and channel water by elevating one end **(Figure 38.4)**.

Step 6: Extend the other end out a door or window.

Using Pike Poles

Step 1: Open the salvage cover.

Step 2: Lay the cover flat at the desired location.

Step 3: Place pike poles at opposite edges of the salvage cover with the pike extending off the end of the cover **(Figure 38.5, p. 822)**.

Step 4: Roll the edges of the cover over the pike poles toward the center of the cover until there is 1 to 3 feet (0.3 m to 1 m) between the rolls **(Figures 38.6 and 38.7, p. 822)**.

Step 5: Turn the cover over, keeping the rolls in place **(Figure 38.8, p. 822)**.

Step 6: Adjust the chute to collect and channel water by elevating one end **(Figure 38.9, p. 822)**.

Step 7: Extend the other end out a door or window.

Figure 38.3

Figure 38.4

Figure 38.1

Figure 38.2

Figure 38.5

Figure 38.8

Figure 38.6

Figure 38.7

Figure 38.9

NOTE: These steps are done with both students performing the steps simultaneously.

Step 1: Open the salvage cover.

Step 2: Lay the cover flat at the desired location **(Figure 39.1)**.

Step 3: Roll the sides inward approximately 3 feet (1 m) **(Figures 39.2 and 39.3)**.

Step 4: Lay the ends of the side rolls over at a 90-degree angle to form the corners of the basin **(Figure 39.4)**.

Step 5: Roll one end into a tight roll on top of the side roll and form a projected flap **(Figure 39.5)**.

Step 6: Lift the edge roll.

Step 7: Tuck the end roll to lock the corners **(Figure 39.6)**.

Step 8: Roll the other end and lock the corners in the same manner **(Figures 39.7 and 39.8)**.

Figure 39.5

Figure 39.1

Figure 39.6

Figure 39.2

Figure 39.3

Figure 39.7

Figure 39.4

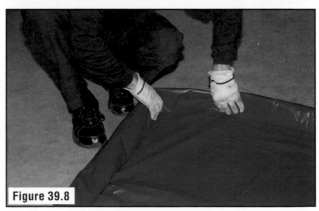

Figure 39.8

Step 1: Open the salvage cover.

Step 2: Lay the cover flat at the desired location **(Figure 40.1)**.

Step 3: Roll the opposite edges of the salvage cover toward the center until there is 1 to 3 feet (0.3 m to 1 m) between the rolls **(Figure 40.2)**.

Step 4: Turn the cover over, keeping the rolls in place and flattening the center to the floor.

Step 5: Slide the end of the chute into the catchall, about 1 to 2 feet (0.3 m to 0.6 m) **(Figure 40.3 and 40.4)**.

Step 6: Unfold the corner of the catchall.

Step 7: Flatten the corner of the catchall to form a seamless path for the water.

Figure 40.3

Figure 40.1

Figure 40.4

Figure 40.2

Step 1: Identify openings to be covered **(Figure 41.1)**.

Step 2: Gather tools, equipment, and materials.

Step 3: Cover or secure openings.

    a. Doors **(Figure 41.2)**

    b. Windows **(Figure 41.3)**

    c. Floor openings

    d. Roof openings

    e. Other openings as necessary.

Step 4: Verify that the building is secure **(Figure 41.4)**.

Figure 41.3

Figure 41.1

Figure 41.2

Figure 41.4

NOTE: Fire brigade members must confirm the order to attack the fire prior to performing suppression operations.

Direct Attack Method

Step 1: Deploy and advance an uncharged attack hoseline to a safe location **(Figure 42.1)**.

Step 2: Signal when ready for water **(Figure 42.2)**.

Step 3: Open the nozzle to bleed air from the line and check for adequate water flow **(Figure 42.3)**.

Step 4: Select the correct nozzle pattern and close the nozzle.

Step 5: Advance to the attack position, extinguishing any fires that are encountered along the way.

Step 6: Cool hot gases overhead as needed using short applications of a solid or straight stream.

Step 7: When in the attack position, direct a solid or straight stream of water onto the base of the fire **(Figure 42.4)**.

NOTE: Locate and suppress any other fires as directed.

Step 8: Close the nozzle when the fire is extinguished.

Indirect Attack Method

Step 1: Deploy and advance an uncharged attack hoseline to a safe location **(Figure 42.5)**.

Step 2: Signal when ready for water.

Step 3: Open the nozzle to bleed air from the line and check for adequate water flow.

Step 4: Select the correct nozzle pattern and close the nozzle.

Step 5: Advance to the attack position, extinguishing any fires that are encountered along the way.

Step 6: Cool hot gases overhead as needed using short applications of a solid or straight stream.

Step 7: When in position, open the nozzle and direct a fog pattern toward the ceiling and upper area of the walls **(Figure 42.6)**.

Step 8: Close the door to the compartment, allowing steam to develop. Crack the door to observe the conditions.

Step 9: Continue to apply water until the fire is extinguished.

Step 10: Close the nozzle when the fire is extinguished.

Combination Attack Method

Step 1: Deploy and advance an uncharged attack hoseline to a safe location **(Figure 42.7, p. 828)**.

Step 2: Signal when ready for water.

Step 3: Open the nozzle to bleed air from the line and check for adequate water flow.

Step 4: Select the correct nozzle pattern and close the nozzle.

Step 5: Enter the structure and advance to the attack position, extinguishing any fires that are encountered along the way.

Step 6: Cool hot gases overhead as needed using short applications of a solid or straight stream.

Step 7: When in position, open the nozzle and direct a straight stream toward the upper edge of the fire at the ceiling level.

Step 8: Apply water using a T, Z, or O pattern, moving the fire stream from high to low **(Figure 42.8, p. 828)**.

NOTE: Ensure that the ceiling and floor are reached by the hose stream.

Step 9: Close the nozzle when the room begins to darken.

Step 10: Apply water using the direct attack method as needed.

Step 11: Close the nozzle when the fire is extinguished.

Figure 42.1

Figure 42.2

Figure 42.3

Figure 42.5

Figure 42.4

Figure 42.6

Figure 42.7

Figure 42.8

CAUTION: Always don appropriate workplace PPE when on the fireground. Approach from uphill and upwind if possible. Maintain communication and situational awareness. Observe fire conditions throughout the operation.

NOTE: Fire brigade members must confirm the order to attack the fire prior to performing suppression operations.

Step 1: Deploy and advance an uncharged attack hoseline **(Figure 43.1)**.

Step 2: Signal when ready for water.

Step 3: Open the nozzle to purge air and ensure that water has reached the nozzle **(Figure 43.2)**.

Step 4: Select the correct nozzle pattern and close the nozzle.

Step 5: Advance toward the structure and position to make fire attack.

Step 6: Direct a straight stream at the structure and extinguish the fire **(Figure 43.3)**.

Step 7: Search for and extinguish hidden fires **(Figure 43.4)**.

    a. Break up material and probe with pike pole for hot spots.

    b. Extinguish hot spots.

Figure 43.2

Figure 43.3

Figure 43.1

Figure 43.4

CAUTION: Always don appropriate workplace PPE when on the fireground. Approach from uphill and upwind. Maintain communication and situational awareness. Observe fire conditions throughout the operation.

NOTE: Fire brigade members must confirm the order to attack the fire prior to performing suppression operations.

Step 1: Deploy and advance an uncharged attack hoseline.

Step 2: Signal when ready for water **(Figure 44.1)**.

Step 3: Open the nozzle to bleed air from the line and check for adequate water flow **(Figure 44.2)**.

Step 4: Select the correct nozzle pattern and close the nozzle.

Step 5: Check for threat to exposures and cool as necessary.

Step 6: Position to make fire attack.

Step 7: Extinguish the fire with a straight stream **(Figure 44.3)**.

Step 8: Expose fire in the debris using a pike pole or trash hook and extinguish any debris fires **(Figure 44.4)**.

Figure 44.2

Figure 44.1

Figure 44.3

Figure 44.4

NOTE: Fire brigade members must wait to perform overhaul until ordered to do so.

Step 1: Locate area(s)/material(s) with potential hidden or smoldering fire **(Figure 45.1)**.

   a. Use thermal imager or similar device.

   b. Observe fire area to detect smoking or smoldering materials.

   c. Observe burn and smoke patterns.

Step 2: Overhaul area(s)/material(s) until hidden fires and smoldering components are exposed.

Step 3: Completely extinguish hidden and smoldering fires with a handline **(Figure 45.2)**.

   a. Use minimal water for extinguishment.

   b. Ensure that no hidden or smoldering fires remain.

Step 4: Remove smoldering materials from structure and overhaul outside.

Figure 45.1

Figure 45.2

Clean

Step 1: Place the ladder flat on the sawhorses **(Figure 46.1)**.

Step 2: Clean all parts of the ladder with a scrub brush and cleaning solution. Remove greasy residues with approved cleaners **(Figure 46.2)**.

Step 3: Rinse the ladder thoroughly with clean water **(Figure 46.3)**.

Step 4: Dry the ladder thoroughly with clean, dry cloths **(Figure 46.4)**.

Inspect

Step 1: Inspect each part of the ladder, noting any:

    a. Looseness **(Figure 46.5, p. 834)**

    b. Cracks

    c. Dents

    d. Unusual wear

    e. Bent rungs or beams

    f. Heat damage, deformities or change in sensor label **(Figure 46.6, p. 834)**

Step 2: Circle any defects with chalk or grease pen.

Step 3: Extension ladders: Inspect the ladder halyard for **(Figure 46.7, p. 834)**:

    a. Fraying or kinking.

    b. Snugness of cable when in bedded position.

Step 4: Extension, roof, and pole ladders: Inspect all movable parts.

Maintain

Step 1: Lubricate parts as needed, using recommended lubricant.

Step 2: Extension ladders: Replace halyard, if necessary.

Step 3: Tag and remove ladder from service for any conditions that cannot be corrected with cleaning, inspection, and simple maintenance. Notify officer.

Step 4: Record cleaning, inspection, and maintenance performed **(Figure 46.8, p. 834)**.

Figure 46.1

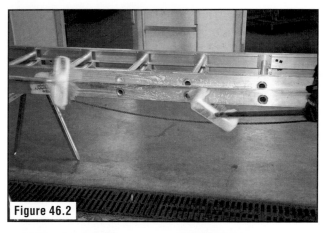

Figure 46.2

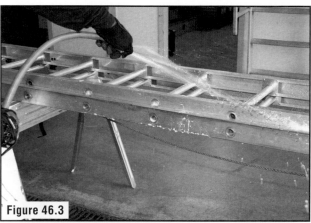

Figure 46.3

Figure 46.4

Figure 46.5

Figure 46.7

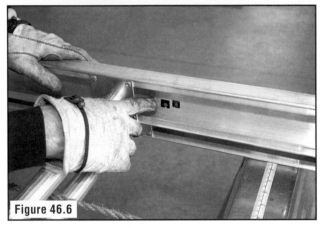

Figure 46.6

Figure 46.8

NOTE: Always use caution when handling couplings. Do not throw, drag, or drop couplings on the ground. Damage to the couplings can result in a bad connection.

Inspect

Step 1: Stretch hose to full length on flat, clean, dry surface **(Figure 47.1)**.

  a. Ensure grease or other chemicals cannot come into contact with hose.

  b. Attempt to unroll hose rather than drag it.

Step 2: Inspect one coupling and its component parts (threads, attachment, lugs, swivel, and/or gasket) **(Figure 47.2)**.

Step 3: Place the coupling back on the surface.

Step 4: Walk along the section of hose, visually inspecting surface for abrasions, burns, or other damage **(Figure 47.3, p. 836)**.

Step 5: Circle any damaged spots with chalk or nonpermanent marker.

Step 6: Inspect the other coupling and its component parts (threads, attachment, lugs, swivel, and/or gasket).

Step 7: Turn hose over to inspect the other side.

  a. Follow same procedure and inspect hose back to the coupling.

  b. Pay particular attention to marked locations on other side of hose.

Step 8: Note general inspection results and update fire hose service log as required by local SOPs.

  a. If hose is damaged or has other defects, tag with out-of-service tag and remove from service until repaired and tested.

  b. If free of damage, return it to the appropriate location.

Clean

Step 1: Hand wash or machine wash the hose according to local SOPs **(Figures 47.4 and 47.5, p. 836)**.

Step 2: Dry hose according to local SOPs.

Maintain - Replace a Hose Gasket

Step 1: Remove old or damaged gasket and discard in the proper receptacle **(Figure 47.6, p. 836)**.

Step 2: Place new gasket into the groove in the swivel in which it is meant to sit, smoothing as necessary to seat **(Figure 47.7, p. 837)**.

Figure 47.1

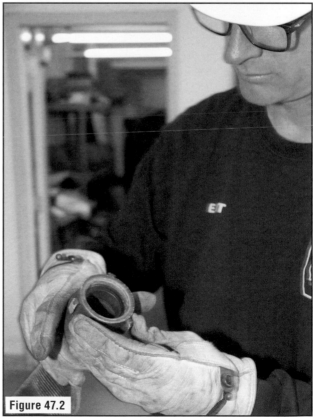

Figure 47.2

Figure 47.3

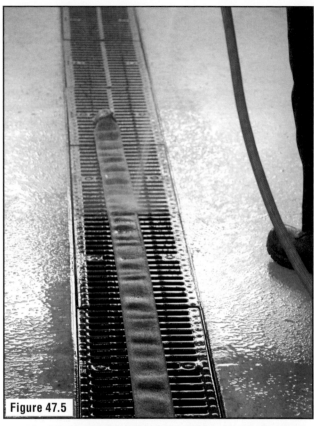

Figure 47.5

Figure 47.4

Figure 47.6

Figure 47.7

Step 1: Visually and physically inspect the entire length of the rope **(Figure 48.1)**.

Step 2: Remove any flawed rope from service, disposing of it or relabeling per local SOPs **(Figure 48.2)**.

Step 3: Record information in the rope logbook.

Step 4: Clean the rope according to manufacturer's guidelines **(Figure 48.3)**.

Step 5: Thoroughly rinse the rope.

Step 6: Dry the rope according to manufacturer's recommendations.

Step 7: Store rope per local SOPs **(Figure 48.4)**.

Figure 48.3

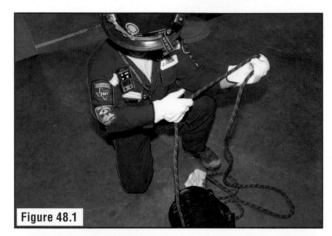

Figure 48.1

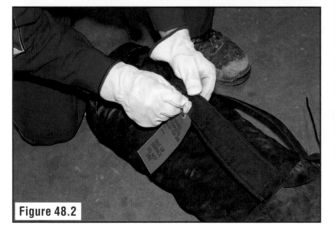

Figure 48.2

Figure 48.4

Tool Cleaning

Step 1: Wash tools with mild detergent per manufacturer's guidelines **(Figure 49.1)**.

Step 2: Rinse tools thoroughly with clean water **(Figure 49.2)**.

Step 3: Dry tools thoroughly **(Figure 49.3, p. 840)**.

Tool Inspection

Step 1: Inspect tools for damage or wear.

    a. Inspect working surface (dullness, cracks, chips, metal fatigue, etc.) **(Figure 49.4, p. 840)**.

    b. Inspect tool handles (e.g. cracks, splinters, or other damage) **(Figure 49.5, p. 840)**.

    c. Inspect tool head.

Step 2: Inspect parts for tightness and function.

Step 3: Place any tools that require maintenance on salvage cover or clean surface.

NOTE: Tools that require maintenance should be tagged out of service.

Tool Maintenance

Step 1: Maintain wooden handles.

    a. Repair loose tool heads.

    b. Sand the handles to eliminate splinters.

    c. Apply a coat of boiled linseed oil to the handles to preserve them and prevent roughness and warping. Do not paint or varnish the handles.

Step 2: Maintain cutting edges.

    a. File the cutting edges **(Figure 49.6, p. 840)**.

    b. Sharpen as specified in local SOPs.

    c. Replace cutting head, if necessary.

Step 3: Maintain unprotected metal surfaces.

    a. Remove rust with steel wool or fine sandpaper **(Figure 49.7, p. 841)**.

    b. File chips, cracks, or sharp edges.

    c. Oil the metal surface lightly, using light machine oil.

Figure 49.1

Figure 49.2

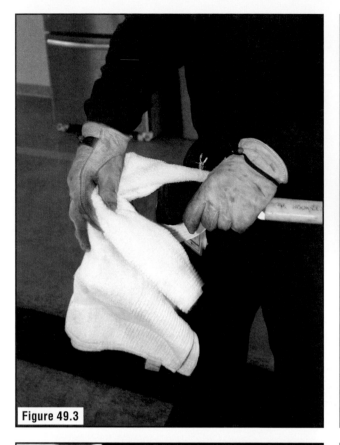

Figure 49.3

Figure 49.5

Figure 49.4

Figure 49.6

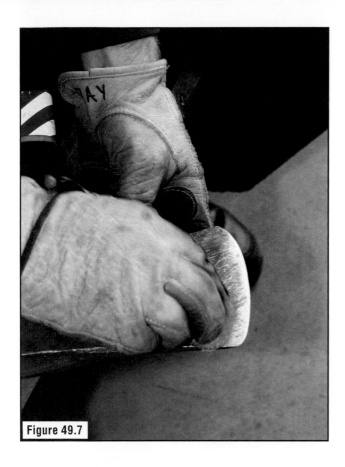

Figure 49.7

Tool Cleaning

Step 1: Clean tools according to manufacturer's guidelines **(Figure 50.1)**.

Step 2: Dry tools thoroughly.

Tool Inspection

Step 1: Inspect tools for damage or wear.

Step 2: Inspect parts for tightness and function **(Figure 50.2)**.

    a. Ensure all guards are functional and in place.

    b. Check all electrical components for cuts or other damage.

Step 3: Place any tools that require maintenance on a salvage cover or clean surface.

NOTE: Tools that require maintenance should be tagged out of service.

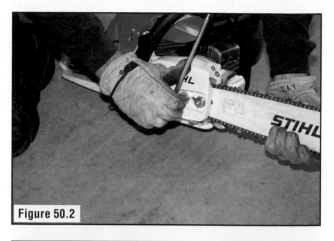

Figure 50.2

Tool Maintenance

Step 1: Maintain cutting blades.

    a. Check blades for damage or wear.

    b. Replace blades that are damaged or worn **(Figure 50.3)**.

Step 2: Check fuel level in all power tools and fill as necessary **(Figure 50.4)**.

    a. Use the correct fuel type.

    b. Ensure that fuel is fresh.

Step 3: Check oil level in all tools and fill as necessary **(Figure 50.5)**.

    a. Use the correct oil type.

    b. Ensure that oil is fresh.

Step 4: Start all power tools and keep them running **(Figure 50.6)**.

    a. Ensure power tools will start.

    b. Ensure battery packs are fully charged.

Step 5: Tag tools that must be placed out of service.

Step 6: Record cleaning, inspection, and maintenance according to local SOPs.

Figure 50.3

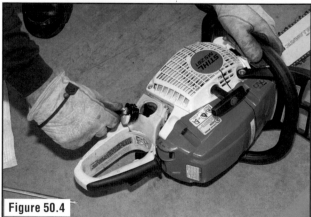

Figure 50.4

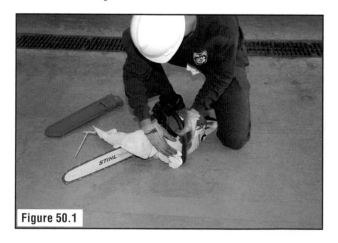

Figure 50.1

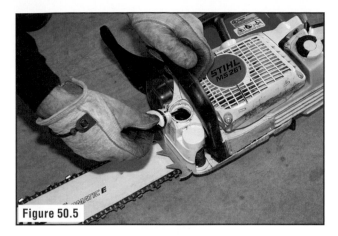

Figure 50.5

Figure 50.6

Step 1: Inspect and maintain spark plugs.

    a. Inspect for damage, visible corrosion, carbon accumulation, or cracks in the porcelain.

    b. Ensure that the spark plug wire is tight **(Figure 51.1)**.

    c. Replace spark plugs if damaged or if the service manual recommends replacement.

Step 2: Inspect the carburetor and identify signs of fuel leaks.

Step 3: Check the fuel level and refill as needed.

Step 4: Check the oil level and refill as needed **(Figure 51.2)**.

Step 5: Start the generator and run tests as required by the service manual **(Figure 51.3)**.

Step 6: Inspect and maintain lighting equipment.

    a. Inspect electrical cords for damaged insulation, exposed wiring, and missing or bent prongs.

    b. Connect each light to the generator one light at a time **(Figure 51.4)**.

    c. Replace light bulbs as necessary and discard faulty bulbs in an approved manner.

Step 7: Record inspection and maintenance according to local SOPs.

Figure 51.3

Figure 51.4

Figure 51.1

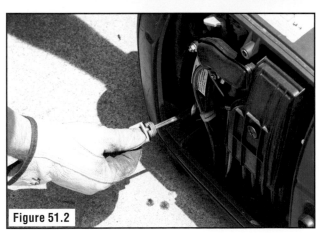
Figure 51.2

Step 1: Access the FACU **(Figure 52.1)**.

Step 2: Using the FACU, identify the type (alarm, trouble, or supervisory) of the alarm **(Figure 52.2)**.

Step 3: Identify appropriate response to alarm type.

Step 4: Using the FACU, identify the location of the alarm.

Step 5: Initiate response to the alarm according to local SOPs **(Figure 52.3)**.

Figure 52.2

Figure 52.1

Figure 52.3

Step 1: Obtain the preincident plan hardcopy or access it on the computer/tablet/mobile display terminal.

Step 2: Identify the components of the preincident plan such as fire suppression and detection systems, structural features, site-specific hazards, and response considerations **(Figure 53.1)**.

Step 3: Implement the preincident plan using all relevant information **(Figure 53.2)**.

Figure 53.1

Figure 53.2

Step 1: Communicate with mutual aid organizations using local SOPs **(Figure 54.1)**.

Step 2: Integrate operational personnel into teams under a unified command.

Step 3: Maintain unified command as operations progress **(Figure 54.2)**.

Figure 54.1

Figure 54.2

SKILL SHEETS

Demonstrate the method for donning thermal personal protective clothing for use at an emergency.
[NFPA 1081 5.2.1, 6.1.2.1]

Step 1: Don pants, suspenders, and boots **(Figure 55.1)**.

Step 2: Don hood **(Figure 55.2)**.

Step 3: Don coat with all closures secure and collar up **(Figure 55.3)**.

Step 4: Don helmet with eye protection on and chin strap in place and fastened **(Figure 55.4)**.

Step 5: Don structural gloves **(Figure 55.5)**.

Figure 55.1

Figure 55.2

Figure 55.3

55

Demonstrate the method for donning thermal personal protective clothing for use at an emergency.
[NFPA 1081 5.2.1, 6.1.2.1]

Figure 55.4

Figure 55.5

56

With thermal personal protective clothing in place, demonstrate the over-the-head and the coat methods of donning SCBA. *[NFPA 1081 5.2.2, 6.1.2.2]*

NOTE: The following are general procedures for donning SCBA. The specific SCBA manufacturer's recommendations for donning and use of the SCBA should always be followed.

Over-the-head Method

Step 1: Ensure the cylinder is full (at least 90 percent capacity) **(Figure 56.1)**.

Step 2: Position the SCBA with the valve end of the cylinder away from the body, the cylinder down, and back frame up. All harness straps are fully extended and untangled.

Step 3: Open cylinder valve fully. Listen for the activation of the integrated PASS Alarm if equipped. Listen for the activation of the Low Air Alarm.

Step 4: Check cylinder and regulator pressure gauges. Pressure readings within 100 psi (700 kPa) OR needles on both pressure gauges indicate same pressure.

Step 5: Grab the back frame so that the shoulder straps will be outside of arms. Using proper lifting techniques, raise the SCBA overhead while guiding elbows into the loops formed by the shoulder straps **(Figure 56.2)**.

Step 6: Release the harness assembly and allow the SCBA to slide down the back.

Step 7: Fasten chest strap, buckle waist strap, and adjust shoulder straps **(Figure 56.3)**.

Step 8: Don facepiece over the head and securely tighten the straps, pulling the straps straight backwards, not out to the side **(Figure 56.4)**.

Step 9: After straps are tightened, test the facepiece for a proper seal and operation of the exhalation valve **(Figure 56.5)**.

NOTE: Not all facepieces are designed for a seal check without the regulator being attached and activated.

Step 10: Don hood, ensure it covers all exposed skin.

Step 11: Connect air supply to facepiece **(Figure 56.6, p. 852)**.

Step 12: Activate external PASS device, if not equipped with integrated device.

Step 13: Don helmet, with chin strap secure and visor lowered.

Step 14: Don gloves **(Figure 56.7, p. 852)**.

Coat Method

Step 1: Ensure the cylinder is full (at least 90 percent capacity) **(Figure 56.8, p. 852)**.

Step 2: Position SCBA with the valve end of the cylinder toward the body, the cylinder down, and back frame up. All harness straps are fully extended and untangled.

Step 3: Open cylinder valve fully. Listen for the activation of the integrated PASS Alarm if equipped. Listen for the activation of the Low Air Alarm.

Step 4: Check cylinder and regulator pressure gauges. Pressure readings within 100 psi (700 kPa) OR needles on both pressure gauges indicate same pressure.

Step 5: Grasp the top of the left shoulder strap on the SCBA with the left hand and raise the SCBA overhead **(Figure 56.9, p. 852)**.

Step 6: Guide left elbow through the loop formed by the left shoulder strap and swing SCBA around left shoulder **(Figure 56.10, p. 853)**.

Step 7: Guide right arm through the loop formed by the right shoulder strap allowing the SCBA to come to rest in proper position.

Step 8: Fasten chest strap, buckle waist strap, and adjust shoulder straps **(Figure 56.11, p. 853)**.

Step 9: Don facepiece over the head and securely tighten the straps, pulling the straps straight backwards, not out to the side.

Step 10: After straps are tightened, test the facepiece for a proper seal and operation of the exhalation valve **(Figure 56.12, p. 853)**.

NOTE: Not all facepieces are designed for a seal check without the regulator being attached and activated.

Step 11: Don hood, ensure it covers all exposed skin.

Step 12: Connect air supply to facepiece **(Figure 56.13, p. 853)**.

Step 13: Activate external PASS device, if not equipped with integrated device.

Step 14: Don helmet, with chin strap secure and facepiece lowered.

Step 15: Don gloves.

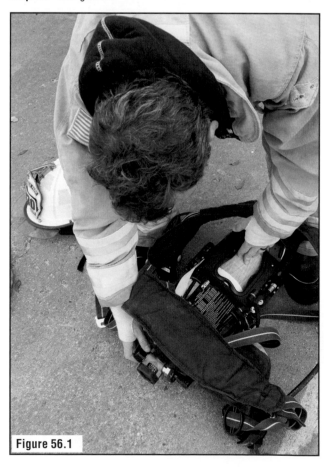

Figure 56.1

56

With thermal personal protective clothing in place, demonstrate the over-the-head and the coat methods of donning SCBA. *[NFPA 1081 5.2.2, 6.1.2.2]*

Figure 56.2

Figure 56.4

Figure 56.3

Figure 56.5

56

SKILL SHEETS

With thermal personal protective clothing in place, demonstrate the over-the-head and the coat methods of donning SCBA. *[NFPA 1081 5.2.2, 6.1.2.2]*

Figure 56.6

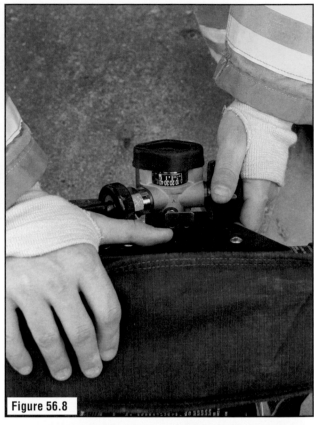

Figure 56.8

Figure 56.7

Figure 56.9

56

With thermal personal protective clothing in place, demonstrate the over-the-head and the coat methods of donning SCBA. *[NFPA 1081 5.2.2, 6.1.2.2]*

SKILL SHEETS

Figure 56.10

Figure 56.12

Figure 56.11

Figure 56.13

SKILL SHEETS

With thermal personal protective clothing in place, demonstrate the method for donning SCBA while seated. *[NFPA 1081 5.2.2, 6.1.2.2]*

Step 1: Position body in seat with back firmly against the SCBA and release the SCBA hold-down device.

Step 2: Insert arms through shoulder straps **(Figure 57.1)**.

Step 3: Fasten chest strap, buckle waist strap, and adjust shoulder straps **(Figure 57.2)**.

Step 4: Fasten seat belt before apparatus gets underway **(Figure 57.3)**.

Step 5: Safely dismount apparatus, using situational awareness **(Figure 57.4)**.

Step 6: Open cylinder valve fully.

Step 7: Check remote gauge.

Step 8: Don facepiece over the head and securely tighten the straps, pulling the straps straight backwards, not out to the side **(Figure 57.5)**.

Step 9: After straps are tightened, test the facepiece for a proper seal and operation of the exhalation valve.

NOTE: Not all facepieces are designed for a seal check without the regulator being attached and activated.

Step 10: Don hood, ensure it covers all exposed skin **(Figure 57.6)**.

Step 11: Connect air supply to facepiece **(Figure 57.7)**.

Step 12: Activate external PASS device, if not equipped with integrated device.

Step 13: Don helmet, with chin strap secure and visor lowered **(Figure 57.8, p. 856)**.

Step 14: Don gloves **(Figure 57.9, p. 856)**.

Figure 57.2

Figure 57.1

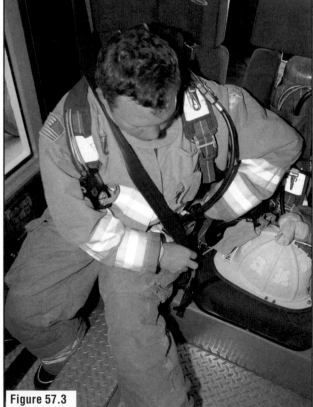

Figure 57.3

57

With thermal personal protective clothing in place, demonstrate the method for donning SCBA while seated. *[NFPA 1081 5.2.2, 6.1.2.2]*

SKILL SHEETS

Figure 57.4

Figure 57.6

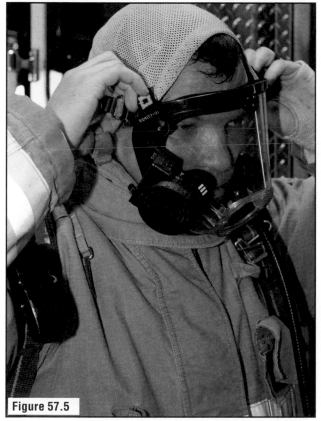

Figure 57.5

Figure 57.7

Figure 57.8

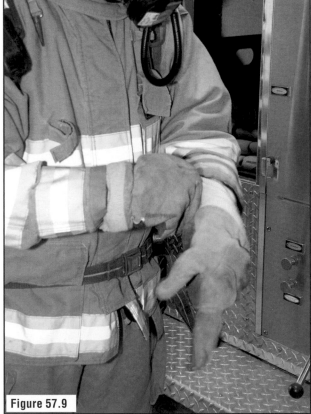

Figure 57.9

Doff SCBA

Step 1: Loosen straps and remove SCBA **(Figures 58.1 and 58.2)**.

Step 2: Close cylinder valve completely.

Step 3: Bleed air from high- and low- pressure hoses. Listen for low air alarm activation **(Figure 58.3)**.

Step 4: Check air cylinder pressure and replace or refill cylinder if less than 90 percent of rated capacity.

Step 5: Return all straps, valves and components back to ready state **(Figure 58.4, p. 858)**.

Step 6: Inspect SCBA and facepiece for damage and need for cleaning **(Figure 58.5, p. 858)**.

Step 7: Clean equipment as needed, remove damaged equipment from service, and report to company officer, if applicable.

Step 8: Place SCBA back in storage area so that it is ready for immediate use.

Doff PPE

Step 1: Remove protective clothing **(Figure 58.6, p. 858)**.

Step 2: Inspect PPE for damage and need for cleaning **(Figure 58.7, p. 858)**.

Step 3: Clean equipment as needed, remove damaged equipment from service, and report to company officer, if applicable.

Step 4: Place clothing in a ready state **(Figure 58.8, p. 859)**.

Figure 58.2

Figure 58.1

Figure 58.3

Figure 58.4

Figure 58.6

Figure 58.5

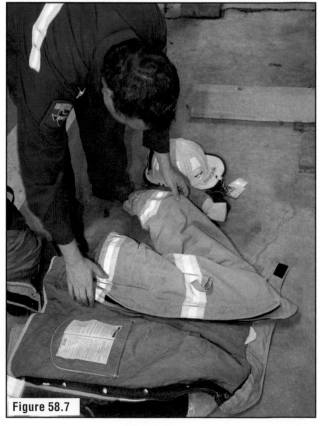

Figure 58.7

58

Doff thermal protective equipment, including SCBA, and prepare for reuse.
[NFPA 1081 5.2.1, 5.2.2, 6.1.2.1, 6.1.2.2]

SKILL SHEETS

Figure 58.8

Step 1: Identify all components of SCBA are present: harness assembly, cylinder, facepiece, and PASS device **(Figure 59.1)**.

Step 2: Inspect all components of SCBA for cleanliness and damage.

Step 3: Immediately clean dirty components if found. If damage is found, remove from service and report to company officer.

Step 4: Check that cylinder is full (90-100 percent capacity) **(Figure 59.2)**.

Step 5: Open the cylinder valve slowly; verify operation of the low-air alarm and the absence of audible air leaks **(Figure 59.3)**.

NOTE: On some SCBA, the audible alarm does not sound when the cylinder valve is opened.

Step 6: If air leaks are detected, determine if connections need to be tightened or if valves, donning switch, etc. need to be adjusted. Otherwise, SCBA with audible leaks due to malfunctions shall be removed from service, tagged, and reported to the company officer.

Step 7: Check that gauges and/or indicators (i.e. heads-up display) are providing similar pressure readings. Manufacturer's guidelines determine the acceptable range **(Figure 59.4)**.

Step 8: Check the function of all modes of PASS device.

Step 9: Don facepiece over the head and securely tighten the straps, pulling the straps straight backwards, not out to the side **(Figure 59.5)**.

Step 10: After straps are tightened, test the facepiece for a proper seal and operation of the exhalation valve **(Figure 59.6)**.

NOTE: Not all facepieces are designed for a seal check without the regulator being attached and activated.

Step 11: Don regulator and check function by taking several normal breaths **(Figure 59.7)**.

Step 12: Check bypass and/or purge valve, if applicable.

Step 13: Remove facepiece and prepare all components for immediate reuse **(Figure 59.8)**.

Step 14: Place SCBA components so that they can be accessed quickly for donning in the event of a reported emergency.

Figure 59.2

Figure 59.3

Figure 59.4

Figure 59.1

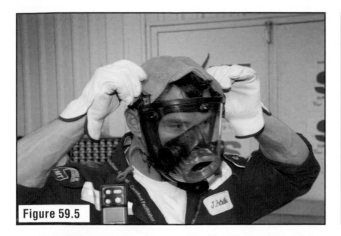

Figure 59.5

Figure 59.8

Figure 59.6

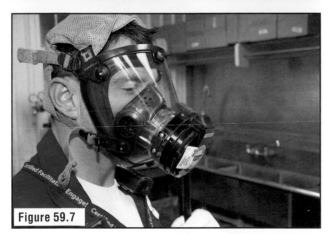

Figure 59.7

Step 1: Prepare cleaning solution, buckets, etc. according to manufacturer's guidelines and departmental policies **(Figure 60.1)**.

Step 2: Clean all components of SCBA unit according to manufacturer's guidelines and departmental policies **(Figure 60.2)**.

Step 3: After equipment is clean, inspect for damage. If any damage is noted, report in accordance with local SOPs **(Figure 60.3)**.

Step 4: Place all components in a manner and location so that they will dry.

Step 5: Assemble components so they are in a state of readiness **(Figure 60.4)**.

Figure 60.2

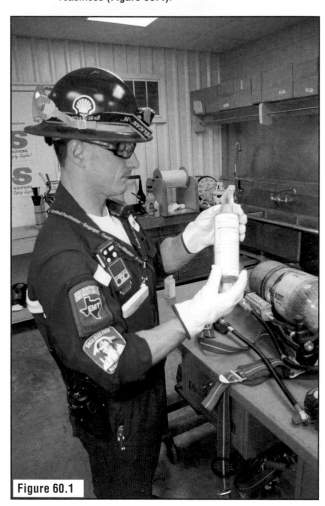

Figure 60.1

Figure 60.3

Figure 60.4

61

⌐Demonstrate the method for filling an SCBA cylinder from a cascade system or an SCBA/SAR compressor/purifier system. *[NFPA 1081, 5.3.10, 6.3.7]*

Using a Cascade System

Step 1: Check the hydrostatic test date and recommended fill pressure of the cylinder.

Step 2: Inspect the SCBA cylinder for damage such as deep nicks, cuts, gouges, or discoloration from heat. If the cylinder is damaged or is out of hydrostatic test date, remove it from service and tag it for further inspection and hydrostatic testing.

Step 3: Place the SCBA cylinder in a fragment-proof fill station **(Figure 61.1)**.

Step 4: Connect the fill hose to the cylinder and close bleed valve on fill hose **(Figure 61.2)**.

Step 5: Open the SCBA cylinder valve **(Figure 61.3)**.

Step 6: Open the valve at the fill hose, the valve at the cascade system manifold, or the valves at both locations if the system is so equipped. Check that the regulator setting is appropriate for the cylinder pressure **(Figures 61.4 and 61.5)**.

Step 7: Open the valve of the cascade cylinder that has the least pressure but that has more pressure than the SCBA cylinder **(Figure 61.6, p. 866)**.

Step 8: Close the cascade cylinder valve when the pressures of the SCBA and the cascade cylinder equalize.

    a. If the SCBA cylinder is not yet completely full, open the valve on the cascade cylinder with the next highest pressure.

    b. Repeat Step 8 until the SCBA cylinder is completely full.

Step 9: Close the valve or valves at the cascade system manifold and/or fill line if the system is so equipped.

Step 10: Close the SCBA cylinder valve **(Figure 61.7, p. 866)**.

Step 11: Open the hose bleed valve to bleed off excess pressure between the cylinder valve and the valve on the fill hose **(Figure 61.8, p. 866)**.

Step 12: Disconnect the fill hose from the SCBA cylinder.

Step 13: Remove the SCBA cylinder from the fill station.

Step 14: Return the cylinder to proper storage.

Using a Compressor/Purifier System

Step 1: Check the hydrostatic test date of the cylinder **(Figure 61.9, p. 866)**.

Step 2: Inspect the SCBA cylinder for damage such as deep nicks, cuts, gouges, or discoloration from heat. If the cylinder is damaged or out of hydrostatic test date, remove it from service and tag it for further inspection and hydrostatic testing **(Figure 61.10, p. 867)**.

Step 3: Place the SCBA cylinder in a shielded fill station **(Figure 61.11, p. 867)**.

Step 4: Connect the fill hose to the cylinder and close bleed valve on fill hose **(Figure 61.12, p. 867)**.

Step 5: Open the SCBA cylinder valve **(Figure 61.13, p. 867)**.

Step 6: Turn on the compressor/purifier and open the outlet valve **(Figure 61.14, p. 868)**.

Step 7: Set the cylinder pressure adjustment on the compressor, if applicable, or manifold to the desired full-cylinder pressure. If there is no cylinder pressure adjustment, watch the pressure gauge on the cylinder during filling to determine when it is full.

Step 8: Open the manifold valve, if applicable, and again check the fill pressure.

NOTE: All valves should be opened slowly.

Step 9: Open the fill station valve and begin filling the SCBA cylinder.

Step 10: Close the fill station valve when the cylinder is full.

Step 11: Close the SCBA cylinder valve **(Figure 61.15, p. 868)**.

Step 12: Open the hose bleed valve to bleed off excess pressure between the cylinder valve and valve on the fill station **(Figure 61.16, p. 868)**.

Step 13: Disconnect the fill hose from the SCBA cylinder **(Figure 61.17, p. 868)**.

Step 14: Remove the SCBA cylinder from the fill station and return the cylinder to proper storage **(Figure 61.18, p. 869)**.

Figure 61.1

61

Demonstrate the method for filling an SCBA cylinder from a cascade system or an SCBA/SAR compressor/purifier system. *[NFPA 1081, 5.3.10, 6.3.7]*

SKILL SHEETS

Figure 61.2

Figure 61.4

Figure 61.3

Figure 61.5

61

Demonstrate the method for filling an SCBA cylinder from a cascade system or an SCBA/SAR compressor/purifier system. *[NFPA 1081, 5.3.10, 6.3.7]*

SKILL SHEETS

Figure 61.6

Figure 61.8

Figure 61.7

Figure 61.9

61

Demonstrate the method for filling an SCBA cylinder from a cascade system or an
SCBA/SAR compressor/purifier system. *[NFPA 1081, 5.3.10, 6.3.7]*

SKILL SHEETS

Figure 61.10

Figure 61.12

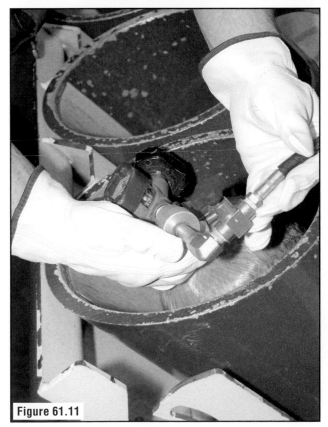

Figure 61.11

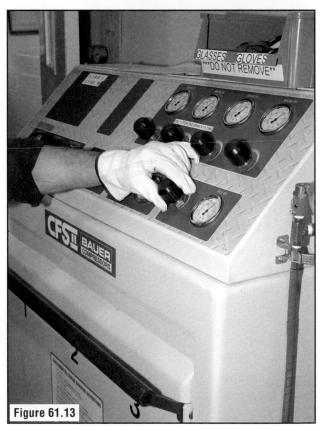

Figure 61.13

61

SKILL SHEETS

Demonstrate the method for filling an SCBA cylinder from a cascade system or an SCBA/SAR compressor/purifier system. *[NFPA 1081, 5.3.10, 6.3.7]*

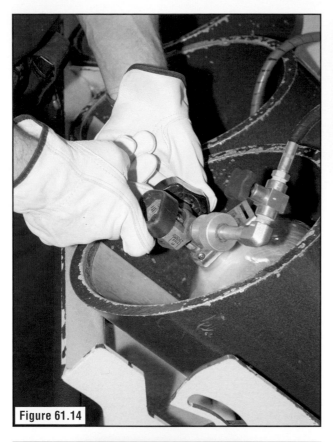

Figure 61.14

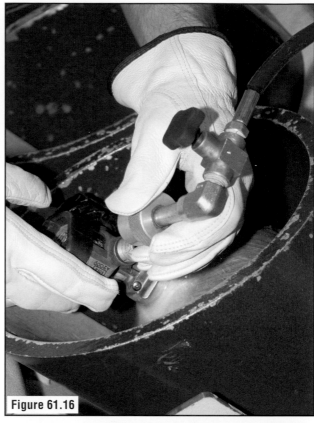

Figure 61.16

Figure 61.15

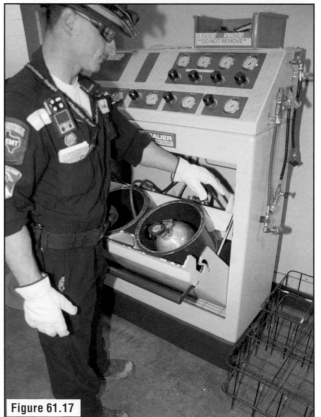

Figure 61.17

61

Demonstrate the method for filling an SCBA cylinder from a cascade system or an
SCBA/SAR compressor/purifier system. *[NFPA 1081, 5.3.10, 6.3.7]*

Figure 61.18

One-Person Method

Step 1: Place the SCBA unit on a firm, clean surface.

Step 2: Fully close the cylinder valve.

Step 3: Release air pressure from high- and low-pressure hoses **(Figure 62.1)**.

Step 4: Disconnect the high-pressure coupling from the cylinder **(Figure 62.2)**.

Step 5: Remove the empty cylinder from harness assembly **(Figure 62.3)**.

Step 6: Verify that replacement cylinder is 90-100 percent of rated capacity **(Figure 62.4)**.

Step 7: Check cylinder valve opening, the high-pressure hose fitting for debris, and the O-ring.

Step 8: Place the new cylinder into the harness assembly.

Step 9: Connect the high-pressure hose to the cylinder and hand-tighten.

Step 10: Slowly and fully open the cylinder valve and listen for an audible alarm and leaks as the system pressurizes **(Figure 62.5)**.

NOTE: On some SCBA, the audible alarm does not sound when the cylinder valve is opened. You must know the operation of your own particular unit.

Step 11: If air leaks are detected, determine if connections need to be tightened or if valves, donning switch, etc. need to be adjusted. Otherwise, SCBA with audible leaks due to malfunctions shall be removed from service, tagged, and reported to the officer.

Step 12: Don regulator and take normal breaths **(Figure 62.6)**.

Step 13: Check pressure reading on remote gauge and/or indicators and report reading.

Two-Person Method

Step 1: Disconnect the regulator from the facepiece or disconnect the low-pressure hose from the regulator **(Figure 62.7)**.

Step 2: Position the cylinder for easy access by kneeling down or bending over.

Step 3: Fully close the cylinder valve **(Figure 62.8, p. 872)**.

Step 4: Release the air pressure from the high- and low-pressure hoses.

Step 5: Disconnect the high-pressure coupling from the cylinder **(Figure 62.9, p. 872)**.

Step 6: Remove the empty cylinder from harness assembly.

Step 7: Inspect replacement cylinder and ensure that cylinder is 90-100 percent of rated capacity.

Step 8: Place new cylinder into the harness assembly **(Figure 62.10, p. 872)**.

Step 9: Check the cylinder valve opening and the high-pressure hose fitting for debris. Clear any debris by quickly opening and closing cylinder valve, and the O-ring.

Step 10: Connect the high-pressure hose to the cylinder and hand-tighten **(Figure 62.11, p. 872)**.

Step 11: Slowly open the cylinder valve fully and listen for an audible alarm and leaks as the system pressurizes **(Figure 62.12, p. 873)**.

NOTE: On some SCBA, the audible alarm does not sound when the cylinder valve is opened. You must know the operation of your own particular unit.

Step 12: If air leaks are detected, determine if connections need to be tightened or if valves, donning switch, etc. need to be adjusted. Otherwise, SCBA with audible leaks due to malfunctions shall be removed from service, tagged, and reported to the officer.

Step 13: Don regulator and take normal breaths.

Step 14: Check pressure reading on remote gauge and/or indicators and report reading.

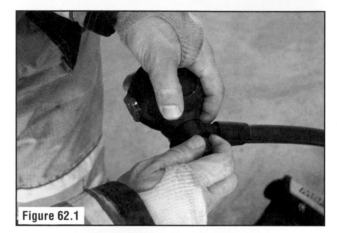

Figure 62.1

Figure 62.2

Figure 62.3

Figure 62.6

Figure 62.4

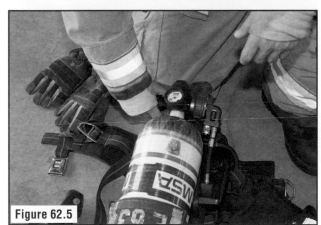

Figure 62.5

Figure 62.7

SKILL SHEETS

Figure 62.8

Figure 62.10

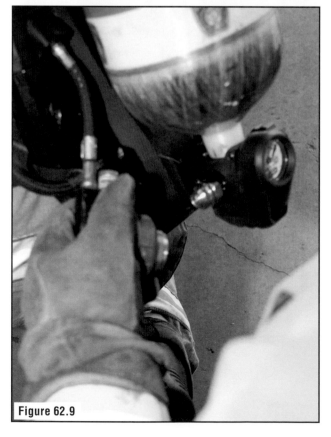

Figure 62.9

Figure 62.11

Figure 62.12

Scenario 1: If bypass resumes air flow

Step 1: Recognize the emergency **(Figure 63.1)**.

Step 2: Drop face to the ground and ensure cylinder valve is fully open, as well as opening regulator bypass valve as directed by local SOPs.

Step 3: If opening on bypass valve returns air supply, immediately exit the IDLH environment only opening the valve as needed **(Figure 63.2)**.

Step 4: Communicate your emergency with your crew and command via MAYDAY transmission.

Step 5: Activate PASS device if trapped or disoriented.

Scenario 2: If bypass results in no return of air flow

Step 1: Recognize the emergency.

Step 2: Drop face to the ground and ensure cylinder valve is fully open, as well as opening regulator bypass valve as directed by local SOPs **(Figure 63.3)**.

Step 3: If still unable to get air with bypass valve fully open, create gap between chin and mask seal to take breath.

NOTE: Ensure that regulator stays in place and protective hood stays sealed around lower lip of mask.

Step 4: Communicate your emergency with your crew and command via MAYDAY transmission.

Step 5: Activate PASS device **(Figure 63.4)**.

Step 6: Stay low to ground and attempt to escape the IDLH environment. Stop to take breaths as needed, ensuring protective hood remains in place to "filter" air as much as possible.

Step 7: If trapped, stay calm and limit breathing until rescue team arrives.

Scenario 3: If air emergency is due to other SCBA malfunction

Step 1: Recognize the emergency.

Step 2: Drop face to the ground and ensure cylinder valve is fully open, as well as opening regulator bypass valve as directed by local SOPs **(Figure 63.5)**.

Step 3: Stay low to the ground. Stop to take breaths as needed, ensuring protective hood remains in place to "filter" air as much as possible **(Figure 63.6)**.

Step 4: Communicate your emergency with your crew and command via MAYDAY transmission **(Figure 63.7, p. 876)**.

Step 5: Activate PASS device **(Figure 63.8, p. 876)**.

Step 6: Assess the situation.

    a. Can malfunction be fixed or bypassed?

    b. Can air from cylinder be used if removed from harness?

Step 7: Attempt to escape the IDLH environment **(Figure 63.9, p. 876)**.

Step 8: If trapped or disoriented, attempt to remove cylinder from pack and utilize air for breathing, conserving after each breath.

Figure 63.1

Figure 63.2

Figure 63.3

Figure 63.5

Figure 63.4

Figure 63.6

Figure 63.7

Figure 63.9

Figure 63.8

Side Technique

Step 1: Remain calm, follow SOPs, and activate an emergency call for assistance.

Step 2: Loosen waist strap and right shoulder strap.

Step 3: Remove right arm from right shoulder strap **(Figure 64.1)**.

Step 4: Shift SCBA to left side and tuck under left armpit.

Step 5: Ensure that waist strap remains buckled and left arm remains in shoulder strap **(Figure 64.2)**.

Step 6: Use tool to sound other side of the wall before exiting room.

Step 7: With SCBA tucked tightly under left armpit, lay on right side to create a low profile and attempt escape through restricted opening **(Figure 64.3)**.

SCBA-First Technique

Step 1: Remain calm, follow SOPs, and activate an emergency call for assistance.

Step 2: Once opening has been made, sound floor on the other side of the opening to ensure safety.

Step 3: Sit with SCBA and back toward the opening.

Step 4: Place one arm and SCBA cylinder into the opening **(Figure 64.4, p. 878)**.

Step 5: Using a backstroke technique, swim other arm through the opening **(Figure 64.5, p. 878)**.

Step 6: Using both arms and wall board for leverage, pull through the space **(Figure 64.6, p. 878)**.

Figure 64.2

Figure 64.1

Figure 64.3

Figure 64.4

Figure 64.6

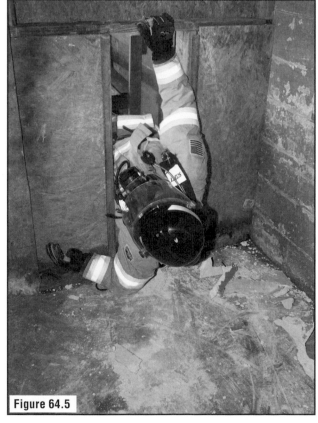

Figure 64.5

65

Exit a hazardous area as a member of a team to a safe haven during vision-obscured conditions.
[NFPA 1081, 5.2.8, 6.2.5]

SKILL SHEETS

NOTE: Instructors must provide a scenario with vision obscured conditions when testing above the incipient level.

Step 1: Recognize the need for evacuation **(Figure 65.1)**.

Step 2: Communicate with appropriate personnel **(Figure 65.2)**.

Step 3: Initiate emergency evacuation methods.

Step 4: Identify hazards.

Step 5: Follow hoseline or guide line to move back toward the entrance of the hazardous area or a safe haven in vision impaired conditions.

Step 6: Monitor air supply **(Figure 65.3)**.

Step 7: Ensure all team members are accounted for and the team remains intact **(Figure 65.4)**.

Figure 65.3

Figure 65.1

Figure 65.2

Figure 65.4

Step 1: Form a loop in the rope **(Figure 66.1)**.

Step 2: Insert the end of the rope through the loop **(Figure 66.2)**.

Step 3: Dress the knot by pulling on both ends of the rope at the same time **(Figure 66.3)**.

Figure 66.1

Figure 66.2

Figure 66.3

Step 1: Select enough rope to form the size of the loop desired.

Step 2: Form an overhand loop in the standing part **(Figure 67.1)**.

Step 3: Pass the working end upward through the loop **(Figure 67.2)**.

Step 4: Pass the working end over the top of the loop under the standing part **(Figure 67.3)**.

Step 5: Bring the working end completely around the standing part and down through the loop.

Step 6: Pull the knot snugly into place, forming an inside bowline with the working end on the inside of the loop **(Figure 67.4)**.

Step 7: Secure the bowline with an overhand safety **(Figure 67.5)**.

Figure 67.1

Figure 67.2

Figure 67.3

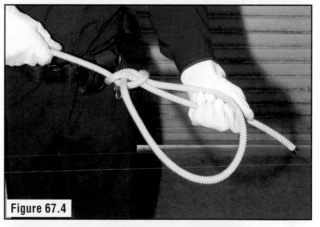

Figure 67.4

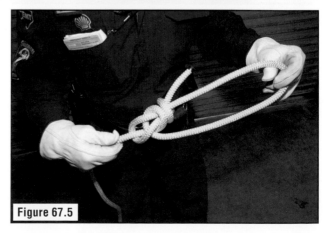

Figure 67.5

Step 1: Form a loop in your left hand with the working end to the right, crossing under the standing part **(Figure 68.1)**.

Step 2: Form another loop in your right hand (creating a round turn) with the working end crossing under the standing part **(Figure 68.2)**.

Step 3: Slide the right-hand loop on top of the left hand loop **(Figure 68.3)**.

Step 4: Hold the two loops together at the rope forming the clove hitch **(Figure 68.4)**.

Step 5: Slide the knot over the object **(Figure 68.5)**.

Step 6: Pull the ends in opposite directions to tighten.

Step 7: Secure with an overhand safety **(Figure 68.6)**.

Figure 68.4

Figure 68.1

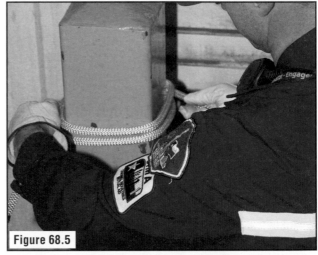

Figure 68.5

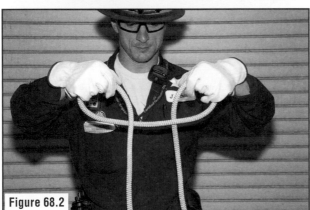

Figure 68.2

Figure 68.3

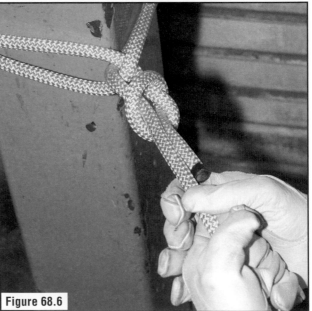

Figure 68.6

Step 1: Make a bight with the rope **(Figure 69.1)**.

Step 2: Pass the working end completely around the standing part **(Figure 69.2)**.

Step 3: Insert the end of the rope back through the bight.

Step 4: Dress the knot by pulling on both the working end and standing part of the rope at the same time **(Figure 69.3)**.

Step 5: Secure with an overhand safety as needed **(Figure 69.4)**.

Figure 69.3

Figure 69.4

Figure 69.1

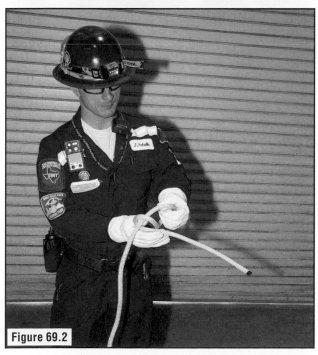

Figure 69.2

Step 1: Form a bight in the working end of the rope **(Figure 70.1)**.

Step 2: Pass the bight over the standing part to form a loop.

Step 3: Pass the bight under the standing part and then over the loop and down through it; this forms the figure-eight **(Figure 70.2)**.

Step 4: Extend the bight through the knot to whatever size working loop is needed.

Step 5: Dress the knot **(Figure 70.3)**.

Step 6: Secure with an overhand safety as needed **(Figure 70.4)**.

Figure 70.1

Figure 70.2

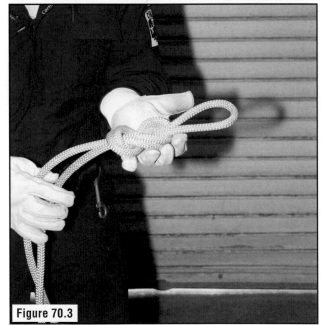

Figure 70.3

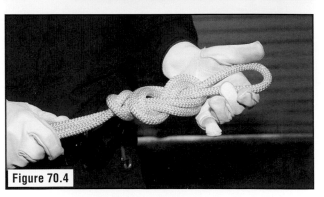

Figure 70.4

Step 1: Tie a loose figure-eight knot **(Figure 71.1)**.

Step 2: Pass the tail end of the rope around the object to be secured **(Figure 71.2)**.

Step 3: Follow the original figure-eight around the entire knot in reverse **(Figure 71.3)**.

Step 4: Exit the rope beside the standing end to complete the knot.

Step 5: Dress the knot **(Figure 71.4)**.

Step 6: Secure with an overhand safety as needed **(Figure 71.5)**.

Figure 71.3

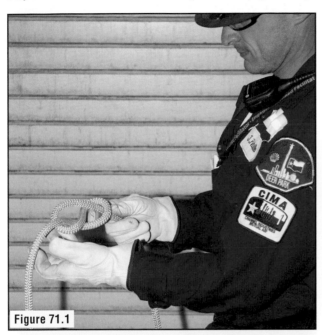

Figure 71.1

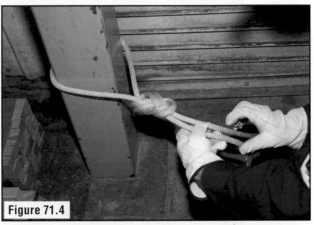

Figure 71.4

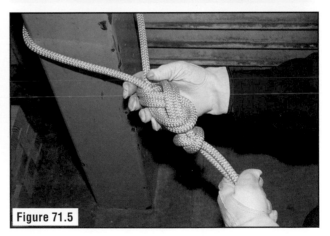

Figure 71.5

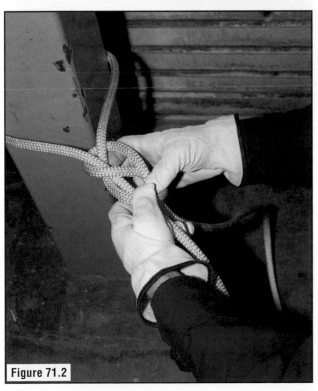

Figure 71.2

Step 1: Tie an overhand knot loosely in the end of the webbing **(Figure 72.1)**.

Step 2: Take the opposite end of the webbing and retrace the overhand knot **(Figures 72.2, 72.3, and 72.4)**.

Step 3: Tighten by pulling both working ends while holding the ends with your thumbs **(Figure 72.5)**.

Step 4: Dress the water knot so it lays flat and no webbing is twisted **(Figure 72.6)**.

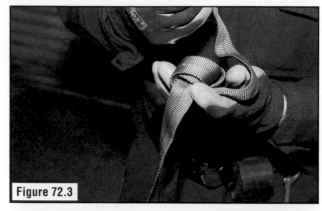

Figure 72.3

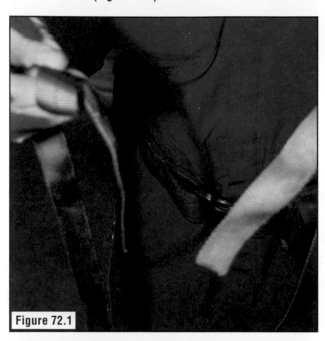

Figure 72.1

Figure 72.4

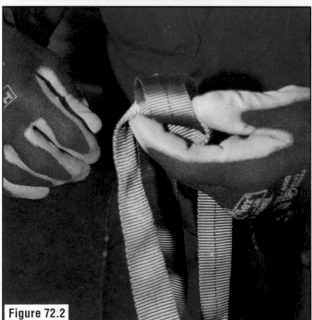

Figure 72.2

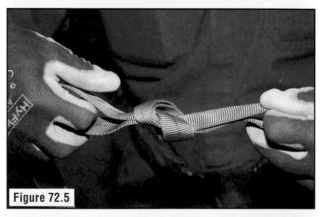

Figure 72.5

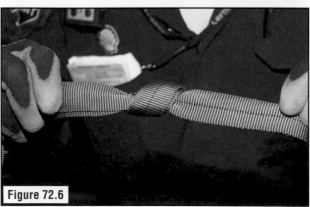

Figure 72.6

Step 1: Lower an appropriate length of rope from the intended destination of the axe **(Figure 73.1)**.

Step 2: Tie a clove hitch or approved knot.

NOTE: If the rope has a loop in the end, the loop may be used instead of a clove hitch.

Step 3: Slide the clove hitch or approved knot down the axe handle to the axe head. The excess running end of the rope becomes the tag/guide line **(Figure 73.2)**.

Step 4: Loop the working end of the rope around the head of the axe and back up the handle **(Figure 73.3)**.

Step 5: Tie a half-hitch or approved knot on the handle a few inches (mm) above the clove hitch.

Step 6: Tie a second half-hitch or approved knot on the handle a few inches (mm) above the first half-hitch **(Figure 73.4, p. 888)**.

Step 7: Hoist the axe **(Figure 73.5, p. 888)**.

Figure 73.2

Figure 73.1

Figure 73.3

Figure 73.4

Figure 73.5

Step 1: Lower an appropriate length of rope from the intended destination of the pike pole **(Figure 74.1)**.

Step 2: Tie a clove hitch or approved knot around the pole opposite the head **(Figure 74.2)**.

Step 3: Leave enough excess running end so that it becomes the tag/guide line.

Step 4: Tie a half-hitch or approved knot around the pike pole under the pike hook **(Figure 74.3)**.

Step 5: Tie a second half-hitch or approved knot around the pike pole under the pike hook **(Figure 74.4, p. 890)**.

Step 6: Hoist the pike pole **(Figure 74.5, p. 890)**.

Figure 74.2

Figure 74.1

Figure 74.3

Figure 74.4

Figure 74.5

Step 1: Lower an appropriate length of rope from the intended destination of the ladder.

Step 2: Make a large loop in the end of the rope using a figure-eight on a bight **(Figure 75.1)**.

Step 3: Place the closed loop under the ladder and bring it up between the rung about one-third the distance from the hoisting end **(Figure 75.2)**.

Step 4: Open the loop and place it over the tip of the ladder.

Step 5: Arrange the standing part under the ladder rungs.

Step 6: Tighten the loop around the beams, pulling the standing part of the rope up behind rungs toward ladder tip **(Figure 75.3)**.

Step 7: Tie a tag/guide line to the ladder **(Figure 75.4)**.

Step 8: Hoist the ladder **(Figure 75.5)**.

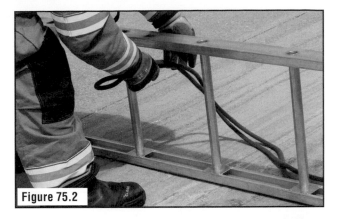

Figure 75.2

Figure 75.3

Figure 75.4

Figure 75.1

Figure 75.5

Step 1: Lower an appropriate length of rope from the intended destination of the hoseline.

Step 2: Fold the nozzle end of the hoseline back over the rest of the hose so that an overlap of 4 to 5 feet (1.2 to 1.5 m) is formed **(Figure 76.1)**.

Step 3: Tie a clove hitch, with an overhand safety knot, around the tip of the nozzle and the hose it is folded against so that they are lashed together **(Figures 76.2 and 76.3)**.

Step 4: Place a half-hitch on the doubled hose about 12 inches (300 mm) from the loop end **(Figure 76.4)**.

Step 5: Hoist hoseline **(Figure 76.5)**.

Figure 76.3

Figure 76.1

Figure 76.4

Figure 76.2

Figure 76.5

Step 1: Lower an appropriate length of rope from the intended destination of the power saw.

Step 2: Secure the rope to the handle of the power saw using a figure-eight on a bight or approved knot **(Figures 77.1 and 77.2)**.

Step 3: Leave enough excess running end so that it becomes the tag/guide line **(Figure 77.3)**.

Step 4: Hoist the power saw **(Figure 77.4)**.

Figure 77.3

Figure 77.1

Figure 77.2

Figure 77.4

Step 1: Remove the unit from the apparatus, and move it to the appropriate location, if applicable **(Figure 78.1)**.

> **WARNING:** Avoid areas containing potentially flammable vapors. Be sure that exhaust fumes are directed away from the working area.

Step 2: Check the on/off switch, fuel level, fuel switch, and the choke **(Figure 78.2)**.

Step 3: Start the unit **(Figure 78.3)**.

Step 4: When the power supply unit is running smoothly, connect power cords for the tools to be used.

NOTE: Check to ensure GFCI is working properly, if applicable.

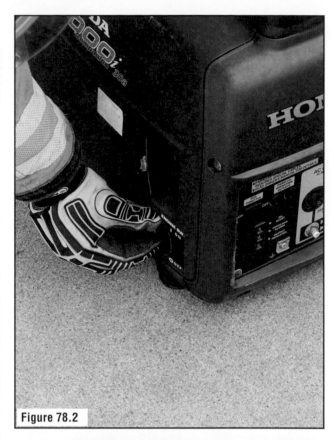

Figure 78.2

Figure 78.1

Figure 78.3

Set Up Apparatus-mounted Lights

Step 1: Unlock the light poles **(Figure 79.1)**.

Step 2: Extend lights to the appropriate height **(Figure 79.2)**.

Step 3: Reset GFCI devices, if necessary.

Step 4: Turn on the lights **(Figure 79.3)**.

Step 5: Adjust direction and angle of the lights in order to best illuminate the scene **(Figure 79.4, p. 896)**.

Set Up Portable Lights

Step 1: Remove portable lights from apparatus.

Step 2: Remove power cord reels or extend power cords from apparatus-mounted reels.

Step 3: Position the portable lights in order to best illuminate the scene **(Figure 79.5, p. 896)**.

Step 4: Connect the lights to power cords **(Figure 79.6, p. 896)**.

Step 5: If power cords are not hard-wired to the apparatus electrical system, plug in power cords to power outlets.

Step 6: Reset GFCI devices, if necessary.

Step 7: Turn on the lights **(Figure 79.7, p. 896)**.

Step 8: Adjust direction and angle of the lights in order to best illuminate the scene **(Figure 79.8, p. 896)**.

Figure 79.2

Figure 79.1

Figure 79.3

Figure 79.4

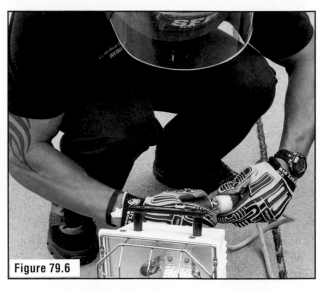

Figure 79.6

Figure 79.5

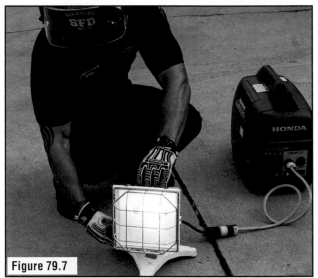

Figure 79.7

Figure 79.8

Step 1: Visually inspect the work area **(Figure 80.1)**.

  a. Inspect terrain for solid, level footing.

  b. Inspect overhead for electrical wires and obstructions.

Step 2: Stand at lifting point near the center of the ladder.

Step 3: Kneel beside the ladder.

Step 4: Grasp the ladder beam **(Figure 80.2)**.

Step 5: Place the ladder on the beam **(Figure 80.3)**.

Step 6: Stand while shouldering the ladder.

Step 7: Position the ladder for carrying.

  a. Secure the upper beam on the shoulder.

  b. Lower the butt of the ladder slightly.

  c. Steady the ladder with both hands.

Step 8: Carry the ladder forward toward the objective **(Figure 80.4)**.

Figure 80.3

Figure 80.1

Figure 80.4

Figure 80.2

Low-Shoulder Method

Step 1: Visually inspect the work area **(Figure 81.1)**.

   a. Inspect terrain for solid, level footing.

   b. Inspect overhead for electrical wires and obstructions.

Step 2: Both fire brigade members: Kneel beside the ladder, facing the same direction.

Step 3: Grasp the ladder beam.

Step 4: Place the ladder on the beam.

Step 5: Stand while shouldering the ladder **(Figure 81.2)**.

Step 6: Position the ladder for carrying.

   a. Secure the upper beam on the shoulder.

   b. Lower the butt of the ladder slightly.

   c. Steady the ladder with both hands.

Step 7: Carry the ladder forward toward the objective **(Figure 81.3)**.

Figure 81.3

Arm's Length On Edge Method

Step 1: Visually inspect the work area.

   a. Inspect terrain for solid, level footing.

   b. Inspect overhead for electrical wires and obstructions.

Step 2: Both fire brigade members: Kneel beside the ladder, facing the same direction.

Step 3: Grasp the ladder beam **(Figure 81.4)**.

Step 4: Place the ladder on the beam **(Figure 81.5)**.

Step 5: Stand and lift the ladder to arm's length.

Step 6: Position the ladder for carrying.

   a. Grasp the beam.

   b. Place the ladder against your body.

Step 7: Carry the ladder forward toward objective **(Figure 81.6)**.

Figure 81.4

Figure 81.1

Figure 81.2

Figure 81.5

Figure 81.6

NOTE: These raises begin from a carry position, with the ladder beam resting on your shoulder.

NOTE: After raising the ladder, it may be used to work from or be lowered.

CAUTION: If working from the ladder, make sure it is properly secured, either by another student or by mechanical means.

Single Ladder – Beam Method

Step 1: Visually inspect the work area **(Figure 82.1, p. 900)**.

    a. Inspect terrain for solid, level footing.

    b. Inspect overhead for electrical wires and obstructions.

Step 2: With the ladder beam still on your shoulder, lower one spur of the butt end to the ground approximately ¼ the usable height from the building **(Figure 82.2, p. 900)**.

Step 3: Raise the ladder and rest both spurs on the ground.

Step 4: Rotate the ladder until both beams are parallel to the building **(Figure 82.3, p. 900)**.

Step 5: Place the ladder against the building **(Figure 82.4, p. 900)**.

Step 6: While supporting the ladder against the building, pull the butt end away from the building to an appropriate climbing angle **(Figure 82.5, p. 900)**.

Step 7: Lower the ladder, reversing the raising procedure.

    a. Inspect the overhead for wires and obstructions that may have changed during operations.

    b. Rotate the ladder away from the building, if necessary.

    c. Lower the ladder and place it flat on the ground.

Single Ladder – Flat Method

Step 1: Visually inspect the work area.

    a. Inspect terrain for solid, level footing.

    b. Inspect overhead for electrical wires and obstructions.

Step 2: Place the ladder flat on the ground perpendicular to the wall **(Figure 82.6, p. 901)**.

Step 3: Slide the ladder so that both spurs are resting against the wall **(Figure 82.7, p. 901)**.

Step 4: Position at the tip of the ladder.

Step 5: Grasp the top rung of the ladder and lift **(Figure 82.8, p. 901)**.

Step 6: Position beneath the ladder and grasp the rungs.

Step 7: Raise the ladder and place it flat against the building **(Figure 82.9, p. 901)**.

Step 8: While supporting the ladder against the building, pull the butt end away from the building to an appropriate climbing angle **(Figure 82.10, p. 901)**.

Step 9: Lower the ladder, reversing the raising procedure.

    a. Inspect the overhead for wires and obstructions that may have changed during operations.

    b. Rotate the ladder away from the building, if necessary.

    c. Lower the ladder and place it flat on the ground.

Extension Ladder – Beam Method

Step 1: Visually inspect the work area **(Figure 82.11, p. 901)**.

    a. Inspect terrain for solid, level footing.

    b. Inspect overhead for electrical wires and obstructions.

Step 2: With the ladder beam still on your shoulder, lower one spur of the butt end to the ground approximately ¼ the usable height from the building **(Figure 82.12, p. 902)**.

Step 3: Raise the ladder and rest both spurs on the ground.

Step 4: Rotate the ladder until both beams are parallel to the building and the fly is properly positioned **(Figure 82.13, p. 902)**.

Step 5: Place the ladder against the building.

Step 6: While maintaining control of the ladder, untie and grasp the halyard.

Step 7: Control the halyard and extend the fly section to the desired elevation **(Figure 82.14, p. 902)**.

Step 8: Engage the ladder locks.

Step 9: While supporting the ladder against the building, pull the butt end away from the building to an appropriate climbing angle **(Figure 82.15, p. 902)**.

Step 10: Secure the halyard **(Figure 82.16, p. 903)**.

Step 11: Lower the ladder, reversing the raising procedure.

    a. Inspect the overhead for wires and obstructions that may have changed during the fire.

    b. Rotate the ladder away from the building, if necessary.

    c. Lower the ladder using a hand-under-hand motion and place it flat on the ground.

Extension Ladder – Flat Method

Step 1: Visually inspect the work area.

    a. Inspect terrain for solid, level footing.

    b. Inspect overhead for electrical wires and obstructions.

Step 2: Place the ladder flat on the ground perpendicular to the wall.

Step 3: Slide the ladder so that both spurs are resting against the wall **(Figure 82.17, p. 903)**.

Step 4: Position at the tip of the ladder.

Step 5: Grasp the top rung of the ladder and lift.

Step 6: Position beneath the ladder and grasp the rungs.

Step 7: Raise the ladder, placing it flat against the building **(Figure 82.18, p. 903)**.

Step 8: Pull the butt of the ladder slightly away from the building.

Step 9: While maintaining control of the ladder, untie and grasp the halyard **(Figure 82.19, p. 903)**.

Step 10: Control the halyard and extend the fly section to the desired elevation.

Step 11: Engage the ladder locks.

Step 12: While supporting the ladder against the building, pull the butt end away from the building to an appropriate climbing angle **(Figure 82.20, p. 903)**.

Step 13: Secure the halyard.

Step 14: Lower the ladder, reversing the raising procedure.

    a. Inspect the overhead for wires and obstructions that may have changed during operations.

    b. Rotate the ladder away from the building, if necessary.

    c. Lower the ladder using a hand-under-hand motion and place it flat on the ground.

Figure 82.1

Figure 82.2

Figure 82.3

Figure 82.4

Figure 82.5

Figure 82.6

Figure 82.9

Figure 82.7

Figure 82.10

Figure 82.8

Figure 82.11

Figure 82.12

Figure 82.14

Figure 82.13

Figure 82.15

Figure 82.16

Figure 82.19

Figure 82.17

Figure 82.20

Figure 82.18

NOTE: These raises begin from a carry position, with the ladder beam resting on your shoulder.

NOTE: These raises begin from a carry position, with the ladder resting on the shoulder. After raising the ladder, it may be used to work from or be lowered.

> **CAUTION:** If working from the ladder, make sure it is properly secured, either by another firefighter or by mechanical means.

Beam Method

Step 1: Visually inspect the work area **(Figure 83.1)**.

    a. Inspect terrain for solid, level footing.

    b. Inspect overhead for electrical wires and obstructions.

Step 2: Fire brigade member #1: Place the ladder beam on the ground approximately ¼ the usable height from the building.

Step 3: Fire brigade member #2: Rest the tip of the lower ladder beam on one shoulder.

Step 4: Fire brigade member #1: Place one foot on the lower beam at the butt end.

Step 5: Fire brigade member #1: Grasp the upper beam with hands apart and the other foot extended back to act as a counterbalance.

Step 6: Fire brigade member #2: Advance down the beam toward the butt end until the ladder is in a vertical position **(Figure 83.2)**.

Step 7: Both fire brigade members: Stand on opposite sides of the ladder.

Step 8: Rotate the ladder to properly position the fly section **(Figure 83.3)**.

Step 9: Untie and grasp the halyard.

Step 10: Control the halyard and extend the fly section to the desired elevation **(Figure 83.4)**.

Step 11: Engage the ladder locks.

Step 12: Place the ladder against the building, maintaining ladder balance.

Step 13: While supporting the ladder against the building, pull the butt end away from the building to an appropriate climbing angle **(Figure 83.5)**.

Step 14: Secure the halyard.

Step 15: Lower the ladder, reversing the raising procedure.

    a. Inspect the overhead for wires and obstructions that may have changed during the fire.

    b. Rotate the ladder away from the building, if necessary.

    c. Lower the ladder using a hand-under-hand motion and place it flat on the ground.

Flat Method

Step 1: Visually inspect the work area.

    a. Inspect terrain for solid, level footing.

    b. Inspect overhead for electrical wires and obstructions.

Step 2: Both fire brigade members: Place the ladder flat on the ground with the butt end perpendicular to and approximately ¼ the usable height from the building **(Figure 83.6, p. 906)**.

Step 3: Fire brigade member #2: Lift the tip of the ladder and position beneath it **(Figure 83.7, p. 906)**.

Step 4: Fire brigade member #1: Heel the ladder.

Step 5: Fire brigade member #1: Crouch to grasp a convenient rung or the beams with both hands.

Step 6: Fire brigade member #1: Lean back.

Step 7: Raise the ladder until it is in a vertical position **(Figure 83.8, p. 906)**.

Step 8: Both fire brigade members: Stand on opposite sides of the ladder.

Step 9: Both fire brigade members: Heel the ladder by placing toes against the beams.

Step 10: Fire brigade member #2: Grasp the beams, ensuring that hands and fingers are on the outside of the beam.

Step 11: Rotate the ladder to properly position the fly section.

Step 12: Untie and grasp the halyard.

Step 13: Control the halyard and extend the fly section to the desired elevation **(Figure 83.9, p. 906)**.

Step 14: Engage the ladder locks.

Step 15: Both fire brigade members: Place the ladder against the building, maintaining ladder balance **(Figure 83.10, p. 906)**.

Step 16: While supporting the ladder against the building, pull the butt end away from the building to an appropriate climbing angle **(Figure 83.11, p. 906)**.

Step 17: Secure the halyard.

Step 18: Lower the ladder, reversing the raising procedure.

    a. Inspect the overhead for wires and obstructions that may have changed during the fire.

    b. Rotate the ladder away from the building, if necessary.

    c. Lower the ladder using a hand-under-hand motion and place it flat on the ground.

Figure 83.1

Figure 83.2

Figure 83.3

Figure 83.4

Figure 83.5

Figure 83.6

Figure 83.9

Figure 83.7

Figure 83.10

Figure 83.8

Figure 83.11

Shift a Ladder – One-Fire brigade member Method

Step 1: Visually inspect the work area **(Figure 84.1, p. 908)**.

    a. Inspect terrain for solid, level footing.

    b. Inspect overhead for electrical wires and obstructions.

Step 2: Face the ladder.

Step 3: Heel the ladder **(Figure 84.2, p. 908)**.

Step 4: Grasp the beams.

Step 5: Slide the butt end of the ladder 1 to 2 feet (0.3 m to 0.6 m) in the desired direction. Maintain control of the ladder and watch the tip at all times **(Figure 84.3, p. 908)**.

Step 6: Heel the ladder.

Step 7: Bring hands higher on the beams and slide the tip of the ladder until it is vertical. If necessary, lift the tip slightly off of the building.

Step 8: Repeat until the desired location is reached.

Step 9: Adjust the height and angle of the ladder, if necessary **(Figure 84.4, p. 908)**.

Shift a Ladder – Two-Fire brigade member Method

Step 1: Visually inspect the work area.

    a. Inspect terrain for solid, level footing.

    b. Inspect overhead for electrical wires and obstructions.

Step 2: Both fire brigade members: Position on opposite sides of the ladder **(Figure 84.5, p. 909)**.

Step 3: Face the ladder.

Step 4: Heel the ladder.

Step 5: Grasp the beams **(Figure 84.6, p. 909)**.

Step 6: Slide the butt end of the ladder 1 to 2 feet (0.3 m to 0.6 m) in the desired direction. Maintain control of the ladder and watch the tip at all times **(Figure 84.7, p. 909)**.

Step 7: Heel the ladder.

Step 8: Bring hands higher on the beams and slide the tip of the ladder until it is vertical. If necessary, lift the tip slightly off of the building.

Step 9: Repeat until the desired location is reached.

Step 10: Adjust the height and angle of the ladder, if necessary **(Figure 84.8, p. 909)**.

Pivot a Ladder – Two-fire brigade member Method

Step 1: Visually inspect the work area.

    a. Inspect terrain for solid, level footing.

    b. Inspect overhead for electrical wires and obstructions.

Step 2: Both fire brigade members: Stand on opposite sides of the ladder **(Figure 84.9, p. 910)**.

NOTE: Fire brigade member #1 is located on the side opposite the building and is in command of the operation.

Step 3: Both fire brigade members: Grasp the ladder beams.

Step 4: Fire brigade member #1: Place a foot against the side of the beam on which the ladder will pivot.

Step 5: Both fire brigade members: Tilt the ladder onto the pivot beam.

Step 6: Pivot the ladder 90 degrees, simultaneously adjusting positions as necessary **(Figure 84.10, p. 910)**.

Step 7: Repeat the process until the ladder is turned a full 180 degrees and the fly is properly positioned **(Figures 84.11 and 84.12, p. 910)**.

Step 8: Place the ladder against the building.

Figure 84.1

Figure 84.3

Figure 84.2

Figure 84.4

Figure 84.5

Figure 84.7

Figure 84.6

Figure 84.8

Figure 84.9

Figure 84.11

Figure 84.10

Figure 84.12

Step 1: Climb to the desired height.

Step 2: Advance one rung higher **(Figure 85.1)**.

Step 3: Slide the leg opposite the working side over and behind the target rung **(Figure 85.2)**.

Step 4: Hook your foot on the rung or on the beam **(Figure 85.3)**.

Step 5: Rest on your thigh.

Step 6: Step down with the opposite leg **(Figure 85.4)**.

Figure 85.3

Figure 85.1

Figure 85.2

Figure 85.4

Step 1: Don the ladder belt or safety harness, securing it tightly around body **(Figure 86.1)**.

Step 2: Climb the ladder to the desired height **(Figure 86.2)**.

NOTE: The hook may be moved to one side while climbing.

Step 3: Upon reaching the desired height, center the hook with the body and attach it to a rung **(Figure 86.3)**.

Figure 86.2

Figure 86.1

Figure 86.3

One-Fire brigade member Method

Step 1: Deploy the hooks of the roof ladder **(Figure 87.1)**.

Step 2: Place the roof ladder against the ground ladder with the hooks facing out **(Figure 87.2)**.

Step 3: Climb the ground ladder until your shoulder is about two rungs above the midpoint of the roof ladder.

Step 4: Reach through the rungs of the roof ladder and hoist it onto your shoulder.

Step 5: Climb the ground ladder to the desired elevation **(Figure 87.3)**.

Step 6: Lock into the ladder using a leg lock or life safety harness.

Step 7: Place the roof ladder on the roof and push it toward the ridge line **(Figure 87.4)**.

Step 8: Lay the ladder flat and secure the hooks over the ridge line **(Figure 87.5)**.

Two-Fire brigade member Method

Step 1: Deploy the hooks of the roof ladder **(Figure 87.6, p. 914)**.

Step 2: Climb the ground ladder several feet.

Step 3: Receive the roof ladder from another student **(Figure 87.7, p. 914)**.

Step 4: Climb the ground ladder the remainder of the distance to the desired elevation, if necessary.

Step 5: Lock into the ladder using a leg lock or life safety harness.

Step 6: Place the roof ladder on the roof and push it toward the ridge line **(Figure 87.8, p. 914)**.

Step 7: Lay the roof ladder flat and secure the hooks over the ridge line **(Figure 87.9, p. 914)**.

Figure 87.1

Figure 87.2

Figure 87.3

Figure 87.4

Figure 87.5

Figure 87.6

Figure 87.8

Figure 87.7

Figure 87.9

NOTE: A rescue manikin is used to practice this skill. A conscious victim will position his or her arms and legs on the ladder beams and rungs during descent.

Assist an Unconscious Victim

Step 1: Position on the ladder to receive the victim.

Step 2: Position the victim facing the rescuer **(Figure 88.1)**.

Step 3: Maintain control of the victim.

NOTE: Examples of methods to maintain control of the victim may include:

    a. On-the-knee method **(Figure 88.2)**

    b. Cross-body method **(Figure 88.3)**

    c. Modified cross-body method **(Figure 88.4, p. 916)**

Step 4: Descend the ladder one rung at a time. Support the victim during descent.

Assist a Conscious Victim

Step 1: Position on the ladder to receive the victim.

Step 2: Position the victim facing the ladder rungs **(Figure 88.5, p. 916)**.

Step 3: Maintain control of the victim.

    a. Place forearms under the victim's armpits **(Figure 88.6, p. 916)**.

    b. Place hands on ladder beams.

Step 4: Descend the ladder one rung at a time. Support and reassure the victim during descent **(Figure 88.7, p. 916)**.

Figure 88.2

Figure 88.1

Figure 88.3

Figure 88.4

Figure 88.6

Figure 88.5

Figure 88.7

> **CAUTION:** Students must maintain communication and coordinate actions at all times during forcible entry. Maintain control of the door at all times.

NOTE: Always remember to "try before you pry" **(Figure 89.1)**.

Two-Fire Brigade Member Method

Step 1: Size up the door and lock.

Step 2: Fire brigade member #1: Place the fork of the Halligan just above or below the lock with the bevel side of the fork against the door **(Figure 89.2)**.

Step 3: Fire brigade member #1: Give the command to strike when ready and reposition the Halligan as necessary between strikes.

Step 4: Fire brigade member #2: As Fire brigade member #1 commands, strike the Halligan with the back of the flat-head axe until commanded to stop **(Figure 89.3, p. 918)**.

Step 5: Make sure the fork end has penetrated between the door and the doorjamb and that approximately three-fourths of the forked end is extending past the door.

Step 6: Exert pressure on the Halligan toward the door, forcing it open **(Figure 89.4, p. 918)**.

Cut-the-Lock-Out-of-the-Door Method

Step 1: Size up the door and lock **(Figure 89.5, p. 918)**.

Step 2: With a rotary saw, cut the lock out using either a three-sided cut or a v-cut **(Figure 89.6, p. 918)**.

Step 3: Remove the cut piece and knob from the door and move it out of the path of ingress **(Figure 89.7, p. 918)**.

Step 4: Open the door.

Figure 89.1

Figure 89.2

Figure 89.3

Figure 89.6

Figure 89.4

Figure 89.7

Figure 89.5

> **CAUTION:** Students must maintain communication and coordinate actions at all times during forcible entry. Maintain control of the door at all times.

NOTE: Always remember to "try before you pry."

Removing the Hinges Method

Step 1: Size up the door and lock.

Step 2: Place the fork end of the Halligan between the top hinge and the door **(Figure 90.1)**.

Step 3: Pry up or down **(Figure 90.2)**.

Step 4: If necessary, twist the Halligan from side to side to loosen the hinge mounting screws **(Figure 90.3)**.

Step 5: Pull the hinge clear of the door **(Figure 90.4, p. 920)**.

Step 6: Repeat to pry and remove the other hinges.

Step 7: Open the door.

Adz-end Method

Step 1: Size up the door and lock.

Step 2: Fire brigade member #1: Place the adz end of the Halligan just above or below the lock. If there are two locks, place the adz between the locks **(Figure 90.5, p. 920)**.

Step 3: Fire brigade member #2: Strike the Halligan using the flat-head axe on the surface behind the adz, driving the adz into the space between the door and the jamb and past the interior door jamb **(Figure 90.6, p. 920)**.

Step 4: Fire brigade member #1: Pry down and out, applying force to the forked end of the tool in order to separate the door from the jamb **(Figure 90.7, p. 920)**.

Step 5: Open the door.

Figure 90.2

Figure 90.1

Figure 90.3

Figure 90.4

Figure 90.6

Figure 90.5

Figure 90.7

NOTE: Always remember to "try before you pry."

Halligan Tool Hook End Method

Step 1: Fire brigade member #1: Insert the hook of the Halligan into the shackle of the lock **(Figure 91.1)**.

Step 2: Fire brigade member #1: Pull the lock out and away from the staple **(Figure 91.2)**.

Step 3: Fire brigade member #2: Strike the Halligan sharply with a flat-head axe to drive the hook through the lock shackle and break it **(Figure 91.3)**.

Halligan Tool Fork End Method

Step 1: Place the fork of the Halligan over the padlock shackle **(Figure 91.4)**.

Step 2: Twist the lock until the shackle or hasp breaks **(Figures 91.5 and 91.6, p. 922)**.

Bolt Cutters Method

Step 1: Cut the shackle of the padlock, the chain, or the staple with bolt cutters **(Figures 91.7 and 91.8, p. 922)**.

NOTE: Do not attempt to cut case-hardened lock shackles with bolt cutters.

Rotary Saw Method

Step 1: Position the lock against the door or frame, exposing both parts of the shackle **(Figure 91.9, p. 922)**.

Step 2: With a rotary saw, cut both shackles at the same time **(Figure 91.10, p. 922)**.

Step 3: Remove the shackle from the door hasp.

Figure 91.1

Figure 91.2

Figure 91.3

Figure 91.4

Figure 91.5

Figure 91.7

Figure 91.8

Figure 91.6

Figure 91.9

Figure 91.10

NOTE: Always remember to "try before you pry."

Step 1: Size up the situation **(Figure 92.1)**.

    a. Try the window first.

    b. Evaluate window construction.

Step 2: Break the window glass **(Figure 92.2)**.

    a. Single-paned windows: Start at the top of the pane.

    b. Multiple-paned windows: Start at the lowest pane of glass.

Figure 92.1

Step 3: Use the tool to clean all broken glass out of the frame **(Figure 92.3)**.

Figure 92.2

Figure 92.3

CAUTION: Students must maintain communication and coordinate actions at all times during forcible entry. Use safe glass breaking techniques when forcing entry through windows.

NOTE: Always remember to "try before you pry."

Step 1: Size up the situation **(Figure 93.1)**.

  a. Try the window first.

  b. Evaluate window construction.

Step 2: Insert the blade of an axe or other prying tool under the center of the bottom sash in line with the locking mechanism **(Figure 93.2)**.

Step 3: Pry upward on the tool handle to force the lock.

Step 4: Push the lower sash upward to open the window **(Figure 93.3)**.

Figure 93.1

Figure 93.2

Figure 93.3

CAUTION: Students must maintain communication and coordinate actions at all times during forcible entry. Confirm that utilities are off prior to forcing entry.

Wood-Framed Wall with Hand Tools

Step 1: Size up the situation.

    a. Confirm that no other existing entry points are available.

    b. Evaluate wall construction.

    c. Consider location of utilities.

Step 2: Remove siding, if necessary, and locate studs **(Figure 94.1)**.

Step 3: Cut an inspection hole (small triangle) and utilize it to ensure that the area is safe to continue forcing entry **(Figure 94.2)**.

Step 4: Make a cut large enough for entry. Studs may be removed, if necessary **(Figure 94.3, p. 926)**.

Step 5: Remove wall and insulation material with a hand tool and place it out of the traffic area.

Step 6: Use a hand tool to push inward and remove the interior wall covering.

Wood-Framed Wall with Rotary Saw or Chainsaw

Step 1: Size up the situation.

    a. Confirm that no other existing entry points are available.

    b. Evaluate wall construction.

    c. Consider location of utilities.

Step 2: Place the saw blade against the wall at about shoulder height **(Figure 94.4, p. 926)**.

Step 3: Cut diagonally to one side, ending about one foot (300 mm) off the ground **(Figure 94.5, p. 926)**.

Step 4: Make a diagonal cut of the same length to the other side **(Figure 94.6, p. 926)**.

Step 5: Make a horizontal cut that connects the two diagonal cuts **(Figure 94.7, p. 927)**.

Step 6: Use a sledgehammer, flat-head axe, or battering ram to knock the material out from between the cuts and place it out of the traffic area.

Step 7: Use a hand tool to push inward and remove the interior wall covering.

Metal Wall with Rotary Saw

Step 1: Size up the situation.

    a. Confirm that no other existing entry points are available.

    b. Evaluate wall construction.

    c. Consider location of utilities.

Step 2: Cut an inspection hole (small triangle) and utilize it to ensure that the area is safe to continue forcing entry **(Figure 94.8, p. 927)**.

Step 3: Locate wall studs (indicated by wall screws).

Step 4: Make a cut near the studs large enough for entry. Studs may be removed, if necessary **(Figure 94.9, p. 927)**.

Step 5: Use a hand tool to remove wall material and insulation and place it out of the traffic area **(Figure 94.10, p. 927)**.

Step 6: Use a hand tool to push inward and remove the interior wall covering.

Figure 94.1

Figure 94.2

Figure 94.3

Figure 94.4

Figure 94.5

Figure 94.6

Figure 94.7

Figure 94.8

Figure 94.9

Figure 94.10

Step 1: Place the victim on his or her back.

Step 2: Kneel at the victim's head **(Figure 95.1)**.

Step 3: Support the victim's head and neck.

NOTE: If head or neck injury is suspected, provide appropriate support for head during movement.

Step 4: Lift the victim's upper body into a sitting position **(Figure 95.2)**.

Step 5: With your right arm, reach under the victim's right arm, across his or her chest, and grasp the wrist of his or her left arm.

Step 6: Repeat for the victim's other arm **(Figure 95.3)**.

Step 7: Stand; the victim can now be eased down a stairway or ramp to safety **(Figure 95.4)**.

Figure 95.3

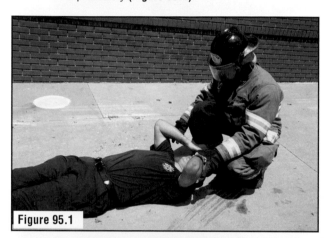

Figure 95.1

Figure 95.4

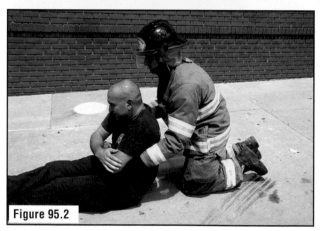

Figure 95.2

> **CAUTION:** Always make sure the victim's air supply is not compromised.

NOTE: All "victims" to be dragged should be mannikins in training scenarios.

Normal Drag Method

Step 1: Extend the DRD handle **(Figure 96.1)**.

Step 2: Place hand through the DRD handle **(Figure 96.2)**.

Step 3: Pull the victim to safety **(Figure 96.3, p. 930)**.

Belt or Harness Method

Step 1: Extend the DRD handle.

Step 2: Unbuckle the rescuer's waist strap of the SCBA and buckle it around the DRD loop or hook the rescuer's drag harness through the DRD loop **(Figure 96.4, p. 930)**.

Step 3: Position the DRD loop on the waist strap or harness so that it falls between the rescuer's legs.

Step 4: Get down on all fours in front of the victim, keeping the line between the legs.

Step 5: Crawl forward and drag the victim behind until safety is reached **(Figure 96.5, p. 930)**.

Tool – One brigade member method

Step 1: Extend the DRD handle.

Step 2: Place the handle of the tool through the DRD handle of the victim **(Figure 96.6, p. 930)**.

NOTE: Twisting the tool may help maintain DRD purchase on the tool.

Step 3: Drag the victim to safety, while keeping the angle of the handle end up to keep the DRD in place against the head of the tool **(Figure 96.7, p. 931)**.

Tool – Two brigade member method

Step 1: Extend the DRD handle.

Step 2: Brigade member #1: Place the handle of the tool through the DRD handle so that the loop rests in the middle of the bar.

Step 3: Brigade member #1: Grip the tool handle on one side of DRD loop.

Step 4: Brigade member #2: Grip the tool handle on the other side of the DRD loop.

Step 5: Brigade member #1 and Brigade member #2: Drag the victim to safety together, keeping the DRD loop in the middle of the handle between their hands **(Figure 96.8, p. 931)**.

Figure 96.1

Figure 96.2

Figure 96.3

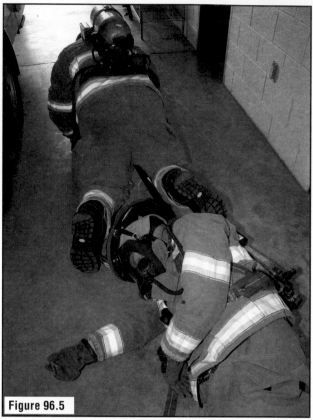

Figure 96.5

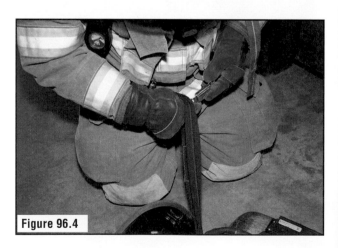

Figure 96.4

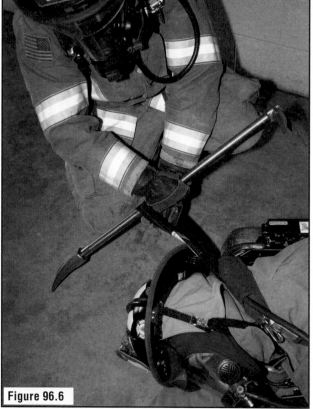

Figure 96.6

Figure 96.7

Figure 96.8

Step 1: Place the victim on his or her back **(Figure 97.1)**.

Step 2: Slide the large webbing loop under victim's head and chest so the loop is even with armpits **(Figure 97.2)**.

Step 3: Position the victim's arms so that they are outside the webbing.

Step 4: Pull the top of the large loop over the victim's head so that it is just past the head.

Step 5: Reach down through the large loop and under the victim's back and grab the webbing **(Figure 97.3)**.

Step 6: Pull the webbing up and through the loop so that each webbing loop is drawn snugly around the victim's shoulders **(Figure 97.4)**.

Step 7: Adjust hand placement on the webbing to support the victim's head **(Figure 97.5)**.

Step 8: Stand behind the victim and drag the victim to safety by pulling on the webbing loop **(Figure 97.6)**.

Figure 97.3

Figure 97.1

Figure 97.2

Figure 97.4

Figure 97.5

Figure 97.6

Step 1: Both fire brigade members: Place the victim on his or her back.

NOTE: Keep head and neck stabilized during rolling to prevent spinal injury.

Step 2: Fire brigade member #1: Kneel at the head of the victim.

Step 3: Fire brigade member #2: Stand between the victim's knees.

Step 4: Fire brigade member #2: Grasp the victim's wrists.

Step 5: Fire brigade member #2: Pull the victim to a sitting position.

Step 6: Fire brigade member #1: Push gently on the victim's back.

Step 7: Fire brigade member #1: Reach under the victim's arms and grasp the victim's wrists as fire brigade member #2 releases them. Grasp the victim's left wrist with the right hand and right wrist with the left hand **(Figure 98.1)**.

Step 8: Fire brigade member #2: Turn around, kneel down, and slip hands under the victim's knees.

Step 9: Both fire brigade members: Stand and move the victim on command from fire brigade member #1 **(Figure 98.2)**.

Figure 98.1

Figure 98.2

Step 1: Raise the victim to a sitting position **(Figure 99.1)**.

Step 2: Link arms across the victim's back.

Step 3: Reach under the victim's knees to form a seat **(Figure 99.2)**.

Step 4: Lift the victim using your legs. Keep your back straight while lifting **(Figure 99.3)**.

Step 5: Move the victim to safety **(Figure 99.4)**.

Figure 99.1

Figure 99.2

Figure 99.3

Figure 99.4

Step 1: Position the backboard/litter so that the victim can be carried to it and placed on it with the least amount of movement. This may require leaving the backboard/litter in the fully raised position.

Step 2: Position fire brigade members on the side of the victim that is easiest to reach and/or that will facilitate placing the victim on the backboard/litter.

Step 3: All fire brigade members: Crouch or kneel as close to the victim as possible, keeping backs straight.

Step 4: Fire brigade member #1: Place one hand under the victim's head and the other hand and arm under the victim's upper back.

Step 5: Other fire brigade members: Place arms under the victim at fire brigade members' respective positions **(Figure 100.1)**.

Step 6: All fire brigade members: Roll the victim carefully toward fire brigade members' chests.

Step 7: All fire brigade members: Stand while holding the victim against fire brigade members' chests **(Figure 100.2)**.

Step 8: Carry the victim to the desired location.

Step 9: Reverse the above procedures on the signal of Fire brigade member #1 to place the victim on the backboard/litter **(Figure 100.3)**.

Figure 100.1

Figure 100.2

Figure 100.3

Step 1: Don appropriate PPE and SCBA.

Step 2: Perform size-up.

Step 3: Gather rescue tools and equipment that may be needed in case of a mayday.

Step 4: Stand by with other RIC members at the entrance of the hazardous area until a mayday is received and orders to enter are given.

Step 5: Determine the most effective means to rescue the victim **(Figure 101.1)**.

Step 6: Ensure all hazard warning systems are established and understood by all participating personnel.

Step 7: Select appropriate specialized tools and equipment.

Step 8: Hook in air supply to SCBA facepiece prior to entry **(Figure 101.2)**.

Step 9: Enter the hazardous area as a team.

Step 10: Follow the orders of the team leader while maintaining situational awareness.

Step 11: Locate the victim.

Step 12: Check the victim's air supply. If necessary, provide additional air supply **(Figure 101.3)**.

Step 13: Disentangle the victim, if necessary.

Step 14: Move the victim to safety **(Figure 101.4)**.

Figure 101.2

Figure 101.3

Figure 101.1

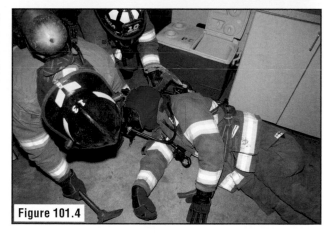

Figure 101.4

NOTE: Fire brigade members must confirm the order to attack the fire prior to performing suppression operations.

Step 1:   Deploy and advance an uncharged attack hoseline **(Figure 102.1)**.

Step 2:   Signal water supply when ready for water.

Step 3:   Open the nozzle to bleed air from the line and check for adequate water flow **(Figure 102.2)**.

Step 4:   Select the correct nozzle pattern and close the nozzle.

Step 5:   Check for threat to exposures and cool as necessary.

Step 6:   Position to make fire attack.

Step 7:   Extinguish the fire with a straight stream **(Figure 102.3)**.

Step 8:   Expose fire in the debris using a pike pole or trash hook and extinguish any debris fires **(Figure 102.4)**.

Figure 102.2

Figure 102.3

Figure 102.1

Figure 102.4

Step 1: Size up the incident scene for hazards.

    a. Fire conditions.

    b. Type of fuel.

    c. Integrity of container.

    d. Wind conditions.

    e. Identify escape route(s) and safe haven(s).

Step 2: Deploy handlines.

    a. Bleed air from the hoselines.

    b. Ensure adequate hoseline to reach the container.

    c. Estimate and maintain adequate waterflow.

Step 3: Cool cylinder or storage tank by applying a straight stream to the container **(Figure 103.1)**.

Step 4: Extend hoselines to isolate the control valve.

    a. Approach from uphill and upwind.

    b. Push flames away from the valve with a fog stream (30-degree pattern) **(Figure 103.2)**.

> **CAUTION:** If the team is unable to push flame away from the valve, immediately withdraw to a safe location and continue to cool the container.

Step 5: Close the control valve completely **(Figure 103.3)**.

Step 6: Cool container from safe distance.

    a. Withdraw the hoselines.

    b. Apply a straight stream to the container.

Step 7: Retreat to safety by backing away from the container.

Figure 103.2

Figure 103.1

Figure 103.3

Step 1: Select the proper type, ratio, and quantity of foam concentrate for the fuel involved **(Figure 104.1)**.

Step 2: Place the foam concentrate at the eductor.

Step 3: Check the eductor and nozzle for hydraulic compatibility (rated for the same flow).

Step 4: Adjust the eductor metering valve to the same percentage rating as that listed on the foam concentrate container **(Figure 104.2)**.

Step 5: Attach the eductor to a hose capable of efficiently flowing the rated capacity of the eductor and the nozzle.

Step 6: Attach the attack hoseline and nozzle to the discharge end of the eductor. Avoid kinks in the hose.

Step 7: Place the eductor suction hose into the foam concentrate **(Figure 104.3)**.

Step 8: Fully open the nozzle **(Figure 104.4)**.

Step 9: Increase the water supply pressure to that required for the eductor. Consult the manufacturer's recommendations for the specific eductor.

Figure 104.2

Figure 104.3

Figure 104.1

Figure 104.4

Ground Level Fire Attack — Rain Down Method

Step 1: Size up the incident scene.

Step 2: Identify escape route.

Step 3: Verify that foam type and concentration are appropriate for fuel, fire, and environmental conditions.

Step 4: Verify that the attack line is functioning and ready by producing a small amount of foam **(Figure 105.1)**.

Step 5: Extend the hoseline to the point of fire attack.

NOTE: Approach from uphill and upwind.

Step 6: Direct the foam stream into the air above the fire or spill so that foam floats gently down onto surface of fuel **(Figure 105.2)**.

   a. Maintain the stream as foam spreads across the surface of the fuel.

   b. Continue applying foam until it spreads across entire surface of the fuel and extinguishes the fire.

Step 7: Direct the stream away from pool before shutting it down.

Step 8: Retreat to safety by backing away.

Step 9: Monitor the fire for reignition and reapply foam as necessary.

Ground Level Fire Attack — Bank Down Method

Step 1: Size up the incident scene.

Step 2: Identify escape route.

Step 3: Verify that foam type and concentration are appropriate for fuel, fire, and environmental conditions.

Step 4: Verify that the attack line is functioning and ready by producing a small amount of foam.

Step 5: Extend the hoseline to the point of fire attack.

   a. Approach from uphill and upwind

   b. Apply and control stream as needed

Step 6: Direct the foam stream onto a nearby elevated object and allow foam to run down onto the surface of fuel **(Figure 105.3)**. Maintain stream as foam spreads across surface of fuel.

Step 7: Direct the stream away from pool before shutting it down.

Step 8: Retreat to safety by backing away.

Step 9: Monitor the fire for reignition and reapply foam as necessary.

Figure 105.1

Figure 105.2

Figure 105.3

Ground Level Fire Attack — Roll-On Method

Step 1: Size up the incident scene.

Step 2: Identify escape route.

Step 3: Verify that foam type and concentration are appropriate for fuel, fire, and environmental conditions.

Step 4: Verify that the attack line is functioning and ready by producing a small amount of foam.

Step 5: Extend the hoseline to the point of fire attack.

    a. Approach from uphill and upwind.

    b. Apply and control stream as needed.

Step 6: Direct the foam stream on the ground near front edge of fire so that foam rolls across surface of fuel **(Figure 105.4).**

NOTE: Maintain stream as foam rolls across surface of fuel.

Step 7: Direct the stream away from pool before shutting it down.

Step 8: Retreat to safety by backing away.

Step 9: Monitor the fire for reignition and reapply foam as necessary.

Figure 105.4

NOTE: When dealing with Class C fires, turn off the power before extinguishment operations if possible.

Step 1: Size up fire, ensuring that it is safe to fight with an extinguisher.

Step 2: Check that the extinguisher is properly charged.

Step 3: Position the unit for operation.

    a. Identify escape route

    b. Hold upright and stable

    c. Position upwind of fire

    d. Deploy entire length of hose from extinguisher **(Figure 106.1)**

Step 4: Activate or, if required, pull pin at top of extinguisher **(Figure 106.2)**.

Step 5: Test to ensure proper operation **(Figure 106.3)**.

    a. Point nozzle/horn in safe direction.

NOTE: If equipped with a horn, use the handle on the horn.

    b. Discharge very short test burst.

Step 6: Aim nozzle toward base of fire.

Step 7: Discharge extinguishing agent **(Figure 106.4)**.

    a. Squeeze handle or operate the bale.

    b. Sweep slowly back and forth across entire width of fire.

Step 8: Cover entire area with extinguishing agent until fire is completely extinguished **(Figure 106.5, p. 944)**.

Step 9: Back away from the fire area **(Figure 106.6, p. 944)**.

Step 10: Verbalize rekindle prevention measures have been established.

Step 11: Tag extinguisher for recharge and inspection.

Figure 106.2

Figure 106.3

Figure 106.1

Figure 106.4

Figure 106.5

Figure 106.6

NOTE: Fire brigade members must wait to perform overhaul until ordered to do so.

Step 1: Locate area(s)/material(s) with potential hidden or smoldering fire.

  a. Use thermal imager or similar device.

  b. Observe fire area to detect smoking or smoldering materials.

  c. Observe burn and smoke patterns.

  d. Recognize and preserve obvious signs of area of origin and fire cause.

Step 2: Overhaul area(s)/material(s) until hidden fires and smoldering components are exposed **(Figure 107.1)**.

Step 3: Completely extinguish hidden and smoldering fires with a handline **(Figure 107.2)**.

  a. Use minimal water for extinguishment.

  b. Ensure that no hidden or smoldering fires remain.

Step 4: Remove smoldering materials from structure and overhaul outside **(Figure 107.3)**.

Figure 107.1

Figure 107.2

Figure 107.3

Step 1: Identify openings to be covered **(Figure 108.1)**.

Step 2: Gather tools, equipment, and materials **(Figure 108.2)**.

Step 3: Cover or secure openings **(Figure 108.3)**.

    a. Doors

    b. Windows

    c. Floor openings

    d. Roof openings

    e. Other openings as necessary

Step 4: Verify that the building is secure **(Figure 108.4)**.

Figure 108.3

Figure 108.1

Figure 108.4

Figure 108.2

On Scene

Step 1: Isolate contaminated tools and equipment according to SOPs **(Figure 109.1)**.

Step 2: Conduct decontamination of tools and equipment according to SOPs.

Step 3: Wash, and/or isolate PPE according to SOPs, doffing as appropriate **(Figure 109.2)**.

Step 4: Use hygienic wipes to wipe potential contaminates from face, head, neck, and hands.

Designated Area

Step 5: Shower thoroughly using soap and water.

Step 6: Clean PPE according to SOPs **(Figure 109.3)**.

Step 7: Inspect and maintain PPE according to manufacturer's recommendations.

Step 8: Store PPE outside of living and sleeping quarters.

Step 9: Complete required reports and supporting documentation.

Figure 109.1

Figure 109.2

Figure 109.3

Step 1: Don appropriate PPE **(Figure 110.1)**.

Step 2: Mount apparatus using handrails and steps per local procedures **(Figure 110.2)**.

NOTE: Be sure to use three points of contact at all times

Step 3: Sit in a seat within the cab and fasten safety belt **(Figure 110.3)**. Follow all local safety regulations.

Step 4: Remain seated with safety belt fastened while vehicle is in motion.

Step 5: When vehicle comes to a complete stop, unfasten safety belt and prepare to dismount.

Step 6: Dismount apparatus using handrails and steps per local procedures **(Figure 110.4)**.

> **CAUTION:** Before fully opening the apparatus door, look for oncoming traffic. Always use situational awareness. If possible, dismount on the side opposite of traffic.

NOTE: Be sure to use three points of contact at all times.

Figure 110.2

Figure 110.1

Figure 110.3

Figure 110.4

NOTE: Fire brigade members must confirm the order to attack the fire prior to performing suppression operations.

Step 1: Deploy and advance an uncharged attack hoseline.

Step 2: Signal when ready for water.

Step 3: Open the nozzle to bleed air from the line and check for adequate water flow **(Figure 111.1)**.

Step 4: Select the correct nozzle pattern and close the nozzle.

Step 5: Advance toward the structure and position to make fire attack **(Figure 111.2)**.

Step 6: Direct a straight stream into the structure using a direct, indirect, and/or combination attack to extinguish the fire **(Figure 111.3)**.

Step 7: Search for and extinguish hidden fires.

    a. Break up material and probe with pike pole for hot spots.

    b. Extinguish hot spots.

Figure 111.2

Figure 111.1

Figure 111.3

CAUTION: Always don appropriate PPE, including SCBA, when on the fireground. Approach from uphill, upwind, and a 45-degree angle from the side of the vehicle, if possible. Maintain communication and situational awareness. Observe fire conditions throughout the operation. Ensure that the vehicle is properly stabilized.

NOTE: Fire brigade members must confirm the order to attack the fire prior to performing suppression operations.

Step 1: Identify automobile fuel type, if possible.

Step 2: Deploy an uncharged attack line.

Step 3: Signal the driver/operator when ready for water.

Step 4: Open the nozzle to bleed air from the line and check for adequate water flow **(Figure 112.1)**.

Step 5: Select the correct nozzle pattern.

Step 6: Advance the attack line to the vehicle, applying water while advancing **(Figure 112.2)**.

Step 7: Extinguish any fire in the line of approach or under the vehicle **(Figure 112.3)**.

Step 8: Extinguish fire in the passenger compartment **(Figure 112.4)**.

Step 9: Open the hood and extinguish the fire in the engine compartment.

NOTE: It may be necessary to force entry to the engine compartment.

Step 10: Open the compartments and extinguish the fire in compartments.

NOTE: It may be necessary to force entry to the trunk.

Step 11: Extinguish hidden and smoldering fires.

Step 12: Isolate fuel and power sources.

Figure 112.2

Figure 112.3

Figure 112.4

Figure 112.1

NOTE: Fire brigade members must confirm the order to attack the fire prior to performing suppression operations.

Step 1: Deploy and advance the uncharged attack hoseline to the selected door or window **(Figure 113.1)**.

Step 2: Signal when ready for water.

Step 3: Open the nozzle to bleed air from the line and check for adequate water flow **(Figure 113.2)**.

Step 4: If using a fog nozzle, select straight stream pattern and close the nozzle.

Step 5: Open the selected door or window and clear any obstructions.

Step 6: Open the nozzle and direct a solid or straight stream toward the ceiling. Kneel to attain a good angle to the ceiling, if necessary **(Figure 113.3)**.

NOTE: The stream may be moved from side to side along the ceiling, but NOT in a circular pattern.

CAUTION: Do not block the opening with the hose stream.

Step 7: Flow water long enough to cool the compartment and control the fire, then shut the nozzle.

Step 8: Close the door or window, if possible.

CAUTION: Always maintain door control to control the flow path.

Step 9: Observe conditions. Apply more water as necessary **(Figure 113.4)**.

Step 10: Enter the building and advance to extinguish the fire, or remain outside as a second team enters the building to extinguish the fire.

Figure 113.2

Figure 113.3

Figure 113.1

Figure 113.4

NOTE: Fire brigade members should be positioned on the same side of the hose.

Step 1: Unload the hose.

Step 2: Face the nozzle with about 15 to 20 feet (5 to 6 m) of hose between each fire brigade member.

Step 3: Place the hose over one shoulder **(Figure 114.1)**.

Step 4: Fully open SCBA before approaching the structure entrance or entering smoke environment.

Step 5: Advance the hose to building entrance, but do not enter the building.

    a. Size up the environment to identify hazards.

    b. Approach the door from the side opposite the hinges.

Step 6: Signal the driver/operator to charge hoseline **(Figure 114.2)**.

Step 7: Open the nozzle fully to ensure adequate water flow and to allow the pump operator to set the pressure **(Figure 114.3)**.

Step 8: Set the desired nozzle pattern and bleed air from the hoseline.

Step 9: Communicate readiness to enter the structure.

Step 10: Enter the structure when directed to do so. Stay low and maintain spacing **(Figure 114.4, p. 954)**.

Figure 114.2

Figure 114.1

Figure 114.3

Figure 114.4

NOTE: Ensure that fire brigade members take stationary positions along the route and on the stairs at critical points (obstructions and corners) to help feed the hose and to keep the hose on the outside of the staircase.

Up Interior Stairs (Uncharged Hoseline)

Step 1: Face the nozzle with about 15 to 20 feet (5 to 6 m) of hose between each fire brigade member.

Step 2: Place the hose over one shoulder **(Figure 115.1)**.

Step 3: Advance the hoseline up a flight of stairs against the outside wall **(Figure 115.2, p. 956)**.
   a. Avoid sharp bends and kinks.
   b. Maintain spacing between fire brigade members.

Step 4: Deploy excess hose up the stairway toward the floor above the fire floor **(Figure 115.3, p. 956)**.

Step 5: Lay the hose down the stairway along outside wall to fire floor.

Step 6: Last fire brigade member: After the hose supply is depleted, advance and assist the nozzle operator in removing kinks and pushing hose to the outside wall of the stairway as necessary **(Figure 115.4, p. 956)**.

Down Interior Stairs (Uncharged Hoseline)

Step 1: Face the nozzle with about 15 to 20 feet (5 to 6 m) of hose between each fire brigade member.

Step 2: Place the hose over one shoulder.

Step 3: Advance the hoseline down a flight of stairs against outside wall **(Figure 115.5, p. 956)**.
   a. Avoid sharp bends and kinks.
   b. Maintain spacing between fire brigade members.

Step 4: Deploy excess hose up the stairway toward the floor above the fire floor **(Figure 115.6, p. 957)**.

Step 5: Lay the hose down the stairway along outside wall to fire floor.

Step 6: Last fire brigade member: After the hose supply is depleted, advance and assist the nozzle operator in removing kinks and pushing hose to the outside wall of the stairway as necessary **(Figure 115.7, p. 957)**.

Up Interior Stairs (Charged Hoseline)

Step 1: Face the nozzle.

Step 2: Advance the hoseline up a flight of stairs against the outside wall.
   a. Use the working line drag **(Figure 115.8, p. 957)**.
   b. Avoid sharp bends and kinks.
   c. Maintain spacing between fire brigade members **(Figure 115.9, p. 957)**.

Step 3: Deploy excess hose up the stairway toward the floor above the fire floor.

Step 4: Advance the hose down the stairway to the fire floor.

Step 5: Last fire brigade member: After the hose supply is depleted, advance and assist the nozzle operator in removing kinks and pushing hose to the outside wall of the stairway as necessary **(Figure 115.10, p. 958)**.

Down Interior Stairs (Charged Hoseline)

Step 1: Face the nozzle.

Step 2: Advance the hoseline down a flight of stairs against the outside wall **(Figure 115.11, p. 958)**.
   a. Use the working line drag.
   b. Avoid sharp bends and kinks.
   c. Maintain spacing between fire brigade members **(Figure 115.12, p. 958)**.

Step 3: Deploy excess hose outside the stairway (such as in a hallway or room adjacent to the stairway) and continue advancing the hose on the fire floor **(Figure 115.13, p. 958)**.

Step 4: Last fire brigade member: After the hose supply is depleted, advance and assist the nozzle operator in removing kinks and pushing hose to the outside wall of the stairway as necessary.

Figure 115.1

Figure 115.2

Figure 115.4

Figure 115.3

Figure 115.5

Figure 115.6

Figure 115.8

Figure 115.7

Figure 115.9

Figure 115.10

Figure 115.12

Figure 115.11

Figure 115.13

NOTE: Students should be positioned on the same side of the hose.

Step 1: Deploy hoseline.

Step 2: Remove the standpipe outlet cap **(Figure 116.1)**.

    a. Check the condition of the outlet threads.

    b. Check for any obstructions in the outlet.

    c. Flush standpipe to ensure proper operation.

    d. Ensure the gasket is in place in the hoseline coupling.

Step 3: Connect the female coupling to the standpipe outlet. Finger tighten the connection **(Figure 116.2)**.

Step 4: Advance the nozzle end of the hoseline to the fire **(Figure 116.3)**.

Step 5: Open the standpipe outlet valve **(Figure 116.4, p. 960)**.

Figure 116.2

Figure 116.1

Figure 116.3

Figure 116.4

CAUTION: Always don appropriate PPE, including SCBA, when on the fireground. Approach from uphill and upwind if possible. Maintain communication and situational awareness. Observe fire conditions throughout the operation.

NOTE: Fire brigade members must confirm the order to attack the fire prior to performing suppression operations.

Direct Attack Method

Step 1: Deploy and advance an uncharged attack hoseline to a safe location near the point of entry.

Step 2: Signal when ready for water.

Step 3: Open the nozzle to bleed air from the line and check for adequate water flow.

Step 4: Select the correct nozzle pattern and close the nozzle.

Step 5: Enter the structure and advance to the seat of the fire, extinguishing any fires that are encountered along the way **(Figure 117.1)**.

CAUTION: Always maintain door control to control the flow path **(Figure 117.2, p. 962)**.

Step 6: Cool hot gases overhead as needed using short applications of a solid or straight stream.

Step 7: When in place near the seat of the fire, direct a solid or straight stream of water onto the base of the fire **(Figure 117.3, p. 962)**.

NOTE: Locate and suppress any interior wall and subfloor fires as directed.

Step 8: Close the nozzle when the fire is extinguished **(Figure 117.4, p. 962)**.

Indirect Attack Method

Step 1: Deploy and advance an uncharged attack hoseline to a safe location near the point of entry.

Step 2: Signal the driver/operator when ready for water.

Step 3: Open the nozzle to bleed air from the line and check for adequate water flow.

Step 4: Select the correct nozzle pattern and close the nozzle.

Step 5: Enter the structure and advance to a location near the seat of the fire, extinguishing any fires that are encountered along the way **(Figure 117.5, p. 962)**.

CAUTION: Always maintain door control to control the flow path. Fire brigade members should not be in the fire compartment during an indirect attack.

Step 6: Cool hot gases overhead as needed using short applications of a solid or straight stream **(Figure 117.6, p. 962)**.

Step 7: When in place near the seat of the fire, open the nozzle and direct a fog pattern toward the ceiling and upper area of the walls **(Figure 117.7, p. 962)**.

Step 8: Close the interior door to the compartment, allowing steam to develop **(Figure 117.8, p. 963)**. Crack the door to observe the conditions.

Step 9: Continue to apply water to the compartment linings (walls and ceiling) until the fire is extinguished.

Step 10: Close the nozzle when the fire is extinguished.

Combination Attack Method

Step 1: Deploy and advance an uncharged attack hoseline to a safe location near the point of entry.

Step 2: Signal the driver/operator when ready for water.

Step 3: Open the nozzle to bleed air from the line and check for adequate water flow.

Step 4: Select the correct nozzle pattern and close the nozzle.

Step 5: Enter the structure and advance to the seat of the fire, extinguishing any fires that are encountered along the way **(Figure 117.9, p. 963)**.

CAUTION: Always maintain door control to control the flow path.

Step 6: Cool hot gases overhead as needed using short applications of a solid or straight stream.

Step 7: When in place near the seat of the fire, open the nozzle and direct a fog or straight stream toward the upper edge of the fire at the ceiling level.

Step 8: Apply water using a T, Z, or O pattern, moving the fire stream from high to low **(Figures 117.10, 117.11, and 117.12, p. 963)**.

NOTE: Ensure that the ceiling and floor are reached by the hose stream.

Step 9: Close the nozzle when the room begins to darken.

Step 10: Apply water using the direct attack method as needed.

Step 11: Close the nozzle when the fire is extinguished.

Figure 117.1

Figure 117.2

Figure 117.5

Figure 117.3

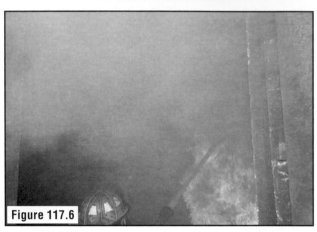
Figure 117.6

Figure 117.4

Figure 117.7

Figure 117.8

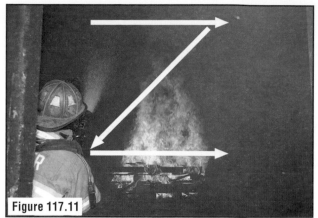

Figure 117.11

Figure 117.9

Figure 117.12

Figure 117.10

CAUTION: Always don appropriate PPE, including SCBA, when on the fireground. Approach from uphill and upwind if possible. Maintain communication and situational awareness. Observe fire conditions throughout the operation.

NOTE: Fire brigade members must confirm the order to attack the fire prior to performing suppression operations.

Above Grade Fire Attack

Step 1: Deploy and advance uncharged attack hoseline to a safe location near the point of entry.

Step 2: Signal when ready for water.

Step 3: Open the nozzle to bleed air from the line and check for adequate water flow.

Step 4: Select correct nozzle pattern and close the nozzle.

Step 5: Advance hoseline into the structure and up the stairwell to the fire floor **(Figure 118.1)**.

NOTE: If the fire is in highrise or multi-story commercial structure, the fire attack may be from a standpipe connection.

Step 6: Apply water using a direct, indirect, or combination attack as directed **(Figure 118.2)**.

Step 7: Close the nozzle when the fire is extinguished.

Below Grade Fire Attack

Step 1: Deploy and advance an uncharged attack hoseline to an exterior opening, if available.

Step 2: Signal when ready for water.

Step 3: Open the nozzle to bleed air from the line and check for adequate water flow **(Figure 118.3)**.

Step 4: Select the correct nozzle pattern and close the nozzle.

Step 5: Apply water to the fire compartment from the exterior to control the fire, if possible **(Figure 118.4)**.

CAUTION: Make access to the building at the level of the fire, if possible. If that is not possible, proceed with the steps below.

Step 6: Reposition the hoseline to the entry point, if necessary.

Step 7: Sound the floor to ensure that the floor is still in place.

Step 8: Advance the hoseline into the structure and down the stairwell **(Figure 118.5)**.

CAUTION: Always maintain door control to control the flow path.

Step 9: Apply water using a direct, indirect, or combination attack as directed **(Figure 118.6)**.

Step 10: Close the nozzle when the fire is extinguished.

Figure 118.1

Figure 118.2

Figure 118.3

Figure 118.4

Figure 118.5

Figure 118.6

NOTE: Make sure the ladder is properly secured, either by another fire brigade member or by mechanical means. Fire brigade members should be positioned on the same side of the hose.

Step 1: Nozzle fire brigade member: Place the line over the shoulder.

Step 2: All fire brigade members: Climb the ladder to the appropriate position **(Figure 119.1)**.

Step 3: Nozzle fire brigade member: Sound the floor for stability and check that no victims are in the way **(Figure 119.2)**.

Step 4: Nozzle fire brigade member: Lay the nozzle in the window, and then enter the window **(Figure 119.3)**.

Step 5: Other fire brigade members on the ladder: Lock in with leg lock or Class I safety harness, leaving hands free to control and advance the hose.

Step 6: Other fire brigade members on the ladder: Feed the hose to the nozzle fire brigade member until signaled to stop.

Step 7: Fire brigade member nearest the top: Secure the hose to the top rung of the ladder with a rope hose tool or utility strap **(Figure 119.4)**.

Step 8: Fire brigade member nearest the top: Advance up the ladder to back up the nozzle fire brigade member.

Figure 119.2

Figure 119.1

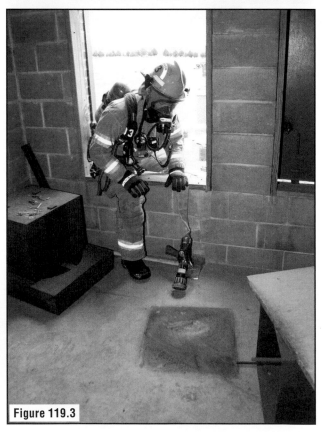

Figure 119.3

Figure 119.4

NOTE: Make sure the ladder is properly secured, either by another fire brigade member or by mechanical means. Fire brigade members should be positioned on the same side of the hose.

Step 1: Nozzle fire brigade member: Climb the ladder, carrying the nozzle **(Figure 120.1)**.

Step 2: Nozzle fire brigade member: Lock in with leg lock or Class I safety harness, leaving hands free to control and advance the hose.

Step 3: Fire brigade members below: Feed the hose to the nozzle fire brigade member.

Step 4: Nozzle fire brigade member: Sound the floor for stability and check that no victims are in the way.

Step 5: Nozzle fire brigade member: Lay the nozzle on the window, and then enter the window **(Figure 120.2)**.

Step 6: Fire brigade members below: Climb the ladder, maintaining appropriate distance from each other.

Step 7: Fire brigade members on the ladder: Lock in with leg lock or Class I safety harness once backup fire brigade member is in position opposite the window. Leave hands free to control and advance the hose.

Step 8: Backup fire brigade member: Enter the window.

Step 9: Fire brigade members on the ladder: Feed the hose to the nozzle and backup fire brigade members until signaled to stop.

Step 10: Fire brigade members on the ladder: Secure the hose to the ladder with a rope hose tool or utility strap **(Figure 120.3)**.

Figure 120.2

Figure 120.1

Figure 120.3

NOTE: Make sure the ladder is properly secured, either by another student or by mechanical means.

Step 1: Advance the hoseline up the ladder using the proper procedure for a charged line.

Step 2: When at the desired elevation, lock in using leg lock or Class I harness, leaving both hands free to control and advance the line.

Step 3: Position the nozzle through the rungs extending it at least 1 foot (0.3 m) beyond the rungs **(Figure 121.1)**.

Step 4: Secure the hose to the top or closest ladder rung with a rope hose tool or utility strap **(Figure 121.2)**.

Step 5: Open the nozzle slowly **(Figure 121.3)**.

Figure 121.2

Figure 121.1

Figure 121.3

> **WARNING:** If the sprinkler system is being supplemented by a fire pump, make sure you shut the pump off prior to attempting to stop the flow.

NOTE: Another fire brigade member should be present to stabilize the ladder.

Wedges

Step 1: Place a step ladder within reach of sprinkler.

Step 2: Climb the ladder.

Step 3: Insert the wedges between the sprinkler arms, flat sides against sprinkler **(Figure 122.1)**.

Step 4: Drive the wedges into the sprinkler with the heel of hand until the water flow stops **(Figures 122.2 and 122.3)**.

Figure 122.2

Clamp-Type Sprinkler Tongs

Step 1: Place a step ladder within reach of sprinkler.

Step 2: Climb the ladder.

Step 3: Insert the tongs into the sprinkler between the arms **(Figure 122.4)**.

Step 4: Open the tongs (by clamping the handles together) until the water flow stops **(Figure 122.5)**.

Step 5: Lock the tongs in the open position, with the keeper pulled as far as it will go toward the end of the handles **(Figure 122.6)**.

Swivel-Type Sprinkler Tongs

Step 1: Place a step ladder within reach of the sprinkler.

Step 2: Climb the ladder.

Step 3: Insert the tongs into the sprinkler between the arms **(Figure 122.7)**.

Step 4: Open the tongs with the handle swiveled upward.

Step 5: Turn the locking knob clockwise to lock the tongs in the open position **(Figure 122.8)**.

Figure 122.3

Figure 122.4

Figure 122.1

Figure 122.5

Figure 122.8

Figure 122.6

Figure 122.7

> **CAUTION:** Fire brigade members must note the wind direction and flow path prior to performing ventilation and continuously size up the fire conditions during ventilation.

NOTE: Fire brigade members must confirm the order to ventilate prior to conducting ventilation operations. Ventilation openings must be large enough to match the fire conditions. If working from the ladder, make sure it is properly secured, either by another fire brigade member or by mechanical means.

Step 1: Clear the intake of all obstructions **(Figure 123.1)**.

Step 2: Place fan near intake opening.

NOTE: The fan should be placed at the appropriate distance based on exhaust opening size and the manufacturer's recommendation.

Step 3: Start fan and temporarily direct away from opening **(Figure 123.2)**.

Step 4: Ensure there is an exhaust opening larger than the intake.

Step 5: Open/close interior doors accordingly to control air flow.

Step 6: Direct fan toward the intake **(Figure 123.3)**.

Step 7: Inspect the site to ensure effectiveness of ventilation **(Figure 123.4)**.

Step 8: If the ventilation is ineffective, discontinue use of the fan and reevaluate the location or size of the intake and exhaust and any obstructions to the flow of air.

Figure 123.2

Figure 123.3

Figure 123.1

Figure 123.4

NOTE: Ventilation openings must be large enough to match the fire conditions. If working from the ladder, make sure it is properly secured, either by another fire brigade member or by mechanical means.

Step 1: Open the exhaust location **(Figure 124.1)**.

Step 2: Clear the opening of all obstructions.

Step 3: Set the fog nozzle pattern wide enough to cover the exhaust location opening **(Figure 124.2)**.

Step 4: Inspect the site to ensure effectiveness of ventilation **(Figure 124.3)**.

Figure 124.1

Figure 124.2

Figure 124.3

NOTE: Ventilation openings must be large enough to match the fire conditions. Fire brigade members must confirm the order to ventilate prior to conducting ventilation operations.

Ventilate Using a Power Saw

Step 1: Ensure that the saw is operating properly before climbing to the roof.

Step 2: Sound the roof for integrity with axe or pike pole before placing weight on the roof.

Step 3: Locate rafters/supports.

Step 4: Select location for ventilation and position upwind of planned opening.

Step 5: Outline ventilation opening with axe or similar tool.

Step 6: Remove gravel or other materials that may limit ability to cut opening from outlines.

Step 7: Remove roof finishing materials.

Step 8: Set the guard depth gauge control, if applicable.

Step 9: Start the saw.

NOTE: When creating ventilation openings, cuts should be made working toward the escape route, if possible. Cut completely through the roof decking, leaving the supports intact.

Step 10: Cut triangular inspection opening in roof, if required by local SOPs **(Figure 125.1)**.

Step 11: Make cut #1: Cut roof deck perpendicular to a roof truss or support. Incorporate the inspection opening, if applicable **(Figure 125.2)**.

Step 12: Make cut #2: Cut the roof deck on one side of the opening parallel to the supports and intersecting cut #1 **(Figure 125.3)**.

Step 13: Make cut #3: Cut roof deck on opposite side of cut #2, perpendicular to and intersecting cut #1 **(Figure 125.4)**.

Step 14: Make cut #4: Complete the ventilation opening by joining cut #2 and cut #3 **(Figure 125.5, p. 976)**.

Step 15: Remove or tilt the decking from the ventilation opening with axe, pike pole, or other sounding tool. Keep decking out of ventilation opening **(Figure 125.6, p. 976)**.

Step 16: Plunge through interior ceiling using pike pole or other long-handled tool, working from upwind side of ventilation opening.

Step 17: Inspect ventilation site and communicate with interior crews to ensure effectiveness of ventilation.

Ventilate Using an Axe

Step 1: Sound the roof for integrity with axe before placing weight on the roof.

Step 2: Locate rafters/supports.

Step 3: Select location for ventilation and position upwind of planned opening.

Step 4: Outline ventilation opening with axe.

Step 5: Remove gravel or other materials that may limit ability to cut opening from outlines and then remove roof finishing materials.

Step 6: Cut triangular inspection opening in roof parallel to farthest roof support, if required by local SOPs **(Figure 125.7, p. 976)**.

NOTE: When creating ventilation openings, cuts should be made away from the escape route, if possible. Cut completely through the roof decking, leaving the supports intact.

Step 7: Make cut #1: Cut the roof deck perpendicular to a roof truss or support. Incorporate inspection opening, if applicable **(Figure 125.8, p. 976)**.

Step 8: Make cut #2: Cut roof deck on one side of opening and intersecting cut #1 **(Figure 125.9, p. 976)**.

Step 9: Make cut #3: Cut roof deck on opposite side of cut #2, perpendicular to and intersecting cut #1 **(Figure 125.10, p. 977)**.

Step 10: Make cut #4: Complete the ventilation opening by joining cut #2 and cut #3 **(Figure 125.11, p. 977)**.

Step 11: Remove or tilt the decking from the ventilation opening with axe, pike pole, or other sounding tool. Keep decking out of ventilation opening **(Figure 125.12, p. 977)**.

Step 12: Plunge through interior ceiling using pike pole or other long-handled tool, working from upwind side of ventilation opening.

Step 13: Inspect ventilation site and communicate with interior crews to ensure effectiveness of ventilation.

Figure 125.1

Figure 125.2

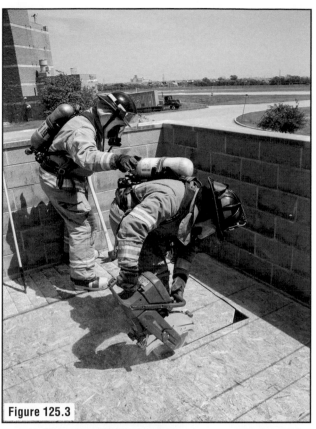

Figure 125.3

Figure 125.4

Figure 125.5

Figure 125.6

Figure 125.7

Figure 125.8

Figure 125.9

Figure 125.10

Figure 125.12

Figure 125.11

> **CAUTION:** Fire brigade members must note the wind direction and flow path prior to performing ventilation and continuously remain aware of the fire location and conditions during ventilation. Maintain footing and a point of contact with the ladder while ventilating.

NOTE: Ventilation openings must be large enough to match the fire conditions. If working from the ladder, make sure it is properly secured, either by another fire brigade member or by mechanical means. Fire brigade members must confirm the order to ventilate prior to conducting ventilation operations.

Ventilate Using a Power Saw

> **CAUTION:** While on the ground, ensure that the saw is operating properly. The saw should NOT be running while ascending to the roof.

Step 1: Sound the roof for integrity with axe or pike pole before placing weight on the roof.

Step 2: Locate rafters/supports.

Step 3: Select location for ventilation.

Step 4: Position and secure roof ladder upwind of planned opening.

NOTE: Maintain footing and a point of contact with the roof ladder while ventilating.

Step 5: Outline ventilation opening with axe or similar tool.

Step 6: Remove gravel or other materials that may limit ability to cut opening from outlines and then remove roof finishing materials.

Step 7: Set the guard depth gauge control, if applicable.

Step 8: Start the saw.

NOTE: When creating ventilation openings, cuts should be made away from the escape route, if possible. Cut completely through the roof decking, leaving the supports intact.

Step 9: Cut triangular inspection opening in roof parallel to farthest roof support, if required by local SOPs **(Figure 126.1)**.

Step 10: Make cut #1: Cut roof deck parallel to a roof truss or support on the side furthest away from ladder or escape route. Incorporate inspection opening, if applicable **(Figure 126.2)**.

Step 11: Make cut #2: Cut roof deck on one side of opening perpendicular to and intersecting cut #1 **(Figure 126.3)**.

Step 12: Make cut #3: Cut roof deck on opposite side of cut #2, perpendicular to and intersecting cut #1 **(Figure 126.4)**.

Step 13: Make cut #4: Complete the ventilation opening by joining cut #2 and cut #3 **(Figure 126.5)**.

Step 14: Remove the decking from the ventilation opening with axe, pike pole, or other sounding tool. Keep decking out of ventilation opening.

Step 15: Plunge through interior ceiling using pike pole, working from upwind side of ventilation opening **(Figure 126.6)**.

Step 16: Inspect site to ensure effectiveness of ventilation.

Ventilate Using an Axe

Step 1: Sound the roof for integrity with axe before placing weight on the roof.

Step 2: Locate rafters/supports.

Step 3: Select location for ventilation.

Step 4: Position and secure roof ladder upwind of planned opening.

NOTE: Maintain footing and a point of contact with the roof ladder while ventilating.

Step 5: Outline ventilation opening with axe.

Step 6: Remove gravel or other materials that may limit ability to cut opening from outlines and then remove roof finishing materials.

NOTE: When creating ventilation openings, cuts should be made away from the escape route, if possible. Cut completely through the roof decking, leaving the supports intact.

Step 7: Cut triangular inspection opening in roof parallel to farthest roof support, if required by local SOPs.

Step 8: Make cut #1: Cut roof deck parallel to a roof truss or support on the side furthest away from ladder or escape route. Incorporate inspection opening, if applicable **(Figure 126.7, p. 980)**.

Step 9: Make cut #2: Cut roof deck on one side of opening perpendicular to and intersecting cut #1 **(Figure 126.8, p. 980)**.

Step 10: Make cut #3: Cut roof deck on opposite side of cut #2, perpendicular to and intersecting cut #1 **(Figure 126.9, p. 980)**.

Step 11: Make cut #4: Complete the ventilation opening by joining cut #2 and cut #3 **(Figure 126.10, p. 980)**.

Step 12: Remove the decking from the ventilation opening with axe, pike pole, or other sounding tool. Keep decking out of ventilation opening.

Step 13: Plunge through interior ceiling using pike pole, working from upwind side of ventilation opening.

Step 14: Inspect site to ensure effectiveness of ventilation.

Figure 126.1

Figure 126.4

Figure 126.2

Figure 126.5

Figure 126.3

Figure 126.6

Figure 126.7

Figure 126.10

Figure 126.8

Figure 126.9

Step 1: Use the initial action plan and size-up information to determine necessary tasks and responsibilities and identify hazards.

Step 2: Assign tasks and responsibilities to qualified members in complete, clear, and concise instructions **(Figure 127.1)**.

Step 3: Ensure the desired outcomes are achieved.

Step 4: Identify hazards **(Figure 127.2)**.

Step 5: Ensure hazards are mitigated and members' safety is maintained.

Step 6: Ensure all members are accounted for at all times.

Figure 127.2

Figure 127.1

Step 1: Instruct fire brigade members which positions to take prior to beginning the training evolution.

Step 2: Identify any potential hazards.

Step 3: Lead members through the steps of the evolution in complete, clear, and concise instructions **(Figure 128.1)**.

Step 4: Ensure hazards are mitigated.

Step 5: Maintain safety of all personnel involved.

Step 6: Evaluate if desired outcomes are achieved **(Figure 128.2)**.

Step 7: Monitor students during assigned tasks.

Figure 128.1

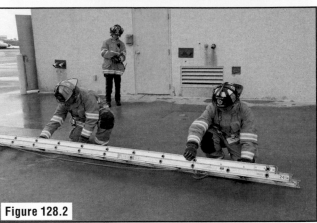

Figure 128.2

Step 1: Review any relevant documentation such as training materials, lesson plans, and SOPs before the start of the classes **(Figure 129.1)**.

Step 2: Impart the necessary information verbally in complete, clear, and concise manner, using appropriate teaching methods **(Figure 129.2)**.

Step 3: Communicate safety considerations.

Step 4: Communicate desired outcomes.

Step 5: Utilize a mixture of direct and indirect questions to help ensure students understand the materials presented **(Figure 129.3)**.

Figure 129.1

Figure 129.2

Figure 129.3

Oral Exam

Step 1: Administer oral exam to individual students one-on-one **(Figure 130.1)**.

Step 2: Speak in clear, articulated voice.

Step 3: Maintain neutral facial expression; limit gestures.

Step 4: Listen carefully to student's answers, asking for clarification as necessary.

Step 5: Record student's answers accurately **(Figure 130.2)**.

Written Exam

Step 1: Arrange classroom/facility to be suitable for written exam testing.

Step 2: Explain test procedures to students **(Figure 130.3)**.

    a. Time permitted for exam

    b. Filling out answer sheets correctly

    c. Standards for passing mark

    d. Cheating policy

    e. What to do when exam is complete

Step 3: Monitor exam **(Figure 130.4)**.

Step 4: Ensure all testing materials are collected at end of exam **(Figure 130.5)**.

Step 5: Record student's test scores accurately.

Performance Exam

Step 1: Arrange classroom/facility to be suitable for performance exam testing.

Step 2: Gather all necessary training aids/equipment appropriate for exam.

Step 3: Explain test procedures to students.

    a. Task required to be completed

    b. Conditions of the testing

    c. Time permitted for the skill

    d. Standards for passing mark

    e. Cheating policy

    f. What to do when exam is complete

Step 4: Observe skill being performed **(Figure 130.6)**.

Step 5: Ensure personnel accountability and safety policies are followed at all times.

Step 6: Use checklist to accurately record skill being performed.

Figure 130.1

Figure 130.2

Figure 130.3

Figure 130.4

Figure 130.5

Figure 130.6

Step 1: Complete and maintain all training forms accurately according to SOPs and all legal requirements **(Figure 131.1)**.

Step 2: File all training records in accordance with local SOPs and accountability systems **(Figure 131.2)**.

Step 3: Update training records as necessary.

Figure 131.1

Figure 131.2

Step 1: Confirm order that you are acting as safety officer for this incident.

Step 2: Obtain briefing from IC **(Figure 132.1)**.

Step 3: Perform size-up as safety officer, looking for hazards or unsafe behavior.

Step 4: Use the incident safety plan and size-up information to identify hazards.

Step 5: Communicate hazards to IC and/or personnel threatened by hazards.

Step 6: Stop and/or correct any unsafe actions and hazards on the scene **(Figure 132.2)**.

Step 7: Continue to oversee operations, ensuring that personnel safety is maintained and resources are safely allocated.

Figure 131.2

Figure 131.1

133

Initiate a response to a reported emergency. *[NFPA 1081, 9.1.7]*

Step 1: Record all necessary information upon receiving the report of an emergency.

Step 2: Initiate a response to the emergency following local SOPs.

Step 3: Relay necessary information.

Step 4: Operate communication equipment properly.

134

Respond to a facility emergency. *[NFPA 1081, 9.1.8]*

Step 1: Acknowledge the order to respond to the emergency.

Step 2: Go to the assigned duty location.

Step 3: Respond to a facility emergency as directed, while recognizing and avoiding hazards.

135

Assist with a building evacuation. *[NFPA 1081, 9.2.1]*

Step 1: Acknowledge the order to assist with the building evacuation.

Step 2: Perform the building evacuation as directed, following the facility evacuation procedures.

Step 3: Ensure all building personnel are evacuated to their assigned assembly point.

Step 4: Report the completion of the task.

136

Operate a fixed fire protection system. *[NFPA 1081, 9.2.2]*

Step 1: Acknowledge the order to operate the fixed fire protection system.

Step 2: Operate the fixed fire protection system as directed, following the facility fixed fire protection equipment operation procedures.

Step 3: Report the completion of the task.

137

Control the facility electrical system. *[NFPA 1081, 9.2.3]*

Step 1: Acknowledge the order to control the facility electrical system.

Step 2: Control the facility electrical system as directed, following the facility electrical equipment operation procedures.

Step 3: Report the completion of the task.

138

Control the facility utilities. *[NFPA 1081, 9.2.4]*

Step 1: Acknowledge the order to control the facility utilities.

Step 2: Control the facility utilities as directed, following the facility utilities operation procedures.

Step 3: Report the completion of the task.

139

Control the process control system. *[NFPA 1081, 9.2.5]*

Step 1: Acknowledge the order to control the process control system.

Step 2: Control the process control system as directed, following the process operation procedures.

Step 3: Report the completion of the task.

140

Control the fire pump/fire water system. *[NFPA 1081, 9.2.6]*

Step 1: Acknowledge the order to control the fire pump/fire water system.

Step 2: Control the fire pump/fire water system as directed, following the fire pump/fire water system procedures.

Step 3: Report the completion of the task.

141

Perform salvage operations. *[NFPA 1081, 9.2.7]*

Step 1: Acknowledge the order to assist with the salvage operations.

Step 2: Perform salvage operations in the cold zone as directed, following the facility evacuation procedures.

Step 3: Report the completion of the task.

142

Perform traffic control and site security duties.
[NFPA 1081, 9.2.8]

Step 1: Acknowledge the order to perform traffic control and site security duties.

Step 2: Perform traffic control and site security duties as directed, following the facility security procedures, so that security outside the fire zone and in the cold zone within the fire area is maintained.

Step 3: Maintain security outside the fire zone and in the cold zone within the fire area.

Step 4: Report the completion of the task.

143

Escort personnel outside the fire zone and in the cold zone.
[9.2.9]

Step 1: Acknowledge the order to escort personnel outside the fire zone and in the cold zone.

Step 2: Escort personnel outside the fire zone and in the cold zone as directed, following the facility escort procedures.

Step 3: Report the completion of the task.

144

Perform general support member services.
[NFPA 1081, 9.2.10]

Step 1: Acknowledge the order to perform general support member services.

Step 2: Perform general support member services as directed, following the specific support services procedures as determined by the facility fire brigade management.

Step 3: Report the completion of the task.

Contents

Appendix A

Chapter and Page Correlation to NFPA 1081, Standard for Facility Fire Brigade Member Professional Qualifications (2018 Edition), Requirements

Incipient Facility Fire Brigade Member

NFPA 1081 JPR Numbers	Chapter References	Page References
4.1.2	3	55-113
4.1.2.1	1	17, 771
4.1.2.2	1	29, 774-775
4.1.2.3	1	18, 771
4.1.2.4	9	277-300, 833-844
4.1.2.5	1	20-21, 772
4.1.3	1	18-20, 27-38, 776
4.2.1	4	122-127, 135-138, 778-780
4.2.2	6, 7	216-239, 244-254, 814-825
4.2.3	1, 8	22-27, 257-262, 773
4.3.1	3, 5, 8	55-65, 82-112, 160-186, 257-272, 788, 799-807, 809-810, 826-832
4.3.2	4, 6	122-135, 216-237, 812-813
4.3.3	5	187-203, 808
4.3.4	5, 6	143-186, 237-239, 784-787, 812
4.3.5	2, 6	43-52, 239, 777

Advanced Exterior Facility Fire Brigade Member

NFPA 1081 JPR Numbers	Chapter References	Page References
5.1.2.1	10, 16	305, 307-315, 480-489, 501, 503-504, 514-516, 846
5.1.2.2	10	315-317, 847
5.2.1	11	321-338, 363-368, 848-849, 857-859, 877-878
5.2.2	11	339-368, 850-859, 870-878
5.2.3	16, 17	480-489, 495-501, 503, 520-524, 532-534, 781-783, 787-807, 809-811, 938, 945, 950
5.2.4	11, 12, 13, 15	339-355, 363-368, 375-403, 409-431, 457-472, 877-878, 880-916, 928-936
5.2.5	16	501, 503-504, 515-516, 518-519, 814-825, 946
5.2.6	12, 16	401-402, 497-500, 520-524, 945
5.2.7	16	485-489, 784-786, 812
5.2.8	16	477, 495-500, 879
5.2.9	11, 12, 15	321-338, 402-403, 472-473, 929-931, 937
5.3.1	16	478-479, 777
5.3.2	13, 14	409-431, 435-452, 897-927
5.3.3	16	495-497, 502, 808
5.3.4	16	505-514, 940-942
5.3.5	16, 17	480-495, 534-550, 939
5.3.6	16, 17	480-495, 514-515, 516-518, 534-550, 943-944
5.3.7	10	305-307, 845
5.3.8	16	503-504, 514-516, 812-813
5.3.9	16	480-489, 495-500, 514-516, 813
5.3.10	11, 12, 14	359-363, 375-403, 437-452, 833-844, 860-869, 880-896, 917-927
5.3.11	13	409-431, 897-916
5.3.12	17	531-532, 948-949
5.3.13	17	551-558, 951

Interior Structural Facility Fire Brigade Member

NFPA 1081 JPR Numbers	Chapter References	Page References
6.1.2.1	11	321-338, 848-849, 857-859
6.1.2.2	11	339-368, 850-859, 870-878
6.1.2.3	10, 16	305, 307-315, 480-489, 501, 503-504, 514-516, 846
6.1.2.4	16	524-525, 947
6.2.1	16, 18	480-489, 495-501, 503, 520-524, 564-580, 781-783, 787-807, 809-811, 938, 945, 952-971
6.2.2	14	434-452, 917-927
6.2.3	19	585-619, 972-980
6.2.4	16	497-500, 520-524, 945
6.2.5	16	477, 495-500, 879
6.2.6	16, 18	485-589, 566-575, 784-786, 812, 959-960
6.2.7	10	315-317, 847
6.2.8	11, 12, 13, 15	339-355, 363-368, 375-403, 409-431, 457-472, 877-878, 880-894, 897-916, 928-936
6.2.9	16, 18	501, 503-504, 515-516, 518-519, 564-565, 814-825, 946, 970-971
6.2.10	11, 12, 15	321-338, 402-403, 472-473, 929-931, 937
6.3.1	10	305-307, 845
6.3.2	16	503-504, 514-516, 812-813
6.3.3	16	495-500, 502, 808
6.3.4	16	505-514, 940-942
6.3.5	16	480-495, 939
6.3.6	16	480-489, 514-515, 516-518, 943-944
6.3.7	11, 12, 14	359-363, 375-403, 437-452, 833-844, 860-869, 880-896, 917-927
6.3.8	13	409-431, 897-916
6.3.9	10	315-317, 847
6.3.10	16	478-479, 777
6.3.11	16	480-489, 495-500, 514-516, 813

Facility Fire Brigade Leader

NFPA 1081 JPR Numbers	Chapter References	Page References
7.1.3	20, 21	626-652, 657-660
7.2.1	21	657-660, 981
7.2.2	21	655-657, 661-666, 668-681, 981
7.2.3	21	661-668, 681-687, 981
7.2.4	21	668-681, 981
7.2.5	21	680-681, 981
7.2.6	21	681-687, 982

Facility Fire Brigade Training Coordinator

NFPA 1081 JPR Numbers	Chapter References	Page References
8.2.1	22	693-711, 983
8.2.2	23	725- 753, 987
8.2.3	22	711-716, 984-985
8.2.4	22	716-719, 986

Support Member

NFPA 1081 JPR Numbers	Chapter References	Page References
9.1.7	24	757-759, 988
9.1.8	24	757-759, 988
9.2.1	24	760, 988
9.2.2	24	760-761, 988
9.2.3	24	761, 988
9.2.4	24	761, 988
9.2.5	24	762, 988
9.2.6	24	762, 988
9.2.7	24	762-763, 988
9.2.8	24	763, 988
9.2.9	24	764, 989
9.2.10	24	764, 989

Appendix B

Sample Facility Emergency Response and Safety Needs Assessment

Incipient Fire Fighting - Employees

The first step in addressing this element of emergency preparedness and response is to determine if your facility has portable fire extinguishers and/or fire hose stations (standpipes) or not. The leading questions below were derived from the standards shown in Appendix 1 (pg. 998), "List of Applicable Standards and Legal Requirements." These questions will help determine if your facility faces this risk.

Leading Questions:

	YES	NO	QUESTION
1			Are portable fire extinguishers available in the workplace?
2			Are fire hose stations (standpipe) available in the workplace?
3			Does a clear written statement, available to employees, exist that defines the intended users of portable fire extinguishers?
4			Does a clear written statement, available to employees, exist that defines the intended users of fire hose stations (standpipes)?
5			Does the emergency action plan state for a total evacuation of the workplace at the time of a fire emergency?
6			Does the emergency action plan state for a partial evacuation of the workplace at the time of a fire emergency except for designated employees remaining behind to operate critical plant operations (i.e. control room) or to fight incipient stage fire or members of the facility fire brigade?

If the answer to all of the questions above (1 – 6) is YES, no further action other than continual education and training for affecter employees.

If the answer to questions 1 and/or 2 is YES and NO to others, select from options below including written statements within the facility's emergency action plan.

Define intended users for fire extinguishers and standpipes:

Fire extinguishers and fire hose stations (standpipes) are commonly found and a clear statement as to the intended users is suggested so that individuals are clear as to the expected reaction upon discover of a fire, training needs identified and managed, and in the case of fire hose stations (standpipes) proper maintenance and testing schedules identified, monitored, thus managed.

Options include, but may not be limited to:

- **Option A:** Fire extinguishers are available for all employees use on incident stage fires.
- **Option B:** Fire extinguishers are available for designated employees.
- **Option C:** Fire extinguishers are available for facility fire brigade and/or public fire department personnel only.

- **Option D:** Fire extinguishers are available for designated employees, facility fire brigade, and/or public fire department personnel.
- **Option E:** Fire extinguishers are available for public fire department personnel only.
- **Option F:** Fire extinguishers are available for contractor personnel who are educated, trained, and designated to perform fire watch. (**Note:** Generally, extinguishers for fire watch are dedicated for that purpose and in addition to the facility's installed compliment.)
- **Option G:** Fire extinguishers and/or fire hose stations (1½ inch) are available for all employees use on incident stage fires.
- **Option H:** Fire extinguishers and/or fire hose stations (1½ inch) are available for designated employees.
- **Option I:** Fire extinguishers and/or fire hose stations are available for facility fire brigade and/or public fire department personnel only.

  Note: Education and training requirements for fire extinguishers and fire hose stations when applicable.

Appendix 1

List of Applicable Standards and Legal Requirements

DEFINITIONS:

- **Designated Employee** - An employee who is not a member of a facility fire brigade but who has been trained to use portable fire extinguishers or small hose lines to fight incipient fires in the employee's immediate work area.
- **Incipient Stage** - A fire which is in the initial or beginning stage and which can be controlled or extinguished by portable fire extinguishers, Class II standpipe or small hose systems without the need for protective clothing or breathing apparatus.
- **Facility (Industrial) Fire Brigade** - An organized group of employees at a facility who are knowledgeable, trained, and skilled in at least basic fire-fighting operations, and whose full-time occupation might or might not be the provision of fire suppression and related activities for their employer.

NFPA 10, *Standard for Portable Fire Extinguishers* – This standard applies to the selection, installation, inspection, maintenance, recharging, and testing of portable fire extinguishers and Class D extinguishing agents.

OSHA 1910.157 – Defines requirements for the placement, use, maintenance, and testing of portable fire extinguishers for the use of employees and education and training for those intended to use them.

INCIDENT BRIEFING (ICS 201)

1. Incident Name: REFRAC 2 FIRE	2. Incident Number: 2019-0009	3. Date/Time Initiated: Date: 04/02/2019 Time: 09:34

4. Map/Sketch (include sketch, showing the total area of operations, the incident site/area, impacted and threatened areas, overflight results, trajectories, impacted shorelines, or other graphics depicting situational status and resource assignment):

5. Situation Summary and Health and Safety Briefing (for briefings or transfer of command): Recognize potential incident Health and Safety Hazards and develop necessary measures (remove hazard, provide personal protective equipment, warn people of the hazard) to protect responders from those hazards.

During a hot work operation on the ground floor of Refrac Unit 2 (RU2), a kerosene product line was damaged creating a spill and igniting a fire. The automatic fire alarm activated and workers evacuated the unit. SU-5 arrived and positioned on the Southeast Corner of RU1 on Delta road. FBM Adams established initial incident command and FBM Kubert set up both monitors to cool the upper levels of RU2 and prevent fire spread. FBL Schwartz and TC Haney, SU-4, SU-6, P-11 and P-12 were dispatched. FBL Schwartz assumed command and set up the ICP on the East side of the Refrac Control Building. TC Haney was assigned as the ISO. SU-4 and 6 were ordered to set up water curtains between RU2 and exposures on the West and East sides. P-11 and P-12 were ordered to lay supply lines and deploy attack lines into the ground floor of RU2.

Evacuated workers were checked for injuries and then reported to the IC to brief her on the conditions within the unit. All personnel on scene were briefed to wear appropriate PPE/SCBA, check in through Accountability prior to entering the hazard area. An ambulance was requested from town and Rehab was set up. Personnel underwent baseline exam and briefing prior to entering RU2.

6. Prepared by: Name: C. Infantino	Position/Title: Planning Chief	Signature: *C. Infantino*
ICS 201, Page 1	Date/Time: 0945 / 04/02/2019	

INCIDENT BRIEFING (ICS 201)

1. Incident Name:	2. Incident Number:	3. Date/Time Initiated:
REFRAC 2 FIRE	2019-0009	Date: 04/02/2019 Time: 09:34

7. Current and Planned Objectives:

1. Evacuate workers from Refrac Units 1 and 2, Buildings 21 through 23, and non-essential workers from the Refrac Control Building. Account for their whereabouts and conditions.
2. Isolate the immediate area around RU2.
3. Isolate flow of product into and out of RU2.
4. Prevent fire spread to RU1 and RU2 and upper levels of RU2.
5. Establish Staging Area in the parking lot south of the RCB in case external support is required.
6. Extinguish fire on ground floor of RU2.
7. Extinguish fire on 2nd floor of RU2.
8. Divert all run-off to Treatment Pond #1.

8. Current and Planned Actions, Strategies, and Tactics:

Time:	Actions:
09:38	N. Adams (SU-5) initiated incident command. J. Kubert connected SU-5 to nearest hydrant and used monitors to cool upper floors.
09:42	J. Schwartz assumed command. Assigns B. Haney as ISO. ICP established eastside of RCB.
09:43	SU-4 and SU-6 arrived and were ordered to set up water curtains between RU2 and RU1 and RU3. P-11 and P-12 on scene.
	Ordered to lay supply lines to nearby hydrants and deploy handlines for fire attack.
09:44	IC ordered RCB Support Personnel to remotely isolate the flow of product into and out of RU2. RCB reported isolation complete.
09:45	RIC personnel setup. Attack Crews 1 and 2 (AC-1 and AC-2) entered RU2 and encountered heavy fire conditions.
09:57	SU-6: Fire spreading from 1st floor to 2nd floor on Northeast corner. SU-5 ordered to deploy a master stream device from P-12.
10:10	AC-3 and AC-4 enter RU2. AC-1 and AC-2 exit RU2 and enter Rehab.
10:19	AC-3: Fire extinguished in the Western half of RU2's 1st floor. AC-4: Slow progress on fire in center of RU2.
10:20	SU-5 ordered to divert water run-off to Treatment Pond #1.
10:45	IC requested mutual aid assistance from Plant #2.
10:55	P-22 arrived. Personnel briefed and ready to enter with AC-1 and AC-2.
10:56	AC-1, AC-2, and AC-5 entered RU2 and relieved AC-3 and AC-4. AC-3 and AC-4 exited RU2 and entered Rehab.
11:04	Fire extinguished on ground floor, AC-1 to conduct overhaul while AC-2 and AC-5 move to 2nd floor.
11:15	Fire extinguished on 2nd floor, overhaul has begun.
11:25	Overhaul completed on both floors.
11:55	All personnel have undergone rehab. Equipment recovery begun. P-22 released to Plant #2.
12:04	Fire watch established: SU-6.
12:05	Incident terminated

6. Prepared by: Name: C. Infantino	Position/Title: Planning Chief	Signature: C. Infantino
ICS 201, Page 2	Date/Time: 04/02/2019 / 12:06	

INCIDENT BRIEFING (ICS 201)

1. Incident Name: REFRAC 2 FIRE	2. Incident Number: 2019-0009	3. Date/Time Initiated: Date: 04/02/2019 Time: 09:34

9. Current Organization (fill in additional organization as appropriate):

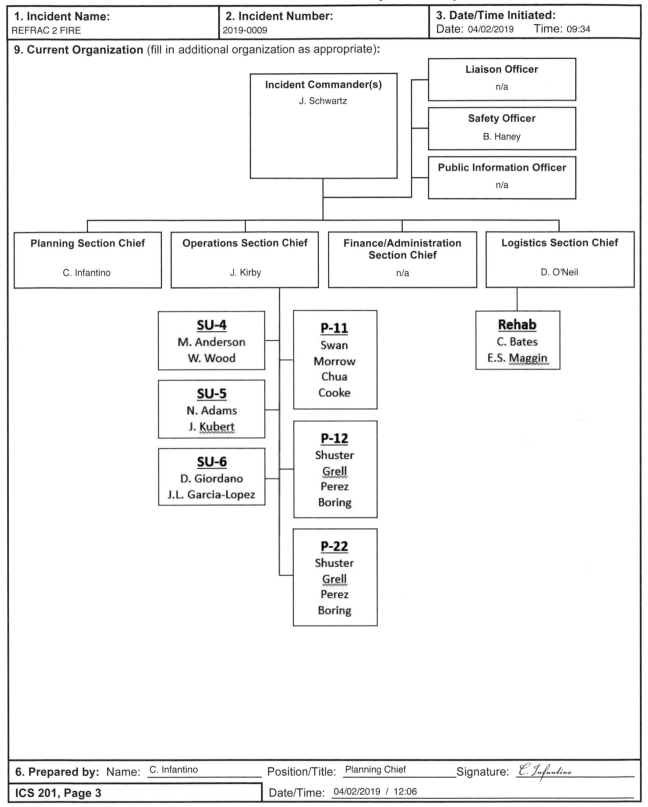

Incident Commander(s)
J. Schwartz

Liaison Officer
n/a

Safety Officer
B. Haney

Public Information Officer
n/a

Planning Section Chief
C. Infantino

Operations Section Chief
J. Kirby

Finance/Administration Section Chief
n/a

Logistics Section Chief
D. O'Neil

SU-4
M. Anderson
W. Wood

SU-5
N. Adams
J. Kubert

SU-6
D. Giordano
J.L. Garcia-Lopez

P-11
Swan
Morrow
Chua
Cooke

P-12
Shuster
Grell
Perez
Boring

P-22
Shuster
Grell
Perez
Boring

Rehab
C. Bates
E.S. Maggin

6. Prepared by: Name: C. Infantino	Position/Title: Planning Chief	Signature: *C. Infantino*
ICS 201, Page 3	Date/Time: 04/02/2019 / 12:06	

INCIDENT BRIEFING (ICS 201)

1. Incident Name:	2. Incident Number:	3. Date/Time Initiated:
REFRAC 2 FIRE	2019-0009	Date: 04/02/2019 Time: 09:34

10. Resource Summary:

Resource	Resource Identifier	Date/Time Ordered	ETA	Arrived	Notes (location/assignment/status)
Adams, Kubert	SU-5	04/02/2019 09:36	09:38	☑	Initiate incident command. Use SU-5's monitor to cool upper floors of RU2. Set up MSD to attack 2nd floor fire spread.
Schwartz Haney	IC ISO	09:39	09:41	☑	Assumed command. Appoint Haney ISO. Set up ICP. Conduct size-up and direct assigned units.
Anderson, Wood Giordano, Garcia-Lopez	SU-4 SU-6	09:39	09:42	☑	Set up water curtains between RU2 and other refrac units.
Bates, Maggin	Rehab	09:39	09:42	☑	Set up Rehab Unit, monitor personnel.
Swan, Morrow, Chua, Cooke Shuster, Grell, Perez, Boring	P-11 and P-12	09:39	09:42	☑	Lay supply lines and deploy handlines for fire attack.
E.N. Bridwell, RCB Support Member	Refrac Ops	09:40	09:44	☑	Use remote isolation valves to shut off product flow into/out of RU2. (Product flow reported shut off at 09:49.)
Andru, Kane, Aparo, Sprang, Newton, Rogers	RIC	09:40	09:43	☑	Set up RIC to support attack crews. Be prepared to rescue lost/injured FB personnel.
Swan, Chua, Cooke Shuster, Perez, Boring	AC-1 AC-2	09:41	09:45	☑	Enter RU2 from Southside, locate and attack the fire on the 1st floor. Later: attack fire on 2nd floor.
Cimarron Ambulance Services	AMB-2	09:41	09:49	☑	Staged just South of the Rehab area. Stand by to receive injured personnel.
Giordano, Conway, Wein Oksner, Goodwin, Colletta	AC-3 AC-4	10:05	10:09	☑	Relieve Attack Crews 1 and 2, continue fire attack on 1st floor, then 2nd floor.
Adams, Kubert	SU-5	10:20	10:20	☑	Divert run-off to Treatment Pond #1.
Shuster, Plastino, Buckler, Dillin	P-22	10:45	10:55	☑	Briefed on incident/actions taken. Set up as Attack Crew 5.
Shuster, Buckler, Dillin	AC-5	10:55	10:56	☑	Enter RU2 with Attack Crews 1 and 2. AC1 overhaul 1st floor, ACs 2 and 5 attack fire on 2nd floor.
Giordano, Garcia-Lopez	SU-6	12:03	12:04	☑	Fire watch.
				☐	
				☐	
				☐	

6. Prepared by: Name: C. Infantino	Position/Title: Planning Chief	Signature: C. Infantino
ICS 201, Page 4	Date/Time: 04/02/2019 / 12:06	

ICS 201
Incident Briefing

Purpose. The Incident Briefing (ICS 201) provides the Incident Commander (and the Command and General Staffs) with basic information regarding the incident situation and the resources allocated to the incident. In addition to a briefing document, the ICS 201 also serves as an initial action worksheet. It serves as a permanent record of the initial response to the incident.

Preparation. The briefing form is prepared by the Incident Commander for presentation to the incoming Incident Commander along with a more detailed oral briefing.

Distribution. Ideally, the ICS 201 is duplicated and distributed before the initial briefing of the Command and General Staffs or other responders as appropriate. The "Map/Sketch" and "Current and Planned Actions, Strategies, and Tactics" sections (pages 1–2) of the briefing form are given to the Situation Unit, while the "Current Organization" and "Resource Summary" sections (pages 3–4) are given to the Resources Unit.

Notes:

- The ICS 201 can serve as part of the initial Incident Action Plan (IAP).
- If additional pages are needed for any form page, use a blank ICS 201 and repaginate as needed.

Block Number	Block Title	Instructions
1	**Incident Name**	Enter the name assigned to the incident.
2	**Incident Number**	Enter the number assigned to the incident.
3	**Date/Time Initiated** • Date, Time	Enter date initiated (month/day/year) and time initiated (using the 24-hour clock).
4	**Map/Sketch** (include sketch, showing the total area of operations, the incident site/area, impacted and threatened areas, overflight results, trajectories, impacted shorelines, or other graphics depicting situational status and resource assignment)	Show perimeter and other graphics depicting situational status, resource assignments, incident facilities, and other special information on a map/sketch or with attached maps. Utilize commonly accepted ICS map symbology. If specific geospatial reference points are needed about the incident's location or area outside the ICS organization at the incident, that information should be submitted on the Incident Status Summary (ICS 209). North should be at the top of page unless noted otherwise.
5	**Situation Summary and Health and Safety Briefing** (for briefings or transfer of command): Recognize potential incident Health and Safety Hazards and develop necessary measures (remove hazard, provide personal protective equipment, warn people of the hazard) to protect responders from those hazards.	Self-explanatory.
6	**Prepared by** • Name • Position/Title • Signature • Date/Time	Enter the name, ICS position/title, and signature of the person preparing the form. Enter date (month/day/year) and time prepared (24-hour clock).
7	**Current and Planned Objectives**	Enter the objectives used on the incident and note any specific problem areas.

Block Number	Block Title	Instructions
8	**Current and Planned Actions, Strategies, and Tactics** • Time • Actions	Enter the current and planned actions, strategies, and tactics and time they may or did occur to attain the objectives. If additional pages are needed, use a blank sheet or another ICS 201 (Page 2), and adjust page numbers accordingly.
9	**Current Organization** (fill in additional organization as appropriate) • Incident Commander(s) • Liaison Officer • Safety Officer • Public Information Officer • Planning Section Chief • Operations Section Chief • Finance/Administration Section Chief • Logistics Section Chief	• Enter on the organization chart the names of the individuals assigned to each position. • Modify the chart as necessary, and add any lines/spaces needed for Command Staff Assistants, Agency Representatives, and the organization of each of the General Staff Sections. • If Unified Command is being used, split the Incident Commander box. • Indicate agency for each of the Incident Commanders listed if Unified Command is being used.
10	**Resource Summary**	Enter the following information about the resources allocated to the incident. If additional pages are needed, use a blank sheet or another ICS 201 (Page 4), and adjust page numbers accordingly.
	• Resource	Enter the number and appropriate category, kind, or type of resource ordered.
	• Resource Identifier	Enter the relevant agency designator and/or resource designator (if any).
	• Date/Time Ordered	Enter the date (month/day/year) and time (24-hour clock) the resource was ordered.
	• ETA	Enter the estimated time of arrival (ETA) to the incident (use 24-hour clock).
	• Arrived	Enter an "X" or a checkmark upon arrival to the incident.
	• Notes (location/ assignment/status)	Enter notes such as the assigned location of the resource and/or the actual assignment and status.

Appendix D

Foam Properties

		Table D.1	Foam Properties		
Type	**Characteristics**	**Storage Range**	**Application Range**	**Application Techniques**	**Primary Uses**
Protein Foam (3% and 6%)	• Protein based • Low expansion • Good reignition (burnback) resistance • Excellent water retention • High heat resistance and stability • Performance can be affected by freezing and thawing • Can freeze protect with antifreeze • Not as mobile or fluid on fuel surface as other low-expansion foams	35–120°F (2°C to 49°C)	0.16 gpm/ft² (6.5 L/min/m²)	• Indirect foam stream; do not mix fuel with foam • Avoid agitating fuel during application; static spark ignition of volatile hydrocarbons can result from plunging and turbulence • Use alcohol-resistant type within seconds of proportioning • Not compatible with dry chemical extinguishing Agents	• Class B fires involving hydrocarbons • Protecting flammable and combustible liquids where they are stored, transported, and processed
Fluoroprotein Foam (3% and 6%)	• Protein and synthetic based; derived from protein foam • Fuel shedding • Long-term vapor suppression • Good water retention • Excellent, long-lasting heat resistance • Performance not affected by freezing and thawing • Maintains low viscosity at low temperatures • Can freeze protect with antifreeze • Use either freshwater or saltwater • Nontoxic and biodegradable after dilution • Good mobility and fluidity on fuel surface • Premixable for short periods of time	35–120°F (2°C to 49°C)	0.16 gpm/ft² (6.5 L/min/m²)	• Direct plunge technique • Subsurface injection • Compatible with simultaneous application of dry chemical extinguishing agents • Deliver through air aspirating equipment	• Hydrocarbon vapor suppression • Subsurface application to hydrocarbon fuel storage tanks • Extinguishing in-depth crude petroleum or other hydrocarbon fuel fires

Type	Characteristics	Storage Range	Application Range	Application Techniques	Primary Uses
Film Forming Fluoroprotein Foam (FFFP) (3% and 6%)	• Protein based; fortified with additional surfactants that reduce the burnback characteristics of other protein-based foams • Fuel shedding • Develops a fast-healing, continuous-floating film on hydrocarbon fuel surfaces • Excellent, long-lasting heat resistance • Good low-temperature viscosity • Fast fire knockdown • Affected by freezing and thawing • Use either freshwater or saltwater • Can store premixed • Can freeze protect with antifreeze • Use alcohol-resistant type on polar solvents at 6% solution and on hydrocarbon fuels at 3% solution • Nontoxic and biodegradable after dilution	35–120°F (2°C to 49°C)	**Ignited Hydrocarbon Fuel:** 0.10 gpm/ft^2 (4.1 L/min/m^2) **Polar Solvent Fuel:** 0.24 gpm/ft^2 (9.8 L/min/m^2)	• Cover entire fuel surface • May apply with dry chemical agents • May apply with spray nozzles • Subsurface injection • Can plunge into fuel during application	• Suppressing vapors in unignited spills of hazardous liquids • Extinguishing fires in hydrocarbon fuels
Aqueous Film Forming Foam (AFFF) (1%, 3%, and 6%)	• Synthetic based • Good penetrating capabilities • Spreads vapor-sealing film over and floats on hydrocarbon fuels • Can use nonaerating nozzles • Performance may be adversely affected by freezing and storing • Has good low temperature viscosity • Can freeze protect with antifreeze • Use either freshwater or saltwater • Can premix	25–120°F (-4°F to 49°C)	0.10 gpm/ft^2 (4.1 L/min/m^2)	• May apply directly onto fuel surface • May apply indirectly by bouncing it off a wall and allowing it to float onto fuel surface • Subsurface injection • May apply with dry chemical agents	• Controlling and extinguishing Class B fire • Handling land or sea crash rescues involving spills • Extinguishing most transportation-related fires • Wetting and penetrating Class A fuels • Securing unignited hydrocarbon spills

Type	Characteristics	Storage Range	Application Range	Application Techniques	Primary Uses
Alcohol-Resistant AFFF (3% and 6%)	• Polymer has been added to AFFF concentrate • Multipurpose: Use on both polar solvents and hydrocarbon fuels (use on polar solvents at 6% solution and on hydrocarbon fuels at 3% solution) • Forms a membrane on polar solvent fuels that prevents destruction of the foam blanket • Forms same aqueous film on hydrocarbon fuels as AFFF • Fast flame knockdown • Good burnback resistance on both fuels • Not easily premixed	25–120°F (-4°C to 49°C) (May become viscous at temperatures under 50°F [10°C])	**Ignited Hydrocarbon Fuel:** 0.10 gpm/ft² (4.1 L/min/m²) **Polar Solvent Fuel:** 0.24 gpm/ft² (9.8 L/min/m²)	• Apply directly but gently onto fuel surface • May apply indirectly by bouncing it off a wall and allowing it to float onto fuel surface • Subsurface injection	• Fires or spills of both hydrocarbon and polar solvent fuels
High-Expansion Foam	• Synthetic detergent based • Special-purpose, low water content • High air-to-solution ratios: 200:1 to 1,000:1 • Performance not affected by freezing and thawing • Poor heat resistance • Prolonged contact with galvanized or raw steel may attack these surfaces	27–110°F (-3°C to 43°C)	Sufficient to quickly cover the fuel or fill the space	• Gentle application; do not mix foam with fuel • Cover entire fuel surface • Usually fills entire space in confined space incidents	• Extinguishing Class A and some Class B fires • Flooding confined spaces • Volumetrically displacing vapor, heat, and smoke • Reducing vaporization from liquefied natural gas spills • Extinguishing pesticide fires • Suppressing fuming acid vapors • Suppressing vapors in coal mines and other subterranean spaces and concealed spaces in basements • Extinguishing agent in fixed extinguishing systems • Not recommended for outdoor use

Type	Characteristics	Storage Range	Application Range	Application Techniques	Primary Uses
Class A Foam	• Synthetic • Wetting agent that reduces surface tension of water and allows it to soak into combustible materials • Rapid extinguishment with less water use than other foams • Use regular water stream equipment • Can premix with water • Mildly corrosive • Requires lower percentage of concentration (0.2 to 1.0) than other foams • Outstanding insulating qualities • Good penetrating capabilities	25–120°F (-4°C to 49°C) (Concentrate is subject to freezing but can be thawed and used if freezing occurs)	Same as the minimum critical flow rate for plain water on similar Class A Fuels; flow rates are not reduced when using Class A foam	• Can propel with compressed-air systems • Can apply with conventional nozzles	• Extinguishing Class A combustibles only
Water Additives (for Fire Control and Vapor Mitigation)	• When added to water in proper quantities, suppresses, cools, mitigates fire and/or vapors, and/or provides insulating properties for fuels exposed to radiant heat or direct flame impingement • Synthetic or Artificial sea water • Reduces surface tension of water • Emulsifier • Miscibility • Use regular water stream equipment • Can premix with water • Requires lower percentage of concentrate than foams • Rapid vapor mitigation • Effective on two and three-dimensional fires • Vapor mitigation	35–130°F (2°C to 54°C)	.5 – 1% for Class A 3% on Class B – polar and non-polar	• Can apply with conventional nozzles	• Classes A, B, C, and D May be used on Class B – polar and Class B - nonpolar